SELECTED PAPERS OF
F.W.J. Olver

Part II

World Scientific Series in 20th Century Mathematics

Published

Vol. 1 The Neumann Compendium
edited by F. Bródy and T. Vámos

Vol. 2 40 Years in Mathematical Physics
by L. D. Faddeev

Vol. 3 Selected Papers of Yu I Manin
by Y. Manin

Vol. 4 A Mathematician and His Mathematical Work
— Selected Papers of S. S. Chern
edited by S. Y. Cheng, P. Li and G. Tian

Vol. 5 Fields Medallists' Lectures
edited by Sir Michael Atiyah and Daniel Iagolnitzer

Vol. 6 Selected Logic Papers
by G. E. Sacks

Vol. 7 Selected Papers of F. W. J. Olver (in 2 Volumes)
edited by Roderick Wong

World Scientific Series in 20th Century Mathematics Vol. 7

SELECTED PAPERS OF F.W.J. Olver

Part II

Edited by

Roderick Wong

Department of Mathematics
City University of Hong Kong

World Scientific
Singapore • New Jersey • London • Hong Kong

Published by

World Scientific Publishing Co. Pte. Ltd.
P O Box 128, Farrer Road, Singapore 912805
USA office: Suite 1B, 1060 Main Street, River Edge, NJ 07661
UK office: 57 Shelton Street, Covent Garden, London WC2H 9HE

British Library Cataloguing-in-Publication Data
A catalogue record for this book is available from the British Library.

The author and publisher would like to thank the following publishers of the various journals and books for their assistance and permission to include the selected reprints found in this volume:
Academic Press
American Mathematical Society
Association for Computing Machinery
Birkhäuser
Cambridge University Press
Elsevier Science Ltd
International Press
London Mathematical Society
Marcel Dekker, Inc.
National Bureau of Standards (now National Institute of Standards and Technology)
Oxford University Press (2 letters)
Royal Irish Academy
Royal Society of Edinburgh
Royal Society of London
SIAM Publications
Utilitas Mathematica

ISBN 981-02-4106-2 (Set)
ISBN 981-02-4995-0 (Vol. 2)

Printed in Singapore by Uto-Print

CONTENTS

Part 2

TRANSACTIONS OF THE
AMERICAN MATHEMATICAL SOCIETY
Volume 226, 1977

SECOND-ORDER DIFFERENTIAL EQUATIONS WITH FRACTIONAL TRANSITION POINTS(1)

BY

F. W. J. OLVER

ABSTRACT. An investigation is made of the differential equation

$$d^2w/dx^2 = \{u^2(x - x_0)^\lambda f(u,x) + g(u,x)/(x - x_0)^2\}w,$$

in which u is a large real (or complex) parameter, λ is a real constant such that $\lambda > -2$, x is a real (or complex) variable, and $f(u,x)$ and $g(u,x)$ are continuous (or analytic) functions of x in a real interval (or complex domain) containing x_0. The interval (or domain) need not be bounded. Previous results of Langer and Riekstiņš giving approximate solutions in terms of Bessel functions of order $1/(\lambda + 2)$ are extended and error bounds supplied.

1. Introduction and summary. A differential equation of the form

$$d^2w/dx^2 = \{u^2f(x) + g(x)\}w, \tag{1.01}$$

in which u is a large parameter and the functions $f(x)$ and $g(x)$ are independent of x, is said to have a simple transition point, or simple turning point, at $x = x_0$ if $f(x_0) = 0$ and $f'(x_0) \neq 0$. More generally, if $f(x)$ has a zero at x_0 of order m, then equation (1.01) is said to have a transition point of order m at $x = x_0$.

The foregoing definition may be extended to cases in which

$$f(x) = (x - x_0)^\lambda h(x),$$

where $h(x)$ is finite and nonvanishing at x_0, and the constant λ is an unrestricted real number, usually to be regarded as fixed. In these circumstances we may say that equation (1.01) has a transition point of *fractional order* λ at x_0. The problem of constructing asymptotic solutions of (1.01) for large u which are uniformly valid in a region containing x_0 was first solved for arbitrary values of λ by Langer [1], [2], [3]. In [1] Langer made the following

Received by the editors January 28, 1975 and, in revised form, November 25, 1975.
AMS (MOS) subject classifications (1970). Primary 34E20; Secondary 33A40.
Key words and phrases. Asymptotic analysis, Bessel functions, error analysis, linear differential equations, transition point, turning point.
(1) This research was supported by the U. S. Army Research Office, Durham under Contract DA-ARO-D-31-124-73-G204, and the National Science Foundation under Grant GP 32841X.

assumptions: $\lambda \geqslant 0$; the variable x ranges over a bounded or unbounded real interval containing the fractional transition point x_0; the function $g(x)$ is bounded as $x \to x_0$; and the large parameter u is real or complex. In [2] these results were extended to the complex x-plane. In the third paper [3] he made further extensions to permit $\lambda > -2$, and $g(x)$ to possess a simple or double pole at x_0. In each case Langer constructed approximations for the solutions in terms of Bessel functions of fixed order, accompanied by asymptotic estimates of the corresponding error terms. These error estimates take one of two forms depending whether $|u^2(x - x_0)^{\lambda+2}|$ is bounded away from infinity or bounded away from zero.

More recently, in a survey paper [8] Riekstiņš extended Langer's result in the case of real variables, by showing that the condition concerning the behavior of the function $(x - x_0)^2 g(x)$ at x_0 can be eased from analyticity to

$$(x - x_0)^2 g(x) = a + O\{(x - x_0)^\alpha\} \qquad (x \to x_0),$$

where a and α are constants, α being positive.

One of the purposes of the present paper is to show that the conditions on $f(x)$ and $g(x)$ given by Langer and Riekstiņš can be further weakened. The primary purpose, however, is to supply strict and realistic error bounds for the known asymptotic solutions, both for real and complex values of u and x. The availability of error bounds is of obvious computational value. Equally important, however, is the theoretical consideration that by examining the asymptotic behavior of the bounds as $|u| \to \infty$, we can cope–in an almost trivial manner–with a considerably enlarged class of differential equations of the form (1.01) in which $f(x)$ and $g(x)$ are replaced by functions $f(u,x)$ and $g(u, x)$ that depend on u as well as x. Furthermore, the bounds facilitate exploration of the uniformity of the approximate solutions with respect to other parameters that may be present in the differential equation, for example λ. These extensions greatly increase the scope of the asymptotic theory. The analysis that we shall give draws heavily on results given in the writer's recent book [5], and it will be assumed that the reader has some familiarity with this work.

The case $\lambda < -2$, for which equation (1.01) possesses an irregular singularity at $x = x_0$, and the case $\lambda = -2$, for which the singularity is regular, were excluded by Langer and Riekstiņš, and will also be excluded in the present investigation. This is because uniform asymptotic approximations in terms of elementary functions, complete with error bounds, have been given for these cases in [5, pp. 203–205 and 220–224]. Other cases for which error bounds have been published include $\lambda = 0$ with $g(x)$ continuous at x_0, $\lambda = 1$ with $g(x)$ continuous at x_0, and $\lambda = -1$ with $(x - x_0)^2 g(x)$ analytic at x_0; see [5, Chapters 6, 11 and 12, respectively]. Also, error bounds for $\lambda = 2$ with $g(x)$

continuous at x_0 are included as a special case of a theory supplied recently by the present writer for differential equations with two coalescing simple turning points [6].

The results given in the present paper for general values of λ specialize into results similar to those just cited for the cases $\lambda = 0, \pm 1$ and 2. The new results also include further cases with $\lambda = 0$ and $g(x)$ unbounded as $x \to x_0$ that are important in the calculation of phase shifts in scattering theory; see [5, pp. 208–211 and 449–451]. Thus the present analysis achieves a unification of the error theory of second-order differential equations in regions containing a singularity or turning point that is analogous to the unification in the asymptotic theory achieved by Langer's work. It needs to be emphasized, however, that each of these unifications is confined to the *first approximations* to the wanted solutions. Except in the cases $\lambda = 0, \pm 1$ it is not known how to construct asymptotic *expansions* for the solutions in descending powers of the large parameter that involve only functions of a single variable; see [4, §§2–6].

The paper is arranged as follows. §§2–5 are concerned with real values of u and x. In §2 the Liouville transformation is applied to convert equation (1.01) into a standard form in which $f(x)$, or more generally $f(u,x)$, is replaced either by $\frac{1}{4}(\lambda+2)^2 x^\lambda$ or by $-\frac{1}{4}(\lambda+2)^2 x^\lambda$, these alternatives being designated Cases I and II, respectively. In §3 we state and prove a theorem for Case I which gives approximations to the solutions of the transformed differential equation in terms of modified Bessel functions, complete with error bounds. In §4 the uniform asymptotic nature of these approximations is demonstrated by an investigation of the behavior of the error bounds as $u \to \infty$. For Case II, a similar theorem and asymptotic investigation appear in §5; in this case the approximants involve ordinary Bessel functions instead of modified ones. The concluding section, §6, supplies the corresponding theory for complex variables.

Of course the cases of real u and x treated in §§2–5 can also be regarded as special cases of the analysis given in §6 for complex variables. Separate treatments of the real cases are desirable, however, because weaker, nonanalytic, assumptions can then be made concerning the functions $f(u,x)$ and $g(u,x)$, and simpler and sharper error bounds can be found. Furthermore, the methods developed for real variables will be applied in a forthcoming paper [7] to the problem of constructing connection formulas for a transition point of any integer multiplicity.

2. Transformation to standard form: real variables. In accordance with the observations made in §1, our starting point is taken to be the differential equation

$$d^2w/dx^2 = \{u^2(x-x_0)^\lambda f(u,x) + g(u,x)/(x-x_0)^2\}w, \tag{2.01}$$

in which u is a positive parameter, λ is a number such that $\lambda > -2$, and $f(u,x)$ and $g(u,x)$ are real.(2) This equation has real solutions when $x > x_0$, but, in general, these solutions become complex when continued along the real axis through x_0. Accordingly, we restrict x to the partly closed interval $[x_0, b)$, where the right endpoint b may be finite or $+\infty$.(3)

For $x \in [x_0, b)$ and each value of u, we assume that $\partial^2 f(u,x)/\partial x^2$ and $g(u,x)$ are continuous functions of x, and $f(u,x)$ is nonzero. All quantities, including x_0, b, and λ, may depend on u. Since $f(u,x)$ is nonvanishing in $[x_0, b)$, its sign is constant. In *Case* I we suppose that this sign is positive, and in *Case* II that the sign is negative.

To convert (2.01) into a standard form, we apply the Liouville transformation. This means that we introduce new variables W and ζ, related by $W = \dot{x}^{-1/2} w$, the dot signifying differentiation with respect to ζ. Then W satisfies

$$\frac{d^2 W}{d\zeta^2} = \left\{ u^2 \dot{x}^2 (x - x_0)^\lambda f(u,x) + \frac{\dot{x}^2 g(u,x)}{(x - x_0)^2} + \dot{x}^{1/2} \frac{d^2}{d\zeta^2}(\dot{x}^{-1/2}) \right\} W. \tag{2.02}$$

The relation between x and ζ is prescribed by setting

$$\dot{x}^2 (x - x_0)^\lambda f(u,x) = \pm \tfrac{1}{4}(\lambda + 2)^2 \zeta^\lambda, \tag{2.03}$$

and stipulating that $\zeta = 0$ corresponds to $x = x_0$. Here, and in what follows, the upper sign pertains to Case I and the lower sign to Case II. Integration of (2.03) yields

$$\zeta^{(\lambda+2)/2} = \int_{x_0}^{x} (t - x_0)^{\lambda/2} |f(u,t)|^{1/2} \, dt. \tag{2.04}$$

This equation defines a one-to-one continuous relationship between ζ and x. We denote by β the value of ζ corresponding to $x = b$; the value of β is positive, and finite or infinite depending whether or not the integral in (2.04) converges as $x \to b$.

Writing

$$\hat{f}(u,x) = (x - x_0)^\lambda |f(u,x)| / \zeta^\lambda$$

and substituting in (2.02) by means of (2.03), we arrive at the required form of

(2) Actually $g(u,x)$ can be complex without any significant complications in the analysis and final results.

(3) When λ is an integer, equation (2.01) also has real solutions in the interval $x < x_0$. These cases can be accommodated in the present theory by replacing x by $-x$. With the further specialization that λ is a nonnegative integer and $f(u,x)$ and $g(u,x)/(x - x_0)^2$ are continuous at x_0, each solution is real on *both* sides of x_0. The problem of continuing the approximate solutions through x_0 in these cases is considered in [7].

differential equation, given by

$$d^2W/d\zeta^2 = \{\pm\tfrac{1}{4}(\lambda+2)^2u^2\zeta^\lambda + \phi(u,\zeta)/\zeta^2\}W, \tag{2.05}$$

in which $W = \hat{f}^{1/4}(u,x)w$, and

$$\phi(u,\zeta) = \frac{(\lambda+2)^2\zeta^2 g(u,x)}{4(x-x_0)^2\hat{f}(u,x)} + \zeta^2\hat{f}^{-1/4}(u,x)\frac{d^2}{d\zeta^2}\{\hat{f}^{1/4}(u,x)\}.$$

On carrying out the differentiations by use of (2.03), we find that when $\phi(u,\zeta)$ is expressed in terms of the original functions it is given by

$$\frac{\lambda(\lambda+4)}{16} \pm \frac{(\lambda+2)^2}{4}\left(\frac{\zeta}{x-x_0}\right)^{\lambda+2}$$
$$\times\left\{\frac{g}{f} - \frac{\lambda(\lambda+4)}{16f} - (x-x_0)\frac{\lambda f'}{8f^2} + (x-x_0)^2\left(\frac{f''}{4f^2} - \frac{5f'^2}{16f^3}\right)\right\}.$$

Here the arguments u and x have been suppressed, and primes denote partial differentiations with respect to x.

The nature of the functions $\zeta \equiv \zeta(u,x)$ and $\phi(u,\zeta)$ is indicated by the following lemma, the proof of which is a straightforward generalization of the proof given in [5, p. 399] for the case $\lambda = 1$, and therefore omitted.

LEMMA. *With the conditions stated in the first two paragraphs of this section, $\zeta/(x-x_0)$ is a positive, twice continuously differentiable function of x in $[x_0, b)$, and $\phi(u,\zeta)$ is continuous in the corresponding ζ-interval* $[0,\beta)$.(4)

3. **Real variables: Case I.** From now on it will be convenient to replace the symbol λ by $\mu - 2$; thus μ is a positive number that is independent of x, though not necessarily independent of u.

By the lemma of §2 the function $\phi(u,\zeta)$ is continuous on the right at $\zeta = 0$. We introduce a number ν defined by the relation

$$\tfrac{1}{4}(\mu^2\nu^2 - 1) = \phi(u,0), \tag{3.01}$$

and a function $\psi(u,\zeta)$ defined by

$$\phi(u,\zeta)/\zeta^2 = (\mu^2\nu^2-1)/4\zeta^2 + \psi(u,\zeta)/\zeta.$$

Clearly $\psi(u,\zeta)$ is a continuous function of ζ in $(0,\beta)$, and $\psi(u,\zeta) = o(1/\zeta)$ as $\zeta \to 0+$. With these substitutions the standard form of differential equation for Case I becomes

(4) At the left endpoints of the intervals, differentiability and continuity apply only on the right.

$$\frac{d^2W}{d\zeta^2} = \left\{\frac{\mu^2 u^2}{4}\zeta^{\mu-2} + \frac{\mu^2\nu^2 - 1}{4\zeta^2} + \frac{\psi(u,\zeta)}{\zeta}\right\}W; \tag{3.02}$$

compare (2.05). The strategy for solving (3.02) will be to approximate the solutions by those of the equation

$$\frac{d^2W}{d\zeta^2} = \left(\frac{\mu^2 u^2}{4}\zeta^{\mu-2} + \frac{\mu^2\nu^2 - 1}{4\zeta^2}\right)W. \tag{3.03}$$

Exact solutions of (3.03) are $\zeta^{1/2}I_\nu(u\zeta^{\mu/2})$ and $\zeta^{1/2}K_\nu(u\zeta^{\mu/2})$, where I_ν and K_ν denote the modified Bessel functions in the usual notation. In the present paper, *we confine attention to nonnegative real values of the order* ν. Referring to (3.01) we see that this implies that $\phi(u,0) \geqslant -\frac{1}{4}$. Cases in which $\phi(u,0) < -\frac{1}{4}$ could be treated by analogous methods using modified (or unmodified) Bessel functions of purely imaginary order, but details will not be pursued in the present investigation.

For reference, we quote here some pertinent well-known properties of modified Bessel functions of nonnegative order and positive argument, given by

$$I_\nu(x) \sim e^x/(2\pi x)^{1/2}, \quad K_\nu(x) \sim (\pi/2x)^{1/2}e^{-x} \qquad (x \to +\infty), \tag{3.04}$$

$$I_\nu(x) \sim (\tfrac{1}{2}x)^\nu/\Gamma(\nu+1), \quad K_\nu(x) \sim \Gamma(\nu)/2(\tfrac{1}{2}x)^\nu \qquad (x \to 0+, \nu > 0), \tag{3.05}$$

$$I_0(x) = 1 + \tfrac{1}{4}x^2 + O(x^4), \quad K_0(x) \sim \ln(x^{-1}) \qquad (x \to 0+). \tag{3.06}$$

Each of these relations may be differentiated with respect to x. For fixed ν, $I_\nu(x)$ is positive and strictly increasing in the interval $0 < x < \infty$, and $K_\nu(x)$ is positive and strictly decreasing in the same interval. Lastly, the Wronskian relation satisfied by the modified Bessel functions is given by

$$\mathscr{W}\{K_\nu(x), I_\nu(x)\} = 1/x. \tag{3.07}$$

Before stating the main result of the present section, we shall also need to introduce a *balancing function* $\Omega_\nu(x)$.[5] This is any conveniently chosen function of x that is continuous and positive in the interval $0 < x < \infty$, and has the properties

$$\Omega_\nu(x) = O(x) \qquad (x \to +\infty), \tag{3.08}$$

$$\begin{aligned} \Omega_\nu(x) &= O(1) \qquad (x \to 0+, \nu > 0),\\ \ln(x^{-1})\Omega_0(x) &= O(1) \qquad (x \to 0+). \end{aligned} \tag{3.09}$$

---

[5] The significance of the name is explained in Remark (i) at the end of this section.

Subject to these conditions the choice of $\Omega_\nu(x)$ is at our disposal. Next, we define

$$l_\nu = \sup_{x\in(0,\infty)} \{2\Omega_\nu(x) I_\nu(x) K_\nu(x)\}. \tag{3.10}$$

From (3.04), (3.05) and (3.06) it is immediately seen that conditions (3.08) and (3.09) are precisely those needed to ensure that l_ν is finite. One possible choice for the balancing function is, in fact, $\Omega_\nu(x) = 1/\{2I_\nu(x)K_\nu(x)\}$, and in this event obviously $l_\nu = 1$.

THEOREM 1. *In the differential equation* (3.02), *let u be a positive parameter and μ and ν numbers that are independent of x and satisfy μ > 0 and ν ⩾ 0. Assume also that for each value of u the function ψ(u, ζ) is continuous in a finite or infinite interval* $0 < \zeta < \beta$, *and denote*

$$H(u,\zeta) \equiv \frac{1}{\mu}\int \frac{\psi(u,\zeta)}{\Omega_\nu(u\zeta^{\mu/2})}\, d\zeta. \tag{3.11}$$

Then in $(0,\beta)$ *equation* (3.02) *has solutions* $W_1(u,\zeta)$ *and* $W_2(u,\zeta)$ *that are twice continuously differentiable functions of ζ, and have the forms*

$$\begin{aligned} W_1(u,\zeta) &= \zeta^{1/2}\{I_\nu(u\zeta^{\mu/2}) + \varepsilon_1(u,\zeta)\}, \\ W_2(u,\zeta) &= \zeta^{1/2}\{K_\nu(u\zeta^{\mu/2}) + \varepsilon_2(u,\zeta)\}, \end{aligned} \tag{3.12}$$

where

$$|\varepsilon_1(u,\zeta)| \leqslant I_\nu(u\zeta^{\mu/2})[\exp\{l_\nu \mathcal{V}_{0,\zeta}(H)\} - 1], \tag{3.13}$$

$$\left|\frac{\partial \varepsilon_1(u,\zeta)}{\partial \zeta}\right| \leqslant \frac{\mu}{2\zeta K_\nu(u\zeta^{\mu/2})}[\exp\{l_\nu \mathcal{V}_{0,\zeta}(H)\} - 1], \tag{3.14}$$

$$|\varepsilon_2(u,\zeta)| \leqslant K_\nu(u\zeta^{\mu/2})[\exp\{l_\nu \mathcal{V}_{\zeta,\beta}(H)\} - 1], \tag{3.15}$$

$$\left|\frac{\partial \varepsilon_2(u,\zeta)}{\partial \zeta}\right| \leqslant \frac{\mu}{2\zeta I_\nu(u\zeta^{\mu/2})}[\exp\{l_\nu \mathcal{V}_{\zeta,\beta}(H)\} - 1], \tag{3.16}$$

provided that these bounds are finite.

In this result $\mathcal{V}$ denotes the variational operator defined in [5, pp. 27–29]; thus, for example,

$$\mathcal{V}_{0,\zeta}(H) = \frac{1}{\mu}\int_0^\zeta \frac{|\psi(u,v)|}{\Omega_\nu(uv^{\mu/2})}\, dv.$$

Moreover, in conformity with this reference, we call $H(u,\zeta)$ the *error-control function* for the present differential equation. In definition (3.11) the choice of integration constant is immaterial, because the bounds (3.13) through (3.16) involve only the variation of H.

To establish (3.13) and (3.14) we begin by substituting the first of (3.12) in (3.02). After subtracting equation (3.03) satisfied by $\zeta^{1/2}I_\nu(u\zeta^{\mu/2})$, we arrive at the following inhomogeneous differential equation for the product of $\zeta^{1/2}$ and the error term $\varepsilon_1(u,\zeta)$:

$$\frac{d^2}{d\zeta^2}\{\zeta^{1/2}\varepsilon_1(u,\zeta)\} - \left(\frac{\mu^2u^2}{4}\zeta^{\mu-2} + \frac{\mu^2\nu^2-1}{4\zeta^2}\right)\{\zeta^{1/2}\varepsilon_1(u,\zeta)\}$$
$$= \frac{\psi(u,\zeta)}{\zeta}\{\zeta^{1/2}I_\nu(u\zeta^{\mu/2}) + \zeta^{1/2}\varepsilon_1(u,\zeta)\}.$$

Then applying the method of variation of parameters and referring to the Wronskian (3.07), we construct an equivalent Volterra integral equation

$$\varepsilon_1(u,\zeta) = \frac{2}{\mu}\int_0^\zeta \mathsf{K}(\zeta,v)\psi(u,v)\{I_\nu(uv^{\mu/2}) + \varepsilon_1(u,v)\}\,dv, \tag{3.17}$$

in which

$$\mathsf{K}(\zeta,v) = I_\nu(u\zeta^{\mu/2})K_\nu(uv^{\mu/2}) - K_\nu(u\zeta^{\mu/2})I_\nu(uv^{\mu/2}). \tag{3.18}$$

When $0 < v \leqslant \zeta$ the monotonicity properties of the modified Bessel functions quoted above show that

$$I_\nu(uv^{\mu/2}) \leqslant I_\nu(u\zeta^{\mu/2}),\quad K_\nu(u\zeta^{\mu/2}) \leqslant K_\nu(uv^{\mu/2}). \tag{3.19}$$

Hence

$$0 \leqslant \mathsf{K}(\zeta,v) < I_\nu(u\zeta^{\mu/2})K_\nu(uv^{\mu/2}) \qquad (0 < v \leqslant \zeta). \tag{3.20}$$

Next, differentiation of (3.18) gives

$$\frac{\partial\mathsf{K}(\zeta,v)}{\partial\zeta} = \tfrac{1}{2}\mu u\zeta^{(\mu-2)/2}\{I'_\nu(u\zeta^{\mu/2})K_\nu(uv^{\mu/2}) - K'_\nu(u\zeta^{\mu/2})I_\nu(uv^{\mu/2})\}.$$

Applying (3.19) and bearing in mind that I'_ν is positive and K'_ν is negative, we see that

$$\left|\frac{\partial\mathsf{K}(\zeta,v)}{\partial\zeta}\right| \leqslant \tfrac{1}{2}\mu u\zeta^{(\mu-2)/2}\Bigg\{I'_\nu(u\zeta^{\mu/2})K_\nu(uv^{\mu/2})$$
$$-K'_\nu(u\zeta^{\mu/2})I_\nu(uv^{\mu/2})\frac{K_\nu(uv^{\mu/2})I_\nu(u\zeta^{\mu/2})}{K_\nu(u\zeta^{\mu/2})I_\nu(uv^{\mu/2})}\Bigg\},$$

and hence, by use of (3.07), obtain

$$\left|\frac{\partial \mathrm{K}(\zeta, v)}{\partial \zeta}\right| \leqslant \frac{\mu}{2\zeta} \frac{K_\nu(uv^{\mu/2})}{K_\nu(u\zeta^{\mu/2})} \qquad (0 < v \leqslant \zeta). \tag{3.21}$$

Having bounded the kernel and its ζ-derivative, we can solve the integral equation (3.17) by the standard procedure of successive approximation,(6) and on using the definitions (3.10) and (3.11) we arrive at the desired bounds (3.13) and (3.14). The proof of (3.15) and (3.16) is similar.

REMARKS. (i) The name "balancing function" is suggested by the following consideration. If $\Omega_\nu(x)$ is changed, then both the quantity l_ν defined by (3.10) and the total variation $\mathcal{V}_{0,\beta}(H)$ of the error-control function (3.11) are affected. Moreover, it is apparent that when one of these quantities increases the other is likely to decrease. To minimize the error bounds (3.13) to (3.16) we need to choose $\Omega_\nu(x)$ in such a way that the best balance is struck between l_ν and $\mathcal{V}_{0,\beta}(H)$ in forming the product of these quantities.(7)

(ii) The inequality (3.13) furnishes direct information concerning the relative error $\varepsilon_1(u,\zeta)/I_\nu(u\zeta^{\mu/2})$ in the first of the approximations (3.12). On the other hand, inequality (3.14) does not supply direct information concerning the ratio of $\partial\varepsilon_1(u,\zeta)/\partial\zeta$ to $dI_\nu(u\zeta^{\mu/2})/d\zeta$, that is, $\frac{1}{2}\mu u\zeta^{(\mu-2)/2}I'_\nu(u\zeta^{\mu/2})$. Meaningful information is available indirectly, however, because the differentiated forms of (3.04), (3.05) and (3.06) show that, except when $\nu = 0$, the ratio of $1/K_\nu(x)$ to $xI'_\nu(x)$ is finite and bounded throughout the interval $x \in (0, \infty)$. The apparent failure in the case $\nu = 0$ is attributable to the presence of a zero in $I'_0(x)$ at $x = 0$.

Similar observations apply to (3.16), except that the case $\nu = 0$ is no longer special. This is because the ratio of $1/I_\nu(x)$ to $xK'_\nu(x)$ is finite and bounded throughout $x \in (0, \infty)$ for each value of ν, including zero.

(iii) The condition that $\psi(u,\zeta)$ be continuous when $\zeta \in (0,\beta)$ is not essential. From the conditions given on p. 218 of [5] it can be seen that relations (3.12) to (3.16) still apply when $\psi(u,\zeta)$ has a finite number of discontinuities in $(0,\beta)$, provided that $\mathcal{V}_{0,\beta}(H)$ is finite. The only change in Theorem 1 is that $\partial^2 W_1/\partial\zeta^2$ and $\partial^2 W_2/\partial\zeta^2$ are discontinuous at the discontinuities of $\psi(u,\zeta)$.

(iv) In the case $\mu = 1$, inequality (3.21) could be applied to the analysis of [5, pp. 441–442], to derive bounds similar to (3.14) and (3.16) for the derivatives of the error terms associated with the series *expansions* of the solutions. These bounds are simpler than those given in [5].

---

(6) For example, by application of Theorem 10.2 on p. 220 of [5].

(7) "Weight function" could be used in place of "balancing function", but this term is used in a different context in §§5 and 6.

4. Asymptotic properties of the approximate solutions. In order that the bounds (3.13) and (3.15) for the relative errors in the approximations to the solutions $W_1(u,\zeta)$ and $W_2(u,\zeta)$ are finite, it suffices that the error-control function $H(u,\zeta)$ defined by (3.11) is of bounded variation in the interval $(0,\beta)$. From condition (3.08) it is clear that by proper choice of the balancing function $\Omega_\nu(x)$ we can arrange for the variation of $H(u,\zeta)$ to converge at $\zeta=\beta$, provided that $\zeta^{-\mu/2}|\psi(u,\zeta)|$ is integrable at β. Similarly, at the other endpoint $\zeta=0$ the variation of $H(u,\zeta)$ can be made to converge as long as $|\psi(u,\zeta)|$ is integrable when $\nu>0$, or $|\psi(u,\zeta)\ln\zeta|$ is integrable when $\nu=0$.

What is the asymptotic behavior of the error bounds as the parameter u tends to infinity? The answer obviously depends on the way in which the function $\psi(u,\zeta)$ involves the parameter u. For illustration, we consider an example in which $\beta=\infty$, and each of μ, ν, and $\psi(u,\zeta)\equiv\psi(\zeta)$ is independent of u. Other cases may be attacked along similar lines.

EXAMPLE. Assume that:

(i) $\psi(\zeta)$ *is continuous in* $(0,\infty)$.

(ii) $\zeta^{-\mu/2}|\psi(\zeta)|$ *is integrable at* $\zeta=+\infty$.

(iii) $\psi(\zeta)=O(\zeta^{\rho-1})$ *as* $\zeta\to 0+$, *where* ρ *is a positive constant.*

We first observe that these conditions ensure that $\psi(\zeta)$ meets all the conditions given in §3 and the first paragraph in the present section. An admissible choice of $\Omega_\nu(x)$ is furnished by

$$\Omega_\nu(x)=1+x\ (\nu>0),\qquad \Omega_0(x)=(1+x)/\ln(e+x^{-1}),$$

where e is the base of natural logarithms. In consequence of condition (iii) there exists a constant A such that $|\psi(\zeta)|\leqslant A\zeta^{\rho-1}$ $(0<\zeta\leqslant 1)$. Hence in the case $\nu>0$ we have

$$\mathcal{V}_{0,1}(H)=\frac{1}{\mu}\int_0^1\frac{|\psi(v)|}{1+uv^{\mu/2}}dv\leqslant\frac{A}{\mu}\int_0^1\frac{v^{\rho-1}\,dv}{1+uv^{\mu/2}}=\frac{2A}{\mu^2u^{2\rho/\mu}}\int_0^u\frac{\tau^{(2\rho/\mu)-1}}{1+\tau}d\tau.$$

The last quantity is estimated by

$$O(u^{-1})\quad(\mu<2\rho),\quad O(u^{-1}\ln u)\quad(\mu=2\rho),\quad\text{or}\quad O(u^{-2\rho/\mu})\quad(\mu>2\rho).\tag{4.01}$$

Next,

$$\mathcal{V}_{1,\infty}(H)=\frac{1}{\mu}\int_1^\infty\frac{|\psi(v)|}{1+uv^{\mu/2}}dv\leqslant\frac{1}{\mu u}\int_1^\infty\frac{|\psi(v)|}{v^{\mu/2}}dv=O\Big(\frac{1}{u}\Big);$$

compare condition (ii). Adding this estimate to that for $\mathcal{V}_{0,1}(H)$ given by (4.01), we see that $\mathcal{V}_{0,\infty}(H)$, also, is estimated by (4.01).

When $\nu = 0$, the analysis is modified by introduction of the factor $\ln(e + u^{-1}\nu^{-\mu/2})$ in the integrals for $\mathcal{V}_{0,1}(H)$ and $\mathcal{V}_{1,\infty}(H)$. It is easy to verify, however, that the final estimates (4.01) continue to apply to $\mathcal{V}_{0,\infty}(H)$.

Bearing in mind that the quantity l_ν defined by (3.10) is independent of u, we see from (3.13) and (3.15) that the relative errors $\varepsilon_1(u,\zeta)/I_\nu(u\zeta^{\mu/2})$ and $\varepsilon_2(u,\zeta)/K_\nu(u\zeta^{\mu/2})$ in the approximations (3.12) each have the estimates (4.01) as $u \to \infty$, uniformly with respect to $\zeta \in (0,\infty)$. Moreover, the same estimates also hold for $\zeta K_\nu(u\zeta^{\mu/2})\partial\varepsilon_1(u,\zeta)/\partial\zeta$ and $\zeta I_\nu(u\zeta^{\mu/2})\partial\varepsilon_2(u,\zeta)/\partial\zeta$.(8) These are the required asymptotic results for the present example.

5. **Real variables: Case** II. The standard form of differential equation for Case II is given by

$$\frac{d^2W}{d\zeta^2} = \left\{-\frac{\mu^2u^2}{4}\zeta^{\mu-2} + \frac{\mu^2\nu^2-1}{4\zeta^2} + \frac{\psi(u,\zeta)}{\zeta}\right\}W. \tag{5.01}$$

The approximating equation is taken to be

$$\frac{d^2W}{d\zeta^2} = \left(-\frac{\mu^2u^2}{4}\zeta^{\mu-2} + \frac{\mu^2\nu^2-1}{4\zeta^2}\right)W, \tag{5.02}$$

with solutions $\zeta^{1/2}J_\nu(u\zeta^{\mu/2})$ and $\zeta^{1/2}Y_\nu(u\zeta^{\mu/2})$.

For nonnegative values of the order ν and positive values of the argument x, relevant properties of the Bessel functions are given, for example, in [5, pp. 436–438]. And exactly as in this reference we introduce auxiliary weight, modulus, and phase functions $E_\nu(x)$, $M_\nu(x)$, and $\theta_\nu(x)$, respectively, such that

$$J_\nu(x) = E_\nu^{-1}(x)M_\nu(x)\cos\theta_\nu(x), \quad Y_\nu(x) = E_\nu(x)M_\nu(x)\sin\theta_\nu(x). \tag{5.03}$$

We shall also need to introduce corresponding modulus and phase functions for the derivatives; thus

$$J'_\nu(x) = E_\nu^{-1}(x)N_\nu(x)\cos\omega_\nu(x), \quad Y'_\nu(x) = E_\nu(x)N_\nu(x)\sin\omega_\nu(x), \tag{5.04}$$

with the same weight function $E_\nu(x)$ as in (5.03).

The balancing function $\Omega_\nu(x)$ and error-control function $H(u,\zeta)$ are defined exactly as in §3 above. Auxiliary positive constants that will be needed are defined by

$$l_{\nu,0} = \sup\{\pi\Omega_\nu(x)M_\nu^2(x)\}, \qquad l_{\nu,1} = \sup\{\pi\Omega_\nu(x)|J_\nu(x)|E_\nu(x)M_\nu(x)\},$$
$$l_{\nu,2} = \sup\{\pi\Omega_\nu(x)|Y_\nu(x)|E_\nu^{-1}(x)M_\nu(x)\},$$

(8) Compare Remark (ii) at the end of §3.

each supremum being taken over the x-interval $(0, \infty)$. It is easily verified that all three suprema are finite; moreover, $l_{\nu,1} \leqslant l_{\nu,0}$ and $l_{\nu,2} \leqslant l_{\nu,0}$.

THEOREM 2. *Let u be a positive parameter and μ and ν be numbers that are independent of x and satisfy $\mu > 0$ and $\nu \geqslant 0$. Assume also that for each value of u the function $\psi(u, \zeta)$ is continuous in a finite or infinite interval $0 < \zeta < \beta$. Then in this interval the differential equation* (5.01) *has solutions $W_1(u, \zeta)$ and $W_2(u, \zeta)$ that are twice continuously differentiable functions of ζ, and have the forms*

$$W_1(u, \zeta) = \zeta^{1/2}\{J_\nu(u\zeta^{\mu/2}) + \varepsilon_1(u, \zeta)\},$$
$$W_2(u, \zeta) = \zeta^{1/2}\{Y_\nu(u\zeta^{\mu/2}) + \varepsilon_2(u, \zeta)\}, \tag{5.05}$$

where

$$|\varepsilon_1(u, \zeta)| \leqslant (l_{\nu,1}/l_{\nu,0}) E_\nu^{-1}(u\zeta^{\mu/2}) M_\nu(u\zeta^{\mu/2})[\exp\{l_{\nu,0} \mathcal{V}_{0,\zeta}(H)\} - 1], \tag{5.06}$$

$$|\partial\varepsilon_1(u, \zeta)/\partial\zeta| \leqslant \tfrac{1}{2}\mu(l_{\nu,1}/l_{\nu,0}) u\zeta^{(\mu-2)/2} E_\nu^{-1}(u\zeta^{\mu/2}) N_\nu(u\zeta^{\mu/2}) \times [\exp\{l_{\nu,0} \mathcal{V}_{0,\zeta}(H)\} - 1], \tag{5.07}$$

$$|\varepsilon_2(u, \zeta)| \leqslant (l_{\nu,2}/l_{\nu,0}) E_\nu(u\zeta^{\mu/2}) M_\nu(u\zeta^{\mu/2}) \times [\exp\{l_{\nu,0} \mathcal{V}_{\zeta,\beta}(H)\} - 1], \tag{5.08}$$

$$|\partial\varepsilon_2(u, \zeta)/\partial\zeta| \leqslant \tfrac{1}{2}\mu(l_{\nu,2}/l_{\nu,0}) u\zeta^{(\mu-2)/2} E_\nu(u\zeta^{\mu/2}) N_\nu(u\zeta^{\mu/2}) \times [\exp\{l_{\nu,0} \mathcal{V}_{\zeta,\beta}(H)\} - 1], \tag{5.09}$$

provided that these bounds are finite.

The proof of this theorem is similar to that of Theorem 1, and it is unnecessary to record details.

Similar observations to those made in §§3 and 4 also apply in the present case. Thus if $\psi(u, \zeta) \equiv \psi(\zeta)$ is independent of u, and satisfies the conditions of the example given in §4, then both

$$\varepsilon_1(u, \zeta)/\{E_\nu^{-1}(u\zeta^{\mu/2}) M_\nu(u\zeta^{\mu/2})\}, \qquad \varepsilon_2(u, \zeta)/\{E_\nu(u\zeta^{\mu/2}) M_\nu(u\zeta^{\mu/2})\},$$

are estimated by (4.01) as $u \to \infty$, uniformly with respect to $\zeta \in (0, \infty)$. Similarly for the derivatives. It may be noted that this particular example was also treated by Riekstiņš, and our results resemble those given on p. 73 of [8].

6. Complex parameter and argument. In this concluding section we consider equation (3.02), that is,

$$\frac{d^2 W}{d\zeta^2} = \left\{\frac{\mu^2 u^2}{4}\zeta^{\mu-2} + \frac{\mu^2 \nu^2 - 1}{4\zeta^2} + \frac{\psi(u, \zeta)}{\zeta}\right\} W \tag{6.01}$$

for complex values of u and ζ. We continue to suppose that μ is real and positive, and ν is real and nonnegative. We assume that for each value of u there is an open domain $\Delta(u)$, which contains $\zeta = 0$ and may be unbounded, and $\psi(u,\zeta)$ is holomorphic in $\Delta(u)$ except possibly at $\zeta = 0$. The domain $\Delta(u)$ need not be confined to a single Riemann sheet.

Relevant properties of the modified Bessel functions for real orders and complex arguments are given in [5, pp. 453–454], and exactly as on pp. 454–457 of this reference we introduce real weight, modulus, and phase functions $\mathfrak{E}_\nu(z)$, $\mathfrak{M}_\nu(z)$, and $\vartheta_\nu(z)$, respectively, such that when $|\mathrm{ph}\, z| \leqslant \frac{1}{2}\pi$,(9)

$$(6.02)\qquad |I_\nu(z)| = \mathfrak{E}_\nu(z)\mathfrak{M}_\nu(z)\cos\vartheta_\nu(z), \qquad |K_\nu(z)| = \mathfrak{E}_\nu^{-1}(z)\mathfrak{M}_\nu(z)\sin\vartheta_\nu(z).$$

With the same weight function $\mathfrak{E}_\nu(z)$ we also introduce corresponding modulus and phase functions for the derivatives, given by

$$(6.03)\qquad |I'_\nu(z)| = \mathfrak{E}_\nu(z)\mathfrak{N}_\nu(z)\cos\varpi_\nu(z), \qquad |K'_\nu(z)| = \mathfrak{E}_\nu^{-1}(z)\mathfrak{N}_\nu(z)\sin\varpi_\nu(z),$$

again valid when $|\mathrm{ph}\, z| \leqslant \frac{1}{2}\pi$.

Next, the balancing function $\Omega_\nu(z)$ is defined to be a real or complex continuous function of z, not necessarily analytic, which is nonvanishing in the sector $|\mathrm{ph}\, z| \leqslant \frac{1}{2}\pi$, except possibly at $z = 0$, and has the following properties in this sector:

$$\begin{aligned} \Omega_\nu(z) &= O(z) && (|z| \to \infty), \\ \Omega_\nu(z) &= O(1) && (|z| \to 0, \nu > 0), \\ \ln(z^{-1})\Omega_0(z) &= O(1) && (|z| \to 0), \end{aligned}$$

each O-term being uniform with respect to $\mathrm{ph}\, z$. The auxiliary positive constants needed in the present case are defined by

$$L_{\nu,0} = \sup\{2|\Omega_\nu(z)|\mathfrak{M}_\nu^2(z)\}, \qquad L_{\nu,1} = \sup\{2|\Omega_\nu(z) I_\nu(z)| \mathfrak{E}_\nu^{-1}(z)\mathfrak{M}_\nu(z)\},$$
$$L_{\nu,2} = \sup\{2|\Omega_\nu(z) K_\nu(z)| \mathfrak{E}_\nu(z)\mathfrak{M}_\nu(z)\}.$$

Each supremum is taken over the sector $|\mathrm{ph}\, z| \leqslant \frac{1}{2}\pi$, and is easily seen to be finite.

Lastly, we again define

$$(6.04)\qquad H(u,\zeta) = \frac{1}{\mu}\int \frac{\psi(u,\zeta)}{\Omega_\nu(u\zeta^{\mu/2})}\, d\zeta,$$

(9) Outside the sector $|\mathrm{ph}\, z| \leqslant \frac{1}{2}\pi$ the auxiliary functions are undefined.

with any convenient choice of the constant of integration.

THEOREM 3. *With the conditions and definitions of the present section, the differential equation* (6.01) *has, for each value of u, solutions* $W_1(u,\zeta)$ *and* $W_2(u,\zeta)$ *which are holomorphic in* $\Delta(u)$, *save at* $\zeta = 0$, *and have the forms*

$$W_1(u,\zeta) = \zeta^{1/2}\{I_\nu(u\zeta^{\mu/2}) + \varepsilon_1(u,\zeta)\},$$
(6.05)
$$W_2(u,\zeta) = \zeta^{1/2}\{K_\nu(u\zeta^{\mu/2}) + \varepsilon_2(u,\zeta)\},$$

where

(6.06) $$|\varepsilon_1(u,\zeta)| \leqslant (L_{\nu,1}/L_{\nu,0})\mathfrak{E}_\nu(u\zeta^{\mu/2})\mathfrak{M}_\nu(u\zeta^{\mu/2})\ [\exp\{L_{\nu,0}\mathcal{V}_{0,\zeta}(H)\} - 1],$$

(6.07) $$|\partial\varepsilon_1(u,\zeta)/\partial\zeta| \leqslant \tfrac{1}{2}\mu(L_{\nu,1}/L_{\nu,0})|u\zeta^{(\mu-2)/2}|\mathfrak{E}_\nu(u\zeta^{\mu/2})\mathfrak{N}_\nu(u\zeta^{\mu/2}) \times [\exp\{L_{\nu,0}\mathcal{V}_{0,\zeta}(H)\} - 1],$$

when $\zeta \in \mathbf{Z}_1(u)$ (*defined below*), *and*

(6.08) $$|\varepsilon_2(u,\zeta)| \leqslant (L_{\nu,2}/L_{\nu,0})\mathfrak{E}_\nu^{-1}(u\zeta^{\mu/2})\mathfrak{M}_\nu(u\zeta^{\mu/2})[\exp\{L_{\nu,0}\mathcal{V}_{\zeta,\beta}(H)\} - 1],$$

(6.09) $$|\partial\varepsilon_2(u,\zeta)/\partial\zeta| \leqslant \tfrac{1}{2}\mu(L_{\nu,2}/L_{\nu,0})|u\zeta^{(\mu-2)/2}|\mathfrak{E}_\nu^{-1}(u\zeta^{\mu/2})\mathfrak{N}_\nu(u\zeta^{\mu/2}) \times [\exp\{L_{\nu,0}\mathcal{V}_{\zeta,\beta}(H)\} - 1],$$

when $\zeta \in \mathbf{Z}_2(u,\beta)$ (*defined below*).

In this result the regions of validity $\mathbf{Z}_1(u)$ and $\mathbf{Z}_2(u,\beta)$ are specified in a similar manner to the case $\mu = 1$ treated in [5, p. 457]. Thus we denote by $\mathbf{Z}(u)$ the intersection of $\Delta(u)$ and the sector $|\mathrm{ph}(u\zeta^{\mu/2})| \leqslant \frac{1}{2}\pi$. Any branch of $\zeta^{\mu/2}$ may be employed, provided that it is continuous and used consistently throughout.(10) Then $\mathbf{Z}_1(u)$ comprises the set of points ζ that can be linked to the origin by a path(11) $\mathfrak{Q}_1$ lying in $\mathbf{Z}(u)$ such that as v passes along $\mathfrak{Q}_1$ from 0 to ζ both $\mathrm{Re}(uv^{\mu/2})$ and $|v|$ are nondecreasing. The other region of validity $\mathbf{Z}_2(u,\beta)$ comprises the set of points ζ that can be linked to an arbitrary point $\beta = \beta(u)$ of $\mathbf{Z}(u)$ (possibly at infinity), by a path $\mathfrak{Q}_2$ lying in $\mathbf{Z}(u)$ such that as v passes along $\mathfrak{Q}_2$ from β to ζ both $\mathrm{Re}(uv^{\mu/2})$ and $|v|$ are nonincreasing. Other matters to be noted are (a) the argument $u\zeta^{\mu/2}$ of each function appearing in (6.04) to (6.09) is the branch satisfying $|\mathrm{ph}(u\zeta^{\mu/2})| \leqslant \frac{1}{2}\pi$; (b) the variations in (6.06) and (6.07) are evaluated along the path $\mathfrak{Q}_1$, and the variations in (6.08)

(10) See also Remark (i) below.

(11) Strictly, here, and in the definition of $\mathbf{Z}_2(u,\beta)$, a "path" means a finite chain of R_2-arcs in the sense of [5, p. 147].

and (6.09) are evaluated along $\mathfrak{Q}_2$; (c) the solution $W_2(u,\zeta)$ depends on the choice of β.

The proof of Theorem 3 is similar to that of Theorem 1 above and Theorem 9.1 of [5, Chapter 12], and details are omitted.

REMARKS. (i) By employing all possible branches of $\zeta^{\mu/2}$ in the definition of the region $\mathbf{Z}(u)$, the whole of the original domain $\Delta(u)$ can be covered by a sequence of abutting sectors of angle $2\pi/\mu$. In each sector, Theorem 3 furnishes a pair of solutions of equation (6.01). The pair differs from sector to sector.

(ii) For large $|u|$ uniform asymptotic properties of the approximate solutions can be investigated by a straightforward extension of the methods indicated in §4.

ACKNOWLEDGMENT. The writer is pleased to acknowledge several suggestions by the referee that improved the presentation of the results.

REFERENCES

1. R. E. Langer, *On the asymptotic solutions of ordinary differential equations, with an application to the Bessel functions of large order*, Trans. Amer. Math. Soc. **33** (1931), 23–64.

2. ———, *On the asymptotic solutions of differential equations, with an application to the Bessel functions of large complex order*, Trans. Amer. Math. Soc. **34** (1932), 447–480.

3. ———, *On the asymptotic solutions of ordinary differential equations, with reference to the Stokes' phenomenon about a singular point*, Trans. Amer. Math. Soc. **37** (1935), 397–416.

4. F. W. J. Olver, *The asymptotic solution of linear differential equations of the second order in a domain containing one transition point*, Philos. Trans. Roy. Soc. London Ser. A **249** (1956), 65–97. MR **18**, 38.

5. ———, *Asymptotics and special functions*, Academic Press, New York, 1974.

6. ———, *Second-order linear differential equations with two turning points*, Philos. Trans. Roy. Soc. London Ser. A **278** (1975), 137–174.

7. ———, *Connection formulas for second-order differential equations with multiple turning points*, SIAM J. Math. Anal. **8** (1977), 127–154.

8. E. Riekstiņš, *On the method of tabulated functions*, Latvijas Valsts Univ. Zinātn. Raksti **20** (1958), 65–86. (Russian) MR **21** #2095; **22**, p. 2545.

INSTITUTE FOR PHYSICAL SCIENCE AND TECHNOLOGY, UNIVERSITY OF MARYLAND, COLLEGE PARK, MARYLAND 20742

APPLIED MATHEMATICS DIVISION, NATIONAL BUREAU OF STANDARDS, WASHINGTON, D.C. 20234

SIAM J. MATH. ANAL.
Vol. 8, No. 1, February 1977

CONNECTION FORMULAS FOR SECOND-ORDER DIFFERENTIAL EQUATIONS WITH MULTIPLE TURNING POINTS*

F. W. J. OLVER†

Abstract. A study is made of the differential equation

$$d^2w/dx^2=\{u^2f(u,x)+g(u,x)\}w, \qquad a_1<x<a_2,$$

in which u is a positive parameter. For each value of u, $\partial^2 f(u,x)/\partial x^2$ and $g(u,x)$ are assumed to be continuous in the finite or infinite open interval (a_1, a_2). The function $f(u,x)$ is real and its only zero within (a_1,a_2) is a single zero of multiplicity $m-2$, where m ($\geqq 2$) is an arbitrary integer. For large values of u, asymptotic approximations for the solutions are constructed in terms of Bessel functions of order $1/m$, subject to certain restrictions on the behavior of $f(u,x)$ and $g(u,x)$ as $u\to\infty$. These restrictions are satisfied, for example, if $f(u,x)$ is independent of u and $g(u,x)=O(u^{\varpi})$, where $\varpi<\min(4/m, 1)$. Each approximation is uniformly valid throughout (a_1,a_2) and is accompanied by a strict and realistic bound for the error term.

In the case in which a_1 and a_2 are singularities of the differential equation, the uniform approximations are applied to solve the problem of connecting the known asymptotic solutions in terms of elementary functions (the Liouville–Green approximations) valid in a neighborhood of a_2, with the corresponding asymptotic solutions valid in a neighborhood of a_1.

1. Introduction and summary

1.1. Introduction. Consider the following two questions concerning a differential equation of the form

$$d^2w/dx^2=f(x)w, \tag{1.01}$$

in which the independent variable x ranges over a finite or infinite interval (a_1,a_2),[1] and $f(x)$ is a real function that has singularities at a_1 and a_2, and is continuous within (a_1,a_2):

What is the nature of the solutions as x approaches the endpoints?

Given a solution with a certain behavior at one endpoint, how does this solution behave as x approaches the other endpoint?

A satisfactory answer to the first question is furnished by the theory of the Liouville–Green approximation given in [23, Chap. 6]. The general result is as follows. Assume that:

(i) *In the neighborhoods of a_1 and a_2, $f(x)$ is nonzero, $f''(x)$ is continuous, and the function*

$$F(x)\equiv\int\frac{1}{|f(x)|^{1/4}}\frac{d^2}{dx^2}\left(\frac{1}{|f(x)|^{1/4}}\right)dx$$

is of bounded variation.

---

* Received by the editors June 12, 1975, and in revised form October 17, 1975. This research was supported by the U.S. Army Research Office, Durham, under Contract DA ARO D 31 124 73 G204, and by the National Science Foundation under Grant GP 32841X2.

† Institute for Physical Science and Technology, University of Maryland, College Park, Maryland 20742, and National Bureau of Standards, Washington, D.C. 20234.

[1] Throughout, we adhere to the convention that (a,b) denotes the open interval $a<x<b$, and $[a,b]$ denotes the corresponding closed interval $a\leqq x\leqq b$; similarly for the partly closed intervals $(a,b]$ and $[a,b)$.

(ii)

$$|\int f^{1/2}(x)\,dx| \to \infty \quad \textit{as } x \to a_1+ \quad \textit{or} \quad a_2-.$$

Then equation (1.01) has solutions $w_1(x)$, $w_2(x)$, $w_3(x)$ and $w_4(x)$, such that

$$(1.02)\qquad \begin{aligned} w_1(x) &\sim f^{-1/4}(x)\exp\left\{\int f^{1/2}(x)\,dx\right\}, \\ w_2(x) &\sim f^{-1/4}(x)\exp\left\{-\int f^{1/2}(x)\,dx\right\}, \end{aligned} \qquad x \to a_1+,$$

$$(1.03)\qquad \begin{aligned} w_3(x) &\sim f^{-1/4}(x)\exp\left\{\int f^{1/2}(x)\,dx\right\}, \\ w_4(x) &\sim f^{-1/4}(x)\exp\left\{-\int f^{1/2}(x)\,dx\right\}, \end{aligned} \qquad x \to a_2-.$$

The following comments on this result are pertinent to the present investigation. First, the given conditions admit almost all kinds of singularities at a_1 and a_2, including most regular singularities and all irregular singularities of finite or infinite rank; see [23, pp. 197–202]. Secondly, the choice of integration constant in the indefinite integral of $f^{1/2}(x)$ appearing in (1.02) and (1.03) is unimportant, since it only affects the solutions by a constant factor. Thirdly, even when this constant of integration is fixed, the solutions may or may not be unique, but this is immaterial at the moment.

To answer the second question posed in the opening paragraph, it suffices to know the coefficients in two of the linear relations holding between any three of the four solutions, for example,

$$w_1(x) = A_1 w_3(x) + B_1 w_4(x), \qquad w_2(x) = A_2 w_3(x) + B_2 w_4(x).$$

These linear relations are called the *connection formulas* for the given differential system. Exact expressions for the coefficients A_1, B_1, A_2 and B_2 can be found only in rare cases, and in general approximate methods have to be employed. In certain physical problems, for example, barrier penetration and the approximate harmonic oscillator [10], [6], [3], $f(x)$ is twice continuously differentiable throughout (a_1, a_2) and contains a real parameter—which we shall denote by u^2—as a factor. Asymptotic approximations for the coefficients in the connection formulas are needed for large values of u. Of great importance in constructing these approximations are the number and multiplicities of the zeros of $f(x)$ within (a_1, a_2). A zero of $f(x)$ of multiplicity m is called a *turning point* (or *transition point*) *of* (1.01) *of multiplicity m*.

Satisfactory approximations, complete with strict error bounds, have been constructed for the solutions of the problem outlined in the preceding paragraph in cases when (a_1, a_2) contains at most two turning points, both of which are simple; see [3] and [23, Chap. 13]. The purpose of the present paper is to supply a similar theory when (a_1, a_2) contains a single turning point of arbitrary (integer) multiplicity. A subsequent paper [26] extends the analysis to the general case in which (a_1, a_2) contains an arbitrary number of turning points of arbitrary multiplicities.

1.2. Summary. The paper is arranged as follows.

In § 2 we consider the simplest form of differential equation having a multiple turning point, obtained by setting $f(x)$ equal to a constant factor times a power of x. Depending on the sign of the constant factor and whether the power is even or odd, three essentially distinct cases arise, which we designate I, II and III. With m denoting a positive integer such that $m \geqq 2$, our classification is given by:

Case I: $f(x) = \frac{1}{4}m^2x^{m-2}$, m even.

Case II: $f(x) = -\frac{1}{4}m^2x^{m-2}$, m even.

Case III: $f(x) = \frac{1}{4}m^2x^{m-2}$, m odd.

Thus in each case the multiplicity of the turning point at the origin is $m-2$. The normalizing factor $\pm\frac{1}{4}m^2$ has been introduced to simplify subsequent notation. In each case, the differential equation is solvable exactly in terms of Bessel functions (or modified Bessel functions) of order $1/m$. Also, in § 2 the correct choice of standard solutions is discussed, and relevant properties of the solutions are supplied, including exact connection formulas and illustrative graphs.[2]

In § 3 we study the equation

$$d^2w/dx^2 = \{u^2f(u, x) + g(u, x)\}w, \qquad a_1 < x < a_2, \tag{1.04}$$

in which u is a positive parameter, and $f(u, x)$ is nonvanishing within (a_1, a_2), except for a zero x_0, say, of multiplicity $m-2$. By means of an appropriate Liouville transformation, equation (1.04) is transformed into one of the forms

$$d^2W/d\zeta^2 = \{\pm\tfrac{1}{4}m^2u^2\zeta^{m-2} + \phi(u, \zeta)\}W,$$

in which the function $\phi(u, \zeta)$ is expressible in terms of $f(u, x)$ and $g(u, x)$. On neglecting $\phi(u, \zeta)$, the transformed equation is solvable in terms of the standard solutions of § 2. Strict error bounds are constructed for the approximations found in this way. The analysis in this section is very similar to that of [25], which treats the more general case in which the zero of $f(u, x)$ may have any multiplicity, integer or fractional. It is not possible to quote needed results directly from this reference however, because solutions are given directly in [25] for only one of the intervals $[x_0, a_2)$ or $(a_1, x_0]$. Moreover, solutions that comprise a numerically satisfactory pair[3] in the neighborhoods of x_0 and a_2 (or a_1), do not comprise a numerically satisfactory pair in the neighborhoods of a_1 and a_2.

In § 4 the results of §§ 2 and 3 are applied to derive the desired connection formulas for (1.04), complete with strict bounds for the error terms in the coefficients.

In § 5 the asymptotic nature of the error bounds of § 4 is explored in the commonly occurring case in which $f(u, x)$ is independent of u and $g(u, x) = O(u^{\varpi})$ as $u \to \infty$, uniformly with respect to x in compact intervals within (a_1, a_2), ϖ denoting a real constant. With suitable supplementary conditions, it is proved that each error bound vanishes as $u \to \infty$, provided that $\varpi < \min(4/m, 1)$. This establishes the asymptotic validity of the approximate connection formulas in these circumstances.

[2] A detailed investigation of solutions of the equation $d^2w/dz^2 = z^m w$ for integer values of m and complex values of z has been carried out by Swanson and Headley [28], and Headley and Barwell [7]. Solutions that are appropriate for complex z, however, are not necessarily the most suitable for real z; in consequence, these references do not supply all the results needed in the present paper.

[3] In the sense of Miller [19]; see also [23, pp. 154–155].

Lastly, in § 6 the work of other writers on the problem is described and related to the present analysis.

2. Standard solutions of the basic equations

2.1. Case I. The basic differential equation is given by

$$d^2w/dt^2 = \tfrac{1}{4}m^2t^{m-2}w, \tag{2.01}$$

where m is an even positive integer.[4] All solutions of this equation are infinitely differentiable when $t \in (-\infty, \infty)$. In defining standard solutions, we are guided by asymptotic behavior as $t \to \pm\infty$. From the theory of the Liouville–Green approximation given in [23, pp. 197–202], we know that there exists a unique solution that is asymptotic to $t^{(2-m)/4}\exp(-t^{m/2})$ as $t \to +\infty$. Since this solution is recessive compared with all linearly independent solutions in these circumstances, we adopt it as one of the standard solutions, and denote it by $U_m(t)$. Thus

$$U_m(t) \sim t^{(2-m)/4}\exp(-t^{m/2}), \qquad t \to +\infty, \tag{2.02}$$

the relative error in this relation being $O(t^{-m/2})$. It is also known from the theory of the Liouville–Green approximation that the last relation is differentiable; thus

$$U_m'(t) \sim -\tfrac{1}{2}mt^{(m-2)/4}\exp(-t^{m/2}), \qquad t \to +\infty, \tag{2.03}$$

again with relative error $O(t^{-m/2})$. Next, from (2.02), (2.03) and the differential equation (2.01), it follows that as t increases from $-\infty$ to $+\infty$, $U_m(t)$ is positive and decreasing, and $U_m'(t)$ is negative and increasing.[5] To determine the asymptotic behavior of $U_m(t)$ as $t \to -\infty$, as well as to derive other properties, we express $U_m(t)$ in terms of modified Bessel functions.

From the properties of Bessel functions collected in [21, Chap. 9], it is known that the general solution of (2.01) is $|t|^{1/2}\mathscr{Z}_{1/m}(|t|^{m/2})$, where $\mathscr{Z}_{1/m}$ denotes any modified cylinder function of order $1/m$. Examination of the asymptotic form of the modified Bessel functions for large positive argument yields the identification

$$U_m(t) = (2t/\pi)^{1/2}K_{1/m}(t^{m/2}), \qquad t > 0. \tag{2.04}$$

Letting $t \to 0$ in this relation and its differentiated form, we find that

$$\begin{aligned} U_m(0) &= \pi^{-1/2}2^{(2-m)/(2m)}\Gamma(1/m), \\ U_m'(0) &= \pi^{-1/2}2^{-(2+m)/(2m)}\Gamma(-1/m). \end{aligned} \tag{2.05}$$

These relations enable $U_m(t)$ to be identified in terms of modified Bessel functions when t is negative; thus

$$U_m(t) = (2|t|/\pi)^{1/2}\{\pi\csc(\pi/m)I_{1/m}(|t|^{m/2}) + K_{1/m}(|t|^{m/2})\}, \qquad t < 0. \tag{2.06}$$

---

[4] Although (2.01) has no turning point when $m = 2$, no complications arise on including this case in the subsequent analysis. In fact, because the solutions of (2.01) are elementary functions when $m = 2$, a useful check on the results becomes available. Similarly in Case II below.

[5] Let t_1 be the (algebraically) largest zero, if any, of $U_m(t)$. From (2.02) and graphical considerations, there exists $t_2 \in (t_1, \infty)$, such that $U_m'(t_2) = 0$. Referring to (2.03), however, we see that this is impossible, since from (2.01) and the fact that m is even it follows that $U_m''(t) \geqq 0$ when $t \in (t_1, \infty)$. Hence for all t, $U_m(t)$ is positive, $U_m''(t)$ is nonnegative, and $U_m'(t)$ is negative.

Thence we derive

$$U_m(t) \sim \csc(\pi/m)|t|^{(2-m)/4} \exp(|t|^{m/2}), \qquad t \to -\infty, \tag{2.07}$$

$$U'_m(t) \sim -\tfrac{1}{2}m \csc(\pi/m)|t|^{(m-2)/4} \exp(|t|^{m/2}), \qquad t \to -\infty, \tag{2.08}$$

with relative errors $O(t^{-m/2})$ in both cases.

As the second standard solution of (2.01) we employ $U_m(-t)$. As t increases from $-\infty$ to $+\infty$, this function and its first derivative increase strictly from 0 to $+\infty$. Clearly $U_m(t)$ and $U_m(-t)$ are linearly independent; they also comprise a numerically satisfactory pair in the sense of Miller [19]. Their Wronskian is easily calculated by letting $t \to +\infty$ or $t \to 0$. Either way yields

$$\mathscr{W}\{U_m(t), U_m(-t)\} = m \csc(\pi/m). \tag{2.09}$$

The connection formulas for equation (2.01) are in effect given by the combination of (2.02) and (2.07).

Lastly, in the special cases $m = 2$ and 4, we have

$$U_2(t) = e^{-t}, \qquad U_4(t) = 2^{1/2}U(0, 2t), \tag{2.10}$$

where $U(a, t)$ is the parabolic cylinder function in the notation of Miller [20], or [21, Chap. 19].

2.2. Case II. The basic differential equation in this case is given by

$$d^2w/dt^2 = -\tfrac{1}{4}m^2t^{m-2}w, \tag{2.11}$$

where m is again an even positive integer. The Liouville–Green approximation shows that as $t \to +\infty$, all solutions of this equation have the form

$$Xt^{(2-m)/4}\{\cos(t^{m/2} + \chi) + O(t^{-m/2})\},$$

where the amplitude X and phase χ are arbitrary constants. Similarly, as $t \to -\infty$, the solutions reduce to

$$\hat{X}|t|^{(2-m)/4}\{\cos(|t|^{m/2} + \hat{\chi}) + O(t^{-m/2})\},$$

where $\hat{X}$ and $\hat{\chi}$ are further constants. Following Miller [19], we seek a pair of solutions that differ in phase by $\frac{1}{2}\pi$ as $t \to +\infty$ *and also as* $t \to -\infty$. The general solution of (2.11) is $|t|^{1/2}\mathscr{C}_{1/m}(|t|^{m/2})$, where $\mathscr{C}_{1/m}$ denotes any cylinder function of order $1/m$. By considering the asymptotic forms of the $J_{1/m}$ and $Y_{1/m}$ functions for large positive argument and connecting the solutions at $t = 0$, we find that an appropriate pair of solutions is $W_m(t)$ and $W_m(-t)$, where[6]

$$W_m(t) = -\left(\frac{\pi t}{2}\right)^{1/2}\left\{\tan\left(\frac{\pi}{2m}\right)J_{1/m}(t^{m/2}) + Y_{1/m}(t^{m/2})\right\}, \qquad t > 0, \tag{2.12}$$

$$W_m(t) = \left(\frac{\pi|t|}{2}\right)^{1/2}\left\{\cot\left(\frac{\pi}{2m}\right)J_{1/m}(|t|^{m/2}) - Y_{1/m}(|t|^{m/2})\right\}, \qquad t < 0. \tag{2.13}$$

[6] The analysis also shows that when $m \geqq 4$, the *only* solutions meeting the stipulated phase conditions are constant multiples of $W_m(t)$ and $W_m(-t)$. The normalizing factor has been chosen to make $W_m(t)$ and $W'_m(t)$ agree with $U_m(t)$ and $U'_m(t)$, respectively, at $t = 0$; compare (2.05) and (2.18) below. This has some notational advantages when we come to Case III.

Relevant properties of these solutions are as follows:

$$(2.14)\quad W_m(t)=\sec\left(\frac{\pi}{2m}\right)t^{(2-m)/4}\{\cos(t^{m/2}+\tfrac{1}{4}\pi)+O(t^{-m/2})\},\qquad t\to+\infty,$$

$$(2.15)\quad W'_m(t)=-\frac{m}{2}\sec\left(\frac{\pi}{2m}\right)t^{(m-2)/4}\{\sin(t^{m/2}+\tfrac{1}{4}\pi)+O(t^{-m/2})\},\qquad t\to+\infty,$$

$$(2.16)\quad W_m(t)=\csc\left(\frac{\pi}{2m}\right)|t|^{(2-m)/4}\{\cos(|t|^{m/2}-\tfrac{1}{4}\pi)+O(t^{-m/2})\},\qquad t\to-\infty,$$

$$(2.17)\quad W'_m(t)=\frac{m}{2}\csc\left(\frac{\pi}{2m}\right)|t|^{(m-2)/4}\{\sin(|t|^{m/2}-\tfrac{1}{4}\pi)+O(t^{-m/2})\},\qquad t\to-\infty,$$

$$(2.18)\quad \begin{aligned} W_m(0)&=\pi^{-1/2}2^{(2-m)/(2m)}\Gamma(1/m),\\ W'_m(0)&=\pi^{-1/2}2^{-(2+m)/(2m)}\Gamma(-1/m),\end{aligned}$$

$$(2.19)\quad \mathscr{W}\{W_m(t),W_m(-t)\}=m\csc(\pi/m).$$

Special cases are:

$$(2.20)\quad W_2(t)=2^{1/2}\cos(t+\tfrac{1}{4}\pi),\qquad W_4(t)=2^{3/4}W(0,2t),$$

where $W(a, t)$ is the modified parabolic cylinder function defined by Miller, as in [20], or [21, Chap. 19].[7]

In order to have a convenient way of assessing the magnitudes of the functions $W_m(t)$ and $W_m(-t)$ and their derivatives in the error analysis in subsequent sections, we introduce auxiliary weight, modulus and phase functions as was done, for example, for the Airy functions in [23, Chap. 11]. Let $t=q_m$ denote the smallest nonnegative root of the equation

$$\cos\left(\frac{\pi}{2m}\right)W_m(t)=\sin\left(\frac{\pi}{2m}\right)W_m(-t);$$

compare (2.14) and (2.16). Then the weight function $E_m(t)$ is defined to be

$$(2.21)\quad \begin{aligned} &\left(\cot\frac{\pi}{2m}\right)^{1/2}, && t\geqq q_m;\\ &\left\{\frac{W_m(-t)}{W_m(t)}\right\}^{1/2}, && -q_m\leqq t\leqq q_m;\\ &\left(\tan\frac{\pi}{2m}\right)^{1/2}, && t\leqq -q_m.\end{aligned}$$

Using (2.19), we see that

$$\frac{d}{dt}\left\{\tan\left(\frac{\pi}{2m}\right)\frac{W_m(-t)}{W_m(t)}\right\}=\frac{m}{2}\sec^2\left(\frac{\pi}{2m}\right)\frac{1}{W_m^2(t)}>0.$$

[7] It is on account of the second of (2.10) and the second of (2.20) that the symbols U and W have been chosen for the solutions of (2.01) and (2.11), respectively.

From this relation and the fact that $W_m(0)>0$, it follows that the functions $W_m(t)$ and $W_m(-t)$ have no zeros in the interval $-q_m \leqq t \leqq q_m$, and hence that $E_m(t)$ *is continuous and nondecreasing in the interval* $(-\infty, \infty)$. It is also clear that $E_m(0)=1$, and if $E_m^{-1}(t)$ denotes $1/E_m(t)$, then

$$E_m(-t)=E_m^{-1}(t). \tag{2.22}$$

Modulus functions $M_m(t)$, $N_m(t)$, and phase functions $\theta_m(t)$, $\omega_m(t)$, are defined by

$$W_m(t)=E_m^{-1}(t)M_m(t)\sin\theta_m(t), \qquad W_m(-t)=E_m(t)M_m(t)\cos\theta_m(t), \tag{2.23}$$

$$W'_m(t)=E_m^{-1}(t)N_m(t)\sin\omega_m(t), \qquad W'_m(-t)=E_m(t)N_m(t)\cos\omega_m(t). \tag{2.24}$$

Each is continuous in $(-\infty, \infty)$. From (2.22) it is seen that $M_m(t)$ and $N_m(t)$ are even in t, and

$$\theta_m(t)+\theta_m(-t)=\tfrac{1}{2}\pi, \qquad \omega_m(t)+\omega_m(-t)=\tfrac{1}{2}\pi. \tag{2.25}$$

Using (2.21), we arrive at the following expressions, valid when $t \geqq q_m$:

$$\begin{aligned} M_m(t)&=\left\{\cot\left(\frac{\pi}{2m}\right)W_m^2(t)+\tan\left(\frac{\pi}{2m}\right)W_m^2(-t)\right\}^{1/2}, \\ N_m(t)&=\left\{\cot\left(\frac{\pi}{2m}\right)W_m'^2(t)+\tan\left(\frac{\pi}{2m}\right)W_m'^2(-t)\right\}^{1/2}, \end{aligned} \tag{2.26}$$

$$\begin{aligned} \theta_m(t)&=\tan^{-1}\left\{\cot\left(\frac{\pi}{2m}\right)\frac{W_m(t)}{W_m(-t)}\right\}, \\ \omega_m(t)&=\tan^{-1}\left\{\cot\left(\frac{\pi}{2m}\right)\frac{W'_m(t)}{W'_m(-t)}\right\}. \end{aligned} \tag{2.27}$$

Similarly, when $-q_m \leqq t \leqq q_m$, we have

$$\begin{aligned} M_m(t)&=\{2W_m(t)W_m(-t)\}^{1/2}, \\ N_m(t)&=\left\{\frac{W_m'^2(t)W_m^2(-t)+W_m'^2(-t)W_m^2(t)}{W_m(t)W_m(-t)}\right\}^{1/2}, \end{aligned} \tag{2.28}$$

$$\theta_m(t)=\tfrac{1}{4}\pi, \qquad \omega_m(t)=\tan^{-1}\left\{\frac{W'_m(t)W_m(-t)}{W'_m(-t)W_m(t)}\right\}. \tag{2.29}$$

Lastly, when $t\to\pm\infty$, we obtain from (2.14) to (2.17) the asymptotic forms

$$\begin{aligned} M_m(t)&\sim\{2\csc(\pi/m)\}^{1/2}|t|^{(2-m)/4}, \\ N_m(t)&\sim m\{\tfrac{1}{2}\csc(\pi/m)\}^{1/2}|t|^{(m-2)/4}. \end{aligned} \tag{2.30}$$

2.3. Case III. The basic differential equation in this case is the same as in Case I, that is,

$$d^2w/dt^2=\tfrac{1}{4}m^2t^{m-2}w, \tag{2.31}$$

except that now $m=3, 5, 7, \cdots$. For positive t, the solutions have exponential-type behavior. As in Case I, the first standard solution, which we denote by $V_m(t)$, is recessive as $t \to +\infty$ and fixed by the condition

$$V_m(t) = t^{(2-m)/4} \exp(-t^{m/2})\{1+O(t^{-m/2})\}, \qquad t \to +\infty. \tag{2.32}$$

Because this relation has the same form as (2.02), the formulas for $U_m(t)$ given in § 2.1 carry over directly to $V_m(t)$ when $t \geqq 0$. Thus

$$V'_m(t) \sim -\tfrac{1}{2} m t^{(m-2)/4} \exp(-t^{m/2}), \qquad t \to +\infty, \tag{2.33}$$

with relative error $O(t^{-m/2})$,

$$V_m(t) = (2t/\pi)^{1/2} K_{1/m}(t^{m/2}), \qquad t > 0, \tag{2.34}$$

and

$$V_m(0) = \pi^{-1/2} 2^{(2-m)/(2m)} \Gamma(1/m), \qquad V'_m(0) = \pi^{-1/2} 2^{-(2+m)/(2m)} \Gamma(-1/m). \tag{2.35}$$

When t is negative, the differential equation (2.31) has the same form as in Case II, hence the solutions are oscillatory. Moreover, since the initial conditions (2.35) agree with (2.18), the formulas for $W_m(t)$ given in § 2.2 carry over to $V_m(t)$ when $t \leqq 0$. Thus

$$V_m(t) = \left(\frac{\pi|t|}{2}\right)^{1/2} \left\{\cot\left(\frac{\pi}{2m}\right) J_{1/m}(|t|^{m/2}) - Y_{1/m}(|t|^{m/2})\right\}, \qquad t < 0, \tag{2.36}$$

$$V_m(t) = \csc\left(\frac{\pi}{2m}\right) |t|^{(2-m)/4} \{\cos(|t|^{m/2} - \tfrac{1}{4}\pi) + O(t^{-m/2})\}, \qquad t \to -\infty, \tag{2.37}$$

$$V'_m(t) = \frac{m}{2} \csc\left(\frac{\pi}{2m}\right) |t|^{(m-2)/4} \{\sin(|t|^{m/2} - \tfrac{1}{4}\pi) + O(t^{-m/2})\}, \qquad t \to -\infty. \tag{2.38}$$

Again, following Miller [19], we choose the second standard solution of (2.31), $\bar{V}_m(t)$, say, in such a way that $V_m(t)$ and $\bar{V}_m(t)$ are $\frac{1}{2}\pi$ out of phase as $x \to -\infty$. A convenient normalization is given by

$$\bar{V}_m(t) = \sec\left(\frac{\pi}{2m}\right) |t|^{(2-m)/4} \{\cos(|t|^{m/2} + \tfrac{1}{4}\pi) + O(t^{-m/2})\}, \qquad t \to -\infty, \tag{2.39}$$

since this has the same form as $W_m(-t)$ when $t \to -\infty$; compare (2.14). Then from § 2.2 we immediately derive

$$\bar{V}'_m(t) = \frac{m}{2} \sec\left(\frac{\pi}{2m}\right) |t|^{(m-2)/4} \{\sin(|t|^{m/2} + \tfrac{1}{4}\pi) + O(t^{-m/2})\}, \qquad t \to -\infty, \tag{2.40}$$

$$\bar{V}_m(t) = -\left(\frac{\pi|t|}{2}\right)^{1/2} \left\{\tan\left(\frac{\pi}{2m}\right) J_{1/m}(|t|^{m/2}) + Y_{1/m}(|t|^{m/2})\right\}, \qquad t < 0, \tag{2.41}$$

and

$$\begin{aligned} \bar{V}_m(0) &= \pi^{-1/2} 2^{(2-m)/(2m)} \Gamma(1/m), \\ \bar{V}'_m(0) &= -\pi^{-1/2} 2^{-(2+m)/(2m)} \Gamma(-1/m). \end{aligned} \tag{2.42}$$

For positive t, we have, as in Case I,

(2.43) $\bar{V}_m(t)=(2t/\pi)^{1/2}\{\pi \csc(\pi/m) I_{1/m}(t^{m/2})+K_{1/m}(t^{m/2})\}, \qquad t>0,$

(2.44) $\bar{V}_m(t)\sim \csc(\pi/m) t^{(2-m)/4} \exp(t^{m/2}), \qquad t\to+\infty,$

(2.45) $\bar{V}'_m(t)\sim \frac{1}{2}m \csc(\pi/m) t^{(m-2)/4} \exp(t^{m/2}), \qquad t\to+\infty,$

the relative error in the last two relations being $O(t^{-m/2})$.

The Wronskian relation in the present case is given by

(2.46) $$\mathscr{W}\{V_m(t), \bar{V}_m(t)\}=m \csc(\pi/m).$$

In the special case $m=3$, the solutions are expressible as Airy functions, as follows:

(2.47) $V_3(t)=2^{5/6}3^{1/6}\pi^{1/2} \operatorname{Ai}\{(\frac{3}{2})^{2/3}t\}, \qquad \bar{V}_3(t)=2^{5/6}3^{-1/3}\pi^{1/2} \operatorname{Bi}\{(\frac{3}{2})^{2/3}t\}.$

Next, when $t\in[0,\infty)$, $V_m(t)$ is positive and decreasing, $V'_m(t)$ is negative and increasing, and both $\bar{V}_m(t)$ and $\bar{V}'_m(t)$ are positive and increasing. In the case of $V_m(t)$ and $V'_m(t)$, this result is proved by similar analysis to that sketched in § 2.1 for $U_m(t)$ and $U'_m(t)$. For $\bar{V}_m(t)$ and $\bar{V}'_m(t)$, the result follows from the Maclaurin series for $\bar{V}_m(t)$.

Auxiliary functions are defined as follows. First, consider the equation

$$\cos\left(\frac{\pi}{2m}\right)\bar{V}_m(t)=\sin\left(\frac{\pi}{2m}\right)V_m(t).$$

There are no positive roots, since the left-hand side exceeds the right-hand side at $t=0$, and the former is increasing and the latter decreasing. Let $t=-q_m$ be the negative root of smallest absolute value. Then the weight function we shall use is defined by

(2.48) $$E_m(t)=\left\{\frac{\bar{V}_m(t)}{V_m(t)}\right\}^{1/2}, \qquad t\geqq -q_m;$$
$$E_m(t)=\left(\tan\frac{\pi}{2m}\right)^{1/2}, \qquad t\leqq -q_m.$$

From (2.46) we have

$$\frac{d}{dt}\frac{\bar{V}_m(t)}{V_m(t)}=m\csc\left(\frac{\pi}{m}\right)\frac{1}{V_m^2(t)}>0.$$

Hence as t decreases continuously from $t=0$, the value $-q_m$ is reached ahead of the first zero of $\bar{V}_m(t)$, which in turn is reached ahead of the first zero of $V_m(t)$. Thus $E_m(t)$ *is continuous and nondecreasing in the interval* $(-\infty,\infty)$.

With $E_m^{-1}(t)$ again denoting $1/E_m(t)$, modulus functions $M_m(t)$, $N_m(t)$ and phase functions $\theta_m(t)$, $\omega_m(t)$, are defined by

(2.49) $V_m(t)=E_m^{-1}(t)M_m(t)\sin\theta_m(t), \qquad \bar{V}_m(t)=E_m(t)M_m(t)\cos\theta_m(t),$

(2.50) $V'_m(t)=E_m^{-1}(t)N_m(t)\sin\omega_m(t), \qquad \bar{V}'_m(t)=E_m(t)N_m(t)\cos\omega_m(t).$

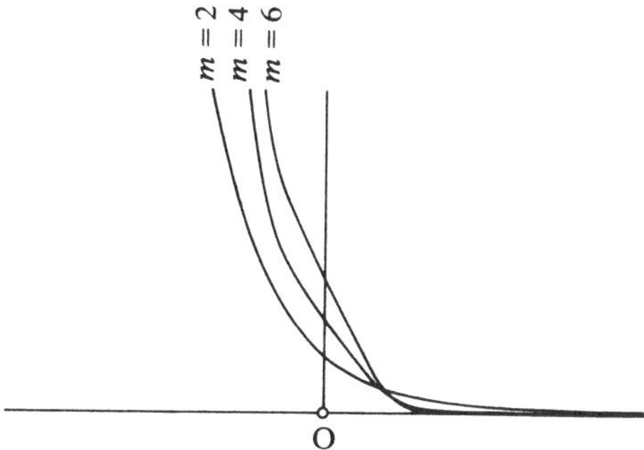

FIG. 2.1. *Case* I. $U_m(t)$, $m = 2, 4, 6$

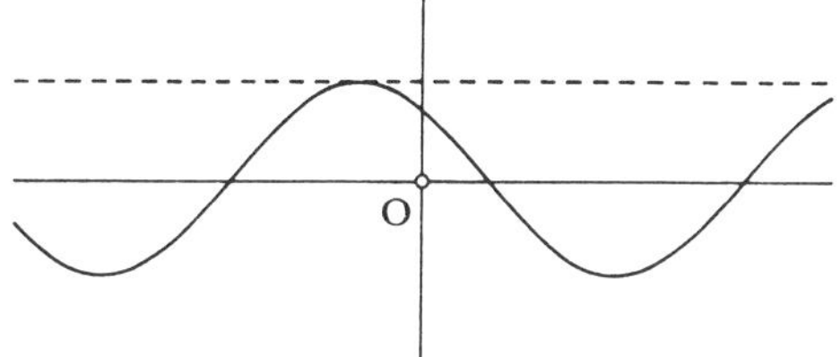

FIG. 2.2. *Case* II. $W_2(t)$ ——; $E_2^{-1}(t)M_2(t)$ - - -

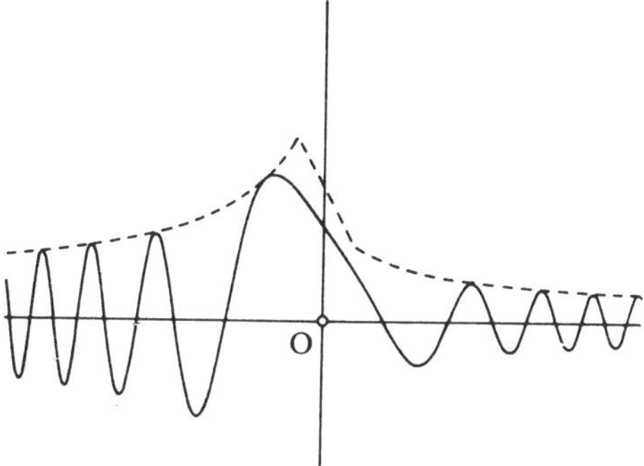

FIG. 2.3. *Case* II. $W_4(t)$ ——; $E_4^{-1}(t)M_4(t)$ - - -

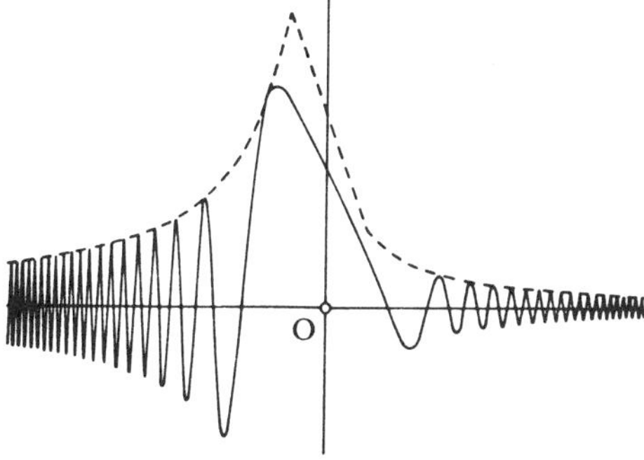

FIG. 2.4. *Case* II. $W_6(t)$ ——; $E_6^{-1}(t)M_6(t)$ - - -

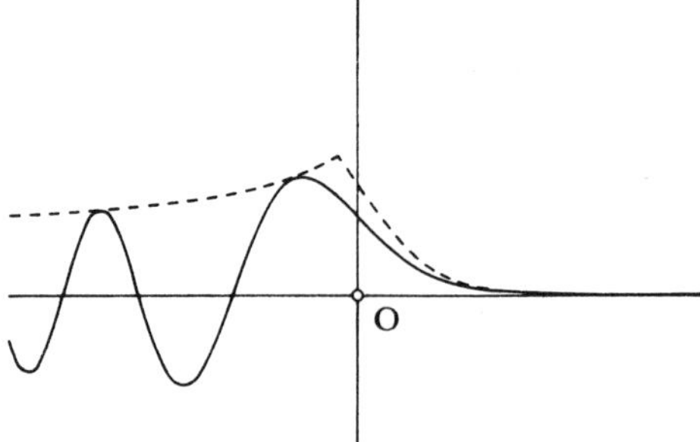

FIG. 2.5. *Case* III. $V_3(t)$ —— ; $E_3^{-1}(t)M_3(t)$ - - -

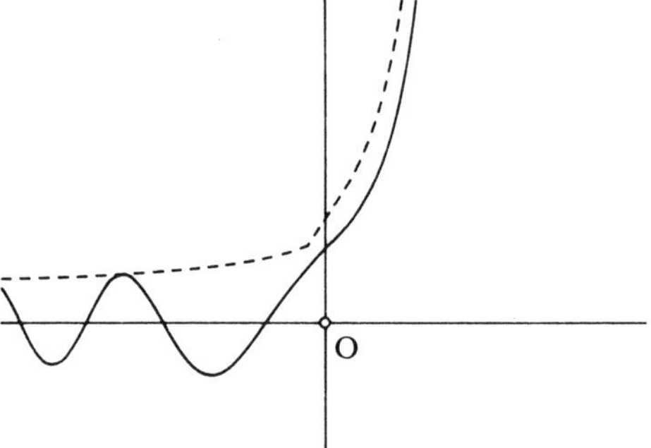

FIG. 2.6. *Case* III. $\bar{V}_3(t)$ —— ; $E_3(t)M_3(t)$ - - -

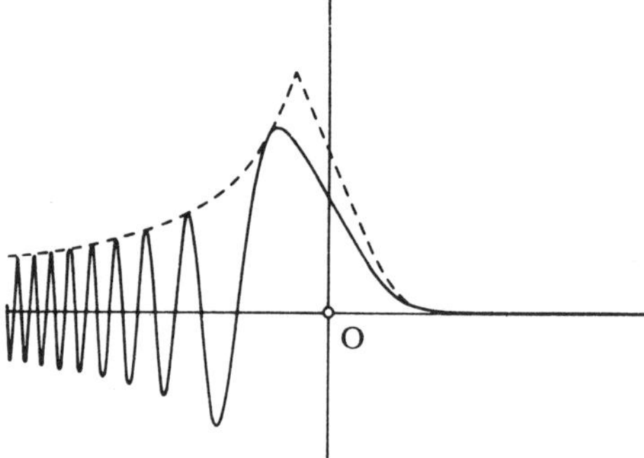

FIG. 2.7. *Case* III. $V_5(t)$ —— ; $E_5^{-1}(t)M_5(t)$ - - -

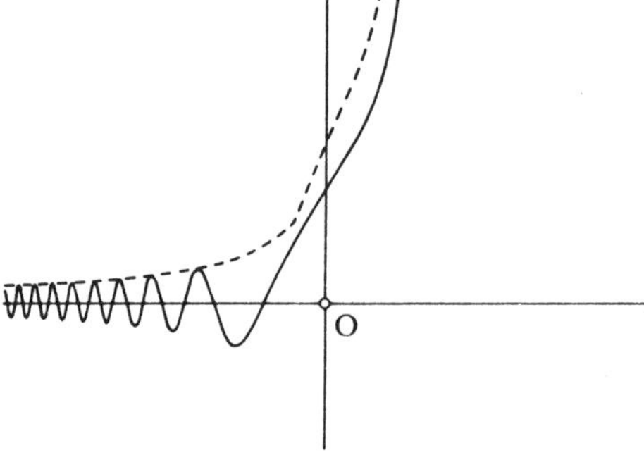

FIG. 2.8. *Case* III. $\bar{V}_5(t)$ —— ; $E_5(t)M_5(t)$ - - -

Each is continuous. Using (2.48), we see that when $t \geqq -q_m$,

$$(2.51)\quad M_m(t)=\{2V_m(t)\bar{V}_m(t)\}^{1/2},\qquad N_m(t)=\left\{\frac{V_m'^2(t)\bar{V}_m^2(t)+\bar{V}_m'^2(t)V_m^2(t)}{V_m(t)\bar{V}_m(t)}\right\}^{1/2},$$

$$(2.52)\qquad \theta_m(t)=\tfrac{1}{4}\pi,\qquad \omega_m(t)=\tan^{-1}\left\{\frac{V_m'(t)\bar{V}_m(t)}{\bar{V}_m'(t)V_m(t)}\right\}.$$

Alternatively, when $t \leqq -q_m$,

$$(2.53)\qquad \begin{aligned} M_m(t)&=\left\{\tan\left(\frac{\pi}{2m}\right)V_m^2(t)+\cot\left(\frac{\pi}{2m}\right)\bar{V}_m^2(t)\right\}^{1/2},\\ N_m(t)&=\left\{\tan\left(\frac{\pi}{2m}\right)V_m'^2(t)+\cot\left(\frac{\pi}{2m}\right)\bar{V}_m'^2(t)\right\}^{1/2},\end{aligned}$$

$$(2.54)\quad \theta_m(t)=\tan^{-1}\left\{\tan\left(\frac{\pi}{2m}\right)\frac{V_m(t)}{\bar{V}_m(t)}\right\},\qquad \omega_m(t)=\tan^{-1}\left\{\tan\left(\frac{\pi}{2m}\right)\frac{V_m'(t)}{\bar{V}_m'(t)}\right\}.$$

Lastly, as $t\to\pm\infty$, we find that

$$(2.55)\quad M_m(t)\sim\{2\csc(\pi/m)\}^{1/2}|t|^{(2-m)/4},\qquad N_m(t)\sim m\{\tfrac{1}{2}\csc(\pi/m)\}^{1/2}|t|^{(m-2)/4}.$$

2.4. Graphs. Typical graphs for the standard solutions in Cases I, II and III are given in the accompanying diagrams.

The continuous curves in Figs. 2.1–2.4 represent the solutions $U_m(t)$, in Case I, and $W_m(t)$, in Case II, for $m=2$ (no turning point), $m=4$ (double turning point) and $m=6$ (quadruple turning point). The graphs of $W_m(t)$ in Figs. 2.2–2.4 are accompanied by broken curves representing the auxiliary function $E_m^{-1}(t)M_m(t)$. This function is used as a majorant for $|W_m(t)|$ in constructing error bounds in subsequent sections; compare the first of equations (2.23). The discontinuities in the direction of the tangent to the broken curves occur at the points $t=\pm q_m$, defined in § 2.2. Numerical values to three decimal places are found to be

$$q_2=0.000,\quad q_4=0.431,\quad q_6=0.596.$$

In a similar manner, the solutions $V_m(t)$ and $\bar{V}_m(t)$ in Case III are represented by the continuous curves in Figs. 2.5–2.8 for $m=3$ (simple turning point) and $m=5$ (triple turning point). The graphs of $V_m(t)$ and $\bar{V}_m(t)$ are accompanied by broken curves representing $E_m^{-1}(t)M_m(t)$, and $E_m(t)M_m(t)$, respectively; compare equations (2.49). The discontinuities in the direction of the tangent to the broken curves occur at $t=-q_m$, defined in § 2.3. Numerical values to three decimal places are given by

$$q_3=0.279,\qquad q_5=0.528.$$

All diagrams are drawn to the same scale, that is, from -5 to 5 horizontally and from -2.75 to 6 vertically, except that the vertical scales in Figs. 2.1 and 2.2 have been shortened to 0 to 6, and -2.75 to 2.75, respectively.

3. Approximations for the solutions

3.1. Preliminary conditions. In this section we investigate solutions of the differential equation

$$d^2w/dx^2=\{u^2f(u,x)+g(u,x)\}w, \tag{3.01}$$

when x ranges over a finite or infinite interval (a_1, a_2) and u is a positive parameter. For each value of u, we suppose that $g(u, x)$ is a real or complex function that is continuous (or sectionally continuous) in (a_1, a_2), and $f(u, x)/(x-x_0)^{m-2}$ is a real function that is nonvanishing and twice continuously differentiable in (a_1, a_2). Here x_0 is a given interior point of (a_1, a_2) (which may depend on u), and m is an integer not less than 2. Thus the only possible zero of $f(u, x)$ in (a_1, a_2) is a zero of multiplicity $m-2$ at $x=x_0$. As in § 2, there are three distinct cases I, II and III to consider, depending on the sign of $f(u,x)/(x-x_0)^{m-2}$ and whether m is even or odd.

Following similar investigations in [24] and [25], we introduce a *balancing function* $\Omega_m(t)$, an *auxiliary variable* $\zeta\equiv\zeta(u,x)$, an *auxiliary function* $\hat{f}(u,x)$ and an *error-control function* $H_m(u,x)$. These are defined as follows.

First, $\Omega_m(t)$ is any conveniently chosen continuous[8] even function of the real variable t that is positive, except possibly at $t=0$, and has the properties

$$\Omega_m(t)=O(t^{(m-2)/2}),\qquad t\to\pm\infty. \tag{3.02}$$

For example, a suitable choice is given by

$$\Omega_m(t)=1+|t|^{(m-2)/2}. \tag{3.03}$$

Secondly,

$$\begin{aligned}\zeta&=-\left\{\int_x^{x_0}|f(u,y)|^{1/2}\,dy\right\}^{2/m}, && a_1<x\leqq x_0;\\ \zeta&=\left\{\int_{x_0}^{x}|f(u,y)|^{1/2}\,dy\right\}^{2/m}, && x_0\leqq x<a_2.\end{aligned} \tag{3.04}$$

Clearly ζ is a continuous and increasing function of x.

Thirdly,

$$\hat{f}(u,x)=4|f(u,x)|/(m^2|\zeta|^{m-2}). \tag{3.05}$$

Fourthly,

$$H_m(u,x)=\int\left\{\frac{1}{\hat{f}^{1/4}(u,x)}\frac{d^2}{dx^2}\left(\frac{1}{\hat{f}^{1/4}(u,x)}\right)-\frac{g(u,x)}{\hat{f}^{1/2}(u,x)}\right\}\frac{dx}{\Omega_m(u^{2/m}\zeta)}, \tag{3.06}$$

the arbitrary constant of integration being immaterial.

For example, in the case of the equation

$$d^2w/dx^2=\tfrac{1}{4}u^2m^2x^{m-2}w$$

---

[8] Actually "continuous" may be replaced here by "sectionally continuous." Also, $\Omega_m(t)$ may depend on u, but this does not need emphasizing in the notation.

we may take $f(u,x)=\frac{1}{4}m^2x^{m-2}$, $x_0=0$ and $g(u,x)=0$. Then $\zeta=x$, $\hat{f}(u,x)=1$, and $H_m(u,x)=0$.

3.2. Case I.

THEOREM I. *Assume the conditions and notation of* § 3.1, *and also that m is even and the sign of* $f(u,x)/(x-x_0)^{m-2}$ *is positive. Then in* (a_1, a_2), *equation* (3.01) *has twice continuously differentiable solutions* $w_1(u,x)$ *and* $w_2(u,x)$ *such that*

$$w_1(u,x)=\hat{f}^{-1/4}(u,x)\{U_m(-u^{2/m}\zeta)+\varepsilon_1(u,x)\}, \tag{3.07}$$

$$w_2(u,x)=\hat{f}^{-1/4}(u,x)\{U_m(u^{2/m}\zeta)+\varepsilon_2(u,x)\}, \tag{3.08}$$

where

$$\frac{|\varepsilon_1(u,x)|}{U_m(-u^{2/m}\zeta)},\ \frac{|\partial\varepsilon_1(u,x)/\partial x|}{\mu_m u^{2/m}\hat{f}^{1/2}(u,x)|U_m'(-u^{2/m}\zeta)|} \leqq \exp\left\{\frac{\lambda_m}{u^{2/m}}\mathcal{V}_{a_1,x}(H_m)\right\}-1, \tag{3.09}$$

$$\frac{|\varepsilon_2(u,x)|}{U_m(u^{2/m}\zeta)},\ \frac{|\partial\varepsilon_2(u,x)/\partial x|}{\mu_m u^{2/m}\hat{f}^{1/2}(u,x)|U_m'(u^{2/m}\zeta)|} \leqq \exp\left\{\frac{\lambda_m}{u^{2/m}}\mathcal{V}_{x,a_2}(H_m)\right\}-1, \tag{3.10}$$

and

$$\lambda_m=\sup_{t\in(-\infty,\infty)}\left\{\frac{1}{m}\sin\left(\frac{\pi}{m}\right)\Omega_m(t)U_m(t)U_m(-t)\right\}, \tag{3.11}$$

$$\mu_m=\sup_{t\in(-\infty,\infty)}\left\{m\csc\left(\frac{\pi}{m}\right)\frac{1}{|U_m'(t)|U_m(-t)}\right\}. \tag{3.12}$$

In this theorem and subsequent analysis, $\mathcal{V}$ denotes the variational operator defined and discussed in [23, pp. 27–29]; thus, for example,

$$\mathcal{V}_{a_1,x}(H_m)=\int_{a_1}^{x}\left|\frac{\partial H_m(u,y)}{\partial y}\right|dy.$$

We note that as a consequence of the behavior of $U_m(t)$ and $U_m'(t)$ as $t\to\pm\infty$, given in § 2.1, and the conditions on $\Omega_m(t)$ imposed in § 3.1, the suprema in (3.11) and (3.12) are finite.

To prove Theorem I, we begin by transforming from x to ζ as independent variable in the differential equation. Let $\zeta=\zeta_1, \zeta_2$ correspond to the endpoints $x=a_1, a_2$, respectively. Either ζ_1 or ζ_2 or both may be at infinity. From (3.04) and the fact that in the present case, $f(u,x)$ is nonnegative, we see that

$$\tfrac{1}{4}m^2\zeta^{m-2}=\dot{x}^2 f(u,x),$$

where the dot signifies differentiation with respect to ζ. In place of w, we adopt a new dependent variable, given by

$$W=\dot{x}^{-1/2}w. \tag{3.13}$$

The transformation from x and w to ζ and W is then a Liouville transformation [23, pp. 190–193]; accordingly the new differential equation is given by

$$d^2W/d\zeta^2 = \{\tfrac{1}{4}m^2u^2\zeta^{m-2} + \phi(u, \zeta)\}W, \tag{3.14}$$

where

$$\phi(u, \zeta) = \dot{x}^{1/2}\{d^2(\dot{x}^{-1/2})/d\zeta^2\} + \dot{x}^2 g(u, x).$$

From the definition (3.05) we see that

$$\hat{f}(u, x) = 1/\dot{x}^2 \tag{3.15}$$

and hence that

$$\phi(u, \zeta) = \frac{1}{\hat{f}^{1/4}}\frac{d^2}{d\zeta^2}(\hat{f}^{1/4}) + \frac{g}{\hat{f}} = -\frac{1}{\hat{f}^{3/4}}\frac{d^2}{dx^2}\left(\frac{1}{\hat{f}^{1/4}}\right) + \frac{g}{\hat{f}}.$$

LEMMA. *With the conditions in the opening paragraph of* § 3.1, $\zeta/(x - x_0)$ *is a positive, twice continuously differentiable function of* x *when* $a_1 < x < a_2$, *and* $\phi(u, \zeta)$ *is sectionally continuous in the corresponding interval* $\zeta_1 < \zeta < \zeta_2$.

The proof of this result in the case $m = 3$ can be found, for example, on p. 399 of [23]. The extension to other values of m is straightforward, and it is unnecessary to record details.

We return to the proof of Theorem I. Substituting $w_2(u, x)$ for w on the right-hand side of (3.13) and using (3.08) and (3.15), we obtain

$$W = U_m(u^{2/m}\zeta) + \varepsilon_2(u, x).$$

On combining (2.01), with $w = U_m$ and $t = u^{2/m}\zeta$, and (3.14), we arrive at the following inhomogeneous differential equation for the error term:

$$(d^2\varepsilon_2/d\zeta^2) - \tfrac{1}{4}m^2u^2\zeta^{m-2}\varepsilon_2 = \phi(u, \zeta)\{U_m(u^{2/m}\zeta) + \varepsilon_2\}.$$

Using the Wronskian (2.09), we construct an equivalent Volterra integral equation:

$$\eta_2(u, \zeta) = \frac{1}{mu^{2/m}}\sin\left(\frac{\pi}{m}\right)\int_\zeta^{\zeta_2} K(\zeta, v)\phi(u, v)\{U_m(u^{2/m}v) + \eta_2(u, v)\}\,dv, \tag{3.16}$$

where $\eta_2(u, \zeta)$ has been written for $\varepsilon_2(u, x)$ and

$$K(\zeta, v) = U_m(u^{2/m}\zeta)U_m(-u^{2/m}v) - U_m(-u^{2/m}\zeta)U_m(u^{2/m}v). \tag{3.17}$$

From the monotonicity properties of the function $U_m(t)$ stated in § 2.1, it follows that the kernel is bounded by

$$0 \leqq K(\zeta, v) < U_m(u^{2/m}\zeta)U_m(-u^{2/m}v), \qquad \zeta \leqq v.$$

Next, if we differentiate (3.17) with respect to ζ and use (2.09), bearing in mind that U_m' is always negative, we find that

$$\left|\frac{\partial K(\zeta, v)}{\partial \zeta}\right| \leqq u^{2/m} m \csc\left(\frac{\pi}{m}\right)\frac{U_m(-u^{2/m}v)}{U_m(-u^{2/m}\zeta)}, \qquad \zeta \leqq v,$$

and hence

$$\left|\frac{\partial K(\zeta, v)}{\partial \zeta}\right| \leqq \mu_m u^{2/m} |U_m'(u^{2/m}\zeta)| U_m(-u^{2/m}v), \qquad \zeta \leqq v,$$

where μ_m is defined by (3.12).

Having bounded the kernel and its ζ-derivative, we can solve the integral equation (3.16) by the standard procedure of successive approximations, for example, by applying Theorem 10.2 of [23, Chap. 6]. Then returning from ζ to x as variable, we arrive at the desired inequalities (3.10). The proof of (3.09) is similar, or we may merely replace x by $-x$ in the result for $w_2(u, x)$ and $\varepsilon_2(u, x)$.

3.3. Case II.

THEOREM II. *Assume the conditions and notation of* § 3.1, *and also that m is even and the sign of* $f(u, x)/(x-x_0)^{m-2}$ *is negative. Then in* (a_1, a_2), *equation* (3.01) *has twice continuously differentiable solutions* $w_1(u, x)$ *and* $w_2(u, x)$ *such that*

$$w_1(u, x) = \hat{f}^{-1/4}(u, x)\{W_m(-u^{2/m}\zeta) + \varepsilon_1(u, x)\}, \tag{3.18}$$

$$w_2(u, x) = \hat{f}^{-1/4}(u, x)\{W_m(u^{2/m}\zeta) + \varepsilon_2(u, x)\}, \tag{3.19}$$

where

$$\frac{|\varepsilon_1(u, x)|}{M_m(u^{2/m}\zeta)}, \frac{|\partial \varepsilon_1(u, x)/\partial x|}{u^{2/m}\hat{f}^{1/2}(u, x) N_m(u^{2/m}\zeta)} \leqq \frac{\sigma_m}{\rho_m} E_m(u^{2/m}\zeta)\left[\exp\left\{\frac{\rho_m}{u^{2/m}} \mathcal{V}_{a_1,x}(H_m)\right\} - 1\right], \tag{3.20}$$

$$\frac{|\varepsilon_2(u, x)|}{M_m(u^{2/m}\zeta)}, \frac{|\partial \varepsilon_2(u, x)/\partial x|}{u^{2/m}\hat{f}^{1/2}(u, x) N_m(u^{2/m}\zeta)} \leqq \frac{\sigma_m}{\rho_m} E_m^{-1}(u^{2/m}\zeta)\left[\exp\left\{\frac{\rho_m}{u^{2/m}} \mathcal{V}_{x,a_2}(H_m)\right\} - 1\right], \tag{3.21}$$

and

$$\rho_m = \sup_{t \in (-\infty, \infty)} \left\{\frac{1}{m} \sin\left(\frac{\pi}{m}\right) \Omega_m(t) M_m^2(t)\right\}, \tag{3.22}$$

$$\sigma_m = \sup_{t \in (-\infty, \infty)} \left\{\frac{1}{m} \sin\left(\frac{\pi}{m}\right) \Omega_m(t) |W_m(t)| E_m(t) M_m(t)\right\}. \tag{3.23}$$

In this theorem the functions $W_m(t)$, $E_m(t)$, $M_m(t)$ and $N_m(t)$ are defined in § 2.2. The proof is similar to that of Theorem I, and it is unnecessary to give details. Again, in consequence of the asymptotic properties of $W_m(t)$ and $M_m(t)$ for large $|t|$ given in § 2.2, the positive constants ρ_m and σ_m are finite. It is also clear from (2.23) that $\sigma_m \leqq \rho_m$; in consequence, σ_m may be replaced by ρ_m in (3.20) and (3.21), thereby simplifying the results.

3.4. Case III.

THEOREM III. *Assume the conditions and notation of* § 3.1, *and also that m is odd and the sign of* $f(u, x)/(x-x_0)^{m-2}$ *is positive.*[9] *Then in* (a_1, a_2), *equation* (3.01) *has twice continuously differentiable solutions* $w_1(u, x)$ *and* $w_2(u, x)$ *such that*

$$w_1(u, x) = \hat{f}^{-1/4}(u, x)\{\bar{V}_m(u^{2/m}\zeta) + \varepsilon_1(u, x)\}, \tag{3.24}$$

$$w_2(u, x) = \hat{f}^{-1/4}(u, x)\{V_m(u^{2/m}\zeta) + \varepsilon_2(u, x)\}, \tag{3.25}$$

where

$$\frac{|\varepsilon_1(u, x)|}{M_m(u^{2/m}\zeta)}, \frac{|\partial\varepsilon_1(u, x)/\partial x|}{u^{2/m}\hat{f}^{1/2}(u, x)N_m(u^{2/m}\zeta)} \leqq \frac{\sigma_{m,1}}{\rho_m} E_m(u^{2/m}\zeta)\left[\exp\left\{\frac{\rho_m}{u^{2/m}} \mathcal{V}_{a_1,x}(H_m)\right\} - 1\right], \tag{3.26}$$

$$\frac{|\varepsilon_2(u, x)|}{M_m(u^{2/m}\zeta)}, \frac{|\partial\varepsilon_2(u, x)/\partial x|}{u^{2/m}\hat{f}^{1/2}(u, x)N_m(u^{2/m}\zeta)} \leqq \frac{\sigma_{m,2}}{\rho_m} E_m^{-1}(u^{2/m}\zeta)\left[\exp\left\{\frac{\rho_m}{u^{2/m}} \mathcal{V}_{x,a_2}(H_m)\right\} - 1\right], \tag{3.27}$$

and

$$\rho_m = \sup_{t\in(-\infty,\infty)} \left\{\frac{1}{m}\sin\left(\frac{\pi}{m}\right)\Omega_m(t)M_m^2(t)\right\}, \tag{3.28}$$

$$\sigma_{m,1} = \sup_{t\in(-\infty,\infty)} \left\{\frac{1}{m}\sin\left(\frac{\pi}{m}\right)\Omega_m(t)|\bar{V}_m(t)|E_m^{-1}(t)M_m(t)\right\}, \tag{3.29}$$

$$\sigma_{m,2} = \sup_{t\in(-\infty,\infty)} \left\{\frac{1}{m}\sin\left(\frac{\pi}{m}\right)\Omega_m(t)|V_m(t)|E_m(t)M_m(t)\right\}. \tag{3.30}$$

In this theorem, the functions $\bar{V}_m(t)$, $V_m(t)$, $E_m(t)$, $M_m(t)$ and $N_m(t)$ are defined in § 2.3. The proof is similar to that of Theorems I and II. Again, the positive constants ρ_m, $\sigma_{m,1}$ and $\sigma_{m,2}$ are finite, and since $\sigma_{m,1}$ and $\sigma_{m,2}$ are both bounded by ρ_m, the ratios $\sigma_{m,1}/\rho_m$ and $\sigma_{m,2}/\rho_m$ in (3.26) and (3.27) may be replaced by unity.

3.5. Remarks on Theorems I, II and III. (i) The present results agree with earlier ones in cases in which there are no turning points or one turning point. Thus Theorems I and II reduce respectively to Theorems 2.1 and 2.2 of [23, Chap. 6] when $m=2$ and $\Omega_2(t)=1$, and Theorem III reduces to Theorem 3.1 of [23, Chap. 11] when $m=3$ and $\Omega_3(t)=|t|^{1/2}$.

(ii) The theorems are essentially inequalities for the solutions of the differential equation, and not asymptotic results *per se*. Subject to the given conditions they are valid for any positive value of the parameter u, not necessarily large. But, of course, the results are of interest only when the error terms $\varepsilon_1(u, x)$ and $\varepsilon_2(u, x)$ are small compared with the corresponding approximants $U_m(\mp u^{2/m}\zeta)$,

[9] Cases in which the sign of $f(u, x)/(x-x_0)^{m-2}$ is negative can be accommodated by replacing x by $-x$ throughout.

$W_m(\mp u^{2/m}\zeta)$, $\bar{V}_m(u^{2/m}\zeta)$ or $V_m(u^{2/m}\zeta)$. When this happens, the graphs in Figs. 2.1–2.8) mirror the behavior of the actual solutions, or more precisely, the products of each solution and the function $\hat{f}^{1/4}(u, x)$. In § 5 it will be shown that with suitable dependence of $f(u, x)$ and $g(u, x)$ on u, the error terms are uniformly vanishingly small compared with the approximants as $u \to \infty$.

4. The connection formulas

4.1. Preliminary conditions. In this section we construct connection formulas for a turning point of arbitrary multiplicity which are analogous to the Gans–Jeffreys formulas for the case of a single turning point given, for example, in [23, pp. 491–494].

As in § 3, we consider the differential equation

$$d^2w/dx^2 = \{u^2 f(u, x) + g(u, x)\}w, \qquad u > 0, \quad a_1 < x < a_2, \tag{4.01}$$

in which the given interval (a_1, a_2) is finite or infinite and contains just one zero x_0, say, of $f(u, x)$, the multiplicity of this zero being $m-2$. In addition, we assume that within (a_1, a_2):

(i) $f(u, x)/(x-x_0)^{m-2}$ *is real and twice continuously differentiable.*

(ii) $g(u, x)$ *is continuous.*

(iii) *As* $x \to a_1+$ *or* a_2-, *the integral* $\int_{x_0}^{x} |f(u, y)|^{1/2}\, dy$ *diverges and* $\mathcal{V}(F)$ *converges, where* $F(u, x)$ *is the error-control function for the Liouville–Green approximation, that is,*

$$F(u, x) \equiv \int \left\{ \frac{1}{|f|^{1/4}} \frac{d^2}{dx^2}\left(\frac{1}{|f|^{1/4}}\right) - \frac{g}{|f|^{1/2}} \right\} dx. \tag{4.02}$$

We first show that these conditions ensure that the error-control function $H_m(u, x)$ defined by (3.06) is of bounded variation in (a_1, a_2), provided that the balancing function $\Omega_m(t)$ is chosen to satisfy the extra condition

$$\Omega_m(t)/|t|^{(m-2)/2} \to \text{const.}, \qquad t \to \pm\infty. \tag{4.03}$$

Substituting in (3.06) by means of (3.05) and using the differential relation $|f|^{1/2}\, dx = \frac{1}{2} m |\zeta|^{(m-2)/2}\, d\zeta$, we find that

$$H_m(u, x) = \frac{m}{2} \int \left\{ \frac{1}{|f|^{1/4}} \frac{d^2}{dx^2}\left(\frac{1}{|f|^{1/4}}\right) - \frac{g}{|f|^{1/2}} \right\} \frac{|\zeta|^{(m-2)/2} dx}{\Omega_m(u^{2/m}\zeta)} - \frac{m^2-4}{16} \int \frac{d\zeta}{\zeta^2 \Omega_m(u^{2/m}\zeta)}. \tag{4.04}$$

Condition (iii) above implies that $\zeta \to -\infty$ as $x \to a_1+$, and $\zeta \to +\infty$ as $x \to a_2-$. Aided also by (4.03), we see that each integral on the right-hand side of (4.04) converges absolutely, and therefore that $\mathcal{V}(H_m)$ converges, as asserted.

4.2. Case I. Here m $(\geqq 2)$ is even and the sign of $f(u, x)/(x-x_0)^{m-2}$ is positive. With the given conditions it is known from the theory of the Liouville–Green approximation [23, pp. 197–200] that for each value of u there exist unique solutions $\hat{w}_1(u, x)$ and $\hat{w}_2(u, x)$, say, of (4.01) having the properties:

$$\text{(4.05)} \qquad \hat{w}_1(u,x) \sim f^{-1/4}(u,x) \exp\left(-u \int_x^{x_0} f^{1/2}(u,y)\, dy\right), \qquad x \to a_1+,$$

$$\text{(4.06)} \qquad \hat{w}_2(u,x) \sim f^{-1/4}(u,x) \exp\left(-u \int_{x_0}^{x} f^{1/2}(u,y)\, dy\right), \qquad x \to a_2-.$$

Our object is to determine the asymptotic form of $\hat{w}_1(u, x)$ as $x \to a_2-$ and the asymptotic form of $\hat{w}_2(u, x)$ as $x \to a_1+$.

All the conditions of Theorem I of § 3.2 are satisfied with the present assumptions, in consequence there exists a solution $w_2(u, x)$ given by (3.08) and (3.10). Furthermore, the right-hand side of (3.10) is finite for each u. Letting $x \to a_2-$, we see that

$$\varepsilon_2(u,x)/U_m(u^{2/m}\zeta) \to 0,$$

and hence from (3.08) that

$$w_2(u,x) \sim \hat{f}^{-1/4}(u,x)\, U_m(u^{2/m}\zeta).$$

Since $\zeta \to +\infty$, we may replace $U_m(u^{2/m}\zeta)$ by its asymptotic form, obtainable from (2.02). Then using (3.04) and (3.05), we derive

$$w_2(u,x) \sim (\tfrac{1}{2}m)^{1/2} u^{(2-m)/(2m)} f^{-1/4}(u,x) \exp\left(-u \int_{x_0}^{x} f^{1/2}(u,y)\, dy\right).$$

On comparing this relation with (4.06), we identify

$$\text{(4.07)} \qquad \hat{w}_2(u,x) = (\tfrac{1}{2}m)^{-1/2} u^{(m-2)/(2m)} w_2(u,x).$$

We now let $x \to a_1+$, that is, $\zeta \to -\infty$. From (3.08), (3.10) and (2.07), we obtain

$$w_2(u,x) \sim (\tfrac{1}{2}m)^{1/2} \csc(\pi/m)\ (1+k_2) u^{(2-m)/(2m)} f^{-1/4}(u,x) \exp\left(u \int_x^{x_0} f^{1/2}(u,y)\, dy\right),$$

where k_2 is a constant bounded by

$$\text{(4.08)} \qquad |k_2| \leqq \exp\{\lambda_m u^{-2/m} \mathcal{V}_{a_1,a_2}(H_m)\} - 1,$$

provided that the right-hand side of this inequality does not exceed unity.[10] Here λ_m is defined by (3.11). Combination of this result with (4.07) immediately yields

$$\text{(4.09)} \quad \hat{w}_2(u,x) \sim (1+k_2) \csc\left(\frac{\pi}{m}\right) f^{-1/4}(u,x) \exp\left(u \int_x^{x_0} f^{1/2}(u,y)\, dy\right), \qquad x \to a_1+.$$

Relations (4.06) and (4.09) comprise one of the wanted connection formulas. By symmetry, the other formula is given by (4.05) and

$$\text{(4.10)} \quad \hat{w}_1(u,x) \sim (1+k_1) \csc\left(\frac{\pi}{m}\right) f^{-1/4}(u,x) \exp\left(u \int_{x_0}^{x} f^{1/2}(u,y)\, dy\right), \qquad x \to a_2-,$$

[10] Actually it is not obvious that k_2 *is* a constant, that is, independent of x, because Theorem I merely states that $|\varepsilon_2(u,x)|/U_m(u^{2/m}\zeta)$ is bounded as $x \to a_1+$. The assertion is justifiable, however, of Theorem 3.1 of [23, Chap. 6].

where k_1 is a constant subject to the same bound (4.08) as k_2.

4.3. Case II. Here m ($\geqq 2$) is even and the sign of $f(u,x)/(x-x_0)^{m-2}$ is negative. With the conditions of § 4.1, for each value of u there are unique solutions $\hat{w}_1(u,x)$ and $\hat{w}_2(u,x)$ of (4.01), such that

$$(4.11)\quad \hat{w}_1(u,x)=|f(u,x)|^{-1/4}\left\{\cos\left(u\int_x^{x_0}|f(u,y)|^{1/2}\,dy+\tfrac{1}{4}\pi\right)+o(1)\right\},\qquad x\to a_1+,$$

$$(4.12)\quad \hat{w}_2(u,x)=|f(u,x)|^{-1/4}\left\{\cos\left(u\int_{x_0}^{x}|f(u,y)|^{1/2}\,dy+\tfrac{1}{4}\pi\right)+o(1)\right\},\qquad x\to a_2-.$$

Using analysis similar to that of the preceding subsection and § 7.2 of [23, Chap. 13], we find that

$$(4.13)\quad \hat{w}_1(u,x)=(1+\gamma_1)\cot\left(\frac{\pi}{2m}\right)|f(u,x)|^{-1/4}\cdot\left\{\cos\left(u\int_{x_0}^{x}|f(u,y)|^{1/2}\,dy-\tfrac{1}{4}\pi+\delta_1\right)+o(1)\right\},\qquad x\to a_2-,$$

$$(4.14)\quad \hat{w}_2(u,x)=(1+\gamma_2)\cot\left(\frac{\pi}{2m}\right)|f(u,x)|^{-1/4}\cdot\left\{\cos\left(u\int_{x}^{x_0}|f(u,y)|^{1/2}\,dy-\tfrac{1}{4}\pi+\delta_2\right)+o(1)\right\},\qquad x\to a_1+,$$

where γ_1, γ_2, δ_1 and δ_2 are constants bounded by

$$(4.15)\qquad |\gamma_1|,|\gamma_2|,\frac{2|\delta_1|}{\pi},\frac{2|\delta_2|}{\pi}\leqq\frac{\sigma_m}{\rho_m}\left[\exp\left\{\frac{\rho_m}{u^{2/m}}\mathcal{V}_{a_1,a_2}(H_m)\right\}-1\right],$$

and ρ_m and σ_m are defined by (3.22) and (3.23). These results are the required connection formulas, and are valid whenever the right-hand side of (4.15) does not exceed unity.

4.4. Case III. In this case, m ($\geqq 3$) is odd and the sign of $f(u,x)/(x-x_0)^m$ is positive.[11] Again, with the conditions of § 4.1, for each u there are unique solutions $\hat{w}_1(u,x)$ and $\hat{w}_2(u,x)$, such that

$$(4.16)\quad \hat{w}_1(u,x)=|f(u,x)|^{-1/4}\left\{\cos\left(u\int_x^{x_0}|f(u,y)|^{1/2}\,dy+\tfrac{1}{4}\pi\right)+o(1)\right\},\qquad x\to a_1+,$$

$$(4.17)\qquad \hat{w}_2(u,x)\sim f^{-1/4}(u,x)\exp\left(-u\int_{x_0}^{x}f^{1/2}(u,y)\,dy\right),\qquad x\to a_2-.$$

[11] As in § 3.4, cases in which $f(u,x)/(x-x_0)^{m-2}$ is negative can be accommodated by reversal of the sign of x.

Using analysis similar to that in Cases I and II, we find that the required connection formulas are given by

$$(4.18)\quad \hat{w}_1(u,x) \sim \tfrac{1}{2}(1+k)\csc\left(\frac{\pi}{2m}\right) f^{-1/4}(u,x)\exp\left(u\int_{x_0}^{x} f^{1/2}(u,y)\,dy\right), \qquad x \to a_2-,$$

$$(4.19)\quad \hat{w}_2(u,x) = (1+\gamma)\csc\left(\frac{\pi}{2m}\right)|f(u,x)|^{-1/4} \cdot\left\{\cos\left(u\int_{x}^{x_0}|f(u,y)|^{1/2}\,dy - \tfrac{1}{4}\pi + \delta\right) + o(1)\right\}, \qquad x \to a_1+,$$

where k, γ and δ are constants bounded by

$$(4.20)\qquad |k| \leqq 2^{1/2}\frac{\sigma_{m,1}}{\rho_m}\left[\exp\left\{\frac{\rho_m}{u^{2/m}}\mathcal{V}_{a_1,a_2}(H_m)\right\} - 1\right],$$

$$(4.21)\qquad |\gamma|, \frac{2|\delta|}{\pi} \leqq \frac{\sigma_{m,2}}{\rho_m}\left[\exp\left\{\frac{\rho_m}{u^{2/m}}\mathcal{V}_{a_1,a_2}(H_m)\right\} - 1\right],$$

and ρ_m, $\sigma_{m,1}$ and $\sigma_{m,2}$ are defined by (3.28), (3.29) and (3.30). The only additional condition needed is that in the case of (4.19), the right-hand side of (4.21) must not exceed unity. It is easily verified that these results reduce to those given in [23, pp. 491–494] in the case $m = 3$.

4.5. Remark. In each of Cases I, II and III, we have constructed connection formulas for two solutions of the given differential equation, complete with bounds on the errors in the approximate coefficients. Provided that the error terms are small compared with the coefficients—and this forms the subject of the next section—each pair of solutions of the differential equation is numerically satisfactory, because the approximating functions were chosen in § 2 to be numerically satisfactory solutions of the corresponding basic equation. In consequence, connection formulas for any other solution can be deduced whenever the problem is not ill-posed. This aspect is discussed more fully in [26].

5. Asymptotic estimates of the error terms

5.1. Preliminary remarks. The error terms $\varepsilon_1(u,x)$ and $\varepsilon_2(u,x)$ appearing in the solutions given by Theorems I, II and III of § 3 depend on the parameter u, as do the error terms k, k_1, k_2, γ, γ_1, γ_2, δ, δ_1 and δ_2 in the connection formulas derived in § 4. The behavior of these error terms as $u \to \infty$ obviously depends on the manner in which u enters the functions $f(u,x)$ and $g(u,x)$ in the given differential equation (3.01).

5.2. A typical case. Let us assume that the endpoints a_1 and a_2 of the x-interval are independent of u, and that the conditions of § 3.1 are satisfied. We also assume that:

(i) $f(u,x) \equiv f(x)$ *is independent of* u, *and the variation of the function* $\int f^{-1/4}(x)\{f^{-1/4}(x)\}''\,dx$ *converges as* $x \to a_1+$ *or* a_2-.

(ii) *There is a real constant* ϖ *such that* $u^{-\varpi}|g(u, x)|$ *is bounded when u is arbitrarily large and x ranges over any fixed compact interval within* (a_1, a_2). *Moreover, the variation of* $\int u^{-\varpi} g(u, x) f^{-1/2}(x)\, dx$ *converges uniformly with respect to u as* $x \to a_1+$ *or* a_2-.

The main problem is to find an asymptotic estimate of $\mathscr{V}_{a_1,a_2}(H_m)$ as $u \to \infty$, where $H_m(u, x)$ is defined by (3.06); thus

$$\mathscr{V}_{a_1,a_2}(H_m) = \int_{a_1}^{a_2} \left| \frac{1}{\hat{f}^{1/4}(x)} \frac{d^2}{dx^2} \left(\frac{1}{\hat{f}^{1/4}(x)} \right) - \frac{g(u, x)}{\hat{f}^{1/2}(x)} \right| \frac{dx}{\Omega_m(u^{2/m}\zeta)}. \tag{5.01}$$

Consider first the interval $[x_1, x_2]$, where x_1 and x_2 are any fixed points such that $a_1 < x_1 < x_0 < x_2 < a_2$. From (3.05), we have

$$\hat{f}(x) \equiv \hat{f}(u, x) = \frac{4}{m^2} \frac{|f(x)|}{|x - x_0|^{m-2}} \left(\frac{x - x_0}{\zeta} \right)^{m-2}.$$

By hypothesis, $|f(x)|/|x - x_0|^{m-2}$ is nonvanishing and twice continuously differentiable, and from the Lemma of § 3.2, and the corresponding results for Cases II and III, we know that the same is true of $(x - x_0)/\zeta$. Hence $\hat{f}^{-1/4}(\hat{f}^{-1/4})''$ is continuous in (a_1, a_2) and therefore bounded in absolute value in $[x_1, x_2]$. Next, using Condition (ii) above, we see that $u^{-\varpi}\hat{f}^{-1/2}(x)|g(u, x)|$ is bounded in $[x_1, x_2]$. Combination of these two results shows that

$$\left| \frac{1}{\hat{f}^{1/4}(x)} \frac{d^2}{dx^2} \left(\frac{1}{\hat{f}^{1/4}(x)} \right) - \frac{g(u, x)}{\hat{f}^{1/2}(x)} \right| \leqq A u^{\varpi_0}, \qquad u \geq 1, \quad x \in [x_1, x_2], \tag{5.02}$$

where A is a constant and

$$\varpi_0 = \max(\varpi, 0). \tag{5.03}$$

We now adopt the choice (3.03) for the balancing function $\Omega_m(t)$. Since $(x - x_0)/\zeta$ is bounded in $[x_1, x_2]$, it follows that

$$\frac{1}{\Omega_m(u^{2/m}\zeta)} \leqq \frac{A}{1 + u^{(m-2)/m}|x - x_0|^{(m-2)/2}},$$

where the symbol A is now being used generically. On combining this inequality with (5.02) and referring to (5.01), we see that

$$\mathscr{V}_{x_1,x_2}(H_m) \leqq A u^{\varpi_0} \int_{x_1}^{x_2} \frac{dx}{1 + u^{(m-2)/m}|x - x_0|^{(m-2)/2}}.$$

With $\xi = u^{2/m}(x - x_0)$ as new integration variable, we have

$$\int_{x_0}^{x_2} \frac{dx}{1 + u^{(m-2)/m}|x - x_0|^{(m-2)/2}} = \frac{1}{u^{2/m}} \int_0^{u^{2/m}(x_2 - x_0)} \frac{d\xi}{1 + \xi^{(m-2)/2}}.$$

For large u, this is $O(u^{-(m-2)/m})$, $O(u^{-2/m} \ln u)$ or $O(u^{-2/m})$, according as $2 \leqq m < 4$, $m = 4$ or $m > 4$. The same estimates hold for the corresponding integral over the interval $[x_1, x_0]$, hence $\mathcal{V}_{x_1,x_2}(H_m)$ is estimated by

$$O(u^{\varpi_0-1+(2/m)}), \qquad m=2,3;$$
$$O(u^{\varpi_0-(1/2)}\ln u), \qquad m=4; \tag{5.04}$$
$$O(u^{\varpi_0-(2/m)}), \qquad m>4.$$

Next, consider the contribution from the interval $[x_2, a_2)$. Instead of (5.01), we shall use the expression (4.04), with the same choice (3.03) for $\Omega_m(t)$. Since ζ is nonzero in the present circumstances, we have

$$\frac{|\zeta|^{(m-2)/2}}{\Omega_m(u^{2/m}\zeta)}=\frac{\zeta^{(m-2)/2}}{1+u^{(m-2)/m}\zeta^{(m-2)/2}}<\frac{1}{u^{(m-2)/m}}.$$

Combining this bound with Conditions (i) and (ii) in turn, we derive

$$\int_{x_2}^{a_2}\left|\frac{1}{f^{1/4}(x)}\frac{d^2}{dx^2}\left\{\frac{1}{f^{1/4}(x)}\right\}\frac{\zeta^{(m-2)/2}}{\Omega_m(u^{2/m}\zeta)}dx\right|=O\left(\frac{1}{u^{(m-2)/m}}\right)$$

and

$$\int_{x_2}^{a_2}\left|\frac{g(u,x)}{f^{1/2}(x)}\frac{\zeta^{(m-2)/2}}{\Omega_m(u^{2/m}\zeta)}dx\right|=O\left(\frac{u^{\varpi}}{u^{(m-2)/m}}\right).$$

For the remaining contribution in (4.04), let ζ_2 again denote the value of ζ corresponding to $x=a_2$, and $z_2(>0)$ the value of ζ corresponding to $x=x_2$. Then we have

$$\int_{z_2}^{\zeta_2}\frac{d\zeta}{\zeta^2\Omega_m(u^{2/m}\zeta)}=\int_{z_2}^{\zeta_2}\frac{d\zeta}{\zeta^2\{1+u^{(m-2)/m}\zeta^{(m-2)/2}\}}$$
$$<\frac{1}{u^{(m-2)/m}}\int_{z_2}^{\infty}\frac{d\zeta}{\zeta^{(m+2)/2}}=O\left(\frac{1}{u^{(m-2)/m}}\right),$$

since the last integral converges when $m\geqq 2$. Substituting in (4.04) by means of these three relations, we see that

$$\mathcal{V}_{x_2,a_2}(H_m)=O(u^{(m\varpi_0-m+2)/m}),$$

which is absorbable in the estimates (5.04) for $\mathcal{V}_{x_1,x_2}(H_m)$. Similarly $\mathcal{V}_{a_1,x_1}(H_m)$ is absorbable in (5.04). Accordingly $\mathcal{V}_{a_1,a_2}(H_m)$, also, is estimated by (5.04).

Uniform estimates for the error terms $\varepsilon_1(u,x)$ and $\varepsilon_2(u,x)$ appearing in Theorems I, II and III are easily available now by substituting (5.04) for the variations of H_m appearing in these theorems. For example, in Case I both $\varepsilon_1(u,x)/U_m(-u^{2/m}\zeta)$ and $\varepsilon_2(u,x)/U_m(u^{2/m}\zeta)$ are estimated by

$$O(u^{\varpi_0-1}), \qquad m=2,3;$$
$$O(u^{\varpi_0-1}\ln u), \qquad m=4; \tag{5.05}$$
$$O(u^{\varpi_0-(4/m)}), \qquad m>4;$$

uniformly for $x\in(a_1,a_2)$. Furthermore, with the additional condition that $\int_{x_0}^{x}|f(y)|^{1/2}dy$ diverges as $x\to a_1+$ or a_2- each of the error terms $k, k_1, k_2, \gamma, \gamma_1, \gamma_2, \delta, \delta_1$ and δ_2 appearing in the connection formulas of § 4 is estimated by (5.05).

5.3. Specializations. If the conditions stated in the first paragraph of § 5.2 are satisfied and $\varpi \leqq 0$, then from (5.03) we have $\varpi = 0$. Accordingly, the estimates (5.05) become

$$O(u^{-1}), \qquad m = 2, 3;$$
$$(5.06) \qquad O(u^{-1} \ln u), \qquad m = 4;$$
$$O(u^{-4/m}), \qquad m > 4.$$

In particular, these estimates apply when $g(u, x)$ is independent of u, provided that $\int |gf^{-1/2}|\, dx$ converges as $x \to a_1 +$ or $a_2 -$.

On the other hand, if $\varpi > 0$, then $\varpi_0 = \varpi$. The estimates (5.05) for the error terms are valid for any ϖ, but they are useful only when they are $o(1)$ as $u \to \infty$. Thus we require $\varpi < 1$ when $m = 2$, 3 or 4, and $\varpi < /4m$ when $m > 4$. When these conditions are fulfilled Theorems I, II and III, and the corresponding connection formulas of § 4 supply useful information, but not otherwise. To put this another way, when $\varpi \geqq \min(1, 4/m)$, the term $g(u, x)$ in (3.01) cannot be treated as a perturbation compared with $u^2 f(u, x)$; at least part of $g(u, x)$ must be taken into account in constructing the basic equation, in consequence Bessel functions no longer furnish adequate approximations to the solutions.

6. Previous results and conclusions

6.1. Simple turning points. In the case of a simple turning point, two types of method are available for the construction of connection formulas. The first consists of approximating, in some manner, the solutions of the differential equation by Airy functions or, equivalently, Bessel functions of order one-third, and then substituting for the approximants by their asymptotic approximations in terms of elementary functions for large positive and negative arguments. In the case $m = 3$, the method used in the present paper is of this type.

The second method is applicable only when the coefficients $f(u, x)$ and $g(u, x)$ in the given differential equation (3.01) are analytic functions of the complex variable x. We first map the so-called *principal curves* (or *anti-Stokes lines*)

$$(6.01) \qquad \mathrm{Re}\left\{\int_{x_0}^{x} f^{1/2}(u, y)\, dy\right\} = 0$$

in the complex x-plane, where x_0 denotes the turning point. Since $f(u, x)$ has a simple zero at x_0, three of these curves emerge from this point, dividing the x-plane into three regions, which we refer to as the *principal subdomains* corresponding to x_0. Associated with each principal subdomain there is a solution of the differential equation which is recessive as $x \to \infty$ within the subdomain, and dominant as $x \to \infty$ in the other two subdomains. Except in the neighborhood of the turning point, each of the three solutions can be approximated uniformly in terms of elementary functions by the Liouville–Green theory. The linear identity holding between the three solutions is, in effect, the required connection formula. Because two of the solutions are dominant in any chosen principal subdomain, they have to cancel each other in the connection formula as $x \to \infty$ in this subdomain. This condition yields exactly the right number of equations to determine the coefficients in the connection formula. An attractive feature of this method is that approximations in terms of elementary functions are continued around the turning point without having to construct approximations in terms of nonelementary functions valid in domains that include the turning point. Another advantage is that a simpler error-control function is used in constructing error bounds (although the variation of this function has to be calculated along curves in the complex plane instead of the real axis).

Wasow [29] appropriately has called the first type of method *central connection*, and the second type *lateral connection*. Detailed accounts of rigorous methods of both types are included in [23, Chap. 13]. These references, and also [11], [9], [6, Chap. 1], [3, Chap. 1], [30], [17] and [1, pp. 292–295], sketch the history and modifications of the methods.

6.2. Multiple turning points. As we have seen in the present paper, the method of central connection can still be used for double and higher turning points. A true analogue of the rigorous lateral connection procedure for a simple turning point has yet to be found, however. All published methods, including those mentioned below, that continue an approximate solution around a multiple turning point in the complex plane are based, directly or indirectly, on approximate representations in terms of Bessel functions valid at the turning point. To distinguish these complex-variable methods from direct central connection procedures along the real axis, we shall call them *pseudo-lateral* methods.

Another way in which the connection formula problem for simple turning points differs from that for multiple turning points is that in the former case, the uniform asymptotic approximations for the solutions of the differential equation can be extended in straightforward manner into uniform asymptotic expansions in descending powers of the large parameter u; see [23, Chap. 11]. Although asymptotic expansions in descending powers of u can be constructed for the solutions in regions containing a multiple turning point [18], [27], [16], [31], in marked contrast to the case of a simple turning point, these expansions are uniformly valid only for bounded values of the independent variable; compare [24, § 11]. Moreover, in the case of [18], [27] and [16] the expansions are in terms of functions of two or more variables.

The earliest paper deriving connection formulas for multiple turning points appears to be that of Goldstein [4]. He treats equation (3.01) with $g(u,x)=0$ and $f(u,x)\equiv f(x)$ independent of x. The zero x_0 of $f(x)$ may have any multiplicity. Goldstein's method is an extension of the procedure successfully employed by Jeffreys for a simple turning point [8]. Thus $f(x)$ is replaced by the first nonvanishing term $f^{(m-2)}(x_0)(x-x_0)^{m-2}/(m-2)!$ in its Taylor series expansion at x_0, where $m-2$ is the multiplicity of the zero. The differential equation is then solvable exactly in terms of Bessel functions (or modified Bessel functions), as we saw in § 2. The connection formulas are found by replacing the Bessel functions by their asymptotic approximations for large positive and negative arguments. Goldstein's connection formulas agree with those obtained by rigorous analysis in the present paper.[12]

---

[12] Misprints on pp. 84 and 86 of [4] are corrected in [5].

A second paper by Goldstein [5] treats the case in which $f(u, x)$ and $u^{-1}g(u, x)$ are independent of x, and $f(u, x)$ has a double zero at x_0. As we perceived in § 5.3, Bessel functions are no longer adequate approximants to the solutions in these circumstances. By using parabolic cylinder functions instead, Goldstein is able to derive connection formulas by analysis similar to that of [8] and [4]. A somewhat more general version of the same problem was treated subsequently by Langer [12]. Langer's analysis is rigorous, and he supplies uniform asymptotic approximations for the solutions in the complex x-plane. It may be noted, incidentally, that recent results of the present writer for the case of two coalescing simple turning points [24] are applicable to this second problem of Goldstein and will yield the connection formulas, complete with error bounds.

Returning to Goldstein's first problem, we note that almost all subsequent writers have espoused the pseudo-lateral approach, deriving rules for the discontinuous changes in the coefficients in the Liouville–Green approximations as the solutions pass from one principal subdomain in the complex plane to the next. The first systematic treatment of this kind for a turning point of arbitrary multiplicity appears to be the formal analysis of Heading on pp. 89–93 and pp. 110–115 of [6]. Similar analysis was given subsequently by Fröman and Fröman [3, pp. 69–74], and also Evgrafov and Fedoryuk [2, pp. 34–35].[13]

Apart from [12], rigorous analyses of the pseudo-lateral methods begin with papers of Lee [13] and Leung [14], [15], which establish the connection formulas for adjacent principal subdomains for a double turning point. Extensions to turning points of any multiplicity have been made by Nishimoto [22], Sibuya [27] and Leung [16].

6.3. Conclusions. The present paper is essentially a rigorous formulation, with extensions, of the results of Goldstein's first paper [4]. For connection formula problems along the real axis, this approach has the following advantages over the complex-variable approach adopted in the references mentioned in § 6.2:

(i) The coefficients $f(u, x)$ and $g(u, x)$ in the given differential equation (3.01) need not be analytic functions of the complex variable x. It suffices that $\partial^2 f(u, x)/\partial x^2$ and $g(u, x)$ are continuous functions of the real variable x (and even this condition could be relaxed to some extent).

(ii) There is no need to investigate the topology in the complex plane of the principal curves (6.01).

(iii) A solution can be continued along the real axis through the turning point by means of a *single* connection formula. With the complex-variable approach, there are m principal subdomains associated with a turning point of multiplicity

[13] Instead of drawing on known properties of Bessel functions in discussing the equation $d^2w/dt^2 = t^{m-2}w$, Fröman and Fröman, and Evgrafov and Fedoryuk, derive the necessary connection formulas *ab initio* by elementary analysis. However, this analysis hinges upon the Fuchs–Frobenius theory of the differential equation as $t \to 0$, and can be regarded simply as a way of establishing the connection formulas for the Bessel functions. Thus the connection procedure of these authors is properly classified as central and not lateral. Incidentally, although the treatment of multiple turning points in [2] and [3] is formal, the analysis of simple turning points in both references is rigorous. It may also be noted that [2] includes a systematic study of the topology of the principal curves (6.01) in the complex plane when any number of turning points are present.

$m-2$, and a total of almost $[\frac{1}{2}m]$ successive steps from one principal subdomain to the next is needed to achieve the connection along the real axis.

(iv) Explicit and realistic bounds are available for the error terms.

Acknowledgment. Figures 2.1–2.8 were plotted mechanically from values of the solutions obtained by numerical integration of the differential equations (2.01), (2.11) and (2.31). The programs for the calculations and plotting were constructed by Mr. R. E. Kaylor, and the author is pleased to acknowledge this assistance.

REFERENCES

[1] R. B. DINGLE, *Asymptotic Expansions: Their Derivation and Interpretation*, Academic Press, New York, 1973.

[2] M. A. EVGRAFOV AND M. V. FEDORYUK, *Asymptotic behaviour as $\lambda \to \infty$ of the solution of the equation $w''(z)-p(z,\lambda)w(z)=0$ in the complex z-plane*, Russian Math. Surveys, 21 (1966), pp. 1–48.

[3] N. FRÖMAN AND P. O. FRÖMAN, *JWKB Approximation—Contributions to the Theory*, North-Holland, Amsterdam, 1965.

[4] S. GOLDSTEIN, *A note on certain approximate solutions of linear differential equations of the second order, with an application to the Mathieu equation*, Proc. London Math. Soc. [2], 28 (1928), pp. 81–90.

[5] ———, *A note on certain approximate solutions of linear differential equations of the second order* (2), Proc. London Math. Soc. [2], 33 (1932), pp. 246–252.

[6] J. HEADING, *An Introduction to Phase-integral Methods*, John Wiley, New York, 1962.

[7] V. B. HEADLEY AND V. K. BARWELL, *On the distribution of the zeros of generalized Airy functions*, Math. Comp., 29 (1975), pp. 863–877.

[8] H. JEFFREYS, *On certain approximate solutions of linear differential equations of the second order*, Proc. London Math. Soc., [2], 23 (1924), pp. 428–436.

[9] ———, *On the use of asymptotic approximations of Green's type when the coefficient has zeros*, Proc. Cambridge Philos. Soc., 52 (1956), pp. 61–66.

[10] N. D. KAZARINOFF AND R. K. RITT, *Scalar diffraction theory and turning-point problems*, Arch. Rational Mech. Anal., 5 (1960), pp. 177–186.

[11] R. E. LANGER, *The asymptotic solutions of ordinary linear differential equations of the second order, with special reference to the Stokes phenomenon*, Bull. Amer. Math. Soc., 40 (1934), pp. 545–582.

[12] ———, *The asymptotic solutions of certain linear ordinary differential equations of the second order*, Trans. Amer. Math. Soc., 36 (1934), pp. 90–106.

[13] R. Y. LEE, *On uniform simplification of linear differential equation in a full neighborhood of a turning point*, J. Math. Anal. Appl., 27 (1969), pp. 501–510.

[14] A. W-K. LEUNG, *Connection formulas for asymptotic solutions of second order turning points in unbounded domains*, this Journal, 4 (1973), pp. 89–103.

[15] ———, *Errata: Connection formulas for asymptotic solutions of second order turning points in unbounded domains*, this Journal, 6 (1975), p. 600.

[16] ———, *Lateral connections for asymptotic solutions around higher order turning points*, J. Math. Anal. Appl., 50 (1975), pp. 560–578.

[17] J. A. M. MCHUGH, *An historical survey of ordinary linear differential equations with a large parameter and turning points*, Arch. History Exact Sci., 7 (1971), pp. 277–324.

[18] R. W. MCKELVEY, *The solutions of second order linear ordinary differential equations about a turning point of order two*, Trans. Amer. Math. Soc., 79 (1955), pp. 103–123.

[19] J. C. P. MILLER, *On the choice of standard solutions for a homogeneous linear differential equation of the second order*, Quart. J. Mech. Appl. Math., 3 (1950), pp. 225–235.

[20] ———, *Tables of Weber Parabolic Cylinder Functions*, H. M. Stationery Office, London, 1955.

[21] NATIONAL BUREAU OF STANDARDS, *Handbook of Mathematical Functions*, Appl. Math. Ser., no. 55, M. Abramowitz and I. A. Stegun, eds., U.S. Govt. Printing Office, Washington, D.C., 1964.

[22] T. NISHIMOTO, *On an extension theorem and its application for turning point problems of large order*, Kōdai Math. Sem. Rep., 25 (1973), pp. 458–489.

[23] F. W. J. OLVER, *Asymptotics and Special Functions*, Academic Press, New York, 1974.

[24] ———, *Second-order linear differential equations with two turning points*, Philos. Trans. Roy. Soc. London Ser. A, 278 (1975), pp. 137–174.

[25] ———, *Second-order differential equations with fractional transition points*, Trans. Amer. Math. Soc., to appear.

[26] ———, *Connection formulas for second-order differential equations having an arbitrary number of turning points of arbitrary multiplicities*, this Journal, to appear.

[27] Y. SIBUYA, *Uniform simplification in a full neighborhood of a transition point*, Mem. Amer. Math. Soc., no. 149, (1974).

[28] C. A. SWANSON AND V. B. HEADLEY, *An extension of Airy's equation*, SIAM J. Appl. Math., 15 (1967), pp. 1400–1412.

[29] W. WASOW, *Connection problems for asymptotic series*, Bull. Amer. Math. Soc., 74 (1968), pp. 831–853.

[30] ———, *Simple turning-point problems in unbounded domains*, this Journal, 1 (1970), pp. 153–170.

[31] B. WILLNER AND L. A. RUBENFELD, *Uniform asymptotic solutions for a linear ordinary differential equation with one μ-th order turning point: analytic theory*, Comm. Pure Appl. Math., 29 (1976), pp. 343–367.

SIAM J. MATH. ANAL.
Vol. 8, No. 4, August 1977

CONNECTION FORMULAS FOR SECOND-ORDER DIFFERENTIAL EQUATIONS HAVING AN ARBITRARY NUMBER OF TURNING POINTS OF ARBITRARY MULTIPLICITIES*

F. W. J. OLVER†

Abstract. Consider the differential equation

$$d^2w/dx^2=\{u^2f(x)+g(x)\}w, \qquad x\in(a,b),$$

in which (a, b) is a finite or infinite open interval, u is a positive parameter, $f(x)$ is real and twice continuously differentiable, and $g(x)$ is continuous. It is well known that in any subinterval of (a, b) not containing a turning point, that is, a zero of $f(x)$, uniform asymptotic solutions for large u can be constructed in terms of the so-called Liouville–Green or WKBJ functions:

$$f^{-1/4}(x)\exp\left\{\pm u\int f^{1/2}(x)\,dx\right\}.$$

If (a, b) contains turning points, then differing combinations of the Liouville–Green functions have to be used in subintervals that are separated by a turning point in order to represent the same solution.

This paper solves the general problem of connecting the Liouville–Green approximations throughout the interval (a, b) for any number of turning points of arbitrary multiplicities. Several illustrative examples are given, including an arbitrary number of turning points of even multiplicity, an arbitrary number of turning points of odd multiplicity, an eigenvalue problem involving four turning points of multiplicities 1, 2, 3, and 4, and a problem with two simple turning points and one multiple turning point that is solvable exactly in terms of Whittaker functions.

1. Introduction and summary.

In this paper we study the differential equation

$$d^2w/dx^2=\{u^2f(x)+g(x)\}w, \tag{1.01}$$

in which the independent variable x ranges over an open, possibly infinite, interval (a, b), and u is a large positive parameter. Our primary assumptions are that within (a, b) the function $f(x)$ is real and twice continuously differentiable, and $g(x)$ is continuous. For simplicity of exposition we shall also suppose that $f(x)$ and $g(x)$ are independent of u, but the analysis that we shall give is extendible in a straightforward manner to a wide variety of cases in which $f(x)$ and $g(x)$ depend on u.[1]

Let $[a_1, b_1]$ be any compact interval lying within (a, b) and not containing any zeros of $f(x)$. Then the theory of the Liouville–Green (LG) approximation, given for example in [24, Chap. 6] shows that when $u\to\infty$ the functions

$$f^{-1/4}(x)\exp\left\{\pm u\int f^{1/2}(x)\,dx\right\} \tag{1.02}$$

furnish asymptotic representations of a pair of linearly independent solutions of (1.01) with relative errors that are uniformly $O(u^{-1})$ in $[a_1, b_1]$. Zeros of $f(x)$ are known as turning points or transition points of equation (1.01), and their exclusion

* Received by the editors December 19, 1975, and in revised form March 15, 1976.

† Institute for Physical Science and Technology, University of Maryland, College Park, Maryland 20742, and National Bureau of Standards, Washington, D.C. 20234. This research was supported by the U.S. Army Research Office, Durham under Contract DA ARO D 31 124 73 G204, and the National Science Foundation under Grant GP 32841X2.

[1] Compare [24, Chap. 13], and [27].

from the intervals of validity of the LG approximation is essential. This is because for each value of u the solutions of (1.01) are twice continuously differentiable throughout (a, b) and therefore bounded in any interior compact interval, whereas the LG functions (1.02) become infinite at a turning point.

Now suppose that $[a_2, b_2]$ is another compact interval that lies within (a, b) and is free from turning points. Suppose also that $[a_1, b_1]$ and $[a_2, b_2]$ are disjoint. For large u any chosen solution of (1.01) may be represented asymptotically in $[a_1, b_1]$ as a certain linear combination of the LG functions (1.02). It is natural to enquire whether this solution is represented by the same combination in $[a_2, b_2]$. If the interval I, say, that separates $[a_2, b_2]$ from $[a_1, b_1]$ is also free from turning points, then the answer is in the affirmative, because the theory of the LG approximation can be applied to the single interval comprising the union of $[a_1, b_1]$, $[a_2, b_2]$, and I. On the other hand, if I contains one or more turning points, then different combinations of LG functions have to be employed in the intervals $[a_1, b_1]$ and $[a_2, b_2]$, in general, in order to represent the same solution of (1.01). As we shall see in later sections, the changes in these combinations depend on the number of turning points in I and also on their multiplicities, that is, the orders of the zeros of $f(x)$. The general problem of finding the manner in which the combinations of the LG functions change is called the *connection formula problem*, and is of considerable importance in quantum mechanics; see, for example, [1], [5], [7].

In the present paper we apply recent results of the present writer [27] concerning single turning points of arbitrary multiplicity to solve the most general connection formula problem for real variables. That is, we show how to calculate the approximate changes in the combinations of the LG functions in $[a_1, b_1]$ and $[a_2, b_2]$ when the intervening interval I contains any number of turning points, each having arbitrary multiplicity.

The paper is arranged as follows. In § 2 we state theorems that supply rules for connecting the LG approximations across a single turning point of any multiplicity. Four distinct cases arise, depending on the sign of $f(x)$ and the parity of the multiplicity of the turning point. An important feature of the rules is that they are readily combinable with each other, thereby facilitating passage through any number of turning points in succession. The rules are given explicitly only for passage from left to right through each turning point; corresponding rules for passage in the other direction are easily found by changing the sign of x in the original differential equation. The theorems of § 2 are proved in § 3, and then discussed briefly in § 4.

In § 5, which is easily the longest section of the paper, the rules are illustrated by six representative examples. Examples 1 and 2 treat the two cases that involve an arbitrary number of turning points of even multiplicity. In Example 1 the sign of $f(x)$ between consecutive pairs of turning points is positive, causing the solutions of (1.01) to be monotonic; in Example 2 this sign is negative, causing the solutions to be oscillatory. In a similar way, Examples 3 and 4 treat the cases involving an arbitrary number of turning points of odd multiplicity, including the solution of the eigenvalue problem that arises in one of these cases. Example 5 gives the solution of an eigenvalue problem involving four turning points whose multiplicities are, in order, 2, 1, 4, and 3. This example serves to illustrate the use of all four rules in the same problem, and the results were checked by direct numerical methods. The final illustration, Example 6, is a problem due to Heading [11] that involves three turning points. Two of the turning points are simple; the third has any even multiplicity and is located midway between the other two. This example is solvable exactly in terms of Whittaker functions, thereby furnishing another useful check on the new asymptotic theory.

In the concluding section, § 6, the work of other writers on connection formulas for second-order differential equations having two or more turning points is described and related to the results of the present investigation.

2. Basic rules. In this section we consider the differential equation (1.01) in the case when the independent variable x ranges over a finite or infinite open interval (a_0, b_0). The function $f(x)$ is real, and $g(x)$ is real or complex. Furthermore, we assume that:

(i) *$f(x)/(x-x_0)^l$ is nonvanishing and twice continuously differentiable within (a_0, b_0), where x_0 is an interior point of (a_0, b_0) and l is a nonnegative integer.*

(ii) *$g(x)$ is continuous within (a_0, b_0).*

(iii) *The integral*

$$\int \left\{ \frac{1}{|f(x)|^{1/4}} \frac{d^2}{dx^2}\left(\frac{1}{|f(x)|^{1/4}}\right) - \frac{g(x)}{|f(x)|^{1/2}} \right\} dx \tag{2.01}$$

is absolutely convergent as $x \to a_0+$ or b_0-.

The following points should be noted. First, in consequence of condition (i) $f(x)$ is a twice continuously differentiable function whose only possible zero within (a_0, b_0) is a zero of multiplicity l at x_0. Secondly, the integral (2.01) diverges as $x \to x_0$ (but this is immaterial). Thirdly, the functions $f(x)$ and $g(x)$ are permitted to become infinite as x tends to either endpoint a_0 or b_0, provided that condition (iii) is satisfied. However, if (a_0, b_0) is finite and conditions (i) and (ii) are satisfied in the closure of (a_0, b_0), then at both endpoints $f(x)$ is finite and nonvanishing, $g(x)$ is finite, and condition (iii) is automatically fulfilled.

Let us denote by $\hat{a}_0$ and $\hat{b}_0$ two arbitrary fixed points such that

$$a_0 < \hat{a}_0 < x_0 < \hat{b}_0 < b_0. \tag{2.02}$$

Then in the intervals $(a_0, \hat{a}_0)$ and $(\hat{b}_0, b_0)$ uniform asymptotic solutions of (1.01) for large u can be constructed in terms of LG functions. In order to formulate concise rules for connecting these asymptotic solutions we introduce the following notations.

First, we define

$$\xi \equiv \xi(x) = \int^x |f(t)|^{1/2}\, dt. \tag{2.03}$$

Any convenient value may be assigned to the lower limit of integration, provided that the same choice is adhered to in a given context. In consequence of condition (i), $\xi(x)$ is continuously differentiable in the interval (a_0, b_0). Moreover, because $\xi(x)$ is increasing the relation between ξ and x is one to one.

Secondly, we suppose that the symbols $\theta(u)$, $\phi(u)$, and $\chi(u)$ denote three conveniently chosen real functions of the positive parameter u that are independent of x. We require $\phi(u)$ and $\chi(u)$ to have the following properties as $u\to\infty$:

$$\phi(u)=O(1), \quad \chi(u)\to 0, \quad \frac{1}{\chi(u)}=O(u). \tag{2.04}$$

We also stipulate that $\chi(u)$ has to be positive, and we shall often write χ for $\chi(u)$. An admissible choice, for example, is $\chi=u^{-1/2}$.

Thirdly, we define $\chi_l\equiv\chi_l(u)$ and $\hat{\chi}_l\equiv\hat{\chi}_l(u)$ by the equations

$$\chi_l(u)=\begin{cases} u^{-1}, & l=0,1 \\ u^{-1}\ln u, & l=2 \\ u^{-4/(l+2)}, & l\geqq 3 \end{cases}, \qquad \hat{\chi}_l(u)=\max\{\chi(u),\chi_l(u)\}. \tag{2.05}$$

Case I. In this case we assume l to be even and the sign of $f(x)/(x-x_0)^l$ to be positive.

THEOREM 1. *Let $w(u,x)$ be a solution of* (1.01) *having the following properties when u is large and $x\in(a_0,\hat{a}_0)$*:

$$f^{1/4}(x)w(u,x)=\{\phi(u)+O(\chi)\}\,e^{u\xi(x)}, \tag{2.06}$$

and

$$\frac{d}{dx}\{f^{1/4}(x)w(u,x)\}=\{\phi(u)+O(\chi)\}uf^{1/2}(x)\,e^{u\xi(x)}, \tag{2.07}$$

the O-terms being uniform with respect to x. Then in the interval $(\hat{b}_0,b_0)$ this solution has the properties

$$f^{1/4}(x)w(u,x)=\csc\left(\frac{\pi}{l+2}\right)\{\phi(u)+O(\hat{\chi}_l)\}\,e^{u\xi(x)}, \tag{2.08}$$

and

$$\frac{d}{dx}\{f^{1/4}(x)w(u,x)\}=\csc\left(\frac{\pi}{l+2}\right)\{\phi(u)+O(\hat{\chi}_l)\}uf^{1/2}(x)\,e^{u\xi(x)}, \tag{2.09}$$

as $u\to\infty$, the O-terms again being uniform with respect to x.

The proof of this result, and also of Theorems 2, 3, and 4 stated below, forms the subject of the next section.

It will be observed that because $d\xi/dx=|f(x)|^{1/2}$, equations (2.07) and (2.09) may be obtained by formal differentiation of (2.06) and (2.08) respectively, ignoring the differentiation of the error terms $O(\chi)$ and $O(\hat{\chi}_l)$. This kind of pairing occurs frequently in the rest of this paper, and in order to avoid excessive repetition *we shall use the symbol $\underset{(2)}{=}$ in place of $=$ to signify that a given equation is valid, and also the corresponding equation obtained by formal differentiation with respect to x ignoring the differentiation of all O-terms.* We also adopt the convention that *whenever an O-term appears in an equation it is uniformly valid with respect to all values of x associated with that equation.* With these understandings Theorem 1 is expressed concisely by the following statement:

$$f^{1/4}(x)w(u,x) \underset{(2)}{=} \{\phi(u)+O(\chi)\}\, e^{u\xi(x)}, \qquad x\in(a_0,\hat{a}_0), \tag{2.10}$$

implies

$$f^{1/4}(x)w(u,x) \underset{(2)}{=} \csc\left(\frac{\pi}{l+2}\right)\{\phi(u)+O(\hat{\chi}_l)\}\, e^{u\xi(x)}, \qquad x\in(\hat{b}_0,b_0). \tag{2.11}$$

Case II. Here l is even and the sign of $f(x)/(x-x_0)^l$ is negative.
THEOREM 2.

$$\begin{aligned}|f(x)|^{1/4}w(u,x) &\underset{(2)}{=} \{\phi(u)+O(\chi)\}\cos\{u\xi(x)-u\xi(x_0)+\theta(u)\}\\ &\quad +O(\chi)\sin\{u\xi(x)-u\xi(x_0)+\theta(u)\}, \qquad x\in(a_0,\hat{a}_0),\end{aligned} \tag{2.12}$$

implies

$$\begin{aligned}|f(x)|^{1/4}w(u,x) &\underset{(2)}{=} \{\Lambda(u)+O(\hat{\chi}_l)\}\cos\{u\xi(x)-u\xi(x_0)+\lambda(u)\}\\ &\quad +O(\hat{\chi}_l)\sin\{u\xi(x)-u\xi(x_0)+\lambda(u)\}, \qquad x\in(\hat{b}_0,b_0),\end{aligned} \tag{2.13}$$

where

$$\begin{aligned}\Lambda(u)=\phi(u)\Big[&\cot^2\left(\frac{\pi}{2l+4}\right)\cos^2\left\{\theta(u)+\frac{1}{4}\pi\right\}\\ &+\tan^2\left(\frac{\pi}{2l+4}\right)\sin^2\left\{\theta(u)+\frac{1}{4}\pi\right\}\Big]^{1/2},\end{aligned} \tag{2.14}$$

and

$$\lambda(u)=-\frac{1}{4}\pi+\tan^{-1}\left[\tan^2\left(\frac{\pi}{2l+4}\right)\tan\left\{\theta(u)+\frac{1}{4}\pi\right\}\right]. \tag{2.15}$$

In the last equation the branch of the inverse tangent is taken to be zero when $\theta(u)=-\frac{1}{4}\pi$, and defined by continuity for other values of $\theta(u)$.

It should be noted that the two terms $O(\chi)$ in (2.12) denote different error terms, in general. The undifferentiated form of (2.12) is equivalent to

$$|f(x)|^{1/4}w(u,x)=\phi(u)\cos\{u\xi(x)-u\xi(x_0)+\theta(u)\}+O(\chi), \qquad x\in(a_0,\hat{a}_0),$$

and the differentiated form is equivalent to

$$\frac{d}{dx}\{|f(x)|^{1/4}w(u,x)\}=-u|f(x)|^{1/2}[\phi(u)\sin\{u\xi(x)-u\xi(x_0)+\theta(u)\}+O(\chi)],$$
$$x\in(a_0,\hat{a}_0).$$

Similarly for (2.13), and also (2.16) and (2.19) below.

Case III. Here l is odd and the sign of $f(x)/(x-x_0)^l$ is positive.

THEOREM 3.

$$\begin{aligned}|f(x)|^{1/4}w(u,x) \underset{(2)}{=} \{\phi(u)+O(\chi)\}\cos\{u\xi(x)-u\xi(x_0)+\theta(u)\}\\ +O(\chi)\sin\{u\xi(x)-u\xi(x_0)+\theta(u)\}, \qquad x\in(a_0,\hat{a}_0),\end{aligned} \tag{2.16}$$

implies

$$\begin{aligned}f^{1/4}(x)w(u,x) \underset{(2)}{=} \frac{1}{2}\csc\left(\frac{\pi}{2l+4}\right)\left[\phi(u)\cos\left\{\theta(u)+\frac{1}{4}\pi\right\}+O(\hat{\chi}_l)\right]\\ \times e^{u\xi(x)-u\xi(x_0)}, \qquad x\in(\hat{b}_0,b_0).\end{aligned} \tag{2.17}$$

Case IV. Here l is odd and the sign of $f(x)/(x-x_0)^l$ is negative.

THEOREM 4.

$$f^{1/4}(x)w(u,x) \underset{(2)}{=} \{\phi(u)+O(\chi)\}\,e^{u\xi(x)}, \qquad x\in(a_0,\hat{a}_0), \tag{2.18}$$

implies

$$\begin{aligned}|f(x)|^{1/4}w(u,x) \underset{(2)}{=} \csc\left(\frac{\pi}{2l+4}\right)e^{u\xi(x_0)}\left[\{\phi(u)+O(\hat{\chi}_l)\}\cos\left\{u\xi(x)-u\xi(x_0)-\frac{1}{4}\pi\right\}\right.\\ \left.+O(\hat{\chi}_l)\sin\left\{u\xi(x)-u\xi(x_0)-\frac{1}{4}\pi\right\}\right], \qquad x\in(\hat{b}_0,b_0).\end{aligned} \tag{2.19}$$

3. Proof of the theorems of § 2. We begin with the proof of Theorem 1. Since $f(x)/(x-x_0)^l$ is positive and l is even, the function $f(x)$ is positive throughout (a_0, b_0), except at x_0. In consequence of conditions (i), (ii), and (iii) stated at the beginning of § 2, there exists a solution $\hat{w}(u,x)$, say, of (1.01) such that for large u

$$f^{1/4}(x)\hat{w}(u,x) \underset{(2)}{=} \{1+O(u^{-1})\}\,e^{u\xi(x)}, \qquad x\in(a_0,\hat{a}_0); \tag{3.01}$$

see [24, p. 203]. If we now define

$$w(u,x)=\{\phi(u)+O(\chi)\}\hat{w}(u,x), \tag{3.02}$$

where the term $O(\chi)$ in this equation is independent of x, then $w(u,x)$ is another solution of (1.01). Hypothesis (2.04) requires $|\phi(u)|$ to be bounded and $O(u^{-1})\subseteq O(\chi)$. Hence from (3.01) and (3.02) it follows that

$$f^{1/4}(x)w(u,x) \underset{(2)}{=} \{\phi(u)+O(\chi)\}\,e^{u\xi(x)}, \qquad x\in(a_0,\hat{a}_0), \tag{3.03}$$

where the term $O(\chi)$ may now depend on x. In other words, with the given conditions a solution $w(u,x)$ having the properties (2.06) and (2.07) certainly exists, but because there is freedom of choice of the term $O(\chi)$ in (3.02) this solution is not unique.

The problem of finding the correct LG approximation to $w(u,x)$ in the interval $(\hat{b}_0, b_0)$ is very similar to the connection formula problem solved in [27,

§ 4.2]. An important difference in the present case, however, is that the endpoints a_0 and b_0 need not be singularities of the differential equation. The effect of this modification is to render the matching of the solutions somewhat more complicated.

Let us define $\zeta \equiv \zeta(x)$ by

$$\zeta(x) = -\left\{\int_x^{x_0} f^{1/2}(t)\,dt\right\}^{2/(l+2)}, \qquad a_0 < x \leqq x_0, \tag{3.04}$$

and

$$\zeta(x) = \left\{\int_{x_0}^{x} f^{1/2}(t)\,dt\right\}^{2/(l+2)}, \qquad x_0 \leqq x < b_0. \tag{3.05}$$

Then in terms of the function $\xi(x)$ defined by (2.03), we have

$$|\zeta(x)|^{(l+2)/2} = |\xi(x) - \xi(x_0)|, \qquad x \in (a_0, b_0). \tag{3.06}$$

From (3.04) and (3.05) it is clear that $\zeta(x)$ is an increasing function of x, and from the lemma of [27, § 3.2] we also know that $\zeta(x)$ is twice continuously differentiable. Furthermore, by taking $m = l+2$ and $\varpi = 0$ in §§ 3.2 and 5.2 of the same reference, we see that (1.01) has twice continuously differentiable solutions $w_-(u, x)$ and $w_+(u, x)$, say, such that for large u and $x \in (a_0, b_0)$

$$\hat{f}^{1/4}(x) w_-(u, x) \underset{(2)}{\equiv} 2^{1/2}(l+2)^{-1/2} u^{l/(2l+4)}\{1 + O(\chi_l)\} U_{l+2}(-u^{2/(l+2)}\zeta), \tag{3.07}$$

and

$$\hat{f}^{1/4}(x) w_+(u, x) \underset{(2)}{\equiv} 2^{1/2}(l+2)^{-1/2} u^{l/(2l+4)}\{1 + O(\chi_l)\} U_{l+2}(u^{2/(l+2)}\zeta). \tag{3.08}$$

In these relations $\hat{f}(x)$ is defined by

$$\hat{f}(x) \equiv \frac{4f(x)}{(l+2)^2|\zeta|^l} = \left(\frac{d\zeta}{dx}\right)^2, \tag{3.09}$$

the normalizing factors $2^{1/2}(l+2)^{-1/2}u^{l/(2l+4)}$ have been introduced for later convenience, the function $\chi_l \equiv \chi_l(u)$ is defined by (2.05), and the function $U_{l+2}(t)$ is defined in terms of modified Bessel functions by the equations

$$U_{l+2}(t) = (2t/\pi)^{1/2} K_{1/(l+2)}(t^{(l+2)/2}), \qquad t > 0,$$

$$U_{l+2}(t) = (2|t|/\pi)^{1/2}[\pi \csc\{\pi/(l+2)\} I_{1/(l+2)}(|t|^{(l+2)/2}) + K_{1/(l+2)}(|t|^{(l+2)/2})], \qquad t < 0.$$

Properties of $U_{l+2}(t)$ are discussed in [27, §2.1].

Suppose now that $x \in (a_0, \hat{a}_0)$. Then from (2.02) and (3.04) it follows that ζ is negative and bounded away from zero. Consequently the functions U_{l+2} in (3.07) and (3.08) may be replaced by their respective asymptotic approximations for large positive and negative arguments, given in [27, § 2.1]; similarly for the derivatives of these functions. Aided by (3.06) and (3.09) and the fact that

$O(u^{-1}) \subseteq O(\chi_l)$, we arrive at

$$(3.10) \quad f^{1/4}(x)w_-(u,x) \underset{(2)}{=} \{1+O(\chi_l)\} \exp\{u\xi(x)-u\xi(x_0)\}, \qquad x \in (a_0, \hat{a}_0),$$

and

$$(3.11) \quad f^{1/4}(x)w_+(u,x) \underset{(2)}{=} \{1+O(\chi_l)\} \csc\left(\frac{\pi}{l+2}\right) \exp\{u\xi(x_0)-u\xi(x)\}, \qquad x \in (a_0, \hat{a}_0).$$

Secondly, suppose that $x \in (\hat{b}_0, b_0)$. Then by similar analysis we find that

$$(3.12) \quad f^{1/4}(x)w_-(u,x) \underset{(2)}{=} \{1+O(\chi_l)\} \csc\left(\frac{\pi}{l+2}\right) \exp\{u\xi(x)-u\xi(x_0)\}, \qquad x \in (\hat{b}_0, b_0),$$

and

$$(3.13) \quad f^{1/4}(x)w_+(u,x) \underset{(2)}{=} \{1+O(\chi_l)\} \exp\{u\xi(x_0)-u\xi(x)\}, \qquad x \in (\hat{b}_0, b_0).$$

Let the linear relation that holds between the wanted solution $w(u,x)$ and the known solutions $w_-(u,x)$ and $w_+(u,x)$ be denoted by

$$(3.14) \qquad w(u,x) = Aw_-(u,x) + Bw_+(u,x),$$

where the coefficients A and B are independent of x (but may depend on u). To find A and B, we let $x \to a_0+$ in the equation

$$(3.15) \qquad f^{1/4}(x)w(u,x) = Af^{1/4}(x)w_-(u,x) + Bf^{1/4}(x)w_+(u,x),$$

and its differentiated form. Assuming for the moment that $\xi(a_0)$ is finite, and referring to (2.06), (2.07), (3.10), and (3.11), we obtain the equations

$$\{\phi(u)+O(\chi)\}\exp\{u\xi(a_0)\} = A\{1+O(\chi_l)\}\exp\{u\xi(a_0)-u\xi(x_0)\} + B\{1+O(\chi_l)\}\csc\left(\frac{\pi}{l+2}\right)\exp\{u\xi(x_0)-u\xi(a_0)\},$$

and

$$\{\phi(u)+O(\chi)\}\exp\{u\xi(a_0)\} = A\{1+O(\chi_l)\}\exp\{u\xi(a_0)-u\xi(x_0)\} - B\{1+O(\chi_l)\}\csc\left(\frac{\pi}{l+2}\right)\exp\{u\xi(x_0)-u\xi(a_0)\}.$$

Solving for A and B, remembering that $|\phi(u)|$ is assumed to be bounded, we derive

$$(3.16) \qquad A = \exp\{u\xi(x_0)\}\{\phi(u)+O(\hat{\chi}_l)\},$$

$$(3.17) \qquad B = \exp\{2u\xi(a_0)-u\xi(x_0)\}O(\hat{\chi}_l),$$

where $\hat{\chi}_l$ is defined by (2.05).

Alternatively, if $\xi(a_0)=-\infty$ then by similar analysis we find that A is again given by (3.16) and B vanishes. In other words, it is legitimate to replace the right-hand side of (3.17) by its limiting value as $\xi(a_0)\to-\infty$.

Uniform asymptotic approximations for $f^{1/4}(x)w(u,x)$ in the interval $(\hat{b}_0, b_0)$ may now be found from (3.15) by substituting (3.12), (3.13), (3.16), and (3.17). When $\xi(a_0)$ is finite it is easily seen that the whole of the contribution from the second solution on the right-hand side of (3.15) is absorbable in the uniform error term associated with the contribution from the first solution. Alternatively, when $\xi(a_0)=-\infty$ there is no contribution from the second solution. Similarly for the derivatives. The final results are given by (2.08) and (2.09) or, equivalently, by (2.11). This completes the proof.

To prove Theorem 2, we begin with the results of §§ 3.3 and 5.2 of [27]. Using methods similar to those just employed for Theorem 1, we find that there exist solutions $w_-(u,x)$ and $w_+(u,x)$, say, of equation (1.01) with the properties

$$|f(x)|^{1/4}w_-(u,x) \underset{(2)}{=} \{1+O(\chi_l)\}\sec\left(\frac{\pi}{2l+4}\right)\cos\left\{u\xi(x)-u\xi(x_0)-\frac{1}{4}\pi\right\}$$
(3.18)
$$+O(\chi_l)\sin\left\{u\xi(x)-u\xi(x_0)-\frac{1}{4}\pi\right\},\qquad x\in(a_0,\hat{a}_0),$$

$$|f(x)|^{1/4}w_+(u,x) \underset{(2)}{=} \{1+O(\chi_l)\}\csc\left(\frac{\pi}{2l+4}\right)\cos\left\{u\xi(x)-u\xi(x_0)+\frac{1}{4}\pi\right\}$$
(3.19)
$$+O(\chi_l)\sin\left\{u\xi(x)-u\xi(x_0)+\frac{1}{4}\pi\right\},\qquad x\in(a_0,\hat{a}_0),$$

and

$$|f(x)|^{1/4}w_-(u,x) \underset{(2)}{=} \{1+O(\chi_l)\}\csc\left(\frac{\pi}{2l+4}\right)\cos\left\{u\xi(x)-u\xi(x_0)-\frac{1}{4}\pi\right\}$$
(3.20)
$$+O(\chi_l)\sin\left\{u\xi(x)-u\xi(x_0)-\frac{1}{4}\pi\right\},\qquad x\in(\hat{b}_0,b_0),$$

$$|f(x)|^{1/4}w_+(u,x) \underset{(2)}{=} \{1+O(\chi_l)\}\sec\left(\frac{\pi}{2l+4}\right)\cos\left\{u\xi(x)-u\xi(x_0)+\frac{1}{4}\pi\right\}$$
(3.21)
$$+O(\chi_l)\sin\left\{u\xi(x)-u\xi(x_0)+\frac{1}{4}\pi\right\},\qquad x\in(\hat{b}_0,b_0).$$

The wanted solution $w(u,x)$ has the property (2.12), and is easily seen to exist by the theory of the Liouville–Green approximation. From (3.18), (3.19), and the fact that $|\phi(u)|$ is assumed to be bounded, we find that the linear relation holding between the three solutions is representable in the form

$$|f(x)|^{1/4}w(u,x)=\left[\phi(u)\cos\left\{\theta(u)+\frac{1}{4}\pi\right\}+O(\hat{\chi}_l)\right]\cos\left(\frac{\pi}{2l+4}\right)|f(x)|^{1/4}w_-(u,x)$$
$$+\left[\phi(u)\sin\left\{\theta(u)+\frac{1}{4}\pi\right\}+O(\hat{\chi}_l)\right]\sin\left(\frac{\pi}{2l+4}\right)|f(x)|^{1/4}w_+(u,x);$$

compare (3.15). The required results (2.13), (2.14), and (2.15) follow on substituting in the right-hand side of this equation, and its differentiated form, by means of (3.20) and (3.21).

The proofs of Theorems 3 and 4 are similar to those of Theorems 1 and 2 and it is unnecessary to record details.

4. Remarks on the theorems of § 2. Theorems 1, 2, 3, and 4 describe the approximate changes in the form of the LG approximations to the solutions of the differential equation (1.01) on passing through the various types of turning point. For example, in Case I the net effect is to multiply the asymptotic forms (2.06) and (2.07) by the factor $\csc\{\pi/(l+2)\}$. In particular, when $l=0$, that is, when there is no turning point, there is no change in the asymptotic forms—as is to be expected.

In comparing the four theorems, we note that there are differences in the number of solutions of the differential equation that are supplied. We discuss here briefly the underlying reasons, taking each case in turn.

Case I. The effect of changing the lower limit in the definition (2.03) of $\xi(x)$ is to multiply the solution $w(u,x)$ by a factor that is independent of x. In consequence, Theorem 1 supplies direct information for only one independent solution of the differential equation. However, the theory of the LG approximation shows that for large u there exists a second solution $w_2(u,x)$, say, having the property

$$f^{1/4}(x)w_2(u,x) \underset{(2)}{=} \{\phi(u)+O(\chi)\}\, e^{-u\xi(x)}, \qquad x\in(a_0,\hat{a}_0);$$

compare (2.10). Like $w(u,x)$ this solution is expressible in the form

$$w_2(u,x)=Aw_-(u,x)+Bw_+(u,x), \tag{4.01}$$

where $w_-(u,x)$ and $w_+(u,x)$ are as in § 3, but A and B have new values. Carrying through the analysis in a similar manner to § 3, we find that

$$A=\exp\{u\xi(x_0)-2u\xi(a_0)\}O(\hat{\chi}_l),$$

$$B=\sin\left(\frac{\pi}{l+2}\right)\exp\{-u\xi(x_0)\}\{\phi(u)+O(\hat{\chi}_l)\},$$

provided that $\xi(a_0)$ is finite. However, on substituting these results in (4.01) we obtain little information concerning $f^{1/4}(x)w_2(u,x)$ and its derivative in $(\hat{b}_0, {}^{\circ}b_0)$, because in this interval $w_-(u,x)$ dominates $w_+(u,x)$ when u is large (compare (3.12) and (3.13)), and the coefficient A of $w_-(u,x)$ is available only as an O-estimate.

Noting that we are able to obtain a satisfactory connection formula for the solution that is growing in magnitude as we pass through the turning point, but not for the solution that is decaying, we perceive that the way to obtain a second connection formula is to reverse the roles of the original solutions by passing through the turning point in the opposite direction, that is, from right to left. Thus the required formula is found by replacing x by $-x$ in (1.01), applying Theorem 1, and then changing the sign of x again. The result is expressible in the form:

$$f^{1/4}(x)w(u,x) \underset{(2)}{=} \{\phi(u)+O(\chi)\}\, e^{-u\xi(x)}, \qquad x\in(\hat{b}_0, b_0),$$

implies

$$f^{1/4}(x)w(u,x) \underset{(2)}{=} \csc\left(\frac{\pi}{l+2}\right)\{\phi(u)+O(\hat{\chi}_l)\}\,e^{-u\xi(x)}, \qquad x\in(a_0,\hat{a}_0).$$

Case II. Since there is no restriction on the choice of the function $\theta(u)$, and the only restriction on $\phi(u)$ is that this function is bounded in absolute value, Theorem 2 informs us directly how any solution of the differential equation continues through the turning point. In particular, if we select $\theta(u)=-\frac{1}{4}\pi$ and $\frac{1}{4}\pi$, then we obtain a pair of solutions that are asymptotically out of phase by $\frac{1}{2}\pi$, both for $x\in(a_0,\hat{a}_0)$ and $x\in(\hat{b}_0,b_0)$; compare (2.15). They therefore comprise a numerically satisfactory pair of solutions in the sense of Miller [19].

The reason for the difference between Theorems 1 and 2 concerning the number of connection formulas that each theorem supplies is traceable to the fact that in Case II no solution grows exponentially in magnitude compared with other solutions as we pass through the turning point.

Case III. Since $\theta(u)$ and $\phi(u)$ again may be freely chosen, subject to $|\phi(u)|$ being bounded, the situation resembles Case II superficially. However, if $\theta(u)-\frac{1}{4}\pi$ is zero or an integer multiple of π, then the factor contained in the square brackets in (2.17) reduces to the error term $O(\hat{\chi}_l)$. Moreover, if we exclude these values of $\theta(u)$, then it is impossible to construct a pair of solutions that are numerically satisfactory in the interval $(\hat{b}_0,b_0)$. To obtain a satisfactory companion connection formula we have to pass through the turning point in the opposite direction, in the manner of Case I. This is effected by reversing the sign of x in the given differential equation and applying Theorem 4.

Case IV. The situation here is analogous to Case I. Theorem 4 supplies direct information for only one independent solution of the differential equation. To obtain a second connection formula we pass through the turning point from right to left with the aid of Theorem 3.

5. Examples. In this section we consider the differential equation (1.01), that is,

$$d^2w/dx^2=\{u^2f(x)+g(x)\}w, \qquad x\in(a,b), \tag{5.01}$$

in various cases for which there is more than one turning point in the finite or infinite open interval (a,b).

As before, we suppose that within (a,b) the function $f(x)$ is real, $f''(x)$ is continuous, $g(x)$ is real or complex and continuous, and the integral (2.01) is absolutely convergent as x approaches the endpoints a and b. We again define $\xi(x)$ by the integral (2.03), with the understanding that we adhere to the same lower limit of integration in each example.

Example 1. *Arbitrary number of even turning points: first case.* As our first example we suppose that there are n turning points x_r, $r=1,2,\cdots,n$, arranged as follows:

$$a<x_1<x_2<\cdots<x_n<b. \tag{5.02}$$

We also suppose that the function

$$(x_1-x)^{-2l_1}(x_2-x)^{-2l_2}\cdots(x_n-x)^{-2l_n}f(x) \tag{5.03}$$

is positive and twice continuously differentiable within (a, b), where $l_1, l_2, \cdots, l_n$ are positive integers. Thus the multiplicity of the turning point x_r is $2l_r$, and $f(x)$ is positive within (a, b) except at the turning points.

We first introduce a set of arbitrary fixed points $a_r, b_r, r=1, 2, \cdots, n$, that satisfy

$$a<a_1<x_1<b_1<a_2<x_2<b_2<\cdots<a_n<x_n<b_n<b. \tag{5.04}$$

With the given conditions, we know from the theory of the LG approximation that there is a solution of (5.01) with the property

$$f^{1/4}(x)w(u, x) \underset{(2)}{=} \{1+O(u^{-1})\}\, e^{u\xi(x)}, \qquad x \in (a, a_1), \tag{5.05}$$

as $u \to \infty$. Applying Theorem 1 of § 2 with $x_0=x_1$, $l=2l_1$, $\phi(u)=1$, and $\chi(u)=1/u$, we find that

$$f^{1/4}(x)w(u, x) \underset{(2)}{=} \csc\left(\frac{\pi}{2l_1+2}\right)\{1+O(\chi_{2l_1})\}\, e^{u\xi(x)}, \qquad x \in (b_1, a_2).$$

Theorem 1 may now be applied a second time to continue $w(u, x)$ across the turning point x_2 to the interval (b_2, a_3), and so on. The final result is evidently given by

$$f^{1/4}(x)w(u, x) \underset{(2)}{=} \left\{\prod_{r=1}^{n} \csc\left(\frac{\pi}{2l_r+2}\right)\right\}\{1+O(\chi_{2l})\}\, e^{u\xi(x)}, \qquad x \in (b_n, b), \tag{5.06}$$

where

$$l=\max(l_1, l_2, \cdots, l_n). \tag{5.07}$$

Remarks. It is interesting to observe that the result (5.06) is independent of the actual location of the turning points in (a, b) and also of the order in which the differing multiplicities occur. It needs to be stressed, however, that we have supposed that the turning points are fixed. In some problems the function $f(x)$ and the turning points may depend continuously on a second parameter ρ, say. Assuming that the given conditions are satisfied uniformly with respect to ρ, we may easily verify that the result (5.06) holds uniformly with respect to ρ, provided that none of the turning points coalesce with each other, or with the endpoints, as ρ varies. If, however, the turning points x_r and x_{r+1}, say, were to coalesce for a certain value of ρ, then in (5.06) the factors

$$\csc\left(\frac{\pi}{2l_r+2}\right) \csc\left(\frac{\pi}{2l_{r+1}+2}\right) \tag{5.08}$$

would have to be replaced by the single factor

$$\csc\left(\frac{\pi}{2l_r+2l_{r+1}+2}\right). \tag{5.09}$$

Unless the expressions (5.08) and (5.09) are equal—as they are when $l_r=l_{r+1}=1$—such an abrupt change cannot possibly be uniform with respect to ρ.

Example 2. *Arbitrary number of even turning points: second case.* We assume the same conditions and notation as in Example 1, except that we now suppose that the sign of the function (5.03) is negative. Thus $f(x)$ is negative, except at the turning points.

From the theory of the LG approximation, there exist solutions $w_{-1}(u, x)$ and $w_1(u, x)$ such that when u is large and $x \in (a, a_1)$

$$|f(x)|^{1/4} w_{-1}(u, x) \underset{(2)}{=} \{1+O(u^{-1})\} \cos\{u\xi(x)-\tfrac{1}{4}\pi\} + O(u^{-1}) \sin\{u\xi(x)-\tfrac{1}{4}\pi\}, \tag{5.10}$$

and

$$|f(x)|^{1/4} w_{1}(u, x) \underset{(2)}{=} \{1+O(u^{-1})\} \cos\{u\xi(x)+\tfrac{1}{4}\pi\} + O(u^{-1}) \sin\{u\xi(x)+\tfrac{1}{4}\pi\}. \tag{5.11}$$

The asymptotic forms of these solutions in the interval (b_1, a_2) can be found by direct application of Theorem 2 of § 2 with $x_0 = x_1$. Subsequent analysis is considerably simplified, however, by taking $\theta(u) = \mp\frac{1}{4}\pi$ in Theorem 2, for from (2.14) and (2.15) we then obtain

$$\Lambda(u) = \phi(u) \cot\left(\frac{\pi}{2l+4}\right), \qquad \lambda(u) = -\tfrac{1}{4}\pi, \quad \text{when } \theta(u) = -\tfrac{1}{4}\pi;$$

or

$$\Lambda(u) = \phi(u) \tan\left(\frac{\pi}{2l+4}\right), \qquad \lambda(u) = \tfrac{1}{4}\pi, \quad \text{when } \theta(u) = \tfrac{1}{4}\pi.$$

Accordingly, we first convert the arguments of the trigonometric functions in (5.10) and (5.11) into the forms $u\xi(x) - u\xi(x_1) - \frac{1}{4}\pi$ and $u\xi(x) - u\xi(x_1) + \frac{1}{4}\pi$, respectively, by setting

$$u\xi(x) \mp \tfrac{1}{4}\pi = u\xi(x_1) + \{u\xi(x) - u\xi(x_1) \mp \tfrac{1}{4}\pi\},$$

and expanding by means of the addition rules. The result is expressed most concisely in matrix form. Let $\mathbf{R}_r$ denote the rotation matrix

$$\mathbf{R}_r = \begin{bmatrix} \cos u\xi(x_r) & \sin u\xi(x_r) \\ -\sin u\xi(x_r) & \cos u\xi(x_r) \end{bmatrix}, \qquad r = 1, 2, \cdots, n.$$

Then we have

$$\begin{bmatrix} |f(x)|^{1/4} w_{-1}(u, x) \\ |f(x)|^{1/4} w_{1}(u, x) \end{bmatrix} \underset{(2)}{=} \mathbf{R}_1 \begin{bmatrix} \{1+O(u^{-1})\} \cos\{u\xi(x) - u\xi(x_1) - \frac{1}{4}\pi\} + O(u^{-1}) \sin\{u\xi(x) - u\xi(x_1) - \frac{1}{4}\pi\} \\ \{1+O(u^{-1})\} \cos\{u\xi(x) - u\xi(x_1) + \frac{1}{4}\pi\} + O(u^{-1}) \sin\{u\xi(x) - u\xi(x_1) + \frac{1}{4}\pi\} \end{bmatrix},$$

valid when $x \in (a, a_1)$.

We now apply Theorem 2 with $x_0=x_1$, $l=2l_1$, $\phi(u)=1$, $\chi(u)=1/u$, and $\theta(u)=-\frac{1}{4}\pi$ and $\frac{1}{4}\pi$ in turn. The result is expressible in the form

$$\begin{bmatrix}|f(x)|^{1/4}w_{-1}(u,x)\\|f(x)|^{1/4}w_1(u,x)\end{bmatrix} \underset{(2)}{=} \mathbf{R}_1\mathbf{D}_1\begin{bmatrix}\{1+O(\chi_{2l_1})\}\cos\{u\xi(x)-u\xi(x_1)-\frac{1}{4}\pi\}\\ \quad +O(\chi_{2l_1})\sin\{u\xi(x)-u\xi(x_1)-\frac{1}{4}\pi\}\\ \{1+O(\chi_{2l_1})\}\cos\{u\xi(x)-u\xi(x_1)+\frac{1}{4}\pi\}\\ \quad +O(\chi_{2l_1})\sin\{u\xi(x)-u\xi(x_1)+\frac{1}{4}\pi\}\end{bmatrix}, \tag{5.12}$$

valid when $x\in(b_1,a_2)$, where

$$\mathbf{D}_r=\begin{bmatrix}\cot\{\pi/(4l_r+4)\} & 0\\ 0 & \tan\{\pi/(4l_r+4)\}\end{bmatrix},\qquad r=1,2,\cdots,n.$$

To prepare for passage through the next turning point x_2 we convert the arguments of the cosine and sine functions appearing in (5.12) into the forms $u\xi(x)-u\xi(x_2)-\frac{1}{4}\pi$ and $u\xi(x)-u\xi(x_2)+\frac{1}{4}\pi$, respectively, by application of the addition formulas. Thus we have

$$\begin{bmatrix}\{1+O(\chi_{2l_1})\}\cos\{u\xi(x)-u\xi(x_1)-\frac{1}{4}\pi\}+O(\chi_{2l_1})\sin\{u\xi(x)-u\xi(x_1)-\frac{1}{4}\pi\}\\ \{1+O(\chi_{2l_1})\}\cos\{u\xi(x)-u\xi(x_1)+\frac{1}{4}\pi\}+O(\chi_{2l_1})\sin\{u\xi(x)-u\xi(x_1)+\frac{1}{4}\pi\}\end{bmatrix}$$

$$\underset{(2)}{=}\begin{bmatrix}\cos\{u\xi(x_2)-u\xi(x_1)\} & \sin\{u\xi(x_2)-u\xi(x_1)\}\\ -\sin\{u\xi(x_2)-u\xi(x_1)\} & \cos\{u\xi(x_2)-u\xi(x_1)\}\end{bmatrix}$$

$$\times\begin{bmatrix}\{1+O(\chi_{2l_1})\}\cos\{u\xi(x)-u\xi(x_2)-\frac{1}{4}\pi\}+O(\chi_{2l_1})\sin\{u\xi(x)-u\xi(x_2)-\frac{1}{4}\pi\}\\ \{1+O(\chi_{2l_1})\}\cos\{u\xi(x)-u\xi(x_2)+\frac{1}{4}\pi\}+O(\chi_{2l_1})\sin\{u\xi(x)-u\xi(x_2)+\frac{1}{4}\pi\}\end{bmatrix}$$

$$\underset{(2)}{=}\mathbf{R}_1^{-1}\mathbf{R}_2\begin{bmatrix}\{1+O(\chi_{2l_1})\}\cos\{u\xi(x)-u\xi(x_2)-\frac{1}{4}\pi\}\\ \quad +O(\chi_{2l_1})\sin\{u\xi(x)-u\xi(x_2)-\frac{1}{4}\pi\}\\ \{1+O(\chi_{2l_1})\}\cos\{u\xi(x)-u\xi(x_2)+\frac{1}{4}\pi\}\\ \quad +O(\chi_{2l_1})\sin\{u\xi(x)-u\xi(x_2)+\frac{1}{4}\pi\}\end{bmatrix},$$

since

$$\mathbf{R}_1^{-1}=\begin{bmatrix}\cos u\xi(x_1) & -\sin u\xi(x_1)\\ \sin u\xi(x_1) & \cos u\xi(x_1)\end{bmatrix}.$$

We may now apply Theorem 2 with $x_0=x_2$, $l=2l_2$, $\phi(u)=1$, $\chi(u)=\chi_{2l_1}(u)$, and $\theta(u)=\mp\frac{1}{4}\pi$, to continue the solutions to the interval (b_2,a_3). The process may then be repeated for successive turning points, and the final result is easily seen to be

$$\begin{bmatrix}|f(x)|^{1/4}w_{-1}(u,x)\\|f(x)|^{1/4}w_1(u,x)\end{bmatrix} \underset{(2)}{=} \mathbf{M}_1\mathbf{M}_2\cdots\mathbf{M}_n\begin{bmatrix}\{1+O(\chi_{2l})\}\cos\{u\xi(x)-\frac{1}{4}\pi\}+O(\chi_{2l})\sin\{u\xi(x)-\frac{1}{4}\pi\}\\ \{1+O(\chi_{2l})\}\cos\{u\xi(x)+\frac{1}{4}\pi\}+O(\chi_{2l})\sin\{u\xi(x)+\frac{1}{4}\pi\}\end{bmatrix}, \tag{5.13}$$

valid when $x \in (b_n, b)$, where l is defined by (5.07), and

$$\mathbf{M}_r = \mathbf{R}_r \mathbf{D}_r \mathbf{R}_r^{-1}, \qquad r = 1, 2, \cdots, n.$$

Equation (5.13) is the required connection formula.

Remarks. It will be observed that each matrix $\mathbf{M}_r$ depends on x_r as well as l_r; thus $\mathbf{M}_r \equiv \mathbf{M}(x_r, l_r)$. In contrast to Example 1, a change in the value of x_r alters the final result (5.13). Furthermore, it is readily verified that

$$\mathbf{M}(x_r, l_r)\mathbf{M}(x_{r+1}, l_{r+1}) \neq \mathbf{M}(x_r, l_{r+1})\mathbf{M}(x_{r+1}, l_r),$$

in general. Hence the final result is also affected by the order in which differing multiplicities occur, again in contrast to Example 1.

Example 3. *Arbitrary number of odd turning points: first case.* In this example we suppose that there are n turning points x_r, $r = 1, 2, \cdots, n$, again enumerated to satisfy (5.02), and that the multiplicity of the turning point at x_r is $2l_r + 1$, where l_r now denotes a nonnegative integer. We also assume that the function

$$(x_1 - x)^{-2l_1 - 1}(x_2 - x)^{-2l_2 - 1} \cdots (x_n - x)^{-2l_n - 1} f(x) \tag{5.14}$$

is negative and twice continuously differentiable within (a, b).

As in Examples 1 and 2, we begin by introducing arbitrary fixed points a_r, b_r, $r = 1, 2, \cdots, n$, that satisfy (5.04).

When $x \in (a, a_1)$ the function $f(x)$ is negative, and with the assumed conditions the theory of the LG approximation shows that there exists a solution $w(u, x)$ having the property

$$\begin{aligned} |f(x)|^{1/4} w(u, x) \underset{(2)}{=} &\{1 + O(u^{-1})\} \cos\{u\xi(x) - u\xi(x_1) + \theta(u) - \tfrac{1}{4}\pi\} \\ &+ O(u^{-1}) \sin\{u\xi(x) - u\xi(x_1) + \theta(u) - \tfrac{1}{4}\pi\}, \qquad x \in (a, a_1), \end{aligned} \tag{5.15}$$

where, as before, $\theta(u)$ is any prescribed real function of the large positive parameter u.

Applying Theorem 3 of § 2 with $x_0 = x_1$, $l = 2l_1 + 1$, $\phi(u) = 1$, $\chi(u) = 1/u$, and $\theta(u)$ replaced by $\theta(u) - \frac{1}{4}\pi$, we see that

$$f^{1/4}(x) w(u, x) \underset{(2)}{=} \frac{1}{2} \csc\left(\frac{\pi}{4l_1 + 6}\right)\{\cos\theta(u) + O(\chi_{2l_1+1})\} e^{u\xi(x) - u\xi(x_1)}, \qquad x \in (b_1, a_2).$$

Then applying Theorem 4 of § 2 with $x_0 = x_2$, $l = 2l_2 + 1$, $\phi(u) = \cos\theta(u)$, and $\chi(u) = \chi_{2l_1+1}(u)$, we obtain

$$\begin{aligned} |f(x)|^{1/4} w(u, x) \underset{(2)}{=} &\frac{1}{2} \csc\left(\frac{\pi}{4l_1 + 6}\right) \csc\left(\frac{\pi}{4l_2 + 6}\right) e^{u\xi(x_2) - u\xi(x_1)} \\ &\times [\{\cos\theta(u) + O(\chi_{l_{1,2}})\} \cos\{u\xi(x) - u\xi(x_2) - \tfrac{1}{4}\pi\} \\ &+ O(\chi_{l_{1,2}}) \sin\{u\xi(x) - u\xi(x_2) - \tfrac{1}{4}\pi\}], \end{aligned}$$

valid when $x \in (b_2, a_3)$, where $l_{1,2} = 2 \max(l_1, l_2) + 1$.

The last formula describes the net effect of passing through the turning points x_1 and x_2, and the process is repeatable in a straightforward manner any number of times. If the total number of turning points n is even, then the final result is given by

$$\begin{aligned}|f(x)|^{1/4}w(u,x) \underset{(2)}{=} \frac{1}{2^{n/2}}\left\{\prod_{r=1}^{n} \csc\left(\frac{\pi}{4l_r+6}\right)\right\} \exp\left\{u \sum_{r=1}^{n} (-)^r \xi(x_r)\right\} \\ \times [\{M(u)+O(\chi_{2l+1})\} \cos\{u\xi(x)-u\xi(x_n)-\tfrac{1}{4}\pi\} \\ +O(\chi_{2l+1}) \sin\{u\xi(x)-u\xi(x_n)-\tfrac{1}{4}\pi\}],\end{aligned} \tag{5.16}$$

valid when $x \in (b_n, b)$, where l is defined by (5.07), and[2]

$$M(u) = \cos\theta(u) \prod_{r=1}^{[(n-1)/2]} \cos\{u\xi(x_{2r+1})-u\xi(x_{2r})\}. \tag{5.17}$$

On the other hand, if n is odd, then with the same definitions of l and $M(u)$, we have

$$\begin{aligned}f^{1/4}(x)w(u,x) \underset{(2)}{=} \frac{1}{2^{(n+1)/2}}\left\{\prod_{r=1}^{n} \csc\left(\frac{\pi}{4l_r+6}\right)\right\} \exp\left\{u \sum_{r=1}^{n} (-)^r \xi(x_r)\right\} \\ \times \{M(u)+O(\chi_{2l+1})\} e^{u\xi(x)}, \qquad x \in (b_n, b).\end{aligned} \tag{5.18}$$

Example 4. *Arbitrary number of odd turning points*: *second case*. We make the same assumptions as in Example 3, except that the sign of the function (5.14) is now assumed to be positive. Using the same notation, we know that there exists a solution $w(u, x)$ having the property

$$f^{1/4}(x)w(u,x) \underset{(2)}{=} \{1+O(u^{-1})\} e^{u\xi(x)}, \qquad x \in (a, a_1). \tag{5.19}$$

The continuation of this solution to the interval (b_n, b) may be achieved by successive application of Theorems 4 and 3, in a similar manner to Example 3. The final result is readily verified to be

$$\begin{aligned}f^{1/4}(x)w(u,x) \underset{(2)}{=} \frac{1}{2^{n/2}}\left\{\prod_{r=1}^{n} \csc\left(\frac{\pi}{4l_r+6}\right)\right\} \exp\left\{u \sum_{r=1}^{n} (-)^{r-1} \xi(x_r)\right\} \\ \times \{N(u)+O(\chi_{2l+1})\} e^{u\xi(x)}, \qquad x \in (b_n, b),\end{aligned} \tag{5.20}$$

when n is even, or

$$\begin{aligned}|f(x)|^{1/4}w(u,x) \underset{(2)}{=} \frac{1}{2^{(n-1)/2}}\left\{\prod_{r=1}^{n} \csc\left(\frac{\pi}{4l_r+6}\right)\right\} \exp\left\{u \sum_{r=1}^{n} (-)^{r-1} \xi(x_r)\right\} \\ \times [\{N(u)+O(\chi_{2l+1})\} \cos\{u\xi(x)-u\xi(x_n)-\tfrac{1}{4}\pi\} \\ +O(\chi_{2l+1}) \sin\{u\xi(x)-u\xi(x_n)-\tfrac{1}{4}\pi\}], \qquad x \in (b_n, b),\end{aligned} \tag{5.21}$$

[2] As usual, $[(n-1)/2]$ denotes the integer part of $(n-1)/2$. When n is even this is, of course $(n/2)-1$ but in the following equation we use the same definition of $M(u)$ when n is odd.

when n is odd. Here l is again defined by (5.07), and

$$N(u)=\prod_{r=1}^{[n/2]}\cos\{u\xi(x_{2r})-u\xi(x_{2r-1})\}. \tag{5.22}$$

A subsidiary problem of physical interest [1, Chap. 13], is the following eigenvalue problem. The number of turning points n is even, $\xi(x)\to-\infty$ as $x\to a+$, $\xi(x)\to+\infty$ as $x\to b-$, and we seek those values of u for which there is a solution that is recessive at both endpoints. From (5.20) it follows that a necessary and sufficient condition for the existence of such a solution is given by[3]

$$N(u)+O(\chi_{2l+1})=0. \tag{5.23}$$

Using (2.03) and (5.22) we derive

$$u=\left\{\int_{x_{2r-1}}^{x_{2r}}|f(x)|^{1/2}\,dx\right\}^{-1}(k+\tfrac{1}{2})\pi+O\{\chi_{2l+1}(k)\}, \tag{5.24}$$

where k is a large positive integer, r has any of the values $1, 2, \cdots, \frac{1}{2}n$, l is defined by (5.07), and $\chi_l(u)$ is defined by (2.05).

It may be noted in passing that as an immediate consequence of Theorem 1, the result (5.24) continues to hold when any (finite) number of even turning points are interposed in the intervals (a, x_1), (x_2, x_3), (x_4, x_5), $\cdots$, (x_{n-2}, x_{n-1}), (x_n, b), provided that $2l+1$ now denotes the highest multiplicity of all the turning points in (a, b).

Example 5. *An eigenvalue problem with four mixed turning points.* In this example, we seek the large eigenvalues of the system

$$d^2w/dx^2=u^2h(x)(x+c_1)^2x(x-c_2)^4(x-c_3)^3w, \qquad -\infty<x<\infty, \tag{5.25}$$

where c_1, c_2, and c_3 are positive constants such that $c_2<c_3$, and $h(x)$ is a positive, twice continuously differentiable function of x with the properties

$$h(x)\sim(\text{constant})x^{\gamma_1}, \quad x\to-\infty; \quad h(x)\sim(\text{constant})x^{\gamma_2}, \quad x\to+\infty, \tag{5.26}$$

where γ_1 and γ_2 are constants such that $\gamma_1>-12$ and $\gamma_2>-12$. We also assume that the relations (5.26) are twice differentiable.[4] This problem has been selected because all the theorems of § 2 are used in its solution.

[3] This may be proved as follows. With the given conditions we know from §§ 2, 3, and 5 of [24, Chap. 6], that (5.01) has solutions of the form $f^{-1/4}(x)\,e^{u\xi(x)}\{1+\varepsilon_1(u,x)\}$ and $f^{-1/4}(x)\,e^{-u\xi(x)}\times\{1+\varepsilon_2(u,x)\}$, such that as $x\to b-$, $\varepsilon_2(u,x)$ vanishes and $\varepsilon_1(u,x)$ tends to a constant value $\varepsilon_1(u,b)$, say. Furthermore $\varepsilon_1(u,b)$ is $O(u^{-1})$ as $u\to\infty$. Denote the error term $O(\chi_{2l+1})$ in (5.20) by $\eta(u,x)$. Then

$$e^{u\xi(x)}\{N(u)+\eta(u,x)\}=A(u)\,e^{u\xi(x)}\{1+\varepsilon_1(u,x)\}+B(u)\,e^{-u\xi(x)}\{1+\varepsilon_2(u,x)\},$$

where $A(u)$ and $B(u)$ are independent of x. Dividing throughout by $e^{u\xi(x)}$ and letting $x\to b-$, we see that $\eta(u,x)$ tends to a constant $\eta(u,b)$, say, and also that

$$A(u)=\{N(u)+\eta(u,b)\}/\{1+\varepsilon_1(u,b)\}=N(u)+O(\chi_{2l+1}).$$

The condition that the solution (5.20) be recessive at b is $A(u)=0$; which yields (5.23).

[4] The interpretation of this condition in the cases in which γ_1 or γ_2 is 0 or 1 is the same as in § 4.2 of [24, Chap. 6].

We begin by fixing the arbitrary constant in the definition (2.03) of $\xi(x)$ by the condition $\xi(0)=0$; thus

(5.27) $$\xi(x)=\int_0^x \{h(t)\}^{1/2}|(t+c_1)t^{1/2}(t-c_2)^2(t-c_3)^{3/2}|\,dt.$$

There are two reasons for introducing the conditions (5.26). First they ensure that $\xi(x)\to-\infty$ as $x\to-\infty$ and $\xi(x)\to+\infty$ as $x\to+\infty$. Secondly, with

$$f(x)=h(x)(x+c_1)^2x(x-c_2)^4(x-c_3)^3,\qquad g(x)=0,$$

they ensure that the integral (2.01) converges absolutely as $x\to\pm\infty$.

Let a be any fixed point such that $a<-c_1$. Then the theory of the LG approximation shows that (5.25) has a solution $w(u,x)$ with the property

$$f^{1/4}(x)w(u,x)\underset{(2)}{=}\{1+O(u^{-1})\}\,e^{u\xi(x)},\qquad x\in(-\infty,a).$$

Furthermore, this solution is recessive as $x\to-\infty$.

Applying Theorem 1, with $x_0=-c_1$, $l=2$, $\phi(u)=1$, and $\chi(u)=1/u$, we find that in any fixed closed interval within $(-c_1,0)$, we have

$$f^{1/4}(x)w(u,x)\underset{(2)}{=}\csc(\tfrac14\pi)\{1+O(u^{-1}\ln u)\}\,e^{u\xi(x)}.$$

The next step is to apply Theorem 4 with $x_0=0$, $l=1$, $\phi(u)=1$, and $\chi(u)=u^{-1}\ln u$. Since $\xi(0)=0$, we find that in any fixed closed interval within $(0,c_2)$

$$|f(x)|^{1/4}w(u,x)\underset{(2)}{=}\csc(\tfrac14\pi)\csc(\tfrac16\pi)[\{1+O(u^{-1}\ln u)\}\cos\{u\xi(x)-\tfrac14\pi\}$$
$$+O(u^{-1}\ln u)\sin\{u\xi(x)-\tfrac14\pi\}].$$

Thirdly, we apply Theorem 2 with $x_0=c_2$ and $l=4$ to obtain

$$|f(x)|^{1/4}w(u,x)\underset{(2)}{=}\csc(\tfrac14\pi)\csc(\tfrac16\pi)[\{\Lambda(u)+O(u^{-2/3})\}\cos\{u\xi(x)-u\xi(c_2)+\lambda(u)\}$$
$$+O(u^{-2/3})\sin\{u\xi(x)-u\xi(c_2)+\lambda(u)\}],$$

valid in any fixed closed interval within (c_2,c_3), where $\Lambda(u)$ and $\lambda(u)$ are given by (2.14) and (2.15) with $\phi(u)=1$ and

(5.28) $$\theta(u)=u\xi(c_2)-\tfrac14\pi.$$

The final continuation is to apply Theorem 3 with $x_0=c_3$, $l=3$, $\phi(u)=\Lambda(u)$, and $\chi(u)=u^{-2/3}$, to obtain

$$f^{1/4}(x)w(u,x)\underset{(2)}{=}\tfrac12\csc(\tfrac14\pi)\csc(\tfrac16\pi)\csc(\tfrac1{10}\pi)\,e^{-u\xi(c_3)}$$
$$\times[\Lambda(u)\cos\{u\xi(c_3)-u\xi(c_2)+\lambda(u)+\tfrac14\pi\}+O(u^{-2/3})]\,e^{u\xi(x)},$$

valid when $x\in(b,\infty)$, where b is any fixed point such that $b>c_3$.

Since $1/\Lambda(u)$ is bounded it follows, as in Example 4, that the eigenvalues are given by

$$\cos\{u\xi(c_3)-u\xi(c_2)+\lambda(u)+\tfrac14\pi\}=O(u^{-2/3}),$$

that is,

$$\{\xi(c_3)-\xi(c_2)\}u+\lambda(u)+\tfrac{1}{4}\pi=(k+\tfrac{1}{2})\pi+O(u^{-2/3}),$$

where k is an integer. On using (2.15), with $l=4$, and (5.28), the last equation becomes

$$\{\xi(c_3)-\xi(c_2)\}u+\tan^{-1}[\tan^2(\tfrac{1}{12}\pi)\tan\{\xi(c_2)u\}]=(k+\tfrac{1}{2})\pi+O(u^{-2/3}). \tag{5.29}$$

To solve (5.29) we first discuss the properties of the function $\omega(u)$ defined by

$$\tan^{-1}\{\tan^2(\tfrac{1}{12}\pi)\tan u\}=u-\omega(u). \tag{5.30}$$

Consistent with § 2, we are using the continuous branch of the left-hand side that vanishes at $u=0$. The following properties are easily verified:

$$\omega(0)=\omega(\tfrac{1}{2}\pi)=\omega(\pi)=0, \qquad \omega(u)=\omega(u+\pi)=-\omega(-u).$$

The graph of $\omega(u)$ is indicated in Figure 5.1 for the interval $(0, \pi)$ and continues by periodicity. By differentiating (5.30) we find that

$$\omega'(u)=1-\frac{\tan^2(\frac{1}{12}\pi)}{\cos^2 u+\tan^4(\frac{1}{12}\pi)\sin^2 u}.$$

Therefore for all u

$$-\{\cot^2(\tfrac{1}{12}\pi)-1\}\leqq\omega'(u)\leqq 1-\tan^2(\tfrac{1}{12}\pi).$$

Returning to (5.29) and substituting by means of (5.30), we obtain

$$\xi(c_3)u-\omega\{\xi(c_2)u\}=(k+\tfrac{1}{2})\pi+O(u^{-2/3}). \tag{5.31}$$

Now consider the equation

$$\xi(c_3)u-\omega\{\xi(c_2)u\}=(k+\tfrac{1}{2})\pi. \tag{5.32}$$

The u-derivative of the left-hand side is

$$\xi(c_3)-\xi(c_2)\omega'\{\xi(c_2)u\}. \tag{5.33}$$

Since $\xi(c_3)>\xi(c_2)>0$ and the (algebraically) largest value of $\omega'\{\xi(c_2)u\}$ is $1-\tan^2(\frac{1}{12}\pi)$, we conclude that (5.33) is always positive and bounded away from zero. Accordingly, for each value of k equation (5.32) has exactly one root $u=u_k$,

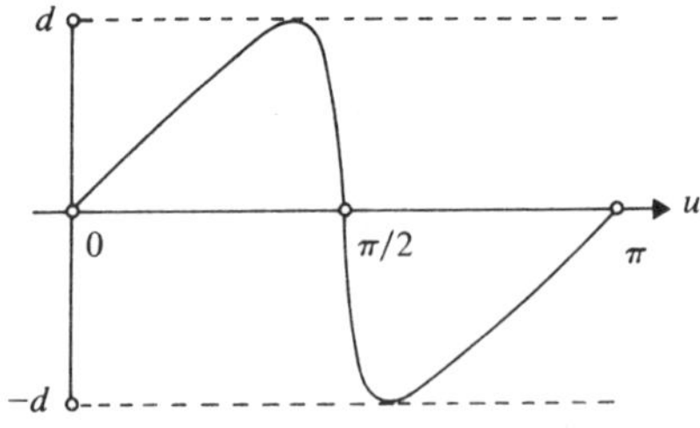

FIG. 5.1. *Graph of* $\omega(u)$. $d=1.047\cdots$

say. Hence from (5.31) and the mean-value theorem we conclude that the required eigenvalues are given by

$$u = u_k + O(k^{-2/3}), \qquad k \to +\infty. \tag{5.34}$$

Remarks. (i) The need to solve a transcendental equation, namely (5.32), in order to obtain adequate approximations to the eigenvalues stems from the presence of a turning point of Case II type. Suppose that instead of (5.25) we had chosen the system

$$d^2w/dx^2 = u^2h(x)(x+c_1)^2x(x-c_3)^3w, \qquad -\infty < x < \infty,$$

with the conditions (5.26) modified by requiring $\gamma_1 > -8$ and $\gamma_2 > -8$. Then by similar analysis we find that the eigenvalues are explicitly given by

$$u = \{\xi(c_3)\}^{-1}(k+\tfrac{1}{2})\pi + O(k^{-4/5}),$$

where k again denotes a large positive integer, and $\xi(x)$ is now defined by

$$\xi(x) = \int_0^x \{h(t)\}^{1/2}|(t+c_1)t^{1/2}(t-c_3)^{3/2}|\,dt.$$

(ii) As in Example 4, the presence of the turning point of Case I type at $x=-c_1$ essentially has no effect on the final result (5.34). Indeed, this turning point may be replaced by an arbitrary finite number of even turning points in the intervals $(-\infty, 0)$ and (c_3, ∞), provided that none is of multiplicity exceeding 4. If the last condition is not fulfilled, then the only change needed is to increase the estimate for the error term in (5.34) from $O(k^{-2/3})$ to $O(k^{-4/(l+2)})$, where l is the multiplicity of the turning point of highest order.

(iii) It is of interest to compare the results yielded by the asymptotic formula (5.34) with those calculated by direct numerical methods, especially as an error bound has not been constructed for the asymptotic estimate. For this purpose we select the following equation:

$$d^2w/dx^2 = u^2(x+1)^2x(x-1)^4(x-2)^3w. \tag{5.35}$$

Thus in the notation of (5.25) we have $h(x)=1$, $c_1=c_2=1$, and $c_3=2$. From (5.27) we find that[5]

$$\xi(1) = \tfrac{3}{32}\pi + \tfrac{2}{15}, \qquad \xi(2) = \tfrac{3}{16}\pi. \tag{5.36}$$

Substituting these values in (5.30) and (5.32) we see that the equation for the estimated eigenvalues u_k is given by

$$(\tfrac{3}{32}\pi - \tfrac{2}{15})u + \tan^{-1}[\tan^2(\tfrac{1}{12}\pi)\tan\{(\tfrac{3}{32}\pi + \tfrac{2}{15})u\}] = (k+\tfrac{1}{2})\pi, \tag{5.37}$$

where, as noted previously, the branch of the inverse ta gent vanishes at $u=0$ and is a continuous function of u.

Corresponding to any prescribed value of k, the desired approximation $u=u_k$ to an eigenvalue of (5.35) is obtained by solving (5.37) by successive

[5] These values were verified by use of the MACSYMA System of the Massachusetts Institute of Technology.

approximation. Taking $k=5$, 6, 7, and 8, we find that

(5.38) $$u_5=29.257,\quad u_6=33.262,\quad u_7=40.347,\quad u_8=47.111,$$

correct to three places of decimals.

To calculate the eigenvalues by numerical analysis the following method was used. Equation (5.35) is integrated numerically from a sufficiently large negative value $x=X_1$, say, to $x=0$, using arbitrary initial values of w and dw/dx at $x=X_1$. The same equation is also integrated numerically from a sufficiently large positive value $x=X_2$, say, to $x=0$ using arbitrary initial values at $x=X_2$. The value of u is then adjusted until the Wronskian of the two solutions vanishes at $x=0$. (The actual values of X_1 and X_2 are not crucial, nor are the initial values at these points; for the present range of values of u and required accuracy it was found that $X_1=-1.1$ and $X_2=2.6$ are adequately large.) This method was used to search the interval $28\leqq u\leqq 48$ systematically for eigenvalues, and the only ones were found to be

(5.39) $$u=28.822,\quad 33.185,\quad 40.265,\quad 46.909,$$

again, correct to three places of decimals. The agreement with the asymptotic estimates (5.38) is clearly quite satisfactory.

Example 6. *A problem with three turning points solvable in terms of Whittaker functions*. Our final example is furnished by the equation

(5.40) $$d^2w/dx^2=u^2x^{2p-2}(c^{2p}-x^{2p})w,$$

in which u is a positive parameter, p is a positive integer, and c is a fixed positive constant. On the real axis there are simple turning points at $x=\pm c$, and a turning point of multiplicity $2p-2$ at $x=0$. The theory of the LG approximation shows that there are unique solutions $w_1(u,x)$, $w_2(u,x)$, and $w_3(u,x)$ with the properties

(5.41) $$|f(x)|^{1/4}w_1(u,x)\sim e^{iu\xi(x)},\qquad x\to-\infty,$$

(5.42) $$|f(x)|^{1/4}w_2(u,x)\sim e^{iu\xi(x)},\qquad x\to+\infty,$$

(5.43) $$|f(x)|^{1/4}w_3(u,x)\sim e^{-iu\xi(x)},\qquad x\to+\infty,$$

where

(5.44) $$f(x)=x^{2p-2}(c^{2p}-x^{2p}),$$

and

(5.45) $$\xi(x)=\int_0^x |t^{p-1}(c^{2p}-t^{2p})^{1/2}|\,dt.$$

Our intention is to find the coefficients A and B in the connection formula

(5.46) $$w_1(u,x)=Aw_2(u,x)+Bw_3(u,x).$$

This problem is of interest in the theory of barrier penetration. In this context the solutions $w_1(u,x)$, $w_2(u,x)$, and $w_3(u,x)$ represent respectively the transmitted, incident, and reflected waves. Heading [11] has solved the problem exactly by transforming (5.40) into Whittaker's equation. A valuable check on the analysis of the present paper is to apply the rules of § 2 to solve the problem approximately for large u, and then compare the answers with the asymptotic forms of the Whittaker functions.

The theory of the LG approximation shows that corresponding to any assigned values of real constants a and θ, with $a > c$, there is a solution $w(\theta, u, x)$ of (5.40) with the properties

$$|f(x)|^{1/4} w(\theta, u, x) = \cos\{u\xi(x) + \theta\} + o(1), \qquad x \to -\infty, \tag{5.47}$$

when u is fixed, and

$$|f(x)|^{1/4} w(\theta, u, x) \underset{(2)}{=} \{1 + O(u^{-1})\} \cos\{u\xi(x) + \theta\} + O(u^{-1}) \sin\{u\xi(x) + \theta\}, \qquad -\infty < x < -a, \tag{5.48}$$

uniformly when u is large. Applying Theorems 3, 1, and 4 in succession in the manner of previous examples, we find that

$$\begin{aligned} \sin\left(\frac{\pi}{2p}\right) e^{u\xi(-c) - u\xi(c)} |f(x)|^{1/4} w(\theta, u, x) &\underset{(2)}{=} [2\cos\{u\xi(-c) + \theta + \tfrac{1}{4}\pi\} + O(\chi_{2p-2})] \cos\{u\xi(x) - u\xi(c) - \tfrac{1}{4}\pi\} \\ &\quad + O(\chi_{2p-2}) \sin\{u\xi(x) - u\xi(c) - \tfrac{1}{4}\pi\}, \end{aligned}$$

valid when $x \in (a, \infty)$. From (5.45) it is clear that $\xi(x)$ is an odd function of x; hence by rearrangement of the last relation we deduce that

$$\begin{aligned} |f(x)|^{1/4} w(\theta, u, x) = \csc\left(\frac{\pi}{2p}\right) e^{2u\xi(c)} [&\cos\{u\xi(x) - 2u\xi(c) + \theta\} \\ &+ \sin\{u\xi(x) - \theta\} + O(\chi_{2p-2})]. \end{aligned} \tag{5.49}$$

From (5.47) it follows that the solution $w_1(u, x)$ having the property (5.41) is given by the linear combination

$$w_1(u, x) = w(0, u, x) + i w(-\tfrac{1}{2}\pi, u, x).$$

Hence from (5.49) we derive

$$|f(x)|^{1/4} w_1(u, x) = \csc\left(\frac{\pi}{2p}\right) e^{2u\xi(c)} \{e^{iu\xi(x) - 2iu\xi(c)} + i e^{-iu\xi(x)} + O(\chi_{2p-2})\},$$

valid when $x \in (a, \infty)$. The values of the coefficients A and B in (5.46) may now be found by letting $x \to \infty$, first through the sequence of values for which $2u\xi(x)$ is an even multiple of π, and secondly through the sequence for which $2u\xi(x)$ is an odd multiple of π. Comparing the resulting expressions with (5.42) and (5.43) we see that

$$A = \csc\left(\frac{\pi}{2p}\right) e^{2(1-i)u\xi(c)} \{1 + O(\chi_{2p-2})\}, \tag{5.50}$$

$$B = i \csc\left(\frac{\pi}{2p}\right) e^{2u\xi(c)} \{1 + O(\chi_{2p-2})\}. \tag{5.51}$$

These are the required results. The necessary value of $\xi(c)$ may be found from (5.45) with the aid of the substitution $t^p = c^p \sin v$; thus

$$\xi(c) = \pi c^{2p}/(4p). \tag{5.52}$$

Let us turn now to the exact solution of (5.40) in terms of Whittaker functions. Following Heading [11] we find that when $x<0$ a solution is $\hat{w}(u,x)$, given by

$$\hat{w}(u,x)=|x|^{(1/2)-p}W_{\kappa,1/(4p)}(iu|x|^{2p}/p), \tag{5.53}$$

where

$$\kappa=iuc^{2p}/(4p), \tag{5.54}$$

and $W_{\kappa,\mu}(z)$ is Whittaker's function in the usual notation. For large $|z|$ it is known that[6]

$$W_{\kappa,\mu}(z)\sim z^{\kappa}e^{-z/2},\qquad |\text{ph}\, z|\leqq\tfrac{3}{2}\pi-\delta(<\tfrac{3}{2}\pi). \tag{5.55}$$

Hence

$$\hat{w}(u,x)\sim|x|^{(1/2)-p}\left(\frac{iu|x|^{2p}}{p}\right)^{\kappa}\exp\left(-\frac{iu|x|^{2p}}{2p}\right),\qquad x\to-\infty. \tag{5.56}$$

In order to compare the last result with (5.41), we first evaluate the integral (5.45) when $x\geqq c$. This may be done by means of the substitution $t^p=c^p\cosh v$; thus

$$\xi(x)=\xi(c)+\frac{c^{2p}}{2p}\left\{\frac{x^p}{c^p}\left(\frac{x^{2p}}{c^{2p}}-1\right)^{1/2}-\cosh^{-1}\left(\frac{x^p}{c^p}\right)\right\},\qquad x\geqq c.$$

Hence

$$\xi(x)=\xi(c)+\frac{c^{2p}}{2p}\left\{\frac{x^{2p}}{c^{2p}}-\frac{1}{2}-\ln\left(\frac{2x^p}{c^p}\right)\right\}+o(1),\qquad x\to+\infty. \tag{5.57}$$

Using this result and the fact that $\xi(-x)=-\xi(x)$, we see from (5.41), (5.54), and (5.56) that the relation between $w_1(u,x)$ and $\hat{w}(u,x)$ is given by

$$w_1(u,x)=e^{\kappa}\kappa^{-\kappa}e^{-iu\xi(c)}\hat{w}(u,x). \tag{5.58}$$

Next, we need the continuation of $\hat{w}(u,x)$ to positive values of x. If we pass from the negative real x-axis to the positive real x-axis via an indentation that lies in the upper half of the x-plane, then from (5.53) we see that

$$\hat{w}(u,x)=(e^{-\pi i}x)^{(1/2)-p}W_{\kappa,1/(4p)}(e^{-2p\pi i}iux^{2p}/p),\qquad x>0.$$

Applying the connection formula for Whittaker functions with arguments $e^{-2p\pi i}z$, z, and $ze^{-\pi i}$ obtainable, for example, from [11] or [24, p. 262], we derive

$$\hat{w}(u,x)=\csc\left(\frac{\pi}{2p}\right)x^{(1/2)-p}\left\{\hat{B}W_{\kappa,1/(4p)}\left(\frac{iux^{2p}}{p}\right)+\hat{A}W_{-\kappa,1/(4p)}\left(-\frac{iux^{2p}}{p}\right)\right\}, \tag{5.59}$$

where

$$\hat{A}=2\pi e^{-\kappa\pi i}\Big/\left\{\Gamma\left(\frac{1}{2}+\frac{1}{4p}-\kappa\right)\Gamma\left(\frac{1}{2}-\frac{1}{4p}-\kappa\right)\right\}, \tag{5.60}$$

$$\hat{B}=i\left\{e^{-2\kappa\pi i}+\cos\left(\frac{\pi}{2p}\right)\right\}. \tag{5.61}$$

---

[6] See, for example, [24, p. 260].

The asymptotic form of $w_1(u, x)$ as $x \to +\infty$ may be found from (5.58) and (5.59) by replacing the Whittaker functions by their asymptotic forms for large argument, again given by (5.55). Then by using (5.44), (5.54), and (5.57) we are able to cast the result into the form

$$|f(x)|^{1/4} w_1(u, x) = \csc\left(\frac{\pi}{2p}\right)\left\{e^{-2iu\xi(c)} e^{\kappa\pi i} e^{2\kappa} \kappa^{-2\kappa} \hat{A} e^{iu\xi(x)} + \hat{B} e^{-iu\xi(x)} + o(1)\right\}.$$

Comparing this result with (5.46) and referring to (5.42) and (5.43), we see that

$$A = \csc\left(\frac{\pi}{2p}\right) e^{-2iu\xi(c)} e^{\kappa\pi i} e^{2\kappa} \kappa^{-2\kappa} \hat{A}, \tag{5.62}$$

$$B = \csc\left(\frac{\pi}{2p}\right) \hat{B}. \tag{5.63}$$

The last two equations give exact expressions for the coefficients in the wanted connection formula (5.46). To check the approximate formulas (5.50) and (5.51) found by our present theory, we assume u (and therefore, also, $|\kappa|$) is large and calculate the asymptotic form of the right-hand side of (5.60) by means of Stirling's formula. On substituting the result in (5.62) and using (5.52) and (5.54), we find that (5.50) agrees with (5.62) within the tolerance of the uniform error term $O(\chi_{2p-2})$; similarly for (5.51) and (5.63). This confirms the soundness of our asymptotic theory as applied to this example.

6. Previous results and conclusions. It will be assumed in this section that the reader is acquainted with the survey that was made in [27, § 6] of work on connection formulas for second-order differential equations having a single turning point. We shall continue to use the terms *central connection*, *lateral connection*, and *pseudo-lateral connection* in the same sense as in this reference, and remind the reader that central connection and pseudo-lateral connection may be used for turning points of any multiplicity, whereas at present true lateral connection may be employed only for simple turning points. The methods developed in the present paper are all of central connection type.

In the first part of this section we survey applications of the methods of central connection, lateral connection, and pseudo-lateral connection to equations having more than one turning point, proceeding roughly in increasing order of complexity. Because all three methods proceed step by step through one turning point at a time, they may be classified as having a *local* nature, even though the regions of validity of the corresponding asymptotic solutions of the differential equation may extend to infinity. Later in this section we discuss a significantly different type of method in which the approach is of *global* nature.

Two simple turning points. As in Examples 3 and 4 of § 5, two distinct cases arise depending whether the function $f(x)$ in (1.01) is positive or negative in the interval between its zeros. In the latter case there is also a subsidiary eigenvalue problem. Physical models corresponding to the two cases are the potential barrier and the potential well, respectively.

Solutions date back almost 50 years, and references can be found, for example, in [7, Chap. 1], [22], and [23]. From the mathematical standpoint, the first fully satisfactory applications of the central connection method were those of Jeffreys [13], [14].

Rigorous solutions by means of lateral connection were published independently (and in the same year) by Fedoryuk [3], Fröman and Fröman [5], and the present writer [23]; the last two references also include error bounds.

Three simple turning points. Special examples have been solved by Nishimoto [21, § 6] and the present writer [24, p. 516, Exercises 15.4 and 15.5], in both cases by lateral connection.

Four simple turning points. This situation arises with double potential barriers or wells. As in the case of two simple turning points there are two cases, depending on the sign of $f(x)$. A formal solution of the barrier problem was given by Bohm [1, pp. 283–295], using central connection. Rigorous solutions by lateral connection, both for barriers and wells, have been supplied in a series of papers by N. Fröman and her collaborators [4], [6], [32]. Other work on these problems has been discussed by Heading [9], [10].

Arbitrary number of simple turning points. Problems of this type have been treated by Murphy and Good [20] (central connection), Fedoryuk [3] (lateral connection), Evgrafov and Fedoryuk [2] (lateral connection), and Heading [9] (lateral connection). Some of the analysis in these references is formal or given incompletely. Sibuya [29] and Weinberg [31] have given completely rigorous analyses, using lateral connection, for the case in which $g(x)=0$ and $f(x)$ is a polynomial, or has polynomial growth rate as $|x|\to\infty$.

Two turning points, at least one of which is multiple. Heading [11, § 8] has solved the general problem in which one of the turning points is simple and the other is of any odd multiplicity by lateral connection, generalizing a device used by the present writer when both turning points are simple [23]. More recently, Heading [12] has made a further extension to solve the general problem in which the two turning points are of arbitrary odd multiplicities.

Leung [15], [16] has treated the example

$$d^2w/dx^2=u^2x^2(x-1)^2w$$

by rigorous application of pseudo-lateral connection although the solution in these references is incomplete.[7]

Arbitrary number of multiple turning points. Again using pseudo-lateral connection, Leung [17] has solved the eigenvalue problem in the general case in which $g(x)\equiv 0$, $f(x)$ is positive as $x\to\pm\infty$, and there are any number of multiple turning points, provided that none of the turning points is of type II (defined in § 2). This problem was treated in Example 4 of § 5; compare the comments in the closing paragraph in this example. Leung's formula for the eigenvalues agrees with (5.24), except that the order of his estimate for the error term is weaker than our $O\{\chi_{2l+1}(k)\}$.

Global central connection. Methods of this type have been proposed by several writers, including Heading [8], Pike [28], and Lynn and Keller [18]. The idea is to try to approximate, in a uniform manner, the solutions of the given

[7] The complete solution has been communicated by Dr. Leung to the present writer. It agrees with the specialization of Example 1 of § 5 above.

differential equation by those of an equation of the form

$$d^2w/dx^2 = u^2P(x)w, \tag{6.01}$$

in which $P(x)$ is a polynomial whose degree is the sum of the order of the turning points in the interval (or complex domain) under consideration.

When we are dealing with problems in which the turning points are fixed this approach has no advantages to offer compared with the methods of the present paper. Indeed, the reverse is true; little is known about the solutions of equations of the form (6.01) even for quite moderate values of the degree of $P(x)$; compare [26, § 6.3], and [30]. Clearly unless connection formulas are independently available for (6.01) there is little to be gained by trying to use the solutions of this equation to approximate those of the original differential equation.

As noted by Lynn and Keller on page 393 of [18], however, if the locations of the turning points are variable owing to the presence of a second parameter in the differential equation, then there is an important potential advantage in the global approach: it may yield connection formulas that are uniform with respect to the second parameter, *even when two or more of the turning points coalesce.* As we noted in the Remarks at the close of Example 1 in § 5, the approach used in the present paper fails in these circumstances.

At present, the only rigorous development of the global approach that permits coalescence of turning points appears to be that of the present writer [25]. This reference treats the case in which $P(x)$ is a quadratic polynomial; the solutions of (6.01) are then expressible as parabolic cylinder functions. Approximate connection formulas are derived for large u, and they continue to be uniformly valid when the two simple turning points in the original differential equation coalesce into a double turning point. These results could be combined with those of the present paper to treat problems in which there are movable turning points, provided that the only kind of coalescence that occurs is of pairs of simple turning points.

Conclusions. The present paper provides a rigorous solution, and in fact the first general solution, of the problem of constructing connection formulas for second-order differential equations having an arbitrary number of turning points of arbitrary multiplicities.

The method used is a generalization of the central connection procedure developed by Jeffreys for two simple turning points, and employs only real-variable theory in the analysis. In consequence, the coefficients in the differential equation need not be analytic functions of the independent variable, nor is there any need to investigate the topology in the complex plane of the principal curves (or anti-Stokes lines).

Acknowledgment. The numerical integrations of the differential equation (5.35) used to check Example 5 were carried out by Mr. R. E. Kaylor. The author is pleased to acknowledge this assistance.

REFERENCES

[1] D. Bohm, *Quantum Theory*, Prentice-Hall, Englewood Cliffs, N.J., 1951.

[2] M. A. Evgrafov and M. V. Fedoryuk, *Asymptotic behavior as $\lambda \to \infty$ of solutions of the equation $w''(z) - p(z, \lambda)w(z) = 0$ in the complex z-plane*, Uspehi Mat. Nauk, 21 (1966), pp. 3–50 = Russian Math. Surveys, 21 (1966), pp. 1–48.

[3] M. V. Fedoryuk, *Asymptotics of the discrete spectrum of the operator $w''(x) - \lambda^2 p(x)w(x)$*, Mat. Sb., 68 (1965), pp. 81–110. (In Russian.)

[4] N. Fröman and Ö. Dammert, *Tunneling and super-barrier transmission through a system of two real potential barriers*, Nuclear Phys. A, 147 (1970), pp. 627–649.

[5] N. Fröman and P. O. Fröman, *JWKB Approximation—Contributions to the Theory*, North-Holland, Amsterdam, 1965.

[6] N. Fröman, P. O. Fröman, U. Myhrman and R. Paulsson, *On the quantal treatment of the double-well potential problem by means of certain phase-integral approximations*, Ann. Physics, 74 (1972), pp. 314–323.

[7] J. Heading, *An Introduction to Phase-integral Methods*, John Wiley, New York, 1962.

[8] ———, *Phase-integral methods I*, Quart, J. Mech. Appl. Math., 15 (1962), pp. 215–244.

[9] ———, *Exact and approximate methods for the investigation of the propagation of waves through a system of barriers*, Proc. Cambridge Philos. Soc., 74 (1973), pp. 161–178.

[10] ———, *The approximate use of the complex gamma function in some wave propagation problems*, J. Phys. A, 6 (1973), pp. 958–973.

[11] ———, *Barriers bounded by a transition point of order greater than unity*, Physica, 77 (1974), pp. 263–278.

[12] ———, *Barriers bounded by two transition points of arbitrary odd order*, Proc. Roy. Soc. Edinburgh, 73A (1974/5), pp. 51–64.

[13] H. Jeffreys, *On approximate solutions of linear differential equations*, Proc. Cambridge Philos. Soc., 49 (1953), pp. 601–611.

[14] ———, *On the use of asymptotic approximations of Green's type when the coefficient has zeros*, Ibid., 52 (1956), pp. 61–66.

[15] A. W-K. Leung, *Connection formulas for asymptotic solutions of second order turning points in unbounded domains*, this Journal, 4 (1973), pp. 89–103.

[16] ———, *Errata: connection formulas for asymptotic solutions of second order turning points in unbounded domains*, this Journal, 6 (1975), p. 600.

[17] ———, *Distribution of eigenvalues in the presence of higher order turning points*, Trans. Amer. Math. Soc., to appear.

[18] R. Y. S. Lynn and J. B. Keller, *Uniform asymptotic solutions of second order linear ordinary differential equations with turning points*, Comm. Pure Appl. Math., 23 (1970), pp. 379–408.

[19] J. C. P. Miller, *On the choice of standard solutions for a homogeneous linear differential equation of the second order*, Quart. J. Mech. Appl. Math., 3 (1950), pp. 225–235.

[20] E. L. Murphy and R. H. Good, Jr., *WKB Connection formulas*, J. Math. and Phys., 43 (1964), pp. 251–254.

[21] T. Nishimoto, *On an extension theorem and its application for turning point problems of large order*, Kōdai Math. Sem. Rep., 25 (1973), pp. 458–489.

[22] F. W. J. Olver, *Error analysis of phase-integral methods. I. General theory for simple turning points*, J. Res. Nat. Bur. Standards Sect. B, 69 (1965), pp. 271–290.

[23] ———, *Error analysis of phase-integral methods. II. Application to wave-penetration problems*, Ibid., 69 (1965), pp. 291–300.

[24] ———, *Asymptotics and Special Functions*, Academic Press, New York, 1974.

[25] ———, *Second-order linear differential equations with two turning points*, Philos. Trans. Roy. Soc. London Ser. A, 278 (1975), pp. 137–174.

[26] ———, *Unsolved problems in the asymptotic estimation of special functions*, Theory and Applications of Special Functions, R. A. Askey, ed., Academic Press, New York, 1975, pp. 99–142.

[27] ———, *Connection formulas for second-order differential equations with multiple turning points*, this Journal, 8 (1977), pp. 127–154.

[28] E. R. Pike, *On the related-equation method of asymptotic approximation (W.K.B. or A-A method) I. A proposed new existence theorem*, Quart. J. Mech. Appl. Math., 17 (1964), pp. 105–124.

[29] Y. SIBUYA, *Subdominant solutions of the differential equation* $y''-\lambda^2(x-a_1)(x-a_2)\cdots(x-a_m)y=0$, Acta Math., 119 (1967), pp. 235–272.

[30] ———, *Global Theory of a Second Order Linear Ordinary Differential Equation with a Polynomial Coefficient*, Mathematics Studies 18, North-Holland, Amsterdam, 1975.

[31] L. WEINBERG, *The asymptotic distribution of eigenvalues for the boundary value problem* $y''(x)-\lambda^2 p(x)y(x)=0$, $y\in L_2(-\infty,+\infty)$, this Journal, 2 (1971), pp. 546–566.

[32] S. YNGVE, *Normalization of certain higher-order phase-integral approximations for wavefunctions of bound states in a potential well. II*, J. Mathematical Phys., 13 (1972), pp. 324–331.

ASYMPTOTIC BEHAVIOUR OF INTEGRALS OF BESSEL FUNCTIONS OF HIGH ORDER*

M. L. Glasser and F. W. J. Olver

ABSTRACT. Two methods are developed for the approximate evaluation of infinite integrals of products of Bessel functions when the order of these functions is large. The first method is to transform the integral into a contour integral of Barnes' type, and then approximate the resulting Gamma functions by Stirling's formula. The second method is to approximate the Bessel functions by their uniform asymptotic approximations in terms of elementary or Airy functions.

1. *Introduction.*

In this paper we consider the integrals

$$U = \int_0^\infty J_\nu(ax) I_\nu(bx) K_\nu(bx) x^{\rho-1} dx \ , \tag{1.1}$$

$$V = \int_0^\infty J_\nu(ax) Y_\nu(ax) I_\nu(bx) K_\nu(bx) x^{\sigma-1} dx \ , \tag{1.2}$$

in which a and b are positive constants, ρ and σ are real or complex constants, and J_ν, Y_ν, I_ν, K_ν are Bessel functions of non-negative real order ν in the usual notation. For certain values of ρ and ν, U can be evaluated in closed form, see for example [2, p.372] and [5, pp.111-115], but a general formula for U and V appears to be unavailable. Our present object is to find the asymptotic forms of U and V as $\nu \to \infty$ and we achieve this by two quite different methods, which may be capable of generalization to integrals of similar type containing more than four Bessel functions in the integrand.

The first method is to represent U (or V) as a Meijer G-function and hence as a contour integral of Barnes' type; this analysis has some features in common with that of [3]. The Gamma functions that depend on ν in the Barnes integral are then approximated by means of Stirling's formula. The reduced integral can be evaluated

*Research supported by NRC Grant No. A9344, USAROD, Durham, Contract DA ARO D 31 124 73 G204 and NSF Grant GP 32841X2.

UTILITAS MATHEMATICA Vol. 12 (1977), pp. 225-239.

in terms of elementary functions, in the case of U, or Legendre functions, in the case of V.

The second method consists of replacing the Bessel functions in (1.1) and (1.2) by their uniform asymptotic approximations for large orders. The reduced integrals involve Airy functions and are evaluated by asymptotic analysis, yielding the same results as in the first method.

The restrictions we impose on the constants ρ and σ are given by

$$\mathrm{Re}\,\rho < 3/2,\ 0 < \mathrm{Re}\,\sigma < 2\ . \tag{1.3}$$

The integral (1.1) then converges absolutely for all sufficiently large ν, and (1.2) converges absolutely for all ν.

It may be noted in passing that the integrals also converge when $3/2 \le \mathrm{Re}\,\rho < 5/2$ and $2 \le \mathrm{Re}\,\sigma < 3$, but convergence at the upper limit is not absolute in these cases, nor does our analysis apply in its present form.

2. *Evaluation of* U: *First Method.*

Setting $t = x^2$ in (1.1) we find that

$$U = \frac{1}{2}\int_0^\infty J_\nu(at^{1/2})I_\nu(bt^{1/2})K_\nu(bt^{1/2})t^{(\rho-2)/2}dt\ . \tag{2.1}$$

From [4, p.226, eq. (7)] we have

$$t^{(\rho-2)/2}J_\nu(at^{1/2}) = (a/2)^{2-\rho}G^{1,0}_{0,2}\left(\frac{1}{4}\,a^2t\,\middle|\,\frac{1}{2}(\rho+\nu-2),\ \frac{1}{2}(\rho-\nu-2)\right),$$

and from p. 229, eq. (31) and p. 149, eq. (1) of the same reference we derive

$$I_\nu(bt^{1/2})K_\nu(bt^{1/2}) = \frac{1}{2\pi^{1/2}}\,G^{2,1}_{1,3}\left(b^2t\,\middle|\,\begin{matrix}\frac{1}{2}\\ \nu,0,-\nu\end{matrix}\right).$$

We substitute these expressions into (2.1) to obtain

$$U = \frac{(a/2)^{2-\rho}}{4\pi^{1/2}} \int_0^\infty G_{0,2}^{1,0}\left(\frac{1}{4}a^2 t \,\middle|\, \frac{1}{2}(\rho+\nu-2),\ \frac{1}{2}(\rho-\nu-2)\right) G_{1,3}^{2,1}\left(b^2 t \,\middle|\, \begin{matrix} \frac{1}{2} \\ \nu,0,-\nu \end{matrix}\right) dt.$$

By using eq. (1) on p. 159 of [4], we see that

$$U = \frac{(a/2)^{2-\rho}}{4b^2\pi^{1/2}} G_{3,3}^{2,2}\left(\frac{1}{4\alpha^2} \,\middle|\, \begin{matrix} -\nu,0,\nu \\ \frac{1}{2}(\rho+\nu-2),\ -\frac{1}{2},\ \frac{1}{2}(\rho-\nu-2) \end{matrix}\right) , \tag{2.2}$$

where we have set

$$\alpha = b/a . \tag{2.3}$$

Here we note in passing that if $\rho = 2+\nu$ then the G-function in (2.2) reduces to an elementary function, and if $\rho = 2-\nu$ then the G-function in (2.2) reduces to a hypergeometric ${}_2F_1$ function. The results obtained in this way agree with formulae (12.22) and (12.26) on pp. 112-113 of [5] .

By using Barnes' integral representation for the G-function in (2.2), we obtain

$$U = \frac{(a/2)^{2-\rho}}{8b^2\pi^{3/2}i} \int_{-i\infty}^{i\infty} p(s)q(\nu,s)ds , \tag{2.4}$$

where

$$p(s) = \Gamma(1+s)\Gamma(-\frac{1}{2}-s)\alpha^{-2s} , \tag{2.5}$$

$$q(\nu,s) = \frac{\Gamma(\nu+1+s)\Gamma(\frac{1}{2}\nu+\frac{1}{2}\rho-1-s)}{\Gamma(\frac{1}{2}\nu-\frac{1}{2}\rho+2+s)\Gamma(\nu-s)} 2^{-2s} , \tag{2.6}$$

and the contour of integration separates the poles of $\Gamma(-\frac{1}{2}-s)\Gamma(\frac{1}{2}\nu+\frac{1}{2}\rho-1-s)$ from the poles of $\Gamma(1+s)\Gamma(\nu+1+s)$. Since $\nu \geq 0$, it is always possible to construct such a contour whenever

$$\operatorname{Re}\rho > 0 , \tag{2.7}$$

and throughout the present section we shall adopt this additional condition. We also note that the contour can be constructed independently of the value of ν.

When ν is real and nonnegative and s is purely imaginary, we find, by application of Stirling's formula, that

$$p(s) = O(|s|^{-1/2}e^{-\pi|s|}), \quad |s| \to \infty, \tag{2.8}$$

and

$$|q(\nu,s)| \sim |\nu+s| \, |\tfrac{1}{2}\nu+s|^{\mathrm{Re}\,\rho-3}, \quad |\tfrac{1}{2}\nu\pm s| \to \infty. \tag{2.9}$$

The right-hand side of the last relation is bounded by $2\left|\frac{1}{2}\nu+s\right|^{\mathrm{Re}\,\rho-2}$. Therefore because $\mathrm{Re}\,\rho-2$ is negative it follows that

$$q(\nu,s) = O(\nu^{\mathrm{Re}\,\rho-2}), \quad \nu \to \infty, \tag{2.10}$$

uniformly with respect to all purely imaginary values of s.

From (1.3), (2.9), and (2.10) it follows that

$$\nu^{2-\rho}q(\nu,s) = O(1)$$

as $|s| \to \infty$, uniformly with respect to $\nu \in [0,\infty)$. From this result and (2.8) it follows that, given any positive number ε, we can find a positive number $S \equiv S(\varepsilon)$, independently of $\nu \in [0,\infty)$, such that each of the following inequalities holds:

$$\left| \int_{iS}^{i\infty} p(s)ds \right| < \varepsilon, \quad \left| \int_{-i\infty}^{-iS} p(s)ds \right| < \varepsilon, \tag{2.11}$$

$$\left| \nu^{2-\rho} \int_{iS}^{i\infty} p(s)q(\nu,s)ds \right| < \varepsilon, \quad \left| \nu^{2-\rho} \int_{-i\infty}^{-iS} p(s)q(\nu,s)ds \right| < \varepsilon. \tag{2.12}$$

Having fixed S, we make a second application of Stirling's formula to (2.6) to obtain

$$q(\nu,s) = 2^{3-\rho}\nu^{\rho-2}\{1+O(\nu^{-1})\}$$

as $\nu \to \infty$, uniformly with respect to bounded values of s, and in particular for those values of s on the part of the contour of integration in (2.4) that joins $\pm iS$. Hence

$$\int_{-iS}^{iS} p(s)q(\nu,s)ds = 2^{3-\rho}\nu^{\rho-2}\left\{\int_{-iS}^{iS} p(s)ds + O(\nu^{-1})\right\},$$

and therefore

$$(2.13) \qquad \left|2^{\rho-3}\nu^{2-\rho}\int_{-iS}^{iS} p(s)q(\nu,s)ds - \int_{-iS}^{iS} p(s)ds\right| < \varepsilon$$

for all $\nu > N(\varepsilon)$ assignable. Combination of (2.11), (2.12), and (2.13) establishes

$$(2.14) \qquad 2^{\rho-3}\nu^{2-\rho}\int_{-i\infty}^{i\infty} p(s)q(\nu,s)ds = \int_{-i\infty}^{i\infty} p(s)ds + o(1),\ \nu \to \infty .$$

Lastly, by translating the contour of integration to the right, summing residues, and using analytic continuation, we find that

$$(2.15) \qquad \frac{1}{2\pi i}\int_{-i\infty}^{i\infty} p(s)ds = \frac{1}{2\pi i}\int_{-i\infty}^{i\infty} \Gamma(1+s)\Gamma(-\tfrac{1}{2}-s)\alpha^{-2s}ds = \frac{\alpha^2\pi^{1/2}}{(1+\alpha^2)^{1/2}} .$$

From (2.3), (2.4), (2.14), and (2.15) we arrive at the required result in the form

$$(2.16) \qquad U = \frac{a^{1-\rho}\nu^{\rho-2}}{2(a^2+b^2)^{1/2}}\{1 + o(1)\},\ \nu \to \infty ,$$

valid when $0 < \operatorname{Re} \rho < 3/2$.

3. *Evaluation of* V: *First Method.*

The analysis in this section parallels that of Section 2, and we only indicate the main steps. Corresponding to (2.1) we have

$$(3.1) \qquad V = \frac{1}{2}\int_0^{\infty} J_\nu(at^{1/2})Y_\nu(at^{1/2})I_\nu(bt^{1/2})K_\nu(bt^{1/2})t^{(\sigma-2)/2}dt .$$

Next ,

$$t^{(\sigma-2)/2}J_\nu(at^{1/2})Y_\nu(at^{1/2}) = -\frac{1}{\pi^{1/2}a^{\sigma-2}}G^{2,0}_{1,3}\left(a^2t\,\middle|\,\begin{matrix}\frac{1}{2}\sigma-\frac{1}{2}\\ \frac{1}{2}\sigma-1,\frac{1}{2}\sigma-1+\nu,\frac{1}{2}\sigma-1-\nu\end{matrix}\right);$$

compare [4, p. 229, eq. (30)]. Hence

$$(3.2)\qquad V = -\frac{1}{4\pi a^\sigma}G^{2,3}_{4,4}\left(\alpha^2\,\middle|\,\begin{matrix}1-\frac{1}{2}\sigma,\ 1-\frac{1}{2}\sigma-\nu,\frac{1}{2},1-\frac{1}{2}\sigma+\nu\\ \nu,\ 0,\ -\nu,\frac{1}{2}-\frac{1}{2}\sigma\end{matrix}\right)$$

$$= -\frac{1}{8\pi^2 ia^\sigma}\int_{-i\infty}^{i\infty}p(s)q(\nu,s)ds\ ,$$

where α is again given by (2.3), and now

$$(3.3)\qquad p(s) = \frac{\Gamma(\frac{1}{2}+s)\Gamma(\frac{1}{2}\sigma+s)\Gamma(-s)}{\Gamma(\frac{1}{2}+\frac{1}{2}\sigma+s)}\alpha^{2s}\ ,$$

$$(3.4)\qquad q(\nu,s) = \frac{\Gamma(\nu+\frac{1}{2}\sigma+s)\Gamma(\nu-s)}{\Gamma(\nu+1+s)\Gamma(\nu+1-\frac{1}{2}\sigma-s)}\ .$$

The contour of integration in (3.2) separates the poles of $\Gamma(-s)\Gamma(\nu-s)$ from those of $\Gamma(\frac{1}{2}+s)\Gamma(\frac{1}{2}\sigma+s)\Gamma(\nu+\frac{1}{2}\sigma+s)$. In consequence of the assumptions $\nu \geq 0$, and $\mathrm{Re}\ \sigma > 0$, it is always possible to construct such a contour; moreover this contour can be chosen independently of ν.

On the contour

$$(3.5)\qquad p(s) = O\left(|s|^{-1}e^{-\pi|s|}\right),\ s \to \pm i\infty\ ,$$

and

$$(3.6)\qquad q(\nu,s) \sim (\nu+s)^{(\sigma-2)/2}(\nu-s)^{(\sigma-2)/2},\ |\nu\pm s| \to \infty\ .$$

By hypothesis, $\mathrm{Re}\ \sigma-2$ is negative; hence we have

$$(3.7)\qquad q(\nu,s) = O(\nu^{\mathrm{Re}\ \sigma-2})$$

as $\nu \to \infty$, uniformly with respect to all values of s on the contour. Next,

(3.8) $$q(\nu,s) = \nu^{\sigma-2}\{1+O(\nu^{-1})\}$$

as $\nu \to \infty$, uniformly with respect to bounded values of s, and corresponding to (2.14) we derive

(3.9) $$\nu^{2-\sigma}\int_{-i\infty}^{i\infty} p(s)q(\nu,s)ds = \int_{-i\infty}^{i\infty} p(s)ds + o(1), \quad \nu \to \infty .$$

The last integral is in the form of Barnes' representation for the hypergeometric function; thus

(3.10) $$\frac{1}{2\pi i}\int_{-i\infty}^{i\infty} p(s)ds = \frac{\pi^{1/2}\Gamma(\frac{1}{2}\sigma)}{\Gamma(\frac{1}{2}\sigma+\frac{1}{2})}\, {}_2F_1(\tfrac{1}{2},\tfrac{1}{2}\sigma;\ \tfrac{1}{2}\sigma+\tfrac{1}{2};\ -\alpha^2) .$$

For this combination of parameters the hypergeometric function is expressible in terms of Ferrers' Legendre function:

(3.11) $${}_2F_1(\tfrac{1}{2},\tfrac{1}{2}\sigma;\tfrac{1}{2}\sigma+\tfrac{1}{2};-\alpha^2) = \frac{\Gamma(\frac{1}{2}\sigma+\frac{1}{2})}{\alpha^{(\sigma-1)/2}(1+\alpha^2)^{1/2}}\, \mathrm{P}_{-1/2}^{(1-\sigma)/2}\left(\frac{1-\alpha^2}{1+\alpha^2}\right);$$

compare [1, pp. 124-125 and 143]. On combining these results with (3.2) and (3.9), we arrive at the required result in the form

(3.12) $$V = -\frac{\Gamma(\frac{1}{2}\sigma)\nu^{\sigma-2}}{4\pi^{1/2}a^{\sigma}\alpha^{(\sigma-1)/2}(1+\alpha^2)^{1/2}}\left\{\mathrm{P}_{-1/2}^{(1-\sigma)/2}\left(\frac{1-\alpha^2}{1+\alpha^2}\right)+o(1)\right\}, \quad \nu \to \infty .$$

4. *Evaluation of* U: *Second Method.*

In (1.1) set $x = \nu z/a$ and again write $\alpha = b/a$. Then

(4.1) $$U = \frac{\nu^{\rho}}{a^{\rho}}\int_0^{\infty} J_{\nu}(\nu z)I_{\nu}(\alpha\nu z)K_{\nu}(\alpha\nu z)z^{\rho-1}dz .$$

For large positive values of ν we have from [6, pp.374-378]

$$I_\nu(\alpha\nu z)K_\nu(\alpha\nu z) = \frac{1}{2\nu(1+\alpha^2 z^2)^{1/2}}\left\{1 + O\left(\frac{1}{\nu}\right)\right\}, \tag{4.2}$$

where the O-term is uniform for $z \in (0,\infty)$. For the remaining Bessel function we have from [6, pp. 419-424]

$$J_\nu(\nu z) = \left(\frac{4\zeta}{1-z^2}\right)^{1/4}\left\{\frac{\mathrm{Ai}(\nu^{2/3}\zeta)}{\nu^{1/3}} + \frac{M(\nu^{2/3}\zeta)}{E(\nu^{2/3}\zeta)}\, O\left(\frac{1}{\nu^{4/3}}\right)\right\}, \tag{4.3}$$

where $\zeta \equiv \zeta(z)$ is a decreasing and C^∞ function of z that is given by

$$\begin{cases} \frac{2}{3}\zeta^{3/2} = \ln\frac{1+(1-z^2)^{1/2}}{z} - (1-z^2)^{1/2}, & 0 < z \le 1, \\ \frac{2}{3}(-\zeta)^{3/2} = (z^2-1)^{1/2} - \sec^{-1} z, & z \ge 1, \end{cases} \tag{4.4}$$

and the auxiliary positive functions $E(\nu^{2/3}\zeta)$ and $M(\nu^{2/3}\zeta)$ are defined and discussed in [6, pp. 394-397].

Let us write

$$f(\zeta) = \frac{z^\rho}{(1+\alpha^2 z^2)^{1/2}}\left(\frac{\zeta}{1-z^2}\right)^{3/4}. \tag{4.5}$$

Since ζ vanishes when $z = 1$ it follows that $f(\zeta)$ is continuous in the interval $-\infty < \zeta < \infty$. On substituting in (4.1) by means of (4.2), (4.3), and (4.5), and using the identity

$$\frac{dz}{d\zeta} = -\left(\frac{\zeta}{1-z^2}\right)^{1/2} z, \tag{4.6}$$

we obtain

$$U = \frac{\nu^{\rho-1}}{a^\rho}\left\{\frac{1}{2^{1/2}\nu^{1/3}}\int_{-\infty}^{\infty} f(\zeta)\mathrm{Ai}(\nu^{2/3}\zeta)\,d\zeta + O\left(\frac{1}{\nu^{4/3}}\right)\int_{-\infty}^{\infty} |f(\zeta)|\,\frac{M(\nu^{2/3}\zeta)}{E(\nu^{2/3}\zeta)}\,d\zeta\right\}. \tag{4.7}$$

To evaluate the limiting form of U we consider separately the ζ-intervals $[0,\infty)$ and $(-\infty,0]$, beginning with the former.

As $\zeta \to +\infty$ we have

$$z \sim 2\exp\left(-\tfrac{2}{3}\zeta^{3/2}-1\right),\quad f(\zeta) \sim 2^{\rho}\zeta^{3/4}\exp\left(-\tfrac{2}{3}\rho\zeta^{3/2}-\rho\right) . \tag{4.8}$$

Hence from [6, p.338] it follows that

$$\int_0^{\infty} f(\zeta)\mathrm{Ai}(\nu^{2/3}\zeta)d\zeta = \frac{f(0)}{3\nu^{2/3}} + O\left(\frac{1}{\nu^{4/3}}\right),\quad \nu \to \infty . \tag{4.9}$$

Moreover, when $\zeta \geq 0$

$$M(\nu^{2/3}\zeta)/E(\nu^{2/3}\zeta) = 2^{1/2}\mathrm{Ai}(\nu^{2/3}\zeta) .$$

Therefore

$$\int_0^{\infty} |f(\zeta)| \frac{M(\nu^{2/3}\zeta)}{E(\nu^{2/3}\zeta)} d\zeta = \frac{2^{1/2}|f(0)|}{3\nu^{2/3}} + O\left(\frac{1}{\nu^{4/3}}\right),\quad \nu \to \infty . \tag{4.10}$$

To assess the contribution from the interval $(-\infty,0]$, we use the relations

$$z = \tfrac{2}{3}|\zeta|^{3/2} + \tfrac{1}{2}\pi + O(|\zeta|^{-3/2}),\quad f(\zeta) = O(|\zeta|^{3(\rho-2)/2}) , \tag{4.11}$$

which are valid when $\zeta \to -\infty$, and also differentiable any number of times. Using [6, pp. 342-344] we find that

$$\int_{-\infty}^{0} f(\zeta)\mathrm{Ai}(\nu^{2/3}\zeta)d\zeta = \frac{2f(0)}{3\nu^{2/3}} + O\left(\frac{1}{\nu^{4/3}}\right),\quad \nu \to \infty . \tag{4.12}$$

Next, when $\zeta \in (-\infty,0]$ and $\nu \in (0,\infty)$ we have

$$\frac{M(\nu^{2/3}\zeta)}{E(\nu^{2/3}\zeta)} \leq \frac{A}{(\nu^{2/3}|\zeta|)^{1/4}} ,$$

where A is an assignable constant. Therefore when $\nu \geq 1$ it follows that

$$\nu^{1/6}\int_{-\infty}^{0} |f(\zeta)| \frac{M(\nu^{2/3}\zeta)}{E(\nu^{2/3}\zeta)} d\zeta \leq A\int_{-\infty}^{0} |\zeta^{-1/4}f(\zeta)|d\zeta < \infty , \tag{4.13}$$

in consequence of the second of (4.11) and the first of (1.3).

Substituting in (4.7) by means of (4.9), (4.10), (4.12), and (4.13), we obtain the required approximation in the form

$$U = \frac{\nu^{\rho-2} f(0)}{2^{1/2} a^{\rho}} \left\{ 1 + O\left(\frac{1}{\nu^{1/2}}\right) \right\}. \tag{4.14}$$

It remains to evaluate $f(0)$. From (4.4) we find that for small ζ

$$z = 1 - 2^{-1/3}\zeta + O(\zeta^2) .$$

Substitution in (4.5) gives

$$f(0) = 2^{-1/2}(1+\alpha^2)^{-1/2} . \tag{4.15}$$

From (2.3), (4.14), and (4.15) we finally arrive at

$$U = \frac{a^{1-\rho}\nu^{\rho-2}}{2(a^2+b^2)^{1/2}} \left\{ 1+O\left(\frac{1}{\nu^{1/2}}\right) \right\}, \quad \nu \to \infty , \tag{4.16}$$

which agrees with the previous result (2.16), and is valid with the less restrictive condition $\operatorname{Re} \rho < 3/2$.

5. *Evaluation of* V : *Second Method.*

Corresponding to (4.3) we have

$$Y_\nu(\nu z) = -\left(\frac{4\zeta}{1-z^2}\right)^{1/4} \left\{ \frac{\operatorname{Bi}(\nu^{2/3}\zeta)}{\nu^{1/3}} + E(\nu^{2/3}\zeta)M(\nu^{2/3}\zeta)O\left(\frac{1}{\nu^{4/3}}\right) \right\} \tag{5.1}$$

this result again applying uniformly for $z \in (0,\infty)$. Multiplying (4.3) and (5.1) together and using the properties of the auxiliary functions E and M given in [6, pp. 394-397], we find that

$$J_\nu(\nu z)Y_\nu(\nu z) = -\left(\frac{4\zeta}{1-z^2}\right)^{1/2} \left\{ \frac{\operatorname{Ai}(\nu^{2/3}\zeta)\operatorname{Bi}(\nu^{2/3}\zeta)}{\nu^{2/3}} + M^2(\nu^{2/3}\zeta)O\left(\frac{1}{\nu^{5/3}}\right) \right\} .$$

Referring to (1.2) and making the same substitutions as in Section 4, we derive

(5.2) $$V = -\frac{\nu^{\sigma-1}}{a^{\sigma}}\left\{\frac{1}{\nu^{2/3}}\int_{-\infty}^{\infty} g(\zeta)\mathrm{Ai}(\nu^{2/3}\zeta)\mathrm{Bi}(\nu^{2/3}\zeta)d\zeta + O\left(\frac{1}{\nu^{5/3}}\right)\int_{-\infty}^{\infty}|g(\zeta)|M^2(\nu^{2/3}\zeta)d\zeta\right\},$$

where

(5.3) $$g(\zeta) = \frac{z^{\sigma}}{(1+\alpha^2 z^2)^{1/2}}\,\frac{\zeta}{1-z^2}.$$

As in the case of $f(\zeta)$ in Section 4, the function $g(\zeta)$ is in $C^{\infty}(-\infty,\infty)$. From the first of (4.8) and the first of (4.11) we find that

$$g(\zeta) \sim 2^{\sigma}\zeta\,\exp(-\tfrac{2}{3}\sigma\zeta^{3/2}-\sigma),\ \zeta \to +\infty;\ g(\zeta) = O(\zeta^{(3\sigma-7)/2}),\ \zeta \to -\infty.$$

In consequence of these results and (1.3) it follows that

(5.4) $$\int_{-\infty}^{\infty}\left|\frac{g(\zeta)}{\zeta^{1/2}}\right|d\zeta < \infty.$$

We shall prove that when ν is large the dominant contribution to V in (5.2) derives from

$$\int_0^{\infty} g(\zeta)\mathrm{Ai}(\nu^{2/3}\zeta)\mathrm{Bi}(\nu^{2/3}\zeta)d\zeta,$$

and may be found by replacing $\mathrm{Ai}(\nu^{2/3}\zeta)$ and $\mathrm{Bi}(\nu^{2/3}\zeta)$ in this integral by their asymptotic approximations for large positive values of $\nu^{2/3}\zeta$.

LEMMA 1.

(5.5) $$\int_0^{\infty} g(\zeta)\mathrm{Ai}(\nu^{2/3}\zeta)\mathrm{Bi}(\nu^{2/3}\zeta)d\zeta = \frac{1}{2\pi\nu^{1/3}}\int_0^{\infty}\frac{g(\zeta)}{\zeta^{1/2}}d\zeta + o\left(\frac{1}{\nu^{1/3}}\right),\quad \nu \to \infty.$$

To establish this result, let $K\ (<\infty)$ be defined by

$$K = \sup_{(-\infty,\infty)} |x^{1/2}\mathrm{Ai}(x)\mathrm{Bi}(x)|,$$

and δ denote any positive number. Then

$$\left|\int_0^\delta g(\zeta)\mathrm{Ai}(\nu^{2/3}\zeta)\mathrm{Bi}(\nu^{2/3}\zeta)d\zeta\right| \le \frac{K}{\nu^{1/3}}\int_0^\delta \frac{|g(\zeta)|}{\zeta^{1/2}}\,d\zeta .$$

In consequence, given any positive number ε we can choose δ, independently of ν, such that

$$2\pi\nu^{1/3}\left|\int_0^\delta g(\zeta)\mathrm{Ai}(\nu^{2/3}\zeta)\mathrm{Bi}(\nu^{2/3}\zeta)d\zeta\right| < \varepsilon , \tag{5.6}$$

and

$$\left|\int_0^\delta \frac{g(\zeta)}{\zeta^{1/2}}\,d\zeta\right| < \varepsilon . \tag{5.7}$$

Having chosen δ, we deduce from the asymptotic forms for the Airy functions of large positive argument that

$$\mathrm{Ai}(\nu^{2/3}\zeta)\mathrm{Bi}(\nu^{2/3}\zeta) = \frac{1}{2\pi\nu^{1/3}\zeta^{1/2}}\left\{1 + O\left(\frac{1}{\nu}\right)\right\}$$

as $\nu \to \infty$, uniformly with respect to $\zeta \in [\delta,\infty)$. Using this result and (5.4) we obtain

$$2\pi\nu^{1/3}\int_\delta^\infty g(\zeta)\mathrm{Ai}(\nu^{2/3}\zeta)\mathrm{Bi}(\nu^{2/3}\zeta)d\zeta = \int_\delta^\infty \frac{g(\zeta)}{\zeta^{1/2}}\,d\zeta + O\left(\frac{1}{\nu}\right) .$$

Hence

$$\left|2\pi\nu^{1/3}\int_\delta^\infty g(\zeta)\mathrm{Ai}(\nu^{2/3}\zeta)\mathrm{Bi}(\nu^{2/3}\zeta)d\zeta - \int_\delta^\infty \frac{g(\zeta)}{\zeta^{1/2}}\,d\zeta\right| < \varepsilon \tag{5.8}$$

for all $\nu > N(\varepsilon)$ assignable. The relation (5.5) now follows on combining (5.6), (5.7), and (5.8).

LEMMA 2.

$$\int_{-\infty}^0 g(\zeta)\mathrm{Ai}(\nu^{2/3}\zeta)\mathrm{Bi}(\nu^{2/3}\zeta)d\zeta = o(\nu^{-1/3}),\quad \nu \to \infty . \tag{5.9}$$

To prove this result, we again assume ε denotes an arbitrary positive number. Given ε we may choose a positive number δ, independently of ν, such that

$$\nu^{1/3}\left|\int_{-\delta}^{0} g(\zeta)\mathrm{Ai}(\nu^{2/3}\zeta)\mathrm{Bi}(\nu^{2/3}\zeta)d\zeta\right| < \varepsilon\ ; \tag{5.10}$$

compare (5.6). Referring to the asymptotic forms for the Airy functions of large negative argument, we see that

$$\mathrm{Ai}(\nu^{2/3}\zeta)\mathrm{Bi}(\nu^{2/3}\zeta) = \frac{1}{2\pi\nu^{1/3}|\zeta|^{1/2}}\left\{\cos\left(\tfrac{4}{3}\nu|\zeta|^{3/2}\right) + O(\nu^{-1})\right\}$$

as $\nu \to \infty$, uniformly with respect to $\zeta \in (-\infty,-\delta]$. Hence

$$\nu^{1/3}\int_{-\infty}^{-\delta} g(\zeta)\mathrm{Ai}(\nu^{2/3}\zeta)\mathrm{Bi}(\nu^{2/3}\zeta)d\zeta = \frac{1}{2\pi}\int_{-\infty}^{-\delta}\frac{g(\zeta)}{|\zeta|^{1/2}}\cos\left(\tfrac{4}{3}\nu|\zeta|^{3/2}\right)d\zeta + O\left(\frac{1}{\nu}\right).$$

By integrating by parts it is easily verified that the integral on the right-hand side is $O(\nu^{-1})$. Therefore

$$\nu^{1/3}\left|\int_{-\infty}^{-\delta} g(\zeta)\mathrm{Ai}(\nu^{2/3}\zeta)\mathrm{Bi}(\nu^{2/3}\zeta)d\zeta\right| < \varepsilon \tag{5.11}$$

for $\nu > N(\varepsilon)$ assignable. Equation (5.9) follows from (5.10) and (5.11).

LEMMA 3.

$$\int_{-\infty}^{\infty} |g(\zeta)|M^2(\nu^{2/3}\zeta)d\zeta = O\left(\frac{1}{\nu^{1/3}}\right), \quad \nu \to \infty . \tag{5.12}$$

This result is an immediate consequence of (5.4) and the inequality

$$M^2(\nu^{2/3}\zeta) \le A|\nu^{2/3}\zeta|^{-1/2} ,$$

in which A is an assignable constant.

Substituting in (5.2) by means of the results given in Lemmas 1, 2, and 3, we obtain the required approximation to V in the form

$$V = -\frac{\nu^{\sigma-2}}{2\pi a^{\sigma}}\int_0^{\infty}\frac{g(\zeta)}{\zeta^{1/2}}\,d\zeta + o(\nu^{\sigma-2}),\quad \nu\to\infty\,. \tag{5.13}$$

To evaluate the integral that appears in this estimate we substitute by means of (4.6) and (5.3). This yields

$$\int_0^{\infty}\frac{g(\zeta)}{\zeta^{1/2}}\,d\zeta = \int_0^{1}\frac{z^{\sigma-1}}{(1-z^2)^{1/2}(1+\alpha^2z^2)^{1/2}}\,dz\,. \tag{5.14}$$

On taking z^2 as integration variable, we arrive at a special case of Euler's integral for the hypergeometric function [1, p. 59]. Hence we obtain

$$V = -\frac{\nu^{\sigma-2}}{4\pi^{1/2}a^{\sigma}}\,\frac{\Gamma(\frac{1}{2}\sigma)}{\Gamma(\frac{1}{2}\sigma+\frac{1}{2})}\,{}_2F_1(\tfrac{1}{2},\tfrac{1}{2}\sigma;\tfrac{1}{2}\sigma+\tfrac{1}{2};-\alpha^2) + o(\nu^{\sigma-2})\,, \tag{5.15}$$

and by referring to (3.11) we see that this result agrees with (3.12), as expected.

REFERENCES

[1] Bateman Manuscript Project, *Higher transcendental functions* (A. Erdélyi, ed.), Vol. 1, McGraw-Hill, New York, 1953.

[2] Bateman Manuscript Project, *Tables of integral transforms* (A. Erdélyi, ed.), Vol. 2, McGraw-Hill, New York, 1954.

[3] J. E. Kilpatrick, S. Katsura, and Y. Inoue, *Calculations of integrals of products of Bessel functions*, Math. Comp. *21* (1967), 407-412.

[4] Y. L. Luke, *The special functions and their approximations*, Vol. 1, Academic Press, New York, 1969.

[5] F. Oberhettinger, *Tables of Bessel transforms*, Springer, New York, 1972.

[6] F. W. J. Olver, *Asymptotics and special functions*, Academic Press, New York, 1974.

Department of Applied Mathematics
University of Waterloo
Ontario

Institute for Physical Science and Technology
University of Maryland
College Park

and

National Bureau of Standards
Washington, D. C.

Received April 15, 1975; revised July 7, 1976.

SIAM J. MATH. ANAL.
Vol. 9, No. 2, April, 1978

SUFFICIENT CONDITIONS FOR ACKERBERG–O'MALLEY RESONANCE*

F. W. J. OLVER†

Abstract. An investigation is made of the asymptotic nature of the solution of the boundary-value problem

$$\varepsilon y''+2xA(\varepsilon, x)y'-A(\varepsilon, x)B(\varepsilon, x)y=0; \qquad y(a)=l, \qquad y(b)=m,$$

as $\varepsilon \to 0$, where $A(\varepsilon, x)$ and $B(\varepsilon, x)$ are continuous real functions of ε and x, $a<0$, $b>0$, and $A(\varepsilon, x)$ is nonzero in $[a, b]$. Particular attention is paid to the problem of resonance, which arises when the limiting form of the solution exhibits an unusual lack of decay (in the case $A(\varepsilon, x)<0$), or an unusual rate of growth (in the case $A(\varepsilon, x)>0$). By application of a recent theory of differential equations with coalescing turning points sufficient conditions for resonance are established, both with and without the assumption that $A(\varepsilon, x)$ and $B(\varepsilon, x)$ are analytic functions of ε and x. Illustrative examples are also included.

1. Introduction. In this paper we study the differential equation

$$\varepsilon y''+2xA(\varepsilon, x)y'-A(\varepsilon, x)B(\varepsilon, x)y=0, \tag{1.01}$$

in which the independent variable x ranges over a compact interval $[a, b]$ with $a<0$ and $b>0$, and ε is a small positive parameter. The coefficients $A(\varepsilon, x)$ and $B(\varepsilon, x)$ are continuous real functions of ε and x, and $A(\varepsilon, x)$ is nonzero in $[a, b]$. The boundary conditions are assumed to be

$$y(a)=l, \qquad y(b)=m, \tag{1.02}$$

where l and m are prescribed real constants, at least one of which is nonzero. The problem stems from the flow of viscous fluid between rotating disks [17], [5], and interest is focused on the asymptotic behavior of the solution y as $\varepsilon \to 0$.

By assuming that the coefficients $A(\varepsilon, x)$ and $B(\varepsilon, x)$ are independent of ε, or, more generally, expandable in asymptotic power series of the form

$$\begin{aligned} A(\varepsilon, x) &\sim A_0(x)+A_1(x)\varepsilon+A_2(x)\varepsilon^2+\cdots, \\ B(\varepsilon, x) &\sim B_0(x)+B_1(x)\varepsilon+B_2(x)\varepsilon^2+\cdots, \end{aligned} \tag{1.03}$$

the problem can be treated by the methods of singular perturbation theory [15]. The nature of the solution depends on the sign of $A(\varepsilon, x)$ in $[a, b]$. When this sign is negative (which is the case of greater physical interest), it is found that in general $y \to 0$ as $\varepsilon \to 0$, uniformly in any closed interval that is properly interior to $[a, b]$. However, certain exceptional situations may arise in which the solution does not decay in this manner. Ackerberg and O'Malley drew attention to this phenomenon in [1] and called it *resonance*. Using two distinct methods, these writers (and also O'Malley [13] and [14, Chap. 8]), showed that a necessary condition for resonance to take place is given by

$$B(0,0)=2s-2, \qquad s=1, 2, 3, \cdots, \tag{1.04}$$

and they included an example in which resonance actually occurs. The first method of Ackerberg and O'Malley is to construct the Liouville–Green (or WKBJ) approximations to the solutions of (1.01) valid in intervals that exclude the turning point at $x=0$ and to link these solutions by skirting the turning point in the complex plane by the method of Zwaan [19]. The second method is based on the uniform reduction theorems

* Received by the editors June 1, 1976, and in revised form October 12, 1976.

† Institute for Physical Science and Technology, University of Maryland, College Park, Maryland 20742, and National Bureau of Standards, Washington, DC 20234. This research was supported by the U.S. Army Research Office, Durham, under Contract DA ARO D 31 124 73 G204, and by the National Science Foundation under Grant GP 32841X2.

of Sibuya [16] and Lee [6], and transforms (1.01) into a differential equation of the same type in which $A(\varepsilon, x)$ and $B(\varepsilon, x)$ are replaced by functions that are independent of x. This yields approximations for the solutions in terms of parabolic cylinder functions that are uniformly valid throughout $[a, b]$. The first method was applied in a formal manner, but the second method was placed on a rigorous foundation by assuming that the coefficients $A(\varepsilon, x)$ and $B(\varepsilon, x)$ are analytic functions of ε and x.

The first method of Ackerberg and O'Malley was reconsidered independently by Watts [17] and Zauderer [18]. Avoiding Zwaan's complex-variable approach, these writers showed that the linking of the Liouville–Green approximations across the turning point can be achieved with the aid of local approximations in terms of parabolic cylinder functions. These local approximations are obtained by making a stretching transformation of the independent variable.

Next, Lakin [5] and Cook and Eckhaus [2] demonstrated independently, by formal methods, that the condition (1.04) is only the first of an infinite sequence of necessary conditions for resonance. Lakin constructed series solutions in terms of parabolic cylinder functions that are uniformly valid in $[a, b]$, whereas Cook and Eckhaus used the method of matched asymptotic expansions.

More recently, Kreiss and Parter [4] and Matkowsky [7], [8] have considered the problem and discussed several examples in detail. The approach of Kreiss and Parter is quite different from the approaches of other writers that have been mentioned, and is based in part on the maximum principle. Matkowsky uses a formal criterion that does not depend on Zwaan's method or on local approximations in the neighborhood of $x = 0$. We shall discuss some of Matkowsky's results more fully later (§ 9).

A similar situation exists when the coefficient $A(\varepsilon, x)$ in (1.01) is positive throughout $[a, b]$. In [13], and also [14, Chap. 8], O'Malley showed that in general the solution y is bounded as $\varepsilon \to 0$, except in the neighborhood of $x = 0$ where it may grow algebraically, that is, at the rate of a negative power of ε. However, in certain exceptional cases the solution grows exponentially in closed intervals that are properly interior to $[a, 0]$ or $[0, b]$. These exceptional cases are again regarded as manifestations of a resonance phenomenon, and O'Malley proved that when the coefficients $A(\varepsilon, x)$ and $B(\varepsilon, x)$ are analytic in ε and x a necessary condition for resonance is given by

$$B(0, 0) = -2s, \qquad s = 1, 2, 3, \cdots. \tag{1.05}$$

Finally, de Groen [3] has considered resonance problems of the same general type for certain elliptic partial differential equations.

None of the references cited establishes sufficient conditions for resonance that are directly applicable to the general case. Furthermore, the only ordinary differential equations for which resonance has been conclusively demonstrated are either solvable exactly in terms of parabolic cylinder functions, or have a nontrivial solution that is independent of ε. In § 8 of the present paper we shall remedy this situation by establishing a sufficient condition for resonance, applicable to each of the cases $A(\varepsilon, x) < 0$ and $A(\varepsilon, x) > 0$. In effect this condition requires (1.01) to be transformable into a particular form of Weber's equation (that is, the differential equation satisfied by the parabolic cylinder functions), except for the inclusion of a coefficient term that may depend x as well as ε and is uniformly and exponentially small in $[a, b]$ as $\varepsilon \to 0$. Not surprisingly, the particular form of Weber's equation has to be one that admits a solution that is recessive both for large positive and large negative arguments. We also give new examples in which the sufficiency condition is satisfied.

The main purpose of the present paper, however, is to reconsider the problem without the requirement that $A(\varepsilon, x)$ and $B(\varepsilon, x)$ be analytic functions of ε and x. By permitting nonanalytic behavior, we shall see that resonance occurs without the need for (1.01) to be transformable into the special form of differential equation that differs from Weber's equation only by an exponentially small term in the coefficient. In fact, from the new standpoint resonance occurs in the general case just as frequently as it does with Weber's equation. This is a more natural state of affairs because with the assumptions (1.03) the original differential equation (1.01) is always transformable into an equation having the same asymptotic structure as Weber's equation.

Another way of viewing the situation is that by imposing analytic behavior on the coefficients $A(\varepsilon, x)$ and $B(\varepsilon, x)$, the boundary-value problem becomes ill-posed when the condition (1.04) (or (1.05)) is satisfied. That is, nonresonant solutions are transformable into resonant solutions by making relatively small numerical changes in the coefficients.

Our approach will be to introduce an extra free parameter κ in the differential equation, which we define by

$$\pm\kappa = 1 + B(0, 0), \tag{1.06}$$

the upper sign applying in the case in which $A(\varepsilon, x)$ is negative, and the lower sign when $A(\varepsilon, x)$ is positive. In order to facilitate applications of the uniform asymptotic theory of linear differential equations, the term in the first derivative in (1.01) is removed by change of dependent variable. From the standpoint of this theory the transformed equation may be regarded as having two simple turning points which depend on ε and κ and coalesce into a double turning point as $\varepsilon \to 0$. This is exactly the situation treated in a recent paper by the present writer [12], and application of the theory given in this reference yields asymptotic solutions of (1.01) for small ε that are uniformly valid with respect to $x \in [0, b]$ or $x \in [a, 0]$, and also with respect to positive values of the parameter κ that are bounded and bounded away from zero. The approximate solutions are expressed in terms of parabolic cylinder functions, accompanied by strict error bounds. On combining the solutions in such a way that the boundary conditions (1.02) are satisfied, we find that the condition for resonance becomes a type of eigenvalue problem resulting in a transcendental equation for κ. The solutions $\kappa = \kappa(\varepsilon)$ of this equation form a continuum, and are therefore not analytic functions of ε. However, $\kappa(\varepsilon)$ can be approximated asymptotically, and the results are consistent with the necessary conditions for resonance given by (1.04) when $A(\varepsilon, x)$ is negative, or (1.05) when $A(\varepsilon, x)$ is positive.

2. Assumptions and preliminary transformations. In the given differential equation (1.01) we shall assume that

$$A(\varepsilon, x) = A_0(x) + A_1(x)\varepsilon + A_2(\varepsilon, x)\varepsilon^2, \tag{2.01}$$

$$B(\varepsilon, x) = \pm\kappa - 1 + x\hat{B}_0(x) + B_1(\varepsilon, x)\varepsilon, \tag{2.02}$$

subject to the following conditions:

(i) $A_0(x)$, $A_1(x)$, and $\hat{B}_0(x)$ are independent of ε.

(ii) $A_0(x)$ is nonvanishing in $[a, b]$, and the upper or lower sign is taken in (2.02) according as $A_0(x)$ is negative or positive.

(iii) $A_0^{\text{vi}}(x)$, $A_1^{\text{v}}(x)$, and $\hat{B}_0^{\text{v}}(x)$ are continuous in $[a, b]$.[1]

(iv) $A_2(\varepsilon, x)$, $\partial A_2(\varepsilon, x)/\partial x$, and $B_1(\varepsilon, x)$ are continuous functions of ε and x when $\varepsilon \in [0, \delta]$ and $x \in [a, b]$, where δ is a positive constant.

[1] As usual, $A_0^{\text{vi}}(x)$ denotes the sixth derivative of $A_0(x)$, and so on. These conditions are stronger than actually needed, but they simplify the exposition.

(v) κ is a free parameter with the range $k_1 \leqq \kappa \leqq k_2$, where k_1 and k_2 are constants such that $0<k_1<k_2<\infty$.

We remove the term in the first derivative from the differential equation (1.01) by taking a new dependent variable $w = w(\varepsilon, \kappa, x)$, defined by

$$w = \exp\left\{\frac{1}{\varepsilon}\int_0^x tA(\varepsilon, t)\,dt\right\}y. \tag{2.03}$$

Then

$$w'' = \varepsilon^{-2}\{x^2A^2 + \varepsilon(xA)' + \varepsilon AB\}w, \tag{2.04}$$

where primes again denote partial differentiations with respect to x. Substituting for A and B by means of (2.01) and (2.02) and rearranging, we find that

$$w'' = \{\varepsilon^{-2}f(\varepsilon, \kappa, x) + g(\varepsilon, \kappa, x)\}w, \tag{2.05}$$

where

$$f(\varepsilon, \kappa, x) = x^2A_0^2 + \{xA_0' \pm \kappa A_0 + 2x^2A_0A_1 + xA_0\hat{B}_0\}\varepsilon, \tag{2.06}$$

$$\begin{aligned} g(\varepsilon, \kappa, x) = {} & x^2A_1^2 + xA_1' \pm \kappa A_1 + 2x^2A_0A_2 + xA_1\hat{B}_0 + A_0B_1 \\ & + (2x^2A_1A_2 + xA_2' \pm \kappa A_2 + xA_2\hat{B}_0 + A_1B_1)\varepsilon \\ & + (x^2A_2^2 + A_2B_1)\varepsilon^2. \end{aligned} \tag{2.07}$$

In consequence of conditions (iii) and (iv), $f(\varepsilon, \kappa, x)$, $g(\varepsilon, \kappa, x)$, and the first five partial x-derivatives of $f(\varepsilon, \kappa, x)$ are continuous functions of ε, κ, and x.

To find the boundary conditions satisfied by w, we introduce the notations

$$P(x) = \int_0^x tA_0(t)\,dt, \qquad Q(x) = \int_0^x tA_1(t)\,dt. \tag{2.08}$$

Then from (2.01) we have

$$\frac{1}{\varepsilon}\int_0^x tA(\varepsilon, t)\,dt = \frac{1}{\varepsilon}P(x) + Q(x) + O(\varepsilon), \tag{2.09}$$

as $\varepsilon \to 0$, uniformly with respect to $x \in [a, b]$. Hence from (1.02) and (2.03) the new boundary conditions are given by

$$w(\varepsilon, \kappa, a) = le^{Q(a)}e^{P(a)/\varepsilon}\{1 + O(\varepsilon)\}, \tag{2.10}$$

$$w(\varepsilon, \kappa, b) = me^{Q(b)}e^{P(b)/\varepsilon}\{1 + O(\varepsilon)\}. \tag{2.11}$$

3. Zeros of $f(\varepsilon, \kappa, x)$. Write

$$\phi(x) = |A_0(x)|, \qquad \omega(x) = \{A_0'(x) + 2xA_0(x)A_1(x) + A_0(x)\hat{B}_0(x)\}/\phi(x). \tag{3.01}$$

Then in $[a, b]$, $\phi(x)$ is nonvanishing and six times continuously differentiable, and $\omega(x)$ is five times continuously differentiable. From (2.06) we see that

$$f(\varepsilon, \kappa, x) = x^2\phi^2(x) - \{\kappa - x\omega(x)\}\phi(x)\varepsilon. \tag{3.02}$$

Let r and R denote the positive constants

$$r = \min_{a \leqq x \leqq b} \phi(x), \qquad R = \max_{a \leqq x \leqq b} |\omega(x)|.$$

In the interval $-k_1/(2R) \leqq x \leqq k_1/(2R)$ the factor $\kappa - x\omega(x)$ is positive; accordingly the zeros of $f(\varepsilon, \kappa, x)$ are given by

$$\pm\Xi(\kappa, x) = \varepsilon^{1/2},$$

where here and elsewhere $\varepsilon^{1/2}$ denotes as usual the positive square root, and

$$\Xi(\kappa, x) = x\{\phi(x)\}^{1/2}\{\kappa - x\omega(x)\}^{-1/2}.$$

It is easily seen that $\Xi(\kappa, x)$ is continuous and $\partial\Xi(\kappa, x)/\partial x$ is positive and continuous in the region $k_1 \leqq \kappa \leqq k_2$, $-k \leqq x \leqq k$, where k is an assignable positive constant. We now apply the implicit function theorem in the form given in [12, p. 144], with κ in the role of a and $\varepsilon^{1/2}$ in the role of ξ. We deduce that as long as the constant δ is small enough, the only zeros of $f(\varepsilon, \kappa, x)$ in the interval $-k \leqq x \leqq k$ are given by $x = z_1(\varepsilon, \kappa)$ and $x = z_2(\varepsilon, \kappa)$, where $z_1(\varepsilon, \kappa)$ and $z_2(\varepsilon, \kappa)$ are continuous functions of ε and κ, $z_1(\varepsilon, \kappa)$ being nonpositive and a decreasing function of ε, and $z_2(\varepsilon, \kappa)$ being nonnegative and an increasing function of ε; furthermore

$$z_1(0, \kappa) = z_2(0, \kappa) = 0. \tag{3.03}$$

Again, by taking δ small enough we can also ensure that $z_1(\varepsilon, \kappa)$ and $z_2(\varepsilon, \kappa)$ are the only zeros of $f(\varepsilon, \kappa, x)$ in the whole of the original interval $[a, b]$; in fact it suffices that

$$\delta < rk^2/\{k_2 + R \max(|a|, b)\}.$$

The asymptotic forms of the zeros $z_1(\varepsilon, \kappa)$ and $z_2(\varepsilon, \kappa)$ are found by equating the right-hand side of (3.02) to zero, and solving by standard asymptotic methods given, for example, in [11, p. 13]. We find that

$$\begin{aligned} z_1(\varepsilon, \kappa) &= -\left\{\frac{\kappa\varepsilon}{\phi(0)}\right\}^{1/2} - \left\{\omega(0) + \kappa\frac{\phi'(0)}{\phi(0)}\right\}\frac{\varepsilon}{2\phi(0)} + O(\varepsilon^{3/2}), \\ z_2(\varepsilon, \kappa) &= \left\{\frac{\kappa\varepsilon}{\phi(0)}\right\}^{1/2} - \left\{\omega(0) + \kappa\frac{\phi'(0)}{\phi(0)}\right\}\frac{\varepsilon}{2\phi(0)} + O(\varepsilon^{3/2}), \end{aligned} \tag{3.04}$$

as $\varepsilon \to 0$, uniformly with respect to κ.

We shall need certain properties of the function $p(\varepsilon, \kappa, x)$, defined by

$$p(\varepsilon, \kappa, x) = f(\varepsilon, \kappa, x)/\{(x - z_1)(x - z_2)\}, \tag{3.05}$$

when $x \neq z_1$ or z_2, or by the limiting form of this quotient when $x = z_1$ or z_2. Clearly $p(\varepsilon, \kappa, x)$ is always positive, and from (3.02) and (3.03) we have

$$p(0, \kappa, x) = \phi^2(x). \tag{3.06}$$

LEMMA 3.1. *The function $p(\varepsilon, \kappa, x)$ and its first three partial x-derivatives are continuous in the cuboid*

$$0 \leqq \varepsilon \leqq \delta, \qquad k_1 \leqq \kappa \leqq k_2, \qquad a \leqq x \leqq b. \tag{3.07}$$

In the proof that follows we suppress the arguments ε and κ of f and p in most places; thus $f(x) \equiv f(\varepsilon, \kappa, x)$ and $p(x) \equiv p(\varepsilon, \kappa, x)$. We continue to use primes to denote partial differentiations with respect to x.

Since $f(x)$ is a continuous function of ε, κ, and x, and z_1 and z_2 are continuous functions of ε and κ, it follows immediately that $p(x)$ is continuous throughout the cuboid (3.07), except possibly at those points for which $x = z_1$ or z_2. Let us define

$$h(x) = f(x)/(x - z_1), \qquad x \neq z_1; \qquad h(z_1) = f'(z_1). \tag{3.08}$$

Then

$$p(x)=h(x)/(x-z_2), \qquad x\neq z_1 \text{ or } z_2. \tag{3.09}$$

By the mean-value theorem $h(x)=f'(c_1)$, where c_1 lies between x and z_1. Since $f'(x)$ is continuous (in all variables) it follows that $h(x)$ is continuous when $x=z_1$, and therefore throughout (3.07). If $\varepsilon\neq 0$, then $z_1\neq z_2$ and it follows from (3.09) that $p(x)$ is continuous when $x=z_1$, and therefore, by symmetry, when $x=z_2$.

It remains to consider the edge $\varepsilon=x=0$ in order to establish the continuity of $p(x)$ throughout the whole of (3.07). Differentiating (3.08), we have

$$h'(x)=\{(x-z_1)f'(x)-f(x)\}/(x-z_1)^2, \qquad x\neq z_1. \tag{3.10}$$

From Taylor's theorem

$$f'(x)=f'(z_1)+(x-z_1)f''(c_2), \qquad f(x)=(x-z_1)f'(z_1)+\tfrac{1}{2}(x-z_1)^2f''(c_3),$$

where c_2 and c_3 lie between x and z_1. Substitution in (3.10) yields

$$h'(x)=f''(c_2)-\tfrac{1}{2}f''(c_3), \qquad x\neq z_1. \tag{3.11}$$

From (3.08) we have by definition

$$h'(z_1)=\lim_{x\to z_1}\left\{\frac{f(x)}{x-z_1}-f'(z_1)\right\}\frac{1}{x-z_1}=\tfrac{1}{2}f''(z_1). \tag{3.12}$$

The last two results show that $h'(x)$ is continuous when $x=z_1$, and therefore throughout (3.07). Now suppose that $\varepsilon\neq 0$. Since $h(z_2)=0$, application of the mean-value theorem gives

$$h(x)=(x-z_2)h'(d_1),$$

where d_1 lies between x and z_2. Substituting for $h'(d_1)$ by means of (3.11) and (3.12), we obtain

$$h(x)=(x-z_2)\{f''(e_1)-\tfrac{1}{2}f''(e_2)\},$$

where e_1 and e_2 lie in the smallest interval I, say, that contains x, z_1, and z_2. Hence

$$p(x)=f''(e_1)-\tfrac{1}{2}f''(e_2), \tag{3.13}$$

provided that $x\neq z_2$. By symmetry, however, (3.13) also holds when $x\neq z_1$. Therefore (3.13) applies at every point of (3.07) except those on the face $\varepsilon=0$. From (3.02) and (3.06) it follows that $p(x)=\tfrac{1}{2}f''(0)$ when $\varepsilon=x=0$. Because $f''(x)$ is continuous, it follows from (3.13) that $p(x)$ is continuous at all points of the edge $\varepsilon=x=0$. This completes the part of the proof concerning the continuity of $p(\varepsilon,\kappa,x)$.

The proofs for the derivatives $\partial p(\varepsilon,\kappa,x)/\partial x$, $\partial^2p(\varepsilon,\kappa,x)/\partial x^2$, and $\partial^3p(\varepsilon,\kappa,x)/\partial x^3$ are similar and it is unnecessary to record details, except perhaps the equations that correspond to (3.13):

$$p'(x)=\tfrac{11}{6}f'''(e_3)-\tfrac{5}{3}f'''(e_4), \qquad p''(x)=\tfrac{53}{12}f^{\text{iv}}(e_5)-\tfrac{13}{3}f^{\text{iv}}(e_6),$$
$$p'''(x)=\tfrac{233}{20}f^{\text{v}}(e_7)-\tfrac{58}{5}f^{\text{v}}(e_8),$$

where $e_3, e_4, \cdots, e_8$ are points in the interval I defined above. In particular, when $\varepsilon=x=0$ we have

$$p'(0)=\tfrac{1}{6}f'''(0), \qquad p''(0)=\tfrac{1}{12}f^{\text{iv}}(0), \qquad p'''(0)=\tfrac{1}{20}f^{\text{v}}(0).$$

LEMMA 3.2. *As* $\varepsilon \to 0$

$$p(\varepsilon, \kappa, x) = \phi^2(x) + O(\varepsilon), \tag{3.14}$$

uniformly with respect to $\kappa \in [k_1, k_2]$ *and* $x \in [a, b]$.

Since $p(0, \kappa, x)$ equals $\phi^2(x)$, in effect this result supplies information concerning the partial derivative $\partial p(\varepsilon, \kappa, x)/\partial\varepsilon$. The proof is as follows. Write

$$\hat{f}(x) \equiv \hat{f}(\varepsilon, \kappa, x) = f(\varepsilon, \kappa, x) - (x - z_1)(x - z_2)\phi^2(x), \tag{3.15}$$

$$\hat{p}(x) \equiv \hat{p}(\varepsilon, \kappa, x) = \hat{f}(\varepsilon, \kappa, x)/\{(x - z_1)(x - z_2)\}. \tag{3.16}$$

Then $\hat{f}(x)$ and its first five partial x-derivatives are continuous in the cuboid (3.07) and $\hat{f}(x)$ vanishes when $x = z_1$ or z_2. Lemma 3.1 may now be applied with $f(x)$ and $p(x)$ replaced by $\hat{f}(x)$ and $\hat{p}(x)$, respectively, and *inter alia* we deduce that

$$\hat{p}(x) = \hat{f}''(\hat{e}_1) - \tfrac{1}{2}\hat{f}''(\hat{e}_2), \tag{3.17}$$

where $\hat{e}_1$ and $\hat{e}_2$ lie in I; compare (3.13). From (3.02) and (3.15) we see that

$$\hat{f}(x) = \{(z_1 + z_2)x - z_1 z_2\}\phi^2(x) - \{\kappa - x\omega(x)\}\phi(x)\varepsilon. \tag{3.18}$$

The approximations (3.04) show that as $\varepsilon \to 0$ both $z_1 + z_2$ and $z_1 z_2$ are uniformly $O(\varepsilon)$. From this result and the twice-differentiated form of (3.18) it is evident that as $\varepsilon \to 0$, $\hat{f}''(x)$ is uniformly $O(\varepsilon)$; hence from (3.17) $\hat{p}(x)$ is uniformly $O(\varepsilon)$. Combination of the last result with (3.05), (3.15), and (3.16) yields the desired relation (3.14).

4. Application of the Liouville transformation. Returning to the differential equation (2.05), we follow [12, § 2], and take a new independent variable ζ, defined by

$$\dot{x}^2 f(\varepsilon, \kappa, x) = \zeta^2 - \alpha^2, \tag{4.01}$$

where the dot signifies differentiation with respect to ζ, and α is a nonnegative real number chosen to make $\zeta = -\alpha$ correspond to $x = z_1$, and $\zeta = \alpha$ correspond to $x = z_2$. Thus $\alpha \equiv \alpha(\varepsilon, \kappa)$ is given by

$$\int_{z_1}^{z_2} \{-f(\varepsilon, \kappa, x)\}^{1/2}\, dx = \int_{-\alpha}^{\alpha} (\alpha^2 - \zeta^2)^{1/2}\, d\zeta = \tfrac{1}{2}\pi\alpha^2. \tag{4.02}$$

Next, integration of (4.01) yields the following relations between x and ζ:

$$\int_{z_1}^{x} \{-f(\varepsilon, \kappa, t)\}^{1/2}\, dt = \int_{-\alpha}^{\zeta} (\alpha^2 - \tau^2)^{1/2}\, d\tau, \qquad z_1 \leqq x \leqq z_2, \tag{4.03}$$

$$\int_{z_2}^{x} \{f(\varepsilon, \kappa, t)\}^{1/2}\, dt = \int_{\alpha}^{\zeta} (\tau^2 - \alpha^2)^{1/2}\, d\tau, \qquad z_2 \leqq x \leqq b, \tag{4.04}$$

$$\int_{x}^{z_1} \{f(\varepsilon, \kappa, t)\}^{1/2}\, dt = \int_{\zeta}^{-\alpha} (\tau^2 - \alpha^2)^{1/2}\, d\tau, \qquad a \leqq x \leqq z_1. \tag{4.05}$$

These equations define ζ as a continuous and increasing function of x in $[a, b]$. We suppose that $\zeta = \bar{a}$ (<0) corresponds to $x = a$, and $\zeta = \bar{b}$ (>0) corresponds to $x = b$.

The Liouville transformation of (2.05) is completed by introducing a new dependent variable W, defined by

$$W = \dot{x}^{-1/2} w. \tag{4.06}$$

Then

$$d^2W/d\zeta^2 = \{\varepsilon^{-2}(\zeta^2 - \alpha^2) + \psi(\alpha, \kappa, \zeta)\}W, \tag{4.07}$$

where

$$\psi(\alpha, \kappa, \zeta) = \dot{x}^2 g(\varepsilon, \kappa, x) + \dot{x}^{1/2} d^2(\dot{x}^{-1/2})/d\zeta^2. \tag{4.08}$$

LEMMA 4.1. *Provided that δ is sufficiently small, $\alpha(\varepsilon, \kappa)$ is a continuous function of ε and κ, and an increasing function of ε in the rectangle*

$$0 \leqq \varepsilon \leqq \delta, \qquad k_1 \leqq \kappa \leqq k_2, \tag{4.09}$$

and $\psi(\alpha, \kappa, \zeta)$ is a continuous function of α, κ, and ζ throughout the region

$$0 \leqq \alpha \leqq \alpha(\delta, \kappa), \qquad k_1 \leqq \kappa \leqq k_2, \qquad \bar{a} \leqq \zeta \leqq \bar{b}. \tag{4.10}$$

For fixed values of κ we obtain this result by applying Lemma I of [12], with ε^{-1} in the role of u, $\frac{1}{2}(z_2 - z_1)$ in the role of a, and $x - \frac{1}{2}(z_1 + z_2)$ in the role of x, and using Lemma 3.1 above to verify that the requisite conditions are satisfied. The added properties of continuity with respect to ε and κ in the case of $\alpha(\varepsilon, \kappa)$, or continuity with respect of α, κ, and ζ in the case of $\psi(\alpha, \kappa, \zeta)$, are verifiable by repeating the steps in the proof of Lemma I of [12] in a straightforward manner.

We shall need asymptotic approximations to the values of α and ζ when ε is small. These estimates are supplied by the next two lemmas.

LEMMA 4.2. *As $\varepsilon \to 0$*

$$\alpha^2 = \kappa\varepsilon + O(\varepsilon^2), \tag{4.11}$$

uniformly with respect to $\kappa \in [k_1, k_2]$.

On substituting in (4.02) by means of (3.05), we obtain

$$\alpha^2 = \frac{2}{\pi} \int_{z_1}^{z_2} \{(z_2 - x)(x - z_1)\}^{1/2} \{p(\varepsilon, \kappa, x)\}^{1/2}\, dx.$$

When $x \in [z_1, z_2]$, we have $x = O(\varepsilon^{1/2})$; compare (3.04). Hence from Taylor's theorem and Lemmas 3.1 and 3.2, we find that

$$\begin{aligned} p(\varepsilon, \kappa, x) &= p(\varepsilon, \kappa, 0) + xp'(\varepsilon, \kappa, 0) + O(x^2) \\ &= \phi^2(0) + xp'(\varepsilon, \kappa, 0) + O(\varepsilon), \end{aligned} \tag{4.12}$$

the last O-term being uniform with respect to κ and x. Therefore

$$\alpha^2 = \frac{2}{\pi} \int_{z_1}^{z_2} \{(z_2 - x)(x - z_1)\}^{1/2} \left\{ \phi(0) + \frac{xp'(\varepsilon, \kappa, 0)}{2\phi(0)} + O(\varepsilon) \right\} dx. \tag{4.13}$$

We now make the substitutions

$$x = \tfrac{1}{2}(z_1 + z_2) + v, \qquad z = \tfrac{1}{2}(z_2 - z_1), \tag{4.14}$$

and note that

$$z = \{\kappa\varepsilon/\phi(0)\}^{1/2} + O(\varepsilon^{3/2}); \tag{4.15}$$

compare (3.04). Then

$$\frac{2}{\pi} \int_{z_1}^{z_2} \{(z_2 - x)(x - z_1)\}^{1/2}\, dx = \frac{2}{\pi} \int_{-z}^{z} (z^2 - v^2)^{1/2}\, dv = z^2 = \frac{\kappa\varepsilon}{\phi(0)} + O(\varepsilon^2),$$

and

$$\frac{2}{\pi}\int_{z_1}^{z_2}\{(z_2-x)(x-z_1)\}^{1/2}x\,dx=\frac{2}{\pi}\int_{-z}^{z}(z^2-v^2)^{1/2}\{\tfrac{1}{2}(z_1+z_2)+v\}\,dv$$

$$=\tfrac{1}{2}z^2(z_1+z_2)=O(\varepsilon^2).$$

Substitution of these results in (4.13) yields the required result (4.11).

LEMMA 4.3. *As* $\varepsilon\to 0$

$$\alpha^2=\kappa\varepsilon+\theta(\varepsilon,\kappa)\varepsilon^2+O(\varepsilon^{5/2}),\tag{4.16}$$

uniformly with respect to κ, *where* $\theta(\varepsilon,\kappa)$ *is continuous in the rectangle*

$$0\leqq\varepsilon\leqq\delta,\qquad k_1\leqq\kappa\leqq k_2.$$

To prove this result, we repeat the steps of the proof of Lemma 4.2, retaining more terms in the expansions. Thus in place of (4.12), we use

$$p(\varepsilon,\kappa,x)=\phi^2(0)+xp'(\varepsilon,\kappa,0)+\tfrac{1}{2}x^2p''(\varepsilon,\kappa,0)+O(\varepsilon^{3/2});$$

compare again Lemma 3.1. Also, the form of the next term in each of the expansions (3.04) is obtained by replacing the error terms $O(\varepsilon^{3/2})$ by $\mp Z(\kappa)\varepsilon^{3/2}+O(\varepsilon^2)$, where $Z(\kappa)$ is a continuous function of κ. Further details are straightforward, and need not be recorded.

LEMMA 4.4. *As* $\varepsilon\to 0$

$$\tfrac{1}{2}\zeta^2=|P(x)|+O(\varepsilon),\tag{4.17}$$

where $P(x)$ *is defined by* (2.08) *and the* O*-term is uniform with respect to* $\kappa\in[k_1,k_2]$ *and* $x\in[a,b]$.

Suppose first that $x\in[z_2,b]$. Then $\zeta\in[\alpha,\bar{b}]$, and the relation between x and ζ is expressed by (4.04). The right-hand side of this equation is evaluable in closed form; thus

$$\int_\alpha^\zeta(\tau^2-\alpha^2)^{1/2}\,d\tau=-\frac{1}{2}\alpha^2\ln\left(\frac{\zeta}{\alpha}\right)-\frac{1}{2}\alpha^2\ln\left\{1+\left(1-\frac{\alpha^2}{\zeta^2}\right)^{1/2}\right\}+\frac{1}{2}\zeta^2\left(1-\frac{\alpha^2}{\zeta^2}\right)^{1/2}.$$

Since $\zeta\geqq\alpha$, it follows that

$$\int_\alpha^\zeta(\tau^2-\alpha^2)^{1/2}\,d\tau=-\frac{1}{2}\alpha^2\ln\left(\frac{\zeta}{\alpha}\right)+\frac{1}{2}\zeta^2+O(\alpha^2)\tag{4.18}$$

as $\alpha\to 0$. Here and in the rest of the proof the O-symbol is understood to be uniform with respect to all variables.

To approximate the left-hand side of (4.04), we substitute by means of (3.05) and use Lemma 3.2. This yields

$$\int_{z_2}^x\{f(\varepsilon,\kappa,t)\}^{1/2}\,dt=\int_{z_2}^x\{(t-z_1)(t-z_2)\}^{1/2}\phi(t)\,dt+O(\varepsilon).$$

On making the substitutions (4.14), with x replaced by t, we obtain

$$\int_{z_2}^x\{f(\varepsilon,\kappa,t)\}^{1/2}\,dt=\int_z^{x-(1/2)(z_1+z_2)}(v^2-z^2)^{1/2}\phi\{\tfrac{1}{2}(z_1+z_2)+v\}\,dv+O(\varepsilon).$$

Since $z_1+z_2=O(\varepsilon)$, this gives

$$\int_{z_2}^{x}\{f(\varepsilon,\kappa,t)\}^{1/2}\,dt=\int_{z}^{x}(v^2-z^2)^{1/2}\phi(v)\,dv+O(\varepsilon)$$

$$=J_1+J_2-J_3+O(\varepsilon),$$

where

$$J_1=\int_{z}^{x}(v^2-z^2)^{1/2}\phi(0)\,dv,\qquad J_2=\int_{z}^{x}v\{\phi(v)-\phi(0)\}\,dv,$$

$$J_3=\int_{z}^{x}\{v-(v^2-z^2)^{1/2}\}\{\phi(v)-\phi(0)\}\,dv.$$

By comparing with (4.18) and recalling that $z=O(\varepsilon^{1/2})$, we see that

$$J_1=\phi(0)\left\{-\frac{1}{2}z^2\ln\left(\frac{x}{z}\right)+\frac{1}{2}x^2\right\}+O(\varepsilon).$$

Secondly,

$$J_2=\int_{0}^{x}v\{\phi(v)-\phi(0)\}\,dv+O(\varepsilon)=\int_{0}^{x}v\phi(v)\,dv-\frac{1}{2}\phi(0)x^2+O(\varepsilon).$$

Thirdly,

$$|J_3|\leqq z^2\int_{z}^{x}\frac{|\phi(v)-\phi(0)|}{v}\,dv\leqq z^2\int_{0}^{x}\frac{|\phi(v)-\phi(0)|}{v}\,dv=O(\varepsilon).$$

Combining these results we obtain

$$\int_{z_2}^{x}\{f(\varepsilon,\kappa,t)\}^{1/2}\,dt=\int_{0}^{x}v\phi(v)\,dv-\frac{1}{2}\phi(0)z^2\ln\left(\frac{x}{z}\right)+O(\varepsilon).$$

In consequence of (4.04), the right-hand side of this relation may be equated to the right-hand side of (4.18). On using Lemma 4.2 and (4.15), we then find that

$$\tfrac{1}{2}\zeta^2=\int_{0}^{x}v\phi(v)\,dv+\tfrac{1}{2}\kappa\varepsilon\ln\left(\frac{\zeta}{x}\right)+O(\varepsilon). \tag{4.19}$$

We now refer to the equation

$$\frac{dx}{d\zeta}=\left\{\frac{\zeta^2-\alpha^2}{(x-z_1)(x-z_2)}\right\}^{1/2}\frac{1}{\{p(\varepsilon,\kappa,x)\}^{1/2}}, \tag{4.20}$$

obtained from (3.05) and (4.01). From the proof of Lemma I of [12] used in establishing Lemma 4.1, it is immediately seen that the right-hand side of (4.20) is continuous and positive. Therefore $dx/d\zeta$ is bounded, and also bounded away from zero. By integration, it follows that $(x-z_2)/(\zeta-\alpha)$ and $(\zeta-\alpha)/(x-z_2)$ are both bounded. Using (3.04) and Lemma 4.2 we then see that x/ζ and ζ/x are both bounded, and hence that $|\ln(\zeta/x)|$ is bounded. Therefore from (4.19)

$$\tfrac{1}{2}\zeta^2=\int_{0}^{x}v\phi(v)\,dv+O(\varepsilon)=|P(x)|+O(\varepsilon);$$

compare (2.08) and (3.01).

We have therefore established the required result (4.17) when $x \in [z_2, b]$. An exactly similar proof holds when $x \in [a, z_1]$. Lastly, if $x \in [z_1, z_2]$, then $|\zeta| \leqq \alpha$ and hence from Lemma 4.2 $\frac{1}{2}\zeta^2$ is $O(\varepsilon)$. Also $P(x)$ is $O(x^2)$ and therefore $O(\varepsilon)$. Thus (4.17) again applies. This completes the proof of Lemma 4.4.

5. Uniform approximations to the solution of the boundary-value problem. Instead of applying the approximation theorems of [12] directly to the differential equation (4.07), we first modify this equation in the following manner. Write

$$\bar{\psi}(\varepsilon, \kappa, \zeta) = \psi(\alpha, \kappa, \zeta) + \varepsilon^{-2}(\kappa\varepsilon - \alpha^2). \tag{5.01}$$

Then (4.07) becomes

$$d^2W/d\zeta^2 = \{\varepsilon^{-2}(\zeta^2 - \kappa\varepsilon) + \bar{\psi}(\varepsilon, \kappa, \zeta)\}W, \tag{5.02}$$

and from Lemmas 4.1 and 4.3 it follows that $\bar{\psi}(\varepsilon, \kappa, \zeta)$ is a continuous function of its arguments.

Applying Theorem I of [12] to (5.02) and using the same notation as in this reference, we deduce that there are solutions $W_1(\zeta) \equiv W_1(\varepsilon, \kappa, \zeta)$ and $W_2(\zeta) \equiv W_2(\varepsilon, \kappa, \zeta)$ having the following forms in the interval $0 \leqq \zeta \leqq \bar{b}$:

$$W_1(\zeta) = U(\zeta\sqrt{2/\varepsilon}) + \eta_1(\zeta), \qquad W_2(\zeta) = \bar{U}(\zeta\sqrt{2/\varepsilon}) + \eta_2(\zeta), \tag{5.03}$$

where the error terms $\eta_1(\zeta) \equiv \eta_1(\varepsilon, \kappa, \zeta)$ and $\eta_2(\zeta) \equiv \eta_2(\varepsilon, \kappa, \zeta)$ are subject to the bounds

(5.04)

$$\frac{|\eta_1(\zeta)|}{\mathbf{M}(\zeta\sqrt{2/\varepsilon})}, \frac{|\eta_1'(\zeta)|}{(2/\varepsilon)^{1/2}\mathbf{N}(\zeta\sqrt{2/\varepsilon})} \leqq \mathbf{E}^{-1}(\zeta\sqrt{2/\varepsilon})[\exp\{\tfrac{1}{2}(\pi\varepsilon)^{1/2}l_1(-\tfrac{1}{2}\kappa)\mathcal{V}_{\zeta,\bar{b}}(F)\} - 1],$$

(5.05)

$$\frac{|\eta_2(\zeta)|}{\mathbf{M}(\zeta\sqrt{2/\varepsilon})}, \frac{|\eta_2'(\zeta)|}{(2/\varepsilon)^{1/2}\mathbf{N}(\zeta\sqrt{2/\varepsilon})} \leqq \mathbf{E}(\zeta\sqrt{2/\varepsilon})[\exp\{\tfrac{1}{2}(\pi\varepsilon)^{1/2}l_1(-\tfrac{1}{2}\kappa)\mathcal{V}_{0,\zeta}(F)\} - 1].$$

Here, and subsequently, $\eta_1'(\zeta)$ and $\eta_2'(\zeta)$ denote $\partial\eta_1/\partial\zeta$ and $\partial\eta_2/\partial\zeta$ respectively, and we have suppressed the argument parameter $-\frac{1}{2}\kappa$ of the parabolic cylinder functions U and $\bar{U}$ and also of the auxiliary functions $\mathbf{E}$, $\mathbf{M}$, and $\mathbf{N}$; thus

$$U(\zeta\sqrt{2/\varepsilon}) \equiv U(-\tfrac{1}{2}\kappa, \zeta\sqrt{2/\varepsilon}),$$

and so on. The error-control function $F \equiv F(\varepsilon, \kappa, \zeta)$ is defined by

$$F(\varepsilon, \kappa, \zeta) = \int \frac{\bar{\psi}(\varepsilon, \kappa, \zeta)}{\Omega(\zeta\sqrt{2/\varepsilon})} d\zeta, \tag{5.06}$$

with the balancing function $\Omega(t)$ subject to the conditions prescribed in [12, § 6.1].

On taking $\Omega(t)$ to be $1 + |t|$ and observing from Lemma 4.4 that $\bar{b}$ is bounded, we see that

$$\mathcal{V}_{0,\bar{b}}(F) = \int_0^{\bar{b}} \frac{|\bar{\psi}(\varepsilon, \kappa, t)|}{1 + t\sqrt{2/\varepsilon}} dt$$

$$= O(1)\int_0^{\bar{b}} \frac{dt}{1 + t\sqrt{2/\varepsilon}} = O\{\varepsilon^{1/2}\ln(1/\varepsilon)\}$$

as $\varepsilon \to 0$, uniformly with respect to $\kappa \in [k_1, k_2]$. Next, the function $l_1(-\frac{1}{2}\kappa)$ is continuous in κ, and therefore bounded. Substituting in (5.04) and (5.05) by means of these results we conclude that

$$\begin{aligned}\eta_1(\zeta) &= \mathbf{E}^{-1}(\zeta\sqrt{2/\varepsilon})\mathbf{M}(\zeta\sqrt{2/\varepsilon})O(\hat{\varepsilon}),\\ \eta_1'(\zeta) &= \varepsilon^{-1/2}\mathbf{E}^{-1}(\zeta\sqrt{2/\varepsilon})\mathbf{N}(\zeta\sqrt{2/\varepsilon})O(\hat{\varepsilon}),\\ \eta_2(\zeta) &= \mathbf{E}(\zeta\sqrt{2/\varepsilon})\mathbf{M}(\zeta\sqrt{2/\varepsilon})O(\hat{\varepsilon}),\\ \eta_2'(\zeta) &= \varepsilon^{-1/2}\mathbf{E}(\zeta\sqrt{2/\varepsilon})\mathbf{N}(\zeta\sqrt{2/\varepsilon})O(\hat{\varepsilon}),\end{aligned} \tag{5.07}$$

as $\varepsilon \to 0$ uniformly with respect to $\kappa \in [k_1, k_2]$ and $\zeta \in [0, \bar{b}]$, where

$$\hat{\varepsilon} = \varepsilon \ln(1/\varepsilon). \tag{5.08}$$

We also note here the properties

$$\eta_1(\bar{b}) = \eta_1'(\bar{b}) = 0, \qquad \eta_2(0) = \eta_2'(0) = 0, \tag{5.09}$$

obtained from (5.04) and (5.05) by setting $\zeta = \bar{b}$ and 0, respectively.

In a similar manner, by applying Theorem I of [12] to (5.02) with ζ replaced by $-\zeta$, we deduce that in the interval $\bar{a} \leqq \zeta \leqq 0$ there are solutions $W_3(\zeta) \equiv W_3(\varepsilon, \kappa, \zeta)$ and $W_4(\zeta) \equiv W_4(\varepsilon, \kappa, \zeta)$, given by

$$W_3(\zeta) = U(-\zeta\sqrt{2/\varepsilon}) + \eta_3(\zeta), \qquad W_4(\zeta) = \bar{U}(-\zeta\sqrt{2/\varepsilon}) + \eta_4(\zeta), \tag{5.10}$$

where

$$\begin{aligned}\eta_3(\zeta) &= \mathbf{E}^{-1}(-\zeta\sqrt{2/\varepsilon})\mathbf{M}(-\zeta\sqrt{2/\varepsilon})O(\hat{\varepsilon}),\\ \eta_3'(\zeta) &= \varepsilon^{-1/2}\mathbf{E}^{-1}(-\zeta\sqrt{2/\varepsilon})\mathbf{N}(-\zeta\sqrt{2/\varepsilon})O(\hat{\varepsilon}),\\ \eta_4(\zeta) &= \mathbf{E}(-\zeta\sqrt{2/\varepsilon})\mathbf{M}(-\zeta\sqrt{2/\varepsilon})O(\hat{\varepsilon}),\\ \eta_4'(\zeta) &= \varepsilon^{-1/2}\mathbf{E}(-\zeta\sqrt{2/\varepsilon})\mathbf{N}(-\zeta\sqrt{2/\varepsilon})O(\hat{\varepsilon}),\end{aligned} \tag{5.11}$$

as $\varepsilon \to 0$ uniformly with respect to $\kappa \in [k_1, k_2]$ and $\zeta \in [\bar{a}, 0]$. Furthermore,

$$\eta_3(\bar{a}) = \eta_3'(\bar{a}) = 0, \qquad \eta_4(0) = \eta_4'(0) = 0. \tag{5.12}$$

To determine the boundary conditions for (5.02) we require the values of $\dot{x}^{-1/2}$ at the endpoints. Using (3.02), (4.01), Lemma 4.2, and Lemma 4.4, and recalling that $\phi(x) = |A_0(x)|$, we find that

$$\dot{x}^2 = 2\{aA_0(a)\}^{-2}|P(a)| + O(\varepsilon) \quad \text{at } x = a,$$

$$\dot{x}^2 = 2\{bA_0(b)\}^{-2}|P(b)| + O(\varepsilon) \quad \text{at } x = b.$$

From these results and equations (2.10), (2.11), and (4.06) it follows that the wanted solution $W(\zeta) \equiv W(\varepsilon, \kappa, \zeta)$ of (5.02) satisfies the conditions

$$W(\bar{a}) = \bar{l}\,e^{P(a)/\varepsilon}(1+\lambda), \qquad W(\bar{b}) = \bar{m}\,e^{P(b)/\varepsilon}(1+\mu), \tag{5.13}$$

where $\bar{l}$ and $\bar{m}$ are constants given by

$$\bar{l} = |aA_0(a)|^{1/2}|2P(a)|^{-1/4}\,e^{Q(a)}l, \qquad \bar{m} = |bA_0(b)|^{1/2}|2P(b)|^{-1/4}\,e^{Q(b)}m, \tag{5.14}$$

and λ and μ are functions of ε and κ with the properties

$$\lambda = O(\varepsilon), \qquad \mu = O(\varepsilon), \tag{5.15}$$

as $\varepsilon \to 0$, uniformly with respect to κ. We now write

$$\begin{aligned} W(\zeta) &= \Lambda_1 W_1(\zeta) + \Lambda_2 W_2(\zeta), \qquad 0 \leqq \zeta \leqq \bar{b}, \\ W(\zeta) &= \Lambda_3 W_3(\zeta) + \Lambda_4 W_4(\zeta), \qquad \bar{a} \leqq \zeta \leqq 0, \end{aligned} \tag{5.16}$$

where the coefficients Λ_1, Λ_2, Λ_3, and Λ_4 are to be determined.

When $\zeta = 0$, the properties of the parabolic cylinder functions and the auxiliary functions given in [12, § 5] show that $\mathbf{E}(0) = 1$ and

$$\begin{aligned} U(0) &= \mathbf{M}(0) \sin \beta, \qquad U'(0) = -\mathbf{N}(0) \cos \beta, \\ \bar{U}(0) &= \mathbf{M}(0) \cos \beta, \qquad \bar{U}'(0) = \mathbf{N}(0) \sin \beta, \end{aligned} \tag{5.17}$$

where

$$\beta = \tfrac{1}{4}\pi(1+\kappa). \tag{5.18}$$

From (5.03), (5.09), (5.10), (5.12), and (5.17), we obtain

$$\begin{aligned} W_1(0) &= \mathbf{M}(0)\,(\sin \beta + \rho_1), \qquad & W_1'(0) &= -(2/\varepsilon)^{1/2}\mathbf{N}(0)(\cos \beta + \sigma_1), \\ W_2(0) &= \mathbf{M}(0) \cos \beta, & W_2'(0) &= (2/\varepsilon)^{1/2}\mathbf{N}(0) \sin \beta, \\ W_3(0) &= \mathbf{M}(0)(\sin \beta + \rho_3), & W_3'(0) &= (2/\varepsilon)^{1/2}\mathbf{N}(0)(\cos \beta + \sigma_3), \\ W_4(0) &= \mathbf{M}(0) \cos \beta, & W_4'(0) &= -(2/\varepsilon)^{1/2}\mathbf{N}(0) \sin \beta, \end{aligned}$$

where

$$\begin{aligned} \rho_1 &= \frac{\eta_1(0)}{\mathbf{M}(0)}, \qquad \sigma_1 = -\left(\frac{\varepsilon}{2}\right)^{1/2} \frac{\eta_1'(0)}{\mathbf{N}(0)}, \\ \rho_3 &= \frac{\eta_3(0)}{\mathbf{M}(0)}, \qquad \sigma_3 = \left(\frac{\varepsilon}{2}\right)^{1/2} \frac{\eta_3'(0)}{\mathbf{N}(0)}. \end{aligned} \tag{5.19}$$

Thus ρ_1, σ_1, ρ_3, and σ_3 are functions of ε and κ, and from (5.07) and (5.11) it follows that

$$\rho_1, \sigma_1, \rho_3, \sigma_3 = O(\hat{\varepsilon}) \tag{5.20}$$

as $\varepsilon \to 0$, uniformly with respect to κ.

On referring to (5.16) and matching the solutions and their ζ-derivatives at $\zeta = 0$, we obtain

$$\begin{aligned} \Lambda_1(\sin \beta + \rho_1) + \Lambda_2 \cos \beta &= \Lambda_3(\sin \beta + \rho_3) + \Lambda_4 \cos \beta, \\ -\Lambda_1(\cos \beta + \sigma_1) + \Lambda_2 \sin \beta &= \Lambda_3(\cos \beta + \sigma_3) - \Lambda_4 \sin \beta. \end{aligned}$$

The boundary conditions (5.13) yield

$$\Lambda_3 U(-\bar{a}\sqrt{2/\varepsilon}) + \Lambda_4 \bar{U}(-\bar{a}\sqrt{2/\varepsilon})(1+\nu_4) = \bar{l}\, e^{P(a)/\varepsilon}(1+\lambda),$$

$$\Lambda_1 U(\bar{b}\sqrt{2/\varepsilon}) + \Lambda_2 \bar{U}(\bar{b}\sqrt{2/\varepsilon})(1+\nu_2) = \bar{m}\, e^{P(b)/\varepsilon}(1+\mu),$$

where ν_2 and ν_4 denote the quantities

$$\nu_2 = \eta_2(\bar{b})/\bar{U}(\bar{b}\sqrt{2/\varepsilon}), \qquad \nu_4 = \eta_4(\bar{a})/\bar{U}(-\bar{a}\sqrt{2/\varepsilon}). \tag{5.21}$$

From (5.07), (5.11), and the properties of the auxiliary functions **E** and **M** given in [12, § 5.8], we see that

(5.22) $$\nu_2,\ \nu_4 = O(\hat{\varepsilon})$$

as $\varepsilon \to 0$, uniformly with respect to κ.

Solving the four simultaneous equations just given for Λ_1, Λ_2, Λ_3, and Λ_4, we obtain, after a straightforward calculation,

(5.23) $$\begin{aligned} D\Lambda_1 &= \bar{m}\, e^{P(b)/\varepsilon}(1+\mu)\sin 2\beta\, U(-\bar{a}\sqrt{2/\varepsilon}) \\ &\quad + \bar{m}\, e^{P(b)/\varepsilon}(1+\mu)(\cos 2\beta + \sigma_3\cos\beta - \rho_3\sin\beta)(1+\nu_4)\bar{U}(-\bar{a}\sqrt{2/\varepsilon}) \\ &\quad - \bar{l}\, e^{P(a)/\varepsilon}(1+\lambda)(1+\sigma_3\cos\beta + \rho_3\sin\beta)(1+\nu_2)\bar{U}(\bar{b}\sqrt{2/\varepsilon}), \end{aligned}$$

(5.24) $$\begin{aligned} D\Lambda_2 &= \bar{l}\, e^{P(a)/\varepsilon}(1+\lambda)(1+\sigma_3\cos\beta + \rho_3\sin\beta)U(\bar{b}\sqrt{2/\varepsilon}) \\ &\quad + \bar{m}\, e^{P(b)/\varepsilon}(1+\mu)(\cos 2\beta + \sigma_1\cos\beta - \rho_1\sin\beta)U(-\bar{a}\sqrt{2/\varepsilon}) \\ &\quad - \bar{m}\, e^{P(b)/\varepsilon}(1+\mu) \\ &\qquad \cdot \{\sin 2\beta + (\rho_1+\rho_3)\cos\beta + (\sigma_1+\sigma_3)\sin\beta + \rho_1\sigma_3 + \rho_3\sigma_1\} \\ &\qquad \cdot (1+\nu_4)\bar{U}(-\bar{a}\sqrt{2/\varepsilon}), \end{aligned}$$

(5.25) $$\begin{aligned} D\Lambda_3 &= \bar{l}\, e^{P(a)/\varepsilon}(1+\lambda)\sin 2\beta\, U(\bar{b}\sqrt{2/\varepsilon}) \\ &\quad + \bar{l}\, e^{P(a)/\varepsilon}(1+\lambda)(\cos 2\beta + \sigma_1\cos\beta - \rho_1\sin\beta)(1+\nu_2)\bar{U}(\bar{b}\sqrt{2/\varepsilon}) \\ &\quad - \bar{m}\, e^{P(b)/\varepsilon}(1+\mu)(1+\sigma_1\cos\beta + \rho_1\sin\beta)(1+\nu_4)\bar{U}(-\bar{a}\sqrt{2/\varepsilon}), \end{aligned}$$

(5.26) $$\begin{aligned} D\Lambda_4 &= \bar{m}\, e^{P(b)/\varepsilon}(1+\mu)(1+\sigma_1\cos\beta + \rho_1\sin\beta)U(-\bar{a}\sqrt{2/\varepsilon}) \\ &\quad + \bar{l}\, e^{P(a)/\varepsilon}(1+\lambda)(\cos 2\beta + \sigma_3\cos\beta - \rho_3\sin\beta)U(\bar{b}\sqrt{2/\varepsilon}) \\ &\quad - \bar{l}\, e^{P(a)/\varepsilon}(1+\lambda) \\ &\qquad \cdot \{\sin 2\beta + (\rho_1+\rho_3)\cos\beta + (\sigma_1+\sigma_3)\sin\beta + \rho_1\sigma_3 + \rho_3\sigma_1\} \\ &\qquad \cdot (1+\nu_2)\bar{U}(\bar{b}\sqrt{2/\varepsilon}), \end{aligned}$$

where

(5.27) $$\begin{aligned} D &= \sin 2\beta\, U(-\bar{a}\sqrt{2/\varepsilon})U(\bar{b}\sqrt{2/\varepsilon}) \\ &\quad + (\cos 2\beta + \sigma_1\cos\beta - \rho_1\sin\beta)(1+\nu_2)U(-\bar{a}\sqrt{2/\varepsilon})\bar{U}(\bar{b}\sqrt{2/\varepsilon}) \\ &\quad + (\cos 2\beta + \sigma_3\cos\beta - \rho_3\sin\beta)(1+\nu_4)\bar{U}(-\bar{a}\sqrt{2/\varepsilon})U(\bar{b}\sqrt{2/\varepsilon}) \\ &\quad - \{\sin 2\beta + (\rho_1+\rho_3)\cos\beta + (\sigma_1+\sigma_3)\sin\beta + \rho_1\sigma_3 + \rho_3\sigma_1\} \\ &\qquad \cdot (1+\nu_2)(1+\nu_4)\bar{U}(-\bar{a}\sqrt{2/\varepsilon})\bar{U}(\bar{b}\sqrt{2/\varepsilon}). \end{aligned}$$

These results supply the desired formulas for the coefficients Λ_1, Λ_2, Λ_3, and Λ_4 in the expressions (5.16) for the wanted solution $W(\zeta)$. This solution is related to that of the original boundary-value problem of § 2 via

$$y(x)=\exp\left\{-\frac{1}{\varepsilon}\int_0^x tA(\varepsilon,t)\,dt\right\}\dot{x}^{1/2}W(\zeta); \tag{5.28}$$

compare (2.03) and (4.06). Hence from (2.09) and (5.16) we have

$$y(x)=\{1+O(\varepsilon)\}\dot{x}^{1/2}e^{-Q(x)}e^{-P(x)/\varepsilon}\{\Lambda_1W_1(\zeta)+\Lambda_2W_2(\zeta)\},\qquad 0\leqq x\leqq b,$$

and

$$y(x)=\{1+O(\varepsilon)\}\dot{x}^{1/2}e^{-Q(x)}e^{-P(x)/\varepsilon}\{\Lambda_3W_3(\zeta)+\Lambda_4W_4(\zeta)\},\qquad a\leqq x\leqq 0,$$

where the O-terms are uniform with respect to κ and x. In the proof of Lemma 4.4 we noted that $\dot{x}$ and its reciprocal are continuous and bounded for all values of the variables. In consequence, *as $\varepsilon\to 0$ the asymptotic rate of growth (or decay) of the solution $y(x)$ is governed entirely by that of the functions*

$$\Lambda_1e^{-P(x)/\varepsilon}W_1(\zeta)+\Lambda_2e^{-P(x)/\varepsilon}W_2(\zeta) \tag{5.29}$$

when $0\leqq x\leqq b$, or

$$\Lambda_3e^{-P(x)/\varepsilon}W_3(\zeta)+\Lambda_4e^{-P(x)/\varepsilon}W_4(\zeta) \tag{5.30}$$

when $a\leqq x\leqq 0$.

Investigation of this growth forms the subject of the next three sections. Because we shall have frequent need of asymptotic estimates for the parabolic cylinder functions, we collect the relevant results here for reference.

By combining Lemma 4.4 with the asymptotic forms of the parabolic cylinder functions of large positive argument given in [10, Chap. 19] or [12, § 5.2], and remembering that the argument parameter of each of these functions is $-\frac{1}{2}\kappa$, we derive

$$\begin{aligned}U(|\zeta|\sqrt{2/\varepsilon})&=\varepsilon^{(1-\kappa)/4}e^{-|P(x)|/\varepsilon}e^{O(1)},\\ \bar{U}(|\zeta|\sqrt{2/\varepsilon})&=\varepsilon^{(1+\kappa)/4}e^{|P(x)|/\varepsilon}e^{O(1)},\end{aligned} \tag{5.31}$$

as $\varepsilon\to 0$, uniformly with respect to κ and x, *provided that $\kappa\in[k_1,k_2]$ and $|x|$ is bounded away from zero.* In the same circumstances,

$$\begin{aligned}\mathbf{E}^{-1}(|\zeta|\sqrt{2/\varepsilon})\mathbf{M}(|\zeta|\sqrt{2/\varepsilon})&=\varepsilon^{(1-\kappa)/4}e^{-|P(x)|/\varepsilon}e^{O(1)},\\ \mathbf{E}(|\zeta|\sqrt{2/\varepsilon})\mathbf{M}(|\zeta|\sqrt{2/\varepsilon})&=\varepsilon^{(1+\kappa)/4}e^{|P(x)|/\varepsilon}e^{O(1)}.\end{aligned} \tag{5.32}$$

Particular cases of (5.31) are given by

$$\begin{aligned}U(-\bar{a}\sqrt{2/\varepsilon})&=\varepsilon^{(1-\kappa)/4}e^{-|P(a)|/\varepsilon}e^{O(1)},\\ \bar{U}(-\bar{a}\sqrt{2/\varepsilon})&=\varepsilon^{(1+\kappa)/4}e^{|P(a)|/\varepsilon}e^{O(1)},\end{aligned} \tag{5.33}$$

$$\begin{aligned}U(\bar{b}\sqrt{2/\varepsilon})&=\varepsilon^{(1-\kappa)/4}e^{-|P(b)|/\varepsilon}e^{O(1)},\\ \bar{U}(\bar{b}\sqrt{2/\varepsilon})&=\varepsilon^{(1+\kappa)/4}e^{|P(b)|/\varepsilon}e^{O(1)},\end{aligned} \tag{5.34}$$

valid when $\varepsilon\to 0$, uniformly with respect to κ.

For the full interval $x \in [a, b]$, we have the weaker estimates

$$U(|\zeta|\sqrt{2/\varepsilon}) = \varepsilon^{(1-\kappa_1)/4} e^{-|P(x)|/\varepsilon} O(1), \qquad (5.35)$$
$$\bar{U}(|\zeta|\sqrt{2/\varepsilon}) = e^{|P(x)|/\varepsilon} O(1),$$

$$\mathbf{E}^{-1}(|\zeta|\sqrt{2/\varepsilon})\mathbf{M}(|\zeta|\sqrt{2/\varepsilon}) = \varepsilon^{(1-\kappa_1)/4} e^{-|P(x)|/\varepsilon} O(1), \qquad (5.36)$$
$$\mathbf{E}(|\zeta|\sqrt{2/\varepsilon})\mathbf{M}(|\zeta|\sqrt{2/\varepsilon}) = e^{|P(x)|/\varepsilon} O(1),$$

valid when $\varepsilon \to 0$, uniformly with respect to κ and x, where

$$\kappa_1 = \max(\kappa, 1). \qquad (5.37)$$

6. Conditions for resonance: Case $A_0(x)$ negative. In this section we use the expressions (5.29) and (5.30) to investigate the asymptotic behavior of the solution of the boundary-value problem of § 2 in the case when the coefficient $A_0(x)$ in (2.01) is negative throughout the given x-interval $[a, b]$. From (2.08) we observe that this condition implies that the function $P(x)$ is negative for all values of x, other than $x = 0$.

Suppose first that the positive parameter κ is independent of ε and not an odd integer. From (5.18) and (2.02) it is seen that this implies both β and $B(0, 0)$ are fixed, $\sin 2\beta \neq 0$, and

$$B(0, 0) \neq 0, 2, 4, \cdots. \qquad (6.01)$$

Referring to (5.20), (5.22), (5.33), and (5.34), we observe that as $\varepsilon \to 0$ the dominant contribution to D in (5.27) derives from the last line; consequently

$$\frac{1}{D} = \frac{O(1)}{\bar{U}(-\bar{a}\sqrt{2/\varepsilon})\bar{U}(\bar{b}\sqrt{2/\varepsilon})}. \qquad (6.02)$$

Next, on substituting in (5.23) by means of (5.15), (5.20), and (5.22) and then referring to (5.33) we see that

$$D\Lambda_1 = O(1)\, e^{P(b)/\varepsilon} \bar{U}(-\bar{a}\sqrt{2/\varepsilon}) + O(1)\, e^{P(a)/\varepsilon} \bar{U}(\bar{b}\sqrt{2/\varepsilon}). \qquad (6.03)$$

Also, from (5.03) and (5.07) we obtain

$$W_1(\zeta) = O(1)\mathbf{E}^{-1}(\zeta\sqrt{2/\varepsilon})\mathbf{M}(\zeta\sqrt{2/\varepsilon}).$$

Combining the last three equations, we see that when $0 \leqq x \leqq b$

$$\Lambda_1 e^{-P(x)/\varepsilon} W_1(\zeta) = O(1)\frac{e^{\{P(b)-P(x)\}/\varepsilon}}{\bar{U}(\bar{b}\sqrt{2/\varepsilon})}\mathbf{E}^{-1}(\zeta\sqrt{2/\varepsilon})\mathbf{M}(\zeta\sqrt{2/\varepsilon}) \qquad (6.04)$$
$$+ O(1)\frac{e^{\{P(a)-P(x)\}/\varepsilon}}{\bar{U}(-\bar{a}\sqrt{2/\varepsilon})}\mathbf{E}^{-1}(\zeta\sqrt{2/\varepsilon})\mathbf{M}(\zeta\sqrt{2/\varepsilon}).$$

Using (5.33), (5.34), and (5.36), and bearing in mind that $P(x) = -|P(x)|$ throughout the present section, we find that

$$\Lambda_1 e^{-P(x)/\varepsilon} W_1(\zeta) = O(1)\varepsilon^{-(\kappa+\kappa_1)/4}\{e^{-2|P(b)|/\varepsilon} + e^{-2|P(a)|/\varepsilon}\}. \qquad (6.05)$$

This vanishes as $\varepsilon \to 0$, uniformly with respect to x.

Next, by similar analysis we obtain from (5.03), (5.07), (5.24), and (6.02)

(6.06) $$\Lambda_2 e^{-P(x)/\varepsilon} W_2(\zeta) = O(1)\frac{e^{\{P(b)-P(x)\}/\varepsilon}}{\bar{U}(\bar{b}\sqrt{2/\varepsilon})}\mathbf{E}(\zeta\sqrt{2/\varepsilon})\mathbf{M}(\zeta\sqrt{2/\varepsilon}),$$

and hence

(6.07) $$\Lambda_2 e^{-P(x)/\varepsilon} W_2(\zeta) = O(1)\varepsilon^{-(1+\kappa)/4} e^{2\{|P(x)|-|P(b)|\}/\varepsilon}.$$

Let b_1 be any constant such that $0<b_1<b$. Because $|P(x)|$ is increasing when x is positive, the right-hand side of (6.07) vanishes as $\varepsilon \to 0$, uniformly with respect to $x \in [0, b_1]$.

In a similar manner it is verifiable that $\Lambda_3 e^{-P(x)/\varepsilon} W_3(\zeta)$ vanishes uniformly in $[a, 0]$, and $\Lambda_4 e^{-P(x)/\varepsilon} W_4(\zeta)$ vanishes uniformly in $[a_1, 0]$, where a_1 is any constant such that $a<a_1<0$.

On combining the foregoing results we conclude that when κ is independent of ε and not an odd integer, the solution $y(x)$ of the boundary-value problem of § 2 vanishes as $\varepsilon \to 0$, uniformly in any closed interval properly interior to the given interval $[a, b]$. That is, there is no resonance in the sense defined in § 1. This conclusion is already well known from the theory of Ackerberg and O'Malley, given in [1], and also [14, Chap. 8].

In order to induce resonance it is clear that as a first step we must arrange for the contribution from the term in $\bar{U}(-\bar{a}\sqrt{2/\varepsilon})\bar{U}(\bar{b}\sqrt{2/\varepsilon})$ in the expression (5.27) for D not to dominate the other terms. This is achieved by imposing the condition[2]

(6.08) $$\sin 2\beta + (\rho_1+\rho_3)\cos\beta + (\sigma_1+\sigma_3)\sin\beta + \rho_1\sigma_3 + \rho_3\sigma_1 = O(e^{-2\varpi/\varepsilon}),$$

where ϖ is any constant such that

(6.09) $$\varpi > \max\{|P(a)|, |P(b)|\}.$$

The condition (6.08) is satisfied by relaxing the requirement that β and κ be independent of ε. Thus (6.08) is to be regarded as an equation for $\beta = \beta(\varepsilon)$, say, and the corresponding value of $\kappa = \kappa(\varepsilon)$ is given by (5.18). From (5.20) we see that for small values of ε the relevant roots are

(6.10) $$\beta = \tfrac{1}{2}s\pi + O(\hat{\varepsilon}),$$

where $s = 1, 2, 3, \cdots$ and $\hat{\varepsilon}$ is given by (5.08). Correspondingly,

(6.11) $$\kappa = 2s - 1 + O(\hat{\varepsilon}).$$

We note that for each value of s, neither the value of β nor that of κ is unique because of the freedom of choice allowed by inclusion of the O-term on the right-hand side of (6.08). All roots satisfy (6.10), however.

We now suppose that $\beta = \beta(\varepsilon)$ is prescribed in the manner just indicated, and distinguish three cases in subsequent analysis, given by $|P(a)| \gtreqless |P(b)|$. In examining these cases in turn, we continue to use the symbols a_1 and b_1 to denote any positive constants such that $a<a_1<0$ and $0<b_1<b$; in addition we use a_2 and b_2 to denote any constants such that $a_1<a_2<0$ and $0<b_2<b_1$.

Case I. $|P(a)|>|P(b)|$. In this case Lemma 4.4 shows that $|\bar{a}|>\bar{b}$ for all sufficiently small values of ε, and referring to (5.33), (5.34), (6.08), and (6.09) and substituting in (5.27) by means of (5.20), (5.22), and (6.10), we see that

(6.12) $$D = (-)^s\{1+O(\hat{\varepsilon})\}\bar{U}(-\bar{a}\sqrt{2/\varepsilon})U(\bar{b}\sqrt{2/\varepsilon}).$$

[2] The condition (6.08) is adequate for the present purposes, but it could be weakened somewhat without affecting the general conclusions.

From (5.23) we derive in a similar manner

$$D\Lambda_1=(-)^s\{1+O(\hat{\varepsilon})\}\bar{m}\,e^{P(b)/\varepsilon}\bar{U}(-\bar{a}\sqrt{2/\varepsilon})-\{1+O(\hat{\varepsilon})\}\bar{l}\,e^{P(a)/\varepsilon}\bar{U}(\bar{b}\sqrt{2/\varepsilon}). \tag{6.13}$$

Therefore

$$\begin{aligned}\Lambda_1\,e^{-P(x)/\varepsilon}W_1(\zeta)&=\{1+O(\hat{\varepsilon})\}\bar{m}\frac{e^{\{P(b)-P(x)\}/\varepsilon}}{U(\bar{b}\sqrt{2/\varepsilon})}\{U(\zeta\sqrt{2/\varepsilon})+\eta_1(\zeta)\}\\&\quad+(-)^{s-1}\{1+O(\hat{\varepsilon})\}\bar{l}\frac{e^{\{P(a)-P(x)\}/\varepsilon}\bar{U}(\bar{b}\sqrt{2/\varepsilon})}{\bar{U}(-\bar{a}\sqrt{2/\varepsilon})U(\bar{b}\sqrt{2/\varepsilon})}\{U(\zeta\sqrt{2/\varepsilon})+\eta_1(\zeta)\}.\end{aligned} \tag{6.14}$$

From (5.07), and also (5.33) through (5.36), the contribution from the second line is estimated by

$$O(1)\varepsilon^{(\kappa-\kappa_1)/4}\,e^{\{2|P(b)|-2|P(a)|\}/\varepsilon},$$

as $\varepsilon\to 0$, and therefore vanishes uniformly in $[0, b]$. On the other hand if $\bar{m}\neq 0$, that is (from (5.14)) if $m\neq 0$, then with the aid of (5.31) and (5.32) we see that in $[b_2, b]$ the contribution from the previous line is $e^{O(1)}$, that is, bounded and bounded away from zero.

Next, from (5.24), (6.08), and (6.10) we derive

$$\begin{aligned}D\Lambda_2&=\{1+O(\hat{\varepsilon})\}\bar{l}e^{P(a)/\varepsilon}U(\bar{b}\sqrt{2/\varepsilon})+(-)^s\{1+O(\hat{\varepsilon})\}\bar{m}\,e^{P(b)/\varepsilon}U(-\bar{a}\sqrt{2/\varepsilon})\\&\quad+O(e^{-2\varpi/\varepsilon})\,e^{P(b)/\varepsilon}\bar{U}(-\bar{a}\sqrt{2/\varepsilon}).\end{aligned} \tag{6.15}$$

Accordingly, from (5.33), (5.34), (6.09), and (6.12) it follows that

$$\Lambda_2=O(1)\,e^{P(a)/\varepsilon}/\bar{U}(-\bar{a}\sqrt{2/\varepsilon}).$$

Hence

$$\Lambda_2\,e^{-P(x)/\varepsilon}W_2(\zeta)=O(1)\frac{e^{\{P(a)-P(x)\}/\varepsilon}}{\bar{U}(-\bar{a}\sqrt{2/\varepsilon})}\mathbf{E}(\zeta\sqrt{2/\varepsilon})\mathbf{M}(\zeta\sqrt{2/\varepsilon}); \tag{6.16}$$

consequently

$$\Lambda_2\,e^{-P(x)/\varepsilon}W_2(\zeta)=O(1)\varepsilon^{-(1+\kappa)/4}\,e^{2\{|P(x)|-|P(a)|\}/\varepsilon}. \tag{6.17}$$

Since $|P(x)|\leqq|P(b)|$ this vanishes as $\varepsilon\to 0$, uniformly in $[0, b]$.

The behavior of the wanted solution in the interval $[a, 0]$ may be investigated in a similar manner. First, we find that as $\varepsilon\to 0$ the term $\Lambda_3\,e^{-P(x)/\varepsilon}W_3(\zeta)$ is bounded and bounded away from zero throughout $[a, a_2]$, unless $m=0$ in which event this term tends to zero uniformly in $[a, 0]$. Secondly, we find that $\Lambda_4\,e^{-P(x)/\varepsilon}W_4(\zeta)$ tends to zero uniformly in $[a_1, 0]$.

Combining the results for the intervals $[0, b]$ and $[a, 0]$ we reach the following conclusion: *when* $|P(a)|>|P(b)|$ *there is resonance if* $m\neq 0$ *but not if* $m=0$.

Case II. $|P(b)|>|P(a)|$. This case may be investigated in a similar manner to Case I, or the results can be deduced by symmetry. The conclusion is that *when* $|P(b)|>|P(a)|$ *there is resonance if* $l\neq 0$, *but not if* $l=0$.

Case III. $P(a)=P(b)$. In order to discuss this case we shall suppose that we know the value of $\gamma(a)-\gamma(b)$, where $\gamma(x)$ denotes the second coefficient in the expansion

$$\tfrac{1}{2}\zeta^2=|P(x)|+\gamma(x)\varepsilon+o(\varepsilon),\qquad \varepsilon\to 0; \tag{6.18}$$

compare Lemma 4.4. The value of $\gamma(a)-\gamma(b)$ can be found by extending the analysis of §§ 3 and 4, but we shall not pursue these details in the present paper. In passing, however, we note one special case in which the value of $\gamma(a)-\gamma(b)$ is already available. This is the case in which the coefficients $A(\varepsilon, x)$ and $B(\varepsilon, x)$ in (1.01) are even functions of x, and $a=-b$. In these circumstances the functions $f(\varepsilon, \kappa, x)$ and $P(x)$ are even in x, and $\zeta\equiv\zeta(x)$ is odd; in consequence $\gamma(a)-\gamma(b)=0$.

Returning to the general case, we see from Lemma 4.4 that when $P(a)=P(b)$ we have

$$\bar{a}=-\{1+O(\varepsilon)\}\bar{b}.$$

From this result, (6.18), and the asymptotic approximations for the parabolic cylinder functions of large positive argument, it follows that

$$U(-\bar{a}\sqrt{2/\varepsilon})=\{1+o(1)\}\,e^{\gamma(b)-\gamma(a)}U(\bar{b}\sqrt{2/\varepsilon}), \tag{6.19}$$

$$\bar{U}(-\bar{a}\sqrt{2/\varepsilon})=\{1+o(1)\}\,e^{\gamma(a)-\gamma(b)}\bar{U}(\bar{b}\sqrt{2/\varepsilon}). \tag{6.20}$$

Substituting in (5.27) by means of these approximations and using (6.08) and (6.10), we find that

$$D=(-)^s\{1+o(1)\}2\cosh\{\gamma(a)-\gamma(b)\}U(\bar{b}\sqrt{2/\varepsilon})\bar{U}(\bar{b}\sqrt{2/\varepsilon}). \tag{6.21}$$

The relation (6.13) remains valid in the present circumstances, and by referring to (6.20) we see that

$$D\Lambda_1=[(-)^s\{1+o(1)\}\bar{m}\,e^{\gamma(a)-\gamma(b)}-\{1+O(\hat{\varepsilon})\}\bar{l}\,]\,e^{P(b)/\varepsilon}\bar{U}(\bar{b}\sqrt{2/\varepsilon}). \tag{6.22}$$

We now impose the restriction

$$\bar{l}\neq(-)^s\bar{m}\,e^{\gamma(a)-\gamma(b)}, \tag{6.23}$$

that is,

$$l\,e^{Q(a)-\gamma(a)}|aA_0(a)|^{1/2}\neq(-)^s m\,e^{Q(b)-\gamma(b)}|bA_0(b)|^{1/2}; \tag{6.24}$$

compare (5.14). From (5.03), (6.21), and (6.22) we then obtain

$$\begin{aligned}\Lambda_1\,e^{-P(x)/\varepsilon}W_1(\zeta)&\\ &=\{1+o(1)\}\frac{\bar{m}\,e^{\gamma(a)-\gamma(b)}-(-)^s\bar{l}}{2\cosh\{\gamma(a)-\gamma(b)\}}\frac{e^{\{P(b)-P(x)\}/\varepsilon}}{U(\bar{b}\sqrt{2/\varepsilon})}\{U(\zeta\sqrt{2/\varepsilon})+\eta_1(\zeta)\}.\end{aligned} \tag{6.25}$$

As $\varepsilon\to 0$ this quantity is uniformly $e^{O(1)}$ in $[b_2, b]$.

Next, equation (6.15) remains valid. With the aid of (6.21) we deduce that

$$\Lambda_2=O(1)\,e^{P(b)/\varepsilon}/\bar{U}(\bar{b}\sqrt{2/\varepsilon}). \tag{6.26}$$

Accordingly,

$$\Lambda_2\,e^{-P(x)/\varepsilon}W_2(\zeta)=O(1)\varepsilon^{-(1+\kappa)/4}\,e^{2\{|P(x)|-|P(b)|\}/\varepsilon};$$

compare (6.17). This vanishes as $\varepsilon\to 0$, uniformly in $[0, b_1]$.

The analysis for the interval $[a, 0]$ is similar, and we find that as $\varepsilon \to 0$ the term $\Lambda_3 e^{-P(x)/\varepsilon} W_3(\zeta)$ is $e^{O(1)}$ uniformly in $[a, a_2]$, and the term $\Lambda_4 e^{-P(x)/\varepsilon} W_4(\zeta)$ vanishes uniformly in $[a_1, 0]$.

On combining the foregoing results we conclude that *when* $P(a) = P(b)$, *resonance takes place, provided that the condition* (6.23) (*or* (6.24)) *is satisfied.*

The problem is more difficult when

$$\bar{l} = (-)^s \bar{m}\, e^{\gamma(a)-\gamma(b)}. \tag{6.27}$$

The explicit terms on the right-hand side of (6.22) then cancel, but in general our analysis does not reveal whether or not the error terms cancel. There is, however, one special case in which we can arrive at a firm conclusion, as follows.

Let us suppose that the coefficients $A(\varepsilon, x)$ and $B(\varepsilon, x)$ in (1.01) are even in x, and $a = -b$. As noted above, the functions $P(x)$ and $\zeta \equiv \zeta(x)$ are then respectively even and odd, and $\gamma(a) = \gamma(b)$. It is also easily seen that $\psi(\varepsilon, \kappa, \zeta)$ is an even function of ζ. From these properties it follows that the error terms are related by $\rho_1 = \rho_3$, $\sigma_1 = \sigma_3$, $\nu_2 = \nu_4$, and $\lambda = \mu$. Hence (6.08) reduces to

$$\sin 2\beta + 2\rho_3 \cos\beta + 2\sigma_3 \sin\beta + 2\rho_3\sigma_3 = O(e^{-2\varpi/\varepsilon}).$$

The left-hand side of this equation factors, and we deduce that either

$$\sin\beta + \rho_3 = O(e^{-2\varpi/\varepsilon}), \tag{6.28}$$

or

$$\cos\beta + \sigma_3 = O(e^{-2\varpi/\varepsilon}). \tag{6.29}$$

From (6.10) it is clear that the former alternative applies when s is even, and the latter when s is odd. In the present case the condition (6.27) reduces to $\bar{l} = (-)^s \bar{m}$. Whether s be even or odd, it is easily verified from (6.28) and (6.29) that

$$\bar{m}(\cos 2\beta + \sigma_3 \cos\beta - \rho_3 \sin\beta) - \bar{l}(1 + \sigma_3 \cos\beta + \rho_3 \sin\beta) = O(e^{-2\varpi/\varepsilon}).$$

Hence from (5.23) we obtain

$$D\Lambda_1 = \bar{m}\, e^{P(b)/\varepsilon}(1+\mu)\sin 2\beta\, U(\bar{b}\sqrt{2/\varepsilon}) + O(e^{-2\varpi/\varepsilon})\, e^{P(b)/\varepsilon}\bar{U}(\bar{b}\sqrt{2/\varepsilon}).$$

In consequence

$$\Lambda_1 e^{-P(x)/\varepsilon} W_1(\zeta) = O(\hat{\varepsilon}) \frac{e^{\{|P(x)|-|P(b)|\}/\varepsilon}}{\bar{U}(\bar{b}\sqrt{2/\varepsilon})} \mathbf{E}^{-1}(\zeta\sqrt{2/\varepsilon})\mathbf{M}(\zeta\sqrt{2/\varepsilon}).$$

This vanishes as $\varepsilon \to 0$, uniformly in $[0, b]$. Similarly $\Lambda_3 e^{-P(x)/\varepsilon} W_3(\zeta)$ vanishes uniformly in $[a, 0]$. Accordingly, in this special case resonance does *not* take place.

7. Conditions for resonance: Case $A_0(x)$ positive. The analysis in this section parallels that of § 6, the essential change being that the function $P(x)$ is now nonnegative. We again use the symbols a_1, a_2, b_1, and b_2 to denote any constants such that $a < a_1 < a_2 < 0$ and $0 < b_2 < b_1 < b$.

Suppose first that the parameter κ is independent of ε and not an odd integer. From (5.18) and (2.02) it is seen that this implies both β and $B(0, 0)$ are fixed, $\sin 2\beta \neq 0$, and

$$B(0, 0) \neq -2, -4, -6, \cdots. \tag{7.01}$$

Equations (6.02), (6.04), and (6.06) again apply, and using (5.32), (5.33), (5.34), (5.36), and the fact that $P(x)$ is increasing when x is positive, we may verify that as $\varepsilon \to 0$, each of the quantities $\Lambda_1 e^{-P(x)/\varepsilon} W_1(\zeta)$ and $\Lambda_2 e^{-P(x)/\varepsilon} W_2(\zeta)$ is uniformly $O(\varepsilon^{-(\kappa+\kappa_1)/4})$ in $[0, b_2]$ and uniformly $O(1)$ in $[b_2, b]$ where κ_1 is given by (5.37). Similarly each of the quantities $\Lambda_3 e^{-P(x)/\varepsilon} W_3(\zeta)$ and $\Lambda_4 e^{-P(x)/\varepsilon} W_4(\zeta)$ is uniformly $O(\varepsilon^{-(\kappa+\kappa_1)/4})$ in $[a_2, 0]$ and uniformly $O(1)$ in $[a, a_2]$. These results accord with those of O'Malley [13, p. 487], and correspond to the nonresonant situation.

In the rest of this section, we again suppose that $\beta = \beta(\varepsilon)$ is a root of the equation (6.08), where ϖ is a constant subject to (6.09). Thus β and κ are estimated by (6.10) and (6.11), respectively.

Case I. $P(a) > P(b)$. Equation (6.14) again applies, and as $\varepsilon \to 0$ both terms on the right–hand side grow uniformly (and exponentially) in $[b_2, b_1]$. Equation (6.16) also holds, and from it we deduce that $\Lambda_2 e^{-P(x)/\varepsilon} W_2(\zeta)$ is uniformly $O(\varepsilon^{-(1+\kappa)/4})$ in $[0, b_2]$ and $O(1)$ in $[b_2, b]$. In order to guarantee resonance for positive values of x we therefore need to ensure that the two terms on the right-hand side of (6.14) do not cancel. As in Case III of § 6 we assume that we know the value of $\gamma(a) - \gamma(b)$, where $\gamma(x)$ is defined by (6.18). Then using the asymptotic approximations for the parabolic cylinder functions of large positive argument and Lemma 4.4, we calculate that the ratio of the first term to the second term is given by

$$(7.02) \qquad (-)^{s-1}\{1+o(1)\}\frac{\bar{m}}{\bar{l}}\left\{\frac{P(b)}{P(a)}\right\}^{(\kappa+1)/4} e^{\gamma(a)-\gamma(b)}.$$

Hence on using (5.14) we see that the requisite condition is given by

$$(7.03) \quad l\, e^{Q(a)-\gamma(a)}\{-aA_0(a)\}^{1/2}\{P(a)\}^{\kappa/4} \neq (-)^s m\, e^{Q(b)-\gamma(b)}\{bA_0(b)\}^{1/2}\{P(b)\}^{\kappa/4}.$$

The interval $[a, 0]$ may be investigated in a similar manner, and our findings are as follows. Let c be the point of $(a, 0)$ for which

$$P(c) = P(b),$$

and restrict a_1 so that $c < a_1 < 0$. Then $\Lambda_3 e^{-P(x)/\varepsilon} W_3(\zeta)$ grows uniformly (and exponentially) in $[a_1, a_2]$ provided that (7.03) applies. And $\Lambda_4 e^{-P(x)/\varepsilon} W_4(\zeta)$ is uniformly $O(\varepsilon^{-(1+\kappa)/4})$ in $[a_2, 0]$ and $O(1)$ in $[a, a_2]$.

Therefore *when* $P(a) > P(b)$ *resonance takes place, provided that* (7.03) *is satisfied.* This is the case, for example, if either l or m is zero, or if l and $(-)^{s-1}m$ have the same sign.

When the condition (7.03) is violated some cancellation takes place on the right-hand side of (6.14) as $\varepsilon \to 0$; similarly for $\Lambda_3 e^{-P(x)/\varepsilon} W_3(\zeta)$. The present analysis is insufficiently delicate to determine whether resonance occurs in these circumstances however.

Case II. $P(b) > P(a)$. This case is treatable in a similar manner, and we find that *when* $P(b) > P(a)$ *resonance takes place, provided that* (7.03) *is satisfied.*

Case III. $P(a) = P(b)$. Equations (6.21) and (6.22) remain valid. Hence (6.25) applies, subject to the condition (6.24). Accordingly, $\Lambda_1 e^{-P(x)/\varepsilon} W_1(\zeta)$ grows uniformly (and exponentially) in $[b_2, b_1]$. Next, (6.26) applies, and from it we conclude that $\Lambda_2 e^{-P(x)/\varepsilon} W_2(\zeta)$ is uniformly $O(\varepsilon^{-(1+\kappa)/4})$ in $[0, b_2]$ and uniformly $O(1)$ in $[b_2, b]$. The analysis for the interval $[a, 0]$ is similar, and the general conclusion is the same as in Cases I and II, that is, *resonance takes place, provided that* (6.24) (or (7.03)) *is satisfied.*

An example in which the condition (6.24) is violated, but a definite conclusion can still be reached, is again supplied by the case in which the coefficients $A(\varepsilon, x)$ and

$B(\varepsilon, x)$ in (1.01) are even in x, and $a=-b$. Similar analysis to that given at the end of § 6 shows that resonance does *not* take place in these circumstances.

8. Exact eigenvalues. In the first parts of §§ 6 and 7 we proved that if $\beta \equiv \frac{1}{4}\pi(1+\kappa)$ is independent of ε and 2β is not an integer multiple of π, then resonance does not take place. We also showed that if β is permitted to depend on ε, then except for certain special boundary conditions resonance occurs whenever β satisfies equation (6.08), that is,

(8.01) $$\sin 2\beta+(\rho_1+\rho_3)\cos\beta+(\sigma_1+\sigma_3)\sin\beta+\rho_1\sigma_3+\rho_3\sigma_1=O(e^{-2\varpi/\varepsilon})$$

as $\varepsilon\to 0$, where ϖ is any constant exceeding both $|P(a)|$ and $|P(b)|$. As we noted in § 6, this equation has roots

$$\beta=\beta_s(\varepsilon), \qquad s=1,2,3,\cdots,$$

where

$$\beta_s(\varepsilon)=\tfrac{1}{2}s\pi+O\{\varepsilon\ \ln(1/\varepsilon)\}$$

as $\varepsilon\to 0$. The corresponding form of the original differential equation (1.01) is obtained by substituting

$$\kappa=(4/\pi)\beta_s(\varepsilon)-1$$

in (2.02). For each value of s there is a continuum of roots $\beta_s(\varepsilon)$; therefore since $\beta_s(\varepsilon)$ is not unique it is not an analytic function of ε.

In the form of the original problem that was investigated rigorously by Ackerberg and O'Malley, [1, § 5] and O'Malley [13, §§ 3 and 4], it was assumed that the coefficients $A(\varepsilon, x)$ and $B(\varepsilon, x)$ in (1.01) are holomorphic functions of ε and x and possess asymptotic expansions as $\varepsilon\to 0$ for x in some complex neighborhood of the interval $[a, b]$ and for ε in a sector $0<|\varepsilon|\leqq\varepsilon_0$, $|\mathrm{ph}\ \varepsilon|\leqq\theta_0$, where $\theta_0>0$. With these assumptions it was proved that necessary conditions for resonance are given by (1.04) or (1.05), that is (in both cases), $\beta=\frac{1}{2}s\pi$, where s is a positive integer. Correspondingly, $\kappa=2s-1$; compare (5.18). As we have already noted, these results are consistent with those of §§ 6 and 7.

In the first part of the present section we investigate circumstances in which (8.01) possesses *exact* roots $\beta=\frac{1}{2}s\pi$, where s is a positive integer. In other words, we seek sufficient conditions for resonance when the conditions (1.04) or (1.05) are fulfilled. Our assumptions will be the same as in § 2; thus no conditions of analyticity are imposed on the coefficients in (1.01).

On substituting $\beta=\frac{1}{2}s\pi$ in (8.01), we obtain either

(8.02) $$(-)^{s/2}(\rho_1+\rho_3)+\rho_1\sigma_3+\rho_3\sigma_1=O(e^{-2\varpi/\varepsilon}), \qquad s \text{ even};$$

or

(8.03) $$(-)^{(s-1)/2}(\sigma_1+\sigma_3)+\rho_1\sigma_3+\rho_3\sigma_1=O(e^{-2\varpi/\varepsilon}), \qquad s \text{ odd}.$$

One obvious situation in which these conditions are satisfied is given by

(8.04) $$\rho_1=\sigma_1=\rho_3=\sigma_3=0.$$

This happens, for example, when the function $\bar{\psi}(\varepsilon, \kappa, \zeta)$ in (5.02) is identically zero; in this event the original differential equation (1.01) is transformable into Weber's equation.

A more general situation in which (8.02), or (8.03), is satisfiable identically for all sufficiently small values of ε arises when the error terms ρ_1, σ_1, ρ_3, and σ_3 are independent of ε. Apart from the case (8.04) this may happen when equation (1.01) has a nontrivial solution that is independent of ε.[3]

Turning to cases in which ρ_1, σ_1, ρ_3, and σ_3 may vary with ε, we observe that (8.02) and (8.03) are satisfied when

$$\bar{\psi}(\varepsilon, 2s-1, \zeta) = O(e^{-2\varpi/\varepsilon}) \tag{8.05}$$

as $\varepsilon \to 0$, uniformly with respect to $\zeta \in [\bar{a}, \bar{b}]$. For in this case by taking the balancing function $\Omega(\zeta\sqrt{2/\varepsilon})$ in (5.06) to be $1+|\zeta|\sqrt{2/\varepsilon}$, we easily deduce from the definitions (5.19) and the error bounds (5.04) that both ρ_1 and σ_1 are $O\{\varepsilon \ln(1/\varepsilon) e^{-2\varpi/\varepsilon}\}$; compare (5.07). *A fortiori* ρ_1 and σ_1 are $O(e^{-2\varpi/\varepsilon})$. Similarly, both ρ_3 and σ_3 are $O(e^{-2\varpi/\varepsilon})$.

Equation (8.05) is therefore an appropriate condition of sufficiency to be adjoined to (1.04) or (1.05).[4] The only additional requirement concerns the boundary conditions, as specified in §§ 6 and 7. It will be observed that (8.05) is not unlike the condition given by Ackerberg and O'Malley on p. 292 of [1] pertaining to a coefficient $\sigma(\varepsilon)$ that appears in a certain transformation of the differential equation. The important difference is that we have explicit formulas for $\bar{\psi}(\varepsilon, 2s-1, \zeta)$, given in §§ 4 and 5, whereas only an existence theorem and asymptotic expansion are available for Ackerberg and O'Malley's $\sigma(\varepsilon)$.

We are now in a position to construct new examples of resonant systems, as follows:

$$\varepsilon y'' - xy' + \{x + s - 1 - \varepsilon + \varepsilon C(\varepsilon, x)\}y = 0, \tag{8.06}$$

and

$$\varepsilon y'' + xy' + \{x + s - \varepsilon + \varepsilon C(\varepsilon, x)\}y = 0. \tag{8.07}$$

In both cases the boundary conditions are again given by $y(a) = l$ and $y(b) = m$, with $l^2 + m^2 \neq 0$. Here s is a fixed positive integer, and $C(\varepsilon, x)$ is any continuous function of ε and x that satisfies

$$C(\varepsilon, x) = O(e^{-2\varpi/\varepsilon}) \tag{8.08}$$

as $\varepsilon \to 0$, uniformly with respect to $x \in [a, b]$, where ϖ is any constant exceeding both $\frac{1}{4}a^2$ and $\frac{1}{4}b^2$.

To establish resonance properties for (8.06) and (8.07), we write

$$P(x) = \mp \tfrac{1}{4}x^2, \tag{8.09}$$

where the upper sign applies in the case of (8.06), and the lower sign in the case of (8.07). On making the substitutions

$$y = e^{-P(x)/\varepsilon} W, \qquad x = 2\varepsilon + \zeta\sqrt{2}, \tag{8.10}$$

we obtain, in both cases,

$$d^2W/d\zeta^2 = \{\varepsilon^{-2}(\zeta^2 - 2s\varepsilon + \varepsilon) - 2C(\varepsilon, 2\varepsilon + \zeta\sqrt{2})\} W. \tag{8.11}$$

This differential equation has the form (5.02) with $-2C(\varepsilon, 2\varepsilon + \zeta\sqrt{2})$ in the role of

[3] When $A(\varepsilon, x)$ and $B(\varepsilon, x)$ are independent of ε, such nontrivial solutions are necessarily linear functions of x or constants. Some examples have been supplied by Kreiss and Parter [4, § 3].

[4] The condition (8.05) could be weakened somewhat with more detailed analysis.

$\bar{\psi}(\varepsilon, \kappa, \zeta)$, and $\kappa = 2s - 1$. The boundary conditions are evidently given by

$$W(\bar{a}) = l\, e^{P(a)/\varepsilon}, \qquad W(\bar{b}) = m\, e^{P(b)/\varepsilon}, \tag{8.12}$$

where

$$\bar{a} = (a - 2\varepsilon)/\sqrt{2}, \qquad \bar{b} = (b - 2\varepsilon)/\sqrt{2}. \tag{8.13}$$

Comparison with (5.13) shows that l and m are now playing the roles of $\bar{l}$ and $\bar{m}$, respectively, and $\lambda = \mu = 0$. Lastly, from (8.08) it is clear that the condition (8.05) is satisfied.

On applying the results of § 6 to (8.06) we immediately conclude that in Case I, that is (in the present instance), $|a| > b$, resonance occurs if $m \neq 0$ but not if $m = 0$. Similarly in Case II, given by $|a| < b$, resonance occurs if $l \neq 0$, but not if $l = 0$. To deal with Case III, given by $a = -b$, we first compare the second of (8.10) with equations (6.18) and (8.09). This shows that $\gamma(x) = -x$. Hence (6.23) becomes

$$l \neq (-)^s m\, e^{2b}, \tag{8.14}$$

and resonance takes place in Case III whenever this condition is satisfied.

In the case of (8.07) we apply the results of § 7. We find that resonance occurs for all boundary conditions, except possibly those satisfying

$$la^s e^a = mb^s e^b; \tag{8.15}$$

compare (7.02), with $\bar{l}$ replaced by l, and $\bar{m}$ replaced by m.

Equations (8.06) and (8.07) appear to be the first established examples of resonance that satisfy the original conditions of Ackerberg and O'Malley and do not fall into either of the categories mentioned in the fourth and fifth paragraphs of this section. That is, neither (8.06) nor (8.07) is transformable into Weber's equation, nor is there a nontrivial solution that is independent of ε.

9. Matkowsky's criterion. Recently, Matkowsky [7] proposed an interesting formal criterion for resonance, applicable when the coefficients in the original differential equation are analytic functions of the parameter ε and independent variable x. His approach is to construct the outer solution of the boundary-value problem via the method of matched asymptotic expansions, and the criterion adopted for resonance is that all the coefficients in the outer expansion must be bounded throughout the interior of the interval of integration, including the turning point $x = 0$. Some applications have since been made to nonlinear problems [9]. Before we consider the validity of the criterion, it is instructive to discuss one of Matkowsky's examples in some detail.

Section 2 of [7] contains four examples, in three of which resonance is claimed in certain circumstances. Two of these examples are forms of Weber's equation and when corrected as in [8] the conclusions agree with the results of the present paper. The other example of resonance is given by

$$\varepsilon y'' - x(1 + x^2)y' + (2 + 12\varepsilon)y = 0. \tag{9.01}$$

In the light of our observations in the preceding section, this differential equation appears to be of unusual interest, because it is not a form of Weber's equation. Unfortunately, however, the analysis in [7] has not been carried sufficiently far for this example, and the conclusions arrived at are incorrect. More complete analysis is as follows.

The outer expansion for the solution of (9.01) is given by

$$y = \sum_{j=0}^{\infty} w_j(x)\varepsilon^j,$$

where

(9.02) $$x(1+x^2)w_j'(x)-2w_j(x)=12w_{j-1}(x)+w_{j-1}''(x), \qquad j=0,1,2,\cdots,$$

with $w_{-1}(x)\equiv 0$; compare [7, eqs. (19) and (20)]. Integration of (9.02) yields

$$w_j(x)=\frac{x^2}{1+x^2}\int \frac{12w_{j-1}(x)+w_{j-1}''(x)}{x^3}\,dx.$$

From this relation it is easily seen that the coefficients have the form

$$w_j(x)=c_0q_j(x)+c_1q_{j-1}(x)+c_2q_{j-2}(x)+\cdots+c_jq_0(x),$$

where $c_0, c_1, c_2, \cdots$ are arbitrary constants of integration. The first three functions $q_j(x)$ may be verified to be

$$q_0(x)=\frac{x^2}{1+x^2}, \qquad q_1(x)=-\frac{1}{1+x^2}-\frac{5x^2}{(1+x^2)^2}-\frac{2x^2}{(1+x^2)^3},$$

$$q_2(x)=\frac{12}{1+x^2}+\frac{42x^2}{(1+x^2)^2}+\frac{33x^2}{(1+x^2)^3}+\frac{30x^2}{(1+x^2)^4}+\frac{12x^2}{(1+x^2)^5}$$
$$+\frac{108x^2}{1+x^2}\ln x-\frac{54x^2}{1+x^2}\ln(1+x^2).$$

Each of the coefficients $w_0(x)$, $w_1(x)$, and $w_2(x)$ is therefore bounded as $x\to 0$, as required by Matkowsky's criterion. On proceeding to the next coefficient, we perceive that each term in $q_0(x)$, $q_1(x)$, and $q_2(x)$ that is analytic at $x=0$ makes a bounded contribution to $w_3(x)$. This takes care of all terms except the penultimate member of $q_2(x)$. For this term we find that

$$\frac{x^2}{1+x^2}\int \frac{1}{x^3}\left(12+\frac{d^2}{dx^2}\right)\left(\frac{x^2\ln x}{1+x^2}\right)dx=\chi(x)-\ln x,$$

where $\chi(x)$ denotes a function that is bounded at $x=0$. Hence $w_3(x)$ is unbounded at $x=0$. Accordingly, when Matkowsky's criterion is applied correctly to this example, it indicates that resonance does not take place. This is contrary to the statement on p. 88 of [7], but in agreement with our present results.

In order to show that Matkowsky's criterion can lead to a false conclusion when applied to the class of problems considered originally by Ackerberg and O'Malley, we consider the following (and final) example, given by

(9.03) $$\varepsilon y''-xy'+(x+1-\varepsilon+\varepsilon e^{-2\varpi/\varepsilon})y=0; \qquad y(a)=l, \quad y(b)=m,$$

where ϖ is a positive constant. It is easily seen that the coefficients in this equation satisfy all the conditions of the Uniform Reduction Theorem quoted in [1, p. 291], including those of analyticity with respect to ε and x.

The differential equation in (9.03) is the special form of the example (8.06) with $s=2$ and $C(\varepsilon,x)=e^{-2\varpi/\varepsilon}$. The results of § 8 therefore show that when

(9.04) $$\varpi>\max\left(\tfrac{1}{4}a^2, \tfrac{1}{4}b^2\right)$$

resonance occurs except for certain special values of l and m. This conclusion is consistent with Matkowsky's criterion, because the outer expansion is found to have the form

$$y = \sum_{j=0}^{\infty} (c_j x - 2c_{j-1})\, e^x \varepsilon^j,$$

in which $c_0, c_1, c_2, \cdots$ are arbitrary constants, and $c_{-1} = 0$. Thus all coefficients in the outer expansion are free from singularity everywhere in $[a, b]$.

Let us now suppose that instead of (9.04) the constant ϖ satisfies the condition

$$0 < \varpi < \min(\tfrac{1}{4}a^2, \tfrac{1}{4}b^2). \tag{9.05}$$

On making the substitutions (8.10) with

$$P(x) = -\tfrac{1}{4}x^2, \tag{9.06}$$

we transform (9.03) into

$$d^2W/d\zeta^2 = \{\varepsilon^{-2}(\zeta^2 - 3\varepsilon) - 2e^{-2\varpi/\varepsilon}\}W; \tag{9.07}$$

compare (8.11). This rearranges into the form (5.02) if we take

$$\kappa = 3 + 2\varepsilon e^{-2\varpi/\varepsilon}, \qquad \bar{\psi}(\varepsilon, \kappa, \zeta) = 0. \tag{9.08}$$

The analysis of § 5 then applies with each of the error terms $\eta_1(\zeta)$, $\eta_2(\zeta)$, $\eta_3(\zeta)$, and $\eta_4(\zeta)$ replaced by zero. Furthermore, because the boundary conditions for (9.07) are given by (8.12) and (8.13), we again see from (5.13) that l and m are playing the roles of $\bar{l}$ and $\bar{m}$, respectively, and $\lambda = \mu = 0$.

From (5.18) and (9.08) it follows that

$$\beta = \pi + \tfrac{1}{2}\pi\varepsilon e^{-2\varpi/\varepsilon}.$$

Hence for small ε

$$\cos 2\beta = 1 + O(\varepsilon^2 e^{-4\varpi/\varepsilon}), \qquad \sin 2\beta = \{1 + O(\varepsilon^2 e^{-4\varpi/\varepsilon})\}\pi\varepsilon e^{-2\varpi/\varepsilon}.$$

Next, from (5.33), (5.34), and (9.06), we see that

$$U(-\bar{a}\sqrt{2/\varepsilon}) = O\{\varepsilon^{-\kappa/2} e^{-a^2/(2\varepsilon)}\}\bar{U}(-\bar{a}\sqrt{2/\varepsilon}),$$

$$U(\bar{b}\sqrt{2/\varepsilon}) = O\{\varepsilon^{-\kappa/2} e^{-b^2/(2\varepsilon)}\}\bar{U}(\bar{b}\sqrt{2/\varepsilon}).$$

Substituting in (5.27) by means of these results and referring to the condition (9.05), we derive

$$D = -\{1 + o(1)\}\pi\varepsilon\, e^{-2\varpi/\varepsilon}\bar{U}(-\bar{a}\sqrt{2/\varepsilon})\bar{U}(\bar{b}\sqrt{2/\varepsilon}).$$

Similarly (5.23) reduces to

$$D\Lambda_1 = \{1 + o(1)\}m\, e^{-b^2/(4\varepsilon)}\bar{U}(-\bar{a}\sqrt{2/\varepsilon}) - l\, e^{-a^2/(4\varepsilon)}\bar{U}(\bar{b}\sqrt{2/\varepsilon}).$$

Dividing the last two equations and using the first of (5.03), we obtain

$$\Lambda_1 e^{-P(x)/\varepsilon} W_1(\zeta) = -\{1 + o(1)\}\frac{m}{\pi\varepsilon} e^{2\varpi/\varepsilon} e^{(x^2-b^2)/(4\varepsilon)} \frac{U(\zeta\sqrt{2/\varepsilon})}{\bar{U}(\bar{b}\sqrt{2/\varepsilon})}$$

$$+ \{1 + o(1)\}\frac{l}{\pi\varepsilon} e^{2\varpi/\varepsilon} e^{(x^2-a^2)/(4\varepsilon)} \frac{U(\zeta\sqrt{2/\varepsilon})}{\bar{U}(-\bar{a}\sqrt{2/\varepsilon})}.$$

Then letting $\varepsilon \to 0$ and referring to (5.33), (5.34), and (5.35), we see that the right-hand side vanishes uniformly in $[0, b]$.

For the second term in (5.29) we find that

$$\Lambda_2 e^{-P(x)/\varepsilon} W_2(\zeta) = -\{1+o(1)\}\frac{l}{\pi\varepsilon} e^{2\varpi/\varepsilon} e^{(x^2-a^2)/(4\varepsilon)} \frac{U(\bar{b}\sqrt{2/\varepsilon})\bar{U}(\zeta\sqrt{2/\varepsilon})}{\bar{U}(\bar{b}\sqrt{2/\varepsilon})\bar{U}(-\bar{a}\sqrt{2/\varepsilon})}$$

$$+\{1+o(1)\} m e^{(x^2-b^2)/(4\varepsilon)} \frac{\bar{U}(\zeta\sqrt{2/\varepsilon})}{\bar{U}(\bar{b}\sqrt{2/\varepsilon})}.$$

As $\varepsilon \to 0$, the first term on the right-hand side vanishes uniformly in $[0, b]$, and the second term vanishes uniformly in $[0, b_1]$, where, as before, $0 < b_1 < b$. The corresponding results for the interval $[a, 0]$ may be arrived at in a similar way or by symmetry: we find that $\Lambda_3 e^{-P(x)/\varepsilon} W_3(\zeta)$ vanishes uniformly in $[a, 0]$, and $\Lambda_4 e^{-P(x)/\varepsilon} W_4(\zeta)$ vanishes uniformly in $[a_1, 0]$, where $a < a_1 < 0$.

The results just obtained show that the system (9.03) never resonates when the condition (9.05) is satisfied. On the other hand, Matkowsky's criterion does not distinguish between the cases (9.04) and (9.05), and would therefore lead to a false conclusion in the latter case. It is also interesting to note that the system (9.03) satisfies the infinite set of necessary conditions for resonance found by Lakin [5] and Cook and Eckhaus [2], irrespective of the value of the positive constant ϖ.

10. Summary and conclusions. In this paper we have studied the asymptotic behavior, for small ε, of the solutions of the boundary-value problem given by (1.01) and (1.02), with differentiability and other conditions on the coefficients $A(\varepsilon, x)$ and $B(\varepsilon, x)$ stated in the opening paragraph of § 2. By transforming the differential equation into a form resembling Weber's equation (§§ 3 and 4), we constructed four asymptotic solutions, complete with error bounds, two of which are uniformly valid in the interval $0 \leqq x \leqq b$, and the other two are uniformly valid in the interval $a \leqq x \leqq 0$ (§ 5). These solutions were then combined to satisfy the boundary conditions, and the asymptotic behavior of the resulting solution as $\varepsilon \to 0$ was examined in the cases $A(\varepsilon, x) < 0$ (§ 6) and $A(\varepsilon, x) > 0$ (§ 7). Particular attention was paid to the phenomenon of resonance, that is, an unusual lack of decay (§ 6) or an unusual growth (§ 7) of the solution as $\varepsilon \to 0$. We showed that in the general case resonance occurs essentially in the same manner as in the special case in which (1.01) is transformable into Weber's equation. That is, corresponding to each value of the positive integer s, there is an infinite set of values of the parameter κ appearing in the expression (2.02) for $B(\varepsilon, x)$ for which resonance takes place. The values of κ depend on ε, and are not known explicitly, except in the case of Weber's equation. Asymptotic estimates of κ are supplied by (6.11), in which $\hat{\varepsilon} = \varepsilon \ln(1/\varepsilon)$.

Next (§ 8), we considered the problem in the form proposed originally by Ackerberg and O'Malley [1], in which the coefficients $A(\varepsilon, x)$ and $B(\varepsilon, x)$ are assumed to be holomorphic functions of ε and x. Hitherto, only necessary conditions for resonance have been found in these circumstances. We completed these results by deriving a sufficient condition, and we illustrated this condition by two examples. In the concluding section (§ 9) we discussed a formal criterion for resonance that has been proposed recently, and showed by means of an example that this test is incomplete in its present form.

We have concentrated on the resonance phenomenon in the present paper, since this has been the least understood feature of the problem. The separation of the solution into boundary layers, which is of physical significance, has been neglected because this has been discussed fully by earlier writers. Nor did we consider details of the interesting oscillatory behavior of the solution in the neighborhood of $x = 0$. If desired, all of this information can be recovered from the uniform asymptotic approximations we have constructed for the solution.

Finally, we comment that we have restricted attention to a finite interval $[a, b]$, since this has been the assumption of earlier writers. However, the theory of differential equations with coalescing turning points that we have used is also applicable with unbounded values of the independent variable. In consequence, the corresponding boundary-value problem with $a = -\infty$ and $b = \infty$ is solvable by similar methods. Indeed, the analysis in this case is somewhat simpler, because *inter alīa* the values of κ that correspond to resonance are eigenvalues of the system and comprise a discrete set.

Acknowledgments. The author is indebted to Dr. R. E. O'Malley for illuminating discussions concerning the implications of the analyticity assumption on the coefficients in the differential equation, and also for providing several references. The author also thanks Dr. B. J. Matkowsky and the referees for several improvements in the presentation of the results.

REFERENCES

[1] R. C. ACKERBERG AND R. E. O'MALLEY, JR., *Boundary layer problems exhibiting resonance*, Studies in Appl. Math., 49 (1970), pp. 277–295.

[2] L. P. COOK AND W. ECKHAUS, *Resonance in a boundary value problem of singular perturbation type*, Ibid., 52 (1973), pp. 129–139.

[3] P. P. N. DE GROEN, *Elliptic singular perturbations of first-order operators with critical points*, Proc. Roy. Soc. Edinburgh Ser. A, 74 (1974/75), pp. 91–113.

[4] H. O. KREISS AND S. V. PARTER, *Remarks on singular perturbations with turning points*, this Journal, 5 (1974), pp. 230–251.

[5] W. D. LAKIN, *Boundary value problems with a turning point*, Studies in Appl. Math., 51 (1972), pp. 261–275.

[6] R. Y. LEE, *On uniform simplification of linear differential equation in a full neighborhood of a turning point*, J. Math. Anal. Appl., 27 (1969), pp. 501–510.

[7] B. J. MATKOWSKY, *On boundary layer problems exhibiting resonance*, SIAM Rev., 17 (1975), pp. 82–100.

[8] ———, *Errata: On boundary layer problems exhibiting resonance*, Ibid., 18 (1976), p. 112.

[9] B. J. MATKOWSKY AND W. L. SIEGMANN, *The flow between counter-rotating disks at high Reynolds number*, SIAM J. Appl. Math., 30 (1976), pp. 720–727.

[10] NATIONAL BUREAU OF STANDARDS, *Handbook of Mathematical Functions*, Appl. Math. Ser. No. 55, M. Abramowitz and I. A. Stegun, eds., U.S. Govt. Printing Office, Washington, DC, 1964.

[11] F. W. J. OLVER, *Asymptotics and Special Functions*, Academic Press, New York and London, 1974.

[12] ———, *Second-order linear differential equations with two turning points*, Philos. Trans. Roy. Soc. London Ser. A, 278 (1975), pp. 137–174.

[13] R. E. O'MALLEY, JR., *On boundary value problems for a singularly perturbed differential equation with a turning point*, this Journal, 1 (1970), pp. 479–490.

[14] ———, *Introduction to Singular Perturbations*, Academic Press, New York and London, 1974.

[15] C. E. PEARSON, *On a differential equation of boundary layer type*, J. Math. and Phys., 47 (1968), pp. 134–154.

[16] Y. SIBUYA, *Asymptotic solutions of a system of linear ordinary differential equations containing a parameter*, Funkcial. Ekvac., 4 (1962), pp. 83–113.

[17] A. M. WATTS, *A singular perturbation problem with a turning point*, Bull. Austral. Math. Soc., 5 (1971), pp. 61–73.

[18] E. ZAUDERER, *Boundary value problems for a second order differential equation with a turning point*, Studies in Appl. Math., 51 (1972), pp. 411–413.

[19] A. ZWAAN, *Intensitäten im Ca-Funkenspektrum*, Arch. Néerlandaises Sci. Exactes Natur. Ser. 3A, 12 (1929), pp. 1–76.

GENERAL CONNECTION FORMULAE FOR LIOUVILLE–GREEN APPROXIMATIONS IN THE COMPLEX PLANE

By F. W. J. OLVER†
The University of Maryland and The National Bureau of Standards

(*Communicated by Sir Harold Jeffreys, F.R.S. – Received* 26 *October* 1977)

CONTENTS

This paper is concerned with differential equations of the form

$$d^2w/dz^2 = \{u^2 f(u, z) + g(u, z)\} w,$$

in which u is a positive parameter and z is a complex variable ranging over a simply connected open domain $\boldsymbol{D}$ that is not necessarily one-sheeted, and may be bounded or unbounded.

In the first part we assume that for each value of u the function $(z-c)^{2-m} f(u, z)$ is holomorphic and non-vanishing throughout $\boldsymbol{D}$, where c is an interior point of $\boldsymbol{D}$ and m is a positive constant. It is also assumed that $g(u, z)$ is holomorphic in $\boldsymbol{D}$, punctured at c,

† Present address: Institute for Physical Science and Technology, University of Maryland, College Park, Maryland 20742, U.S.A.

and $g(u,z) = O\{(z-c)^{\gamma-1}\}$ as $z \to c$, where γ is another positive constant. Thus c is a fractional transition point of the differential equation of multiplicity (or order) $m-2$, and there are no other transition points in $\boldsymbol{D}$. Uniform asymptotic approximations for the solutions, when u is large, are constructed in terms of Bessel functions of order $1/m$, complete with error bounds.

In the second part the Bessel function approximants are replaced by their uniform asymptotic approximations for large argument, yielding the connection formulae for the Liouville–Green (or J.W.K.B.) approximations to the solutions, again complete with error bounds. These results are then applied to solve the general problem of connecting the Liouville–Green approximations when $\boldsymbol{D}$ contains any (finite) number of transition points of arbitrary multiplicities, integral or fractional.

The third, and concluding, part illustrates the theory by means of three examples.

An appendix describes a numerical method for the automatic computation and plotting of the boundary curves of the Liouville–Green approximations, defined by

$$\mathrm{Re}\int_c^z f^{\frac{1}{2}}(u,t)\,\mathrm{d}t = 0,$$

where c again denotes a transition point.

1. Introduction and summary

1.1. *Introduction*

The problem of constructing asymptotic solutions of differential equations of the form

$$\mathrm{d}^2w/\mathrm{d}x^2 = \{u^2 f(u,x) + g(u,x)\}\,w \tag{1.1}$$

for large values of the positive real parameter u has been studied by many physicists and mathematicians, including the present writer. In Olver (1977*a*) I considered the case in which the independent variable x ranges over a finite or infinite open interval, within which $f(u,x)$ and $g(u,x)$ are free from singularity and $f(u,x)$ has a single zero of arbitrary multiplicity. Zeros of $f(u,x)$ are called *turning points* or *transition points* of (1.1), and in Olver (1977*b*) I considered the necessary modifications when the interval of integration is permitted to contain any (finite) number of turning points of arbitrary multiplicities. The object in these two papers was to connect the Liouville–Green approximations† that represent the solutions in the neighbourhood of an end-point of the interval of integration with the corresponding approximations valid near the other end-point.

The present paper develops a similar theory when the independent variable, which we now denote by z, ranges over a bounded or unbounded domain $\boldsymbol{D}$ in the complex plane. This extension has a variety of promising physical applications, including scattering and optical potential problems in quantum mechanics (Pokrovskii & Khalatnikov 1961; Mott & Massey 1965; Brander 1966; Berry & Mount 1972; Child 1974; Connor, Jakubetz & Sukumar 1976; Knoll & Schaeffer 1976), transmission of radio waves (Budden & Smith 1974), trapping of water waves (Lozano & Meyer 1976), and hydrodynamic instability (Drazin 1974).

A new feature in the complex case is that the functions $f(u,z)$ and $g(u,z)$ in the differential equation

$$\mathrm{d}^2w/\mathrm{d}z^2 = \{u^2 f(u,z) + g(u,z)\}\,w \tag{1.2}$$

are required to be analytic functions of the complex variable z. Another important difference is that the Liouville–Green (L.G.) approximations are valid only in restricted regions of $\boldsymbol{D}$. Suppose,

† Also known as J.W.K.B. approximations.

for example, that $\boldsymbol{D}$ contains a single turning point c of multiplicity $m-2$, where m is an integer not less than 2. Then we first construct the curves

$$\operatorname{Re}\int_c^z f^{\frac{1}{2}}(u,t)\,\mathrm{d}t = 0,$$

called the *principal curves* (or *anti-Stokes lines*) *associated with c*. It is easily verified that m such curves emerge from c, dividing $\boldsymbol{D}$ into m regions, which we call the *principal regions*† *associated with c*. Each L.G. approximation for a given solution of (1.2) is valid in at most three adjoining principal regions, and then only after deletion of a domain that contains the boundary of their union.

Hitherto, methods used for connecting L.G. approximations in the complex plane have depended on the construction of *transition* (or *transmission*) *matrices* that relate pairs of solutions in two adjoining principal regions. To pass through several regions we form the product of the corresponding transition matrices. In Olver (1977*a*) methods of this type were classified as *lateral* or *pseudo-lateral*, depending on the way in which the transition matrices are derived. The earliest investigation of transition matrices for turning points of arbitrary multiplicity appears to be the formal analysis of Heading (1962, pp. 89–93, and 110–115). Leung (1975) supplied a rigorous proof, based on a uniform reduction theorem due to Sibuya (1974), for the case in which $f(u,z)$ is a polynomial in z that is independent of u, $g(u,z) \equiv 0$ and $\boldsymbol{D}$ contains a single multiple turning point. More recently, Leung (1977) has applied his results to solve an eigenvalue problem involving several turning points. Further historical details may be found in Olver (1977*a*, §6) and Olver (1977*b*, §6) and will not be repeated here.

In the present paper it is shown how to continue a solution that is recessive in any given principal region directly to *any* other principal region associated with the same turning point, without the need for passage through each of the intervening regions. The method is of *central connection* type, as defined by Wasow (1968) and Olver (1977*a*). The procedure has the obvious advantage of reducing substantially the number of steps needed in the connection process. When $\boldsymbol{D}$ contains n turning points, at most n steps are needed to trace any solution, whatever the multiplicities of the turning points. In practice, the number of steps is often very much less than n. Also, in contrast to the procedures of Heading and Leung, there are no restrictions on the configuration of the turning points.‡

The present theory differs from earlier investigations in two other respects. First, explicit and realistic error bounds are found for the approximate coefficients in the connection formulae in a form that is suitable for a single transition point or several transition points. In the real-variable theory of Olver (1977*a*, *b*) error bounds were constructed only for the case of a single transition point. The present extension to several transition points was stimulated by the work of Taylor (1978).

Secondly, the theory admits *fractional transition points*, that is, points c at which $f(u,z)/(z-c)^{m-2}$ is analytic, m now denoting *any* positive constant. In general, such points are branch-points of the solutions of the differential equation. The analysis in these cases is more difficult, but apart from the need to introduce Riemann sheets the final connection formulae are essentially the same. This extension covers the commonly occurring case in which $f(u,z)$ has a simple pole at c; in this event $m = 1$.

† Other names are *Stokes regions* (Wasow 1968) and *principal subdomains* (Olver 1965).

‡ *Added in proof*, 8 *May* 1978. Restrictions on the number and configuration of the turning points have also been removed in a recent paper by Heading (1977). The object in this reference is to develop a method that can be applied easily, and it is achieved by use of pseudo-lateral connection with formal analysis.

1.2. *Summary*

The paper is divided into three parts, the contents of which are as follows.

In part A, comprising §§2–4, the given complex domain $\boldsymbol{D}$ is assumed to contain a single transition point of any multiplicity, integral or fractional. In §2 we collect relevant properties of standard solutions of the basic comparison equation

$$d^2w/dt^2 = \tfrac{1}{4}m^2t^{m-2}w, \tag{1.3}$$

especially connection formulae and uniform asymptotic approximations for large $|t|$. We also introduce auxiliary weight, modulus and phase functions. In §3 we state and prove the main approximation theorem for solutions of (1.2). This theorem furnishes approximations for large values of the parameter u in terms of solutions of (1.3). Except for the usual possible shadow zones (see, for example, Cherry 1950; Olver 1974, pp. 223 and 417) these approximations are uniformly valid in the whole of $\boldsymbol{D}$, even when $\boldsymbol{D}$ is unbounded or has irregular singularities of (1.2) on its boundary. This problem is of considerable importance in its own right, quite apart from the connection formula problem. It has been considered previously by Langer (1932, 1935) and Olver (1977*c*), but the asymptotic solutions constructed in these references are not the ones that are pertinent to the present investigation, and new proofs are needed, especially when m is not an integer. The approximations found in §3 are accompanied by inequalities satisfied by the error terms, and are valid when the coefficients $f(u,z)$ and $g(u,z)$ in (1.2) depend on the parameter u in a fairly general manner. For the approximations to be meaningful, however, the error terms must vanish as $u \to \infty$, and in §4 we derive asymptotic estimates of the error bounds in the common case in which $f(u,z)$ and $g(u,z)$ are independent of u.

In part B, comprising §§5–7, the uniform approximations of §3 are re-approximated away from the transition point by replacing the basic functions, that is, the standard solutions of (1.3), by their asymptotic approximations for large argument. This yields the L.G. approximations in each principal region. The main connection theorem, giving the L.G. approximations complete with inequalities satisfied by the error terms, is stated and proved in §5. In §6 we derive asymptotic estimates of the error bounds in the case when $f(u,z)$ and $g(u,z)$ are independent of u by application of the results of §4. Applications of the theorems of §§5 and 6 are discussed in §7. To solve the general problem in which there are any number of transition points, it suffices to consider a domain $\boldsymbol{D}$ containing two transition points of arbitrary multiplicities. Two distinct cases arise, depending whether or not these points are joined by a common principal curve.

Part C, comprising §§8–10, illustrates the theory by means of three examples. The first (§8) is an eigenvalue problem involving four real turning points of multiplicities 2, 1, 4 and 3. This example was solved previously in Olver (1977*b*, §5) and therefore serves as a check on the present analysis. The second example (§9) has three triple turning points, distributed equidistantly around the unit circle. The final example (§10) involves four singularities. Two of these are located on the real axis and are simple poles of $f(u,z)$; thus $m = 1$ for each. The other two are branch-points of $f(u,z)$ situated on the imaginary axis, and $m = \frac{5}{2}$ for each.

An appendix outlines the numerical method that was used for the automatic computation and plotting of the principal curves for the examples described in part C.

For the reader who is concerned only with applying the connection formulae in the case when the functions $f(u,z)$ and $g(u,z)$ are independent of u, and not with the proofs of the theorems or the evaluation of error bounds, the relevant parts of this paper are §§5.1, 6.1, 6.2, 6.4, 7.1–7.4, the examples treated in §§8–10, and the appendix.

PART A. UNIFORM APPROXIMATIONS FOR THE SOLUTIONS

2. Standard solutions of the basic equation

2.1. *Primary solution*

In this section we derive properties of solutions of the equation

$$d^2w/dt^2 = \tfrac{1}{4}m^2t^{m-2}w. \tag{2.1}$$

For the case in which t is a real variable and $m-2$ is a non-negative integer, Olver (1977*a*), with a slight change in notation, adopted the function

$$U(t) = (2t/\pi)^{\frac{1}{2}}K_{1/m}(t^{\frac{1}{2}m}) \tag{2.2}$$

as a standard solution, K denoting the modified Bessel function in the usual notation. We continue to employ this solution in the more general circumstances which we now contemplate, that is, when t is a complex variable and m has any positive real value. The functions on the right hand side of (2.2) are understood to assume their principal values when $\operatorname{ph} t = 0$, and be defined by continuity for other values of $\operatorname{ph} t$.

Properties of $U(t)$ are easily deduced from those of Bessel functions, given for example in National Bureau of Standards (1964, ch. 9). Thus if m is an integer such that $m \geqslant 2$, then $U(t)$ is entire. For other values of m, $U(t)$ has a branch-point at $t = 0$ and is analytic at all other finite points of the t-plane.

As $t \to 0$

$$U(t) \to \frac{2^{(2-m)/(2m)}}{\pi^{\frac{1}{2}}}\Gamma\left(\frac{1}{m}\right). \tag{2.3}$$

In the same circumstances the asymptotic form of $U'(t)$ is given by

$$-\frac{2^{(2-5m)/(2m)}m}{\pi^{\frac{1}{2}}}\Gamma\left(\frac{1}{m}-1\right)t^{m-1}, \quad \frac{\ln t}{(8\pi)^{\frac{1}{2}}} \quad \text{or} \quad \frac{2^{-(2+m)/(2m)}}{\pi^{\frac{1}{2}}}\Gamma\left(-\frac{1}{m}\right), \tag{2.4}$$

according as $m < 1$, $m = 1$ or $m > 1$.

As $t \to \infty$

$$U(t) \sim t^{\frac{1}{4}(2-m)}\exp(-t^{\frac{1}{2}m}), \quad U'(t) \sim -\tfrac{1}{2}mt^{\frac{1}{4}(m-2)}\exp(-t^{\frac{1}{2}m}), \tag{2.5}$$

each of these relations being valid when $|\operatorname{ph} t| \leqslant (3-\delta)\pi/m$. Here δ denotes any constant such that $0 < \delta < 1$.

We shall use the approximations (2.5) only in the sector $|\operatorname{ph} t| \leqslant 2\pi/m$, and in this region uniform error bounds are supplied by the following results:

$$U(t) = t^{\frac{1}{4}(2-m)}\exp(-t^{\frac{1}{2}m})\{1+\vartheta(t)\}, \tag{2.6}$$

$$d\{t^{\frac{1}{4}(m-2)}U(t)\}/dt = -\tfrac{1}{2}mt^{\frac{1}{2}(m-2)}\exp(-t^{\frac{1}{2}m})\{1+\vartheta^1(t)\}, \tag{2.7}$$

where

$$|\vartheta(t)|,\ |\vartheta^1(t)| \leqslant \Theta(t^{\frac{1}{2}m}) \quad (|\operatorname{ph} t| \leqslant 2\pi/m), \tag{2.8}$$

and

$$\Theta(t) = \exp\left|\frac{\pi(4-m^2)}{8m^2t}\right| - 1. \tag{2.9}$$

Thus $\vartheta(t)$ and $\vartheta^1(t)$ are both $O(t^{-\frac{1}{2}m})$ as $t \to \infty$ in the sector. To verify (2.8) set $z = t^{\frac{1}{2}m}$ and

$\vartheta(t) = e^z h(z)$. Then from (2.6) and (2.7) we find that $\vartheta^1(t) = -e^z h'(z)$. Using the differential equation

$$\frac{d^2}{dz^2}\{z^{\frac{1}{2}}K_{1/m}(z)\} = \left(1+\frac{4-m^2}{4m^2z^2}\right)\{z^{\frac{1}{2}}K_{1/m}(z)\},$$

and making the substitution

$$z^{\frac{1}{2}}K_{1/m}(z) = (\tfrac{1}{2}\pi)^{\frac{1}{2}}\{e^{-z}+h(z)\},$$

we obtain

$$h''(z)-h(z) = (4-m^2)(4m^2z^2)^{-1}\{e^{-z}+h(z)\},$$

and hence, by variation of parameters,

$$h(z) = \frac{4-m^2}{8m^2}\int_z^\infty (e^{v-z}-e^{z-v})\{e^{-v}+h(v)\}\frac{dv}{v^2}.$$

On solving this integral equation by means of theorem 10.2 of Olver (1974, ch. 6), and using the relations (13.03) and (13.05) of the same reference, we conclude that $|h(z)|$ and $|h'(z)|$ are both bounded by $|e^{-z}|\,\Theta(z)$ when $|\mathrm{ph}\,z| \leqslant \pi$. This result is clearly equivalent to (2.8). Compare also Olver (1964, §§5 and 7).

Asymptotic forms of $U(t)$ as $t\to\infty$ in other phase ranges will be found in §2.4 below.

When $m-2$ is a positive integer further properties of $U(t)$, particularly the location of its zeros, may be derived from results of Swanson & Headley (1967) and Headley & Barwell (1975). In the notation of these authors

$$U(t) = (\tfrac{1}{2}\pi)^{\frac{1}{2}}(2/m)^{1/m}m\,\mathrm{cosec}\,(\pi/m)\,A_{m-2}\{(\tfrac{1}{2}m)^{2/m}t\}.$$

2.2. *Secondary solutions*

We define†

$$U_j(t) = U(t\,e^{-2j\pi i/m}) \quad (j = 0,\ \pm1,\ \pm2,\ \ldots). \tag{2.10}$$

Clearly $U_j(t)$ is a solution of equation (2.1) that is recessive as $t\to\infty$ in the sector S_j, defined by

$$(2j-1)\,\pi/m \leqslant \mathrm{ph}\,t \leqslant (2j+1)\,\pi/m. \tag{2.11}$$

These sectors are indicated in figure 1. From (2.6) to (2.9) we obtain

$$U_j(t) = i^j e^{-j\pi i/m} t^{\frac{1}{4}(2-m)} \exp\{-(t\,e^{-2j\pi i/m})^{\frac{1}{2}m}\}\{1+\vartheta_j(t)\}, \tag{2.12}$$

$$d\{t^{\frac{1}{4}(m-2)}U_j(t)\}/dt = -\tfrac{1}{2}m i^{-j} e^{-j\pi i/m} t^{\frac{1}{2}(m-2)} \exp\{-(t\,e^{-2j\pi i/m})^{\frac{1}{2}m}\}\{1+\vartheta_j^1(t)\}, \tag{2.13}$$

where

$$|\vartheta_j(t)|,\ |\vartheta_j^1(t)| \leqslant \Theta(t^{\frac{1}{2}m}), \tag{2.14}$$

valid when

$$(2j-2)\,\pi/m \leqslant \mathrm{ph}\,t \leqslant (2j+2)\,\pi/m. \tag{2.15}$$

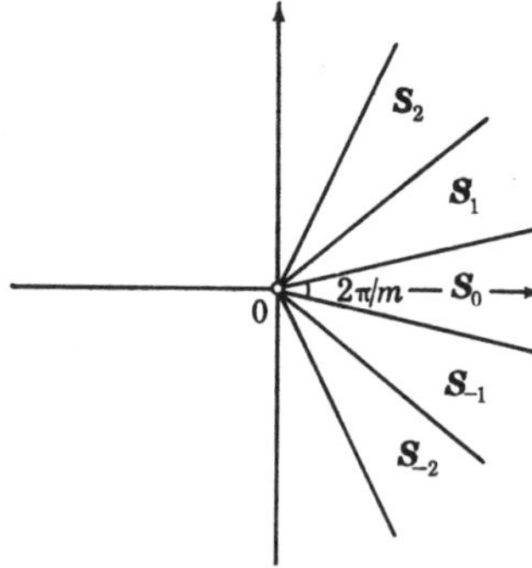

FIGURE 1. Sectors S_j.

† This notation should not be confused with that of Olver (1977*a*).

When $m > 1$ the Wronskian of any pair of solutions $U_j(t)$ and $U_k(t)$ is easily calculated by letting $t \to 0$ and referring to (2.3) and (2.4); thus

$$\mathscr{W}\{U_j(t),\, U_k(t)\} = (\mathrm{e}^{-2k\pi\mathrm{i}/m} - \mathrm{e}^{-2j\pi\mathrm{i}/m})\, U(0)\, U'(0) = m\mathrm{i}\,\mathrm{e}^{-(j+k)\pi\mathrm{i}/m}\lambda_{j,k}, \tag{2.16}$$

where

$$\lambda_{j,k} = \frac{\sin(k-j)\,\pi/m}{\sin \pi/m}. \tag{2.17}$$

The validity of (2.16) when $0 < m \leqslant 1$ is then inferred by temporarily supposing m to be a complex variable and appealing to analytic continuation. When $1/m$ happens to be an integer the ratio of the sine functions in (2.17) is to be replaced by its limiting value, that is,

$$\lambda_{j,k} = (-)^{(k-j-1)/m}(k-j), \quad 1/m = \text{an integer}. \tag{2.18}$$

From (2.16), (2.17) and (2.18) we conclude that $U_j(t)$ and $U_k(t)$ are linearly independent solutions of (2.1), provided that

$$k \neq j, \quad \text{when } 1/m = \text{an integer}, \tag{2.19}$$

or

$$k \neq j \,(\operatorname{mod} m), \quad \text{when} \quad 1/m \neq \text{an integer}. \tag{2.20}$$

We also note that if $1/m$ is not an integer and $k = j \,(\operatorname{mod} m)$, then m is necessarily rational and the sector $\boldsymbol{S}_k$ is a superimposition of $\boldsymbol{S}_j$ in the complex plane. In particular, if m is an integer such that $m \geqslant 2$, then there are only m distinct sectors $\boldsymbol{S}_j$ and m distinct solutions $U_j(t)$.

2.3. *Connection formulae*

The linear relation satisfied by any three secondary solutions may be found as follows. From the connection formulae for the modified Bessel functions given on page 376 of National Bureau of Standards (1964) we have

$$\sin(\pi/m)\, K_{1/m}(z\,\mathrm{e}^{-j\pi\mathrm{i}}) = \sin(\pi/m)\, \mathrm{e}^{j\pi\mathrm{i}/m} K_{1/m}(z) + \pi\mathrm{i} \sin(j\pi/m)\, I_{1/m}(z).$$

On replacing j by k and l in turn and eliminating $K_{1/m}(z)$ and $I_{1/m}(z)$ from the resulting three equations, we arrive at

$$\sin\{(k-l)\,\pi/m\}\, K_{1/m}(z\,\mathrm{e}^{-j\pi\mathrm{i}}) + \sin\{(l-j)\,\pi/m\}\, K_{1/m}(z\,\mathrm{e}^{-k\pi\mathrm{i}}) + \sin\{(j-k)\,\pi/m\}\, K_{1/m}(z\,\mathrm{e}^{-l\pi\mathrm{i}}) = 0.$$

Hence from (2.2) and (2.10) the desired formula is seen to be

$$\sin\{(k-l)\,\pi/m\}\,\mathrm{e}^{j\pi\mathrm{i}/m} U_j(t) + \sin\{(l-j)\,\pi/m\}\,\mathrm{e}^{k\pi\mathrm{i}/m} U_k(t) + \sin\{(j-k)\,\pi/m\}\,\mathrm{e}^{l\pi\mathrm{i}/m} U_l(t) = 0. \tag{2.21}$$

Special cases that will be required in the next subsection are given by

$$U_j(t) = \mp\,\mathrm{e}^{(k-j\pm 1)\pi\mathrm{i}/m}\lambda_{j,k}\, U_{k\pm 1}(t) \pm \mathrm{e}^{(k-j)\pi\mathrm{i}/m}\lambda_{j,k\pm 1}\, U_k(t), \tag{2.22}$$

the upper or lower signs being taken consistently throughout.

2.4. *Further asymptotic forms of the secondary solutions*

Let us assume that $2k\pi/m \leqslant \operatorname{ph} t \leqslant (2k+2)\pi/m$. Then $\operatorname{ph} t$ satisfies (2.15) with j replaced by either k or $k+1$. Substituting in the right hand side of (2.22), with upper signs, by means of (2.12) we derive

$$\begin{aligned} U_j(t) = {} & \mathrm{i}^{k-1}\mathrm{e}^{-j\pi\mathrm{i}/m}\lambda_{j,k}\, t^{\frac{1}{4}(2-m)} \exp\{(t\,\mathrm{e}^{-2k\pi\mathrm{i}/m})^{\frac{1}{2}m}\}\{1 + \vartheta_{k+1}(t)\} \\ & + \mathrm{i}^{k}\mathrm{e}^{-j\pi\mathrm{i}/m}\lambda_{j,k+1}\, t^{\frac{1}{4}(2-m)} \exp\{-(t\,\mathrm{e}^{-2k\pi\mathrm{i}/m})^{\frac{1}{2}m}\}\{1 + \vartheta_k(t)\}, \end{aligned} \tag{2.23}$$

where $\vartheta_k(t)$ and $\vartheta_{k+1}(t)$ are subject to (2.14).

At this stage it is convenient to introduce some terminology apropos the sector $\boldsymbol{S}_k$. First, we call the ray $\operatorname{ph} t = (2k+1)\,\pi/m$ the *left boundary of* $\boldsymbol{S}_k$, owing to its orientation when viewed from the vertex at $t = 0$. Similarly $\operatorname{ph} t = (2k-1)\,\pi/m$ is called the *right boundary of* $\boldsymbol{S}_k$. Next, we call the sectors

$$2k\pi/m \leqslant \operatorname{ph} t \leqslant (2k+1)\,\pi/m, \quad (2k-1)\,\pi/m \leqslant \operatorname{ph} t \leqslant 2k\pi/m,$$

the *left* and *right parts of* $\boldsymbol{S}_k$, respectively. And if δ is a constant such that $0 < \delta < 1$ we call

$$(2k-\delta)\,\pi/m \leqslant \operatorname{ph} t \leqslant (2k+\delta)\,\pi/m$$

an *internal part of* $\boldsymbol{S}_k$.

With these definitions, (2.23) is valid in the left part of $\boldsymbol{S}_k$, and also in the right part of $\boldsymbol{S}_{k+1}$. The corresponding asymptotic approximation in the right part of $\boldsymbol{S}_k$ and the left part of $\boldsymbol{S}_{k-1}$ may be obtained by use of (2.22), with lower signs, or by changing k into $k-1$ in (2.23). Either way yields

$$\begin{aligned} U_j(t) = {} & \mathrm{i}^{k-1}\mathrm{e}^{-j\pi\mathrm{i}/m}\lambda_{j,k}\, t^{\frac{1}{4}(2-m)} \exp\{(t\,\mathrm{e}^{-2k\pi\mathrm{i}/m})^{\frac{1}{2}m}\}\{1+\vartheta_{k-1}(t)\} \\ & - \mathrm{i}^{k}\mathrm{e}^{-j\pi\mathrm{i}/m}\lambda_{j,k-1}\, t^{\frac{1}{4}(2-m)} \exp\{-(t\,\mathrm{e}^{-2k\pi\mathrm{i}/m})^{\frac{1}{2}m}\}\{1+\vartheta_{k}(t)\}. \end{aligned} \tag{2.24}$$

Analogous results for the derivative are expressed by

$$\begin{aligned} \mathrm{d}\{t^{\frac{1}{4}(m-2)}U_j(t)\}/\mathrm{d}t = {} & \tfrac{1}{2}m\mathrm{i}^{-k-1}\mathrm{e}^{-j\pi\mathrm{i}/m}\lambda_{j,k}\, t^{\frac{1}{2}(m-2)} \exp\{(t\,\mathrm{e}^{-2k\pi\mathrm{i}/m})^{\frac{1}{2}m}\}\{1+\vartheta^1_{k\pm1}(t)\} \\ & \mp \tfrac{1}{2}m\mathrm{i}^{-k}\mathrm{e}^{-j\pi\mathrm{i}/m}\lambda_{j,k\pm1}\, t^{\frac{1}{2}(m-2)} \exp\{-(t\,\mathrm{e}^{-2k\pi\mathrm{i}/m})^{\frac{1}{2}m}\}\{1+\vartheta^1_{k}(t)\}, \end{aligned} \tag{2.25}$$

the upper signs being taken when t lies in the left part of $\boldsymbol{S}_k$ (or the right part of $\boldsymbol{S}_{k+1}$), and the lower signs being taken when t lies in the right part of $\boldsymbol{S}_k$ (or the left part of $\boldsymbol{S}_{k-1}$).

2.5. *Auxiliary functions*

Throughout this subsection we assume that the conditions (2.19) and (2.20) are fulfilled, ensuring that $\lambda_{j,k} \neq 0$.

From (2.12), (2.23) and (2.24), we see that as $t \to \infty$ the solution $U_j(t)$ is recessive in $\boldsymbol{S}_j$ and dominant in $\boldsymbol{S}_k$; by symmetry $U_k(t)$ is dominant in $\boldsymbol{S}_j$ and recessive in $\boldsymbol{S}_k$. In consequence, $U_j(t)$ and $U_k(t)$ comprise a numerically satisfactory pair of solutions in the closed region $\boldsymbol{S}_j \cup \boldsymbol{S}_k$, except possibly in the neighbourhood of $t = 0$. For our purposes $U_j(t)$ and $U_k(t)$ comprise an appropriate solution basis in $\boldsymbol{S}_j \cup \boldsymbol{S}_k$, and in order to majorize these solutions in a satisfactory manner, we follow the procedure of § 8.3 of Olver (1974, ch. 11), and introduce auxiliary weight, modulus and phase functions, as follows.

We define a function $e(t)$ by the formula

$$e(t) = |\exp\{(-)^j t^{\frac{1}{2}m}\}| \quad (t \in \boldsymbol{S}_j), \tag{2.26}$$

for every integer j, where the branch of $t^{\frac{1}{2}m}$ is $|t|^{\frac{1}{2}m} \exp(\frac{1}{2}m\mathrm{i} \operatorname{ph} t)$. On the boundaries of $\boldsymbol{S}_j$ we have $e(t) = 1$, hence $e(t)$ is continuous everywhere. Furthermore, $e(t) \geqslant 1$. As weight function in $\boldsymbol{S}_j \cup \boldsymbol{S}_k$ we shall adopt $E_{j,k}(t)$, defined by

$$E_{j,k}(t) = 1/e(t) \quad (t \in \boldsymbol{S}_j); \quad E_{j,k}(t) = e(t) \quad (t \in \boldsymbol{S}_k). \tag{2.27}$$

Clearly $E_{j,k}$ is continuous, and $E_{j,k}(0) = 1$. Also, with $E^{-1}_{j,k}(t)$ denoting $1/E_{j,k}(t)$, we have

$$E_{k,j}(t) = E^{-1}_{j,k}(t) \quad (t \in \boldsymbol{S}_j \cup \boldsymbol{S}_k). \tag{2.28}$$

Modulus and phase functions are defined in $\boldsymbol{S}_j \cup \boldsymbol{S}_k$ by the equations

$$|U_j(t)| = E_{j,k}(t)\, M_{j,k}(t) \cos\theta_{j,k}(t), \quad |U_k(t)| = E^{-1}_{j,k}(t)\, M_{j,k}(t) \sin\theta_{j,k}(t), \tag{2.29}$$

$$|U'_j(t)| = E_{j,k}(t)\, N_{j,k}(t) \cos\omega_{j,k}(t), \quad |U'_k(t)| = E^{-1}_{j,k}(t)\, N_{j,k}(t) \sin\omega_{j,k}(t). \tag{2.30}$$

In consequence

$$M_{j,k}(t) = \{E_{j,k}^{-2}(t)\,|U_j(t)|^2 + E_{j,k}^2(t)\,|U_k(t)|^2\}^{\frac{1}{2}},$$

$$N_{j,k}(t) = \{E_{j,k}^{-2}(t)\,|U_j'(t)|^2 + E_{j,k}^2(t)\,|U_k'(t)|^2\}^{\frac{1}{2}},$$

$$\theta_{j,k}(t) = \arctan\{E_{j,k}^2(t)\,|U_k(t)/U_j(t)|\},$$

$$\omega_{j,k}(t) = \arctan\{E_{j,k}^2(t)\,|U_k'(t)/U_j'(t)|\}.$$

Each of the functions $M_{j,k}(t)$, $\theta_{j,k}(t)$, $N_{j,k}(t)$ and $\omega_{j,k}(t)$ is continuous in $\boldsymbol{S}_j \cup \boldsymbol{S}_k$, except that $N_{j,k}(t)$ has an infinity at $t = 0$ when $0 < m \leqslant 1$. Symmetry properties follow from (2.28), and are given by

$$M_{j,k}(t) = M_{k,j}(t), \quad \theta_{j,k}(t) + \theta_{k,j}(t) = \tfrac{1}{2}\pi, \tag{2.31}$$

$$N_{j,k}(t) = N_{k,j}(t), \quad \omega_{j,k}(t) + \omega_{k,j}(t) = \tfrac{1}{2}\pi. \tag{2.32}$$

At the origin

$$M_{j,k}(0) = 2^{\frac{1}{2}}|U(0)|, \quad \theta_{j,k}(0) = \omega_{j,k}(0) = \tfrac{1}{4}\pi, \tag{2.33}$$

$$N_{j,k}(0) = 2^{\frac{1}{2}}|U'(0)| \quad (m > 1); \quad N_{j,k}(0) = \infty \quad (0 < m \leqslant 1). \tag{2.34}$$

The asymptotic behaviour of the modulus functions for large $|t|$ may be deduced from (2.12), (2.13), (2.23), (2.24) and (2.25). In internal parts of $\boldsymbol{S}_j$ and $\boldsymbol{S}_k$ we find that

$$M_{j,k}(t) \sim (1+\lambda_{j,k}^2)^{\frac{1}{2}}|t|^{\frac{1}{4}(2-m)}, \tag{2.35}$$

$$N_{j,k}(t) \sim \tfrac{1}{2}m(1+\lambda_{j,k}^2)^{\frac{1}{2}}|t|^{\frac{1}{4}(m-2)}. \tag{2.36}$$

And in these circumstances the phase functons $\theta_{j,k}(t)$ and $\omega_{j,k}(t)$ tend to constant values, both values being arctan $|\lambda_{j,k}|$ in internal parts of $\boldsymbol{S}_j$ and arccot $|\lambda_{j,k}|$ in internal parts of $\boldsymbol{S}_k$.

In the full domain $\boldsymbol{S}_j \cup \boldsymbol{S}_k$ the modulus and phase functions fluctuate as $t \to \infty$. In the case of $M_{j,k}(t)$ we shall employ the following uniform bound, again derived from (2.12), (2.23) and (2.24):

$$M_{j,k}(t) \leqslant C_{j,k}\,|t|^{\frac{1}{4}(2-m)}\{1+\mathcal{O}(t^{\frac{1}{2}m})\} \quad (t \in \boldsymbol{S}_j \cup \boldsymbol{S}_k), \tag{2.37}$$

where

$$C_{j,k} = \max[\{1+(|\lambda_{j,k}|+|\lambda_{j,k+1}|)^2\}^{\frac{1}{2}}, \ \{1+(|\lambda_{j,k}|+|\lambda_{j,k-1}|)^2\}^{\frac{1}{2}}]. \tag{2.38}$$

No such simple bound is available for $N_{j,k}(t)$, and for this reason we shall sometimes find it convenient to work in terms of another pair of modulus and phase functions, defined by

$$|\mathrm{d}\{t^{\frac{1}{4}(m-2)}U_j(t)\}/\mathrm{d}t| = |t|^{\frac{1}{4}(m-2)}E_{j,k}(t)\,\hat{N}_{j,k}(t)\cos\hat{\omega}_{j,k}(t), \tag{2.39}$$

$$|\mathrm{d}\{t^{\frac{1}{4}(m-2)}U_k(t)\}/\mathrm{d}t| = |t|^{\frac{1}{4}(m-2)}E_{j,k}^{-1}(t)\,\hat{N}_{j,k}(t)\sin\hat{\omega}_{j,k}(t). \tag{2.40}$$

Some of the corresponding properties of $\hat{N}_{j,k}(t)$ and $\hat{\omega}_{j,k}(t)$ are given by

$$\left.\begin{aligned} \hat{N}_{j,k}(t) &= |t|^{\frac{1}{4}(2-m)}[E_{j,k}^{-2}(t)\,|\mathrm{d}\{t^{\frac{1}{4}(m-2)}U_j(t)\}/\mathrm{d}t|^2 + E_{j,k}^2(t)\,|\,\mathrm{d}\{t^{\frac{1}{4}(m-2)}U_k(t)\}/\mathrm{d}t|^2]^{\frac{1}{2}},\\ \hat{\omega}_{j,k}(t) &= \arctan[E_{j,k}^2(t)\,|\mathrm{d}\{t^{\frac{1}{4}(m-2)}U_k(t)\}/\mathrm{d}t|/|\mathrm{d}\{t^{\frac{1}{4}(m-2)}U_j(t)\}/\mathrm{d}t|],\\ \hat{N}_{j,k}(t) &= \hat{N}_{k,j}(t), \quad \hat{\omega}_{j,k}(t)+\hat{\omega}_{k,j}(t) = \tfrac{1}{2}\pi, \quad \hat{\omega}_{j,k}(0) = \tfrac{1}{4}\pi, \end{aligned}\right\} \tag{2.41}$$

and

$$\hat{N}_{j,k}(t) \sim \tfrac{1}{2}m(1+\lambda_{j,k}^2)^{\frac{1}{2}}|t|^{\frac{1}{4}(m-2)} \tag{2.42}$$

as $t \to \infty$ in internal parts of $\boldsymbol{S}_j$ and $\boldsymbol{S}_k$. Lastly,

$$\hat{N}_{j,k}(t) \leqslant \tfrac{1}{2}mC_{j,k}|t|^{\frac{1}{4}(m-2)}\{1+\mathcal{O}(t^{\frac{1}{2}m})\} \quad (t \in \boldsymbol{S}_j \cup \boldsymbol{S}_k). \tag{2.43}$$

3. Main approximation theorem

3.1. *Primary assumptions*

In this section we seek approximate solutions of the differential equation

$$d^2w/dz^2 = \{u^2f(u,z)+g(u,z)\}w, \tag{3.1}$$

in which u is a positive parameter and z ranges over a bounded or unbounded open complex domain $\boldsymbol{D}$, which may depend on u. We suppose c to be a given interior point of $\boldsymbol{D}$, which may depend on u, and m to be a positive constant. Then $(z-c)^{2-m}f(u,z)$ is assumed to be holomorphic and non-vanishing throughout $\boldsymbol{D}$, including c. The function $g(u,z)$, also, is assumed to be holomorphic in $\boldsymbol{D}$ except possibly at c; at this point we require

$$g(u,z) = O\{(z-c)^{\gamma-1}\} \quad (z\to c), \tag{3.2}$$

where γ is a positive constant. (Condition (3.2) suffices for our present purposes, but it could be eased somewhat without affecting the final conclusions.)

Because $f(u,z)$ and $g(u,z)$ may have branch-points at c, we do not confine $\boldsymbol{D}$ to a single Riemann sheet. Any number of sheets may be used, provided that $\boldsymbol{D}$ is simply connected on the aggregate Riemann surface.

3.2. *Preliminary definitions and transformations*

Following the treatment of the real-variable case given in Olver (1977*a*, §3.1), we introduce a new variable $\zeta = \zeta(u,z)$, defined by

$$\zeta = \left\{\int_c^z f^{\frac{1}{2}}(u,t)\,dt\right\}^{2/m}. \tag{3.3}$$

The branches of the fractional powers in this relation are determined as follows. Let the Taylor-series expansion of $(z-c)^{2-m}f(u,z)$ in the neighbourhood of c be denoted by

$$(z-c)^{2-m}f(u,z) = f_0+f_1(z-c)+f_2(z-c)^2+\dots, \tag{3.4}$$

where $f_0 \neq 0$. Substituting for $f(u,z)$ in (3.3) and integrating term by term, we find that ζ has a Taylor-series expansion that begins

$$\zeta = \left(\frac{2}{m}\right)^{2/m} f_0^{1/m}(z-c)\left\{1+\frac{1}{m+2}\frac{f_1}{f_0}(z-c)+\dots\right\}. \tag{3.5}$$

We select any branch of the coefficient $f_0^{1/m}$ that is convenient. This fixes the relation between ζ and z in the neighbourhood of c; elsewhere ζ is determined by continuity.

Having prescribed $\zeta(u,z)$ in a unique manner we define $\boldsymbol{\Delta}$ to be the map of $\boldsymbol{D}$ on the ζ-plane. Like $\boldsymbol{D}$, $\boldsymbol{\Delta}$ is a domain that may lie on an enumerable set of Riemann sheets. We suppose, however, that $\boldsymbol{D}$ *is restricted in such a way that the mapping from* $\boldsymbol{D}$ *on to* $\boldsymbol{\Delta}$ *is one-to-one*. In particular, this means that the only point of $\boldsymbol{D}$ at which the right hand side of (3.3) may vanish is c. And since the only possible zero or singularity of $f(u,z)$ is located at c, it follows that $\zeta(u,z)$ is holomorphic in $\boldsymbol{D}$, and therefore that the mapping from $\boldsymbol{D}$ on to $\boldsymbol{\Delta}$ is conformal.

Next, for every integer j we define $\boldsymbol{D}_j$ to be the map on the z-plane of $\boldsymbol{\Delta} \cap \boldsymbol{S}_j$, where $\boldsymbol{S}_j$ is the sector defined in §2.2. We call $\boldsymbol{D}_j$ a *principal region associated with the transition point* c. (Although $\boldsymbol{D}_j$ is simply connected, it is not necessarily connected, and therefore may not be a domain in the ordinary sense.)

A simple illustration is provided by taking

$$f(u,z) = z^2/(1-z)^6, \quad g(u,z) = 0,$$

with $\boldsymbol{D}$ comprising the z-plane after removal of the interval $[1,\infty)$. In this case equation (3.1) has a double turning point at the origin and an irregular singularity at $z=1$. From (3.3) with $c=0$ and $m=4$, we find that ζ is given in terms of z by the fractional linear transformation

$$\zeta = z/\{2^{\frac{1}{2}}(1-z)\}.$$

Corresponding regions of the mapping are indicated in figures 2 and 3. The turning point remains at the origin, and the points $z=1$ and ∞ are projected to $\zeta=\infty$ and $-2^{-\frac{1}{2}}$, respectively. Thus $\varDelta$ comprises the whole ζ-plane with the interval $(-\infty, -2^{-\frac{1}{2}}]$ deleted. The mapping is one-to-one, as required, and the boundaries of the principal regions are circular arcs and also, in the case of $\boldsymbol{D}_2$, the interval $[1,\infty)$.

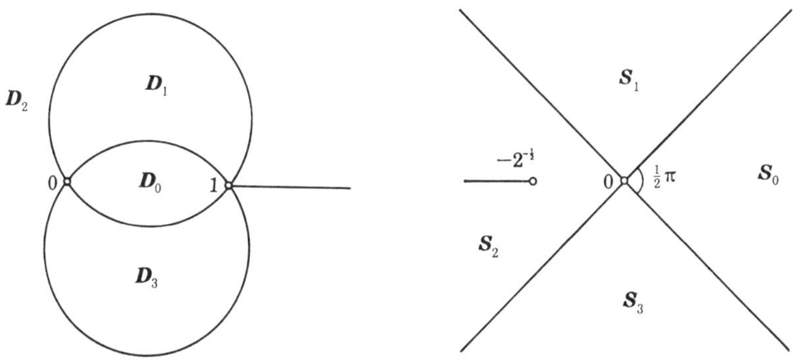

FIGURE 2. z-plane.

FIGURE 3. ζ-plane.

Returning to the general problem, we continue to follow Olver (1977*a*, §3.1), and define

$$\hat{f}(u,z) = \frac{4f(u,z)}{m^2\zeta^{m-2}} = \left(\frac{d\zeta}{dz}\right)^2; \tag{3.6}$$

compare (3.3). Evidently $\hat{f}(u,z)$ is holomorphic and non-vanishing in $\boldsymbol{D}$.

Next, we introduce a balancing function $\Omega(t)$. This is any convenient positive real function of the complex variable t that is continuous and satisfies the condition

$$\Omega(t) = O(t^{\frac{1}{2}(m-2)}), \tag{3.7}$$

uniformly in the neighbourhood of $t=\infty$. An admissible choice is given by†

$$\Omega(t) = (1+|t|^{\frac{1}{2}m})/(1+|t|). \tag{3.8}$$

Associated with $\Omega(t)$ we define $\rho_{j,k}$ to be the constant

$$\rho_{j,k} = \sup_{t\in \boldsymbol{S}_j \cup \boldsymbol{S}_k} \{\Omega(t)\, M^2_{j,k}(t)\}. \tag{3.9}$$

In consequence of (2.37), (3.7) and the fact that $M_{j,k}(t)$ is continuous in $\boldsymbol{S}_j \cup \boldsymbol{S}_k$, the value of $\rho_{j,k}$ is always finite.

† The choice $1+|t|^{\frac{1}{2}(m-2)}$ that was used in the real-variable case is also suitable here when $m \geqslant 2$, but not when $0 < m < 2$ because of discontinuous behaviour at the origin.

Lastly, we introduce the *error-control function*

$$H(u,z) \equiv \int \left\{ \frac{1}{f^{\frac{1}{4}}(u,z)} \frac{d^2}{dz^2} \left(\frac{1}{f^{\frac{1}{4}}(u,z)} \right) - \frac{g(u,z)}{f^{\frac{1}{2}}(u,z)} \right\} \frac{dz}{\Omega(u^{2/m}\zeta)}. \tag{3.10}$$

Any branches of $f^{\frac{1}{4}}(u,z)$ and $f^{\frac{1}{2}}(u,z)$ may be used, provided they are continuous in $\boldsymbol{D}$ and the latter is the square of the former. The choice of integration constant is immaterial.

3.3. *Statement of theorem*

THEOREM 3.1. *With the assumptions of* § 3.1 *and the definitions of* §§ 2 *and* 3.2, *let A and B be arbitrary real or complex constants, and a_j be an arbitrarily chosen reference point in the closure of $\boldsymbol{D}_j$, including the point at infinity. Let $\boldsymbol{H}_k(a_j)$ comprise the set of points z in $\boldsymbol{D}_j \cup \boldsymbol{D}_k$ that can be joined to a_j by a path*† *$\mathscr{P}$ that lies in $\boldsymbol{D}_j \cup \boldsymbol{D}_k$ and satisfies the following monotonicity condition: as t travels along $\mathscr{P}$ from a_j to z the real part of*

$$\xi(u,z) \equiv \int_c^z f^{\frac{1}{2}}(u,t)\, dt \tag{3.11}$$

is non-decreasing, where the branch of this integral is continuous and has non-positive real part in $\boldsymbol{D}_j$ and non-negative real part in $\boldsymbol{D}_k$. Then with conditions (i), (ii) *and* (iii) *given below, equation* (3.1) *has a solution $w(u,z)$ that depends on A, B and a_j, is holomorphic in $\boldsymbol{D}$ punctured at c, and is continuous at c. Furthermore, when $z \in \boldsymbol{H}_k(a_j)$*

$$w(u,z) = f^{-\frac{1}{4}}(u,z)\{AU_j(u^{2/m}\zeta) + BU_k(u^{2/m}\zeta) + \epsilon(u,\zeta)\}, \tag{3.12}$$

where‡

$$\frac{|\epsilon(u,\zeta)|}{M_{j,k}(u^{2/m}\zeta)},\quad \frac{|\partial\epsilon(u,\zeta)/\partial\zeta|}{u^{2/m}N_{j,k}(u^{2/m}\zeta)},\quad \frac{|\partial\{\zeta^{\frac{1}{4}(m-2)}\epsilon(u,\zeta)\}/\partial\zeta|}{u^{2/m}|\zeta|^{\frac{1}{4}(m-2)}\hat{N}_{j,k}(u^{2/m}\zeta)}$$
$$\leqslant \frac{\sigma_{j,k}}{\rho_{j,k}} E_{j,k}(u^{2/m}\zeta)\left[\exp\left\{\frac{\rho_{j,k}}{m|\lambda_{j,k}|u^{2/m}} \mathscr{V}_{a_j,z}(H)\right\} - 1\right], \tag{3.13}$$

and

$$\sigma_{j,k} = \sup_{v \in \mathscr{Q}} \{\Omega(u^{2/m}v)\, E^{-1}_{j,k}(u^{2/m}v)\, M_{j,k}(u^{2/m}v)\, |AU_j(u^{2/m}v) + BU_k(u^{2/m}v)|\}, \tag{3.14}$$

$\lambda_{j,k}$ being defined by (2.17) *and* (2.18), *$\mathscr{Q}$ denoting the ζ-map of $\mathscr{P}$, and the variation of H in* (3.13) *being evaluated along $\mathscr{P}$.*

The supplementary conditions are as follows:

(i) k is an integer other than j. If m is a rational number of the form m_1/m_2 where $m_1 \neq 1$ and m_1 and m_2 are mutually prime positive integers, then we require $|k-j| < m_1$. For all other values of m, k is unrestricted.

(ii) If the ζ-map of a_j is at infinity, then we suppose that it is the point at infinity on a path $\mathscr{L}$ in $\boldsymbol{S}_j$ and require $\mathscr{P}$ to coincide with $\mathscr{L}$ in the neighbourhood of a_j.

(iii) When $z \in \boldsymbol{D}_k$ the bounds (3.13) apply only to the branch of $w(u,z)$ obtained by analytic continuation from $\boldsymbol{D}_j$ in the neighbourhood of c by rotation through an angle $2(k-j)\pi/m$, the sense of this angle being the same as the sign of $k-j$.

Remarks. (*a*) Any path $\mathscr{P}$ that satisfies the monotonicity condition of the theorem will be called a *progressive path*. It should be observed that when $z \in \boldsymbol{D}_k$ and $k-j = \pm 1$ it is possible to satisfy the monotonicity condition without the need for $\mathscr{P}$ to pass through c.

† Strictly, by 'path' we mean a Jordan arc composed of a finite chain of R_2 arcs in the sense defined in § 3.4 of Olver (1974, ch. 5).

‡ The symbol $\mathscr{V}$ denotes the variational operator as defined in § 11.5 of Olver (1974, ch. 1).

(*b*) For the theorem to be meaningful it is necessary that the right hand side of (3.13) be finite. In the first place this condition requires $\mathscr{V}_{\mathscr{P}}(H)$ to converge. Next, if k and j satisfy condition (i), then it is easily verified that (2.19) and (2.20) are satisfied, ensuring $1/|\lambda_{j,k}|$ is finite. It is also essential that $\sigma_{j,k}$ be finite. From the properties of the auxiliary functions given in § 2.5 and the assumed property (3.7) of the balancing function, it is seen that the content of the braces in (3.14) is finite at all finite points v in $\boldsymbol{S}_j \cup \boldsymbol{S}_k$, and bounded as $v \to \infty$ in $\boldsymbol{S}_k$. As $v \to \infty$ in an internal part of $\boldsymbol{S}_j$, however, the content of the braces in (3.14) is unbounded, unless $B = 0$. Accordingly, *if the ζ-map of a_j lies at infinity in an internal part of $\boldsymbol{S}_j$ then the theorem may be applied only in the case $B = 0$.*

(*c*) The asymptotic nature of the error bounds (3.13) for large values of u is investigated in section 4.

3.4. *Proof when c is a multiple turning point*

Throughout this subsection we suppose that m is a positive integer other than 1, and $g(u, z)$ is analytic at c. Thus the differential equation (3.1) has a turning point of multiplicity $m-2$ at c, and all solutions are analytic at c (as well as at all other points of $\boldsymbol{D}$).

On introducing a new dependent variable W given by

$$w = \dot{z}^{\frac{1}{2}} W, \tag{3.15}$$

where the dot signifies differentiation with respect to ζ, we have a Liouville transformation of (3.1) from the variables w and z to the variables W and ζ. The transformed equation is given by

$$\mathrm{d}^2 W/\mathrm{d}\zeta^2 = \{\tfrac{1}{4}m^2 u^2 \zeta^{m-2} + \phi(u, \zeta)\}\, W, \tag{3.16}$$

where

$$\phi(u, \zeta) = \dot{z}^{\frac{1}{2}}\{\mathrm{d}^2(\dot{z}^{-\frac{1}{2}})/\mathrm{d}\zeta^2\} + \dot{z}^2 g(u, z). \tag{3.17}$$

In the present circumstances $g(u, z)$ is holomorphic in $\boldsymbol{D}$. We also know that $z \equiv z(u, \zeta)$ is a holomorphic function of ζ in $\boldsymbol{\Delta}$ and $\dot{z}$ is non-vanishing. Hence $\phi(u, \zeta)$ is holomorphic in $\boldsymbol{\Delta}$.

From (3.6), (3.12) and (3.15) we see that

$$W = AU_j(u^{2/m}\zeta) + BU_k(u^{2/m}\zeta) + \epsilon(u, \zeta). \tag{3.18}$$

Next, from (2.1) with $t = u^{2/m}\zeta$ we derive

$$\mathrm{d}^2\{AU_j(u^{2/m}\zeta) + BU_k(u^{2/m}\zeta)\}/\mathrm{d}\zeta^2 = \tfrac{1}{4}m^2 u^2 \zeta^{m-2}\{AU_j(u^{2/m}\zeta) + BU_k(u^{2/m}\zeta)\}. \tag{3.19}$$

On substituting in (3.16) by means of (3.18) and then subtracting (3.19), we arrive at the following inhomogeneous differential equation for $\epsilon(u, \zeta)$:

$$\mathrm{d}^2\epsilon/\mathrm{d}\zeta^2 - \tfrac{1}{4}m^2 u^2 \zeta^{m-2}\epsilon = \phi(u, \zeta)\,\{AU_j(u^{2/m}\zeta) + BU_k(u^{2/m}\zeta) + \epsilon\}. \tag{3.20}$$

An equivalent integral equation is obtained by applying the method of variation of parameters and using the Wronskian relation (2.16); thus

$$\epsilon(u, \zeta) = \frac{\mathrm{i}}{mu^{2/m}} \int_{\alpha_j}^{\zeta} K(\zeta, v)\, \phi(u, v)\, \{AU_j(u^{2/m}v) + BU_k(u^{2/m}v) + \epsilon(u, v)\}\, \mathrm{d}v, \tag{3.21}$$

where $\zeta = \alpha_j$ corresponds to the reference point a_j, and

$$K(\zeta, v) = \mathrm{e}^{(j+k)\pi \mathrm{i}/m} \lambda_{j,k}^{-1} \{U_j(u^{2/m}\zeta)\, U_k(u^{2/m}v) - U_k(u^{2/m}\zeta)\, U_j(u^{2/m}v)\}. \tag{3.22}$$

The integration path in (3.21) is taken to be the ζ-map $\mathscr{Q}$ of $\mathscr{P}$. It therefore lies in $\boldsymbol{S}_j \cup \boldsymbol{S}_k$.

From (2.26), (2.27) and the definition of $\xi(u,z)$ it is seen that $E_{j,k}(u^{2/m}\zeta) = |e^{u\xi}|$. Hence in consequence of the monotonicity condition we have

$$E_{j,k}(u^{2/m}v) \leqslant E_{j,k}(u^{2/m}\zeta) \quad (v \in \mathscr{Q}). \tag{3.23}$$

Substituting in (3.22) by means of (2.29) and using (3.23), we find that

$$|K(\zeta,v)| \leqslant |\lambda_{j,k}^{-1}| E_{j,k}(u^{2/m}\zeta)\, E_{j,k}^{-1}(u^{2/m}v)\, M_{j,k}(u^{2/m}\zeta)\, M_{j,k}(u^{2/m}v). \tag{3.24}$$

Similarly,

$$|\partial K(\zeta,v)/\partial\zeta| \leqslant |\lambda_{j,k}^{-1}|\, u^{2/m} E_{j,k}(u^{2/m}\zeta)\, E_{j,k}^{-1}(u^{2/m}v)\, N_{j,k}(u^{2/m}\zeta)\, M_{j,k}(u^{2/m}v). \tag{3.25}$$

The integral equation (3.21) may now be solved by successive approximation, for example, by application of theorem 10.2 of Olver (1974, ch. 6). Provided that $\int \{|\phi(u,v)|/\Omega(u^{2/m}v)\}|dv|$ converges as $v \to \alpha_j$ along $\mathscr{Q}$ – and this will be justified shortly – we conclude that there is a unique solution $\epsilon(u,v)$ that is twice continuously differentiable along $\mathscr{Q}$ and enjoys the properties

$$\frac{\epsilon(u,v)}{E_{j,k}(u^{2/m}v)\, M_{j,k}(u^{2/m}v)}, \quad \frac{\partial\epsilon(u,v)/\partial v}{E_{j,k}(u^{2/m}v)\, N_{j,k}(u^{2/m}v)} \to 0$$

as $v \to \alpha_j$ along $\mathscr{Q}$. Furthermore, when $v \in \mathscr{Q}$

$$\frac{|\epsilon(u,v)|}{E_{j,k}(u^{2/m}v)\, M_{j,k}(u^{2/m}v)}, \quad \frac{|\partial\epsilon(u,v)/\partial v|}{u^{2/m}E_{j,k}(u^{2/m}v)\, N_{j,k}(u^{2/m}v)} \leqslant \frac{\sigma_{j,k}}{\rho_{j,k}}\left[\exp\left\{\frac{\rho_{j,k}}{m|\lambda_{j,k}|u^{2/m}}\int_{\alpha_j}^{v}\frac{|\phi(u,\tau)|}{\Omega(u^{2/m}\tau)}|d\tau|\right\} - 1\right], \tag{3.26}$$

where $\rho_{j,k}$ and $\sigma_{j,k}$ are defined by (3.9) and (3.14), respectively. In particular, these inequalities hold when $v = \zeta$. We now transform back to the z-plane in the manner of § 11.2 of Olver (1974, ch. 6) using the identity

$$H(u,z) = -\int \frac{\phi(u,\zeta)}{\Omega(u^{2/m}\zeta)}\, d\zeta, \tag{3.27}$$

obtained from (3.6), (3.10) and (3.17). This yields the first and second of the inequalities (3.13); it also establishes the convergence of the integral within the braces in (3.26) since $\mathscr{V}_{\mathscr{P}}(H)$ converges, by hypothesis.

To establish the remaining inequality in (3.13), we use the bound

$$|\partial\{\zeta^{\frac{1}{4}(m-2)}K(\zeta,v)\}/\partial\zeta| \leqslant |\lambda_{j,k}^{-1}|u^{2/m}|\zeta|^{\frac{1}{4}(m-2)}E_{j,k}(u^{2/m}\zeta)\, E_{j,k}^{-1}(u^{2/m}v)\, \hat{N}_{j,k}(u^{2/m}\zeta)\, M_{j,k}(u^{2/m}v), \tag{3.28}$$

obtained from (3.22) with the aid of (2.39) and (2.40).

Remark. With the conditions adopted in the opening paragraph of this subsection passage around any closed circuit in $\boldsymbol{D}$ leaves the solution $w(u,z)$ unchanged. Also, $M_{j,k+m}(u^{2/m}\zeta)$ is the same as $M_{j,k}(u^{2/m}\zeta)$, and so on. Hence in the present circumstances condition (i) of § 3.3 may be eased to $k \neq j \pmod m$.

3.5. *Proof in the general case: preliminaries*

When m is permitted to assume positive values other than 2, 3, 4, ..., and $g(u,z)$ may be singular at c, the analysis of § 3.4 can be retraced until we reach the integral equation (3.21), with the modification that $\phi(u,\zeta)$ may be singular at $\zeta = 0$. As we saw in §§ 2.1 and 2.2, $U_j(u^{2/m}\zeta)$ is continuous at $\zeta = 0$, but its derivative $U_j'(u^{2/m}\zeta)$ is infinite at this point for certain values of m. Similarly for $U_k(u^{2/m}\zeta)$. Hence although $\epsilon(u,v)$ represents a continuously differentiable solution of (3.20) on $\mathscr{Q} \cap \boldsymbol{S}_j$ and another continuously differentiable solution on $\mathscr{Q} \cap \boldsymbol{S}_k$, because of the discontinuity in $\partial e(u,v)/\partial v$ at $v = 0$ it is no longer obvious how the two solutions are related.

In order to resolve this difficulty we now suppose that $\mathscr{Q}$ denotes an arbitrary path in $\varDelta \cap (\boldsymbol{S}_j \cup \boldsymbol{S}_k)$ that begins at α_j and terminates at an arbitrary point β_k in $\boldsymbol{S}_k$. We shall suppose that $E_{j,k}(u^{2/m}v)$ is non-decreasing as v travels along $\mathscr{Q}$ from α_j to β_k; in other words, $\mathscr{Q}$ has to be the map of a progressive path in the sense defined in remark (*a*) of § 3.3. Next, we denote by $\boldsymbol{S}_{j,k}$ the union of $\boldsymbol{S}_j$, $\boldsymbol{S}_k$ and all intervening sectors, that is, $\boldsymbol{S}_{j+1}, \boldsymbol{S}_{j+2}, \ldots, \boldsymbol{S}_{k-1}$ if $k > j$, or $\boldsymbol{S}_{j-1}, \boldsymbol{S}_{j-2}, \ldots, \boldsymbol{S}_{k+1}$ if $k < j$. Instead of solving (3.21) directly on $\mathscr{Q}$, we first indent $\mathscr{Q}$ in the neighbourhood of the origin by a circular arc of radius $\varpi^{2/m}$, where ϖ is a positive constant that is sufficiently small to ensure that this indentation is contained in $\varDelta \cap \boldsymbol{S}_{j,k}$. The indented path will be denoted by $\mathscr{Q}_\varpi$. As we travel along $\mathscr{Q}_\varpi$ from α_j to β_k, we suppose that the origin is passed in the positive or negative rotational sense according as $k > j$ or $k < j$; compare figure 4.

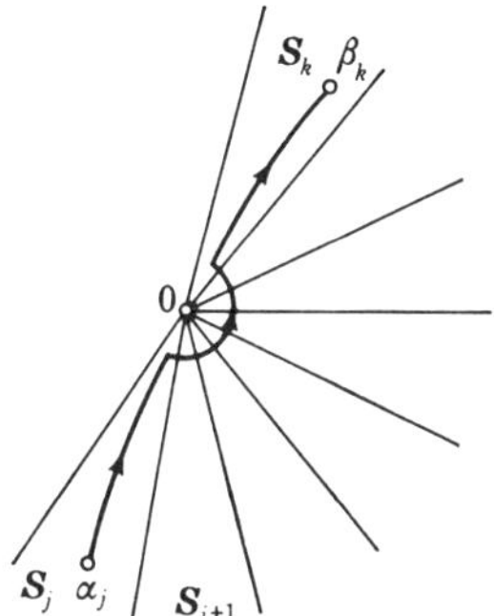

FIGURE 4. ζ-plane: path $\mathscr{Q}_\varpi$ when $k > j$.

We shall need another expression for the kernel of the integral equation (3.21), given by

$$K(\zeta, v) = e^{(p+q)\pi i/m}\lambda_{p,q}^{-1}\{U_p(u^{2/m}\zeta)\, U_q(u^{2/m}v) - U_q(u^{2/m}\zeta)\, U_p(u^{2/m}v)\}. \tag{3.29}$$

Here p and q are any two integers such that $\lambda_{p,q} \neq 0$. This formula is obtainable from (2.21) and (3.22) by straightforward substitutions.

We shall also need to associate certain auxiliary functions with $\boldsymbol{S}_{j,k}$ in addition to those of § 2.5. First, we define a weight function $\bar{E}_{j,k}(t)$ by the formulae

$$\bar{E}_{j,k}(t) = 1/e(t) \quad (t \in \boldsymbol{S}_j); \quad \bar{E}_{j,k}(t) = e(t) \quad (t \notin \boldsymbol{S}_j).$$

Clearly $\bar{E}_{j,k}(t)$ is continuous in $\boldsymbol{S}_{j,k}$. Secondly, we denote by $\{j,k\}$ the set of all integers from j to k, inclusive. Then for every $p \in \{j,k\}$ and $t \in \boldsymbol{S}_p$ we define

$$\bar{M}_{j,k}(t) = \max_{q \neq p}\{M_{p,q}(t)\} \quad (q \in \{j,k\}).$$

Since each modulus function $M_{p,q}(t)$ is continuous in $\boldsymbol{S}_p$ it is easily seen that $\bar{M}_{j,k}(t)$ is continuous in $\boldsymbol{S}_{j,k}$, except possibly on the boundaries of the sectors that intervene between $\boldsymbol{S}_j$ and $\boldsymbol{S}_k$. In order to prove that $\bar{M}_{j,k}(t)$ is continuous on these boundaries, we assume temporarily that $k > j$, and let t be any point on the left boundary of $\boldsymbol{S}_p$, where $j \leqslant p \leqslant k-1$. On referring to the definition (2.10) and rotating the t-plane, we see that $U_p(t) = U_{p+1}(t')$, where t' is the point on the left boundary of $\boldsymbol{S}_{p+1}$ such that $|t'| = |t|$. Again, from (2.10) and the fact that $U(t)$ is real on the positive real t-axis it follows that $U_{p+1}(t)$ and $U_{p+1}(t')$ are complex conjugates. Hence $|U_p(t)| = |U_{p+1}(t)|$. This implies that $\bar{M}_{j,k}(t)$ has the same value whether t be counted as a member of

S_p or S_{p+1}. Therefore $\bar{M}_{j,k}(t)$ is continuous on the boundary $S_p \cap S_{p+1}$. Similar analysis may also be used when $k < j$, and we therefore conclude that $\bar{M}_{j,k}(t)$ *is continuous throughout* $S_{j,k}$.

In an analogous manner, for every $p \in \{j,k\}$ and $t \in S_p$ we define

$$\bar{N}_{j,k}(t) = \max_{q \neq p} \{N_{p,q}(t)\} \quad (q \in \{j,k\}).$$

By similar analysis we see that $\bar{N}_{j,k}(t)$ is continuous in $S_{j,k}$, except at $t = 0$ when $0 < m \leqslant 1$.

From the definitions of $\bar{M}_{j,k}(t)$ and $\bar{N}_{j,k}(t)$ it is immediately clear that

$$\bar{M}_{j,k}(t) = \bar{M}_{k,j}(t), \quad \bar{N}_{j,k}(t) = \bar{N}_{k,j}(t). \tag{3.30}$$

Also, from the asymptotic properties of $M_{j,k}(t)$ and $N_{j,k}(t)$ given in §2.5, we derive

$$\bar{M}_{j,k}(t) = O(t^{\frac{1}{4}(2-m)}), \quad \bar{N}_{j,k}(t) = O(t^{\frac{1}{4}(m-2)}), \quad (t \to \infty \text{ in } S_{j,k}). \tag{3.31}$$

3.6. *Proof in the general case: conclusion*

Lemma. *If v and ζ are points of $\mathcal{Q}_\varpi$ in the order α_j, v, ζ, β_k, then*

$$|K(\zeta, v)| \leqslant \bar{\lambda}_{j,k}^{-1} e^{2u\varpi} \bar{E}_{j,k}(u^{2/m}\zeta)\, \bar{E}_{j,k}^{-1}(u^{2/m}v)\, \bar{M}_{j,k}(u^{2/m}\zeta)\, \bar{M}_{j,k}(u^{2/m}v), \tag{3.32}$$

$$|\partial K(\zeta, v)/\partial \zeta| \leqslant \bar{\lambda}_{j,k}^{-1} u^{2/m} e^{2u\varpi} \bar{E}_{j,k}(u^{2/m}\zeta)\, \bar{E}_{j,k}^{-1}(u^{2/m}v)\, \bar{N}_{j,k}(u^{2/m}\zeta)\, \bar{M}_{j,k}(u^{2/m}v), \tag{3.33}$$

where

$$\bar{\lambda}_{j,k} = \min_{p \neq q} |\lambda_{p,q}| \quad (p \in \{j,k\}, \quad q \in \{j,k\}). \tag{3.34}$$

To prove this result, we note first that the constant $\bar{\lambda}_{j,k}$ is non-zero. This follows from condition (i) of §3.3 and the definitions (2.17) and (2.18) by observing that $0 < |q-p| \leqslant |k-j|$. Next, we observe that details of the proof need be supplied only when $k > j$: the analysis for $k < j$ is exactly similar. We denote the part of $\mathcal{Q}_\varpi$ that coincides with the circular arc of radius $\varpi^{2/m}$ by $\mathcal{I}_\varpi$. There are five cases to consider.

(i) Suppose that $\zeta \in S_j$. Then $v \in S_j$. The inequality (3.23) applies unless $\zeta \in \mathcal{I}_\varpi \cap S_j$. However, from the definition of $E_{j,k}$ (§2.5) it is easily verified that the weaker inequality

$$E_{j,k}(u^{2/m}v) \leqslant e^{u\varpi} E_{j,k}(u^{2/m}\zeta) \tag{3.35}$$

applies without restriction. Substituting in (3.22) by means of (2.29) and using (3.35), we find that

$$|K(\zeta, v)| \leqslant |\lambda_{j,k}^{-1}|\, e^{2u\varpi} E_{j,k}(u^{2/m}\zeta)\, E_{j,k}^{-1}(u^{2/m}v)\, M_{j,k}(u^{2/m}\zeta)\, M_{j,k}(u^{2/m}v); \tag{3.36}$$

compare (3.24).

(ii) Suppose that $\zeta \in S_q$, where $j+1 \leqslant q \leqslant k$, and $v \in S_j$. Then from (3.29) with $p = j$ we have

$$|K(\zeta, v)| \leqslant \bar{\lambda}_{j,k}^{-1} |U_j(u^{2/m}\zeta)\, U_q(u^{2/m}v) - U_q(u^{2/m}\zeta)\, U_j(u^{2/m}v)|.$$

Referring to (2.29) and (2.27) and recalling that $e(t) \geqslant 1$ for all t, we derive

$$|K(\zeta, v)| \leqslant \bar{\lambda}_{j,k}^{-1} e(u^{2/m}\zeta)\, e(u^{2/m}v)\, M_{j,q}(u^{2/m}\zeta)\, M_{j,q}(u^{2/m}v).$$

(iii) Suppose that $\zeta \in S_q$ and $v \in S_p$, where $j+1 \leqslant p \leqslant q-1$ and $j+2 \leqslant q \leqslant k$. Then $v \in \mathcal{I}_\varpi$. From (3.29) we derive

$$|K(\zeta, v)| \leqslant \bar{\lambda}_{j,k}^{-1} |U_p(u^{2/m}\zeta)\, U_q(u^{2/m}v) - U_q(u^{2/m}\zeta)\, U_p(u^{2/m}v)|.$$

Since $|v| = \varpi^{2/m}$ it follows that

$$e(u^{2/m}v) \leqslant e^{2u\varpi} e^{-1}(u^{2/m}v),$$

and hence that

$$|K(\zeta, v)| \leqslant \bar{\lambda}_{j,k}^{-1} e^{2u\varpi} e(u^{2/m}\zeta)\, e^{-1}(u^{2/m}v)\, M_{p,q}(u^{2/m}\zeta)\, M_{p,q}(u^{2/m}v).$$

(iv) Suppose that $\zeta \in S_q$ and $v \in S_q$, where $j+1 \leqslant q \leqslant k-1$. Then we use (3.29) with p replaced by j. Using reasoning similar to that of (iii), we arrive at

$$|K(\zeta, v)| \leqslant \bar{\lambda}_{j,k}^{-1} e^{2u\varpi} e(u^{2/m}\zeta)\, e^{-1}(u^{2/m}v)\, M_{j,q}(u^{2/m}\zeta)\, M_{j,q}(u^{2/m}v).$$

(v) Lastly, suppose that $\zeta \in S_k$ and $v \in S_k$. Then (3.35) holds and from (3.22) we deduce that (3.36) again applies.

All possible combinations have now been covered, and by combining the results and referring to the definitions and properties of $E_{j,k}$, $M_{j,k}$, $\bar{E}_{j,k}$ and $\bar{M}_{j,k}$ given in §§2.5 and 3.5, we perceive that (3.32) applies in all cases. The proof of (3.33) is similar.

Having established the bounds (3.32) and (3.33), we may solve the integral equation (3.21) along $\mathscr{Q}_\varpi$ by application of theorem 10.2 of Olver (1974, ch. 6). Corresponding to (3.26) we find that

$$\frac{|\epsilon(u,\zeta)|}{\bar{E}_{j,k}(u^{2/m}\zeta)\, \bar{M}_{j,k}(u^{2/m}\zeta)}, \quad \frac{|\partial\epsilon(u,\zeta)/\partial\zeta|}{u^{2/m}\bar{E}_{j,k}(u^{2/m}\zeta)\, \bar{N}_{j,k}(u^{2/m}\zeta)} \leqslant \frac{\bar{\sigma}_{j,k}}{\bar{\rho}_{j,k}}\left[\exp\left\{\frac{e^{2u\varpi}\bar{\rho}_{j,k}}{m\bar{\lambda}_{j,k}u^{2/m}}\int_{\alpha_j}^{\zeta}\frac{|\phi(u,v)|}{\Omega(u^{2/m}v)}|dv|\right\}-1\right], \tag{3.37}$$

where the integral is evaluated along $\mathscr{Q}_\varpi$,

$$\bar{\rho}_{j,k} = \sup_{t \in S_{j,k}} \{\Omega(t)\, \bar{M}_{j,k}^2(t)\}, \tag{3.38}$$

and

$$\bar{\sigma}_{j,k} = \sup_{v \in \mathscr{Q}_\varpi} \{\Omega(u^{2/m}v)\, \bar{E}_{j,k}^{-1}(u^{2/m}v)\, \bar{M}_{j,k}(u^{2/m}v)\, |AU_j(u^{2/m}v) + BU_k(u^{2/m}v)|\}. \tag{3.39}$$

In consequence of (3.7) and the first of (3.31) $\bar{\rho}_{j,k}$ is always finite. Also, $\bar{\sigma}_{j,k}$ is finite whenever $\sigma_{j,k}$ is finite; compare remark (*b*) of §3.3. Moreover, because $\epsilon(u,\zeta)$ is twice continuously differentiable along $\mathscr{Q}_\varpi$, it satisfies the differential equation (3.20) everywhere on $\mathscr{Q}_\varpi$.

Let us now suppose that ζ is any prescribed point of $\mathscr{Q} \cap S_k$, other than the origin, and consider the behaviour of the integral

$$\int_{\mathscr{I}_\varpi} K(\zeta, v)\, \phi(u,v)\, \{AU_j(u^{2/m}v) + BU_k(u^{2/m}v) + \epsilon(u,v)\}\, dv \tag{3.40}$$

as $\varpi \to 0$. First, since each of the functions appearing within the braces on the right hand side of (3.39) is a continuous function of v at the origin, it follows that $\bar{\sigma}_{j,k}$ is bounded as $\varpi \to 0$. Next, from (3.2), (3.5) and (3.17) we deduce that

$$\phi(u,v) = O(v^{\gamma_1 - 1}) \quad (v \to 0),$$

where $\gamma_1 = \min(\gamma, 1)$. Substituting in (3.37) by means of these results, we conclude that $|\epsilon(u,v)|$ is bounded as $\varpi \to 0$, the bound being uniform with respect to $v \in \mathscr{I}_\varpi$. Lastly, since we also know that $K(\zeta, v)$ is a continuous function of v we deduce that the integral (3.40) vanishes as $\varpi \to 0$.

We have therefore established that when $\zeta \in \mathscr{Q} \cap S_k$ and $\zeta \neq 0$, the solution $\epsilon(u,\zeta)$ of the differential equation (3.20) obtained by analytic continuation along $\mathscr{I}_\varpi$ from S_j to S_k also satisfies the integral equation (3.21) along $\mathscr{Q}$. Furthermore, $\epsilon(u,\zeta)$ is continuous on $\mathscr{Q}$, including the origin. Now we can also construct a solution of (3.21) on $\mathscr{Q}$ by use of (3.24) and direct application of the method of successive approximations.† Furthermore, this method also shows that: (i) there is only one solution that is continuous on $\mathcal{Q}$ and has the property

$$\epsilon(u, \zeta) = \bar{E}_{j,k}(u^{2/m}\zeta)\, \bar{M}_{j,k}(u^{2/m}\zeta)\, O(1)$$

as $\zeta \to \alpha_j$ and also as $\zeta \to \beta_k$; (ii) this solution is subject to the bounds (3.26).

The remainder of the proof is completed as in §3.4.

3.7. *Additional remark on theorem* 3.1

It might be thought that the condition on k imposed by §3.3 (i) is a consequence of the method of proof that we have adopted. This is not so, however, and the underlying reason is as follows. Let $m = m_1/m_2$, where m_1 and m_2 are mutually prime and $m_1 > 1$. Suppose also that $B = 0$ and $k-j = \pm m_1$. Then $\lambda_{j,k} = 0$, and from (2.23) and (2.24) we see that the approximant $f^{-\frac{1}{4}}(u, z)\, AU_j(u^{2/m}\zeta)$ in (3.12) is recessive as $\zeta \to \infty$ in $\boldsymbol{S}_k$, in contrast to its dominant behaviour in all sectors that intervene between $\boldsymbol{S}_j$ and $\boldsymbol{S}_k$. We cannot expect the true solution $w(u, z)$ to be recessive in exactly the same circumstances.

4. Asymptotic estimates of the error terms

4.1. *Preliminary remarks*

The inequalities for the error term and its derivative supplied by theorem 3.1 are valid for *any* value of the positive parameter u. In §1 it was stated that the object of the present paper is to construct uniform asymptotic solutions of the differential equation (1.2) as $u \to \infty$. Accordingly, we now consider circumstances in which the error term is sufficiently small for the theorem to supply meaningful approximations when u is large. On referring to (2.29), (2.30) and (3.12) we see that in the archetypal case, $A = 1$ and $B = 0$, we require

$$\epsilon(u, \zeta) = E_{j,k}(u^{2/m}\zeta)\, M_{j,k}(u^{2/m}\zeta)\, o(1), \quad \partial\epsilon(u, \zeta)/\partial\zeta = E_{j,k}(u^{2/m}\zeta)\, N_{j,k}(u^{2/m}\zeta)\, o(u^{2/m}),$$

as $u \to \infty$, uniformly with respect to z. Again, when $A = 1$ and $B = 0$ it is seen from (2.29), (3.9) and (3.14) that $\sigma_{j,k} \leqslant \rho_{j,k}$. Hence from (3.13) both asymptotic conditions just given are met when

$$\mathscr{V}_{a_j, a_k}(H) = o(u^{2/m}) \quad (u \to \infty), \tag{4.1}$$

this variation being taken along the progressive path $\mathscr{P}$.

Whether the condition (4.1) is satisfied depends largely on the manner in which the parameter u enters the functions $f(u, z)$ and $g(u, z)$, and each application may be examined on its merits. In practice, a commonly occurring case is that in which $f(u, z)$ and $g(u, z)$ are independent of u. Some simplifications then become available; for example, the principal regions are independent of u. In the present section we shall examine this case in detail, using analysis similar to that for real variables given in §5 of Olver (1977*a*).

Before we begin, we introduce the L.G. error-control function defined by

$$F(u, z) = \int \left\{ \frac{1}{f^{\frac{1}{4}}(u, z)} \frac{\mathrm{d}^2}{\mathrm{d}z^2}\left(\frac{1}{f^{\frac{1}{4}}(u, z)}\right) - \frac{g(u, z)}{f^{\frac{1}{2}}(u, z)} \right\} \mathrm{d}z. \tag{4.2}$$

For this integral we shall not use paths that intersect c. Any branches may be adopted for $f^{\frac{1}{4}}(u, z)$ and $f^{\frac{1}{2}}(u, z)$, provided that they are continuous and the latter is the square of the former.

† But not, in this instance, by use of theorem 10.2 of Olver (1974, ch. 6), because not all the conditions are satisfied. However, the general method of successive approximations is still applicable, and yields the stated results.

Next, we give the following expression for the error-control function $H(u,z)$, obtained by substituting (3.6) in (3.10):

$$H(u,z) = \frac{m}{2}\int\left\{\frac{1}{f^{\frac{1}{4}}(u,z)}\frac{\mathrm{d}^2}{\mathrm{d}z^2}\left(\frac{1}{f^{\frac{1}{4}}(u,z)}\right)-\frac{g(u,z)}{f^{\frac{1}{2}}(u,z)}\right\}\frac{\zeta^{\frac{1}{2}(m-2)}\,\mathrm{d}z}{\Omega(u^{2/m}\zeta)}-\frac{m^2-4}{16}\int\frac{\mathrm{d}\zeta}{\zeta^2\Omega(u^{2/m}\zeta)}. \tag{4.3}$$

The two integrals in this expression may not converge separately at $z = c$, but this is immaterial.

4.2. *Asymptotic estimates for paths*

THEOREM 4.1. (i) *Assume the conditions of* §§ 3.1 *and* 3.2 *are satisfied, and that the functions f and g are independent of u. Let a_j and a_k be arbitrary points in the closures of $\mathbf{D}_j$ and $\mathbf{D}_k$, respectively, including the point at infinity, and $\mathscr{P}$ be a progressive path connecting a_j and a_k. Assume also that each of the functions $1/\xi(z)$ and $F(z)$, defined by* (3.11) *and* (4.2), *is of bounded variation as $z \to a_j$ or a_k along $\mathscr{P}$. Then*

$$u^{-2/m}\mathscr{V}_{\mathscr{P}}(H) = O(\psi_m) \quad (u\to\infty), \tag{4.4}$$

where

$$\left.\begin{aligned}\psi_m &= u^{-1} \quad (0<m<2(1+\gamma_1)),\\ \psi_m &= u^{-1}\ln u \quad (m=2(1+\gamma_1)),\\ \psi_m &= u^{-2(1+\gamma_1)/m} \quad (m>2(1+\gamma_1)),\end{aligned}\right\} \tag{4.5}$$

and

$$\gamma_1 = \min(\gamma, 1). \tag{4.6}$$

(ii) *If, in addition, $g(z)$ is analytic at c, then*

$$u^{-2/m}\mathscr{V}_{\mathscr{P}}(H) = O(\chi_m) \quad (u\to\infty), \tag{4.7}$$

where† $\chi_m = u^{-1}$ $(0<m<4)$, $\chi_m = u^{-1}\ln u$ $(m=4)$, $\chi_m = u^{-4/m}$ $(m>4)$. (4.8)

The proof is given in the following two subsections.

4.3. *Proof of theorem* 4.1 *when a_j, a_k, $\zeta(a_j)$ and $\zeta(a_k)$ are finite*

In this subsection we assume that a_j and a_k are finite and ζ remains finite as $z\to a_j$ or a_k along $\mathscr{P}$. We also assume that $c\in\mathscr{P}$. (Compare remark (*a*) in § 3.3.)

Let α_j, α_k and $\mathscr{Q}$ again denote the ζ-maps of a_j, a_k and $\mathscr{P}$, respectively. Referring to (3.10) and transforming to the ζ-plane, we find that

$$\mathscr{V}_{\mathscr{P}}(H) = \int_{\alpha_j}^{\alpha_k}\left|\left\{\frac{1}{f^{\frac{1}{4}}(z)}\frac{\mathrm{d}^2}{\mathrm{d}z^2}\left(\frac{1}{f^{\frac{1}{4}}(z)}\right)-\frac{g(z)}{f^{\frac{1}{2}}(z)}\right\}\frac{\mathrm{d}z}{\mathrm{d}\zeta}\right|\frac{|\mathrm{d}\zeta|}{\Omega(u^{2/m}\zeta)}, \tag{4.9}$$

where the integral is evaluated along $\mathscr{Q}$. Because $\mathrm{d}z/\mathrm{d}\zeta$, $f^{-\frac{1}{4}}(z)$ and the derivatives of $f^{-\frac{1}{4}}(z)$ are continuous on $\mathscr{P}$, it follows that

$$\left|\frac{1}{f^{\frac{1}{4}}(z)}\frac{\mathrm{d}^2}{\mathrm{d}z^2}\left(\frac{1}{f^{\frac{1}{4}}(z)}\right)\frac{\mathrm{d}z}{\mathrm{d}\zeta}\right| \leqslant A \quad (\zeta\in\mathscr{Q}),$$

where A is an assignable finite constant. Hence on making the choice (3.8) for Ω we have

$$\int_{\alpha_j}^{\alpha_k}\left|\frac{1}{f^{\frac{1}{4}}(z)}\frac{\mathrm{d}^2}{\mathrm{d}z^2}\left(\frac{1}{f^{\frac{1}{4}}(z)}\right)\frac{\mathrm{d}z}{\mathrm{d}\zeta}\right|\frac{|\mathrm{d}\zeta|}{\Omega(u^{2/m}\zeta)} \leqslant A\int_{\alpha_j}^{\alpha_k}\frac{1+u^{2/m}|\zeta|}{1+u|\zeta|^{\frac{1}{2}m}}|\mathrm{d}\zeta|.$$

† This notation differs slightly from that of Olver (1977*b*). Also, when $g(z)$ is analytic at c we have $\gamma_1 = 1$, and the estimates (4.4) and (4.7) are the same.

Denote the arc parameter of $\mathscr{Q}$, measured from $\zeta = 0$, by τ and let $\tau_j(<0)$ and $\tau_k(>0)$ correspond to α_j and α_k, respectively. Then on $\mathscr{Q}$

$$1 \leqslant |\tau/\zeta| \leqslant A,$$

where the symbol A is now being used generically. Since $|\mathrm{d}\zeta/\mathrm{d}\tau| = 1$, it follows that

$$\frac{1}{u^{2/m}}\int_{\alpha_j}^{\alpha_k}\left|\frac{1}{f^{\frac{1}{4}}(z)}\frac{\mathrm{d}^2}{\mathrm{d}z^2}\left(\frac{1}{f^{\frac{1}{4}}(z)}\right)\frac{\mathrm{d}z}{\mathrm{d}\zeta}\right|\frac{|\mathrm{d}\zeta|}{\Omega(u^{2/m}\zeta)} \leqslant \frac{A}{u^{2/m}}\int_{\tau_j}^{\tau_k}\frac{1+u^{2/m}|\tau|}{1+u|\tau|^{\frac{1}{2}m}}\mathrm{d}\tau. \tag{4.10}$$

On transforming to the integration variable $v \equiv \pm u^{2/m}\tau$, we obtain

$$\frac{1}{u^{2/m}}\int_{\tau_j}^{\tau_k}\frac{1+u^{2/m}|\tau|}{1+u|\tau|^{\frac{1}{2}m}}\mathrm{d}\tau = \frac{1}{u^{4/m}}\left(\int_0^{u^{2/m}\tau_k}+\int_0^{u^{2/m}|\tau_j|}\right)\frac{1+v}{1+v^{\frac{1}{2}m}}\mathrm{d}v = O(\chi_m), \tag{4.11}$$

as $u\to\infty$, where χ_m is defined by (4.8).

Next, if $g(z)$ is analytic at c, then $|g(z)f^{-\frac{1}{2}}(z)|$ is bounded on $\mathscr{P}$. By similar analysis we derive

$$\frac{1}{u^{2/m}}\int_{\alpha_j}^{\alpha_k}\left|\frac{g(z)}{f^{\frac{1}{2}}(z)}\frac{\mathrm{d}z}{\mathrm{d}\zeta}\right|\frac{|\mathrm{d}\zeta|}{\Omega(u^{2/m}\zeta)} = O(\chi_m). \tag{4.12}$$

Alternatively, assume that $g(z)$ is singular at c. From (3.2) we have

$$|g(z)| \leqslant A|z-c|^{\gamma-1} \quad (z\in\mathscr{P}),$$

and hence

$$|g(z)| \leqslant A|\zeta|^{\gamma-1} \quad (\zeta\in\mathscr{Q}).$$

Using this inequality we find that

$$\frac{1}{u^{2/m}}\int_{\alpha_j}^{\alpha_k}\left|\frac{g(z)}{f^{\frac{1}{2}}(z)}\frac{\mathrm{d}z}{\mathrm{d}\zeta}\right|\frac{|\mathrm{d}\zeta|}{\Omega(u^{2/m}\zeta)} \leqslant \frac{A}{u^{2(1+\gamma)/m}}\left(\int_0^{u^{2/m}\tau_k}+\int_0^{u^{2/m}|\tau_j|}\right)\frac{1+v}{1+v^{\frac{1}{2}m}}v^{\gamma-1}\,\mathrm{d}v; \tag{4.13}$$

compare (4.11). For large u the right hand side is

$$O(u^{-1}) \quad (0<m<2(1+\gamma)), \quad O(u^{-1}\ln u) \quad (m=2(1+\gamma)), \quad O(u^{-2(1+\gamma)/m}) \quad (m>2(1+\gamma)). \tag{4.14}$$

To complete the proof of part (i) of theorem 4.1 in the present circumstances, we combine (4.10), (4.11), (4.13) and (4.14), and absorb all the error terms in the estimate $O(\psi_m)$, where ψ_m is given by (4.5) and (4.6). To prove part (ii) we combine (4.10), (4.11) and (4.12).

4.4. *Conclusion of the proof of theorem* 4.1

Suppose now that $c\in\mathscr{P}$ and either a_j is at infinity, or $|\zeta|\to\infty$ as $z\to a_j$ along $\mathscr{P}$. We introduce an arbitrary fixed point $\hat{a}_j$ on $\mathscr{P}$ between a_j and c. The analysis of §4.3 shows that $u^{-2/m}\mathscr{V}_{\hat{a}_j,a_k}(H)$ is estimated by $O(\psi_m)$ or $O(\chi_m)$, according as the hypotheses of (i) or (ii) apply.

To estimate the contribution from the part of $\mathscr{P}$ lying between a_j and $\hat{a}_j$, we use the expression (4.3) for H, again with the choice (3.8) for Ω. Since $|\zeta|$ is bounded away from zero on the part of $\mathscr{P}$ under consideration, we have

$$\frac{|\zeta|^{\frac{1}{2}(m-2)}}{\Omega(u^{2/m}\zeta)} = \frac{(u^{2/m}|\zeta|)^{\frac{1}{2}(m-2)}}{u^{(m-2)/m}}\,\frac{1+u^{2/m}|\zeta|}{1+(u^{2/m}|\zeta|)^{\frac{1}{2}m}} \leqslant \frac{A}{u^{(m-2)/m}},$$

provided that u, also, is bounded away from zero. Hence

$$\frac{m}{2}\int_{a_j}^{\hat{a}_j}\left|\left\{\frac{1}{f^{\frac{1}{4}}(z)}\frac{\mathrm{d}^2}{\mathrm{d}z^2}\left(\frac{1}{f^{\frac{1}{4}}(z)}\right)-\frac{g(z)}{f^{\frac{1}{2}}(z)}\right\}\frac{\zeta^{\frac{1}{2}(m-2)}\mathrm{d}z}{\Omega(u^{2/m}\zeta)}\right| \leqslant \frac{A}{u^{(m-2)/m}}\mathscr{V}_{a_j,\hat{a}_j}(F), \tag{4.15}$$

the last quantity being finite, by hypothesis.

For the other term in (4.3), let $\hat{\alpha}_j$ be the ζ-map of $\hat{a}_j$. Since $|\zeta|$ is bounded away from zero, we may choose u so that $u^{2/m}|\zeta| \geqslant 1$ everywhere. Then

$$\int_{\alpha_j}^{\hat{\alpha}_j}\left|\frac{d\zeta}{\zeta^2\Omega(u^{2/m}\zeta)}\right| = \int_{\alpha_j}^{\hat{\alpha}_j}\frac{1+u^{2/m}|\zeta|}{1+u|\zeta|^{\frac{1}{2}m}}\left|\frac{d\zeta}{\zeta^2}\right| \leqslant \int_{\alpha_j}^{\hat{\alpha}_j}\frac{2u^{2/m}|\zeta|}{u|\zeta|^{\frac{1}{2}m}}\left|\frac{d\zeta}{\zeta^2}\right| = \frac{4}{m}u^{(2-m)/m}\mathscr{V}_{\alpha_j,\hat{\alpha}_j}(\zeta^{-\frac{1}{2}m}). \tag{4.16}$$

Since $\zeta^{-\frac{1}{2}m}$ is a multiple of $1/\xi(z)$ the last expression is finite, by hypothesis. On combining this bound with (4.15) we conclude that

$$u^{-2/m}\mathscr{V}_{a_j,\hat{a}_j}(H) = O(u^{-1}) \quad (u\to\infty).$$

This estimate is absorbable in $O(\psi_m)$ or $O(\chi_m)$; in consequence (4.4) and (4.7) again apply.

A similar proof holds when a_k is at infinity or $|\zeta|\to\infty$ as $z\to a_k$ along $\mathscr{P}$.

Lastly, suppose that $c\notin\mathscr{P}$. Then we use the same proof as in the present subsection, except that $\hat{a}_j$ now denotes a point on the common boundary of $\mathbf{D}_j$ and $\mathbf{D}_k$. Clearly in this case we have the stronger result

$$u^{-2/m}\mathscr{V}_{\mathscr{P}}(H) = O(u^{-1}) \quad (u\to\infty),$$

valid for all values of m.

This completes the proof of theorem 4.1.

4.5. *Asymptotic estimates for domains*

Sometimes we need an estimate for the error term of theorem 3.1 that is uniform for a region rather than a single path. A typical result of this nature is as follows:

THEOREM 4.2. *Assume the conditions of §§3.1 and 3.2 are satisfied, and that the functions f and g are independent of u. Let a_k be a boundary point of $\mathbf{D}_k$ (possibly at infinity) such that $|\xi(a_k)| = \infty$, and θ_1 and θ_2 be constants such that $-\frac{1}{2}\pi \leqslant \theta_1 < \theta_2 \leqslant \frac{1}{2}\pi$. Assume also that for every value of θ in the closed interval $[\theta_1,\theta_2]$ there is a path $\mathscr{P}_\theta$ that has the equation*

$$\operatorname{ph}\xi(z) = \theta \tag{4.17}$$

and lies in $\mathbf{D}_k$. If

$$\mathscr{V}_{z,a_k}(F)\to 0 \quad (z\to a_k), \tag{4.18}$$

where the variation is evaluated along $\mathscr{P}_\theta$, then

$$u^{-2/m}\mathscr{V}_{c,a_k}(H) = O(\psi_m) \quad (u\to\infty), \tag{4.19}$$

again with the variation evaluated along $\mathscr{P}_\theta$. Furthermore, if (4.18) applies uniformly with respect to θ, then so does (4.19).

It will be observed that the condition (4.17) ensures that $\mathscr{P}_\theta$ is a progressive path. The proof of theorem 4.2 is a straightforward extension of that of theorem 4.1, and it is unnecessary to include details. The condition of uniform convergence, as applied to (4.18), could be eased to bounded convergence (see, for example, Apostol 1957, p. 405), but this is unlikely to be important in applications.

PART B. CONNECTION FORMULAE

5. MAIN CONNECTION THEOREM

5.1. *Preliminary definitions*

Throughout the present section we suppose that the conditions of §3.1 are satisfied. Before stating the main result we reformulate the geometric concepts introduced in §§3.2 and 3.3 in terms of a new variable $\xi_c(u,z)$, defined below, in order to avoid explicit reference to the variables $\zeta(u,z)$ and $\xi(u,z)$ in applications.

The curves in the z-plane having the equation

$$\operatorname{Re}\int_c^z f^{\frac{1}{2}}(u,t)\,\mathrm{d}t = 0 \tag{5.1}$$

are called the *principal curves associated with the transition point* c. Either branch of $f^{\frac{1}{2}}(u,t)$ may be used in this definition, provided that continuity is maintained. When $m = 2, 3, 4, \ldots$, there are m distinct principal curves and they occupy the same Riemann sheet. For other values of m the principal curves lie on two or more Riemann sheets. In all cases, however, adjacent principal curves intersect at c at an angle $2\pi/m$. The theory of conformal mapping shows that a principal curve can terminate only at c or a boundary point of $\boldsymbol{D}$, and also that no principal curve can intersect itself or any other principal curve on the same Riemann sheet, except at c.

The principal curves are evidently boundaries of the principal regions introduced in §3.2, and we note that each principal region includes its bounding principal curves. *We shall suppose that in each principal region there is a one-to-one relation between* z *and any continuous branch of the integral* $\int f^{\frac{1}{2}}(u,z)\,\mathrm{d}z$. This is equivalent to the assumption of §3.2 that the mapping from $\boldsymbol{D}$ on to $\boldsymbol{\Delta}$ is one-to-one.

Starting with an arbitrarily designated principal region $\boldsymbol{D}_0$, we define $\boldsymbol{D}_1, \boldsymbol{D}_2, \ldots$, to be the successive principal regions that are encountered as we pass around c in the positive rotational sense; similarly $\boldsymbol{D}_{-1}, \boldsymbol{D}_{-2}, \ldots$, denote the successive principal regions encountered in the negative rotational sense. Whatever choice is adopted for $\boldsymbol{D}_0$, the labelling can be made consistent with that of §3.2 by appropriate choice of branch of $f_0^{1/m}$ in the expansion (3.5). We shall refer to $\boldsymbol{D}_j \cap \boldsymbol{D}_{j+1}$ and $\boldsymbol{D}_j \cap \boldsymbol{D}_{j-1}$ as the *left* and *right boundaries*, respectively, of $\boldsymbol{D}_j$; compare §2.4.

Next, in each principal region $\boldsymbol{D}_j$ we define

$$\xi_c(u,z) = \int_c^z f^{\frac{1}{2}}(u,t)\,\mathrm{d}t, \tag{5.2}$$

taking the branch that is continuous and has non-negative real part. This determines a function of z that is continuous throughout $\boldsymbol{D}$, except on the principal curves. Clearly $\xi_c(u,z)$ is positive imaginary on the left boundary of $\boldsymbol{D}_j$ and negative imaginary on the right boundary of $\boldsymbol{D}_j$. Since the left boundary of $\boldsymbol{D}_j$ is also the right boundary of $\boldsymbol{D}_{j+1}$, and the right boundary of $\boldsymbol{D}_j$ is also the left boundary of $\boldsymbol{D}_{j-1}$, it is clear that $\xi_c(u,z)$ changes sign on crossing a principal curve.

In addition to the left and right boundaries, we also need to define the *left, right* and *internal parts* of $\boldsymbol{D}_j$. These are the point sets in $\boldsymbol{D}_j$ that satisfy

$$0 \leqslant \operatorname{ph}\xi_c(u,z) \leqslant \tfrac{1}{2}\pi, \quad -\tfrac{1}{2}\pi \leqslant \operatorname{ph}\xi_c(u,z) \leqslant 0, \quad |\operatorname{ph}\xi_c(u,z)| \leqslant \tfrac{1}{2}\delta\pi, \tag{5.3}$$

respectively, where δ again denotes an arbitrary positive constant less than unity; compare again §2.4.

The last concept is that of a *progressive path*. This is any Jordan arc $\mathscr{P}$ comprising a finite chain of R_2 arcs, in the sense of Olver (1974, p. 147), and having the property that $\operatorname{Re}\xi_c(u,z)$ is monotonic on the intersection of $\mathscr{P}$ with any principal region. It needs to be clarified that this does not require $\operatorname{Re}\xi_c(u,z)$ to be monotonic along the whole of $\mathscr{P}$; $\operatorname{Re}\xi_c(u,z)$ may be non-increasing in one principal region and non-decreasing in another.

It is easily verified that the definition just given is consistent with that of §3.3. Thus $\mathscr{P}$ can lie in at most two principal regions $\boldsymbol{D}_j$ and $\boldsymbol{D}_k$, say. Furthermore, unless $k-j = \pm 1$, $\mathscr{P}$ has to pass through c in order to enter one principal region from the other. Typical progressive paths are indicated in figure 5.

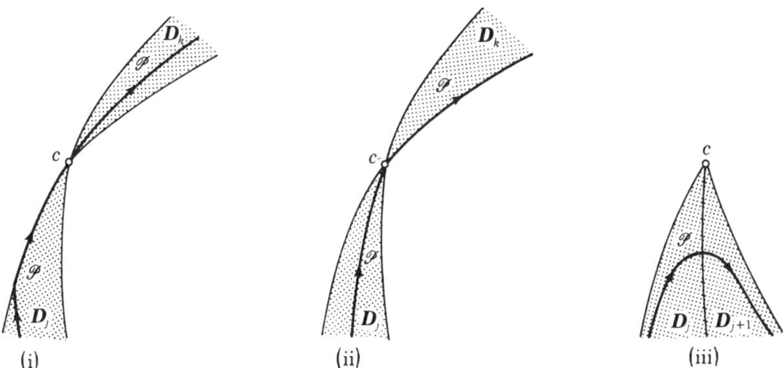

FIGURE 5. z-plane: progressive paths $\mathscr{P}$.

5.2. *Statement of theorem*

In this subsection we assume the conditions and notation of § 5.1, and also that j and k are integers satisfying condition (i) of § 3.3. We suppose that a_j and a_k are given points (other than c) in the closures of $\boldsymbol{D}_j$ and $\boldsymbol{D}_k$, respectively, including boundary points or points at infinity, and $\mathscr{P}$ is a progressive path connecting a_j and a_k. We also suppose that $\hat{\delta}$ denotes a given number that is independent of z (but may depend on u) and satisfies $0 \leqslant \hat{\delta} < 1$. Before stating the main theorem in this section we introduce the following notations.

First,

$$\Delta_j(u) = (1+\hat{\delta})\,[1+\Theta\{u\xi_c(u,a_j)\}]-1, \tag{5.4}$$

where $\Theta(t)$ is defined by (2.9).

Secondly,

$$X_{j,k}(u) = \Delta_j(u)\,\{1+T_j|\lambda_{j,k}^{-1}\lambda_{j,k\mp1}\,\mathrm{e}^{-2u\xi_c(u,a_j)}|\}, \tag{5.5}$$

where the upper or lower sign is taken according as a_j lies in the left or right part of $\boldsymbol{D}_j$, $\lambda_{j,k}$ is defined by (2.17) and (2.18), and $T_j = 1$ or 0 according as $|\xi_c(u,a_j)|$ is finite or infinite. Thus when $|\xi_c(u,a_j)| = \infty$ we have $\Theta\{u\xi_c(u,a_j)\} = 0$ and $X_{j,k}(u) = \Delta_j(u) = \hat{\delta}$.

Lastly, when $z \in \mathscr{P}$

$$A_{j,k}(u,z) = C_{j,k}\{1+X_{j,k}(u)+T_j|\lambda_{j,k}^{-1}|\Delta_j(u)\}[\exp\{m^{-1}|\lambda_{j,k}^{-1}|\rho_{j,k}\,u^{-2/m}\mathscr{V}_{a_j,z}(H)\}-1], \tag{5.6}$$

where $C_{j,k}$, $\rho_{j,k}$ and $H \equiv H(u,z)$ are defined by (2.38), (3.9) and (3.10), and the variation of H is evaluated along $\mathscr{P}$.

THEOREM 5.1. *Let $w(u,z)$ be a solution of* (3.1) *with the properties*

$$f^{\frac{1}{4}}(u,z)\,w(u,z) \sim (1+\eta)\,\mathrm{e}^{-u\xi_c(u,z)}, \tag{5.7}$$

$$\partial\{f^{\frac{1}{4}}(u,z)\,w(u,z)\}/\partial z \sim -(1+\eta^1)\,uf^{\frac{3}{4}}(u,z)\,\mathrm{e}^{-u\xi_c(u,z)}, \tag{5.8}$$

as $z \to a_j$ along $\mathscr{P}$, where η and η^1 are independent of z and $|\eta|$, $|\eta^1| \leqslant \hat{\delta}$. Assume also that $1/\xi_c(u,z)$ and $F(u,z)$ are each of bounded variation as $z \to a_j$ or a_k along $\mathscr{P}$, where $F(u,z)$ is defined by (4.2). *Then the* *analytic continuation of $w(u,z)$ – obtained by passing around the neighbourhood of c from $\mathbf{D}_j$ to $\mathbf{D}_k$ in the same sense as the sign of $(k-j)$ – has the following properties:*

(i) *If $z\in\mathscr{P}\cap\mathbf{D}_k$, then*

$$f^{\frac{1}{4}}(u,z)\,w(u,z) = \mathrm{i}^{k-j-1}\{\lambda_{j,k}+\epsilon_{\pm1}(u,z)\}\,\mathrm{e}^{u\xi_c(u,z)} \pm \mathrm{i}^{k-j}\{\lambda_{j,k\pm1}+\epsilon_{\pm2}(u,z)\}\,\mathrm{e}^{-u\xi_c(u,z)}, \tag{5.9}$$

$$\partial\{f^{\frac{1}{4}}(u,z)\,w(u,z)\}/\partial z = \mathrm{i}^{k-j-1}\{\lambda_{j,k}+\epsilon^1_{\pm1}(u,z)\}\,uf^{\frac{1}{2}}(u,z)\,\mathrm{e}^{u\xi_c(u,z)} \mp \mathrm{i}^{k-j}\{\lambda_{j,k\pm1}+\epsilon^1_{\pm2}(u,z)\}\,uf^{\frac{1}{2}}(u,z)\,\mathrm{e}^{-u\xi_c(u,z)}, \tag{5.10}$$

where

$$|\epsilon_{\pm1}(u,z)|,\quad |\epsilon^1_{\pm1}(u,z)| \leqslant [1+\Theta\{u\xi_c(u,z)\}]\,[\Lambda_{j,k}(u,z)+|\lambda_{j,k}|\{1+X_{j,k}(u)\}]-|\lambda_{j,k}|, \tag{5.11}$$

$$|\epsilon_{\pm2}(u,z)|,\quad |\epsilon^1_{\pm2}(u,z)| \leqslant [1+\Theta\{u\xi_c(u,z)\}]\,[|\lambda_{j,k\pm1}|\{1+X_{j,k}(u)\} + T_j\,\Delta_j(u)\,|\lambda^{-1}_{j,k}\,\mathrm{e}^{-2u\xi_c(u,a_j)}|]-|\lambda_{j,k\pm1}|, \tag{5.12}$$

the upper or lower signs being taken throughout according as z lies in the left or right part of $\mathbf{D}_k$.

(ii) *If $\operatorname{Re}\xi_c(u,z)\to\infty$ as $z\to a_k$ along $\mathscr{P}$, then*

$$f^{\frac{1}{4}}(u,z)\,w(u,z) \sim \mathrm{i}^{k-j-1}(\lambda_{j,k}+\kappa_0)\,\mathrm{e}^{u\xi_c(u,z)}, \tag{5.13}$$

$$\partial\{f^{\frac{1}{4}}(u,z)\,w(u,z)\}/\partial z \sim \mathrm{i}^{k-j-1}(\lambda_{j,k}+\kappa_0)uf^{\frac{1}{2}}(u,z)\,\mathrm{e}^{u\xi_c(u,z)}, \tag{5.14}$$

as $z\to a_k$ along $\mathscr{P}$, where κ_0 is independent of z and

$$|\kappa_0| \leqslant \Lambda_{j,k}(u,a_k)+|\lambda_{j,k}|\,X_{j,k}(u). \tag{5.15}$$

(iii) *If $\mathscr{P}\cap\mathbf{D}_k$ coincides with the left or right boundary of $\mathbf{D}_k$ and $|\xi_c(u,a_k)|=\infty$, then*

$$f^{\frac{1}{4}}(u,z)\,w(u,z) = \mathrm{i}^{k-j-1}(\lambda_{j,k}+\kappa_{\pm1})\,\mathrm{e}^{u\xi_c(u,z)} \pm \mathrm{i}^{k-j}(\lambda_{j,k\pm1}+\kappa_{\pm2})\,\mathrm{e}^{-u\xi_c(u,z)}+o(1), \tag{5.16}$$

$$\partial\{f^{\frac{1}{4}}(u,z)\,w(u,z)\}/\partial z = uf^{\frac{1}{2}}(u,z)\,\{\mathrm{i}^{k-j-1}(\lambda_{j,k}+\kappa_{\pm1})\,\mathrm{e}^{u\xi_c(u,z)} \mp \mathrm{i}^{k-j}(\lambda_{j,k\pm1}+\kappa_{\pm2})\,\mathrm{e}^{-u\xi_c(u,z)}+o(1)\}, \tag{5.17}$$

as $z\to a_k$ along $\mathscr{P}$, where $\kappa_{\pm1}$ and $\kappa_{\pm2}$ are independent of z and subject to the bounds

$$|\kappa_{\pm1}| \leqslant \Lambda_{j,k}(u,a_k)+|\lambda_{j,k}|\,X_{j,k}(u), \tag{5.18}$$

$$|\kappa_{\pm2}| \leqslant \Lambda_{j,k}(u,a_k)+|\lambda_{j,k\pm1}|\,X_{j,k}(u)+T_j\,\Delta_j(u)\,|\,\lambda^{-1}_{j,k}\,\mathrm{e}^{-2u\xi_c(u,a_j)}|, \tag{5.19}$$

and the upper or lower signs are taken throughout according as a_k lies on the left or right boundary of $\mathbf{D}_k$.

In (5.9) *to* (5.17) *$f^{\frac{1}{4}}(u,z)$ denotes the branch obtained by analytic continuation from that used in* (5.7) *and* (5.8) *in the same manner as for $w(u,z)$, and the branch of $f^{\frac{1}{2}}(u,z)$ is the same as that used in* (5.2) *in constructing $\xi_c(u,z)$.*

This theorem is proved in the next three subsections.

Remarks. (*a*) If a_j lies in the intersection of the left and right parts of $\mathbf{D}_j$, that is, if $\operatorname{ph}\xi_c(u,a_j)=0$, then either ambiguous sign may be chosen in (5.5). Similarly, when $\operatorname{ph}\xi_c(u,z)=0$ either upper or lower signs may be adopted throughout (5.9) to (5.12).

(*b*) The relations (5.13) and (5.14) are valid whenever the right hand side of (5.15) is less than $|\lambda_{j,k}|$: this condition ensures that the factor $\lambda_{j,k}+\kappa_0$ does not vanish.

5.3. *Asymptotic forms of the solutions at boundary points of* $\mathbf{D}$

Theorem 5.1 applies only when there actually exists a solution $w(u,z)$ with the properties (5.7) and (5.8). If a_j is an interior point of $\mathbf{D}$, then $f(u,a_j)$, $1/f(u,a_j)$ and $\xi_c(u,a_j)$ are all finite, and from the theory of linear differential equations we know that $w(u, z)$ exists whatever values are assigned to η and η^1. In other circumstances, however, $w(u, z)$ may exist only when $\eta = \eta^1$. This is illustrated by the following result:

LEMMA 5.1. *Assume the conditions and notation of* § 5.1 *and let a_j be a boundary point of $\mathbf{D}_j$ or a point at infinity in $\mathbf{D}_j$. Assume also that $|\xi_c(u, z)| \to \infty$ and $\mathscr{V}(F)$ converges as $z \to a_j$ along a given progressive path $\mathscr{P}$ in $\mathbf{D}_j$. Then the differential equation* (3.1) *has a unique solution $w_j(u, z)$ that is holomorphic in $\mathbf{D}$ and has the property*

$$w_j(u, z) \sim f^{-\frac{1}{4}}(u, z)\, \mathrm{e}^{-u\xi_c(u, z)} \quad (z \to a_j \text{ along } \mathscr{P}). \tag{5.20}$$

Furthermore,

$$\partial\{f^{\frac{1}{4}}(u, z)\, w_j(u, z)\}/\partial z \sim -u f^{\frac{1}{2}}(u, z)\, \mathrm{e}^{-u\xi_c(u, z)} \quad (z \to a_j \text{ along } \mathscr{P}). \tag{5.21}$$

The existence of $w_j(u, z)$ is an immediate consequence of theorem 11.1 of Olver (1974, ch. 6). This theorem also shows that $w_j(u, z)$ has the property (5.21). Next, if $\mathrm{Re}\, \xi_c(u, z) \to \infty$ as $z \to a_j$, then $w_j(u, z)$ is a recessive solution and known to be unique.

It therefore remains to show that $w_j(u, z)$ is unique in the case when $\mathrm{Re}\, \xi_c(u, z)$ is bounded as $z \to a_j$. Because $\mathrm{Re}\, \xi_c(u, z)$ is non-decreasing it must tend to a constant. Hence $|\mathrm{Im}\, \xi_c(u, z)| \to \infty$. Another deduction from theorem 11.1 of Olver (1974, ch. 6) is that there is a second solution $\tilde{w}_j(u, z)$, say, such that

$$\tilde{w}_j(u, z) = f^{-\frac{1}{4}}(u, z)\, \mathrm{e}^{u\xi_c(u, z)}\{1 + \tilde{\epsilon}_j(u, z)\}, \tag{5.22}$$

where

$$|\tilde{\epsilon}_j(u, z)| < \tfrac{1}{2}, \quad |u^{-1} f^{-\frac{1}{2}}(u, z)\, \partial\tilde{\epsilon}_j(u, z)/\partial z| < \tfrac{1}{2}, \tag{5.23}$$

for all points on $\mathscr{P}$ that are sufficiently close to a_j. On letting $z \to a_j$ in the Wronskian relation for $f^{\frac{1}{4}}(u, z)\, w_j(u, z)$ and $f^{\frac{1}{4}}(u, z)\, \tilde{w}_j(u, z)$ and using (5.20)–(5.23), we see that $w_j(u, z)$ and $\tilde{w}_j(u, z)$ are linearly independent. Also,

$$f^{\frac{1}{4}}(u, z)\, \mathrm{e}^{u\xi_c(u, z)} \tilde{w}_j(u, z) = \mathrm{e}^{2u\xi_c(u, z)}\{1 + \tilde{\epsilon}_j(u, z)\}.$$

In consequence of the first of (5.23) and the facts that $\mathrm{Re}\, \xi_c(u, z) \to$ a constant and $|\mathrm{Im}\, \xi_c(u, z)| \to \infty$, the right hand side of the last relation cannot tend to a constant value as $z \to a_j$ along $\mathscr{P}$. Hence the solution $w_j(u, z)$ determined by (5.20) is unique, and the lemma is established.

5.4. *Proof of theorem* 5.1: *determination of A and B*

To prove theorem 5.1 we shall use the uniform approximation supplied by theorem 3.1, and replace the functions $U_j(u^{2/m}\zeta)$ and $U_k(u^{2/m}\zeta)$ by their appropriate asymptotic representations for large arguments. We must first show that the conditions of theorem 3.1 are satisfied; in particular that the error-control function $H(u, z)$ is of bounded variation along $\mathscr{P}$. On any compact segment of $\mathscr{P}$ that does not include a_j or a_k this result follows immediately from the definition (3.10) and the properties of the functions $g(u, z)$, $f(u, z)$ and $\Omega(u^{2/m}\zeta)$ given in §§ 3.1 and 3.2. To show $\mathscr{V}(H)$ converges as $z \to a_j$ or a_k, we impose an extra condition on the balancing function, given by

$$\Omega(t) \sim \nu |t|^{\frac{1}{2}(m-2)} \tag{5.24}$$

as $t \to \infty$, uniformly with respect to $\mathrm{ph}\, t$, where ν is a positive constant, and use analysis similar to that of § 4.4. We note, incidentally, that (3.7) is satisfied whenever (5.24) holds.

The remaining conditions of theorem 3.1 are easily verified. Hence the solution $w(u, z)$ satisfying (5.7) and (5.8) can be expressed in the form (3.12). The first problem is to evaluate the coefficients A and B. Considerable care will be needed in the choice of branches of the fractional powers that occur in subsequent analysis.

For brevity, we write temporarily

$$\hat{U}_j(\zeta) = \zeta^{\frac{1}{4}(m-2)}U_j(u^{2/m}\zeta), \quad \hat{U}_k(\zeta) = \zeta^{\frac{1}{4}(m-2)}U_k(u^{2/m}\zeta), \quad \hat{\epsilon}(u,\zeta) = \zeta^{\frac{1}{4}(m-2)}\epsilon(u,\zeta), \tag{5.25}$$

where in each equation the branch of $\zeta^{\frac{1}{4}(m-2)}$ is determined as in § 3, that is,

$$|\zeta|^{\frac{1}{4}(m-2)} \exp\{\mathrm{i}\tfrac{1}{4}(m-2)\,\mathrm{ph}\,\zeta\}$$

with $\mathrm{ph}\,\zeta$ in the interval $[(2j-1)\,\pi/m,\ (2j+1)\,\pi/m]$ when $\zeta \in \boldsymbol{S}_j$. Substituting in (3.12) by means of (3.6), we find that

$$(\tfrac{1}{2}m)^{-\frac{1}{2}}f^{\frac{1}{4}}(u,z)\,w(u,z) = A\hat{U}_j(\zeta) + B\hat{U}_k(\zeta) + \hat{\epsilon}(u,\zeta), \tag{5.26}$$

where we may suppose the branch of $f^{\frac{1}{4}}(u,z)$ to be the same as on the left hand side of (5.7). We shall also require the identity

$$\frac{\mathrm{d}\zeta}{\mathrm{d}z} = (-)^j\frac{2}{m}\frac{f^{\frac{1}{2}}(u,z)}{\zeta^{\frac{1}{2}(m-2)}}, \quad (\zeta \in \boldsymbol{S}_j), \tag{5.27}$$

in which the branch of $f^{\frac{1}{2}}(u,z)$ is the same as that used in (5.2) in constructing $\xi_c(u,z)$, and $\zeta^{\frac{1}{2}(m-2)}$ denotes the square of the branch of $\zeta^{\frac{1}{4}(m-2)}$ in (5.25). Equation (5.27) is obtained by dividing the equations

$$\mathrm{d}\xi_c/\mathrm{d}z = f^{\frac{1}{2}}(u,z), \quad \mathrm{d}\xi_c/\mathrm{d}\zeta = (-)^j\,\tfrac{1}{2}m\zeta^{\frac{1}{2}(m-2)},$$

obtained from (3.3) and (5.2).

Let us again denote by α_j the value of ζ corresponding to $z = a_j$, and at first suppose that α_j is finite (and therefore, also, $\xi_c(u, a_j)$ is finite). If $z \to a_j$ then $\mathscr{V}_{a_j,z}(H) \to 0$, and from (3.13) it follows that $\hat{\epsilon}(u,\alpha_j) = 0$. Substituting in (5.26) by means of this result and referring to (5.7), we obtain

$$A\hat{U}_j(\alpha_j) + B\hat{U}_k(\alpha_j) = (\tfrac{1}{2}m)^{-\frac{1}{2}}(1+\eta)\,\mathrm{e}^{-u\xi_c(u,a_j)}.$$

Similarly, on differentiating (5.26) with the aid of (5.27) and comparing the result with (5.8) as $z \to a_j$, we find that

$$A\hat{U}'_j(\alpha_j) + B\hat{U}'_k(\alpha_j) = (-)^{j-1}(\tfrac{1}{2}m)^{\frac{1}{2}}(1+\eta^1)\,u\alpha_j^{\frac{1}{4}(m-2)}\,\mathrm{e}^{-u\xi_c(u,a_j)}.$$

Solving the last two equations for A and B with the aid of the Wronskian relation

$$\hat{U}_j(\alpha_j)\,\hat{U}'_k(\alpha_j) - \hat{U}_k(\alpha_j)\,\hat{U}'_j(\alpha_j) = m\mathrm{i}\,\mathrm{e}^{-(j+k)\pi\mathrm{i}/m}\lambda_{j,k}\,u^{2/m}\alpha_j^{\frac{1}{2}(m-2)}$$

obtained from (2.16) and (5.25), we arrive at

$$A = \frac{\mathrm{e}^{(j+k)\pi\mathrm{i}/m}}{m\mathrm{i}\lambda_{j,k}\,u^{2/m}}\,\mathrm{e}^{-u\xi_c(u,a_j)}\{(\tfrac{1}{2}m)^{-\frac{1}{2}}(1+\eta)\,\alpha_j^{\frac{1}{2}(2-m)}\hat{U}'_k(\alpha_j) + (-)^j(\tfrac{1}{2}m)^{\frac{1}{2}}(1+\eta^1)\,u\hat{U}_k(\alpha_j)\},$$

$$B = \frac{\mathrm{i}\mathrm{e}^{(j+k)\pi\mathrm{i}/m}}{m\lambda_{j,k}\,u^{2/m}}\,\mathrm{e}^{-u\xi_c(u,a_j)}\{(\tfrac{1}{2}m)^{-\frac{1}{2}}(1+\eta)\,\alpha_j^{\frac{1}{2}(2-m)}\hat{U}'_j(\alpha_j) + (-)^j(\tfrac{1}{2}m)^{\frac{1}{2}}(1+\eta^1)\,u\hat{U}_j(\alpha_j)\}.$$

We now refer to (5.25) and substitute for $\hat{U}_j(\alpha_j)$ and $\hat{U}'_j(\alpha_j)$ by means of (2.12) and (2.13), and for $\hat{U}_k(\alpha_j)$ and $\hat{U}'_k(\alpha_j)$ by means of (2.23), (2.24) and (2.25), with the symbols j and k interchanged in the case of the last three equations. This analysis yields

$$A = (\tfrac{1}{2}m)^{-\frac{1}{2}}\mathrm{i}^{-j}\mathrm{e}^{j\pi\mathrm{i}/m}u^{(m-2)/(2m)}(1+\hat{A}), \tag{5.28}$$

$$B = (\tfrac{1}{2}m)^{-\frac{1}{2}}\mathrm{i}^{-j-1}\mathrm{e}^{k\pi\mathrm{i}/m}\lambda_{j,k}^{-1}\,u^{(m-2)/(2m)}\hat{B}, \tag{5.29}$$

where

$$\hat{A} = \tfrac{1}{2}(1+\eta)\,\{1+\vartheta^1_{j\pm1}(u^{2/m}\alpha_j)\} + \tfrac{1}{2}(1+\eta^1)\,\{1+\vartheta_{j\pm1}(u^{2/m}\alpha_j)\} - 1 \mp \mathrm{i}\lambda_{j,k}^{-1}\,\lambda_{j,k\mp1}\,\hat{B}, \tag{5.30}$$

$$\hat{B} = \mathrm{e}^{-2u\xi_c(u,a_j)}[\tfrac{1}{2}(1+\eta)\{1+\vartheta^1_j(u^{2/m}\alpha_j)\} - \tfrac{1}{2}(1+\eta^1)\,\{1+\vartheta_j(u^{2/m}\alpha_j)\}]. \tag{5.31}$$

In (5.30) the upper or lower signs are taken according as a_j lies in the left or right part of $\boldsymbol{D}_j$.

Alternatively, assume that α_j is infinite. Then $\xi_c(u, a_j) = \infty$ and from lemma 5.1 we know that we must have $\eta^1 = \eta$. First, if $\mathrm{Re}\,\xi_c(u, a_j) = +\infty$ then $B = 0$; compare remark (*b*) in §3.3. On forming the ratio of the two sides of (5.26) and letting $z \to a_j$ we find that (5.28) applies with $\hat{A} = \eta$. Secondly, if $\mathrm{Re}\,\xi_c(u, a_j)$ is finite then $\mathrm{Im}\,\xi_c(u, a_j)$ must be infinite. By using similar analysis we again conclude that $B = 0$ and $\hat{A} = \eta$. Since the terms $\vartheta_j(u^{2/m}\alpha_j)$, $\vartheta_j^1(u^{2/m}\alpha_j)$, $\vartheta_{j\pm 1}(u^{2/m}\alpha_j)$ and $\vartheta_{j\pm 1}^1(u^{2/m}\alpha_j)$ all vanish when $\alpha_j = \infty$, these results show that (5.30) and (5.31) may be replaced by their limiting forms as $\alpha_j \to \infty$.

Bounds for $\hat{A}$ and $\hat{B}$ may be constructed from (5.30) and (5.31) by use of the hypotheses $|\eta|, |\eta^1| \leqslant \hat{\delta}$ and the bound for $\vartheta_j(u^{2/m}\alpha_j)$ and the other error terms obtained from (2.14). In this way we derive

$$|(1+\eta)\{1+\vartheta_{j\pm 1}^1(u^{2/m}\alpha_j)\}-1|, \quad |(1+\eta^1)\{1+\vartheta_{j\pm 1}(u^{2/m}\alpha_j)\}-1| \leqslant (1+\hat{\delta})\{1+\Theta(u\alpha_j^{\frac{1}{2}m})\}-1,$$

and $$|(1+\eta)\{1+\vartheta_j^1(u^{2/m}\alpha_j)\}-(1+\eta^1)\{1+\vartheta_j(u^{2/m}\alpha_j)\}| \leqslant 2(1+\hat{\delta})\{1+\Theta(u\alpha_j^{\frac{1}{2}m})\}-2.$$

Hence, whether or not $\xi_c(u, a_j)$ be finite, we have

$$|\hat{A}| \leqslant X_{j,k}(u), \quad |\hat{B}| \leqslant T_j \Delta_j(u)\,|\mathrm{e}^{-2u\xi_c(u,a_j)}|, \tag{5.32}$$

where $\Delta_j(u)$, $X_{j,k}(u)$ and T_j are defined in §5.2.

5.5. *Proof of theorem* 5.1: *conclusion*

Theorem 3.1 shows that the representation (5.26) persists as z passes along $\mathscr{P}$ and approaches a_k. To evaluate the error bounds (3.13) we note that when $v \in \mathscr{Q}$ we have, from (2.29),

$$\Omega(u^{2/m}v)\,E_{j,k}^{-1}(u^{2/m}v)\,M_{j,k}(u^{2/m}v)\,|U_j(u^{2/m}v)| \leqslant \Omega(u^{2/m}v)\,M_{j,k}^2(u^{2/m}v) \leqslant \rho_{j,k};$$

compare (3.9). If $|\xi_c(u, a_j)| = \infty$ then, as shown above, $B = 0$. Alternatively, if $\xi_c(u, a_j)$ is finite then we have

$$\Omega(u^{2/m}v)\,E_{j,k}^{-1}(u^{2/m}v)\,M_{j,k}(u^{2/m}v)\,|U_k(u^{2/m}v)\,\mathrm{e}^{-2u\xi_c(u,a_j)}|$$
$$\leqslant \Omega(u^{2/m}v)\,M_{j,k}^2(u^{2/m}v)\,E_{j,k}^{-2}(u^{2/m}v)\,E_{j,k}^2(u^{2/m}\alpha_j).$$

The right hand side is bounded by $\rho_{j,k}$, because $E_{j,k}(u^{2/m}v)$ is non-decreasing on $\mathscr{Q}$. Referring to (3.14), (5.28) and (5.29) we deduce that

$$\sigma_{j,k}/\rho_{j,k} \leqslant (\tfrac{1}{2}m)^{-\frac{1}{2}}u^{(m-2)/(2m)}(|1+\hat{A}| + |\lambda_{j,k}^{-1}\,\mathrm{e}^{2u\xi_c(u,a_j)}\hat{B}|),$$

and hence, with the aid of (5.32),

$$\sigma_{j,k}/\rho_{j,k} \leqslant (\tfrac{1}{2}m)^{-\frac{1}{2}}u^{(m-2)/(2m)}\{1+X_{j,k}(u)+T_j|\lambda_{j,k}^{-1}|\,\Delta_j(u)\},$$

this inequality holding whether or not $\xi_c(u, a_j)$ be finite. On substituting in (3.13) by means of this result and referring to (2.37), (2.43), (5.6) and (5.25), we perceive that

$$(\tfrac{1}{2}m)^{\frac{1}{2}}|\mathrm{e}^{-u\xi_c(u,z)}\hat{\epsilon}(u,\zeta)|, \quad (\tfrac{1}{2}m)^{-\frac{1}{2}}u^{-1}|\mathrm{e}^{-u\xi_c(u,z)}\zeta^{\frac{1}{2}(2-m)}\hat{\epsilon}'(u,\zeta)| \leqslant \Lambda_{j,k}(u,z)\,[1+\Theta\{u\xi_c(u,z)\}], \tag{5.33}$$

valid when $z \in \mathscr{P} \cap \mathbf{D}_k$, where we have denoted $\partial\hat{\epsilon}(u,\zeta)/\partial\zeta$ by $\hat{\epsilon}'(u,\zeta)$, for brevity.

The remaining step is to identify the representation (5.26), and its z-derivative, in the explicit forms given by the theorem in cases (i), (ii) and (iii). In (5.26) we substitute for A and B by means of (5.28) and (5.29), and for $\hat{U}_j(\zeta)$ and $\hat{U}_k(\zeta)$ by means of (5.25), (2.12), (2.23) and (2.24), with the symbol j replaced by k in the case of (2.12). This yields

$$f^{\frac{1}{4}}(u,z)\,w(u,z) = \mathrm{i}^{k-j-1}(1+\hat{A})\,[\lambda_{j,k}\,\mathrm{e}^{u\xi_c(u,z)}\{1+\vartheta_{k\pm 1}(u^{2/m}\zeta)\} \pm \mathrm{i}\lambda_{j,k\pm 1}\,\mathrm{e}^{-u\xi_c(u,z)}\{1+\vartheta_k(u^{2/m}\zeta)\}]$$
$$+\mathrm{i}^{k-j-1}\hat{B}\lambda_{j,k}^{-1}\,\mathrm{e}^{-u\xi_c(u,z)}\{1+\vartheta_k(u^{2/m}\zeta)\} + (\tfrac{1}{2}m)^{\frac{1}{2}}\hat{\epsilon}(u,\zeta), \tag{5.34}$$

the upper or lower signs being taken according as z lies in the left or right part of $\boldsymbol{D}_k$. Next, if we differentiate (5.26) by use of (5.27), with the symbol j replaced by k, and use similar analysis we arrive at

$$\begin{aligned} &u^{-1}f^{-\frac{1}{4}}(u,z)\,\partial\{f^{\frac{1}{4}}(u,z)\,w(u,z)\}/\partial z \\ &\quad = \mathrm{i}^{k-j-1}(1+\hat{A})\,[\lambda_{j,k}\,\mathrm{e}^{u\xi_c(u,z)}\{1+\vartheta^1_{k\pm1}(u^{2/m}\zeta)\}\mp \mathrm{i}\lambda_{j,k\pm1}\,\mathrm{e}^{-u\xi_c(u,z)}\{1+\vartheta^1_k(u^{2/m}\zeta)\}] \\ &\quad\quad -\mathrm{i}^{k-j-1}\hat{B}\lambda^{-1}_{j,k}\,\mathrm{e}^{-u\xi_c(u,z)}\{1+\vartheta^1_k(u^{2/m}\zeta)\}+(-)^k u^{-1}(\tfrac{1}{2}m)^{-\frac{1}{2}}\zeta^{\frac{1}{2}(2-m)}\hat{\epsilon}'(u,\zeta), \end{aligned} \tag{5.35}$$

with the same sign convention.

Case (i). We compare (5.9) and (5.34). Since there are two error terms in (5.9) there is a degree of freedom in the identification. The actual choice does not appear to be critical from the standpoint of applications. We shall adopt

$$\epsilon_{\pm1}(u,z) = (\tfrac{1}{2}m)^{\frac{1}{2}}\mathrm{i}^{-k+j+1}\mathrm{e}^{-u\xi_c(u,z)}\hat{\epsilon}(u,\zeta)+(1+\hat{A})\,\lambda_{j,k}\{1+\vartheta_{k\pm1}(u^{2/m}\zeta)\}-\lambda_{j,k}, \tag{5.36}$$

$$\epsilon_{\pm2}(u,z) = \{(1+\hat{A})\,\lambda_{j,k\pm1}\mp \mathrm{i}\hat{B}\lambda^{-1}_{j,k}\}\{1+\vartheta_k(u^{2/m}\zeta)\}-\lambda_{j,k\pm1}. \tag{5.37}$$

Similarly on comparing (5.10) and (5.35) we see that we can set

$$\epsilon^1_{\pm1}(u,z) = (\tfrac{1}{2}m)^{-\frac{1}{2}}\mathrm{i}^{k+j+1}u^{-1}\mathrm{e}^{-u\xi_c(u,z)}\zeta^{\frac{1}{2}(2-m)}\hat{\epsilon}'(u,\zeta)+(1+\hat{A})\,\lambda_{j,k}\{1+\vartheta^1_{k\pm1}(u^{2/m}\zeta)\}-\lambda_{j,k}, \tag{5.38}$$

$$\epsilon^1_{\pm2}(u,z) = \{(1+\hat{A})\,\lambda_{j,k\pm1}\mp \mathrm{i}\hat{B}\lambda^{-1}_{j,k}\}\{1+\vartheta^1_k(u^{2/m}\zeta)\}-\lambda_{j,k\pm1}. \tag{5.39}$$

Case (ii). We divide (5.13) and (5.34) by $\mathrm{e}^{u\xi_c(u,z)}$, let $z\to a_k$ and compare the results. Since $\mathrm{e}^{-2u\xi_c(u,z)}$, $\vartheta_k(u^{2/m}\zeta)$ and $\vartheta_{k\pm1}(u^{2/m}\zeta)$ all vanish in these circumstances, we obtain

$$\kappa_0 = (\tfrac{1}{2}m)^{\frac{1}{2}}\mathrm{i}^{-k+j+1}\lim_{z\to a_k}\{\mathrm{e}^{-u\xi_c(u,z)}\hat{\epsilon}(u,\zeta)\}+\hat{A}\lambda_{j,k}, \tag{5.40}$$

the existence of the limit on the right hand side being a consequence of theorem 12.1 of Olver (1974, ch. 6). Another consequence of the same theorem is that (5.14) is implied by (5.13).

Case (iii). The analysis in this case is more complicated, because although it is evident from (5.33) that $\mathrm{e}^{-u\xi_c(u,z)}\hat{\epsilon}(u,\zeta)$ is bounded in absolute value, this quantity does not tend to a limit as $z\to a_k$ along $\mathscr{P}$. Bearing in mind that we have $\operatorname{Re}\xi_c(u,z) = 0$ when $z\in\mathscr{P}\cap\boldsymbol{D}_k$, we proceed as follows.

By applying lemma 5.1 with $j = k$ and $k\pm 1$ in turn, we see that when $z\to a_k$ along $\mathscr{P}$ the solution $w(u,z)$ can be expressed in the forms (5.16) and (5.17) in which the terms $\kappa_{\pm1}$ and $\kappa_{\pm2}$ are independent of z. On comparing (5.16) with the limiting form of (5.34), we obtain

$$\begin{aligned}\kappa_{\pm1}\,\mathrm{e}^{u\xi_c(u,z)}\pm \mathrm{i}\kappa_{\pm2}\,\mathrm{e}^{-u\xi_c(u,z)}+o(1) &= \hat{A}\{\lambda_{j,k}\,\mathrm{e}^{u\xi_c(u,z)}\pm \mathrm{i}\lambda_{j,k\pm1}\,\mathrm{e}^{-u\xi_c(u,z)}\} \\ &\quad +\hat{B}\lambda^{-1}_{j,k}\,\mathrm{e}^{-u\xi_c(u,z)}+(\tfrac{1}{2}m)^{\frac{1}{2}}\mathrm{i}^{-k+j+1}\hat{\epsilon}(u,\zeta).\end{aligned}$$

Let $\{\zeta_n\}$, $n = 1, 2, 3, \ldots$ denote the infinite sequence of values of ζ on $\mathscr{Q}\cap\boldsymbol{S}_k$ for which the corresponding values of $\xi_c(u,z)$ are given by

$$2u\xi_c(u,z) = \pm n\pi\mathrm{i},$$

the upper or lower sign being taken according as $\mathscr{Q}$ coincides with the left or right boundary of $\boldsymbol{S}_k$. On letting $\zeta\to\alpha_k$ through the sequence $\{\zeta_{2n}\}$, we derive

$$\kappa_{\pm1}\pm \mathrm{i}\kappa_{\pm2} = \hat{A}(\lambda_{j,k}\pm \mathrm{i}\lambda_{j,k\pm1})+\hat{B}\lambda^{-1}_{j,k}+(-)^n(\tfrac{1}{2}m)^{\frac{1}{2}}\mathrm{i}^{-k+j+1}\hat{\epsilon}(u,\zeta_{2n})+o(1).$$

Similarly on letting $\zeta \to \alpha_k$ through the sequence $\{\zeta_{2n-1}\}$, we obtain

$$\kappa_{\pm 1} \mp i\kappa_{\pm 2} = \hat{A}(\lambda_{j,k} \mp i\lambda_{j,k\pm 1}) - \hat{B}\lambda_{j,k}^{-1} \pm i(-)^n(\tfrac{1}{2}m)^{\frac{1}{2}} i^{-k+j+1}\hat{\epsilon}(u, \zeta_{2n-1}) + o(1).$$

The last two equations may be solved for $\kappa_{\pm 1}$ and $\kappa_{\pm 2}$. In this way we find that

$$\kappa_{\pm 1} = (-)^n\tfrac{1}{2}(\tfrac{1}{2}m)^{\frac{1}{2}} i^{-k+j+1}\{\hat{\epsilon}(u, \zeta_{2n}) \pm i\hat{\epsilon}(u, \zeta_{2n-1})\} + \hat{A}\lambda_{j,k} + o(1), \tag{5.41}$$

$$\kappa_{\pm 2} = (-)^n\tfrac{1}{2}(\tfrac{1}{2}m)^{\frac{1}{2}} i^{-k+j+1}\{\mp i\hat{\epsilon}(u, \zeta_{2n}) - \hat{\epsilon}(u, \zeta_{2n-1})\} + \hat{A}\lambda_{j,k\pm 1} \mp i\hat{B}\lambda_{j,k}^{-1} + o(1). \tag{5.42}$$

Equations (5.36) to (5.42) supply exact formulae for the wanted error terms in the approximations (5.9), (5.10), (5.13), (5.14), (5.16) and (5.17). The desired inequalities (5.11), (5.12), (5.15), (5.18) and (5.19) immediately follow on substituting for the absolute values of $\vartheta_k(u^{2/m}\zeta)$, $\vartheta_k^1(u^{2/m}\zeta)$, $\vartheta_{k\pm 1}(u^{2/m}\zeta)$ and $\vartheta_{k\pm 1}^1(u^{2/m}\zeta)$ by means of their common bound $\Theta\{u\xi_c(u, z)\}$ obtained from (2.14), for $\hat{A}$ and $\hat{B}$ by means of (5.32), and for the terms involving values, or limiting values, of $\hat{\epsilon}(u, \zeta)$ and $\hat{\epsilon}'(u, \zeta)$ by means of (5.33). This completes the proof of theorem 5.1.

5.6. *A special case*

An important case of theorem 5.1 arises when both $\xi_c(u, a_j)$ and $\xi_c(u, a_k)$ are at infinity. Since several simplifications then become available, we state the result as a separate theorem. This may be compared with corresponding results for real variables given by Olver (1977*a*, §4).

THEOREM 5.2. *Assume the conditions of theorem* 5.1 *and also that* $|\xi_c(u, z)| \to \infty$ *as* $z \to a_j$ *or* a_k *along* $\mathscr{P}$. *Then the solution of* (3.1) *defined by*

$$w(u, z) \sim f^{-\frac{1}{4}}(u, z)\, e^{-u\xi_c(u, z)} \quad (z \to a_j \text{ along } \mathscr{P}), \tag{5.43}$$

is unique. Furthermore if $z \to a_k$ *along* $\mathscr{P}$, *then* $w(u, z)$ *has the properties* (5.13) *and* (5.14) *when* $\operatorname{Re} \xi_c(u, a_k) = \infty$, *or the properties* (5.16) *and* (5.17) *when* $\operatorname{Re} \xi_c(u, a_k) = 0$, *where*

$$|\kappa_0|, \quad |\kappa_{\pm 1}|, \quad |\kappa_{\pm 2}| \leqslant C_{j,k}\left[\exp\left\{\frac{\rho_{j,k}}{m|\lambda_{j,k}|u^{2/m}} \mathscr{V}_{\mathscr{P}}(H)\right\} - 1\right], \tag{5.44}$$

provided that, when (5.13) *and* (5.14) *hold, the right hand side of* (5.44) *is less than* $|\lambda_{j,k}|$.

It may also be noted that by constructing a direct proof for this special case it is not difficult to sharpen the bound (5.44) for $|\kappa_0|$ (but not for $|\kappa_{\pm 1}|$ or $|\kappa_{\pm 2}|$) by replacing $C_{j,k}$ by $(1 + \lambda_{j,k}^2)^{\frac{1}{2}}$; compare (2.38).

6. Asymptotic forms of the connection theorem

6.1. *Assumptions*

By supposing that the functions f and g are independent of the parameter u, we may construct asymptotic estimates of the error terms in theorem 5.1 for large values of u by application of the results of §4. The results we shall obtain in the present section are analogous to those for real variables given in Olver (1977*b*, §2) but the method of proof is somewhat different.

We consider the equation

$$d^2w/dz^2 = \{u^2 f(z) + g(z)\}w, \tag{6.1}$$

in which $z \in \boldsymbol{D}$, again a bounded or unbounded open complex domain occupying one or more Riemann sheets, and the functions $f(z)$ and $g(z)$ are independent of the positive parameter u. We suppose that $(z-c)^{2-m}f(z)$ is holomorphic and non-vanishing in $\mathbf{D}$, where c is an interior point of $\mathbf{D}$ and m is a positive constant. Also, $g(z)$ is holomorphic in $\mathbf{D}$, punctured at c, and

$$g(z) = O\{(z-c)^{\gamma-1}\} \quad (z\to c), \tag{6.2}$$

where γ is a positive constant.

As in § 5.1 we define

$$\xi_c(z) = \int_c^z f^{\frac{1}{2}}(t)\,\mathrm{d}t, \tag{6.3}$$

taking the branch that has non-negative real part. We also adopt the other conditions and definitions associated with theorem 5.1, with the specialization that the functions $f(z)$ and $g(z)$ are now independent of u; for example,

$$F(z) = \int\left\{\frac{1}{f^{\frac{1}{4}}(z)}\frac{\mathrm{d}^2}{\mathrm{d}z^2}\left(\frac{1}{f^{\frac{1}{4}}(z)}\right) - \frac{g(z)}{f^{\frac{1}{2}}(z)}\right\}\mathrm{d}z. \tag{6.4}$$

The following conventions were introduced in Olver (1977*b*), and will be followed in this and subsequent sections. First, the *symbol* $\underset{(2)}{=}$ *is used to signify that a given equation is valid, and also the corresponding equation obtained by formal differentiation with respect to z ignoring the differentiation of all O-terms*. Secondly, *whenever an O-term appears in an equation it is understood to be uniform with respect to all values of z associated with that equation*. Thirdly, *the symbol* $\chi(u)$ *denotes an arbitrary positive function of u having the properties*

$$\chi(u)\to 0, \quad 1/\chi(u) = O(u) \quad (u\to\infty). \tag{6.5}$$

Lastly, let a and b be any two points on a path $\mathscr{P}$. Then following Olver (1974, p. 121) we denote the part of $\mathscr{P}$ that lies between a and b by $(a,b)_{\mathscr{P}}$ or $[a,b]_{\mathscr{P}}$, according as a and b are both excluded or both included. Similarly for $(a,b]_{\mathscr{P}}$ and $[a,b)_{\mathscr{P}}$.

6.2. *Connection theorem for paths*

THEOREM 6.1. (i) *Assume the conditions and notation of* § 6.1 *and that j and k are integers satisfying condition* (i) *of* § 3.3. *Let* $\mathscr{P}$ *be a progressive path lying in* $\mathbf{D}_j \cup \mathbf{D}_k$ *and* a_j, b_j, b_k *and* a_k *be points, in that order, on* $\mathscr{P}$, *none of which depends on u or coincides with c; furthermore,* a_j *is in the closure of* $\mathbf{D}_j$, a_k *is in the closure of* $\mathbf{D}_k$, $b_j\in\mathbf{D}_j$ *and* $b_k\in\mathbf{D}_k$.† *Assume also that both* $1/\xi_c(z)$ *and* $F(z)$ *are of bounded variation on* $(a_j,b_j]_{\mathscr{P}}$ *and* $[b_k,a_k)_{\mathscr{P}}$, *and that* $w(u,z)$ *is a solution of the differential equation* (6.1) *having the properties*

$$f^{\frac{1}{4}}(z)\,w(u,z) \underset{(2)}{=} \{1+O(\chi)\}\,\mathrm{e}^{-u\xi_c(z)} \quad (z\in(a_j,b_j]_{\mathscr{P}}), \tag{6.6}$$

as $u\to\infty$, *and*

$$\mathrm{e}^{u\xi_c(z)}f^{\frac{1}{4}}(z)\,w(u,z),\quad f^{-\frac{1}{2}}(z)\,\mathrm{e}^{u\xi_c(z)}\partial\{f^{\frac{1}{4}}(z)\,w(u,z)\}/\partial z \to \text{non-zero finite limits}, \tag{6.7}$$

as $z\to a_j$ *along* $\mathscr{P}$.

Then on $[b_k,a_k)_{\mathscr{P}}$ *the analytic continuation of* $w(u,z)$ – *obtained by passing around the neighbourhood of c from* $\mathbf{D}_j$ *to* $\mathbf{D}_k$ *in the same sense as the sign of* $(k-j)$ – *is given by*

$$w(u,z) = w_{\mathrm{I}}(u,z), \tag{6.8}$$

$$w(u,z) = w_{\mathrm{I},1}(u,z) + w_{\mathrm{L}}(u,z), \tag{6.9}$$

or

$$w(u,z) = w_{\mathrm{I},-1}(u,z) + w_{\mathrm{R}}(u,z), \tag{6.10}$$

† Thus a_j and a_k (but not b_j and b_k) may be boundary points of $\mathbf{D}$, including the point at infinity.

according as b_k *is interior to* $\boldsymbol{D}_k$, $[b_k, a_k)_{\mathscr{P}}$ *coincides with the left boundary of* $\boldsymbol{D}_k$, *or* $[b_k, a_k)_{\mathscr{P}}$ *coincides with the right boundary of* $\boldsymbol{D}_k$. *Here* $w_{\mathrm{I}}(u,z)$, $w_{\mathrm{I},\pm1}(u,z)$, $w_{\mathrm{L}}(u,z)$ *and* $w_{\mathrm{R}}(u,z)$ *are solutions of* (6.1) *having the following asymptotic forms on* $[b_k, a_k)_{\mathscr{P}}$ *as* $u\to\infty$:

$$f^{\frac{1}{4}}(z)\,w_{\mathrm{I}}(u,z),\quad f^{\frac{1}{4}}(z)\,w_{\mathrm{I},1}(u,z),\quad f^{\frac{1}{4}}(z)\,w_{\mathrm{I},-1}(u,z) \underset{(2)}{=} \mathrm{i}^{k-j-1}\{\lambda_{j,k}+O(\hat{\chi}_m)\}\,\mathrm{e}^{u\xi_c(z)}, \tag{6.11}$$

$$f^{\frac{1}{4}}(z)\,w_{\mathrm{L}}(u,z) \underset{(2)}{=} \mathrm{i}^{k-j}\{\lambda_{j,k+1}+O(\hat{\chi}_m)\}\,\mathrm{e}^{-u\xi_c(z)}, \tag{6.12}$$

$$f^{\frac{1}{4}}(z)\,w_{\mathrm{R}}(u,z) \underset{(2)}{=} -\mathrm{i}^{k-j}\{\lambda_{j,k-1}+O(\hat{\chi}_m)\}\,\mathrm{e}^{-u\xi_c(z)}. \tag{6.13}$$

In these relations $\lambda_{j,k}$ *is defined by* (2.17) *and* (2.18), $f^{\frac{1}{4}}(z)$ *denotes the branch obtained from that used in* (6.6) *by analytic continuation in the same manner as for* $w(u,z)$, *and* $\hat{\chi}_m \equiv \hat{\chi}_m(u)$ *is defined by*

$$\hat{\chi}_m(u) = \max\{\chi(u), \psi_m(u)\}, \tag{6.14}$$

where $\psi_m(u)$ *is given by* (4.5) *and* (4.6).

(ii) *If, in addition,* $g(z)$ *is analytic at* c, *then in* (6.11), (6.12) *and* (6.13) *we may take*

$$\hat{\chi}_m(u) = \max\{\chi(u), \chi_m(u)\}, \tag{6.15}$$

where $\chi_m(u)$ *is given by* (4.8).

The proof of this theorem is given in the next subsection.

Remarks. (*a*) Although $w_{\mathrm{I}}(u,z)$, $w_{\mathrm{I},1}(u,z)$ and $w_{\mathrm{I},-1}(u,z)$ have the same asymptotic form (6.11), they are distinct solutions of (6.1).

(*b*) The given conditions permit b_j to coincide with a_j, provided that a_j is not on the boundary of $\boldsymbol{D}$. In this event $(a_j, b_j]_{\mathscr{P}}$ is to be interpreted simply as a_j. Similarly for a_k and b_k.

(*c*) The left boundary of $\boldsymbol{D}_k$ is also the right boundary of $\boldsymbol{D}_{k+1}$. Consequently a simple consistency check is furnished on replacing k by $k+1$ in (6.10) and comparing the result with (6.9) by means of (6.11), (6.12) and (6.13). Bearing in mind that $\xi_c(u,z)$ changes sign on crossing the boundary, we perceive that consistency is maintained. Similarly for the right boundary of $\boldsymbol{D}_k$.

When $g(u,z)$ is analytic at $z=c$, another consistency check is furnished by taking m to be a positive integer, other than unity, and replacing k by $k+m$. In effect, this describes a simple closed circuit of c once in the positive sense, and therefore changes $f^{\frac{1}{4}}(u,z)$ by the factor $\mathrm{e}^{\frac{1}{2}(m-2)\pi\mathrm{i}}$. Using this result we easily verify that the net effect is to leave (6.8) to (6.13) unchanged, as we expect, since $w_j(u,z)$ is analytic at c for these values of m.

(*d*) In the various cases that arise when c is real, $f(z)$ is real on the real axis and m is an integer exceeding unity, theorem 6.1 yields the same results as theorems 1, 2, 3 and 4 of Olver (1977*b*). This assertion is verifiable in a straightforward manner and details will not be included.

6.3. *Proof of theorem* 6.1

In consequence of the assumed conditions, equation (6.1) has a solution $\hat{w}(u,z)$ with the properties

$$f^{\frac{1}{4}}(z)\,\hat{w}(u,z) \underset{(2)}{=} \{1+O(u^{-1})\}\,\mathrm{e}^{-u\xi_c(z)} \quad (z\in(a_j, b_j]_{\mathscr{P}}), \tag{6.16}$$

as $u\to\infty$, and

$$\mathrm{e}^{u\xi_c(z)}f^{\frac{1}{4}}(z)\,\hat{w}(u,z)\to 1,\quad f^{-\frac{1}{4}}(z)\,\mathrm{e}^{u\xi_c(z)}\partial\{f^{\frac{1}{4}}(z)\,\hat{w}(u,z)\}/\partial z\to -u, \tag{6.17}$$

as $z\to a_j$ along $\mathscr{P}$; compare §§ 11 and 12 of Olver (1974, ch. 6). If we define

$$w(u,z) = \{1+O(\chi)\}\,\hat{w}(u,z), \tag{6.18}$$

where the term $O(\chi)$ is independent of z, then $w(u,z)$ is another solution of (6.1). On combining

(6.16) and (6.18) and observing that in consequence of (6.5) $O(u^{-1}) \subseteq O(\chi)$, we obtain (6.6) with the term $O(\chi)$ now depending on z. In other words, a solution $w(u,z)$ having the properties (6.6) and (6.7) certainly exists. This solution is obviously not unique, however, because of the freedom of choice of the term $O(\chi)$ in (6.18).

Next, it is easily verified that all the conditions of theorem 5.1 are satisfied. On comparing (5.7) and (5.8) with (6.6) and (6.7) we see that we may set $\delta = O(\chi)$ as $u \to \infty$. In $[b_k, a_k)_{\mathscr{P}}$ the wanted solution $w(u,z)$ is given by (5.9) and (5.10), and we now seek uniform asymptotic estimates for the error terms in these representations when u is large.

From (5.4), (5.5) and the facts that

$$\Theta\{u\xi_c(a_j)\} = O(u^{-1}), \quad |e^{-2u\xi_c(a_j)}| \leqslant 1,$$

we obtain $\Lambda_j(u) = O(\chi)$ and $X_{j,k}(u) = O(\chi)$. If we assume the conditions of part (i) of theorem 6.1, then theorem 4.1 (i) is applicable; hence we have $u^{-2/m}\mathscr{V}_{\mathscr{P}}(H) = O(\psi_m)$. Since $\mathscr{V}_{a_j,z}(H) \leqslant \mathscr{V}_{\mathscr{P}}(H)$ when $z \in [b_k, a_k)_{\mathscr{P}}$, we deduce from (5.6) that $\Lambda_{j,k}(u,z) = O(\psi_m)$ uniformly with respect to $z \in [b_k, a_k)_{\mathscr{P}}$. We also have $\Theta\{u\xi_c(z)\} = O(u^{-1})$ in the same circumstances.

Substituting in the right hand sides of (5.11) and (5.12) by means of the estimates found in the preceding paragraph, we conclude that

$$\epsilon_{\pm 1}(u,z), \quad \epsilon^1_{\pm 1}(u,z), \quad \epsilon_{\pm 2}(u,z), \quad \epsilon^1_{\pm 2}(u,z) = O(\hat{\chi}_m) \quad (z \in [b_k, a_k)_{\mathscr{P}}), \tag{6.19}$$

where $\hat{\chi}_m$ is defined by (6.14). The required results (6.11), (6.12) and (6.13) are obtained by combining (5.9) and (5.10) with (6.19), and also, when b_k is interior to $\boldsymbol{D}_k$, absorbing the terms

$$\pm\, i^{k-j}\{\lambda_{j,k\pm 1} + \epsilon_{\pm 2}(u,z)\}\, e^{-u\xi_c(z)}, \quad \mp\, i^{k-j}\{\lambda_{j,k\pm 1} + \epsilon^1_{\pm 2}(u,z)\}\, e^{-u\xi_c(z)}$$

in the uniform error estimate $O(\hat{\chi}_m)\, e^{u\xi_c(z)}$, since in this event $\operatorname{Re}\xi_c(z) \geqslant \operatorname{Re}\xi_c(b_k) > 0$.

To complete the proof of part (i) of the theorem we have to show that the individual components $w_{\mathrm{I},1}(u,z)$, $w_{\mathrm{L}}(u,z)$, $w_{\mathrm{I},-1}(u,z)$ and $w_{\mathrm{R}}(u,z)$ in (6.9) and (6.10) can be chosen in such a way that in addition to possessing the asymptotic forms exhibited by (6.11) to (6.13) each is an exact solution of (6.1). In the case of $w_{\mathrm{I},1}(u,z)$ and $w_{\mathrm{L}}(u,z)$ this is verifiable in the following way.

From L.G. theory we know that there exist independent solutions $w_+(u,z)$ and $w_-(u,z)$, say, of (6.1) with the properties

$$f^{\frac{1}{4}}(z)\, w_+(u,z) \underset{(2)}{=} \{1 + O(u^{-1})\}\, e^{u\xi_c(z)}, \quad f^{\frac{1}{4}}(z)\, w_-(u,z) \underset{(2)}{=} \{1 + O(u^{-1})\}\, e^{-u\xi_c(z)}, \tag{6.20}$$

when $z \in [b_k, a_k)_{\mathscr{P}}$; compare (6.16). Let

$$f^{\frac{1}{4}}(z)\, w(u,z) = Af^{\frac{1}{4}}(z)\, w_+(u,z) + Bf^{\frac{1}{4}}(z)\, w_-(u,z), \tag{6.21}$$

where A and B are independent of z. To find these coefficients we substitute on the left hand side by means of (6.9), (6.11) and (6.12), and on the right hand side by means of (6.20). This gives one equation for A and B. A second equation is found in a similar way from the differentiated form of (6.21). Solving the two equations, and recalling that $|e^{\pm u\xi_c(z)}| = 1$ in the present circumstances, we find that

$$A = i^{k-j-1}\{\lambda_{j,k} + O(\hat{\chi}_m)\}, \quad B = i^{k-j}\{\lambda_{j,k+1} + O(\hat{\chi}_m)\}. \tag{6.22}$$

On combining these results with (6.20) we see that $Af^{\frac{1}{4}}(z)\, w_+(u,z)$ and $Bf^{\frac{1}{4}}(z)\, w_-(u,z)$ have the properties (6.11) and (6.12) respectively, when $z \in [b_k, a_k)_{\mathscr{P}}$.

A similar analysis may be constructed for $w_{\mathrm{I},-1}(u,z)$ and $w_{\mathrm{R}}(u,z)$. This concludes the proof of part (i) of the theorem.

To prove part (ii) we observe that if $g(z)$ is analytic at c, then theorem 4.1 (ii) permits ψ_m to be replaced by χ_m everywhere; in particular (6.15) may be used instead of (6.14).

6.4. *Connection theorem for domains*

Theorem 6.1 supplies the L.G. form of the solution $w(u,z)$ when z is confined to a path. In some applications we need asymptotic estimates for $w(u,z)$ that are uniform in subregions of $\boldsymbol{D}_k$. To construct a result of this nature we adopt the conditions of theorem 6.1, but now suppose that $|\xi_c(a_k)| = \infty$ and in $\boldsymbol{D}_k$ the path $\mathscr{P} \equiv \mathscr{P}_\theta$ coincides with the curve having the equation $\operatorname{ph}\xi_c(z) = \theta$, where θ is a parameter in the closed interval $[\theta_1, \theta_2]$. Here θ_1 and θ_2 are constants such that $-\frac{1}{2}\pi \leqslant \theta_1 < \theta_2 \leqslant \frac{1}{2}\pi$. In consequence, the point $b_k \equiv b_k(\theta)$ depends on θ. We assume that $|\xi_c\{b_k(\theta)\}|$ is bounded and bounded away from zero, and also that

$$\mathscr{V}_{z,\,a_k}(F) \to 0 \quad (z \to a_k), \tag{6.23}$$

uniformly with respect to θ, where the variation is evaluated along $\mathscr{P}_\theta$.

Theorem 6.2. *With the assumptions of this subsection, the solution* $w(u,z)$ *of* (6.1) *having the property* (6.6) *has the following asymptotic form on* $[b_k(\theta), a_k)_{\mathscr{P}_\theta}$:

$$f^{\frac{1}{4}}(z)\, w(u,z) \underset{(2)}{=} \mathrm{i}^{k-j-1}\{\lambda_{j,k} + O(\hat{\chi}_m)\}\, \mathrm{e}^{u\xi_c(z)} \pm \mathrm{i}^{k-j}\{\lambda_{j,k\pm1} + O(\hat{\chi}_m)\}\, \mathrm{e}^{-u\xi_c(z)}, \tag{6.24}$$

as $u \to \infty$, *the upper or lower signs being taken throughout according as* $\theta \geqslant 0$ *or* $\theta \leqslant 0$.† *Furthermore, the* O*-terms are uniform with respect to* θ *(as well as* z*).*

This result is based on theorem 4.2, and the modifications to the proof of theorem 6.1 are quite straightforward.

Remark. If, in addition, we restrict $[b_k(\theta), a_k)_{\mathscr{P}_\theta}$ to an internal part of $\boldsymbol{D}_k$ (§5.1) then the contribution of the whole of the second term on the right hand side of (6.24) is absorbable in the uniform error estimate $O(\hat{\chi}_m)\, \mathrm{e}^{u\xi_c(z)}$ included in the first term, because $|\mathrm{e}^{-2u\xi_c(z)}|$ is exponentially and uniformly small in these circumstances.

7. Application of the connection theorem

7.1. *Classification of cases*

Assume $\boldsymbol{D}$ to be a simply connected open domain that contains n transition points, and let the L.G. approximation of a solution of the differential equation (6.1) be given at a point in the closure of $\boldsymbol{D}$, other than one of the transition points. Then the L.G. approximation of the same solution at any other point, except a transition point, can be found by at most n applications of theorem 6.1. Or, if we require the L.G. approximation of the solution in any appropriate subregion of $\boldsymbol{D}$, then it suffices to make $n-1$ or fewer applications of theorem 6.1, followed by one application of theorem 6.2. The process is completely illustrated by the case in which $\boldsymbol{D}$ contains just two transition points c and $\hat{c}$, say, of multiplicities $m-2$ and $\hat{m}-2$, respectively, m and $\hat{m}$ being arbitrary positive numbers.

As in §§5.1 and 6.1 we associate with c the function

$$\xi_c(z) = \int_c^z f^{\frac{1}{2}}(t)\, \mathrm{d}t, \tag{7.1}$$

† Again, either sign may be adopted when $\theta = 0$.

where the branch of the integral has non-negative real part and is continuous except where $\operatorname{Re}\xi_c(z) = 0$. The last equation defines a set of curves emanating from c which we shall call the *c-principal curves*. In a similar way, if

$$\xi_{\hat{c}}(z) = \int_{\hat{c}}^{z} f^{\frac{1}{2}}(t)\,\mathrm{d}t, \tag{7.2}$$

with $\operatorname{Re}\xi_{\hat{c}}(z) \geqslant 0$, then the curves on which $\xi_{\hat{c}}(z)$ is discontinuous, given by $\operatorname{Re}\xi_{\hat{c}}(z) = 0$, will be called the *ĉ-principal curves*.

In the plane of the variable

$$\xi(z) = \int f^{\frac{1}{2}}(z)\,\mathrm{d}z, \tag{7.3}$$

in which the integration constant is arbitrary and the branch is chosen in a continuous manner, the c-principal curves and the $\hat{c}$-principal curves are mapped as straight lines parallel to the imaginary axis. The theory of conformal mapping shows that the c-principal curves intersect each other on the same Riemann sheet only at c; similarly the $\hat{c}$-principal curves intersect only at $\hat{c}$. Nor may a c-principal curve intersect a $\hat{c}$-principal curve on the same Riemann sheet. It is possible, however, for c and $\hat{c}$ to be linked by a common principal curve; this occurs when the join of $\xi(c)$ and $\xi(\hat{c})$ is parallel to the imaginary axis. The absence or presence of a common principal curve gives rise to two distinct cases, which we designate I and II. They are discussed in turn in the next two subsections. Further details will become clear from the examples treated in part C.

7.2. *Case I: no common principal curve*

Figure 6 indicates the disposition of the two sets of principal curves. We denote the region bounded by four principal curves, two from each set, either by $\boldsymbol{D}_0$ or $\hat{\boldsymbol{D}}_0$, depending whether it is being associated with c or $\hat{c}$ in the connection process. Starting from $\boldsymbol{D}_0$ we enumerate the successive regions bounded by adjacent c-principal curves as $\boldsymbol{D}_1, \boldsymbol{D}_2, \ldots$, or $\boldsymbol{D}_{-1}, \boldsymbol{D}_{-2}, \ldots$, depending whether we are proceeding in the positive or negative sense around c. Similarly, starting from $\hat{\boldsymbol{D}}_0$ we denote the successive regions bounded by adjacent $\hat{c}$-principal curves by $\hat{\boldsymbol{D}}_1, \hat{\boldsymbol{D}}_2, \ldots$, or $\hat{\boldsymbol{D}}_{-1}, \hat{\boldsymbol{D}}_{-2}, \ldots$, depending whether we are proceeding in the positive or negative sense around $\hat{c}$. If m is a positive integer exceeding unity, then there are m distinct regions $\boldsymbol{D}_j$. In other cases the $\boldsymbol{D}_j$ may be finite or infinite in number, and occupy two or more Riemann sheets. Similarly for the $\hat{\boldsymbol{D}}_j$.

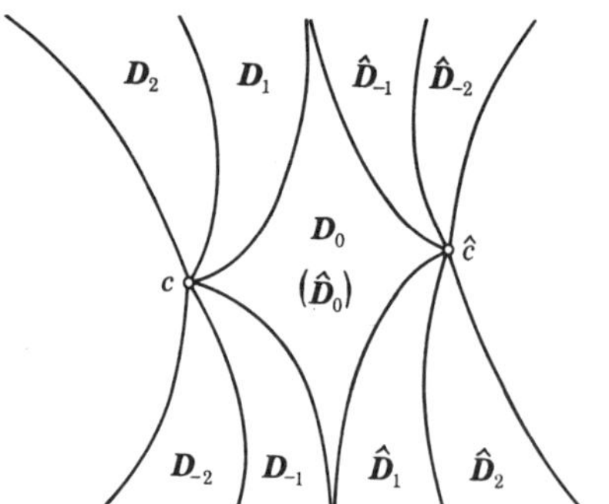

FIGURE 6. Case I: z-plane.

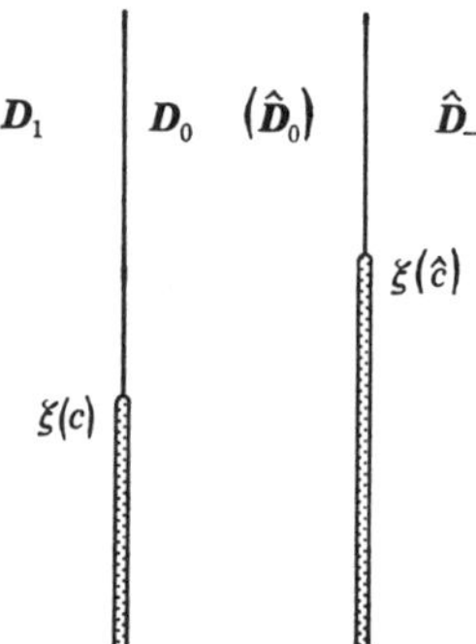

FIGURE 7. Case I: ξ-plane.

When $j \neq 0$ the regions $\boldsymbol{D}_j$ and $\hat{\boldsymbol{D}}_j$ are principal regions in the sense of § 5.1. But $\boldsymbol{D}_0$ (or $\hat{\boldsymbol{D}}_0$) comprises only part of a principal region associated with c (or $\hat{c}$). In the ξ-plane the maps of $\boldsymbol{D}_j$ and $\hat{\boldsymbol{D}}_j$ may extend over a half-plane when $j \neq 0$, but the map of $\boldsymbol{D}_0$ (or $\hat{\boldsymbol{D}}_0$) is confined to a vertical strip; compare figure 7.

Let us assume that we are given the L.G. approximation (6.6) of a solution $w(u, z)$ of (6.1), where $(a_j, b_j]_{\mathscr{P}}$ is a segment of a progressive path $\mathscr{P}$ in $\boldsymbol{D}_j$, j being arbitrary. As special cases $(a_j, b_j]_{\mathscr{P}}$ may coincide with the left or right boundary of $\boldsymbol{D}_j$, or reduce to a single point in $\boldsymbol{D}_j$, other than a boundary point of $\boldsymbol{D}$. Our problem is to construct the L.G. approximation of the same solution on a segment $[\hat{b}_k, \hat{a}_k)_{\hat{\mathscr{P}}}$ of a progressive path $\hat{\mathscr{P}}$ in $\hat{\boldsymbol{D}}_k$, where k is arbitrary. When $j = 0$ the problem is immediately solvable by regarding $\boldsymbol{D}_0$ as $\hat{\boldsymbol{D}}_0$, and passing from $\hat{\boldsymbol{D}}_0$ to $\hat{\boldsymbol{D}}_k$ by means of a single application of theorem 6.1, with c replaced by $\hat{c}$. Similarly when $k = 0$.

When j and k are both non-zero we select an arbitrary point a_0 in the interior of $\boldsymbol{D}_0$ that can be joined to b_j by an extension of $\mathscr{P}$ that passes through c and is progressive, that is, $\operatorname{Re}\xi_c(z)$ is non-increasing as z travels from a_j to c and non-decreasing as z travels from c to a_0. The L.G. form of $w(u, z)$ at a_0 is found by applying theorem 6.1 with $k = 0$, the relevant formulae being (6.8) and (6.11).

To prepare for passage through the second transition point we compare (7.1) and (7.2). Recalling that both $\operatorname{Re}\xi_c(z)$ and $\operatorname{Re}\xi_{\hat{c}}(z)$ are non-negative, we see that

$$\xi_c(z) + \xi_{\hat{c}}(z) = \xi_c(\hat{c}) = \xi_{\hat{c}}(c) \quad (z \in \boldsymbol{D}_0). \tag{7.4}$$

Hence $\operatorname{Re}\xi_c(z)$ is non-increasing on $[c, a_0]_{\mathscr{P}}$, *which implies that this segment of $\mathscr{P}$ is also a progressive path with respect to $\hat{c}$.* We now relabel a_0 as $\hat{a}_0$ and extend $\hat{\mathscr{P}}$, still progressive, to pass through $\hat{c}$ and continue to $\hat{a}_0$. The aggregate path $\mathscr{P} + \hat{\mathscr{P}}$ is indicated by the broken curve in figure 8. Using the

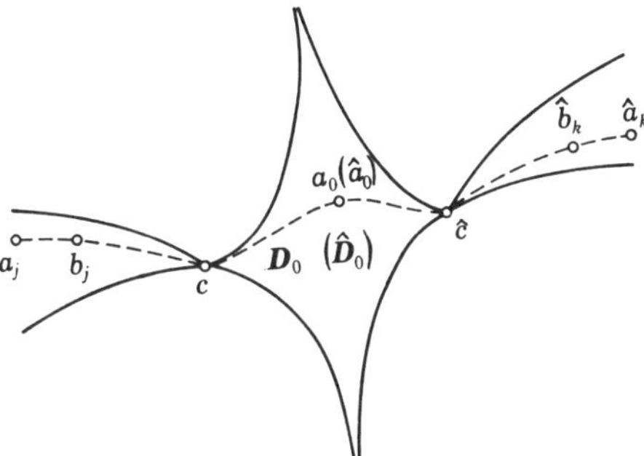

FIGURE 8. Case I: z-plane. --- progressive path.

L.G. form of $w(u, z)$ that is available at $\hat{a}_0$ after passage through c, we replace $e^{u\xi_c(z)}$ by $e^{u\xi_c(\hat{c})}\,e^{-u\xi_{\hat{c}}(z)}$; compare (7.4). Theorem 6.1 is then applied, with c replaced by $\hat{c}$ and $j = 0$, and we select (6.8), (6.9) or (6.10), depending whether b_k is an interior point of $\hat{\boldsymbol{D}}_k$, $[\hat{b}_k, \hat{a}_k)_{\hat{\mathscr{P}}}$ coincides with the left boundary of $\hat{\boldsymbol{D}}_k$ or $[\hat{b}_k, \hat{a}_k)_{\hat{\mathscr{P}}}$ coincides with the right boundary of $\hat{\boldsymbol{D}}_k$. The desired L.G. form on $[\hat{b}_k, \hat{a}_k)_{\hat{\mathscr{P}}}$ is then available from (6.11), (6.12) and (6.13).

7.3. *Case II: common principal curve*

Figure 9 indicates the disposition of the two sets of principal curves and the labelling of the corresponding regions. There are now two regions $\boldsymbol{D}_0$ ($\equiv \hat{\boldsymbol{D}}_1$) and $\boldsymbol{D}_1$ ($\equiv \hat{\boldsymbol{D}}_0$) that have both c and

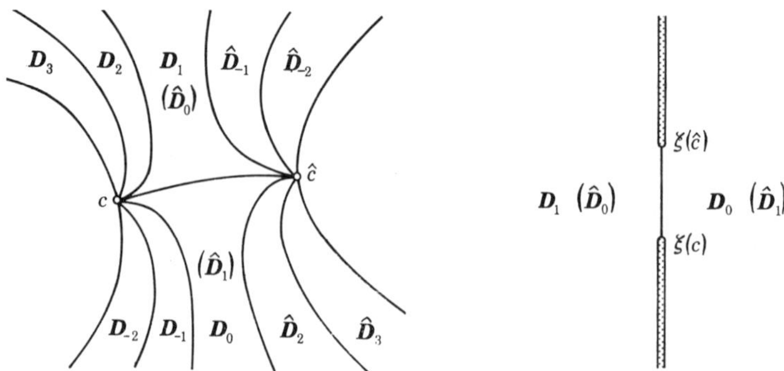

FIGURE 9. Case II: z-plane.

FIGURE 10. Case II: ξ-plane.

$\hat{c}$ on their boundaries; furthermore each is a principal region in the sense of § 5.1 with respect to either transition point. Part of the mapping on the ξ-plane is indicated in figure 10. Again, our problem is to connect the L.G. form (6.6) on a given segment $(a_j, b_j]_{\mathscr{P}}$ of a progressive path $\mathscr{P}$ in $\boldsymbol{D}_j$, with the L.G. form of the same solution on a segment $[\hat{b}_k, \hat{a}_k)_{\hat{\mathscr{P}}}$ of a progressive path $\hat{\mathscr{P}}$ in $\hat{\boldsymbol{D}}_k$, for arbitrary values of j and k. As in case I, when j or k is zero or unity this problem can be solved by a single application of theorem 6.1. We therefore exclude these cases in the remainder of this subsection.

The essential difference from the previous case is that there is a change of sign in the relation between $\xi_c(z)$ and $\xi_{\hat{c}}(z)$: in place of (7.4) we now have

$$\xi_c(z) - \xi_{\hat{c}}(z) = \xi_c(\hat{c}) = -\xi_{\hat{c}}(c) \quad (z \in \boldsymbol{D}_0 \text{ or } \boldsymbol{D}_1). \tag{7.5}$$

In consequence, if we choose an arbitrary point a_0 in the interior of $\boldsymbol{D}_0$ and try to follow the method of I, we encounter a difficulty as soon as we prepare for passage through the second transition point. This is because $e^{u\xi_c(z)}$ is replaced by $e^{u\xi_c(\hat{c})}e^{u\xi_{\hat{c}}(z)}$, and the absence of a negative sign in the argument of the last exponential function precludes a second application of theorem 6.1.

To overcome the difficulty, we place a_0 on the common principal curve linking c and $\hat{c}$, as indicated in figure 11. Then $[c, a_0]_{\mathscr{P}}$ coincides with this principal curve, and the L.G. form of

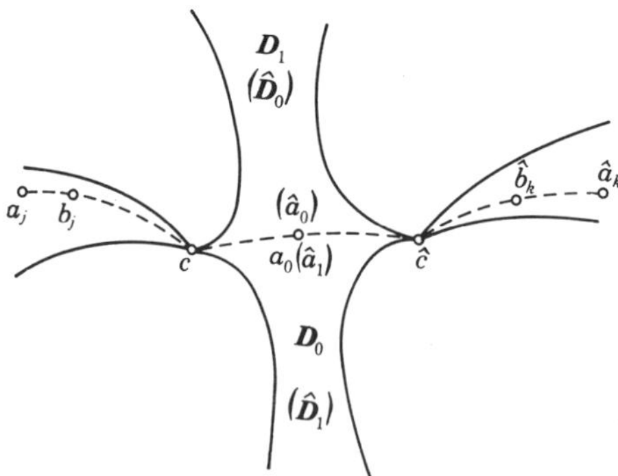

FIGURE 11. Case II: z-plane. --- progressive path.

$w(u,z)$ at a_0 is given by (6.9), (6.11) and (6.12) with $k = 0$. To prepare for passage through $\hat{c}$, we observe that $\boldsymbol{D}_0 \equiv \hat{\boldsymbol{D}}_1$. Consequently we relabel a_0 as $\hat{a}_1$, and extend $\hat{\mathscr{P}}$, still progressive, to pass through $\hat{c}$ and continue along the common principal curve until $\hat{a}_1$ is reached. The aggregate path $\mathscr{P}+\hat{\mathscr{P}}$ is indicated by the broken curve in figure 11. In the L.G. form of $w(u,z)$ at $\hat{a}_1$ found by passage through c, there are now two terms $w_{\mathrm{I},1}(u,z)$ and $w_{\mathrm{L}}(u,z)$. The contribution from $w_{\mathrm{L}}(u,z)$ to the L.G. form on $[\hat{b}_k, \hat{a}_k)_{\hat{\mathscr{P}}}$ is obtained by replacing $\mathrm{e}^{-u\xi_c(z)}$ by $\mathrm{e}^{-u\xi_c(\hat{c})}\,\mathrm{e}^{-u\xi_{\hat{c}}(z)}$ and applying theorem 6.1, with c replaced by $\hat{c}$ and $j = 1$. To handle the contribution from $w_{\mathrm{I},1}(u,z)$, the key step is to regard a_0 as a member of $\hat{\boldsymbol{D}}_0$, and relabel it $\hat{a}_0$. Since this entails crossing a principal curve, $\xi_{\hat{c}}(z)$ is replaced by $-\xi_{\hat{c}}(z)$. Thus $\mathrm{e}^{u\xi_c(z)}$ becomes $\mathrm{e}^{u\xi_c(\hat{c})}\,\mathrm{e}^{-u\xi_{\hat{c}}(z)}$, where $\hat{c}$ is regarded as a member of $\boldsymbol{D}_0$ in calculating $\xi_c(\hat{c})$ (so that $\xi_c(\hat{c})$ is positive imaginary), and z is regarded as a member of $\hat{\boldsymbol{D}}_0$. The contribution from $w_{\mathrm{I},1}(u,z)$ to the L.G. form on $[\hat{b}_k, \hat{a}_k)_{\hat{\mathscr{P}}}$ is then found by applying theorem 6.1, with c replaced by $\hat{c}$ and $j = 0$.

7.4. *Remarks on cases I and II*

(*a*) Instead of using theorem 6.1 for passage through $\hat{c}$ in cases I and II, we may use theorem 6.2. This modification will yield a subregion (in place of curves) in $\hat{\boldsymbol{D}}_k$ in which the L.G. approximation is uniformly valid for large u.

(*b*) If, in case I, $k = \pm 1$ and $\hat{\mathscr{P}}$ lies in an internal part of $\hat{\boldsymbol{D}}_k$, then it may be possible to link $(a_j, b_j]_{\mathscr{P}}$ to $[\hat{b}_k, \hat{a}_k)_{\hat{\mathscr{P}}}$ by a path in $\boldsymbol{D}_j \cup \boldsymbol{D}_0 \cup \hat{\boldsymbol{D}}_k$ that does not intersect $\hat{c}$ and is progressive with respect to c along its entire length. (For $k = -1$ this can be seen from the ξ-map depicted in figure 7). In this event a *single* application of theorem 6.1 suffices to trace the L.G. forms from $(a_j, b_j]_{\mathscr{P}}$ to $[\hat{b}_k, \hat{a}_k)_{\hat{\mathscr{P}}}$.

(*c*) When both transition points are of fractional multiplicity, it may happen that they are joined by a common principal curve on one Riemann sheet but not on others. In this event either the method of case I or that of case II may be employed (though the former is, of course, somewhat simpler).

PART C. EXAMPLES

8. Example 1: four real turning points of differing multiplicities

8.1. *Topology of the principal regions*

Each of the six examples treated in §5 of Olver (1977*b*) can be solved by the methods of the present paper in all cases in which the coefficients in the differential equation are analytic functions of the independent variable. For the purpose of illustration we consider a special case of the fifth example. With a slight change of notation, this is given by

$$\mathrm{d}^2w/\mathrm{d}z^2 = u^2 f(z)\, w, \tag{8.1}$$

where

$$f(z) = (z-c_1)^2(z-c_2)\,(z-c_3)^4(z-c_4)^3, \tag{8.2}$$

c_1, c_2, c_3 and c_4 being real constants such that $c_1 < c_2 < c_3 < c_4$. Thus there are turning points of multiplicities 2, 1, 4 and 3 at c_1, c_2, c_3 and c_4, respectively. The problem is to calculate the eigenvalues of the system for the interval $(-\infty, \infty)$, that is, the values of u for which equation (8.1) admits a non-trivial solution that is recessive as $z \to \pm\infty$.

The numbers of principal curves that emerge from c_1, c_2, c_3 and c_4 are 4, 3, 6 and 5, respectively. Their configuration is indicated in figure 12, only one Riemann sheet being necessary. The points c_2 and c_3 are joined by a common principal curve along the real axis, as are c_3 and c_4. As $|z| \to \infty$

the asymptotic form of the function $\xi(z)$ defined by (7.3) and (8.2) is given by $\xi(z) \sim \pm\frac{1}{6}z^6$. Hence the principal curves approach the point at infinity in the 12 directions specified by

$$\operatorname{ph} z = \tfrac{1}{12}(2s+1)\,\pi \quad (s = 0, 1, \ldots, 11).$$

Of the 14 curves that pass to infinity, one pair from c_1 and c_2 share the asymptotic direction $\frac{3}{4}\pi$ and another (conjugate) pair from the same points share the asymptotic direction $\frac{5}{4}\pi$.

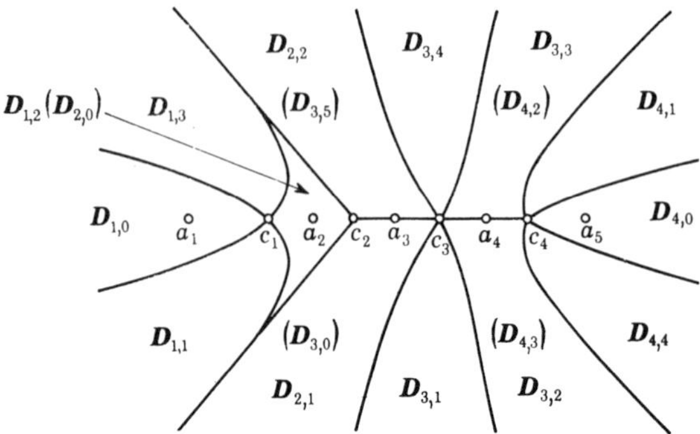

FIGURE 12. Example 1: z-plane.

The 16 principal curves divide the z-plane into 13 closed domains. Those with c_1 on the boundary are labelled $\boldsymbol{D}_{1,0}$, $\boldsymbol{D}_{1,1}$, $\boldsymbol{D}_{1,2}$ and $\boldsymbol{D}_{1,3}$ in the positive rotational sense; those with c_2 on the boundary are labelled $\boldsymbol{D}_{2,0}$, $\boldsymbol{D}_{2,1}$ and $\boldsymbol{D}_{2,2}$, and so on. These notations overlap; as indicated on the diagram $\boldsymbol{D}_{2,0} \equiv \boldsymbol{D}_{1,2}$, and so on. The ξ-map of each domain is a half-plane, except that of $\boldsymbol{D}_{2,0}$, which is a vertical strip.

8.2. *Construction of the connection formula*

Let a_1, a_2, a_3, a_4 and a_5 be arbitrarily chosen fixed points on the real axis such that

$$-\infty < a_1 < c_1 < a_2 < c_2 < a_3 < c_3 < a_4 < c_4 < a_5 < \infty.$$

By L.G. theory, all solutions of (8.1) that are recessive as $z \to -\infty$ are multiples of the solution $w(u,z)$ that is real on the real axis and has the properties

$$f^{\frac{1}{4}}(z)\, w(u,z) \underset{(2)}{=} \{1 + O(u^{-1})\}\, \mathrm{e}^{-u\xi_{c_1}(z)} \quad (z \in (-\infty, a_1])$$

as $u \to \infty$, and

$$f^{\frac{1}{4}}(z)\, w(u,z) \sim \mathrm{e}^{-u\xi_{c_1}(z)}$$

as $z \to -\infty$. The choice of branch of $f^{\frac{1}{4}}(z)$ in these relations is immaterial, as long as it is continuous. The L.G. form of this solution at a_2 is immediately found by applying theorem 6.1 with $c = c_1$, $\chi(u) = u^{-1}$, $j = 0$, $k = 2$ and $m = 4$. From (6.8) and (6.11), we obtain

$$f^{\frac{1}{4}}(z)\, w(u,z) \underset{(2)}{=} 2^{\frac{1}{2}}\mathrm{i}\{1 + O(\chi_4)\}\, \mathrm{e}^{u\xi_{c_1}(z)} \quad (z = a_2).$$

To prepare for passage through c_2, we follow the method of §7, case I and substitute in the last equation by means of the identity

$$\xi_{c_1}(z) = \xi_{c_1}(c_2) - \xi_{c_2}(z) \quad (z \in \boldsymbol{D}_{2,0}(\equiv \boldsymbol{D}_{1,2})),$$

to obtain

$$A_1(u) f^{\frac{1}{4}}(z)\, w(u,z) \underset{(2)}{=} \{1 + O(\chi_4)\}\, \mathrm{e}^{-u\xi_{c_2}(z)} \quad (z = a_2),$$

where

$$A_1(u) = -2^{-\frac{1}{2}}\mathrm{i}\, \mathrm{e}^{-u\xi_{c_1}(c_2)}.$$

At this stage we regard a_3 as belonging to the left boundary of $\boldsymbol{D}_{2,1}$, and therefore apply theorem 6.1 with $c = c_2$, $\chi = \chi_4$, $j = 0$, $k = 1$ and $m = 3$. Recalling that $O(\chi_3) \subset O(\chi_4)$, we obtain from (6.9), (6.11) and (6.12)

$$A_1(u) f^{\frac{1}{4}}(z)\, w(u,z) \underset{(2)}{=} \{1+O(\chi_4)\}\, \mathrm{e}^{u\xi_{c_2}(z)} + \mathrm{i}\{1+O(\chi_4)\}\, \mathrm{e}^{-u\xi_{c_2}(z)} \quad (z = a_3(\in \boldsymbol{D}_{2,1})).$$

To prepare for passage through c_3, we follow the method of § 7, case II and use the identity

$$\xi_{c_2}(z) = \xi_{c_2}(c_3) + \xi_{c_3}(z) \quad (z \in \boldsymbol{D}_{2,1});$$

compare (7.5). Substitution in the preceding relation produces

$$A_1(u) f^{\frac{1}{4}}(z)\, w(u,z) \underset{(2)}{=} A_2(u)\, \{1+O(\chi_4)\}\, \mathrm{e}^{u\xi_{c_3}(z)} + \mathrm{i}A_2^{-1}(u)\, \{1+O(\chi_4)\}\, \mathrm{e}^{-u\xi_{c_3}(z)} \quad (z = a_3(\in \boldsymbol{D}_{2,1}), \tag{8.3}$$

where

$$A_2(u) = \mathrm{e}^{u\xi_{c_2}(c_3)}, \quad A_2^{-1}(u) = \mathrm{e}^{-u\xi_{c_2}(c_3)} \quad (c_3 \in \boldsymbol{D}_{2,1}). \tag{8.4}$$

Again, at this stage we regard a_4 as belonging to the left boundary of $\boldsymbol{D}_{3,2}$. The contribution from the second term on the right hand side of (8.3) is found by applying theorem 6.1 with $c = c_3$, $\chi = \chi_4$, $j = 0$, $k = 2$ and $m = 6$. From (6.9), (6.11) and (6.12) this contribution is calculated to be

$$\mathrm{i}A_2^{-1}(u)\, [3^{\frac{1}{2}}\mathrm{i}\{1+O(\chi_6)\}\, \mathrm{e}^{u\xi_{c_3}(z)} - 2\{1+O(\chi_6)\}\, \mathrm{e}^{-u\xi_{c_3}(z)}] \quad (z = a_4(\in \boldsymbol{D}_{3,2})). \tag{8.5}$$

To trace the contribution of the first term on the right hand side of (8.3), the method of § 7, case II requires us to regard a_3 as a left boundary point of $\boldsymbol{D}_{3,5}$. This replaces $\mathrm{e}^{u\xi_{c_3}(z)}$ by $\mathrm{e}^{-u\xi_{c_3}(z)}$. We then apply theorem 6.1 with $c = c_3$, $\chi = \chi_4$, $j = 5$, $k = 2$ and $m = 6$. From (6.9), (6.11) and (6.12) the contribution is found to be

$$A_2(u)\, [-2\{1+O(\chi_6)\}\, \mathrm{e}^{u\xi_{c_3}(z)} - 3^{\frac{1}{2}}\mathrm{i}\{1+O(\chi_6)\}\, \mathrm{e}^{-u\xi_{c_3}(z)}] \quad (z = a_4(\in \boldsymbol{D}_{3,2})). \tag{8.6}$$

Because $\xi_{c_2}(c_3)$ is purely imaginary it follows from (8.4) that $|A_2(u)| = 1$. Hence the result of combining (8.5) and (8.6) is expressible in the form

$$A_1(u) f^{\frac{1}{4}}(z)\, w(u,z) \underset{(2)}{=} \{A_3(u) + O(\chi_6)\}\, \mathrm{e}^{u\xi_{c_3}(z)} + \{A_4(u) + O(\chi_6)\}\, \mathrm{e}^{-u\xi_{c_3}(z)} \quad (z = a_4(\in \boldsymbol{D}_{3,2})),$$

where

$$A_3(u) = -3^{\frac{1}{2}}A_2^{-1}(u) - 2A_2(u), \quad A_4(u) = -2\mathrm{i}A_2^{-1}(u) - 3^{\frac{1}{2}}\mathrm{i}A_2(u). \tag{8.7}$$

We pass through the remaining turning point c_4 in a similar manner to c_3. This calculation is slightly easier, because (6.8) is used in place of (6.9). The result is found to be

$$A_1(u) f^{\frac{1}{4}}(z)\, w(u,z) \underset{(2)}{=} -2\cos(\tfrac{1}{5}\pi)\, [\{A_4(u) + O(\chi_6)\}\, \mathrm{e}^{-u\xi_{c_3}(c_4)} + \mathrm{i}\{A_3(u) + O(\chi_6)\}\, \mathrm{e}^{u\xi_{c_3}(c_4)}]\, \mathrm{e}^{u\xi_{c_4}(z)} \quad (z \in [a_5, \infty)),$$

where $\xi_{c_3}(c_4)$ is calculated on the assumption that $c_4 \in \boldsymbol{D}_{3,2}$.

8.3. *Determination of the eigenvalues*

The condition that $w(u,z)$ be recessive as $z \to +\infty$ is that the content of the square brackets in the last equation is zero. (Compare the first footnote on page 689 of Olver 1977*b*.) Since $|\mathrm{e}^{\pm u\xi_{c_3}(c_4)}|$ is unity and $\chi_6 = u^{-\frac{6}{5}}$, we find that

$$A_3(u)\, \mathrm{e}^{u\xi_{c_3}(c_4)} - \mathrm{i}A_4(u)\, \mathrm{e}^{-u\xi_{c_3}(c_4)} = O(u^{-\frac{6}{5}}). \tag{8.8}$$

To express the last equation in real form, we have by definition $\xi_{c_2}(c_3) = \mathrm{i}\rho$, $\xi_{c_3}(c_4) = \mathrm{i}\sigma$, where

$$\rho = \int_{c_2}^{c_3} |f(t)|^{\frac{1}{2}}\,\mathrm{d}t, \quad \sigma = \int_{c_3}^{c_4} |f(t)|^{\frac{1}{2}}\,\mathrm{d}t.$$

On referring to (8.4) and (8.7), we find that (8.8) reduces to

$$3^{\frac{1}{2}}\cos\{(\sigma-\rho)u\}+2\cos\{(\sigma+\rho)u\} = O(u^{-\frac{2}{3}}),$$

or, equivalently,

$$\cos[\sigma u+\arctan\{\tan^2(\tfrac{1}{12}\pi)\tan(\rho u)\}] = O(u^{-\frac{2}{3}}). \tag{8.9}$$

Therefore

$$\sigma u+\arctan\{\tan^2(\tfrac{1}{12}\pi)\tan(\rho u)\} = (n+\tfrac{1}{2})\pi+O(u^{-\frac{2}{3}}), \tag{8.10}$$

where n is an arbitrary integer. After making appropriate notational changes we see that the last equation is the same as (5.29) of Olver (1977*b*), and the rest of the analysis proceeds as in this reference.

9. Example 2: three triple turning points on the unit circle

9.1. *Topology of the principal regions*

In this section we consider the differential equation (8.1) with

$$f(z) = (z^3-1)^3. \tag{9.1}$$

The transition points are turning points of third order, situated at 1, ω and $1/\omega$, where $\omega = e^{\frac{2}{3}\pi i}$. Five principal curves emerge from each turning point, the phases of their initial directions being $\frac{1}{5}(2s+1)\pi$, s being an integer. One of these curves is the real interval $(-\infty, 1]$. The configuration of the others is indicated in figure 13, only one Riemann sheet being necessary.

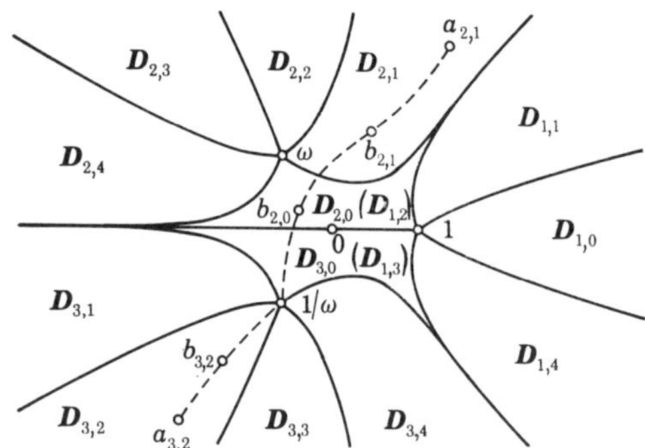

FIGURE 13. Example 2: z-plane. --- progressive path $\mathscr{P}$.

With $\xi(z)$ defined by (7.3) and (9.1), we have $\xi(z) \sim \pm\frac{2}{11}z^{\frac{11}{2}}$ as $|z|\to\infty$. Hence the principal curves approach the point at infinity in the 11 directions given by

$$\operatorname{ph} z = \tfrac{1}{11}(2s+1)\pi \quad (s = 0, 1, \ldots, 10).$$

Two curves, one from 1 and one from ω, share the asymptotic direction $\frac{3}{11}\pi$; similarly two curves from 1 and $1/\omega$ share the asymptotic direction $\frac{19}{11}\pi$. Three curves, one from each turning point, approach infinity in the direction π.

The enumeration of the 13 closed domains bounded by the principal curves is done in a similar manner to that of example 1; the actual labelling we employ is indicated in figure 13. Each domain is mapped on the ξ-plane as a half-plane, except $\boldsymbol{D}_{1,2}$ $(\equiv \boldsymbol{D}_{2,0})$ and $\boldsymbol{D}_{1,3}$ $(\equiv \boldsymbol{D}_{3,0})$, which are mapped as vertical strips.

9.2. *Construction of the connection formulae*

Although there are three turning points in this example, at most two connections are needed to trace the L.G. forms of any given solution from one domain to another. For example, let us consider a solution that is recessive at infinity in $\boldsymbol{D}_{3,2}$. A single application of theorem 6.1 (or theorem 6.2) with $c = 1/\omega$ enables the L.G. form of this solution to be found in each of the following domains: $\boldsymbol{D}_{3,0}$, $\boldsymbol{D}_{3,1}$, $\boldsymbol{D}_{3,3}$, $\boldsymbol{D}_{3,4}$, the left part of $\boldsymbol{D}_{2,4}$, the right parts of $\boldsymbol{D}_{1,4}$ and $\boldsymbol{D}_{2,1}$, and a part of $\boldsymbol{D}_{2,0}$. To reach $\boldsymbol{D}_{1,0}$, $\boldsymbol{D}_{1,1}$ and the remaining parts of $\boldsymbol{D}_{1,4}$ and $\boldsymbol{D}_{2,0}$ two connections are needed, one via $1/\omega$ to an interior point of $\boldsymbol{D}_{3,0}$, then one via 1. Similarly two connections suffice to reach $\boldsymbol{D}_{2,2}$, $\boldsymbol{D}_{2,3}$ and the remaining parts of $\boldsymbol{D}_{2,1}$ and $\boldsymbol{D}_{2,4}$, one via $1/\omega$ to an interior point of $\boldsymbol{D}_{2,0} \cup \boldsymbol{D}_{3,0}$, then one via ω.

For illustration, we consider in detail the problem of tracing the L.G. forms from $\boldsymbol{D}_{3,2}$ to $\boldsymbol{D}_{2,1}$. By considering the ξ-map it is easily seen that a doubly infinite path $\mathscr{P}$ can be found in the union of $\boldsymbol{D}_{3,2}$, $\boldsymbol{D}_{3,0}$, $\boldsymbol{D}_{2,0}$ and any internal part of $\boldsymbol{D}_{2,1}$ that is progressive with respect to the turning point at $1/\omega$ along its entire length. This path is indicated by the broken curve in figure 13. Let $a_{3,2}$ and $a_{2,1}$ be the points at infinity on $\mathscr{P}$ in $\boldsymbol{D}_{3,2}$ and $\boldsymbol{D}_{2,1}$, respectively, and $b_{3,2}$, $b_{2,0}$ and $b_{2,1}$ be points on $\mathscr{P}$ in the interiors of $\boldsymbol{D}_{3,2}$, $\boldsymbol{D}_{2,0}$ and $\boldsymbol{D}_{2,1}$, respectively. By L.G. theory, any solution of the differential equation that is recessive as $z \to \infty$ in $\boldsymbol{D}_{3,2}$ is a multiple of the solution $w(u,z)$ having the properties

$$\left.\begin{aligned} f^{\frac{1}{4}}(z)\, w(u,z) &\underset{(2)}{=} \{1+O(u^{-1})\}\,\mathrm{e}^{-u\xi_{1/\omega}(z)} \quad (z \in (a_{3,2}, b_{3,2}]_{\mathscr{P}}) \\ f^{\frac{1}{4}}(z)\, w(u,z) &\sim \mathrm{e}^{-u\xi_{1/\omega}(z)} \end{aligned}\right\} \tag{9.2}$$

as $u \to \infty$, and (second relation) as $z \to a_{3,2}$ along $\mathscr{P}$. Any continuous branch of $f^{\frac{1}{4}}(z)$ may be adopted in these relations. To find the asymptotic form of $w(u,z)$ on $[b_{2,1}, a_{2,1})_{\mathscr{P}}$, we apply theorem 6.1 with $c = 1/\omega$, $\chi(u) = u^{-1}$, $j = 2$, $k = 0$ and $m = 5$. From (6.8) and (6.11) we obtain

$$f^{\frac{1}{4}}(z)\, w(u,z) \underset{(2)}{=} -2\mathrm{i}\cos(\tfrac{1}{5}\pi)\,\{1+O(u^{-\frac{4}{5}})\}\,\mathrm{e}^{u\xi_{1/\omega}(z)} \quad (z \in [b_{2,1}, a_{2,1})_{\mathscr{P}}). \tag{9.3}$$

Because $k-j$ is negative, it also follows from theorem 6.1 that the branch of $f^{\frac{1}{4}}(z)$ in (9.3) is obtained from that used in (9.2) by continuous passage along $\mathscr{P}$, skirting $1/\omega$ in the clockwise sense. Had we enumerated the domains having $1/\omega$ on their boundary in a different manner, we could have taken $k-j = 3$. In place of (9.3) we would then obtain

$$f^{\frac{1}{4}}(z)\, w(u,z) \underset{(2)}{=} -2\cos(\tfrac{1}{5}\pi)\,\{1+O(u^{-\frac{4}{5}})\}\,\mathrm{e}^{u\xi_{1/\omega}(z)} \quad (z \in [b_{2,1}, a_{2,1})_{\mathscr{P}}), \tag{9.4}$$

where the continuation of $f^{\frac{1}{4}}(z)$ is now achieved by skirting $1/\omega$ in the anticlockwise sense. That (9.3) and (9.4) are consistent is easily seen from the fact that on completion of a simple closed circuit of $1/\omega$ in the positive sense the solution $w(u,z)$ is unaffected, but because $f(z)$ has a triple zero at $1/\omega$ the branch of $f^{\frac{1}{4}}(z)$ is changed by the factor $\mathrm{e}^{\frac{3}{2}\pi\mathrm{i}}$.

9.3. *Extension to domains*

Suppose now that instead of tracing the L.G. form of the solution $w(u,z)$, defined by (9.2), from one path segment to another, we seek asymptotic approximations of $w(u,z)$ for large u that are uniform with respect to z in the intersection of $\boldsymbol{D}_{2,1}$ with the annulus $\boldsymbol{A}_\omega$ defined by $|z-\omega| \geqslant r$, where r is an arbitrary small positive constant. We first construct the L.G. approximation to $w(u,z)$ at the interior point $b_{2,0}$ of $\boldsymbol{D}_{2,0}$ by passage along $\mathscr{P}$ through $1/\omega$. The result is evidently given by (9.3) with $z = b_{2,0}$. To prepare for passage through ω, we use the identity

$$\xi_{1/\omega}(z) = \xi_{1/\omega}(\omega) - \xi_\omega(z) \quad (z \in \boldsymbol{D}_{2,0} \cup \boldsymbol{D}_{3,0});$$

compare (7.4). We take a new progressive path with respect to ω that begins at $b_{2,0}$, passes through ω and continues in $\boldsymbol{D}_{2,1}$ along the curve having the equation $\operatorname{ph} \xi_\omega(z) = \theta$, where θ is a parameter in the closed interval $[-\frac12\pi, \frac12\pi]$. (This path is not indicated in figure 13.) Theorem 6.2 is applied with $c = \omega$, $\chi(u) = u^{-\frac45}$, $j = 0$, $k = 1$ and $m = 5$. Using (6.24), with lower signs, we obtain†

$$f^{\frac14}(z)\, w(u,z) \underset{(2)}{=} -2\mathrm{i}\cos(\tfrac15\pi)\{1+O(u^{-\frac45})\}\, \mathrm{e}^{u\xi_{1/\omega}(\omega)+u\xi_\omega(z)} \tag{9.5}$$

as $u \to \infty$, uniformly in the intersection of $\boldsymbol{A}_\omega$ and the right part of $\boldsymbol{D}_{2,1}$. Similarly from (6.24), with upper signs, we obtain

$$f^{\frac14}(z)\, w(u,z) \underset{(2)}{=} -2\mathrm{i}\cos(\tfrac15\pi)\{1+O(u^{-\frac45})\}\, \mathrm{e}^{u\xi_{1/\omega}(\omega)+u\xi_\omega(z)} + 4\cos^2(\tfrac15\pi)\{1+O(u^{-\frac45})\}\, \mathrm{e}^{u\xi_{1/\omega}(\omega)-u\xi_\omega(z)} \tag{9.6}$$

as $u \to \infty$, uniformly in the intersection of $\boldsymbol{A}_\omega$ and the left part of $\boldsymbol{D}_{2,1}$.

In both (9.5) and (9.6) the branch of $f^{\frac14}(z)$ is obtained from that used in (9.2) by continuous change from $(a_{3,2}, b_{3,2}]_{\mathscr{P}}$ to $\boldsymbol{D}_{2,1}$ passing the branch-points $1/\omega$ and 1 on the right, and ω on the left.

The regions of validity that we have quoted for (9.5) and (9.6) are not maximal. For example, we may pass from $b_{2,0}$ into $\boldsymbol{D}_{2,2}$ by using theorem 6.2 with $c = \omega$, $j = 0$, $k = 2$ and $m = 5$. We then find (9.6) is also uniformly valid in the intersection of $\boldsymbol{A}_\omega$ and the right part of $\boldsymbol{D}_{2,2}$, provided that $\xi_\omega(z)$ is replaced by $-\xi_\omega(z)$ at both occurrences (because $\xi_\omega(z)$ changes sign on crossing the boundary $\boldsymbol{D}_{2,1} \cap \boldsymbol{D}_{2,2}$).

10. Example 3: two fractional transition points and two simple poles

10.1. *Formulation of the problems*

The final example is furnished by the differential equation (8.1) with

$$f(z) = (z^2+\beta^2)^{\frac12}/(z^2-\alpha^2), \tag{10.1}$$

α and β being positive constants. Thus $f(z)$ has simple poles at $\pm\alpha$, and branch-points at $\pm\mathrm{i}\beta$. From our standpoint we regard $\pm\alpha$ as fractional transition points of order -1, and $\pm\mathrm{i}\beta$ as fractional transition points of order $\frac12$. Taking the branch of $f(z)$ that is positive in the interval (α, ∞), we know from L.G. theory that there is a unique solution $w(u,z)$ of the differential equation with the property

$$w(u,z) \sim z^{\frac14}\,\mathrm{e}^{-2uz^{\frac12}} \quad (z \to +\infty), \tag{10.2}$$

the branches of $z^{\frac14}$ and $z^{\frac12}$ both being real and positive. The problems that we set ourselves are to find the asymptotic behaviour of $w(u,z)$ as $z \to -\infty$ in the following cases:

(*a*) $w(u,z)$ is continued from $z = +\infty$ along the positive real axis until the neighbourhood of α is reached. We then make $p+\frac12$ circuits of α, arriving at a point in the interval $(-\alpha, \alpha)$. We continue along the real axis until the neighbourhood of $-\alpha$ is reached and then make $q+\frac12$ circuits of $-\alpha$, arriving at a point in the interval $(-\infty, -\alpha)$. Finally $w(u,z)$ is continued along the negative real axis until $-\infty$ is approached. The integers p and q may have any values, positive, zero or negative.

(*b*) This begins as in problem (*a*), but on reaching the origin we make a detour along the positive imaginary axis, encircle $\mathrm{i}\beta$ once in the positive sense and return to the origin along the positive imaginary axis. The rest of the journey, from 0 to $-\infty$, is completed as in (*a*).

(*c*) This begins as in problem (*b*), but on returning to the origin after passing around $\mathrm{i}\beta$ we continue along the negative imaginary axis, encircle $-\mathrm{i}\beta$ once in the positive sense and return to

† In (6.24) the term $\lambda_{j,k-1}$ disappears, and the error term $O(u^{-\frac45})\,\mathrm{e}^{-u\xi_\omega(z)}$ is absorbable in the other error term.

the origin along the negative imaginary axis. The rest of the journey, from 0 to $-\infty$, is completed as in (a).

These are not the only continuations from $+\infty$ to $-\infty$ that are possible around the four singularities, but they suffice for the purpose of illustration. It should be noted, however, that because all solutions of the differential equation are expansible in convergent series of ascending powers of $(z-\mathrm{i}\beta)^{\frac{1}{2}}$ in the neighbourhood of $\mathrm{i}\beta$, the effect of making any even number of circuits around this point is to leave $w(u, z)$ unchanged, and the effect of making any odd number of circuits is the same as making a single circuit. Similarly for circuits around $-\mathrm{i}\beta$.

10.2. *Topology of the principal regions*

The statements in the following three paragraphs are easily verified by means of conformal mapping on the plane of the function $\xi(z)$ defined by (7.3) and (10.1).

Five principal curves emerge from $\mathrm{i}\beta$. They occupy two Riemann sheets, and the phases of their initial directions are $\frac{1}{10}(8s-9)\,\pi$, $s = 1, 2, 3, 4, 5$. The first of these curves lies in the first and fourth quadrants, is symmetric with respect to the real axis and terminates at $-\mathrm{i}\beta$. The curve for $s = 2$ is confined to the second quadrant and tends to infinity asymptotically as a parabolic arc, with axis along the real axis. The curve for $s = 3$ is the segment of the imaginary axis from $\mathrm{i}\beta$ to $-\mathrm{i}\beta$. For $s = 4$ and 5 the curves are the reflections in the imaginary axis of those for $s = 2$ and 1, respectively.

Five principal curves emerge from $-\mathrm{i}\beta$. They are the complex conjugates of those emerging from $\mathrm{i}\beta$.

Associated with α there is an infinity of Riemann sheets, and only one principal curve lies on each. If we are using the branch of $f(z)$ for which $(z^2-\alpha^2)f(z)$ is positive on the real axis, then the principal curve is the interval $[-\alpha, \alpha]$. On the other hand, when $(z^2-\alpha^2)\,f(z)$ is negative on the real axis, the principal curve is the interval $[\alpha, \infty)$. Similarly for the transition point $-\alpha$.

The complete set of principal curves is indicated by the straight lines and curves sketched in figures 14, 15 and 16. Associated with the transition point $\mathrm{i}\beta$ there are five closed domains bounded by principal curves emanating from all four transition points. They are labelled $\boldsymbol{D}_{1,0}$, $\boldsymbol{D}_{1,1}$, $\boldsymbol{D}_{1,2}$, $\boldsymbol{D}_{1,3}$ and $\boldsymbol{D}_{1,4}$ on proceeding in the anticlockwise sense, and they occupy two Riemann sheets. When associated with $-\mathrm{i}\beta$ the same domains are relabelled $\boldsymbol{D}_{2,0}$, $\boldsymbol{D}_{2,4}$, $\boldsymbol{D}_{2,3}$, $\boldsymbol{D}_{2,2}$, $\boldsymbol{D}_{2,1}$, as indicated in the diagrams.

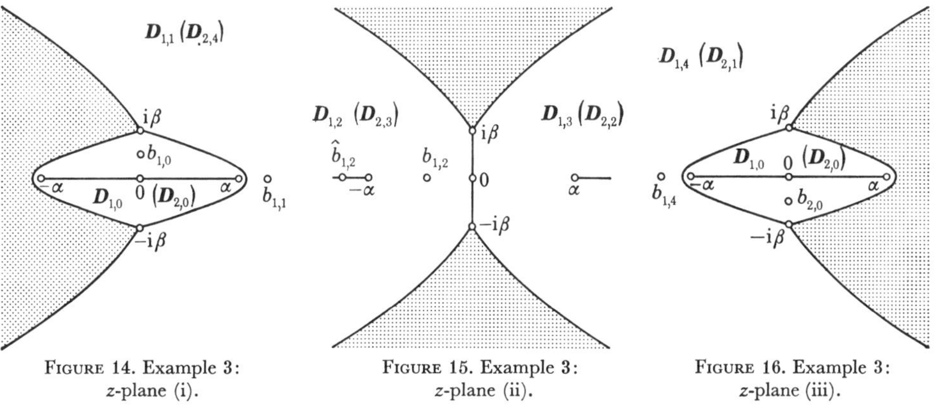

FIGURE 14. Example 3: z-plane (i).

FIGURE 15. Example 3: z-plane (ii).

FIGURE 16. Example 3: z-plane (iii).

The boundaries of $\boldsymbol{D}_{1,0}$ (or $\boldsymbol{D}_{2,0}$) are the two principal curves that join $\mathrm{i}\beta$ and $-\mathrm{i}\beta$, and the interval $[-\alpha, \alpha]$. Thus $\boldsymbol{D}_{1,0}$ is multiply connected, and continuous passage around any closed contour in $\boldsymbol{D}_{1,0}$ that contains the interval $[-\alpha, \alpha]$ in its interior alters the value of each solution of the differential equation and also the value of the function $\xi(z)$, defined by (7.3) and (10.1). If we permit any number of such circuits, then the map of $\boldsymbol{D}_{1,0}$ on the ξ-plane is a vertical strip. The other domains are simply connected. The ξ-maps of $\boldsymbol{D}_{1,1}$ and $\boldsymbol{D}_{1,4}$ are half-planes, and those of $\boldsymbol{D}_{1,2}$ and $\boldsymbol{D}_{1,3}$ are vertical strips.

10.3. *Problem* (*a*)

Let $b_{1,1}$ and $b_{1,4}$ be arbitrary fixed points on the real axis such that $b_{1,1} > \alpha$ and $b_{1,4} < -\alpha$; see figures 14 and 16. From L.G. theory there is a solution $\hat{w}(u, z)$ of the differential equation with the properties

$$f^{\frac{1}{4}}(z)\,\hat{w}(u,z) \sim \mathrm{e}^{-u\xi_\alpha(z)} \tag{10.3}$$

as $z \to +\infty$, and

$$f^{\frac{1}{4}}(z)\,\hat{w}(u,z) \underset{(2)}{=} \{1+O(u^{-1})\}\,\mathrm{e}^{-u\xi_\alpha(z)} \quad (z \in [b_{1,1}, \infty)) \tag{10.4}$$

as $u \to \infty$. The branch of $f^{\frac{1}{4}}(z)$ is taken to be real and positive in both relations. From (10.1) and the definition of $\xi_\alpha(z)$, given by (7.1) with $c = \alpha$, we see that

$$\xi_\alpha(z) = 2z^{\frac{1}{2}} + \kappa + O(z^{-\frac{3}{2}}) \quad (z \to +\infty),$$

where κ is the real constant defined by

$$\kappa = \int_\alpha^\infty \left\{\frac{(t^2+\beta^2)^{\frac{1}{4}}}{(t^2-\alpha^2)^{\frac{1}{4}}} - \frac{1}{t^{\frac{1}{2}}}\right\} \mathrm{d}t - 2\alpha^{\frac{1}{2}}. \tag{10.5}$$

On comparing (10.2) and (10.3), we see that the relation of $\hat{w}(u, z)$ to the wanted solution $w(u, z)$ is given by

$$w(u,z) = \mathrm{e}^{\kappa u}\hat{w}(u,z). \tag{10.6}$$

Let us continue $\hat{w}(u, z)$ from $[b_{1,1}, \infty)$ to the point $0+0\mathrm{i}$ on the upper side of the principal curve joining α and $-\alpha$, making p circuits of α *en route* but not encircling any of the other transition points. In applying theorem 6.1 we take the progressive path $\mathscr{P}$ along the positive real axis, $c = \alpha$, $\chi(u) = u^{-1}$, $k - j = p$ and $m = 1$. Because $0+0\mathrm{i}$ is a left boundary point when viewed from α, the appropriate formulae are (6.9), (6.11) and (6.12). Referring to (2.18) and (4.8), we find that

$$f^{\frac{1}{4}}(z)\,\hat{w}(u,z) \underset{(2)}{=} \mathrm{i}^{1-p}p\{1+O(u^{-1})\}\,\mathrm{e}^{u\xi_\alpha(z)} + \mathrm{i}^{-p}(p+1)\{1+O(u^{-1})\}\,\mathrm{e}^{-u\xi_\alpha(z)} \quad (z = 0+0\mathrm{i}). \tag{10.7}$$

To prepare for passage around $-\alpha$ we observe that if z tends to $-\alpha$ along the upper side of the interval $[-\alpha, \alpha]$, then $\xi_\alpha(z)$ tends to $2\mathrm{i}\rho$ where ρ is the positive real constant defined by

$$\rho = \int_0^\alpha |f^{\frac{1}{2}}(t)\,\mathrm{d}t| = \int_0^\alpha \frac{|\beta^2+t^2|^{\frac{1}{4}}}{|\alpha^2-t^2|^{\frac{1}{4}}}\,\mathrm{d}t; \tag{10.8}$$

compare §5.1. We therefore recast (10.7) in the form

$$f^{\frac{1}{4}}(z)\,\hat{w}(u,z) \underset{(2)}{=} \mathrm{i}^{1-p}p\,\mathrm{e}^{2\mathrm{i}\rho u}\{1+O(u^{-1})\}\,\mathrm{e}^{u\xi_{-\alpha}(z)} + \mathrm{i}^{-p}(p+1)\,\mathrm{e}^{-2\mathrm{i}\rho u}\{1+O(u^{-1})\}\,\mathrm{e}^{-u\xi_{-\alpha}(z)}, \tag{10.9}$$

again with $z = 0+0\mathrm{i}$; compare (7.5). After completing $q+\frac{1}{2}$ circuits of $-\alpha$ and arriving in the interval $(-\infty, b_{1,4}]$ (figure 16), we calculate the contribution from the second term on the right hand side of (10.9) by applying theorem 6.1 with $c = -\alpha$, $\chi(u) = u^{-1}$, $k - j = q$ and $m = 1$. This yields

$$\mathrm{i}^{-p}(p+1)\,\mathrm{e}^{-2\mathrm{i}\rho u}\,\mathrm{i}^{1-q}q\{1+O(u^{-1})\}\,\mathrm{e}^{u\xi_{-\alpha}(z)}. \tag{10.10}$$

To handle the contribution of the first term on the right hand side of (10.9), we proceed as in §7, case II and cross the principal curve joining α and $-\alpha$, passing from $0+0\mathrm{i}$ to $0-0\mathrm{i}$. This replaces $\xi_{-\alpha}(z)$ by $-\xi_{-\alpha}(z)$, and also takes us into another principal region associated with $-\alpha$. Accordingly, theorem 6.1 is now applied with $j=-1$, $k=q$ and $m=1$. This yields

$$\mathrm{i}^{1-p}p\,\mathrm{e}^{2\mathrm{i}\rho u}\,\mathrm{i}^{-q}(q+1)\,\{1+O(u^{-1})\}\,\mathrm{e}^{u\xi_{-\alpha}(z)}. \tag{10.11}$$

Combining (10.10) and (10.11) we obtain

$$f^{\frac{1}{4}}(z)\,\hat{w}(u,z) \underset{(2)}{=} \mathrm{i}^{1-p-q}\{(p+1)q\,\mathrm{e}^{-2\mathrm{i}\rho u}+p(q+1)\,\mathrm{e}^{2\mathrm{i}\rho u}+O(u^{-1})\}\,\mathrm{e}^{u\xi_{-\alpha}(z)} \quad (z\in(-\infty,b_{1,4}]). \tag{10.12}$$

The theory of the L.G. approximation shows that when the positive branch of $f(z)$ is used in the interval $(-\infty,-\alpha)$, the wanted solution $w(u,z)$ is expressible in the form

$$w(u,z) = A(u)\,|z|^{\frac{1}{4}}\,\mathrm{e}^{2u|z|^{\frac{1}{2}}}\{1+O(z^{-\frac{3}{2}})\}+B(u)\,|z|^{\frac{1}{4}}\,\mathrm{e}^{-2u|z|^{\frac{1}{2}}}\{1+O(z^{-\frac{3}{2}})\} \tag{10.13}$$

as $z\to-\infty$, where $A(u)$ and $B(u)$ are independent of z. The coefficient $B(u)$ of the recessive component cannot be found by the present analysis, but $A(u)$ can be estimated for large u as follows. From the definition (7.1) of $\xi_{-\alpha}(z)$, we calculate that

$$\xi_{-\alpha}(z) = 2|z|^{\frac{1}{2}}+\kappa+O(z^{-\frac{1}{2}}) \quad (z\to-\infty), \tag{10.14}$$

where κ is defined by (10.5). Next, because $f(z)$ has simple poles at $\pm\alpha$, the branch of $f^{\frac{1}{4}}(z)$ used in (10.12) is given by

$$\mathrm{e}^{-\frac{1}{4}(2p+1)\pi\mathrm{i}-\frac{1}{4}(2q+1)\pi\mathrm{i}}\,|z^2+\beta^2|^{\frac{1}{8}}\,|z^2-\alpha^2|^{-\frac{1}{4}}, \tag{10.15}$$

and is therefore asymptotic to $\mathrm{i}^{-p-q-1}|z|^{-\frac{1}{4}}$ as $z\to-\infty$. Substituting these estimates in (10.12) and comparing the result with (10.6) and (10.13), we see that

$$A(u) = -\,\mathrm{e}^{2\kappa u}\{(p+1)\,q\,\mathrm{e}^{-2\mathrm{i}\rho u}+p(q+1)\,\mathrm{e}^{2\mathrm{i}\rho u}+O(u^{-1})\}; \tag{10.16}$$

compare theorem 3.1 of Olver (1974, ch. 6). This is the required result.

10.4. *Problem* (*b*)

We follow the analysis of §10.3 until we reach (10.6). Instead of continuing $\hat{w}(u,z)$ from $[b_{1,1},\infty)$ to $0+0\mathrm{i}$, we continue this solution to a point $b_{1,0}$ in $\boldsymbol{D}_{1,0}$ on the join of 0 and $\mathrm{i}\beta$; see figure 14. By applying theorem 6.1, using (6.8) and (6.11), we obtain

$$f^{\frac{1}{4}}(z)\,\hat{w}(u,z) \underset{(2)}{=} \mathrm{i}^{1-p}p\{1+O(u^{-1})\}\,\mathrm{e}^{u\xi_{\alpha}(z)} \quad (z=b_{1,0}); \tag{10.17}$$

compare (10.7).

To prepare for passage around $\mathrm{i}\beta$, we note that when $\mathrm{i}\beta$ is regarded as a member of $\boldsymbol{D}_{1,0}$ we have $\xi_{\alpha}(\mathrm{i}\beta)=\sigma+\mathrm{i}\rho$, where ρ is defined by (10.8) and σ is the positive real constant given by

$$\sigma = \int_0^{\mathrm{i}\beta}|f^{\frac{1}{2}}(t)\,\mathrm{d}t| = \int_0^{\beta}\frac{|\beta^2-t^2|^{\frac{1}{4}}}{|\alpha^2+t^2|^{\frac{1}{2}}}\,\mathrm{d}t. \tag{10.18}$$

Equation (10.17) is therefore recast in the form

$$f^{\frac{1}{4}}(z)\,\hat{w}(u,z) \underset{(2)}{=} \mathrm{i}^{1-p}p\,\mathrm{e}^{(\sigma+\mathrm{i}\rho)u}\{1+O(u^{-1})\}\,\mathrm{e}^{-u\xi_{\mathrm{i}\beta}(z)} \quad (z=b_{1,0}); \tag{10.19}$$

compare (7.4). We now continue $\hat{w}(u,z)$ to an interior point $b_{1,2}$ of $\boldsymbol{D}_{1,2}$; see figure 15. This continuation is achieved by applying theorem 6.1 with $c=\mathrm{i}\beta$, $\chi(u)=u^{-1}$, $j=0$, $k=2$ and $m=\frac{5}{2}$. From (6.8) and (6.11) we obtain

$$f^{\frac{1}{4}}(z)\,\hat{w}(u,z) \underset{(2)}{=} 2\cos\left(\tfrac{2}{5}\pi\right)\mathrm{i}^{2-p}p\,\mathrm{e}^{(\sigma+\mathrm{i}\rho)u}\{1+O(u^{-1})\}\,\mathrm{e}^{u\xi_{\mathrm{i}\beta}(z)} \quad (z=b_{1,2}).$$

To prepare for passage around $-\alpha$ we note that when $-\alpha$ is regarded as a member of $\boldsymbol{D}_{1,2}$ we have $\xi_{1\beta}(-\alpha) = \rho + \mathrm{i}\sigma$, where ρ and σ are defined by (10.8) and (10.18). Accordingly, we recast the last equation in the form

$$f^{\frac{1}{4}}(z)\,\hat{w}(u,z) \underset{(2)}{=} 2\cos\left(\tfrac{2}{5}\pi\right)\mathrm{i}^{2-p}p\,\mathrm{e}^{(\rho+\sigma)(1+\mathrm{i})u}\{1+O(u^{-1})\}\,\mathrm{e}^{-u\xi_{-\alpha}(z)} \quad (z = b_{1,2});$$

compare (7.4). Theorem 6.1 is now applied with $c = -\alpha$, $\chi(u) = u^{-1}$, $k-j = q$ and $m = 1$. From (6.9), (6.11) and (6.12), we obtain

$$f^{\frac{1}{4}}(z)\,\hat{w}(u,z) \underset{(2)}{=} 2\cos\left(\tfrac{2}{5}\pi\right)\mathrm{i}^{2-p}p\,\mathrm{e}^{(\rho+\sigma)(1+\mathrm{i})u}[\mathrm{i}^{1-q}q\{1+O(u^{-1})\}\,\mathrm{e}^{u\xi_{-\alpha}(z)} + \mathrm{i}^{-q}(q+1)\{1+O(u^{-1})\}\,\mathrm{e}^{-u\xi_{-\alpha}(z)}] \quad (z\in(-\infty,\hat{b}_{1,2}]), \tag{10.20}$$

where $\hat{b}_{1,2}$ is an arbitrary fixed point of the interval $(-\infty, -\alpha)$; see figure 15.

The theory of the L.G. approximation shows that when the negative branch of $f(z)$ is used in the interval $(-\infty, -\alpha)$ the wanted solution $w(u, z)$ is expressible in the form

$$w(u,z) = A_1(u)\,|z|^{\frac{1}{4}}\,\mathrm{e}^{2\mathrm{i}u|z|^{\frac{1}{2}}}\{1+O(z^{-\frac{1}{2}})\} + A_2(u)\,|z|^{\frac{1}{4}}\,\mathrm{e}^{-2\mathrm{i}u|z|^{\frac{1}{2}}}\{1+O(z^{-\frac{1}{2}})\} \tag{10.21}$$

as $z\to-\infty$, where $A_1(u)$ and $A_2(u)$ are independent of z. In the present circumstances we have

$$\xi_{-\alpha}(z) = 2\mathrm{i}|z|^{\frac{1}{2}} + \mathrm{i}\kappa + O(z^{-\frac{1}{2}}) \quad (z\to-\infty);$$

compare (10.14). Also, the appropriate branch of $f^{\frac{1}{4}}(z)$ is $\mathrm{e}^{\frac{1}{4}\pi\mathrm{i}}$ times the expression (10.15); accordingly

$$f^{\frac{1}{4}}(z) \sim \mathrm{e}^{-\frac{1}{4}\pi\mathrm{i}}\,\mathrm{i}^{-p-q}|z|^{-\frac{1}{4}} \quad (z\to-\infty).$$

On substituting these estimates in (10.20) and comparing the result with (10.6) and (10.21), we conclude that

$$\left.\begin{aligned} A_1(u) &= 2\cos\left(\tfrac{2}{5}\pi\right)pq\,\mathrm{e}^{-\frac{1}{4}\pi\mathrm{i}}\,\mathrm{e}^{(\rho+\sigma+\kappa)(1+\mathrm{i})u}\{1+O(u^{-1})\},\\ A_2(u) &= -2\cos\left(\tfrac{2}{5}\pi\right)p(q+1)\,\mathrm{e}^{\frac{1}{4}\pi\mathrm{i}}\,\mathrm{e}^{(\rho+\sigma)(1+\mathrm{i})u}\,\mathrm{e}^{\kappa(1-\mathrm{i})u}\{1+O(u^{-1})\}.\end{aligned}\right\} \tag{10.22}$$

This is the required result.

10.5. *Problem* (*c*)

The analysis in this case is similar to that of §§ 10.3 and 10.4 and it suffices to sketch the main steps and state the result.

After reaching (10.19) we continue to $z = 0$ ($\in \boldsymbol{D}_{1,2}$) by use of (6.9), (6.11) and (6.12). We then pass around $-\mathrm{i}\beta$ by the method of § 7, case II, arriving at an arbitrary point $b_{2,0}$ on the join of 0 and $-\mathrm{i}\beta$ in $\boldsymbol{D}_{2,0}$; see figure 16. Lastly, we pass around $-\alpha$ by the method of § 7, case I, arriving at $(-\infty, b_{1,4}]$. The final result is expressed by (10.13), with

$$A(u) = -2\cos\left(\tfrac{2}{5}\pi\right)\sec\left(\tfrac{1}{5}\pi\right)p(q+1)\,\mathrm{e}^{2(\kappa+\sigma+\mathrm{i}\rho)u}\{\cos(2\sigma u) + O(u^{-1})\}, \tag{10.23}$$

and $B(u)$ again undetermined.

Appendix. Computation of principal curves

The principal curves in figures 12, 13, 14, 15 and 16 were computed on the UNIVAC 1108 computer and plotted on the TEKTRONIX 4013 plotter at the University of Maryland, using the following method.

Let c again denote the transition point under consideration and $m-2$ its multiplicity. Then

$$f(z) = (z-c)^{m-2}\tilde{f}(z), \tag{A 1}$$

where $\tilde{f}(z)$ is analytic and non-vanishing at c. Each principal curve emerging from c has the equation

$$\mathrm{Re}\int_c^z f^{\frac{1}{2}}(t)\,\mathrm{d}t = 0. \tag{A 2}$$

These curves are computed in parametric form

$$z = x(\tau) + \mathrm{i}y(\tau), \tag{A 3}$$

where τ is the arc parameter measured from c, and $x(\tau)$ and $y(\tau)$ denote the real and imaginary parts of z, respectively.

Differentiation yields

$$\frac{\mathrm{d}}{\mathrm{d}\tau}\int_c^z f^{\frac{1}{2}}(t)\,\mathrm{d}t = (z-c)^{\frac{1}{2}(m-2)}\tilde{f}^{\frac{1}{2}}(z)\left(\frac{\mathrm{d}x}{\mathrm{d}\tau}+\mathrm{i}\frac{\mathrm{d}y}{\mathrm{d}\tau}\right). \tag{A 4}$$

Let $\theta(\tau)$ denote the inclination of the curve (A 3) to the real axis, so that

$$\mathrm{d}x/\mathrm{d}\tau = \cos\theta, \quad \mathrm{d}y/\mathrm{d}\tau = \sin\theta. \tag{A 5}$$

The condition that the real part of the right hand side of (A 4) be zero yields

$$\theta = -\tfrac{1}{2}(m-2)\arctan\left(\frac{y-c_{\mathrm{I}}}{x-c_{\mathrm{R}}}\right) - \tfrac{1}{2}\arctan\left\{\frac{\tilde{f}_{\mathrm{I}}(x+\mathrm{i}y)}{\tilde{f}_{\mathrm{R}}(x+\mathrm{i}y)}\right\} + (mp+q+\tfrac{1}{2})\pi, \tag{A 6}$$

where c_{R}, c_{I}, $\tilde{f}_{\mathrm{R}}(x+\mathrm{i}y)$ and $\tilde{f}_{\mathrm{I}}(x+\mathrm{i}y)$ denote the real part of c, the imaginary part of c, the real part of $\tilde{f}(z)$ and the imaginary part of $\tilde{f}(z)$, respectively. Also, p and q are arbitrary integers, and it is assumed that the inverse tangents occupy the same quadrants as the points $(x-c_{\mathrm{R}})+\mathrm{i}(y-c_{\mathrm{I}})$ and $\tilde{f}_{\mathrm{R}}(x+\mathrm{i}y)+\mathrm{i}\tilde{f}_{\mathrm{I}}(x+\mathrm{i}y)$, respectively.

The principal curves are computed by numerical integration of the simultaneous nonlinear differential equations represented by (A 5) and (A 6), using the initial conditions

$$x(0) = c_{\mathrm{R}}, \quad y(0) = c_{\mathrm{I}}, \quad \theta(0) = \{(2s+1)\pi - \mathrm{ph}\tilde{f}(c)\}/m,$$

where s is an integer that corresponds to the particular curve under consideration.

The integers p and q in (A 6) are determined by continuity. Thus if τ_{n-1} and τ_n are successive discrete values of τ, then $|\theta(\tau_n)-\theta(\tau_{n-1})|$ is required to lie within a prescribed tolerance. For each of the examples treated in part C a suitable value for this tolerance was found to be $\frac{1}{4}\pi$.

No problems of stiffness arise in the integration of equations (A 5) and (A 6); in consequence any appropriate initial-value method may be employed. The program actually used was based on the codes DE, STEP and INTRP described in ch. 10 of Shampine & Gordon (1975). Each of the principal curves in examples 1, 2 and 3 of part C was computed for a total arc length of 12 units (the arc lengths in the diagrams are somewhat less), the average computing time being just under 4 seconds.

Remark. In place of (A 6), we could employ the simpler formula

$$\theta = -\tfrac{1}{2}\arctan\{f_{\mathrm{I}}(x+\mathrm{i}y)/f_{\mathrm{R}}(x+\mathrm{i}y)\} + (q+\tfrac{1}{2})\pi, \tag{A 7}$$

where $f_{\mathrm{R}}(x+\mathrm{i}y)$ and $f_{\mathrm{I}}(x+\mathrm{i}y)$ denote the real and imaginary parts of $f(z)$, respectively. The disadvantage of (A 7) compared with (A 6) is that $f_{\mathrm{R}}(x+\mathrm{i}y)$ and $f_{\mathrm{I}}(x+\mathrm{i}y)$ often underflow when τ is small, owing to the presence of the factor $(z-c)^{m-2}$ on the right hand side of (A 1).

This research was supported by the U.S. Army Research Office, Durham under Contract DAAG 29-77-G-0003, and the National Science Foundation under Grant GP 32841X2. The writer is indebted to Dr C. Lozano for stimulating discussions and several references to physical applications, and to Dr J. G. Taylor for permission to use some of his unpublished work. He also wishes to acknowledge the assistance of Mr R. E. Kaylor with the computation and plotting of the principal curves described in the appendix.

References

Apostol, T. M. 1957 *Mathematical analysis*. London: Addison-Wesley.

Berry, M. V. & Mount, K. E. 1972 Semiclassical approximations in wave mechanics. *Rep. Prog. Phys.* **35**, 315–397.

Brander, O. 1966 Asymptotic behaviour of the *S*-matrix in complex angular momentum for singular potentials. *Ark. Fys.* **32**, 131–165.

Budden, K. G. & Smith, M. S. 1974 The coalescence of coupling points in the theory of radio waves in the ionosphere. *Proc. R. Soc. Lond.* A **341**, 1–30.

Cherry, T. M. 1950 Uniform asymptotic formulae for functions with transition points. *Trans. Am. math. Soc.* **68**, 224–257.

Child, M. S. 1974 *Molecular collision theory*. London: Academic Press.

Connor, J. N. L., Jakubetz, W. & Sukumar, C. V. 1976 Exact quantum and semiclassical calculation of the positions and residues of Regge poles for interatomic potentials. *J. Phys.* B **9**, 1783–1799.

Drazin, P. G. 1974 Kelvin–Helmholtz instability of a slowly varying flow. *J. Fluid Mech.* **65**, 781–797.

Heading, J. 1962 *An introduction to phase-integral methods*. London: Methuen.

Heading, J. 1977 Global phase-integral methods. *Quart. J. Mech. appl. Math.* **30**, 281–302.

Headley, V. B. & Barwell, V. K. 1975 On the distribution of the zeros of generalized Airy functions. *Math. Comp.* **29**, 863–877.

Knoll, J. & Schaeffer, R. 1976 Semiclassical scattering theory with complex trajectories. I. Elastic waves. *Ann. Phys.* **97**, 307–366.

Langer, R. E. 1932 On the asymptotic solutions of differential equations, with an application to the Bessel functions of large complex order. *Trans. Am. math. Soc.* **34**, 447–480.

Langer, R. E. 1935 On the asymptotic solutions of ordinary differential equations, with reference to the Stokes' phenomenon about a singular point. *Trans. Am. math. Soc.* **37**, 397–416.

Leung, A. 1975 Lateral connections for asymptotic solutions around higher order turning points. *J. Math. Anal. Applics* **50**, 560–578.

Leung, A. 1977 Distribution of eigenvalues in the presence of higher order turning points. *Trans. Am. math. Soc.* **229**, 111–135.

Lozano, C. & Meyer, R. E. 1976 Leakage and response of waves trapped by round islands. *Phys. Fluids* **19**, 1075–1088.

Mott, N. F. & Massey, H. S. W. 1965 *The theory of atomic collisions*, 3rd ed. Oxford: Clarendon Press.

National Bureau of Standards 1964 *Handbook of mathematical functions*. Appl. Math. Ser. no. 55 (eds. M. Abramowitz & I. A. Stegun). Washington: U.S. Government Printing Office.

Olver, F. W. J. 1964 Error bounds for asymptotic expansions, with an application to cylinder functions of large argument. In *Asymptotic solutions of differential equations and their applications* (ed. C. H. Wilcox), pp. 163–183. London: Wiley.

Olver, F. W. J. 1965 Error analysis of phase-integral methods. I. General theory for simple turning points. *J. Res. natn. Bur. Stands* B **69**, 271–290.

Olver, F. W. J. 1974 *Asymptotics and special functions*. London: Academic Press.

Olver, F. W. J. 1977*a* Connection formulas for second-order differential equations with multiple turning points. *SIAM J. Math. Anal.* **8**, 127–154.

Olver, F. W. J. 1977*b* Connection formulas for second-order differential equations having an arbitrary number of turning points of arbitrary multiplicities. *SIAM J. Math. Anal.* **8**, 673–700.

Olver, F. W. J. 1977*c* Second-order differential equations with fractional transition points. *Trans. Am. math. Soc.*, **226**, 227–241.

Pokrovskii, V. L. & Khalatnikov, I. M. 1961 On the problem of above-barrier reflection of high-energy particles. *Soviet Phys. JETP* **13**, 1207–1210.

Shampine, L. F. & Gordon, M. K. 1975 *Computer solution of ordinary differential equations. The initial value problem.* San Francisco: W. H. Freeman.

Sibuya, Y. 1974 Uniform simplification in a full neighborhood of a transition point. *Mem. Am. math. Soc.* no. 149.

Swanson, C. A. & Headley, V. B. 1967 An extension of Airy's equation. *SIAM J. appl. Math.* **15**, 1400–1412.

Taylor, J. G. 1978 Error bounds for the Liouville–Green approximation to initial-value problems. *Z. Angew. Math. Mech.* (In the press.)

Wasow, W. 1968 Connection problems for asymptotic series. *Bull. Am. math. Soc.* **74**, 831–853.

SIAM REVIEW
Vol. 22, No. 2, April 1980

ASYMPTOTIC APPROXIMATIONS AND ERROR BOUNDS*

F. W. J. OLVER†

Abstract. The purpose of this paper is to demonstrate that well-constructed error bounds for asymptotic approximations can provide useful analytical insight into the nature and reliability of the approximations, enable somewhat unsatisfactory concepts such as multiple asymptotic expansions and generalized asymptotic expansions to be avoided, and lead to significant extensions of asymptotic results.

Also included are numerical values of error terms in the asymptotic expansion of Macdonald's modified Bessel function $K_\nu(z)$, and some new results pertaining to the Stokes phenomenon for this expansion.

1. Introduction. The obvious answer to the question "Why do we need error bounds for asymptotic approximations?" is "to bound the errors", or, in other words, "for computational purposes." In a paper presented at a symposium honoring the late Rudolf Langer (Olver (1964)), I discussed various computational aspects of asymptotic expansions and illustrated the conclusions with new error bounds for the well-known expansions of Bessel functions of large complex argument. During the intervening years it has become increasingly clear that there are other reasons for seeking error bounds, which are at least as important as computational justifications. A detailed discussion of these reasons is the theme of the present paper.

2. Insight. The analytic form of a well-constructed error bound provides insight into the nature and reliability of the corresponding asymptotic approximation. For example, it is possible to understand the Stokes phenomenon in a fairly general way by use of O-estimates of the error terms. But a full understanding, including the optimum location of the lines of discontinuity, requires a realistic knowledge of error bounds.

To illustrate these observations, let us again turn to the asymptotic expansion of the modified Bessel function $K_\nu(z)$ for large absolute values of the argument z, and fixed real or complex values of the order ν, given by

$$K_\nu(z) \sim \left(\frac{\pi}{2z}\right)^{1/2} e^{-z} \sum_{s=0}^{\infty} \frac{A_s(\nu)}{z^s}, \qquad |z| \to \infty, \tag{2.01}$$

where $A_0(\nu)=1$ and

$$A_s(\nu) = \frac{(4\nu^2-1^2)(4\nu^2-3^2)\cdots\{4\nu^2-(2s-1)^2\}}{s!8^s}, \qquad s \geqq 1. \tag{2.02}$$

This expansion is uniformly valid in the sector $|\mathrm{ph}\, z| \leqq \frac{3}{2}\pi - \delta$ for arbitrarily small values of the positive constant δ. The word "uniformly" however, has to be interpreted according to its narrow mathematical definition, and not in the sense of Webster's dictionary. Suppose we take a fixed number of terms in the expansion with a fixed (and sufficiently large) value of $|z|$, and consider what happens as ph z is varied. When

* Received by the editors November 29, 1978, and in revised form May 4, 1979. Presented at a Symposium on Precision Asymptotics, SIAM 1978 Spring Meeting, University of Wisconsin, Madison, Wisconsin.

† Institute for Physical Science and Technology, and Mathematics Department, University of Maryland, College Park, Maryland 20742, and National Bureau of Standards, Washington, D.C. 20234. This work was supported by the U.S. Army Research Office, Durham under Grant DAAG 29-77-G-0003 and by the National Science Foundation under Grant GP 32841X2.

ph $z = 0$ the error is comparable with the first neglected term in the expansion.[1] As ph z increases from 0 to π (or decreases from 0 to $-\pi$) the relative error changes fairly slowly. However, unless 2ν happens to equal or be close to an odd integer, after ph z passes through π (or $-\pi$) the relative error grows rapidly and as the extreme values ph $z = \pm\frac{3}{2}\pi$ are approached the absolute error becomes comparable in magnitude with the value of $K_\nu(z)$ itself.

The behavior just described is illustrated numerically in Table 1 in the case $\nu = 0$ for $|z| = 4$ and 10.[2] The arguments in the table are θ (in degrees) and n, where $\theta \equiv \text{ph}\, z$ and n denotes the number of terms taken in (2.01). The entries give 3-figure values of $|\rho_n(0, z)|$, where $\rho_n(\nu, z)$ is defined by

$$K_\nu(z) = \left(\frac{\pi}{2z}\right)^{1/2} e^{-z}\left\{\sum_{s=0}^{n-1} \frac{A_s(\nu)}{z^s} + \rho_n(\nu, z)\frac{A_n(\nu)}{z^n}\right\}; \tag{2.03}$$

thus $\rho_n(\nu, z)$ is the ratio of the absolute error to the first neglected term in the expansion.

By way of comparison, Table 2 exhibits 3-figure values of the corresponding error bounds, as derived in Olver (1964) (and subsequently reproduced on p. 269 of Olver (1974)). In the present notation these bounds are given by

$$|\rho_n(\nu, z)| \leqq 2 \exp(|\nu^2 - \tfrac{1}{4}|/|z|), \qquad |\text{ph}\, z| \leqq \tfrac{1}{2}\pi, \tag{2.04}$$

$$|\rho_n(\nu, z)| \leqq 2\chi(n) \exp(\tfrac{1}{2}\pi|\nu^2 - \tfrac{1}{4}|/|z|), \qquad \tfrac{1}{2}\pi \leqq |\text{ph}\, z| \leqq \pi, \tag{2.05}$$

$$|\rho_n(\nu, z)| \leqq 4\chi(n)|\sec(\text{ph}\, z)|^n \exp\{\pi|\sec(\text{ph}\, z)|\,|\nu^2 - \tfrac{1}{4}|/|z|\}, \quad \pi \leqq |\text{ph}\, z| < \tfrac{3}{2}\pi, \tag{2.06}$$

where

$$\chi(n) = \pi^{1/2}\Gamma(\tfrac{1}{2}n + 1)/\Gamma(\tfrac{1}{2}n + \tfrac{1}{2}). \tag{2.07}$$

It is evident from the tables that the bounds behave in a manner that is reasonably similar to the actual values of the $|\rho_n(0, z)|$.

Corresponding computations to those in Tables 1 and 2 have also been carried out in the cases $\nu = 1$ and i. These results are not reproduced here, but the conclusions are the same.

To understand the meaning of the bounds (2.04), (2.05), and (2.06) in the general case, we first note that in all applications in which the expansion (2.01) would actually be used for the computation of $K_\nu(z)$, the value of $|z|$ is sufficiently large compared with $|\nu^2 - \frac{1}{4}|$ to cause the exponential factors in (2.04) and (2.05) to reduce approximately to unity. In consequence, the truncation error is bounded in absolute value roughly by twice the first neglected term when $|\text{ph}\, z| \leqq \frac{1}{2}\pi$ or $2\chi(n)$ times the first neglected term when $\frac{1}{2}\pi \leqq |\text{ph}\, z| \leqq \pi$. From the estimate

$$\chi(n) = (\tfrac{1}{2}\pi n)^{1/2}\{1 + O(n^{-1})\}, \qquad n \to \infty, \tag{2.08}$$

it is seen that $\chi(n)$ grows fairly slowly as n increases. Hence we conclude that if the asymptotic expansion (2.01) is used in a straightforward manner, then accurate values of $K_\nu(z)$ are obtained provided that $|\text{ph}\, z| \leqq \pi$. In the remaining sectors $\pi < |\text{ph}\, z| < \frac{3}{2}\pi$, however, the factors involving sec (ph z) lead to large bounds for $\rho_n(\nu, z)$, especially near ph $z = \pm\frac{3}{2}\pi$. In summary, the essential message conveyed by the error bounds (2.04), (2.05), and (2.06) is that the direct computational use of (2.01) should be confined to the sector $|\text{ph}\, z| \leqq \pi$, if possible.

---

[1] In fact, if ν is real, $|\text{ph}\, z| \leqq \frac{1}{2}\pi$, and at least $[|\nu| + \frac{1}{2}]$ terms are taken, then the truncation error is bounded in absolute value by the first neglected term; see Watson (1944, p. 219). Compare also Table 1.

[2] The computation of Table 1 is described in the Appendix.

TABLE 1

Relative errors $|\rho_n(0, z)|$.

θ \ n	$\lvert z\rvert = 4$					$\lvert z\rvert = 10$				
	1	2	3	4	5	1	2	3	4	5
0°	.886	.807	.739	.681	.630	.949	.909	.872	.836	.810
10°	.888	.809	.741	.683	.632	.949	.910	.873	.838	.811
20°	.891	.814	.747	.689	.638	.951	.913	.877	.843	.812
30°	.896	.822	.756	.699	.649	.954	.918	.884	.852	.817
40°	.904	.833	.770	.714	.664	.959	.926	.893	.864	.828
50°	.914	.848	.788	.733	.683	.964	.935	.906	.878	.848
60°	.926	.867	.810	.758	.709	.971	.946	.920	.896	.874
70°	.941	.889	.838	.788	.741	.978	.959	.938	.917	.897
80°	.958	.916	.872	.826	.781	.987	.974	.959	.942	.931
90°	.977	.948	.912	.872	.830	.996	.990	.982	.971	.962
100°	.999	.984	.960	.928	.891	1.01	1.01	1.01	1.00	1.00
110°	1.02	1.03	1.02	.996	.966	1.02	1.03	1.04	1.04	1.04
120°	1.05	1.07	1.08	1.08	1.06	1.03	1.05	1.06	1.08	1.09
130°	1.08	1.13	1.16	1.18	1.18	1.04	1.07	1.09	1.12	1.15
140°	1.11	1.19	1.26	1.31	1.33	1.04	1.08	1.12	1.16	1.20
150°	1.14	1.26	1.37	1.47	1.54	1.05	1.10	1.15	1.21	1.26
160°	1.17	1.33	1.51	1.68	1.81	1.06	1.11	1.17	1.24	1.31
170°	1.19	1.41	1.67	1.95	2.20	1.06	1.12	1.19	1.27	1.37
180°	1.21	1.48	1.86	2.32	2.79	1.06	1.12	1.20	1.28	1.39
190°	1.21	1.54	2.10	2.89	3.77	1.06	1.12	1.19	1.27	1.37
200°	1.19	1.56	2.42	3.83	5.60	1.06	1.11	1.17	1.24	1.31
210°	1.12	1.49	2.95	5.81	9.66	1.05	1.10	1.15	1.21	1.28
220°	.983	1.26	4.46	11.0	20.3	1.04	1.08	1.12	1.15	1.27
230°	.751	1.80	10.1	27.2	52.7	1.04	1.07	1.10	.803	1.21
240°	1.06	7.14	31.2	83.1	163	1.02	1.12	2.29	8.48	39.0
250°	4.07	28.1	112	293	578	.850	2.66	29.8	191	937
260°	15.9	112	432	1.13×10^3	2.23×10^3	4.44	87.1	845	5.52×10^3	2.72×10^4
270°	63.8	453	1.74×10^3	4.55×10^3	8.99×10^3	159	2.84×10^3	2.73×10^4	1.78×10^5	8.80×10^5

TABLE 2
Bounds for $|\rho_n(0, z)|$.

	$\|z\|=4$					$\|z\|=10$				
θ \ n	1	2	3	4	5	1	2	3	4	5
0°	2.13	2.13	2.13	2.13	2.13	2.05	2.05	2.05	2.05	2.05
10°	2.13	2.13	2.13	2.13	2.13	2.05	2.05	2.05	2.05	2.05
20°	2.13	2.13	2.13	2.13	2.13	2.05	2.05	2.05	2.05	2.05
30°	2.13	2.13	2.13	2.13	2.13	2.05	2.05	2.05	2.05	2.05
40°	2.13	2.13	2.13	2.13	2.13	2.05	2.05	2.05	2.05	2.05
50°	2.13	2.13	2.13	2.13	2.13	2.05	2.05	2.05	2.05	2.05
60°	2.13	2.13	2.13	2.13	2.13	2.05	2.05	2.05	2.05	2.05
70°	2.13	2.13	2.13	2.13	2.13	2.05	2.05	2.05	2.05	2.05
80°	2.13	2.13	2.13	2.13	2.13	2.05	2.05	2.05	2.05	2.05
90°	2.13	2.13	2.13	2.13	2.13	2.05	2.05	2.05	2.05	2.05
100°	3.47	4.41	5.20	5.88	6.50	3.27	4.16	4.90	5.55	6.13
110°	3.47	4.41	5.20	5.88	6.50	3.27	4.16	4.90	5.55	6.13
120°	3.47	4.41	5.20	5.88	6.50	3.27	4.16	4.90	5.55	6.13
130°	3.47	4.41	5.20	5.88	6.50	3.27	4.16	4.90	5.55	6.13
140°	3.47	4.41	5.20	5.88	6.50	3.27	4.16	4.90	5.55	6.13
150°	3.47	4.41	5.20	5.88	6.50	3.27	4.16	4.90	5.55	6.13
160°	3.47	4.41	5.20	5.88	6.50	3.27	4.16	4.90	5.55	6.13
170°	3.47	4.41	5.20	5.88	6.50	3.27	4.16	4.90	5.55	6.13
180°	3.47	4.41	5.20	5.88	6.50	3.27	4.16	4.90	5.55	6.13
190°	7.79	10.1	12.0	13.8	15.5	6.91	8.93	10.7	12.3	13.8
200°	8.24	11.2	14.0	16.9	19.8	7.27	9.85	12.3	14.9	17.5
210°	9.10	13.4	18.2	23.8	30.3	7.94	11.7	15.9	20.8	26.5
220°	10.6	17.6	27.1	40.0	57.7	9.09	15.1	23.2	34.3	49.5
230°	13.3	26.3	48.2	84.8	146	11.0	21.9	40.1	70.6	121
240°	18.6	47.4	112	253	558	14.7	37.4	88.2	200	441
250°	32.6	121	418	1.38×10^3	4.47×10^3	23.1	86.0	296	981	3.17×10^3
260°	112	822	5.58×10^3	3.63×10^4	2.31×10^5	56.9	417	2.83×10^3	1.84×10^4	1.17×10^5
270°	∞	∞	∞	∞	∞	∞	∞	∞	∞	∞

How may $K_\nu(z)$ be computed accurately for large values of $|z|$ outside the sector $|\text{ph}\, z| \leqq \pi$? The answer is to combine (2.01) with connection formulae. For example, on replacing z in (2.01) by $z\,e^{-\pi i}$ and $z\,e^{-2\pi i}$ in turn, and substituting the results in the identity

$$K_\nu(z) = 2\cos(\nu\pi) K_\nu(z\,e^{-\pi i}) - K_\nu(z\,e^{-2\pi i}), \tag{2.09}$$

we obtain the compound asymptotic expansion

$$K_\nu(z) \sim \left(\frac{\pi}{2z}\right)^{1/2} e^{-z}\left\{\sum_{s=0}^{\infty} \frac{A_s(\nu)}{z^s} + 2i\cos(\nu\pi)\, e^{2z} \sum_{s=0}^{\infty} (-)^s \frac{A_s(\nu)}{z^s}\right\}, \tag{2.10}$$

valid when $z \to \infty$ in the sector $\frac{1}{2}\pi + \delta \leqq \text{ph}\, z \leqq \frac{5}{2}\pi - \delta$. When 2ν is not an odd integer the expansion (2.10) differs from (2.01) by the inclusion of the second series. In the common region of validity, given by $\frac{1}{2}\pi + \delta \leqq \text{ph}\, z \leqq \frac{3}{2}\pi - \delta$, the factor e^{2z} is exponentially small for large z. Therefore (as we already know from (2.01)) the second series in (2.10) can be neglected—in the Poincaré sense. There is, however, no a priori reason to suppose that this series is numerically small, and, as we shall now show, its neglect can introduce serious errors.

Let us suppose that 2ν is not an odd integer, and the same number of terms is taken in each of the three summations in (2.01) and (2.10). Which of (2.01) and (2.10) will then yield the greater accuracy in their common region of validity? To answer this question, we need the full form of (2.10), given by

$$\begin{aligned} K_\nu(z) = \left(\frac{\pi}{2z}\right)^{1/2} e^{-z}\Bigg[&\sum_{s=0}^{n-1} \frac{A_s(\nu)}{z^s} + \rho_n(\nu, z\,e^{-2\pi i})\frac{A_n(\nu)}{z^n} \\ &+ 2i\cos(\nu\pi)\, e^{2z}\Bigg\{\sum_{s=0}^{n-1} (-)^s \frac{A_s(\nu)}{z^s} \\ &\qquad + (-)^n \rho_n(\nu, z\,e^{-\pi i})\frac{A_n(\nu)}{z^n}\Bigg\}\Bigg], \end{aligned} \tag{2.11}$$

in which the bounds for $\rho_n(\nu, z\,e^{-\pi i})$ and $\rho_n(\nu, z\,e^{-2\pi i})$ have the same forms as in (2.04), (2.05), and (2.06), but with different regions of validity; for example,

$$|\rho_n(\nu, z\,e^{-\pi i})| \leqq 2\exp(|\nu^2 - \tfrac{1}{4}|/|z|), \qquad \tfrac{1}{2}\pi \leqq \text{ph}\, z \leqq \tfrac{3}{2}\pi.$$

When $\frac{1}{2}\pi + \delta \leqq \text{ph}\, z < \pi$, the bound for $\rho_n(\nu, z)$ is given by (2.05), whereas the bounds for $\rho_n(\nu, z\,e^{-\pi i})$ and $\rho_n(\nu, z\,e^{-2\pi i})$ are found from (2.04) and (2.06), respectively. By using (2.01) we avoid introducing errors that are bounded by the undesirable "secant" form (2.06); accordingly (2.01) should yield greater accuracy than (2.10).

When $\pi < \text{ph}\, z \leqq \frac{3}{2}\pi - \delta$ the situation is reversed. The bound for $\rho_n(\nu, z)$ now involves secant factors, whereas neither of the bounds for $\rho_n(\nu, z\,e^{-\pi i})$ and $\rho_n(\nu, z\,e^{-2\pi i})$ does so. Hence (2.10) should yield greater accuracy than (2.01).

It is now evident that by selecting the ray $\text{ph}\, z = \pi$ as the place to change over from the expansion (2.01) to the compound expansion (2.10), we completely avoid the undesirable secant forms of error bound. This indicates that $\text{ph}\, z = \pi$ is the correct location of the Stokes line (or curve) for the two expansions, that is, the line on which the coefficient of the series associated with the factor e^{2z} changes discontinuously from 0 to $2i\cos(\nu\pi)$ in order to preserve maximum accuracy. In the following eight paragraphs we seek to confirm this conclusion by analysis of the error bounds.

We are concerned with the asymptotic expansion of $K_\nu(z)$ for large $|z|$. However, as we shall see shortly, the *minimum* error bounds for (2.03) and (2.11)—minimized, that is, with respect to n—occur when $n = 2|z| + \frac{1}{2}$, approximately, and therefore we will be concerned also with $n \gg |\nu|$. First, we introduce the notation

$$B_n(\nu, |z|) \equiv 2\chi(n) \exp\left(\frac{\pi|\nu^2 - \frac{1}{4}|}{2|z|}\right)\frac{|A_n(\nu)|}{|z|^n}, \tag{2.12}$$

in terms of which the bound (2.05) may be recast in the form

$$\left|\rho_n(\nu, z)\frac{A_n(\nu)}{z^n}\right| \leqq B_n(\nu, |z|), \tag{2.13}$$

valid when $\frac{1}{2}\pi \leqq \text{ph } z \leqq \pi$. In the other sector of immediate interest, namely $\pi \leqq \text{ph } z \leqq \frac{3}{2}\pi$, we have $-\pi \leqq \text{ph }(z\,e^{-2\pi i}) \leqq -\frac{1}{2}\pi$. In consequence, the bound for the first error term in (2.11) also may be expressed in terms of $B_n(\nu, |z|)$; thus

$$\left|\rho_n(\nu, z\,e^{-2\pi i})\frac{A_n(\nu)}{z^n}\right| \leqq B_n(\nu, |z|). \tag{2.14}$$

In order to find the minimum values of these bounds we examine the asymptotic form of $B_n(\nu, |z|)$ for n large compared with $|\nu|$. On writing (2.02) in the form

$$A_s(\nu) = (-)^s \frac{\cos(\nu\pi)}{\pi} \frac{\Gamma(s + \frac{1}{2} - \nu)\Gamma(s + \frac{1}{2} + \nu)}{s!2^s}, \tag{2.15}$$

and then using Stirling's series, we find that

$$A_n(\nu) = (-)^n \cos(\nu\pi)\left(\frac{2}{\pi n}\right)^{1/2}\left(\frac{n}{2e}\right)^n\left\{1 + \frac{\nu^2 - \frac{1}{6}}{n} + O\left(\frac{1}{n^2}\right)\right\}, \qquad n \gg \nu. \tag{2.16}$$

Similarly from (2.07) we have

$$\chi(n) = \left(\frac{\pi n}{2}\right)^{1/2}\left\{1 + \frac{1}{4n} + O\left(\frac{1}{n^2}\right)\right\}, \qquad n \to \infty. \tag{2.17}$$

Substituting in (2.12) by means of these results, we obtain the required estimate

$$B_n(\nu, |z|) = 2|\cos(\nu\pi)|\left(\frac{n}{2e|z|}\right)^n \exp\left(\frac{\pi|\nu^2 - \frac{1}{4}|}{2|z|}\right)\left|1 + \frac{\nu^2 + \frac{1}{12}}{n} + O\left(\frac{1}{n^2}\right)\right|, \tag{2.18}$$

which is valid as $n \to \infty$, uniformly with respect to z.

Next, we see from (2.18) that except in the trivial case in which 2ν is an odd integer we have

$$\frac{B_n(\nu, |z|)}{B_{n-1}(\nu, |z|)} = \frac{n}{2|z|}\left\{1 - \frac{1}{2n} + O\left(\frac{1}{n^2}\right)\right\},$$

as $n \to \infty$, again uniformly with respect to z. For large $|z|$ the right-hand side equals unity when

$$n = 2|z| + \tfrac{1}{2} + O(|z|^{-1}).$$

Bearing in mind that n is an integer, we perceive that for large $|z|$ the smallest value of $B_n(\nu, |z|)$ is obtained by taking $n = 2|z| + \vartheta$, where

$$|\vartheta| \leqq \tfrac{1}{2} + O(|z|^{-1}). \tag{2.19}$$

On making this substitution for n in (2.18) we obtain

(2.20)
$$B_n(\nu, |z|) = 2|\cos(\nu\pi)|\, e^{-2|z|}\left\{1 + \frac{\frac{1}{4}\vartheta^2 + \frac{1}{2}\pi|\nu^2 - \frac{1}{4}|}{|z|} + O\left(\frac{1}{|z|^2}\right)\right\}\left|1 + \frac{\nu^2 + \frac{1}{12}}{2|z|} + O\left(\frac{1}{z^2}\right)\right|,$$

as $|z| \to \infty$.

We are now in a position to determine for which part of the sector $\frac{1}{2}\pi \leqq \mathrm{ph}\, z \leqq \frac{3}{2}\pi$ we should choose the asymptotic expansion (2.01) and for which part we should choose (2.10), in order to achieve maximum accuracy.

First, consider the sector $\frac{1}{2}\pi \leqq \mathrm{ph}\, z \leqq \pi$. For the error term associated with the truncated series

$$\sum_{s=0}^{n-1} \frac{A_s(\nu)}{z^s} \tag{2.21}$$

in (2.01) the minimum bound is $B_n(\nu, |z|)$ with $n = 2|z| + \vartheta$. From (2.19) and (2.20) it is evident that this minimum bound is itself bounded by

$$2|\cos(\nu\pi)|\, e^{-2|z|}\left\{1 + \left(\tfrac{1}{16} + \tfrac{1}{2}\pi|\nu^2 - \tfrac{1}{4}| + \tfrac{1}{2}|\nu^2 + \tfrac{1}{12}|\right)\frac{1}{|z|} + O\left(\frac{1}{|z|^2}\right)\right\}. \tag{2.22}$$

In comparison, as long as we take at least two terms (and therefore certainly if we take the optimum number of terms) the absolute value of the *whole* contribution of the second series within the braces in (2.10) has the form

$$2|\cos(\nu\pi)||e^{2z}|\left|1 - \frac{A_1(\nu)}{z} + O\left(\frac{1}{z^2}\right)\right|. \tag{2.23}$$

Clearly $e^{-2|z|} \leqq |e^{2z}|$. Hence except when

$$|e^{2z}|\left|1 - \frac{A_1(\nu)}{z} + O\left(\frac{1}{z^2}\right)\right| \leqq 2e^{-2|z|}\left\{1 + \left(\tfrac{1}{16} + \tfrac{1}{2}\pi|\nu^2 - \tfrac{1}{4}| + \tfrac{1}{2}|\nu^2 + \tfrac{1}{12}|\right)\frac{1}{|z|} + O\left(\frac{1}{|z|^2}\right)\right\}, \tag{2.24}$$

the inclusion of the second series (that is, the use of (2.10) rather than (2.01)) will perturb the sum (2.21) by an amount that exceeds, in absolute value, twice the known error bound associated with (2.21). In consequence, the inclusion of the second series will necessarily increase the *actual* error in the computed value of $K_\nu(z)$. Since $A_1(\nu) = \frac{1}{2}(\nu^2 - \frac{1}{4})$, the region determined by the condition (2.24) is included in that determined by

$$2|z| + 2\,\mathrm{Re}\, z \leqq \ln 2 + \frac{c - (\frac{1}{2}\ln 2)^2}{|z|} + O\left(\frac{1}{|z|^2}\right),$$

where

$$c = (\tfrac{1}{2}\ln 2)^2 + \tfrac{1}{16} + \tfrac{1}{2}(\pi + 1)|\nu^2 - \tfrac{1}{4}| + \tfrac{1}{2}|\nu^2 + \tfrac{1}{12}|, \tag{2.25}$$

or, equivalently, in that determined by

$$0 \leqq y \leqq \{-x \ln 2 + c + O(|x|^{-1})\}^{1/2}, \tag{2.26}$$

where x and y denote the real and imaginary parts of z, respectively.

Secondly, consider the sector $\pi \leqq \mathrm{ph}\, z \leqq \frac{3}{2}\pi$. For the nth error term associated with the first series in (2.10) we again have the minimum bound $B_n(\nu, |z|)$, with $n = 2|z| + \vartheta$, but *only* if the second series (together with its error term) is included. The absolute value of this contribution of the second series again has the form (2.23). Therefore except when the condition (2.24) is satisfied, the omission of the second series will necessarily increase the *actual* error in the computed value of $K_\nu(z)$. The region determined by (2.24) is now included in that determined by the condition

$$0 \geqq y \geqq -\{-x \ln 2 + c + O(|x|^{-1})\}^{1/2}, \tag{2.27}$$

where the constant c is again given by (2.25).

Now let $\hat{c}$ denote any positive number exceeding c. Then we may summarize our findings concerning the sector $\frac{1}{2}\pi \leqq \text{ph}\, z \leqq \frac{3}{2}\pi$ in the following way:

(i) Suppose that $z \equiv x + iy$ does not lie in the region **P** defined by

$$y^2 \leqq -x \ln 2 + \hat{c}, \qquad x \leqq 0, \tag{2.28}$$

(Figure 1). Then for all sufficiently large values of $|z|$ the optimum form of the expansion (2.01) will yield greater or lesser accuracy than the optimum form of (2.10) according as ph $z \lesseqgtr \pi$.

(ii) When $z \in \mathbf{P}$ we cannot determine which of (2.01) and (2.10) will yield the greater accuracy.

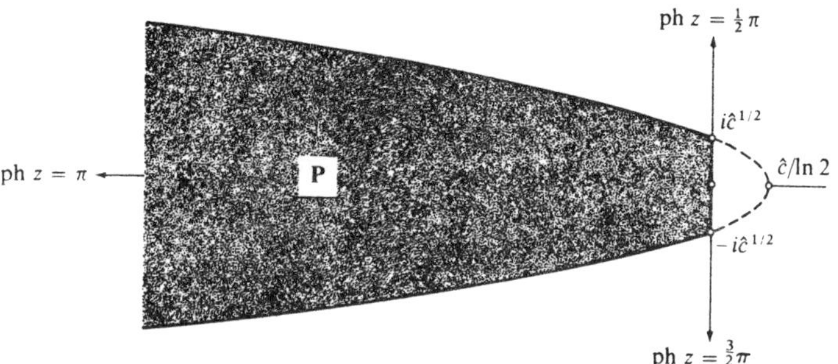

FIG. 1. *Region of uncertainty. z-plane*: $\frac{1}{2}\pi \leqq \text{ph}\, z \leqq \frac{3}{2}\pi$.

As a further deduction, let us suppose that in constructing a computing algorithm it is decided that the changeover from (2.01) to (2.10) is to take place along a ray emanating from the origin. Then to preserve maximum accuracy this ray has to be ph $z = \pi$, since no other ray is completely contained in **P**. On the ray ph $z = \pi$ itself either (2.01) or (2.10) may be used, since the whole contribution of the second series in (2.10) has approximately the same magnitude as the smallest error bound associated with the first series.

Another conclusion to be drawn from (2.11) is that the compound expansion (2.10) will yield accurate values of $K_\nu(z)$ for large $|z|$ throughout the sector $\pi \leqq \text{ph}\, z \leqq 2\pi$, because from (2.11), (2.04), and (2.05) it is clear that the corresponding error bounds do not contain the undesirable secant factors in this region. Other ranges of ph z can be treated in a similar manner by use of appropriate connection formulae. For example, if we employ the formula that expresses $K_\nu(z)$ in terms of $K_\nu(z\,e^{-2\pi i})$ and $K_\nu(z\,e^{-3\pi i})$ in place of (2.09), and follow the same procedure, then we obtain a compound expansion that is valid in Poincaré's sense in the sector $\frac{3}{2}\pi + \delta \leqq \text{ph}\, z \leqq \frac{7}{2}\pi - \delta$, but numerically reliable only in the smaller sector $2\pi \leqq \text{ph}\, z \leqq 3\pi$.

The example described above illustrates two general principles. First, asymptotic approximations or expansions should not normally be used near the natural boundaries of their regions of validity. Secondly, inclusion of exponentially small contributions may lead to substantial improvements in numerical accuracy, despite the fact that they are negligible in Poincaré's sense. Numerical analysts have long been aware of these principles, especially the second one. As we have seen in the present example, there is little difficulty in justifying the conclusions mathematically in cases where realistic error bounds are at hand. Systematic methods for constructing error bounds have evolved only recently, however, and during the better part of a century that has elapsed since Poincaré formulated the definition of an asymptotic expansion there have been several attempts to construct general mathematical theories that would serve to place the two principles on a sound basis. Unfortunately, as we shall see in the next section, none of these attempts has proved fully successful from *both* practical and mathematical standpoints.

3. Unsatisfactory concepts. With a view to handling exponentially small contributions to asymptotic expansions G. N. Watson (1911) established sufficient conditions to ensure that a function possessing a prescribed asymptotic expansion of Poincaré type is unique. Stemming from Watson's theory J. C. P. Miller (1964) and R. B. Dingle (1962 and 1973, especially pp. 17–21) introduced heuristic theories of what they term "complete asymptotic expansions in the sense of Watson". Essentially, an asymptotic expansion is said to be complete when it includes all relevant contributions, whether or not they are exponentially small compared with other terms. In the case of the example treated in § 2, the expansion (2.01) is regarded as complete in the sector $|\text{ph}\, z| \leqq \pi$, but not in the sector $|\text{ph}\, z| \leqq \frac{3}{2}\pi - \delta$ when $\delta < \frac{1}{2}\pi$. Similarly, (2.10) is complete in $\pi \leqq \text{ph}\, z \leqq 2\pi$, but not in any larger sector.

Watson's theory is mathematically sound, but in order to apply it we need properties of the error term that are likely to be available only when a realistic bound is known. In this event the theory is largely unnecessary. In particular, this is true of the only example treated in Watson's paper, the expansion of the logarithmic integral of small argument. In contrast, the theories of Miller and Dingle are often effective in practice, but lack rigorous mathematical bases.

The most recent attempt in the same direction is that of K. D. Shere (1971, 1972b). Shere attacked the problem directly by extending the definition of an asymptotic expansion from single power series to double series of the form

$$\sum_{m=0}^{\infty} \sum_{n=0}^{\infty} a_{m,n} e^{-\lambda m z} z^{-n}, \tag{3.01}$$

in which z is the large asymptotic variable and the coefficients $a_{m,n}$ and the exponent λ are constants. Shere designated such expansions "multiple asymptotic expansions" and investigated various general properties. Some applications to physical problems were given by Shere (1971, 1972a), and have also been made by other writers, including W. Bühring (1977a,b). Unfortunately, serious flaws have been detected in this theory. First, double series of the form (3.01) that happen to converge are not necessarily multiple asymptotic expansions of their sum, in contrast to single series with the usual Poincaré definition. Secondly, linear operations are not necessarily valid. For example, although a given function $f(z)$ may possess a multiple asymptotic expansion of the form (3.01), owing to the particular definition chosen by Shere it is not necessarily true that on replacing each coefficient $a_{m,n}$ by $2a_{m,n}$ we obtain a multiple asymptotic expansion of $2f(z)$. These shortcomings have been pointed out recently by R. D. Gregory (1979). In this article Gregory shows how the difficulties can be overcome by reformulating Shere's definition of a multiple asymptotic expansion; in fact, this reformulation can be done successfully in infinitely many ways. However, Gregory also notes that in order to select the correct definition in any particular application we are likely to need so much extra information about the function that is being expanded as to render the theory unnecessary. In other words, the objection to Watson's theory raised above again applies.

In summary, at the present time the theory of error bounds appears to furnish the only way of assessing contributions from exponentially small terms in a manner that is both effective in practice and mathematically sound.

A complete asymptotic expansion is not the only concept that has given rise to fundamental difficulties that are avoidable by comprehensive theories of error bounds. Another is the so-called generalized asymptotic expansion. The development of a generalized theory has taken place in several stages, important contributions being due to H. Schmidt (1937) and A. Erdélyi and M. Wyman (1963). Schmidt introduced the idea of an asymptotic scale, that is, an infinite sequence of functions $\phi_s(x)$, $s = 0, 1, 2, \ldots$, of steadily diminishing asymptotic order as the asymptotic variable x approaches infinity (or some other distinguished point). More precisely, we have

$$\phi_{s+1}(x) = o\{\phi_s(x)\}$$

as $x \to \infty$ for every s. For a given scale, following Schmidt we say that a function $f(x)$ possesses a generalized expansion

$$f(x) \sim \sum_{s=0}^{\infty} \psi_s(x), \qquad x \to \infty,$$

where $\psi_s(x)$, $s = 0, 1, 2, \ldots$, is another sequence of functions (not necessarily forming a scale) if

$$f(x) = \sum_{s=0}^{n-1} \psi_s(x) + O\{\phi_n(x)\}, \qquad x \to \infty,$$

for every n.

Erdélyi and Wyman introduced the concise notation

$$f(x) \sim \sum_{s=0}^{\infty} \psi_s(x); \qquad \{\phi_s(x)\} \quad \text{as } x \to \infty,$$

to emphasize the role of the scale. They also extended the definition by introducing the notion of composite asymptotic variables. For example, Debye's well-known asymptotic expansion for the modified Bessel function $K_\nu(z)$ of large order ν also happens to be asymptotic in nature as $z \to \infty$ with ν fixed.[3] Consequently, in this case $|z| + |\nu|$ would be an appropriate composite variable, with properly chosen regions of validity.

Unfortunately, and perhaps surprisingly, although the steps that were made in the course of generalizing Poincaré's definition appear to be quite reasonable, the final definition admits expansions that are useless numerically and have no conceivable value in an analytical sense. This is illustrated by the following striking example, due to E. Riekstiņš (1966):

$$\frac{\sin x}{x} \sim \sum_{s=1}^{\infty} \frac{s!\, e^{-(s+1)x/(2s)}}{(\ln x)^s}; \qquad \{(\ln x)^{-s}\} \quad \text{as } x \to \infty.$$

Since the asymptotic scale here is the sequence $(\ln x)^{-s}$, $s = 1, 2, \ldots$, the $\sim$ sign means that when the series is truncated at $n - 1$ terms the error is $O\{(\ln x)^{-n}\}$ for large x. This is true, but quite useless from a practical viewpoint, because exactly the same expansion also "represents" the function $(\cos x)/x$, for example, in a similar manner.

[3] These results may be found, for example, in Chapter 10, §§ 7 and 8, of Olver (1974).

It should also be noted that many of the elementary properties of Poincaré expansions, including uniqueness, multiplication, and division, disappear with generalized expansions. In other words, there is no longer a viable calculus, which was the *raison d'être* of the Poincaré definition. In the present writer's view, we may as well dispense with the formal generalized definition and simply use truncated expansions accompanied by appropriate O-estimates (or o-estimates) for the error terms. Or better still, of course, we should aim at truncated expansions accompanied by bounds that reflect the analytical and numerical character of the error term.

4. Generalizations. The third reason for seeking error bounds is that they often lead to significant generalizations of asymptotic results—as distinct from generalizations of definitions. In the Introduction to a very useful monograph on asymptotic analysis, N. G. de Bruijn (1958) included an account of what appears to be a typical procedure for constructing error bounds. This takes the form of an imaginary (and amusing) conversation between a certain Miss N. A., a Numerical Analyst, and a Dr. A. A., an Asymptotic Analyst. The theme is that reasonably good estimates of the implied constants associated with error bounds, that is, the numerical coefficients hiding under the O-symbols, often can be obtained by retracing existing asymptotic proofs and tightening up all inequalities as much as possible. In the experience of the present writer this approach rarely proves to be fruitful. With the exception of the method of integration by parts (including the Euler–Maclaurin formula), most of the older methods[4] for finding asymptotic approximations for functions defined by definite integrals or as solutions of ordinary differential equations are unsuitable for the purpose of constructing realistic error bounds. Quite different and more powerful analyses are needed as a rule, and it is from these newer proofs that useful generalizations stem.

An excellent example is provided by the so-called Liouville–Green (LG or JWKB) approximation for solutions of differential equations of the form

$$d^2w/dx^2 = \{f(x) + g(x)\}w. \tag{4.01}$$

The theory of this approximation is developed in detail in Chapter 6 of Olver (1974); here we confine attention to the pertinent results.

For simplicity, let us suppose that x ranges over a real interval (a, b), possibly infinite, and that $f(x)$ is positive (thereby ruling out turning-point problems). The function $g(x)$ is understood to be small in some sense compared with $f(x)$. One of the attractive features of the error-analysis approach is that at the outset—and indeed throughout most of the analysis—our suppositions concerning $g(x)$ need be no more precise than this. Subsequently, *the bounds themselves* will let us know exactly what kind of growth in $g(x)$ can be tolerated without disturbing the asymptotic estimates obtained for the solutions.

The LG approximations to the solutions of (4.01) are given by

$$w_\pm(x) = f^{-1/4}(x)\, e^{\pm\int f^{1/2}(x)\,dx}\{1 + \eta_\pm(x)\}, \tag{4.02}$$

with either the upper signs or the lower signs taken throughout. The error terms are subject to the inequalities

$$|\eta_+(x)| \leqq \exp\{\tfrac{1}{2}\mathcal{V}_{a,x}(F)\} - 1, \qquad |\eta_-(x)| \leqq \exp\{\tfrac{1}{2}\mathcal{V}_{x,b}(F)\} - 1, \tag{4.03}$$

[4] Described, for example, in Erdélyi (1956) and de Bruijn (1958).

in which $F(x)$ denotes the indefinite integral ("error-control function")

$$F(x)=\int\{f^{-1/4}(f^{-1/4})''-gf^{-1/2}\}\,dx, \tag{4.04}$$

and $\mathcal{V}_{a,x}(F)$, $\mathcal{V}_{x,b}(F)$ denote the total variations of $F(x)$ over the intervals (a, x) and (x, b), respectively; thus

$$\begin{aligned}\mathcal{V}_{a,x}(F)&=\int_a^x|f^{-1/4}(f^{-1/4})''-gf^{-1/2}|\,dx,\\ \mathcal{V}_{x,b}(F)&=\int_x^b|f^{-1/4}(f^{-1/4})''-gf^{-1/2}|\,dx.\end{aligned} \tag{4.05}$$

The bounds (4.03) are valid whenever the necessary derivatives exist and the integrals (4.05) converge. In these circumstances, we have by definition

$$\mathcal{V}_{a,x}(F)\to 0, \qquad x\to a+. \tag{4.06}$$

Hence from the first of (4.03) we see that $\eta_+(x)\to 0$, and then from (4.02) we derive

$$w_+(x)\sim f^{-1/4}\,e^{\int f^{1/2}dx}, \qquad x\to a+. \tag{4.07}$$

Similarly,

$$w_-(x)\sim f^{-1/4}\,e^{-\int f^{1/2}dx}, \qquad x\to b-. \tag{4.08}$$

In other words, with explicit and well-defined conditions the LG representations provide asymptotic approximations to the solutions as the endpoints are approached.

Now we invert the problem. Instead of seeking the behavior of the solutions at a and b for given functions f and g, we enquire what kind of behavior can be tolerated in f and g at the endpoints without violating the condition that $\mathcal{V}(F)$ converges? In other words, given the asymptotic solutions, what are the problems that they solve? When the question is put in this form, numerical analysts will recognize some similarity to the process of backward numerical error analysis that is frequently used for problems in linear algebra.[5]

Suppose, for example, that all necessary derivatives of f exist and also that as $x\to a$ or b, f tends to a nonzero constant and g tends to a constant. Then it immediately follows that $\mathcal{V}_{a,b}(F)<\infty$. This result is unexciting, however, since a and b are ordinary points of the differential equation (4.01) in these circumstances. Much more interesting are cases in which f is unbounded as x approaches an endpoint. Provided that g does not grow too quickly in comparison with f, the variation $\mathcal{V}(F)$ will generally converge. (Furthermore, the faster f grows, that is, the more fierce the singularity, the more rapidly $\mathcal{V}(F)$ will converge, as a rule.) In particular, all irregular singularities of finite rank admit convergent behavior of $\mathcal{V}(F)$. It should also be observed that in these cases—as in all others in which $\mathcal{V}(F)$ converges—*the LG approximations automatically supply the asymptotic forms of the solutions*. This contrasts with the traditional approach in which the first step of the asymptotic analysis has been to guess the form of the approximation; see, for example, Coddington and Levinson (1955, Chap. 5, § 2), or Erdélyi (1956, § 3.2).

Not only can singularities of finite rank be handled by the present approach; most irregular singularities of infinite or unclassifiable rank also are amenable. Examples are

[5] See, for example, J. H. Wilkinson (1963, Chapt. I, § 6).

furnished by

$$(4.09) \qquad f = x + \ln x, \qquad g = 0, \qquad b = \infty,$$

and

$$(4.10) \qquad f = x^x, \qquad g = e^x, \qquad b = \infty.$$

The first of these was treated in Chapter 6, § 3.6 of Olver (1974); solutions are given by

$$w_\pm(x) \sim x^{-(1/4)\pm\sqrt{x}} \exp\{\pm(\tfrac{2}{3}x^{3/2} - 2x^{1/2})\}, \qquad x \to +\infty.$$

In the case of (4.10) the rate of change of the solutions is extremely rapid, and it is appropriate to express the solutions in logarithmic form, given by[6]

$$(4.11) \qquad \ln w_\pm(x) = \pm\frac{2x^{x/2}}{1+\ln x}\left[1 + O\left\{\frac{1}{x(\ln x)^2}\right\}\right], \qquad x \to +\infty.$$

The reader should reflect how difficult it would be just to get started with traditional methods of proof by guessing the asymptotic forms in these two examples. These examples also suggest that from the new viewpoint the concept of rank of an irregular singularity is of diminished importance, at least as far as differential equations of the second order are concerned. The concept now serves mainly to separate those cases that are amenable to the traditional approach from the more general problem.

Asymptotic behavior of solutions at irregular singularities is only one type of problem that is handled very effectively by the use of error bounds. Another concerns the uniform asymptotic behavior of solutions for extreme values of a parameter. For example, we may seek asymptotic solutions of differential equations of the form

$$d^2w/dx^2 = \{f(\varepsilon, x) + g(\varepsilon, x)\}w$$

that are uniform with respect to $x \in (a, b)$ as the parameter ε tends to zero.[7] In this second type of problem the error-control function F depends on ε as well as x. Since $\mathcal{V}_{a,x}(F)$ and $\mathcal{V}_{x,b}(F)$ are both bounded by $\mathcal{V}_{a,b}(F)$, it is evident from (4.03) that the LG approximations (4.02) supply the desired uniform asymptotic approximations to the solutions, provided that $\mathcal{V}_{a,b}(F)$ is finite and vanishes as $\varepsilon \to 0$. Again, this contrasts with the traditional approach in which we need to specify *in advance* precisely how $f(\varepsilon, x)$ and $g(\varepsilon, x)$ depend on ε; for example, as polynomials in ε or ε^{-1}. (Furthermore, if it is decided to modify the dependence of $f(\varepsilon, x)$ and $g(\varepsilon, x)$ on ε at a later stage by inclusion of extra terms, then frequently it is necessary to restart the asymptotic analysis from the beginning.) Lastly, it should be observed that the error-bound approach applies both to regular perturbation problems, for which $f(\varepsilon, x)$ and $g(\varepsilon, x)$ tend to finite limits as $\varepsilon \to 0$, and to singular perturbation problems, for which at least one of these functions becomes infinite as $\varepsilon \to 0$; compare R. E. O'Malley (1974).

5. Conclusions. In § 1 I mentioned the 1964 Madison symposium on the asymptotic solutions of differential equations and their applications. An an earlier Madison symposium, on numerical approximation, M. Golomb and H. F. Weinberger (1959) described the O-symbol in approximation formulae as a "figleaf" whose purpose is to cover the offending member, that is, the error term. The object of the present paper is to encourage asymptotic analysts to peer intently at what is hidden by this particular

[6] In arriving at the result for $w_+(x)$ use has been made of Theorem 3.1 of Olver (1974, Chap. 6).

[7] Actually, the LG approximation was introduced originally by J. Liouville (1837) and G. Green (1837) to solve certain problems of this type. The application to irregular singularities, described above, is quite recent.

figleaf, with the following intentions:

(i) To legitimize computation.
(ii) To provide analytical insight.
(iii) To avoid unsatisfactory concepts.
(iv) To facilitate extensions.

The practical importance of (i) is obvious. Reasons (ii), (iii), and (iv) are important because each is connected with significant advances in the general theory of asymptotic analysis.

The examples in this paper have all been drawn from the theory of differential equations. However, the error theory of asymptotic expansions derived from integral representations is gaining momentum, especially since the introduction of techniques based on the use of generalized functions and the Mellin transform. Readers who are interested in these developments should consult a forthcoming survey paper by R. Wong (1980).

Appendix. Computation of Table 1. Values of the function $L_\nu(z) \equiv (2z/\pi)^{1/2} e^z K_\nu(z)$ needed in the preparation of Table 1 were generated by a specially constructed algorithm which is applicable for real or complex values of ν and z. The algorithm proceeds in three stages, described briefly as follows.

(i) The differential equation

$$\frac{d^2w}{dz^2} - 2\frac{dw}{dz} - \frac{\nu^2 - \frac{1}{4}}{z^2}w = 0, \tag{A.1}$$

satisfied by $w = L_\nu(z)$, is integrated along the positive real axis from $z = X$ down to $z = r$. Here r corresponds to the values of $|z|$ used in Table 1, and X is an arbitrary positive number which is sufficiently large to ensure that the starting values

$$L_\nu(X) = 1, \qquad L'_\nu(X) = 0, \tag{A.2}$$

can be used to the working accuracy. The minimum value of X is easily estimated by reference to (2.02), (2.03), and (2.04) with $n = 1$: in order to attain an accuracy of S decimal figures we require $X = |\nu^2 - \frac{1}{4}| \times 10^S$, approximately.

(ii) With the same value of r as in stage (i), the differential equation

$$\frac{d^2w}{d\theta^2} - i(1 + 2re^{i\theta})\frac{dw}{d\theta} + (\nu^2 - \tfrac{1}{4})w = 0, \tag{A.3}$$

satisfied by $w = L_\nu(re^{i\theta})$, is integrated from $\theta = 0$ to $\theta = \pi$, and also (for nonreal ν) from $\theta = 0$ to $\theta = -\pi$. Initial values at $\theta = 0$ are derived from the values of $L_\nu(r)$ and $L'_\nu(r)$ found in stage (i) by use of the relations

$$w = L_\nu(r), \qquad dw/d\theta = irL'_\nu(r), \qquad \theta = 0. \tag{A.4}$$

(iii) Again, with the same value of r, the connection formulae

$$L_\nu(re^{i\theta}) = 2i\cos(\nu\pi)\exp(2re^{i\theta})L_\nu\{re^{i(\theta-\pi)}\} + L_\nu\{re^{i(\theta-2\pi)}\},$$
$$L_\nu(re^{i\theta}) = -2i\cos(\nu\pi)\exp(2re^{i\theta})L_\nu\{re^{i(\theta+\pi)}\} + L_\nu\{re^{i(\theta+2\pi)}\},$$

are employed to extend the range of θ to include the intervals $[\pi, \frac{3}{2}\pi]$ and $[-\frac{3}{2}\pi, -\pi]$, respectively. For real values of ν values of $L_\nu\{re^{i(\theta-2\pi)}\}$ for negative values of the phase $\theta - 2\pi$ are obtainable from the corresponding values for positive phase by taking complex conjugates. Similarly for $L_\nu\{re^{i(\theta+\pi)}\}$ when $\theta + \pi$ is negative.

After completing the computation of $L_\nu(r e^{i\theta})$ by means of the algorithm, corresponding values of the error coefficient $\rho_n(\nu, z)$ were generated by means of the formula

$$\rho_n(\nu, r e^{i\theta}) = \left\{L_\nu(r e^{i\theta}) - \sum_{s=0}^{n-1} \frac{A_s(\nu)}{r^s e^{si\theta}}\right\} \frac{r^n e^{ni\theta}}{A_n(\nu)}; \tag{A.5}$$

compare (2.03).

All computations were carried out on the UNIVAC 1108 computer at the National Bureau of Standards, the numerical integration of the differential equations (A.1) and (A.3) being implemented by the GEAR subroutine, described by A. C. Hindmarsh (1974). Single-length precision (approximately 8 decimal figures) was aimed at in the final values of $L_\nu(z)$; some of the intermediate calculations were carried out to double precision to achieve this. As n increases there is a steady loss of accuracy in the computed values of $\rho_n(\nu, z)$ owing to cancellation of the terms within the braces in equation (A.5). Nevertheless, the values of $|\rho_n(\nu, z)|$ given in Table 1 are believed to be correct within two or three units of the last figure given.

Remarks. (a) In addition to $L_\nu(z)$, corresponding values of $K_\nu(z)$ and the Hankel functions $H_\nu^{(1)}(z)$ and $H_\nu^{(2)}(z)$ were generated in stages (ii) and (iii) for checking purposes. These were found from the relations

$$K_\nu(z) = \left(\frac{\pi}{2z}\right)^{1/2} e^{-z} L_\nu(z),$$

$$H_\nu^{(1)}(z) = \frac{2}{\pi i} e^{-\nu\pi i/2} K_\nu(z e^{-\pi i/2}), \qquad H_\nu^{(2)}(z) = \frac{2i}{\pi} e^{\nu\pi i/2} K_\nu(z e^{\pi i/2}).$$

The results were then compared with various tables, including those of M. I. Žurina and L. N. Karmazina (1967), K. L. Zimmerman, A. S. Elder, and A. K. Depue (1978), and the National Bureau of Standards (1947, 1950). (In the case of the N.B.S. tables use was made of the identities $H_\nu^{(1)}(z) = J_\nu(z) + iY_\nu(z)$, $H_\nu^{(2)}(z) = J_\nu(z) - iY_\nu(z)$.) Agreement was satisfactory for all entries examined.

(b) Stage (i) of the algorithm is not really essential, since the initial values required in stage (ii) could all be found from (A.4) and the tables mentioned in (a) above. It is also possible to shorten drastically the integration range in stage (i) by using the asymptotic expansions of $L_\nu(z)$ and $L_\nu'(z)$ to calculate the initial values at $z = X$ in place of (A.2). However, in the interest of having adequate independent checks, as well as in constructing a program that could be used for values of ν not covered by existing tables (especially complex ν) neither course was adopted.

(c) It is not possible to circumvent stage (iii) simply by continuing the numerical integration of the differential equation (A.3) beyond $\theta = \pi$ or $-\pi$, owing to instability. In the interval $[\pi, \frac{3}{2}\pi]$ there is an increasing solution, for increasing θ, given by $w = (2z/\pi)^{1/2} e^z K_\nu(z e^{-\pi i})$ with $z = r e^{i\theta}$. A similar observation applies to the interval $[-\frac{3}{2}\pi, -\pi]$.

Acknowledgments. The computation of Tables 1 and 2 was carried out at the National Bureau of Standards by Ms. Sydney Burton under the direction of Mr. Martin Cordes. The author is pleased to acknowledge this assistance, and also several improvements that were suggested by Dr. L. Maximon of the National Bureau of Standards.

REFERENCES

W. BÜHRING (1977a), *Schrödinger equation with Yukawa potential, a differential equation with two singular points*, J. Mathematical Phys., 18, pp. 1121–1136.

——— (1977b), *Das Zusammenhangsproblem bei der Schrödinger-Gleichung mit Yukawa-Potential*, Z. Angew. Math. Mech., 57, pp. T226–T227.

N. G. DE BRUIJN (1958), *Asymptotic Methods in Analysis* (2nd ed. 1961), Wiley–Interscience, New York.

E. A. CODDINGTON AND N. LEVINSON (1955), *Theory of ordinary differential equations*, McGraw-Hill, New York.

R. B. DINGLE (1962), *Asymptotic expansion and converging factors*, Bul. Inst. Politehn. Iaşi, 8, pp. 53–60.

——— (1973), *Asymptotic Expansions: Their Derivation and Interpretation*, Academic Press, New York.

A. ERDÉLYI (1956), *Asymptotic Expansions*, Dover, New York.

A. ERDÉLYI AND M. WYMAN (1963), *The asymptotic evaluation of certain integrals*, Arch. Rational Mech. Anal., 14, pp. 217–260.

M. GOLOMB AND H. F. WEINBERGER (1959), *Optimal approximation and error bounds*, On Numerical Approximation, R. E. Langer, ed., University of Wisconsin Press, Madison, WI, pp. 117–190.

G. GREEN (1837), *On the motion of waves in a variable canal of small depth and width*, Trans. Cambridge Philos. Soc., 6, pp. 457–462.

R. D. GREGORY (1979), *A note on multiple asymptotic series*, SIAM J. Math. Anal., 11 (1980), pp. 115–118.

A. C. HINDMARSH (1974), *GEAR: Ordinary differential equation system solver*, Rep. No. UCID-30001, Rev. 3, Lawrence Livermore Laboratory, Univ. of California, Livermore, CA.

J. LIOUVILLE (1837), *Sur le développement des fonctions ou parties de fonctions en séries dont les divers termes sont assujettis à satisfaire à une même équation différentielle du second ordre contenant un paramètre variable*, J. Math. Pures Appl. [1], 2, pp. 16–35.

J. C. P. MILLER (1964), *Parabolic cylinder functions*, Handbook of Mathematical Functions, National Bureau of Standards, Appl. Math. Ser. No. 55, M. Abramowitz and I. A. Stegun, eds., U.S. Govt. Printing Office, Washington, DC, pp. 685–720.

NATIONAL BUREAU OF STANDARDS (1947), *Table of the Bessel Functions $J_0(z)$ and $J_1(z)$ for Complex Arguments* (2nd ed.), Columbia University Press, New York.

——— (1950), *Table of the Bessel Functions $Y_0(z)$ and $Y_1(z)$ for Complex Arguments*, Columbia University Press, New York.

F. W. J. OLVER (1964), *Error bounds for asymptotic expansions, with an application to cylinder functions of large argument*, Asymptotic Solutions of Differential Equations and their Applications, C. H. Wilcox, ed., pp. 163–183, Wiley, New York.

——— (1974), *Asymptotics and Special Functions*, Academic Press, New York.

R. E. O'MALLEY, JR. (1974), *Introduction to Singular Perturbations*, Academic Press, New York.

E. RIEKSTIŅŠ (1966), *On the use of neutrices for asymptotic representation of some integrals*, Latvian Math. Yearbook, pp. 5–21. (In Russian.)

H. SCHMIDT (1937), *Beiträge zu einer Theorie der allgemeinen asymptotischen Darstellungen*, Math. Ann., 113, pp. 629–656.

K. D. SHERE (1971), *Introduction to multiple asymptotic series with an application to elastic scattering*, J. Mathematical Phys., 12, pp. 78–82.

——— (1972a), *Multiple asymptotic expansions and singular problems*, SIAM J. Math. Anal., 3, pp. 263–271.

——— (1972b), *On multiple asymptotic expansions*, Ibid., 3, pp. 272–284.

G. N. WATSON (1911), *A theory of asymptotic series*, Philos. Trans. Roy. Soc. London Ser. A, 211, pp. 279–313.

——— (1944), *A Treatise on the Theory of Bessel Functions* (2nd ed.), Cambridge University Press, London and New York.

J. H. WILKINSON (1963), *Rounding Errors in Algebraic Processes*, National Physical Laboratory Notes on Appl. Sci. No. 32, H.M. Stationery Office, London.

R. WONG (1980), *Error bounds for asymptotic expansions of integrals*, to appear.

K. L. ZIMMERMAN, A. S. ELDER AND A. K. DEPUE (1978), *User's manual for the BRL subroutine to calculate Bessel functions of integral order and complex argument*, Tech. Rep. ARBRL-TR-02068, Ballistic Research Laboratory, Aberdeen Proving Ground, MD.

M. I. ŽURINA AND L. N. KARMAZINA (1967), *Tables of Modified Bessel Functions with Imaginary Index $K_{i\tau}(x)$*, Vyčisl. Centr Akad. Nauk SSSR, Moscow. (In Russian.)

Proceedings of the Royal Society of Edinburgh, **86A**, 213–234, *1980*

Whittaker functions with both parameters large: uniform approximations in terms of parabolic cylinder functions

F. W. J. Olver
University of Maryland, College Park, Maryland 20742,
and The National Bureau of Standards, Washington D.C. 20234

(MS received 28 May 1979)

Synopsis

Asymptotic approximations are derived for the Whittaker functions $W_{\kappa,\mu}(z)$, $M_{\kappa,\mu}(z)$, $W_{i\kappa,i\mu}(iz)$ and $M_{i\kappa,i\mu}(iz)$ for large positive values of the parameter μ that are uniform with respect to unrestricted values of the argument z in the open interval $(0,\infty)$, and bounded real values of the ratio κ/μ. The approximations are in terms of parabolic cylinder functions, and in most instances are accompanied by strict error bounds.

The results are derived by application of a recently-developed asymptotic theory of second-order differential equations having coalescing turning points, and an extension of the general theory of equations of this kind is also included.

1. Introduction

The purpose of this paper is to derive approximations for solutions of Whittaker's equation

$$\frac{d^2W}{dz^2}=\left(\frac{1}{4}-\frac{\kappa}{z}+\frac{\mu^2-\frac{1}{4}}{z^2}\right)W, \tag{1.01}$$

and the modified form of this equation

$$\frac{d^2W}{dz^2}=\left(-\frac{1}{4}+\frac{\kappa}{z}-\frac{\mu^2+\frac{1}{4}}{z^2}\right)W, \tag{1.02}$$

which is obtained from (1.01) on replacing κ, μ and z, by $i\kappa$, $i\mu$ and iz, respectively. For both equations, we shall suppose throughout that the parameters κ and μ, and the variable z, are real; furthermore, both μ and z are restricted to be positive. We seek asymptotic approximations to the solutions of (1.01) and (1.02), for large μ, that are uniformly valid with respect to z in the unbounded open interval $(0,\infty)$, and also uniformly valid with respect to bounded values of the ratio κ/μ. In a recent survey [**6**, §6.2], I indicated that this was one of several outstanding problems pertaining to the asymptotic behaviour of confluent hypergeometric functions. This reference should be consulted for information concerning the relationship of the present investigation to existing results.

More recently, Temme [**8**] has published some new uniform asymptotic expansions of solutions of the confluent hypergeometric equation

$$z\frac{d^2W}{dz^2}+(b-z)\frac{dW}{dz}-aW=0,$$

for large positive real values of the parameter b and real values of both z (>0) and the other parameter a. These expansions are derived from integral representations of the solutions by application of Bleistein's method (see e.g. [**3**, Ch. 9, §§9, 10]), and they are expressed in terms of parabolic cylinder functions, as are the uniform asymptotic appproximations that are derived in the present paper. Temme's results can be interpreted in terms of Whittaker functions, the parameters a and b being related to the κ and μ of (1.01) by the equations $a=\mu-\kappa+\frac{1}{2}$, $b=2\mu+1$. In this notation, Temme's expansions apply for large μ uniformly with respect to values of z that satisfy $\mu\delta \leqq z \leqq \mu\Delta$, where δ and Δ are arbitrary positive constants, and also with respect to values of κ for which $|\mu-\kappa|$ is bounded. Both conditions are significantly more restrictive than those adopted in the present investigation. Apart from the methods employed, other differences are that the present results are accompanied by explicit error bounds and they apply to (1.02) as well as (1.01). On the other hand, Temme gives full asymptotic expansions in terms of descending powers of b (or, equivalently, $\mu+\frac{1}{2}$), whereas only a single term can be constructed for the more comprehensive approximations (compare [**4**, §11]).

On taking new variables

$$x=z/\mu, \quad \lambda=\kappa/\mu, \tag{1.03}$$

equations (1.01) and (1.02) become, respectively,

$$\frac{d^2W}{dx^2}=\left(\mu^2\frac{x^2-4\lambda x+4}{4x^2}-\frac{1}{4x^2}\right)W, \tag{1.04}$$

$$\frac{d^2W}{dx^2}=\left(-\mu^2\frac{x^2-4\lambda x+4}{4x^2}-\frac{1}{4x^2}\right)W. \tag{1.05}$$

These differential equations are characterized by a regular singularity at $x=0$, an irregular singularity at $x=\infty$, and also, for large μ, turning points at $x=x_1$ and x_2 where

$$x_1=2\lambda-2(\lambda^2-1)^{\frac{1}{2}}, \quad x_2=2\lambda+2(\lambda^2-1)^{\frac{1}{2}}. \tag{1.06}$$

The nature of the turning points depends on the value of λ. First, if $\lambda>1$ then $0<x_1<x_2<\infty$; hence both turning points lie in the (transformed) interval of interest, given by $0<x<\infty$. By hypothesis, λ is bounded; hence x_1 is bounded away from the singularity at the origin and x_2 is bounded away from the singularity at infinity. Secondly, if $\lambda=1$ then the turning points coalesce: $x_1=x_2=2$. Thirdly, if $-1<\lambda<1$ then both x_1 and x_2 lie off the real axis. Lastly, if $\lambda\leqq-1$ then both x_1 and x_2 are real and negative and therefore lie outside the interval of interest; furthermore since $|\lambda|$ is bounded both points are bounded away from this interval.

Let us introduce the symbols Δ and $\hat{\Delta}$ to denote arbitrary real constants such that

$$\Delta>0, \quad 0<\hat{\Delta}<2.$$

As already indicated in the preceding paragraph, when $-1-\Delta\leqq\lambda\leqq-1+\hat{\Delta}$ the turning points x_1 and x_2 are bounded away from the interval of interest. Hence in this case uniform asymptotic approximations to the solutions of (1.04) and (1.05), for large μ, can be constructed in terms of elementary functions, the uniformity extending to the whole of the open x-interval $(0,\infty)$ as well as to the closed

λ-interval $[-1-\Delta, -1+\hat{\Delta}]$. For (1.04) these results are supplied in [**3**, pp. 260–261]. This reference treats explicitly only values of λ in the interval $[0, -1+\hat{\Delta}]$ with $1<\hat{\Delta}<2$. However, as noted in [**6**, p. 128], the results do in fact hold in the larger interval $[-1-\Delta, -1+\hat{\Delta}]$ with $0<\hat{\Delta}<2$. Similar approximations for (1.05) can be found by the same method. In view of these observations, it suffices to restrict λ to the interval $[-1+\hat{\Delta}, 1+\Delta]$ in the present investigation.

In order to arrive at the desired approximations, we shall apply the asymptotic theory of second-order differential equations with coalescing turning points, as developed in [**4**] and [**7**], and previously applied to the approximation of Legendre functions in [**5**]. Equation (1.04) is treated in §§2 and 3 in the case $1 \leqq \lambda \leqq 1+\Delta$ and in §4 in the case $-1+\hat{\Delta} \leqq \lambda \leqq 1$. Equation (1.05) is treated in both cases in §5. The principal results are collected together in the concluding section, §6.

Also included is an Appendix that supplies an extension of the general theory of [**4**] in cases when the turning points are complex conjugates. This extension is needed in §§4 and 5.

Various properties of Whittaker functions and parabolic cylinder functions (which are used as approximants) are quoted as needed. Derivations of these properties may be found in [**1**, Ch. VI; **2**; **3**, Ch. 7; **4**]. We shall adhere to the definitions and notation common to these sources, except where indicated otherwise.

2. Real parameters and real turning points: preliminary transformations

Throughout this section we suppose that $1 \leqq \lambda < \infty$. From [**4**, §2.2], with $u=\mu$, it is seen that the appropriate Liouville transformation is given by

$$W=\left(\frac{dx}{d\zeta}\right)^{\frac{1}{2}} w, \quad \left(\frac{d\zeta}{dx}\right)^2 = \frac{x^2-4\lambda x+4}{4x^2(\zeta^2-\alpha^2)}, \tag{2.01}$$

where α is the non-negative number defined by

$$2\int_{-\alpha}^{\alpha} (\alpha^2-\zeta^2)^{\frac{1}{2}}\, d\zeta = \int_{x_1}^{x_2} \frac{(-x^2+4\lambda x-4)^{\frac{1}{2}}}{x}\, dx, \tag{2.02}$$

x_1 and x_2 being given by (1.06). Evaluation of the two integrals yields

$$\alpha = \{2(\lambda-1)\}^{\frac{1}{2}}. \tag{2.03}$$

The relation between ζ and x is one-to-one, with the points x_1 and x_2 corresponding respectively to $-\alpha$ and α. On taking the positive square root in the second of (2.01) and integrating, we obtain

$$2\int_{\alpha}^{\zeta} (\tau^2-\alpha^2)^{\frac{1}{2}}\, d\tau = \int_{x_2}^{x} \frac{(t^2-4\lambda t+4)^{\frac{1}{2}}}{t}\, dt, \qquad x_2 \leqq x < \infty; \tag{2.04}$$

$$2\int_{-\alpha}^{\zeta} (\alpha^2-\tau^2)^{\frac{1}{2}}\, d\tau = \int_{x_1}^{x} \frac{(-t^2+4\lambda t-4)^{\frac{1}{2}}}{t}\, dt, \quad x_1 \leqq x \leqq x_2; \tag{2.05}$$

$$2\int_{\zeta}^{-\alpha} (\tau^2-\alpha^2)^{\frac{1}{2}}\, d\tau = \int_{x}^{x_1} \frac{(t^2-4\lambda t+4)^{\frac{1}{2}}}{t}\, dt, \quad 0 < x \leqq x_1. \tag{2.06}$$

From these relations it is evident that ζ is an increasing function of x, with $\zeta = -\infty$ and $+\infty$ corresponding to $x = 0$ and ∞, respectively.

Assume first that $\lambda > 1$, so that $x_1 \neq x_2$ and $\alpha > 0$, and write

$$X \equiv |x^2 - 4\lambda x + 4|^{\frac{1}{2}}. \tag{2.07}$$

On evaluating the integrals in (2.04), (2.05) and (2.06) we find that

$$\zeta(\zeta^2-\alpha^2)^{\frac{1}{2}} - \alpha^2 \cosh^{-1}\left(\frac{\zeta}{\alpha}\right) = X - 2\lambda \ln\left\{\frac{X + x - 2\lambda}{2(\lambda^2-1)^{\frac{1}{2}}}\right\} - 2\ln\left\{\frac{\lambda x - 2 - X}{(\lambda^2-1)^{\frac{1}{2}} x}\right\},$$
$$\alpha \leqq \zeta < \infty, \quad x_2 \leqq x < \infty; \tag{2.08}$$

$$\alpha^2 \sin^{-1}\left(\frac{\zeta}{\alpha}\right) + \zeta(\alpha^2-\zeta^2)^{\frac{1}{2}} = X + 2\lambda \tan^{-1}\left(\frac{x - 2\lambda}{X}\right) - 2\tan^{-1}\left(\frac{\lambda x - 2}{X}\right),$$
$$-\alpha \leqq \zeta \leqq \alpha, \quad x_1 \leqq x \leqq x_2; \tag{2.09}$$

$$-\zeta(\zeta^2-\alpha^2)^{\frac{1}{2}} - \alpha^2 \cosh^{-1}\left(-\frac{\zeta}{\alpha}\right) = -X + 2\lambda \ln\left\{\frac{2\lambda - x - X}{2(\lambda^2-1)^{\frac{1}{2}}}\right\} + 2\ln\left\{\frac{X + 2 - \lambda x}{(\lambda^2-1)^{\frac{1}{2}} x}\right\},$$
$$-\infty < \zeta \leqq -\alpha, \quad 0 < x \leqq x_1. \tag{2.10}$$

Alternatively, assume that $\lambda = 1$, so that $x_1 = x_2 = 2$ and $\alpha = 0$. Then we find that

$$\zeta^2 = x - 2 - 2\ln(\tfrac{1}{2}x), \quad -\infty < \zeta < \infty, \quad 0 < x < \infty, \tag{2.11}$$

positive values of ζ corresponding to $x \in (2, \infty)$ and negative values of ζ corresponding to $x \in (0, 2)$.

Whether or not $\lambda = 1$, the differential equation (1.04) transforms into

$$d^2w/d\zeta^2 = \{\mu^2(\zeta^2 - \alpha^2) + \psi(\alpha^2, \zeta)\}w, \tag{2.12}$$

in which

$$\psi(\alpha^2, \zeta) = -\frac{\dot{x}^2}{4x^2} + \dot{x}^{\frac{1}{2}} \frac{d^2}{d\zeta^2}(\dot{x}^{-\frac{1}{2}}), \tag{2.13}$$

dots signifying differentiations with respect to ζ; compare [**4**], (2.9) and (2.10). On carrying out the differentiations by means of the second of (2.01), we arrive at the explicit formula

$$\psi(\alpha^2, \zeta) = \frac{3\zeta^2 + 2\alpha^2}{4(\zeta^2-\alpha^2)^2} - \{x^3 + 4(\lambda^2-4)x + 16\lambda\} \frac{(\zeta^2-\alpha^2)x}{(x^2 - 4\lambda x + 4)^3}, \tag{2.14}$$

the right-hand side being replaced by its limiting form when $\zeta = \pm\alpha$. Lemma I of [**4**] establishes that $\psi(\alpha^2, \zeta)$ is a continuous function of α and ζ in the region given by $\alpha \in [0, \sqrt{2}]$ and $\zeta \in (-\infty, \infty)$. The restriction $\alpha \leqq \sqrt{2}$ (or equivalently $\lambda \leqq 2$) arises from Condition (iv) of the cited lemma. However, by use of (2.13) and the second of (2.01) it is not difficult to see that the region of continuity is extendible to $\alpha \in [0, \infty)$ and $\zeta \in (-\infty, \infty)$.

In identifying the solutions of equation (1.04) in terms of those of (2.12), we shall need to know the asymptotic behaviour of x, regarded as a function of ζ, as

$\zeta \to \pm\infty$, and also the behaviour of the function $\psi(\alpha^2, \zeta)$ in the same circumstances. Suppose first that $\zeta \to +\infty$, so that $x \to +\infty$. Then from (2.08) we derive

$$\zeta^2 - \tfrac{1}{2}\alpha^2 - \alpha^2 \ln\left(\frac{2\zeta}{\alpha}\right) + O\left(\frac{1}{\zeta^2}\right) = x - 2\lambda - 2\lambda \ln\left\{\frac{x}{(\lambda^2-1)^{\frac{1}{2}}}\right\} - \ln\left(\frac{\lambda-1}{\lambda+1}\right) + O\left(\frac{1}{x}\right).$$

By reversion and use of (2.03) to express λ in terms of α, we obtain

$$x = \zeta^2 + (4+\alpha^2)\ln\zeta - c(\alpha^2) + O(\zeta^{-2}\ln\zeta), \quad \zeta \to +\infty, \tag{2.15}$$

where

$$c(\alpha^2) = (2+\tfrac{1}{2}\alpha^2)\{\ln(1+\tfrac{1}{4}\alpha^2) - 1\} + (2+\alpha^2)\ln 2; \tag{2.16}$$

compare [**3**, p. 13]. Moreover, by expansion of the integrals in (2.04) we perceive that (2.15) is uniform with respect to α in the closed interval $[0, \mathrm{A}]$, where A denotes an arbitrary positive constant. From (2.03) it is seen that this corresponds to $\lambda \in [1, 1+\Delta]$ with $\Delta = \frac{1}{2}\mathrm{A}^2$. Next, substituting in (2.14) by means of (2.15) we find that

$$\psi(\alpha^2, \zeta) \sim -\frac{1}{4\zeta^2}, \quad \zeta \to +\infty, \tag{2.17}$$

uniformly with respect to $\alpha \in [0, \mathrm{A}]$.

Alternatively, suppose that $\zeta \to -\infty$, so that $x \to 0+$. From (2.10) we obtain

$$\zeta^2 - \tfrac{1}{2}\alpha^2 - \alpha^2 \ln\left(-\frac{2\zeta}{\alpha}\right) + O\left(\frac{1}{\zeta^2}\right) = -2 + 2\ln\left\{\frac{4}{(\lambda^2-1)^{\frac{1}{2}}x}\right\} + \lambda\ln\left(\frac{\lambda-1}{\lambda+1}\right) + O(x),$$

and hence

$$x \sim e^{-d(\alpha^2)}\,|\zeta|^{\frac{1}{2}\alpha^2} e^{-\frac{1}{2}\zeta^2}, \quad \zeta \to -\infty, \tag{2.18}$$

where

$$d(\alpha^2) = (1+\tfrac{1}{4}\alpha^2)\ln(1+\tfrac{1}{4}\alpha^2) - \ln 2 + 1 - \tfrac{1}{4}\alpha^2, \tag{2.19}$$

this result being uniform with respect to $\alpha \in [0, \mathrm{A}]$. Substitution in (2.14) then yields

$$\psi(\alpha^2, \zeta) \sim \frac{3}{4\zeta^2}, \quad \zeta \to -\infty, \tag{2.20}$$

again uniformly with respect to $\alpha \in [0, \mathrm{A}]$.

3. Real parameters and real turning points: identification of solutions

On applying [**4**, §6, Theorem I] to equation (2.12), with $u = \mu$ and $\zeta_2 = +\infty$, we obtain the following solutions

$$w_1(\mu^2, \alpha^2, \zeta) = U(-\tfrac{1}{2}\mu\alpha^2, \zeta\sqrt{2\mu}) + \varepsilon_1(\mu^2, \alpha^2, \zeta), \tag{3.01}$$

$$\bar{w}_1(\mu^2, \alpha^2, \zeta) = \bar{U}(-\tfrac{1}{2}\mu\alpha^2, \zeta\sqrt{2\mu}) + \bar{\varepsilon}_1(\mu^2, \alpha^2, \zeta), \tag{3.02}$$

where U and $\bar{U}$ denote the parabolic cylinder functions, and the error terms are bounded by

$$|\varepsilon_1(\mu^2,\alpha^2,\zeta)|\leqq \mathsf{E}^{-1}(-\tfrac{1}{2}\mu\alpha^2,\zeta\sqrt{2\mu})\mathsf{M}(-\tfrac{1}{2}\mu\alpha^2,\zeta\sqrt{2\mu})\times$$
$$\times\left[\exp\left\{\frac{1}{2}\left(\frac{\pi}{\mu}\right)^{\frac{1}{2}} l_1(-\tfrac{1}{2}\mu\alpha^2)\mathcal{V}_{\zeta,\infty}\{F(\mu^2,\alpha^2,\zeta)\}\right\}-1\right], \quad (3.03)$$

$$|\bar{\varepsilon}_1(\mu^2,\alpha^2,\zeta)|\leqq \mathsf{E}(-\tfrac{1}{2}\mu\alpha^2,\zeta\sqrt{2\mu})\mathsf{M}(-\tfrac{1}{2}\mu\alpha^2,\zeta\sqrt{2\mu})\times$$
$$\times\left[\exp\left\{\frac{1}{2}\left(\frac{\pi}{\mu}\right)^{\frac{1}{2}} l_1(-\tfrac{1}{2}\mu\alpha^2)\mathcal{V}_{0,\zeta}\{F(\mu^2,\alpha^2,\zeta)\}\right\}-1\right], \quad (3.04)$$

both inequalities being valid when $\alpha\in[0,\infty)$ and $\zeta\in[0,\infty)$. In these results, the auxiliary functions E, M and l_1 are defined as in [**4**, §§5.8 and 6.1], and the error-control function $F(\mu^2,\alpha^2,\zeta)$ is given by

$$F(\mu^2,\alpha^2,\zeta)=\int\frac{\psi(\alpha^2,\zeta)}{\Omega(\zeta\sqrt{2\mu})}\,d\zeta, \quad (3.05)$$

with an appropriate choice of balancing function Ω; again see [**4**, §6.1]. The next step is to identify $w_1(\mu^2,\alpha^2,\zeta)$ and $\bar{w}_1(\mu^2,\alpha^2,\zeta)$ in terms of standard solutions of (1.01).

As $\zeta\to+\infty$, $w_1(\mu^2,\alpha^2,\zeta)$ is recessive and $\bar{w}_1(\mu^2,\alpha^2,\zeta)$ is dominant. Hence $w_1(\mu^2,\alpha^2,\zeta)$ is a multiple of the solution of (1.01) that is recessive as $z\to+\infty$, that is, the Whittaker function $W_{\kappa,\mu}(z)$. Using (1.03) and (2.01) we perceive that

$$Sw_1(\mu^2,\alpha^2,\zeta)=\left(\frac{x^2-4\lambda x+4}{\zeta^2-\alpha^2}\right)^{\frac{1}{4}}x^{-\frac{1}{2}}W_{\kappa,\mu}(\mu x), \quad (3.06)$$

where the coefficient S is independent of x. To determine S we evaluate the limiting value of the ratio of the two sides of this equation as $\zeta\to+\infty$, with κ and μ held fixed. We require the asymptotic formula

$$W_{\kappa,\mu}(z)\sim e^{-\frac{1}{2}z}z^{\kappa},\quad z\to+\infty.$$

On referring to (1.03), (2.03) and (2.15), we find that the right-hand side of (3.06) is asymptotic to

$$e^{\frac{1}{2}\mu c(\alpha^2)}\mu^{\mu(1+\frac{1}{2}\alpha^2)}\zeta^{\frac{1}{2}\mu\alpha^2-\frac{1}{2}}e^{-\frac{1}{2}\mu\zeta^2}. \quad (3.07)$$

On the other hand, for the left-hand side we have

$$U(-\tfrac{1}{2}\mu\alpha^2,\zeta\sqrt{2\mu})\sim(\zeta\sqrt{2\mu})^{\frac{1}{2}\mu\alpha^2-\frac{1}{2}}e^{-\frac{1}{2}\mu\zeta^2},\quad \zeta\to+\infty, \quad (3.08)$$

and from the bound (3.03) and the properties of the auxiliary functions E and M given in [**4**, §5.8], it is seen that the ratio of $\varepsilon_1(\mu^2,\alpha^2,\zeta)$ to $U(-\frac{1}{2}\mu\alpha^2,\zeta\sqrt{2\mu})$ vanishes as $\zeta\to+\infty$. Hence on dividing (3.07) by (3.08) we deduce that

$$S=e^{\frac{1}{2}\mu c(\alpha^2)}2^{\frac{1}{4}-\frac{1}{4}\mu\alpha^2}\mu^{\frac{1}{4}\mu\alpha^2+\mu+\frac{1}{4}},$$

exactly. Substituting for $c(\alpha^2)$ by means of (2.16) we find that this expression may be reduced to

$$S=(2\mu)^{\frac{1}{4}}\{2\mu(1+\tfrac{1}{4}\alpha^2)/e\}^{\mu(1+\frac{1}{4}\alpha^2)}. \quad (3.09)$$

And on substituting this result in (3.06), we derive the first of the desired representations, given by

$$W_{\kappa,\mu}(\mu x) = (2\mu)^{\frac{1}{4}}\{\mu(2+\tfrac{1}{2}\alpha^2)/e\}^{\mu(1+\frac{1}{4}\alpha^2)}\times$$
$$\times\left(\frac{\zeta^2-\alpha^2}{x^2-4\lambda x+4}\right)^{\frac{1}{4}} x^{\frac{1}{2}}\{U(-\tfrac{1}{2}\mu\alpha^2, \zeta\sqrt{2\mu})+\varepsilon_1(\mu^2, \alpha^2, \zeta)\}, \quad (3.10)$$

valid when $\alpha\in[0,\infty)$ and $\zeta\in[0,\infty)$. This result is restated in terms of the original parameters in §6, as are all subsequent identifications.

An asymptotic estimate for $\varepsilon_1(\mu^2, \alpha^2, \zeta)$ for large μ is immediately available from the results of [**4**, §6.3]. As a consequence of (2.17) we see that $|\psi(\alpha^2, \zeta)|\,\zeta^{-\frac{1}{3}}$ is integrable at $\zeta=+\infty$, uniformly with respect to $\alpha\in[0, \mathrm{A}]$, where A again denotes an arbitrary positive constant. Hence we may prescribe the balancing function $\Omega(t)$ to be $|t|^{\frac{1}{3}}$, and so obtain

$$\varepsilon_1(\mu^2, \alpha^2, \zeta) = \mathsf{E}^{-1}(-\tfrac{1}{2}\mu\alpha^2, \zeta\sqrt{2\mu})\mathsf{M}(-\tfrac{1}{2}\mu\alpha^2, \zeta\sqrt{2\mu})O(\mu^{-\frac{2}{3}}), \quad \mu\to\infty, \quad (3.11)$$

uniformly with respect to $\alpha\in[0, \mathrm{A}]$ and $\zeta\in[0,\infty)$.

The results (3.10) and (3.11) apply only when $\zeta\geqq 0$. In order to treat negative values of ζ, we first apply [**4**, Theorem I] to equation (2.12) with ζ replaced throughout by $-\zeta$ to obtain the following solutions:

$$w_2(\mu^2, \alpha^2, \zeta) = U(-\tfrac{1}{2}\mu\alpha^2, -\zeta\sqrt{2\mu})+\varepsilon_2(\mu^2, \alpha^2, \zeta), \quad (3.12)$$
$$\bar{w}_2(\mu^2, \alpha^2, \zeta) = \bar{U}(-\tfrac{1}{2}\mu\alpha^2, -\zeta\sqrt{2\mu})+\bar{\varepsilon}_2(\mu^2, \alpha^2, \zeta), \quad (3.13)$$

where

$$|\varepsilon_2(\mu^2, \alpha^2, \zeta)| \leqq \mathsf{E}^{-1}(-\tfrac{1}{2}\mu\alpha^2, -\zeta\sqrt{2\mu})\mathsf{M}(-\tfrac{1}{2}\mu\alpha^2, -\zeta\sqrt{2\mu})\times$$
$$\times\left[\exp\left\{\frac{1}{2}\left(\frac{\pi}{\mu}\right)^{\frac{1}{2}} l_1(-\tfrac{1}{2}\mu\alpha^2)\mathcal{V}_{-\infty,\zeta}\{F(\mu^2, \alpha^2, \zeta)\}\right\}-1\right], \quad (3.14)$$

$$|\bar{\varepsilon}_2(\mu^2, \alpha^2, \zeta)| \leqq \mathsf{E}(-\tfrac{1}{2}\mu\alpha^2, -\zeta\sqrt{2\mu})\mathsf{M}(-\tfrac{1}{2}\mu\alpha^2, -\zeta\sqrt{2\mu})\times$$
$$\times\left[\exp\left\{\frac{1}{2}\left(\frac{\pi}{\mu}\right)^{\frac{1}{2}} l_1(-\tfrac{1}{2}\mu\alpha^2)\mathcal{V}_{\zeta,0}\{F(\mu^2, \alpha^2, \zeta)\}\right\}-1\right], \quad (3.15)$$

valid when $\alpha\in[0,\infty)$ and $\zeta\in(-\infty, 0]$, with $F(\mu^2, \alpha^2, \zeta)$ again defined by (3.05). Furthermore, for large μ we have

$$\varepsilon_2(\mu^2, \alpha^2, \zeta) = \mathsf{E}^{-1}(-\tfrac{1}{2}\mu\alpha^2, -\zeta\sqrt{2\mu})\mathsf{M}(-\tfrac{1}{2}\mu\alpha^2, -\zeta\sqrt{2\mu})O(\mu^{-\frac{2}{3}}), \quad (3.16)$$
$$\bar{\varepsilon}_2(\mu^2, \alpha^2, \zeta) = \mathsf{E}(-\tfrac{1}{2}\mu\alpha^2, -\zeta\sqrt{2\mu})\mathsf{M}(-\tfrac{1}{2}\mu\alpha^2, -\zeta\sqrt{2\mu})O(\mu^{-\frac{2}{3}}), \quad (3.17)$$

uniformly with respect to $\alpha\in[0, \mathrm{A}]$ and $\zeta\in(-\infty, 0]$; compare (3.11). We now apply the connection formula (6.23) of [**4**], with the estimates for the error terms sharpened from $O(\mu^{-\frac{2}{3}}\ln\mu)$ to $O(\mu^{-\frac{2}{3}})$, again as a consequence of the uniform integrability of $|\psi(\alpha^2, \zeta)\zeta^{-\frac{1}{3}}|$ at $\zeta=\pm\infty$. The final result is given by

$$W_{\kappa,\mu}(\mu x) = (2\mu)^{\frac{1}{4}}\{\mu(2+\tfrac{1}{2}\alpha^2)/e\}^{\mu(1+\frac{1}{4}\alpha^2)}\left(\frac{\zeta^2-\alpha^2}{x^2-4\lambda x+4}\right)^{\frac{1}{4}} x^{\frac{1}{2}}\times$$
$$\times[\{\sin(\tfrac{1}{2}\pi\mu\alpha^2)+O(\mu^{-\frac{2}{3}})\}w_2(\mu^2, \alpha^2, \zeta)+$$
$$+\{\cos(\tfrac{1}{2}\pi\mu\alpha^2)+O(\mu^{-\frac{2}{3}})\}\bar{w}_2(\mu^2, \alpha^2, \zeta)], \quad (3.18)$$

the O-terms here being independent of ζ and uniform with respect to $\alpha\in[0, \mathrm{A}]$.

As a partial check on the last approximation, we compare its asymptotic form as $\zeta \to -\infty$ with the known behaviour of the Whittaker function as its argument vanishes. For simplicity, we consider only cases in which 2μ is not an integer. We then have

$$W_{\kappa,\mu}(z) = \frac{\Gamma(-2\mu)}{\Gamma(\frac{1}{2}-\mu-\kappa)} z^{\mu+\frac{1}{2}}\{1+O(z)\} + \frac{\Gamma(2\mu)}{\Gamma(\frac{1}{2}+\mu-\kappa)} z^{-\mu+\frac{1}{2}}\{1+O(z)\}, \quad z \to 0+,$$

or, in terms of the new variables,

$$W_{\kappa,\mu}(\mu x) = \frac{\mu^{\mu+\frac{1}{2}}\Gamma(-2\mu)}{\Gamma(\frac{1}{2}-\frac{1}{2}\mu\alpha^2-2\mu)} x^{\mu+\frac{1}{2}}\{1+O(x)\} + \\ + \frac{\mu^{-\mu+\frac{1}{2}}\Gamma(2\mu)}{\Gamma(\frac{1}{2}-\frac{1}{2}\mu\alpha^2)} x^{-\mu+\frac{1}{2}}\{1+O(x)\}, \quad x \to 0+. \tag{3.19}$$

Suppose first that $\frac{1}{2}\mu\alpha^2-\frac{1}{2}$ is not zero or a positive integer. Then the term involving $x^{-\mu+\frac{1}{2}}$ dominates that involving $x^{\mu+\frac{1}{2}}$, and we have

$$\lim_{x\to 0}\{x^{\mu-\frac{1}{2}}W_{\kappa,\mu}(\mu x)\} = \frac{\mu^{-\mu+\frac{1}{2}}\Gamma(2\mu)}{\Gamma(\frac{1}{2}-\frac{1}{2}\mu\alpha^2)},$$

or, on using the reflection formula for the Gamma function,

$$\lim_{x\to 0}\{x^{\mu-\frac{1}{2}}W_{\kappa,\mu}(\mu x)\} = \pi^{-1}\mu^{-\mu+\frac{1}{2}}\Gamma(2\mu)\Gamma(\tfrac{1}{2}+\tfrac{1}{2}\mu\alpha^2)\cos(\tfrac{1}{2}\pi\mu\alpha^2). \tag{3.20}$$

On the right-hand side of (3.18) the contribution from $\bar{w}_2(\mu^2, \alpha^2, \zeta)$ dominates that from $w_2(\mu^2, \alpha^2, \zeta)$, since $\bar{U}(-\frac{1}{2}\mu\alpha^2, -\zeta\sqrt{2\mu})/U(-\frac{1}{2}\mu\alpha^2, -\zeta\sqrt{2\mu})$ tends to infinity as $\zeta \to -\infty$ in the present circumstances. Therefore as $x \to 0$ the limiting form of the product of $x^{\mu-\frac{1}{2}}$ and the right member of (3.18) is given by

$$(\tfrac{1}{2}\mu)^{\frac{1}{4}}\{\mu(2+\tfrac{1}{2}\alpha^2)/e\}^{\mu(1+\frac{1}{4}\alpha^2)}\{\cos(\tfrac{1}{2}\pi\mu\alpha^2)+O(\mu^{-\frac{2}{3}})\}\times \lim_{\zeta\to-\infty}\{x^{\mu}\,|\zeta|^{\frac{1}{2}}\bar{w}_2(\mu^2,\alpha^2,\zeta)\}.$$

On using the asymptotic forms of the functions $\bar{U}$, E and M for large positive argument that are available from [**4**, §§5.2 and 5.8], and also the relations (2.18), (3.13) and (3.17), we find that the last expression reduces to

$$\pi^{-\frac{1}{2}}\{\mu(2+\tfrac{1}{2}\alpha^2)/e\}^{\mu(1+\frac{1}{4}\alpha^2)}(2\mu)^{-\frac{1}{4}\mu\alpha^2}\Gamma(\tfrac{1}{2}+\tfrac{1}{2}\mu\alpha^2)e^{-\mu d(\alpha^2)}\{\cos(\tfrac{1}{2}\pi\mu\alpha^2)+O(\mu^{-\frac{2}{3}})\},$$

and hence, by substitution of (2.19), to

$$\pi^{-\frac{1}{2}}(4\mu/e^2)^{\mu}\Gamma(\tfrac{1}{2}+\tfrac{1}{2}\mu\alpha^2)\{\cos(\tfrac{1}{2}\pi\mu\alpha^2)+O(\mu^{-\frac{2}{3}})\}.$$

Then by use of Stirling's formula for $\Gamma(2\mu)$ we perceive that this agrees with (3.20), within the tolerance of the error term.

A similar verification may be made in the case in which equation (2.12) has a non-trivial solution that is recessive at both $\zeta = \pm\infty$. On the right-hand side of (3.18) the coefficient of $\bar{w}_2(\mu^2, \alpha^2, \zeta)$ has to vanish. This yields the condition

$$\tfrac{1}{2}\mu\alpha^2-\tfrac{1}{2} = p + O(\mu^{-\frac{2}{3}}), \tag{3.21}$$

where p is an arbitrary non-negative integer. This is consistent with the known condition that $\frac{1}{2}\mu\alpha^2-\frac{1}{2}$ has to be exactly a non-negative integer in order that

$W_{\kappa,\mu}(\mu x)$ be recessive as $x \to 0$; compare (3.19). Furthermore, in these circumstances the product of $x^{-\mu-\frac{1}{2}}$ and the right member of (3.18) assumes the limiting form

$$(\tfrac{1}{2}\mu)^{\frac{1}{4}}\{\mu(2+\tfrac{1}{2}\alpha^2)/e\}^{\mu(1+\frac{1}{4}\alpha^2)}\{\sin(\tfrac{1}{2}\pi\mu\alpha^2)+O(\mu^{-\frac{2}{3}})\}\times \lim_{\zeta\to-\infty}\{x^{-\mu}\,|\zeta|^{\frac{1}{2}}w_2(\mu^2,\alpha^2,\zeta)\}.$$

Again, using (3.12) and (3.16) together with the asymptotic forms of the functions U, E^{-1} and M and the relations (2.18) and (2.19), we see that this limit becomes

$$2^{\frac{1}{2}\mu\alpha^2-\frac{1}{2}}e^{-\frac{1}{2}\mu\alpha^2}(1+\tfrac{1}{4}\alpha^2)^{\mu(2+\frac{1}{2}\alpha^2)}\mu^{\mu(1+\frac{1}{2}\alpha^2)}\{\sin(\tfrac{1}{2}\pi\mu\alpha^2)+O(\mu^{-\frac{2}{3}})\}.$$

Then substituting for α^2 by means of (3.21), and regarding p as fixed, we find that the limit reduces to

$$(-)^p 2^p \mu^{\mu+p+\frac{1}{2}}\{1+O(\mu^{-\frac{2}{3}}\ln\mu)\}. \tag{3.22}$$

This is to be compared with the result

$$\lim_{x\to 0}\{x^{-\mu-\frac{1}{2}}W_{\kappa,\mu}(\mu x)\} = \mu^{\mu+\frac{1}{2}}\Gamma(-2\mu)/\Gamma(-p-2\mu),$$

obtained from (3.19), with the condition $\frac{1}{2}\mu\alpha^2-\frac{1}{2}=p$. Thus for large μ and fixed p we have

$$\begin{aligned}\lim_{x\to 0}\{x^{-\mu-\frac{1}{2}}W_{\kappa,\mu}(\mu x)\} &= (-)^p(2\mu+1)(2\mu+2)\dots(2\mu+p)\mu^{\mu+\frac{1}{2}}\\ &= (-)^p(2\mu)^p\mu^{\mu+\frac{1}{2}}\{1+O(\mu^{-1})\}.\end{aligned}$$

This agrees with (3.22), apart from the estimates for the error term.

Having identified and checked one standard solution of the differential equation (1.04) in terms of an asymptotic solution of (2.12), we now consider a second standard solution of (1.04). We select the Whittaker function $M_{\kappa,\mu}(\mu x)$ for this purpose, since it is recessive as $x \to 0$ for all positive values of μ. Because $x=0$ corresponds to $\zeta=-\infty$, $M_{\kappa,\mu}(\mu x)$ must be a multiple of the solution $w_2(\mu^2,\alpha^2,\zeta)$ given by (3.12), (3.14) and (3.16). Thus the desired identification has the form

$$Tw_2(\mu^2,\alpha^2,\zeta) = \left(\frac{x^2-4\lambda x+4}{\zeta^2-\alpha^2}\right)^{\frac{1}{4}}x^{-\frac{1}{2}}M_{\kappa,\mu}(\mu x), \tag{3.23}$$

where the coefficient T is independent of x; compare (3.06). To determine T we evaluate the limiting value of the ratio of the two sides of this equation as $\zeta\to-\infty$, with κ and μ held fixed, using the asymptotic formula

$$M_{\kappa,\mu}(z) \sim z^{\mu+\frac{1}{2}}, \quad z\to 0+,$$

which is valid for all positive values of μ. In this way we arrive at the formula

$$T = (2\mu)^{\frac{3}{4}}(2\mu/e)^{\mu(1-\frac{1}{4}\alpha^2)}(1+\tfrac{1}{4}\alpha^2)^{-\mu(1+\frac{1}{4}\alpha^2)}; \tag{3.24}$$

compare the derivation of (3.09). On substituting in (3.23) by means of this expression and (3.12), we obtain the second required identification in the form

$$\begin{aligned}M_{\kappa,\mu}(\mu x) = {} & (2\mu)^{\frac{3}{4}}(2\mu/e)^{\mu(1-\frac{1}{4}\alpha^2)}(1+\tfrac{1}{4}\alpha^2)^{-\mu(1+\frac{1}{4}\alpha^2)}\times\\ & \times\left(\frac{\zeta^2-\alpha^2}{x^2-4\lambda x+4}\right)^{\frac{1}{4}}x^{\frac{1}{2}}\{U(-\tfrac{1}{2}\mu\alpha^2,-\zeta\sqrt{2\mu})+\varepsilon_2(\mu^2,\alpha^2,\zeta)\},\end{aligned} \tag{3.25}$$

valid when $\alpha\in[0,\infty)$ and $\zeta\in(-\infty,0]$.

For positive values of ζ we again apply the connection formula of [**4**, §6.4]. In this way we find that

$$M_{\kappa,\mu}(\mu x)=(2\mu)^{\frac{3}{4}}(2\mu/e)^{\mu(1-\frac{1}{4}\alpha^2)}(1+\tfrac{1}{4}\alpha^2)^{-\mu(1+\frac{1}{4}\alpha^2)}\left(\frac{\zeta^2-\alpha^2}{x^2-4\lambda x+4}\right)^{\frac{1}{4}}x^{\frac{1}{2}}\times$$
$$\times[\{\sin(\tfrac{1}{2}\pi\mu\alpha^2)+O(\mu^{-\frac{2}{3}})\}w_1(\mu^2,\alpha^2,\zeta)+$$
$$+\{\cos(\tfrac{1}{2}\pi\mu\alpha^2)+O(\mu^{-\frac{2}{3}})\}\bar{w}_1(\mu^2,\alpha^2,\zeta)],\quad(3.26)$$

where $w_1(\mu^2, \alpha^2, \zeta)$ and $\bar{w}_1(\mu^2, \alpha^2, \zeta)$ are the solutions of (2.12) that are given by (3.01) and (3.02). The O-terms in (3.26) are independent of ζ and uniform with respect to $\alpha \in [0, A]$.

The last result may be checked by letting $\zeta \to +\infty$ and comparing the result with the known approximation

$$M_{\kappa,\mu}(z)=\frac{\Gamma(2\mu+1)}{\Gamma(\mu+\kappa+\frac{1}{2})}e^{(\mu-\kappa+\frac{1}{2})\pi i}z^{\kappa}e^{-\frac{1}{2}z}\{1+O(z^{-1})\}+$$
$$+\frac{\Gamma(2\mu+1)}{\Gamma(\mu-\kappa+\frac{1}{2})}z^{-\kappa}e^{\frac{1}{2}z}\{1+O(z^{-1})\},\quad z\to+\infty.$$

Again it is found that there is agreement within the tolerances of the error terms, both in the case in which $M_{\kappa,\mu}(z)$ is dominant as $z \to \infty$, and also in the case in which $M_{\kappa,\mu}(z)$ is recessive as $z \to \infty$. This verification resembles that supplied above for $W_{\kappa,\mu}(z)$ in the case $z \to 0$, and details are omitted.

4. Real parameters and imaginary turning points

In this section we consider equation (1.04) in the case $-1 < \lambda \leq 1$. The turning points x_1 and x_2 defined by (1.06) are now complex conjugates, with non-zero imaginary parts, except in the case $\lambda = 1$ when they coalesce at $x = 2$.

The appropriate Liouville transformation is given by

$$W=\left(\frac{dx}{d\zeta}\right)^{\frac{1}{2}}w,\quad\left(\frac{d\zeta}{dx}\right)^2=\frac{x^2-4\lambda x+4}{4x^2(\zeta^2+\alpha^2)},\quad(4.01)$$

where α is a non-negative real number to be determined shortly. Taking the positive square root in the second of these equations and integrating, we obtain

$$2\int(\zeta^2+\alpha^2)^{\frac{1}{2}}\,d\zeta=\int\frac{(x^2-4\lambda x+4)^{\frac{1}{2}}}{x}\,dx.\quad(4.02)$$

Suppose first that $\alpha \neq 0$ and $\lambda \neq 1$. Then an indefinite integral of the left member of (4.02) is given by

$$2\int(\zeta^2+\alpha^2)^{\frac{1}{2}}\,d\zeta=\zeta(\zeta^2+\alpha^2)^{\frac{1}{2}}+\alpha^2\ln\{\zeta+(\zeta^2+\alpha^2)^{\frac{1}{2}}\}.\quad(4.03)$$

For the right member we have

$$\int\frac{(x^2-4\lambda x+4)^{\frac{1}{2}}}{x}\,dx=X-2\lambda\ln(X+x-2\lambda)-2\ln\left(\frac{X-\lambda x+2}{x}\right),\quad(4.04)$$

where

$$X = (x^2 - 4\lambda x + 4)^{\frac{1}{2}}; \tag{4.05}$$

compare (2.07). (We observe that because $\lambda \in (-1, 1)$ and $x \in (0, \infty)$, the value of X exceeds both $|2\lambda - x|$ and $|\lambda x - 2|$; in consequence the right member of (4.04) is always real.) In order to apply the theory of **[4]**, we need to choose the arbitrary constants of integration in (4.02) in such a way that when the two sides are continued analytically into the complex ζ and x planes, the point $\zeta = i\alpha$ corresponds to $x = x_2$, and the point $\zeta = -i\alpha$ corresponds to $x = x_1$. These conditions are satisfiable by appropriate choice of α and integration constants, as follows.

Let us start at $\zeta = 0$ and proceed along the imaginary axis to $\zeta = \pm i\alpha$. Adhering to continuous branches of the square root and logarithm, we find that the right member of (4.03) tends to

$$\alpha^2(\ln \alpha \pm \tfrac{1}{2}\pi i), \tag{4.06}$$

the upper sign corresponding to $i\alpha$ and the lower sign to $-i\alpha$. Next, if we proceed in the x-plane along a line parallel to the imaginary axis from 2λ to x_2 or x_1, and again adhere to continuous branches of all multi-valued functions, then we find that the right member of (4.04) tends to

$$-\lambda\{2 \ln 2 + \ln(1-\lambda^2) \pm \pi i\} - \ln(1-\lambda^2) \pm \pi i, \tag{4.07}$$

upper signs corresponding to x_2 and lower signs corresponding to x_1. The imaginary parts in (4.06) and (4.07) agree if we take

$$\alpha = \{2(1-\lambda)\}^{\frac{1}{2}}; \tag{4.08}$$

compare (2.03). And on subtracting the real parts from the right members of (4.03) and (4.04), respectively, we arrive at the desired relation between ζ and x in the form

$$\zeta(\zeta^2 + \alpha^2)^{\frac{1}{2}} + \alpha^2 \sinh^{-1}\left(\frac{\zeta}{\alpha}\right) = X - 2\lambda \ln\left\{\frac{X + x - 2\lambda}{2(1-\lambda^2)^{\frac{1}{2}}}\right\} - 2 \ln\left\{\frac{X + 2 - \lambda x}{(1-\lambda^2)^{\frac{1}{2}} x}\right\}, \tag{4.09}$$

valid when $\lambda \in (-1, 1)$ and $x \in (0, \infty)$. This determines ζ as an increasing function of x, with $\zeta = -\infty$ and $+\infty$ corresponding to $x = 0$ and ∞, respectively.

Alternatively, suppose that $\lambda = 1$. Then $x_1 = x_2 = 2$. By evaluating the integrals in (4.02), we see that we can continue to arrange for $\zeta = \pm i\alpha$ to correspond to $x = x_2$ and x_1 if we take $\alpha = 0$ and

$$\zeta^2 = x - 2 - 2 \ln(\tfrac{1}{2}x), \quad -\infty < \zeta < \infty, \quad 0 < x < \infty, \tag{4.10}$$

exactly as in (2.11).

Whether or not $\lambda = 1$, the transformed differential equation is given by

$$d^2w/d\zeta^2 = \{\mu^2(\zeta^2 + \alpha^2) + \psi(-\alpha^2, \zeta)\}w, \tag{4.11}$$

where $\psi(-\alpha^2, \zeta)$ is found from (2.13) and (2.14) by replacing α^2 by $-\alpha^2$ throughout. The theory of **[4]** is insufficiently general to show that $\psi(-\alpha^2, \zeta)$ is continuous in the relevant region, given by $\alpha \in [0, 2)$ (these endpoints are obtained from (4.08) by setting $\lambda = \pm 1$) and $\zeta \in (-\infty, \infty)$. This result is established in the Appendix to the present paper, however.

Next, by analysis similar to that of §2 above, we may verify that the numbered relations (2.15) to (2.20) continue to hold when α^2 is replaced everywhere by $-\alpha^2$—provided that the interval of uniform validity is replaced by $\alpha \in [0, \hat{A}]$, where $\hat{A}$ is any prescribed constant such that $0 < \hat{A} < 2$. From (4.08) it is seen that this corresponds to $\lambda \in [-1+\hat{\Delta}, 1]$ with $\hat{\Delta} = 2 - \frac{1}{2}\hat{A}^2$.

On applying [**4**, §7, Theorem II] to (4.11), and also to the same equation with ζ replaced by $-\zeta$ throughout, we obtain the following solutions of (4.11):

$$w_1(\mu^2, -\alpha^2, \zeta) = U(\tfrac{1}{2}\mu\alpha^2, \zeta\sqrt{2\mu}) + \varepsilon_1(\mu^2, -\alpha^2, \zeta), \tag{4.12}$$

$$w_2(\mu^2, -\alpha^2, \zeta) = U(\tfrac{1}{2}\mu\alpha^2, -\zeta\sqrt{2\mu}) + \varepsilon_2(\mu^2, -\alpha^2, \zeta), \tag{4.13}$$

where

$$|\varepsilon_1(\mu^2, -\alpha^2, \zeta)| \leqq U(\tfrac{1}{2}\mu\alpha^2, \zeta\sqrt{2\mu})\left[\exp\left\{\frac{l_2(\frac{1}{2}\mu\alpha^2)}{2(\pi\mu)^{\frac{1}{2}}}\mathcal{V}_{\zeta,\infty}\{F(\mu^2, -\alpha^2, \zeta)\}\right\} - 1\right], \tag{4.14}$$

$$|\varepsilon_2(\mu^2, -\alpha^2, \zeta)| \leqq U(\tfrac{1}{2}\mu\alpha^2, -\zeta\sqrt{2\mu})\left[\exp\left\{\frac{l_2(\frac{1}{2}\mu\alpha^2)}{2(\pi\mu)^{\frac{1}{2}}}\mathcal{V}_{-\infty,\zeta}\{F(\mu^2, -\alpha^2, \zeta)\}\right\} - 1\right], \tag{4.15}$$

valid when $\alpha \in [0, 2)$ and $\zeta \in (-\infty, \infty)$. In these inequalities the function l_2 is defined as in [**4**, (7.5)], and the error-control function $F(\mu^2, -\alpha^2, \zeta)$ is found from (3.05) by replacing α^2 by $-\alpha^2$.

As $\zeta \to +\infty$ the solution $w_1(\mu^2, -\alpha^2, \zeta)$ is recessive and $w_2(\mu^2, -\alpha^2, \zeta)$ is dominant; as $\zeta \to -\infty$ these roles are interchanged. Therefore $w_1(\mu^2, -\alpha^2, \zeta)$ is a multiple of $W_{\kappa,\mu}(\mu x)$ and $w_2(\mu^2, -\alpha^2, \zeta)$ is a multiple of $M_{\kappa,\mu}(\mu x)$. The actual identifications may be made in a manner similar to that used in §3. The final results are found to be expressible in the forms (3.10) and (3.25) with α^2 replaced by $-\alpha^2$ throughout. Both relations are now valid with the conditions $\alpha \in [0, 2)$ and $\zeta \in (-\infty, \infty)$.

Uniform asymptotic estimates for the error terms are immediately available from the results of [**4**, §7.3]. Thus we obtain

$$\varepsilon_1(\mu^2, -\alpha^2, \zeta) = U(\tfrac{1}{2}\mu\alpha^2, \zeta\sqrt{2\mu})O(\mu^{-1}\ln\mu), \tag{4.16}$$

$$\varepsilon_2(\mu^2, -\alpha^2, \zeta) = U(\tfrac{1}{2}\mu\alpha^2, -\zeta\sqrt{2\mu})O(\mu^{-1}\ln\mu), \tag{4.17}$$

as $\mu \to \infty$, uniformly with respect to $\alpha \in [0, \hat{A}]$ and $\zeta \in (-\infty, \infty)$.

5. Imaginary parameters

In this section we consider equation (1.05) in both cases $1 \leqq \lambda < \infty$ and $-1 < \lambda \leqq 1$.

When $1 \leqq \lambda < \infty$ we apply the Liouville transformation given by (2.01) and (2.03) to obtain

$$d^2w/d\zeta^2 = \{-\mu^2(\zeta^2 - \alpha^2) + \psi(\alpha^2, \zeta)\}w; \tag{5.01}$$

compare (2.12). Alternatively, when $-1 < \lambda \leqq 1$ we apply the transformation given by (4.01) and (4.08) to obtain

$$d^2w/d\zeta^2 = \{-\mu^2(\zeta^2 + \alpha^2) + \psi(-\alpha^2, \zeta)\}w; \tag{5.02}$$

compare (4.11). In (5.01) the variable ζ and the function $\psi(\alpha^2, \zeta)$ are defined as in §2, and in (5.02) ζ and $\psi(-\alpha^2, \zeta)$ are defined as in §4.

On applying the approximation theorem of [**7**, §3] with $u=\mu$, $\zeta_1=-\infty$ and $\zeta_2=+\infty$, we find that equation (5.01) has solutions $w_1(-\mu^2, \alpha^2, \zeta)$ and $w_2(-\mu^2, \alpha^2, \zeta)$, and equation (5.02) has solutions $w_1(-\mu^2, -\alpha^2, \zeta)$ and $w_2(-\mu^2, -\alpha^2, \zeta)$, where

$$w_1(-\mu^2, \pm\alpha^2, \zeta) = W(\pm\tfrac{1}{2}\mu\alpha^2, \zeta\sqrt{2\mu}) + \varepsilon_1(-\mu^2, \pm\alpha^2, \zeta), \tag{5.03}$$

$$w_2(-\mu^2, \pm\alpha^2, \zeta) = W(\pm\tfrac{1}{2}\mu\alpha^2, -\zeta\sqrt{2\mu}) + \varepsilon_2(-\mu^2, \pm\alpha^2, \zeta). \tag{5.04}$$

Here W denotes the modified parabolic cylinder function, and the error terms are bounded by

$$|\varepsilon_1(-\mu^2, \pm\alpha^2, \zeta)| \leqq E^{-1}(\pm\tfrac{1}{2}\mu\alpha^2, \zeta\sqrt{2\mu})M(\pm\tfrac{1}{2}\mu\alpha^2, \zeta\sqrt{2\mu}) \times \\ \times \left[\exp\left\{\frac{l(\pm\frac{1}{2}\mu\alpha^2)}{(2\mu)^{\frac{1}{2}}} \mathscr{V}_{\zeta,\infty}\{F(\mu^2, \pm\alpha^2, \zeta)\}\right\} - 1\right], \tag{5.05}$$

$$|\varepsilon_2(-\mu^2, \pm\alpha^2, \zeta)| \leqq E(\pm\tfrac{1}{2}\mu\alpha^2, \zeta\sqrt{2\mu})M(\pm\tfrac{1}{2}\mu\alpha^2, \zeta\sqrt{2\mu}) \times \\ \times \left[\exp\left\{\frac{l(\pm\frac{1}{2}\mu\alpha^2)}{(2\mu)^{\frac{1}{2}}} \mathscr{V}_{-\infty,\zeta}\{F(\mu^2, \pm\alpha^2, \zeta)\}\right\} - 1\right]. \tag{5.06}$$

In these bounds E, M and l denote the auxiliary functions introduced in [**7**, §§2 and 3], and the error-control function F is defined as in §§3 and 4 above. In each of (5.03), (5.04), (5.05) and (5.06) either the upper sign or the lower sign is to be taken throughout; moreover, when upper signs are used the results are valid for $\alpha \in [0, \infty)$ and $\zeta \in (-\infty, \infty)$, whereas when lower signs are used the results are valid for $\alpha \in [0, 2)$ and $\zeta \in (-\infty, \infty)$.

The next step is to identify these solutions in terms of standard Whittaker functions. As $\zeta \to +\infty$, with μ and α held fixed, we have

$$W(\pm\tfrac{1}{2}\mu\alpha^2, \zeta\sqrt{2\mu}) \\ = (\tfrac{1}{2}\mu)^{-\frac{1}{4}}\{k(\pm\tfrac{1}{2}\mu\alpha^2)\}^{\frac{1}{2}}\zeta^{-\frac{1}{2}} \cos\{\tfrac{1}{2}\mu\zeta^2 \mp \tfrac{1}{2}\mu\alpha^2 \ln(\zeta\sqrt{2\mu}) + \phi(\pm\tfrac{1}{2}\mu\alpha^2)\} + O(\zeta^{-\frac{5}{2}}),$$

where the functions k and ϕ are defined by

$$k(b) = (1+e^{2\pi b})^{\frac{1}{2}} - e^{\pi b}, \quad \phi(b) = \tfrac{1}{4}\pi + \tfrac{1}{2}\,\mathrm{ph}\,\{\Gamma(\tfrac{1}{2}+ib)\}, \tag{5.07}$$

for unrestricted values of the real argument b, the branch of the phase in the second of (5.07) being determined by continuity and the condition $\phi(0) = \frac{1}{4}\pi$. Referring to the bound (5.05) and using the asymptotic properties of the functions E^{-1} and M for large positive argument supplied in [**7**, §2], we see that

$$(\zeta^2 \mp \alpha^2)^{\frac{1}{4}} w_1(-\mu^2, \pm\alpha^2, \zeta) \\ = (\tfrac{1}{2}\mu)^{-\frac{1}{4}}\{k(\pm\tfrac{1}{2}\mu\alpha^2)\}^{\frac{1}{2}} \cos\{\tfrac{1}{2}\mu\zeta^2 \mp \tfrac{1}{2}\mu\alpha^2 \ln(\zeta\sqrt{2\mu}) + \phi(\pm\tfrac{1}{2}\mu\alpha^2)\} + o(1). \tag{5.08}$$

On the other hand, as $x \to \infty$ we have

$$(x^2 - 4\lambda x + 4)^{\frac{1}{4}} x^{-\frac{1}{2}} W_{i\kappa, i\mu}(i\mu x) \sim e^{-\frac{1}{2}\pi\kappa - \frac{1}{2}i\mu x}(\mu x)^{i\kappa}.$$

Substituting for x in terms of ζ by means of (2.15), or the corresponding formula with α^2 replaced by $-\alpha^2$, and using the relation $\kappa = (1 \pm \frac{1}{2}\alpha^2)\mu$ obtained from

(1.03), (2.03) and (4.08), we find that

$$(x^2-4\lambda x+4)^{\frac{1}{4}}x^{-\frac{1}{2}}W_{i\kappa,i\mu}(i\mu x)$$
$$\sim \exp\{-\tfrac{1}{2}i\mu\zeta^2 \pm \tfrac{1}{2}i\mu\alpha^2 \ln(\mu\zeta)+i\mu \ln \mu+\tfrac{1}{2}i\mu c(\pm\alpha^2)-\tfrac{1}{2}\pi\mu(1\pm\tfrac{1}{2}\alpha^2)\}. \quad (5.09)$$

Comparison of (5.08) and (5.09) yields the required identification, in the form

$$\operatorname{Re}\{e^{i\omega_1}W_{i\kappa,i\mu}(i\mu x)\}=(\tfrac{1}{2}\mu)^{\frac{1}{4}}\frac{e^{-\frac{1}{2}\pi\mu(1\pm\frac{1}{2}\alpha^2)}}{\{k(\pm\frac{1}{2}\mu\alpha^2)\}^{\frac{1}{2}}}\left(\frac{\zeta^2\mp\alpha^2}{x^2-4\lambda x+4}\right)^{\frac{1}{4}}x^{\frac{1}{2}}w_1(-\mu^2,\pm\alpha^2,\zeta), \quad (5.10)$$

where

$$\omega_1=-\mu\ln\mu\mp\tfrac{1}{4}\mu\alpha^2\ln(\tfrac{1}{2}\mu)-\tfrac{1}{2}\mu c(\pm\alpha^2)-\phi(\pm\tfrac{1}{2}\mu\alpha^2). \quad (5.11)$$

With upper signs taken throughout this result is valid with the conditions $\alpha\in[0,\infty)$, or equivalently $\lambda\in[1,\infty)$, and $\zeta\in(-\infty,\infty)$. With lower signs, the conditions are $\alpha\in[0,2)$, or equivalently $\lambda\in(-1,1]$, and $\zeta\in(-\infty,\infty)$.

For the second solution, the result corresponding to (5.08) is given by

$$(\zeta^2\mp\alpha^2)^{\frac{1}{4}}w_2(-\mu^2,\pm\alpha^2,\zeta)$$
$$=(\tfrac{1}{2}\mu)^{-\frac{1}{4}}\{k(\pm\tfrac{1}{2}\mu\alpha^2)\}^{\frac{1}{2}}\cos\{\tfrac{1}{2}\mu\zeta^2\mp\tfrac{1}{2}\mu\alpha^2\ln(|\zeta|\sqrt{2\mu})+\phi(\pm\tfrac{1}{2}\mu\alpha^2)\}+o(1), \quad (5.12)$$

as $\zeta\to-\infty$, with μ and α held fixed. On the other hand, as $x\to 0$ we have

$$(x^2-4\lambda x+4)^{\frac{1}{4}}x^{-\frac{1}{2}}M_{i\kappa,i\mu}(i\mu x)\sim(2\mu)^{\frac{1}{2}}e^{-\frac{1}{2}\pi\mu+\frac{1}{4}\pi i}(\mu x)^{i\mu}.$$

Substituting for x in terms of ζ by means of (2.18), or the corresponding result with α^2 replaced by $-\alpha^2$, we find that

$$(x^2-4\lambda x+4)^{\frac{1}{4}}x^{-\frac{1}{2}}M_{i\kappa,i\mu}(i\mu x)$$
$$\sim(2\mu)^{\frac{1}{2}}\exp\{-\tfrac{1}{2}i\mu\zeta^2\pm\tfrac{1}{2}i\mu\alpha^2\ln|\zeta|-\tfrac{1}{2}\pi\mu+\tfrac{1}{4}\pi i+i\mu\ln\mu-i\mu d(\pm\alpha^2)\}. \quad (5.13)$$

Comparison of (5.12) and (5.13) leads to the last of the required identifications, in the form

$$\operatorname{Re}\{e^{i\omega_2}M_{i\kappa,i\mu}(i\mu x)\}=2^{\frac{1}{4}}\mu^{\frac{3}{4}}\frac{e^{-\frac{1}{2}\pi\mu}}{\{k(\pm\frac{1}{2}\mu\alpha^2)\}^{\frac{1}{2}}}\left(\frac{\zeta^2\mp\alpha^2}{x^2-4\lambda x+4}\right)^{\frac{1}{4}}x^{\frac{1}{2}}w_2(-\mu^2,\pm\alpha^2,\zeta), \quad (5.14)$$

where

$$\omega_2=-\tfrac{1}{4}\pi-\mu\ln\mu\pm\tfrac{1}{4}\mu\alpha^2\ln(2\mu)+\mu d(\pm\alpha^2)-\phi(\pm\tfrac{1}{2}\mu\alpha^2), \quad (5.15)$$

this result being valid with the same conditions as (5.10) and (5.11).

Asymptotic estimates for the error terms in (5.03) and (5.04) for large μ are available from the estimates (3.7) and (3.8) of [**7**]. Thus with A again denoting an arbitrary positive constant we have

$$\varepsilon_1(-\mu^2,\alpha^2,\zeta)=E^{-1}(\tfrac{1}{2}\mu\alpha^2,\zeta\sqrt{2\mu})M(\tfrac{1}{2}\mu\alpha^2,\zeta\sqrt{2\mu})O(\mu^{-\frac{2}{3}}\ln\mu), \quad (5.16)$$
$$\varepsilon_2(-\mu^2,\alpha^2,\zeta)=E(\tfrac{1}{2}\mu\alpha^2,\zeta\sqrt{2\mu})M(\tfrac{1}{2}\mu\alpha^2,\zeta\sqrt{2\mu})O(\mu^{-\frac{2}{3}}\ln\mu), \quad (5.17)$$

uniformly with respect to $\alpha\in[0, \mathrm{A}]$ and $\zeta\in(-\infty,\infty)$. Similarly, with $\hat{\mathrm{A}}$ denoting an arbitrary constant such that $0<\hat{\mathrm{A}}<2$ we have

$$\varepsilon_1(-\mu^2,-\alpha^2,\zeta)=E^{-1}(-\tfrac{1}{2}\mu\alpha^2,\zeta\sqrt{2\mu})M(-\tfrac{1}{2}\mu\alpha^2,\zeta\sqrt{2\mu})O(\mu^{-1}\ln\mu), \quad (5.18)$$
$$\varepsilon_2(-\mu^2,-\alpha^2,\zeta)=E(-\tfrac{1}{2}\mu\alpha^2,\zeta\sqrt{2\mu})M(-\tfrac{1}{2}\mu\alpha^2,\zeta\sqrt{2\mu})O(\mu^{-1}\ln\mu), \quad (5.19)$$

uniformly with respect to $\alpha\in[0,\hat{\mathrm{A}}]$ and $\zeta\in(-\infty,\infty)$.

As a check on (5.10) we may fix α and compare the asymptotic forms of the two sides as $x \to 0$, or correspondingly, $\zeta \to -\infty$. Similarly as a check on (5.14) we may compare the asymptotic forms of the two sides as $x \to \infty$, or correspondingly, $\zeta \to +\infty$. These analyses resemble that given in §3 to check the approximation (3.18) by letting $\zeta \to -\infty$. For each approximation, three distinct cases arise according as α is zero or non-zero and in the latter event whether upper or lower signs are taken. In all cases it is found that the results agree within the uniform tolerances of the various error terms. These calculations are relatively straightforward but details are too lengthy to include here.

6. Summary

In this section we collect the principal results of this paper, re-expressed in terms of the original variable z and original parameters κ and μ. In all cases μ is assumed to be positive. Throughout $W_{\kappa,\mu}(z)$ and $M_{\kappa,\mu}(z)$ denote the Whittaker functions in the notation used, for example, in [**1**] and [**3**]. Also U, $\bar{U}$, E and M denote the parabolic cylinder functions and auxiliary functions defined in [**4**, §5]; W, k and ϕ denote the modified parabolic cylinder function and auxiliary functions defined in [**4**, §8]; E and M denote the auxiliary functions introduced in [**7**]. Furthermore,

$$Z = |z^2 - 4\kappa z + 4\mu^2|^{\frac{1}{2}}, \quad \alpha = \{2\,|\kappa - \mu|/\mu\}^{\frac{1}{2}}, \tag{6.01}$$

and we shall use the symbols K and $\hat{\mathrm{K}}$ to denote arbitrary constants such that $1 < \mathrm{K}$ and $-1 < \hat{\mathrm{K}} < 1$. Other notational changes include the following:

$$\begin{gathered} \eta_j(\kappa, \mu, \zeta) = \varepsilon_j(\mu^2, \pm\alpha^2, \zeta), \quad \bar{\eta}_j(\kappa, \mu, \zeta) = \bar{\varepsilon}_j(\mu^2, \pm\alpha^2, \zeta), \\ \eta_{-j}(\kappa, \mu, \zeta) = \varepsilon_j(-\mu^2, \pm\alpha^2, \zeta), \end{gathered} \tag{6.02}$$

with $j = 1$ or 2.

I. *Equation* (1.01) *with* $\mu \leqq \kappa$

Let z_1 and z_2 denote the (real) zeros of Z, given by

$$z_1 = 2\kappa - 2(\kappa^2 - \mu^2)^{\frac{1}{2}}, \quad z_2 = 2\kappa + 2(\kappa^2 - \mu^2)^{\frac{1}{2}}. \tag{6.03}$$

We introduce a transformed independent variable ζ that is an increasing function of z, and a continuous function of κ, μ and z, with $\zeta = -\infty, -\alpha, \alpha$ and $+\infty$ corresponding to $z = 0$, z_1, z_2 and ∞, respectively. When $\mu < \kappa$, ζ is defined implicitly in terms of z by the following equations:

$$\zeta(\zeta^2 - \alpha^2)^{\frac{1}{2}} - \alpha^2 \cosh^{-1}\left(\frac{\zeta}{\alpha}\right) = \frac{Z}{\mu} - \frac{2\kappa}{\mu} \ln\left\{\frac{Z + z - 2\kappa}{2(\kappa^2 - \mu^2)^{\frac{1}{2}}}\right\} - 2\ln\left\{\frac{\kappa z - 2\mu^2 - \mu Z}{(\kappa^2 - \mu^2)^{\frac{1}{2}} z}\right\}, \quad z_2 \leqq z, \tag{6.04}$$

$$\alpha^2 \sin^{-1}\left(\frac{\zeta}{\alpha}\right) + \zeta(\alpha^2 - \zeta^2)^{\frac{1}{2}} = \frac{Z}{\mu} + \frac{2\kappa}{\mu} \tan^{-1}\left(\frac{z - 2\kappa}{Z}\right) - 2\tan^{-1}\left(\frac{\kappa z - 2\mu^2}{\mu Z}\right), \quad z_1 \leqq z \leqq z_2, \tag{6.05}$$

$$-\zeta(\zeta^2 - \alpha^2)^{\frac{1}{2}} - \alpha^2 \cosh^{-1}\left(-\frac{\zeta}{\alpha}\right) = -\frac{Z}{\mu} + \frac{2\kappa}{\mu} \ln\left\{\frac{2\kappa - z - Z}{2(\kappa^2 - \mu^2)^{\frac{1}{2}}}\right\} + 2\ln\left\{\frac{\mu Z + 2\mu^2 - \kappa z}{(\kappa^2 - \mu^2)^{\frac{1}{2}} z}\right\}, \quad z \leqq z_1. \tag{6.06}$$

When $\mu=\kappa$ we have $\alpha=0$, and ζ is defined by

$$\zeta=\pm\left\{\frac{z}{\mu}-2-2\ln\left(\frac{z}{2\mu}\right)\right\}^{\frac{1}{2}}, \tag{6.07}$$

the upper or lower sign being taken according as $z\gtrless 2\mu$.

Lastly, we write

$$\Phi(\kappa,\mu,z)=\left(\frac{\mu^2\zeta^2-2\kappa\mu+2\mu^2}{z^2-4\kappa z+4\mu^2}\right)^{\frac{1}{4}}z^{\frac{1}{2}}, \tag{6.08}$$

replacing the right-hand side by its limiting value when $z=z_1$ or z_2.

The approximations for the Whittaker functions have the forms

$$W_{\kappa,\mu}(z)=(\tfrac{1}{2}\mu)^{-\frac{1}{4}}\{(\kappa+\mu)/e\}^{\frac{1}{2}(\kappa+\mu)}\Phi(\kappa,\mu,z)\{U(\mu-\kappa,\zeta\sqrt{2\mu})+\eta_1(\kappa,\mu,\zeta)\}, \tag{6.09}$$

$$\begin{aligned}M_{\kappa,\mu}(z)=2^{\frac{3}{4}}\mu^{\frac{1}{4}}(2\mu/e)^{2\mu}\{e/(\kappa+\mu)\}^{\frac{1}{2}(\kappa+\mu)}\Phi(\kappa,\mu,z)\times\\ \times[\{\sin(\pi\kappa-\pi\mu)+\delta_1(\kappa,\mu)\}\{U(\mu-\kappa,\zeta\sqrt{2\mu})+\eta_1(\kappa,\mu,\zeta)\}+\\ +\{\cos(\pi\kappa-\pi\mu)+\bar{\delta}_1(\kappa,\mu)\}\{\bar{U}(\mu-\kappa,\zeta\sqrt{2\mu})+\bar{\eta}_1(\kappa,\mu,\zeta)\}],\end{aligned} \tag{6.10}$$

$$\begin{aligned}W_{\kappa,\mu}(z)=(\tfrac{1}{2}\mu)^{-\frac{1}{4}}\{(\kappa+\mu)/e\}^{\frac{1}{2}(\kappa+\mu)}\Phi(\kappa,\mu,z)\times\\ \times[\{\sin(\pi\kappa-\pi\mu)+\delta_2(\kappa,\mu)\}\{U(\mu-\kappa,-\zeta\sqrt{2\mu})+\eta_2(\kappa,\mu,\zeta)\}+\\ +\{\cos(\pi\kappa-\pi\mu)+\bar{\delta}_2(\kappa,\mu)\}\{\bar{U}(\mu-\kappa,-\zeta\sqrt{2\mu})+\bar{\eta}_2(\kappa,\mu,\zeta)\}],\end{aligned} \tag{6.11}$$

$$\begin{aligned}M_{\kappa,\mu}(z)=2^{\frac{3}{4}}\mu^{\frac{1}{4}}(2\mu/e)^{2\mu}\{e/(\kappa+\mu)\}^{\frac{1}{2}(\kappa+\mu)}\Phi(\kappa,\mu,z)\times\\ \times\{U(\mu-\kappa,-\zeta\sqrt{2\mu})+\eta_2(\kappa,\mu,\zeta)\}.\end{aligned} \tag{6.12}$$

The error terms satisfy the boundary conditions

$$\lim_{\zeta\to\infty}\{\eta_1(\kappa,\mu,\zeta)/U(\mu-\kappa,\zeta\sqrt{2\mu})\}=\lim_{\zeta\to-\infty}\{\eta_2(\kappa,\mu,\zeta)/U(\mu-\kappa,-\zeta\sqrt{2\mu})\}=0, \tag{6.13}$$

$$\bar{\eta}_1(\kappa,\mu,0)=\bar{\eta}_2(\kappa,\mu,0)=0, \tag{6.14}$$

and they possess the following asymptotic properties as $\mu\to\infty$:

$$\mathsf{E}(\mu-\kappa,\zeta\sqrt{2\mu})\eta_1(\kappa,\mu,\zeta),\ \mathsf{E}^{-1}(\mu-\kappa,\zeta\sqrt{2\mu})\bar{\eta}_1(\kappa,\mu,\zeta)=\mathsf{M}(\mu-\kappa,\zeta\sqrt{2\mu})O(\mu^{-\frac{2}{3}}), \tag{6.15}$$

uniformly with respect to $\kappa\in[\mu,\mathrm{K}\mu]$ and $\zeta\in[0,\infty)$;

$$\begin{aligned}\mathsf{E}(\mu-\kappa,-\zeta\sqrt{2\mu})\eta_2(\kappa,\mu,\zeta),\ \mathsf{E}^{-1}(\mu-\kappa,-\zeta\sqrt{2\mu})\bar{\eta}_2(\kappa,\mu,\zeta)\\ =\mathsf{M}(\mu-\kappa,-\zeta\sqrt{2\mu})O(\mu^{-\frac{2}{3}}),\end{aligned} \tag{6.16}$$

uniformly with respect to $\kappa\in[\mu,\mathrm{K}\mu]$ and $\zeta\in(-\infty,0]$;

$$\delta_1(\kappa,\mu),\ \bar{\delta}_1(\kappa,\mu),\ \delta_2(\kappa,\mu),\ \bar{\delta}_2(\kappa,\mu)=O(\mu^{-\frac{2}{3}}), \tag{6.17}$$

uniformly with respect to $\kappa\in[\mu,\mathrm{K}\mu]$.

Bounds for $\eta_1(\kappa,\mu,\zeta)$ and $\bar{\eta}_1(\kappa,\mu,\zeta)$, valid when $\zeta\in[0,\infty)$, are supplied by (3.03) and (3.04); compare (6.02). Similarly, bounds for $\eta_2(\kappa,\mu,\zeta)$ and $\bar{\eta}_2(\kappa,\mu,\zeta)$, valid when $\zeta\in(-\infty,0]$, are supplied by (3.14) and (3.15).

II. *Equation* (1.01) *with* $-\mu<\kappa\leqq\mu$

When $\kappa<\mu$ a transformed variable ζ is defined implicitly by

$$\zeta(\zeta^2+\alpha^2)^{\frac{1}{2}}+\alpha^2\sinh^{-1}\left(\frac{\zeta}{\alpha}\right)=\frac{Z}{\mu}-\frac{2\kappa}{\mu}\ln\left\{\frac{Z+z-2\kappa}{2(\mu^2-\kappa^2)^{\frac{1}{2}}}\right\}-2\ln\left\{\frac{\mu Z+2\mu^2-\kappa z}{(\mu^2-\kappa^2)^{\frac{1}{2}}z}\right\}, \tag{6.18}$$

and when $\kappa=\mu$, ζ is again defined by (6.07). Whether or not $\kappa=\mu$, ζ is an increasing function of z, and a continuous function of κ, μ and z, with $\zeta=-\infty$ and $+\infty$ corresponding to $z=0$ and ∞, respectively. With $\Phi(\kappa,\mu,z)$ again defined by (6.08), the approximations for the Whittaker functions have the forms (6.09) and (6.12). The error terms $\eta_1(\kappa,\mu,\zeta)$ and $\eta_2(\kappa,\mu,\zeta)$ continue to satisfy the boundary conditions (6.13), but their asymptotic behaviour as $\mu\to\infty$ is now given by

$$\begin{aligned}\eta_1(\kappa,\mu,\zeta)&=U(\mu-\kappa,\zeta\sqrt{2\mu})O(\mu^{-1}\ln\mu),\\ \eta_2(\kappa,\mu,\zeta)&=U(\mu-\kappa,-\zeta\sqrt{2\mu})O(\mu^{-1}\ln\mu),\end{aligned} \tag{6.19}$$

uniformly with respect to $\kappa\in[\hat{\mathrm{K}}\mu,\mu]$ and $\zeta\in(-\infty,\infty)$.

Bounds for $\eta_1(\kappa,\mu,\zeta)$ and $\eta_2(\kappa,\mu,\zeta)$, again valid when $\zeta\in(-\infty,\infty)$, are supplied by (4.14) and (4.15); compare the first of (6.02).

III. *Equation* (1.02) *with* $\mu\leqq\kappa$

With ζ defined as in I above, the approximations for the Whittaker functions have the forms

$$\operatorname{Re}\{e^{i\omega_1}W_{i\kappa,i\mu}(iz)\}=(2\mu)^{-\frac{1}{4}}e^{-\frac{1}{2}\pi\kappa}\{k(\kappa-\mu)\}^{-\frac{1}{2}}\Phi(\kappa,\mu,z)\times\\ \times\{W(\kappa-\mu,\zeta\sqrt{2\mu})+\eta_{-1}(\kappa,\mu,\zeta)\}, \tag{6.20}$$

$$\operatorname{Re}\{e^{i\omega_2}M_{i\kappa,i\mu}(iz)\}=(2\mu)^{\frac{1}{4}}e^{-\frac{1}{2}\pi\mu}\{k(\kappa-\mu)\}^{-\frac{1}{2}}\Phi(\kappa,\mu,z)\times\\ \times\{W(\kappa-\mu,-\zeta\sqrt{2\mu})+\eta_{-2}(\kappa,\mu,\zeta)\}, \tag{6.21}$$

where $\Phi(\kappa,\mu,z)$ is defined by (6.08), and

$$\omega_1=\tfrac{1}{2}(\kappa+\mu)\{1-\ln(\kappa+\mu)\}-\phi(\kappa-\mu), \tag{6.22}$$

$$\omega_2=\tfrac{1}{2}(\kappa+\mu)\ln(\kappa+\mu)-2\mu\ln(2\mu)-\tfrac{1}{2}\kappa+\tfrac{3}{2}\mu-\tfrac{1}{4}\pi-\phi(\kappa-\mu). \tag{6.23}$$

The error terms in (6.20) and (6.21) satisfy the boundary conditions

$$\lim_{\zeta\to\infty}\{\zeta^{\frac{1}{2}}\eta_{-1}(\kappa,\mu,\zeta)\}=\lim_{\zeta\to-\infty}\{|\zeta|^{\frac{1}{2}}\eta_{-2}(\kappa,\mu,\zeta)\}=0, \tag{6.24}$$

and have the following asymptotic properties as $\mu\to\infty$:

$$\eta_{-1}(\kappa,\mu,\zeta)=E^{-1}(\kappa-\mu,\zeta\sqrt{2\mu})M(\kappa-\mu,\zeta\sqrt{2\mu})O(\mu^{-\frac{2}{3}}\ln\mu), \tag{6.25}$$

$$\eta_{-2}(\kappa,\mu,\zeta)=E(\kappa-\mu,\zeta\sqrt{2\mu})M(\kappa-\mu,\zeta\sqrt{2\mu})O(\mu^{-\frac{2}{3}}\ln\mu), \tag{6.26}$$

these relations being uniformly valid with respect to $\kappa\in[\mu,\mathrm{K}\mu]$ and $\zeta\in(-\infty,\infty)$.

Bounds for the error terms, valid when $\zeta\in(-\infty,\infty)$, are supplied by (5.05) and (5.06) with upper signs; compare (6.02).

IV. *Equation* (1.02) *with* $-\mu<\kappa\leqq\mu$

With ζ defined as in II above, equations (6.20) to (6.24) again apply. Bounds for the error terms, again valid when $\zeta\in(-\infty,\infty)$, are supplied by (5.05) and (5.06) with lower signs. Asymptotic properties as $\mu\to\infty$ are supplied by

$$\eta_{-1}(\kappa,\mu,\zeta)=E^{-1}(\kappa-\mu,\zeta\sqrt{2\mu})M(\kappa-\mu,\zeta\sqrt{2\mu})O(\mu^{-1}\ln\mu), \tag{6.27}$$

$$\eta_{-2}(\kappa,\mu,\zeta)=E(\kappa-\mu,\zeta\sqrt{2\mu})M(\kappa-\mu,\zeta\sqrt{2\mu})O(\mu^{-1}\ln\mu), \tag{6.28}$$

these relations being uniformly valid with respect to $\kappa\in[\hat{K}\mu,\mu]$ and $\zeta\in(-\infty,\infty)$.

Appendix: Continuity of the Schwarzian derivative

In this appendix we give a more general form of [**4**, Lemma II]. The main change is to remove the requirement that $f(u,a,x)$ be an even function of x. Precise conditions are as follows:

We assume that $f(u,a,x)$ has zeros located at $\pm ia$, where a is a real parameter ranging over a compact interval $[0,A]$. The range of x is the union of an open real interval (x_1,x_2), and an open segment of the imaginary axis joining two points $\pm i\hat{x}_1$. Each of the quantities x_1, x_2 and $\hat{x}_1$ may depend on a and u, provided that the dependence on a is continuous, or they can be infinite. It is assumed, however, that $x_1<0$, $x_2>0$ and $\hat{x}_1>a$. We again define $p(u,a,x)$ by the equation

$$f(u,a,x)=(a^2+x^2)p(u,a,x). \tag{A.1}$$

Lemma II (extended). *For each value of u assume that*:

(i) *In the region given by $a\in[0,A]$ and $x\in(x_1,x_2)$, the functions $p(u,a,x)$, $\partial p(u,a,x)/\partial x$, $\partial^2p(u,a,x)/\partial x^2$ and $g(u,a,x)$ are continuous, and $p(u,a,x)$ is real and positive.*

(ii) *In the region given by $a\in[0,A]$ and $ix\in(-\hat{x}_1,\hat{x}_1)$, the function $p(u,a,x)$ is continuous and takes conjugate values for conjugate values of x; furthermore, the principal value of $p^{\frac{1}{2}}(u,a,x)$ has non-zero real part.*

(iii) *The values of $\partial p(u,a,x)/\partial x$, $\partial^2p(u,a,x)/\partial x^2$ and $\partial^3p(u,a,x)/\partial x^3$ at $x=0$ obtained by differentiation along the imaginary x-axis are the same as the corresponding values obtained by differentiation along the real axis. In addition, $\partial^3p(u,a,x)/\partial x^3$ is continuous and $|\partial^4p(u,a,x)/\partial x^4|$ is bounded in a neighbourhood of the point $a=x=0$, both for real and purely imaginary values of x.*

(iv) $\operatorname{Re}\int_0^\alpha(a^2-t^2)^{\frac{1}{2}}p^{\frac{1}{2}}(u,a,it)\,dt$ *is a strictly increasing function of a when $a\in[0,A]$ and the square roots have their principal values.*

Then the function $\psi(u,\alpha,\zeta)$ defined by (2.10) *of* [**4**] *is continuous in the region of the (α,ζ)-plane corresponding to $a\in[0,A]$, $x\in(x_1,x_2)$.*

The proof of this result is similar to the proofs of Lemmas I and II of [**4**], and we merely sketch the main steps.

The relation between the transformed variable ζ and the original variable x is prescribed by

$$\int_0^x f^{\frac{1}{2}}(u,a,t)\,dt=\int_{\zeta_0}^{\zeta}(\alpha^2+\tau^2)^{\frac{1}{2}}\,d\tau, \tag{A.2}$$

with the principal value assigned to each square root. The value of α, the transformed (non-negative) parameter, and the value of ζ_0, the (real) value of ζ corresponding to $x=0$, are found by stipulating that the points $\zeta=\pm i\alpha$ correspond respectively to $x=\pm ia$. Thus we have

$$\int_0^{\pm ia} f^{\frac{1}{2}}(u, a, t)\,dt=\int_{\zeta_0}^{\pm i\alpha}(\alpha^2+\tau^2)^{\frac{1}{2}}\,d\tau,$$

that is,

$$\pm i\int_0^a f^{\frac{1}{2}}(u, a, \pm it)\,dt=\pm\tfrac{1}{4}\pi i\alpha^2-\int_0^{\zeta_0}(\alpha^2+\tau^2)^{\frac{1}{2}}\,d\tau.$$

Taking imaginary parts, and referring to (A.1) and the conjugacy property mentioned in Condition (ii), we obtain an explicit (and unique) formula for α^2, given by

$$\alpha^2=\frac{4}{\pi}\operatorname{Re}\int_0^a(a^2-t^2)^{\frac{1}{2}}p^{\frac{1}{2}}(u, a, it)\,dt. \tag{A.3}$$

Similarly, by taking real parts we obtain an implicit formula for ζ_0:

$$\int_0^{\zeta_0}(\alpha^2+\tau^2)^{\frac{1}{2}}\,d\tau=\operatorname{Im}\int_0^a(a^2-t^2)^{\frac{1}{2}}p^{\frac{1}{2}}(u, a, it)\,dt. \tag{A.4}$$

In consequence of Conditions (ii) and (iv), the right member of (A.3) is a continuous and strictly increasing function of a. Accordingly, if $\alpha=\mathrm{A}$ corresponds to $a=A$, then there is a one-to-one continuous correspondence between these variables in the intervals $[0, \mathrm{A}]$ and $[0, A]$. Next, since the integral on the left of equation (A.4) is a strictly increasing function of its upper limit, the value of ζ_0 is uniquely determined by this equation. Furthermore, since the right member is continuous in a, ζ_0 is a continuous function of a, and therefore also of α.

In consequence of Condition (iii) and Taylor's theorem, we have

$$p^{\frac{1}{2}}(u, a, it)=p^{\frac{1}{2}}(0)+\frac{p'(0)}{2p^{\frac{1}{2}}(0)}it+\left\{\frac{p''(0)}{4p^{\frac{1}{2}}(0)}-\frac{p'^2(0)}{8p^{\frac{3}{2}}(0)}\right\}(it)^2+$$
$$+\left\{\frac{p'''(0)}{12p^{\frac{1}{2}}(0)}-\frac{p'(0)p''(0)}{8p^{\frac{3}{2}}(0)}+\frac{p'^3(0)}{16p^{\frac{5}{2}}(0)}\right\}(it)^3+t^4O(1),$$

uniformly for $t\in[0, a]$ and all sufficiently small a, where for brevity we have written $p(0)\equiv p(u, a, 0)$, $p'(0)\equiv[\partial p(u, a, x)/\partial x]_{x=0}$, and so on. Substituting in (A.3) by means of this expansion and integrating, we derive

$$\alpha=p^{\frac{1}{4}}(0)a\left\{1+\left(\frac{p'^2(0)}{64p^2(0)}-\frac{p''(0)}{32p(0)}\right)a^2+O(a^4)\right\},\quad a\to 0;$$

compare [**4**, (3.7)]. Similarly, from (A.4) we obtain

$$\zeta_0=\frac{p'(0)}{6p^{\frac{1}{2}}(0)}\frac{a^3}{\alpha}+O(a^4)=\frac{p'(0)}{6p^{\frac{3}{4}}(0)}a^2+O(a^4).$$

The proof of the lemma when $\alpha\neq 0$, or when $\alpha=0$ (so that $a=0$ and $\zeta_0=0$) but $\zeta\neq 0$, is a straightforward application of the implicit function theorem, and is similar to the analysis given in [**4**, §§3.4 and 3.5]. It therefore remains to consider the continuity of $\psi(u, \alpha, \zeta)$ at the point $\alpha = \zeta = 0$.

Referring to (A.1) and (A.2) and again suppressing the arguments u and a of the function p, we have

$$\int_0^x (a^2+t^2)^{\frac{1}{2}} p^{\frac{1}{2}}(t)\, dt = \int_{\zeta_0}^{\zeta} (\alpha^2+\tau^2)^{\frac{1}{2}}\, d\tau, \tag{A.5}$$

where from now on all variables are real. Let us set

$$\alpha_0 = (\alpha^2+\zeta_0^2)^{\frac{1}{2}}. \tag{A.6}$$

Then for fixed non-zero values of a and α an expansion of x for small $|\zeta-\zeta_0|$ may be verified to be

$$x = X_1(\zeta-\zeta_0)+X_2(\zeta-\zeta_0)^2+X_3(\zeta-\zeta_0)^3+O\{(\zeta-\zeta_0)^4\}, \tag{A.7}$$

where

$$X_1 = \frac{\alpha_0}{p^{\frac{1}{2}}(0)a}, \quad X_2 = \frac{\zeta_0}{2\alpha_0^2}X_1 - \frac{p'(0)}{4p(0)}X_1^2, \tag{A.8}$$

$$X_3 = \left(1-\frac{\zeta_0^2}{\alpha_0^2}\right)\frac{X_1}{6\alpha_0^2} - \frac{p'(0)\zeta_0}{4p(0)\alpha_0^2}X_1^2 + \left(\frac{p'^2(0)}{6p^2(0)} - \frac{p''(0)}{12p(0)} - \frac{1}{6a^2}\right)X_1^3. \tag{A.9}$$

For small values of α (or equivalently a), these coefficients are approximated by

$$X_1 = \frac{1}{p^{\frac{1}{4}}(0)} + \left(\frac{17p'^2(0)}{576p^{\frac{9}{4}}(0)} - \frac{p''(0)}{32p^{\frac{5}{4}}(0)}\right)a^2 + O(a^4), \tag{A.10}$$

$$X_2 = -\frac{p'(0)}{6p^{\frac{3}{2}}(0)} + O(a^2), \quad X_3 = \frac{29p'^2(0)}{288p^{\frac{11}{4}}(0)} - \frac{p''(0)}{16p^{\frac{7}{4}}(0)} + O(a^2). \tag{A.11}$$

It is easy to verify that the expansion (A.7) also applies with $a = \alpha = 0$ (so that $\zeta_0 = 0$) and X_1, X_2 and X_3 replaced by the limiting forms of (A.10) and (A.11). The key step in the proof is to show that the error term in (A.7) is uniform in a closed neighbourhood of $\alpha = 0$. To achieve this, we denote this error term by η, and rearrange (A.5) in the form

$$I = \int_{\zeta_0}^{\zeta} (\alpha^2+\tau^2)^{\frac{1}{2}}\, d\tau - J, \tag{A.12}$$

where

$$I = \int_{X_1(\zeta-\zeta_0)+X_2(\zeta-\zeta_0)^2+X_3(\zeta-\zeta_0)^3}^{X_1(\zeta-\zeta_0)+X_2(\zeta-\zeta_0)^2+X_3(\zeta-\zeta_0)^3+\eta} (a^2+t^2)^{\frac{1}{2}} p^{\frac{1}{2}}(t)\, dt, \tag{A.13}$$

$$J = \int_0^{X_1(\zeta-\zeta_0)+X_2(\zeta-\zeta_0)^2+X_3(\zeta-\zeta_0)^3} (a^2+t^2)^{\frac{1}{2}} p^{\frac{1}{2}}(t)\, dt. \tag{A.14}$$

We introduce a new integration variable y, defined by

$$t = X_1 y + X_2 y^2 + X_3 y^3, \tag{A.15}$$

so that in J the limits of integration become $y = 0$ and $y = \zeta - \zeta_0$, and we express

$$a^2+t^2 = (\alpha_0^2+2\zeta_0 y+y^2)(Y_0+Y_1y+Y_2y^2+Y_3y^3+Y_4y^4)+Y_5y^5+Y_6y^6, \tag{A.16}$$

where the coefficients Y_s are determined recursively in terms of the X_s by substituting for t by means of (A.15) and equating coefficients. With the aid of (A.10) and (A.11) it may be verified that each of these coefficients is bounded as $a \to 0$. Next, by means of the substitutions $y = \tau - \zeta_0$ and $\alpha_0^2 = \alpha^2 + \zeta_0^2$ it is easily shown that $y^2/(\alpha_0^2 + 2\zeta_0 y + y^2)$ is bounded for all sufficiently small α; hence from (A.16) we obtain

$$a^2 + t^2 = (\alpha_0^2 + 2\zeta_0 y + y^2)\{Y_0 + Y_1 y + Y_2 y^2 + O(y^3)\},$$

in the neighbourhood of $\alpha = \zeta = 0$. Then by using analysis similar to that of [**4**, §3.7], we find that

$$J = \int_0^{\zeta - \zeta_0} (\alpha_0^2 + 2\zeta_0 y + y^2)^{\frac{1}{2}}\{1 + O(y^3)\}\, dy,$$

and hence that

$$\int_{\zeta_0}^{\zeta} (\alpha^2 + \tau^2)^{\frac{1}{2}}\, d\tau - J = \int_0^{\zeta - \zeta_0} (\alpha_0^2 + 2\zeta_0 y + y^2)^{\frac{1}{2}}\, dy - J = (\alpha^2 + \zeta^2)^{\frac{1}{2}} O\{(\zeta - \zeta_0)^4\}, \tag{A.17}$$

in the neighbourhood of $\alpha = \zeta = 0$. From (A.12), (A.13) and (A.17) it is an elementary deduction that η is uniformly $O\{(\zeta - \zeta_0)^4\}$, as required.

The completion of the proof of the lemma proceeds in a similar manner to §§3.8 and 3.9 of [**4**], and it is unnecessary to record further details.

In order to apply the new result to equations (1.04) and (1.05) in the case $-1 < \lambda \leqq 1$, as required in §§4 and 5, we first replace the variable x by $x + 2\lambda$ in order to translate the turning points to the imaginary axis. We then set $a = 2(1 - \lambda^2)^{\frac{1}{2}}$, $x_1 = -2\lambda (= -(4 - a^2)^{\frac{1}{2}})$, $x_2 = \infty$, $\hat{x}_1 = \infty$, $p(\mu, a, x) = \frac{1}{4}(x + 2\lambda)^{-2}$, $g(\mu, a, x) = -\frac{1}{4}(x + 2\lambda)^{-2}$. The conditions of Lemma II (extended) are satisfied, provided that $0 < \lambda \leqq 1$, or correspondingly, $0 \leqq \alpha < \sqrt{2}$. The proof of the continuity of $\psi(-\alpha^2, \zeta)$ for the region $\alpha \in [\sqrt{2}, 2)$, $\zeta \in (-\infty, \infty)$ is achievable in a similar manner to that of $\psi(\alpha^2, \zeta)$ for the region $\alpha \in [\sqrt{2}, \infty)$, $\zeta \in (-\infty, \infty)$, as sketched in §2.

Acknowledgment

This research was supported by the U.S. Army Research Office, Durham under Grant DAAG 29-77-G-0003, and the National Science Foundation under Grant MCS 78-02111.

References

1 Bateman Manuscript Project. *Higher transcendental functions*, vol. I (A. Erdélyi, ed.). (New York: McGraw-Hill, 1953).

2 J. C. P. Miller. *Tables of Weber parabolic cylinder functions* (London: H. M. Stationery Office, 1955).

3 F. W. J. Olver. *Asymptotics and special functions* (London: Academic Press, 1974).

4 ——. Second-order linear differential equations with two turning points. *Philos. Trans. Roy. Soc. London Ser. A* **278** (1975), 137–174.

5 ——. Legendre functions with both parameters large. *Philos. Trans. Roy. Soc. London Ser. A* **278** (1975), 175–185.

6 ——. Unsolved problems in the asymptotic estimation of special functions. In *Theory and application of special functions* (R. A. Askey, ed.), pp. 99–142. (London: Academic Press, 1975).

7 ——. Improved error bounds for second-order differential equations with two turning points, *J. Res. Nat. Bur. Standards Sect. B* **80** (1976), 437–440.

8 N. M. Temme. Uniform asymptotic expansions of confluent hypergeometric functions. *J. Inst. Math. Appl.* **22** (1978), 215–223.

(*Issued 6 October* 1980)

IMA Journal of Numerical Analysis (1982) **2,** 377–406

A Posteriori Error Bounds for Gaussian Elimination

F. W. J. OLVER

University of Maryland and National Bureau of Standards, U.S.A.

AND

J. H. WILKINSON

Department of Computer Science, Stanford University, U.S.A.

[Received 28 June 1982]

Explicit bounds are constructed for the error in the solution of a system of linear algebraic equations obtained by Gaussian elimination using floating-point arithmetic. The bounds take account of inherent errors in the data and all abbreviations (choppings or roundings) introduced during the process of solution. The bounds are strict and agree with the estimate for the maximum error obtained by linearized perturbation theory. The formulation of the bounds avoids the need for specially directed rounding procedures in the hardware or software; in consequence the bounds can be evaluated on most existing computers. The cost of computing the bounds is comparable with the cost of computing the original solution.

1. Introduction and Summary

WE CONSIDER the numerical solution, using floating-point arithmetic, of a system of linear algebraic equations

$$Ax = b, \tag{1.1}$$

in which A is a non-singular real $n \times n$ matrix, b is a real column vector with n elements and x is the required solution vector. Errors in the solution stem from two sources. First, there may be uncertainties in the given numerical values of A and b; these are the so-called *inherent errors*. Secondly, chopping or rounding errors may be introduced at each step of the calculation; these are the so-called *abbreviation errors*. Usually both sources of error are present. Even when the elements of A and components of b are known exactly they may become contaminated with errors from base conversion during the input process (unless special precautions are taken). And unless the system process is solved by methods of the type described by Newman (1967), abbreviation errors inevitably intrude.

The purpose of this paper is to show how to construct explicit bounds for the cumulative error contributed by both sources to the computed solution $\bar{x}$, say. The bounds we shall obtain are (i) strict; (ii) realistic, in the sense that they agree with first-order estimates obtained by perturbation expansions; (iii) calculable on almost any existing computer without the need for special software devices such as directed rounding; (iv) of reasonable cost, in that their computation time is comparable with that required to compute $\bar{x}$. Furthermore, the method used is not dependent on scaling, other than possible scalings of exponents to avoid overflow or underflow, and it applies whether or not a pivoting strategy is followed.

The paper is arranged as follows. Section 2 outlines the three stages of the form of the Gaussian elimination process that will be used, and introduces preliminary notations. Section 3 treats the first stage, forward elimination, and traces the maximum effect of the inherent errors as well as that of the abbreviation errors introduced during this stage. Section 4 treats the second and third stages, respectively backward elimination and normalization, in a similar manner. Section 5 describes and analyses the computation of the inverse matrix. Section 6 supplies explicit bounds for error in the solution $\bar{x}$ arising from all sources, and it is demonstrated that these bounds agree with estimates yielded by linearized perturbation theory. Section 7 converts the error bounds of Section 6 from analytical form into computable form, and also examines the cost of the computations. Section 8 illustrates the process of solution and the computation of the error bounds by means of a numerical example. The concluding section, Section 9, summarizes the main features of the method, and also includes some comparisons with the work of other error analysts. *In order to make a quick assessment of the nature of the main results of the paper, the reader is advised to begin with Sections* 2 *and* 8.

The whole investigation draws heavily on the theory of absolute and relative precisions developed in Olver (1978, 1982). It will be assumed that the reader is familiar with the more important results of the latter paper, and they will not be repeated here.

The following commonly used notations for matrices and vectors will be employed. If a_{ij} is the element of A in the ith row and jth column, then sometimes A will be denoted by $[a_{ij}]$. Similarly we may write $b = [b_i]$, where b_i is the ith component of b. Conversely, the (i, j)th element of A may be denoted by $(A)_{ij}$ and the ith component of b by $(b)_i$. Absolute values are defined by

$$|A| = [|a_{ij}|], \qquad |b| = [|b_i|], \tag{1.2}$$

and the norm that will be employed is the maximum or infinity norm, defined by

$$\|A\| = \max_i \Big(\sum_j |a_{ij}|\Big), \qquad \|b\| = \max_i |b_i|. \tag{1.3}$$

Lastly, the meaning of inequality signs is typified by

$$A \leqslant Z \Leftrightarrow (A)_{ij} \leqslant (Z)_{ij}, \quad \forall\, i, j. \tag{1.4}$$

2. Process of Solution and Preliminary Notations

Detailed descriptions of Gaussian elimination may be found, for example, in Fox (1964, Chapter 3) or Stewart (1973, Chapter 3). Here we record the main stages, in matrix form, in order to establish notation. To begin with, it is convenient to attach the superscript $^{(1)}$ to the symbols A and b in Equation (1.1). Thus we are considering the solution of a non-singular system

$$A^{(1)}x = b^{(1)}, \tag{2.1}$$

or, in full,

$$\left.\begin{array}{l} a_{11}^{(1)}x_1+a_{12}^{(1)}x_2+\ldots+a_{1n}^{(1)}x_n=b_1^{(1)},\\ a_{21}^{(1)}x_1+a_{22}^{(1)}x_2+\ldots+a_{2n}^{(1)}x_n=b_2^{(1)},\\ \vdots \\ a_{n1}^{(1)}x_1+a_{n2}^{(1)}x_2+\ldots+a_{nn}^{(1)}x_n=b_n^{(1)}. \end{array}\right\} \tag{2.2}$$

The first stage is *forward elimination*. We shall suppose that the variables are eliminated in their natural order, without interchange of equations at any step. Any other order of elimination can be converted into the natural order, without affecting the error analysis, by multiplication of the system by suitably chosen permutation matrices; compare Wilkinson (1961, section 14) or Stewart (1973, Chapter 3, section 2). After $x_1, x_2, \ldots, x_{k-1}$ have been eliminated the system assumes the form

$$\left.\begin{array}{r} a_{11}^{(k)}x_1+a_{12}^{(k)}x_2+\ldots\ldots+a_{1n}^{(k)}x_n=b_1^{(k)},\\ a_{22}^{(k)}x_2+\ldots\ldots+a_{2n}^{(k)}x_n=b_2^{(k)},\\ \vdots \\ a_{kk}^{(k)}x_k+\ldots+a_{kn}^{(k)}x_n=b_k^{(k)},\\ \vdots \\ a_{nk}^{(k)}x_k+\ldots+a_{nn}^{(k)}x_n=b_n^{(k)}, \end{array}\right\} \tag{2.3}$$

or, in matrix notation,

$$A^{(k)}x=b^{(k)}. \tag{2.4}$$

The next step is to eliminate x_k. This is carried out according to the equations

$$a_{ij}^{(k+1)}=a_{ij}^{(k)}, \qquad b_i^{(k+1)}=b_i^{(k)}, \quad i\leqslant k, \tag{2.5}$$

$$a_{ij}^{(k+1)}=-m_{ik}a_{kj}^{(k)}+a_{ij}^{(k)}, \qquad b_i^{(k+1)}=-m_{ik}b_k^{(k)}+b_i^{(k)}, \quad i\geqslant k+1, \tag{2.6}$$

where $m_{k+1,k}, m_{k+2,k}, \ldots, m_{nk}$ are *multipliers* defined by

$$m_{ik}=a_{ik}^{(k)}/a_{kk}^{(k)}, \quad i=k+1, k+2, \ldots, n. \tag{2.7}$$

In "backward form", and in matrix notation, this step may be expressed as

$$L^{(k)}A^{(k+1)}=A^{(k)}, \qquad L^{(k)}b^{(k+1)}=b^{(k)}, \tag{2.8}$$

where $L^{(k)}$ is the elementary lower triangular matrix comprising the unit matrix I with its kth column replaced by

$$[0, \ldots, 0, 1, m_{k+1,k}, m_{k+2,k}, \ldots, m_{nk}]^{\mathrm{T}}. \tag{2.9}$$

The forward elimination stage is complete after $n-1$ steps, and we arrive at the triangularized system

$$A^{(n)}x=b^{(n)}, \tag{2.10}$$

or, in full,

$$\left.\begin{aligned} a_{11}^{(1)}x_1+a_{12}^{(1)}x_2+\ldots+a_{1n}^{(1)}x_n &= b_1^{(1)},\\ a_{22}^{(2)}x_2+\ldots+a_{2n}^{(2)}x_n &= b_2^{(2)},\\ \vdots\quad & \quad\vdots\\ a_{nn}^{(n)}x_n &= b_n^{(n)}. \end{aligned}\right\} \tag{2.11}$$

If we denote the full matrix of multipliers by

$$L \equiv \begin{bmatrix} 1 & 0 & \ldots & 0\\ m_{21} & 1 & \ldots & 0\\ \vdots & \vdots & \vdots\vdots\vdots & \vdots\\ m_{n1} & m_{n2} & \ldots & 1 \end{bmatrix}, \tag{2.12}$$

then it is easily verified by induction that

$$L = L^{(1)}L^{(2)}\ldots L^{(n-1)}. \tag{2.13}$$

Hence we have

$$LA^{(n)} = A^{(1)}, \qquad Lb^{(n)} = b^{(1)}. \tag{2.14}$$

The second stage is *backward elimination*. The kth step is carried out according to the equations

$$a_{i,n-k+1}^{(n+k)} = 0, \quad i \leqslant n-k; \qquad a_{ij}^{(n+k)} = a_{ij}^{(n+k-1)}, \quad \forall \text{ other } i,j; \tag{2.15}$$

$$\begin{aligned} b_i^{(n+k)} &= b_i^{(n+k-1)} - m_{i,n-k+1}b_{n-k+1}^{(n+k-1)}, \quad i \leqslant n-k;\\ b_i^{(n+k)} &= b_i^{(n+k-1)}, \quad i \geqslant n-k+1. \end{aligned} \tag{2.16}$$

Here the multipliers $m_{1k}, m_{2k}, \ldots, m_{k-1,k}$ are defined by

$$m_{ik} = a_{ik}^{(n)}/a_{kk}^{(n)} = a_{ik}^{(i)}/a_{kk}^{(k)}, \quad i = 1, 2, \ldots, k-1. \tag{2.17}$$

In contrast to the forward elimination, all the multipliers needed in the backward elimination can be computed at the outset of this stage. Corresponding to (2.8), the kth step may be expressed as

$$U^{(n-k+1)}A^{(n+k)} = A^{(n+k-1)}, \qquad U^{(n-k+1)}b^{(n+k)} = b^{(n+k-1)}, \tag{2.18}$$

where $A^{(n+k)} = [a_{ij}^{(n+k)}]$, $b^{(n+k)} = [b_i^{(n+k)}]$, and $U^{(k)}$ is the elementary upper triangular matrix comprising the unit matrix I with its kth column replaced by

$$[m_{1k}, m_{2k}, \ldots, m_{k-1,k}, 1, 0, \ldots, 0]^{\mathrm{T}}. \tag{2.19}$$

The backward elimination stage is complete after $n-1$ steps, and the system becomes

$$A^{(2n-1)}x = b^{(2n-1)}, \tag{2.20}$$

where $A^{(2n-1)}$ is diagonal. From (2.11) and (2.15) it is seen that the ith diagonal element of $A^{(2n-1)}$ is given by

$$a_{ii}^{(2n-1)} = a_{ii}^{(n)} = a_{ii}^{(i)}. \tag{2.21}$$

Corresponding to (2.12) we write

$$U = \begin{bmatrix} 1 & m_{12} & \dots & m_{1n} \\ 0 & 1 & \dots & m_{2n} \\ \vdots & \vdots & \vdots\vdots\vdots & \vdots \\ 0 & 0 & \dots & 1 \end{bmatrix}. \tag{2.22}$$

Then we have

$$U = U^{(n)}U^{(n-1)}\dots U^{(2)}, \tag{2.23}$$

and hence

$$UA^{(2n-1)} = A^{(n)}, \qquad Ub^{(2n-1)} = b^{(n)}. \tag{2.24}$$

The third, and final, stage of the process of solution is *normalization*. This is given by

$$x_i = b_i^{(2n-1)}/a_{ii}^{(2n-1)} = b_i^{(2n-1)}/a_{ii}^{(i)}, \quad i = 1, 2, \dots, n. \tag{2.25}$$

In matrix notation analogous to that of the preceding stages we write

$$C = A^{(2n-1)}. \tag{2.26}$$

Then after normalization we have

$$A^{(2n)}x = b^{(2n)}, \tag{2.27}$$

with $A^{(2n)} = I$. Thus

$$CA^{(2n)} = A^{(2n-1)}, \qquad Cb^{(2n)} = b^{(2n-1)}. \tag{2.28}$$

Lastly, from (2.14), (2.24) and (2.26), we observe that the matrices L, U and C are related to the triangular decomposition of $A^{(1)}$ by the formula

$$A^{(1)} = LUC. \tag{2.29}$$

3. Error Analysis of the Forward Elimination

We shall use the symbols γ and γ_l as in Olver (1982, section 2) to denote the common rp error bounds of all internal arithmetic operations in the main mode ($\mathscr{M}$) and lower mode ($\mathscr{L}$), respectively, and we assume that $\gamma, \gamma_l \in \mathscr{L}$ and $\gamma \leqslant \gamma_l$. Again, bars will be used to signify stored values, single bars implying storage in $\mathscr{M}$ and double bars implying storage in $\mathscr{L}$.

With these conventions $\bar{A}^{(1)}$ and $\bar{b}^{(1)}$ denote the stored values, in $\mathscr{M}$, of the matrix $A^{(1)}$ and vector $b^{(1)}$, respectively. We connect these values to the true values $A^{(1)}$ and $b^{(1)}$ by the equations

$$A^{(1)} = \bar{A}^{(1)} + \Delta A^{(1)}, \qquad b^{(1)} = \bar{b}^{(1)} + \Delta b^{(1)}. \tag{3.1}$$

In consequence, the system (2.1) is reformulated as

$$(\bar{A}^{(1)} + \Delta A^{(1)})x = \bar{b}^{(1)} + \Delta b^{(1)}. \tag{3.2}$$

The elements of the matrix $\Delta A^{(1)}$ and the components of the vector $\Delta b^{(1)}$ stem from inherent errors in the original data, or the input process, or from both these sources.

Their actual values are unknown, in general, but we shall assume that

$$|\Delta A^{(1)}| \leqslant \phi A^{(1)}, \qquad |\Delta b^{(1)}| \leqslant \phi b^{(1)}, \tag{3.3}$$

where the elements of $\phi A^{(1)}$ and components of $\phi b^{(1)}$ are known and belong to $\mathscr{L}$.†

All of the steps described in Section 2 are implemented numerically in $\mathscr{M}$. Thus, for example, $\bar{A}^{(k+1)}$ and $\bar{b}^{(k+1)}$, with $k \leqslant n-1$, denote the stored values, in $\mathscr{M}$, of the matrix of coefficients and vector of right-hand sides, respectively, after k steps of the forward elimination have been carried out. On the other hand, all steps in the computation of the error bounds are assumed to be carried out in $\mathscr{L}$, except where indicated otherwise.

The object of this section is to bound the matrix $\bar{L}\bar{A}^{(n)} - A^{(1)}$ and the vector $\bar{L}\bar{b}^{(n)} - b^{(1)}$; compare (2.14).

The kth elimination step is given by Equations (2.5) and (2.6). To analyse the errors incurred in their implementation on a computer, we recast them in backward form:

$$a_{ij}^{(k+1)} = a_{ij}^{(k)}, \qquad b_i^{(k+1)} = b_i^{(k)}, \quad i \leqslant k; \tag{3.4}$$

$$m_{ik} a_{kj}^{(k+1)} + a_{ij}^{(k+1)} = a_{ij}^{(k)}, \qquad m_{ik} b_k^{(k+1)} + b_i^{(k+1)} = b_i^{(k)}, \quad i \geqslant k+1; \tag{3.5}$$

compare (2.8) and (2.9).

To obtain the corresponding relations for the stored values suppose first that $i \leqslant k$. Then from (3.4) we obtain

$$\bar{a}_{ij}^{(k+1)} = \bar{a}_{ij}^{(k)}, \qquad \bar{b}_i^{(k+1)} = \bar{b}_i^{(k)}, \quad i \leqslant k. \tag{3.6}$$

Secondly, consider the annihilation positions, given by $i \geqslant k+1$ and $j = k$. From (2.7) and the definition of γ we see that

$$\bar{m}_{ik} \simeq \bar{a}_{ik}^{(k)}/\bar{a}_{kk}^{(k)}; \quad \mathrm{rp}\,(\gamma), \tag{3.7}$$

and hence

$$\bar{m}_{ik}\bar{a}_{kk}^{(k)} \simeq \bar{a}_{ik}^{(k)}; \quad \mathrm{rp}\,(\gamma). \tag{3.8}$$

On applying the conversion rule from rp to ap [Olver, 1982, (4.6)], we derive

$$\bar{m}_{ik}\bar{a}_{kk}^{(k)} \simeq \bar{a}_{ik}^{(k)}; \quad \mathrm{ap}\,(|\bar{a}_{ik}^{(k)}|\gamma\, e^{\gamma}). \tag{3.9}$$

Next, use of the exponential rule (Olver, 1982, Section 3) and the inequality $\gamma \leqslant \gamma_l$ yields

$$|\bar{a}_{ik}^{(k)}|\gamma e^{\gamma} \leqslant |\bar{a}_{ik}^{(k)}|\gamma e^{2\gamma_l}.$$

Therefore if we denote

$$\phi a_{ij}^{(k+1)} = |a_{ij}^{(k)}|, \quad i \geqslant k+1, \quad j = k, \tag{3.10}$$

and observe that $\bar{a}_{kk}^{(k)} = \bar{a}_{kk}^{(k+1)}$, then we may replace (3.9) by

$$\bar{m}_{ik}\bar{a}_{kk}^{(k+1)} = \bar{a}_{ik}^{(k)} - \Delta a_{ik}^{(k+1)}, \quad i \geqslant k+1, \tag{3.11}$$

where

$$|\Delta a_{ik}^{(k+1)}| \leqslant \overline{\overline{\phi a_{ik}^{(k+1)}}}\,\gamma\, e^{2\gamma_l}. \tag{3.12}$$

† The symbol ϕ is to be regarded as an "error bound operator" just as Δ is an "error operator", similarly for the symbols ∇, ψ, δ and χ introduced in section 4 below.

Lastly, suppose that $i \geqslant k+1$ and $j \geqslant k+1$. Corresponding to (3.8) and (3.9) we have

$$-\bar{m}_{ik}\bar{a}_{kj}^{(k)} \simeq -\overline{m_{ik}a_{kj}^{(k)}}; \quad \text{rp}\,(\gamma),$$

and

$$-\bar{m}_{ik}\bar{a}_{kj}^{(k)} \simeq -\overline{m_{ik}a_{kj}^{(k)}}; \quad \text{ap}\,(\overline{|m_{ik}a_{kj}^{(k)}|}\gamma\, e^{\gamma}).$$

Addition of $\bar{a}_{ij}^{(k)}$ to both sides followed by abbreviation of the right member to rp (γ) yields

$$-\bar{m}_{ik}\bar{a}_{kj}^{(k)} + \bar{a}_{ij}^{(k)} \simeq \bar{a}_{ij}^{(k+1)}; \quad \text{ap}\,\{(\overline{|m_{ik}a_{kj}^{(k)}|} + |\bar{a}_{ij}^{(k+1)}|)\gamma\, e^{\gamma}\}; \tag{3.13}$$

compare the first of (2.6). A further application of the exponential rule yields

$$\overline{|m_{ik}a_{kj}^{(k)}|} + |\bar{a}_{ij}^{(k+1)}| \leqslant \overline{\overline{|m_{ik}a_{kj}^{(k)}|}}\, e^{\gamma_l} + |\bar{\bar{a}}_{ij}^{(k+1)}| e^{\gamma_l} \leqslant \overline{\overline{\phi a_{ij}^{(k+1)}}}\, e^{2\gamma_l}, \tag{3.14}$$

where

$$\phi a_{ij}^{(k+1)} = |m_{ik}a_{kj}^{(k)}| + |a_{ij}^{(k+1)}|, \quad i,j \geqslant k+1. \tag{3.15}$$

As indicated in (3.14), in computing $\overline{\overline{\phi a_{ij}^{(k+1)}}}$ we assume that the product $|m_{ik}a_{kj}^{(k)}|$ and the term $|a_{ij}^{(k+1)}|$ are abbreviated separately from $\mathscr{M}$ to $\mathscr{L}$ and then added.† Using the inequality $\gamma \leqslant \gamma_l$ and substituting (3.14) in (3.13), we obtain

$$-\bar{m}_{ik}\bar{a}_{kj}^{(k)} + \bar{a}_{ij}^{(k)} \simeq \bar{a}_{ij}^{(k+1)}; \quad \text{ap}\,(\overline{\overline{\phi a_{ij}^{(k+1)}}}\gamma\, e^{3\gamma_l}). \tag{3.16}$$

Then by use of (3.6) we may recast this relation in the form

$$\bar{m}_{ik}\bar{a}_{kj}^{(k+1)} + \bar{a}_{ij}^{(k+1)} = \bar{a}_{ij}^{(k)} - \Delta a_{ij}^{(k+1)}, \quad i,j \geqslant k+1, \tag{3.17}$$

where

$$|\Delta a_{ij}^{(k+1)}| \leqslant \overline{\overline{\phi a_{ij}^{(k+1)}}}\gamma\, e^{3\gamma_l}. \tag{3.18}$$

In a similar manner we derive

$$\bar{m}_{ik}\bar{b}_{k}^{(k+1)} + \bar{b}_{i}^{(k+1)} = \bar{b}_{i}^{(k)} - \Delta b_{i}^{(k+1)}, \quad i \geqslant k+1, \tag{3.19}$$

where

$$|\Delta b_{i}^{(k+1)}| \leqslant \overline{\overline{\phi b_{i}^{(k+1)}}}\gamma\, e^{3\gamma_l}, \tag{3.20}$$

and

$$\phi b_{i}^{(k+1)} = |m_{ik}b_{k}^{(k)}| + |b_{i}^{(k+1)}|, \quad i \geqslant k+1. \tag{3.21}$$

Equations (3.6), (3.11), (3.17) and (3.19) may be combined into matrix form:

$$\bar{L}^{(k)}\bar{A}^{(k+1)} = \bar{A}^{(k)} - \Delta A^{(k+1)}, \qquad \bar{L}^{(k)}\bar{b}^{(k+1)} = \bar{b}^{(k)} - \Delta b^{(k+1)}, \tag{3.22}$$

where

$$\Delta A^{(k+1)} = \left[\begin{array}{c|ccc} 0 & & 0 & \\ \hline & \Delta a_{k+1,k}^{(k+1)} & \cdots & \Delta a_{k+1,n}^{(k+1)} \\ 0 & \vdots & \vdots & \vdots \\ & \Delta a_{nk}^{(k+1)} & \cdots & \Delta a_{nn}^{(k+1)} \end{array}\right], \qquad \Delta b^{(k+1)} = \left[\begin{array}{c} 0 \\ \hline \Delta b_{k+1}^{(k+1)} \\ \vdots \\ \Delta b_{n}^{(k+1)} \end{array}\right]. \tag{3.23}$$

† It is essential that the value of the product $m_{ik}a_{kj}^{(k)}$ be extracted from the main computations. However, the needed relation (3.16) would remain valid if $\phi a_{ij}^{(k+1)}$ were to be computed by adding $|m_{ik}a_{kj}^{(k)}|$ and $|a_{ij}^{(k+1)}|$ in $\mathscr{M}$ and then abbreviating the result to $\mathscr{L}$.

Equations (3.22) correspond to (2.8). In consequence of (3.12), (3.18) and (3.20) the error terms satisfy

$$|\Delta A^{(k+1)}| \leqslant \overline{\phi A^{(k+1)}}\,\gamma\, e^{3\gamma_l}, \qquad |\Delta b^{(k+1)}| \leqslant \overline{\phi b^{(k+1)}}\,\gamma\, e^{3\gamma_l}, \quad k = 1, 2, \ldots, n-1, \tag{3.24}$$

where

$$\phi A^{(k+1)} = \left[\begin{array}{c|ccc} O & & O & \\ \hline & \phi a_{k+1,k}^{(k+1)} & \ldots & \phi a_{k+1,n}^{(k+1)} \\ O & \vdots & \vdots\vdots\vdots & \vdots \\ & \phi a_{nk}^{(k+1)} & \ldots & \phi a_{nn}^{(k+1)} \end{array}\right], \qquad \phi b^{(k+1)} = \left[\begin{array}{c} O \\ \hline \phi b_{k+1}^{(k+1)} \\ \vdots \\ \phi b_n^{(k+1)} \end{array}\right]. \tag{3.25}$$

The elements of $\phi A^{(k+1)}$ and $\phi b^{(k+1)}$ are defined by (3.10), (3.15) and (3.21), and the bounds (3.24) apply whether the additions in (3.15) and (3.21) are carried out in $\mathscr{L}$ or $\mathscr{M}$, as long as the products $|m_{ik}a_{kj}^{(k)}|$ and $|m_{ik}b_k^{(k)}|$ are extracted from the main-mode computations.

The error analyses for all $n-1$ steps may be combined, as follows. From (3.1) and (3.22), with $k = 1$, we see that

$$\bar{L}^{(1)}\bar{A}^{(2)} = A^{(1)} - \Delta A^{(1)} - \Delta A^{(2)}. \tag{3.26}$$

Setting $k = 2$ in the first of (3.22) and premultiplying by $\bar{L}^{(1)}$, we obtain

$$\bar{L}^{(1)}\bar{L}^{(2)}\bar{A}^{(3)} = \bar{L}^{(1)}\bar{A}^{(2)} - \bar{L}^{(1)}(\Delta A^{(3)}). \tag{3.27}$$

Owing to the fact that $\bar{L}^{(1)}$ differs from I only in its first column and $\Delta A^{(3)}$ has a null first row, we have $\bar{L}^{(1)}(\Delta A^{(3)}) = \Delta A^{(3)}$. Substituting in (3.27) by means of this result and (3.26), we find that

$$\bar{L}^{(1)}\bar{L}^{(2)}\bar{A}^{(3)} = A^{(1)} - \Delta A^{(1)} - \Delta A^{(2)} - \Delta A^{(3)}.$$

Continuing in this manner, we may verify by induction that

$$\bar{L}^{(1)}\bar{L}^{(2)}\ldots\bar{L}^{(k)}\bar{A}^{(k+1)} = A^{(1)} - \Delta A^{(1)} - \Delta A^{(2)} - \ldots - \Delta A^{(k+1)}.$$

Forward elimination concludes at $k = n-1$. We then have

$$\bar{L}\bar{A}^{(n)} = A^{(1)} - \Delta A, \tag{3.28}$$

where $\bar{L}$ is given by (2.12) with each multiplier m_{ij} replaced by $\bar{m}_{ij}$, and

$$\Delta A = \Delta A^{(1)} + \Delta A^{(2)} + \ldots + \Delta A^{(n)}. \tag{3.29}$$

In a similar manner we arrive at

$$\bar{L}\bar{b}^{(n)} = b^{(1)} - \Delta b, \tag{3.30}$$

where

$$\Delta b = \Delta b^{(1)} + \Delta b^{(2)} + \ldots + \Delta b^{(n)}. \tag{3.31}$$

These are the required results. Bounds for the error terms ΔA and Δb are given above, and may be summarized as follows. Write

$$\phi A = \phi A^{(1)} + (\phi A^{(2)} + \phi A^{(3)} + \ldots + \phi A^{(n)})\gamma, \tag{3.32}$$

$$\phi b = \phi b^{(1)} + (\phi b^{(2)} + \phi b^{(3)} + \ldots + \phi b^{(n)})\gamma, \tag{3.33}$$

where $\phi A^{(k)}$ and $\phi b^{(k)}$ are defined as in (3.3) when $k = 1$, and by (3.10), (3.15), (3.21) and (3.25) for other values of k. Then by use of (3.24) and the exponential rule we have

$$|\Delta A| \leqslant \overline{\overline{\phi A}}\, e^{(n+3)\gamma_1}, \qquad |\Delta b| \leqslant \overline{\overline{\phi b}}\, e^{(n+3)\gamma_1}. \tag{3.34}$$

4. Error Analyses of the Backward Elimination and Normalization

The object of this section is to bound the matrices $\bar{U}\bar{A}^{(2n-1)} - \bar{A}^{(n)}$, $\bar{C}\bar{A}^{(2n)} - \bar{A}^{(2n-1)}$ and the vectors $\bar{U}\bar{b}^{(2n-1)} - \bar{b}^{(n)}$, $\bar{C}\bar{b}^{(2n)} - \bar{b}^{(2n-1)}$; compare (2.24) and (2.28). The analysis is similar to that of Section 3, and we merely state the main results.

The kth step of the backward elimination is given by (2.18). To obtain the corresponding equations satisfied by the stored values we proceed as follows. For $k = 1, 2, \ldots, n-1$ define

$$\psi A^{(n+k)} = \left[\begin{array}{c|c|c} & |a^{(n)}_{1,n-k+1}| & \\ O & \vdots & O \\ & |a^{(n)}_{n-k,n-k+1}| & \\ \hline O & O & O \end{array}\right], \qquad \psi b^{(n+k)} = \left[\begin{array}{c} \psi b^{(n+k)}_1 \\ \vdots \\ \psi b^{(n+k)}_{n-k} \\ \hline O \end{array}\right], \tag{4.1}$$

where

$$\psi b^{(n+k)}_i = |m_{i,n-k+1} b^{(n+k-1)}_{n-k+1}| + |b^{(n+k)}_i|. \tag{4.2}$$

Then

$$\bar{U}^{(n-k+1)}\bar{A}^{(n+k)} = \bar{A}^{(n+k-1)} - \nabla A^{(n+k)}, \qquad \bar{U}^{(n-k+1)}\bar{b}^{(n+k)} = \bar{b}^{(n+k-1)} - \nabla b^{(n+k)}, \tag{4.3}$$

where

$$|\nabla A^{(n+k)}| \leqslant \overline{\overline{\psi A^{(n+k)}}}\, \gamma\, e^{2\gamma_1}, \qquad |\nabla b^{(n+k)}| \leqslant \overline{\overline{\psi b^{(n+k)}}}\, \gamma\, e^{3\gamma_1}. \tag{4.4}$$

As in the case of (3.21), it is assumed that in the computation of $\overline{\overline{\psi b^{(n+k)}_i}}$ from (4.2) the product term is extracted from the main-mode computations.

The desired relations may now be expressed in the form:

$$\bar{U}\bar{A}^{(2n-1)} = \bar{A}^{(n)} - \nabla A, \tag{4.5}$$

$$\bar{U}\bar{b}^{(2n-1)} = \bar{b}^{(n)} - \nabla b, \tag{4.6}$$

where $\bar{U}$ is given by (2.22) with each multiplier m_{ij} replaced by $\bar{m}_{ij}$, and

$$\begin{aligned} \nabla A &= \nabla A^{(n+1)} + \nabla A^{(n+2)} + \ldots + \nabla A^{(2n-1)}, \\ \nabla b &= \nabla b^{(n+1)} + \nabla b^{(n+2)} + \ldots + \nabla b^{(2n-1)}. \end{aligned} \tag{4.7}$$

From (4.4) and the exponential rule we derive

$$|\nabla A| \leqslant \overline{\overline{\psi A}}\, \gamma\, e^{2\gamma_1}, \qquad |\nabla b| \leqslant \overline{\overline{\psi b}}\, \gamma\, e^{(n+1)\gamma_1}, \tag{4.8}$$

where

$$\psi A = \begin{bmatrix} 0 & |a_{12}^{(n)}| & \dots & |a_{1n}^{(n)}| \\ 0 & 0 & \dots & |a_{2n}^{(n)}| \\ \vdots & \vdots & \vdots\vdots\vdots & \vdots \\ 0 & 0 & \dots & 0 \end{bmatrix}, \tag{4.9}$$

and

$$\psi b = \psi b^{(n+1)} + \psi b^{(n+2)} + \dots + \psi b^{(2n-1)}. \tag{4.10}$$

For the normalization, we observe that $\bar{A}^{(2n)} = I$. Hence from (2.26) we have immediately

$$\bar{C}\bar{A}^{(2n)} = \bar{A}^{(2n-1)} - \delta A, \tag{4.11}$$

with

$$\delta A = 0. \tag{4.12}$$

Next, from (2.25) we have†

$$\bar{x}_i \simeq (\bar{a}_{ii}^{(2n-1)})^{-1} \bar{b}_i^{(2n-1)}; \quad \text{rp } (2\gamma). \tag{4.13}$$

From (2.27) we have $\bar{x}_i = \bar{b}_i^{(2n)}$. Hence we derive

$$\bar{a}_{ii}^{(2n-1)} \bar{b}_i^{(2n)} \simeq \bar{b}_i^{(2n-1)}; \quad \text{rp } (2\gamma), \tag{4.14}$$

or, in matrix ap form,

$$\bar{C}\bar{b}^{(2n)} = \bar{b}^{(2n-1)} - \delta b, \tag{4.15}$$

where

$$|\delta b| \leqslant 2\overline{\overline{\chi b}}\, \gamma\, e^{3\gamma_1}, \tag{4.16}$$

and

$$\chi b = |b^{(2n-1)}|. \tag{4.17}$$

5. Computation of the Inverse Matrix

As a preliminary to bounding $x - \bar{x}$ we first compute the inverse of $A^{(1)}$. An economical procedure is to compute in succession a diagonal matrix D, an upper triangular matrix E and a matrix F to satisfy the equations

$$DC = I, \qquad EU = D, \qquad FL = E. \tag{5.1}$$

Then from these equations and (2.29) we see that

$$FA^{(1)} = I. \tag{5.2}$$

† In constructing (4.13) we are assuming that two abbreviations are incurred in computing each component $\bar{x}_i$, one when the reciprocal of $\bar{a}_{ii}^{(2n-1)}$ is stored, the other when the product of this stored reciprocal and $\bar{b}_i^{(2n-1)}$ is stored. If, instead, $\bar{x}_i$ is formed by dividing $\bar{b}_i^{(2n-1)}$ directly by $\bar{a}_{ii}^{(2n-1)}$, then the error bound rp (2γ) in (4.13) may be reduced to rp (γ). The resulting overall gain is insignificant, however.

If we denote D, E and F in full by

$$D = \begin{bmatrix} d_1 & & & & \\ & d_2 & & & O \\ & & \cdot & & \\ O & & & \cdot & \\ & & & & d_n \end{bmatrix}, \qquad E = \begin{bmatrix} e_{11} & e_{12} & \dots & e_{1n} \\ 0 & e_{22} & \dots & e_{2n} \\ \vdots & \vdots & \vdots\vdots\vdots & \vdots \\ 0 & 0 & \dots & e_{nn} \end{bmatrix}, \tag{5.3}$$

$$F = \begin{bmatrix} f_{11} & f_{12} & \dots & f_{1n} \\ f_{21} & f_{22} & \dots & f_{2n} \\ \vdots & \vdots & \vdots\vdots\vdots & \vdots \\ f_{n1} & f_{n2} & \dots & f_{nn} \end{bmatrix}, \tag{5.4}$$

then the formulae for computing their elements are given by, in order,

$$d_i = 1/a_{ii}^{(2n-1)} = 1/a_{ii}^{(i)}, \tag{5.5}$$

$$e_{ii} = d_i, \tag{5.6}$$

$$e_{ij} = -e_{ii}m_{ij} - e_{i,i+1}m_{i+1,j} - \dots - e_{i,j-1}m_{j-1,j}, \quad j = i+1, i+2, \dots, n, \tag{5.7}$$

$$f_{in} = e_{in}, \tag{5.8}$$

and

$$f_{ij} = e_{ij} - f_{i,j+1}m_{j+1,j} - f_{i,j+2}m_{j+2,j} - \dots - f_{in}m_{nj}, \quad j = n-1, n-2, \dots, 1. \tag{5.9}$$

In (5.9) it is understood, of course, that $e_{ij} = 0$ when $i > j$.

We shall suppose that all of these computations are carried out in $\mathscr{L}$ (Section 3), and we now analyse propagation of the abbreviation errors. From (5.5) we derive

$$\bar{\bar{d}}_i \simeq (\bar{a}_{ii}^{(2n-1)})^{-1}; \quad \text{rp}\,(2\gamma_l), \tag{5.10}$$

and hence

$$\bar{\bar{D}}\bar{C} = I + \delta D, \tag{5.11}$$

where

$$|\delta D| \leqslant 2I\gamma_l\, e^{2\gamma_l}. \tag{5.12}$$

This result applies whether the abbreviation from $\mathscr{M}$ to $\mathscr{L}$ takes place before or after forming the reciprocal of $\bar{a}_{ii}^{(2n-1)}$.

For the diagonal elements of E, we have from (5.6)

$$\bar{e}_{ii} = \bar{\bar{d}}_i. \tag{5.13}$$

In the computation of the off-diagonal elements $\bar{e}_{ij}$ from (5.7) we suppose that each of the multipliers $m_{ij}, m_{i+1,j}, \dots, m_{j-1,j}$ is abbreviated from $\mathscr{M}$ to $\mathscr{L}$ before use, and each product and also each partial sum is abbreviated to $\mathscr{L}$ as soon as it is formed. Furthermore, the products are summed in the order given. Then by use of the relations (7.6) and (7.7) of Olver (1982) we derive

$$\bar{e}_{ij} \simeq -\bar{e}_{ii}\bar{m}_{ij} - \bar{e}_{i,i+1}\bar{m}_{i+1,j} - \dots - \bar{e}_{i,j-1}\bar{m}_{j-1,j};$$

$$\text{ap}\left\{\left(\sum_{s=i}^{j-1} \overline{\overline{|e_{is}m_{sj}|}}\right)(e^{2\gamma_l}-1) + \left(\sum_{s=i+1}^{j-1} \overline{\overline{|e_{ii}m_{ij} + e_{i,i+1}m_{i+1,j} + \dots + e_{is}m_{sj}|}}\right)(e^{\gamma_l}-1)\right\}.$$

If we define

$$\psi e_{ij} = 2\left(\sum_{s=i}^{j-1} |e_{is}m_{sj}|\right) + \left(\sum_{s=i+1}^{j-1} |e_{ii}m_{ij}+e_{i,i+1}m_{i+1,j}+\ldots+e_{is}m_{sj}|\right), \quad i<j, \tag{5.14}$$

then by use of the inequalities $e^{2\gamma_l}-1 \leqslant 2\gamma_l e^{2\gamma_l}$, $e^{\gamma_l}-1 \leqslant \gamma_l e^{\gamma_l}$ and the exponential rule, we conclude that

$$\bar{e}_{ii}\bar{m}_{ij}+\bar{e}_{i,i+1}\bar{m}_{i+1,j}+\ldots+\bar{e}_{i,j-1}\bar{m}_{j-1,j}+\bar{e}_{ij} = \nabla e_{ij}, \tag{5.15}$$

where

$$|\nabla e_{ij}| \leqslant \overline{\overline{\psi e_{ij}}}\,\gamma_l\, e^{(j-i+3)\gamma_l}, \quad i<j. \tag{5.16}$$

In computing $\overline{\overline{\psi e_{ij}}}$ from (5.14) it is to be understood that the brackets are to be obeyed, and the values of $\overline{\overline{e_{is}m_{sj}}}$ and $\overline{\overline{e_{ii}m_{ij}+e_{i,i+1}m_{i+1,j}+\ldots+e_{is}m_{sj}}}$ to be used are those already available from the computation of the right-hand side of (5.7). From (5.13) and (5.15) it follows that

$$\bar{\bar{E}}\bar{U} = \bar{\bar{D}}+\nabla E, \tag{5.17}$$

where ∇E is the triangular matrix defined by $(\nabla E)_{ij} = \nabla e_{ij}$ or 0, according to whether $i<j$ or $i \geqslant j$. On referring to (5.16) and noting that $j-i \leqslant n-1$, we see that

$$|\nabla E| \leqslant \overline{\overline{\psi E}}\,\gamma_l\, e^{(n+2)\gamma_l}, \tag{5.18}$$

where

$$\psi E = \begin{bmatrix} 0 & \psi e_{12} & \ldots & \psi e_{1n} \\ 0 & 0 & \ldots & \psi e_{2n} \\ \vdots & \vdots & \vdots\vdots\vdots & \vdots \\ 0 & 0 & \ldots & 0 \end{bmatrix}. \tag{5.19}$$

The error analysis of the third of (5.1) is similar. On defining

$$\phi f_{ij} = 2\left(\sum_{s=j+1}^{n} |f_{is}m_{sj}|\right) + \left(\sum_{s=j+1}^{n}{}' |e_{ij}-f_{i,j+1}m_{j+1,j}-f_{i,j+2}m_{j+2,j}-\ldots-f_{is}m_{sj}|\right), \quad j<n, \tag{5.20}$$

where the prime means that the term for $s=j+1$ is omitted when $j<i$ (that is, when $e_{ij}=0$), we have

$$\bar{f}_{in} = \bar{e}_{in}, \tag{5.21}$$

and

$$\bar{f}_{ij}+\bar{f}_{i,j+1}\bar{m}_{j+1,j}+\bar{f}_{i,j+2}\bar{m}_{j+2,j}+\ldots+\bar{f}_{in}\bar{m}_{nj} = \bar{e}_{ij}+\Delta f_{ij}, \quad j<n, \tag{5.22}$$

where

$$|\Delta f_{ij}| \leqslant \overline{\overline{\phi f_{ij}}}\,\gamma_l\, e^{(n-j+3)\gamma_l}. \tag{5.23}$$

Similar observations apply to the computation of $\overline{\overline{\phi f_{ij}}}$ from (5.20) to those made above concerning the computation of $\overline{\overline{\psi e_{ij}}}$ from (5.14). The matrix result that is equivalent to (5.21), (5.22) and (5.23) is given by

$$\bar{F}\bar{L} = \bar{E}+\Delta F, \tag{5.24}$$

where

$$|\Delta F| \leqslant \overline{\overline{\phi F}}\, \gamma_l\, e^{(n+2)\gamma_l}, \tag{5.25}$$

and

$$\phi F = \begin{bmatrix} \phi f_{11} & \phi f_{12} & \cdots & \phi f_{1,n-1} & 0 \\ \phi f_{21} & \phi f_{22} & \cdots & \phi f_{2,n-1} & 0 \\ \vdots & \vdots & \vdots\vdots\vdots & \vdots & \vdots \\ \phi f_{n1} & \phi f_{n2} & \cdots & \phi f_{n,n-1} & 0 \end{bmatrix}. \tag{5.26}$$

We now combine (5.11), (5.17) and (5.24) with (3.28), (4.5) and (4.11) to obtain an expression for $\bar{\bar{F}}A^{(1)}-I$. Premultiplying (3.28) throughout by $\bar{\bar{F}}$ and substituting for $\bar{\bar{F}}\bar{L}$ by means of (5.24), we obtain

$$\bar{\bar{F}}A^{(1)} - \bar{\bar{E}}\bar{A}^{(n)} = \bar{\bar{F}}(\Delta A) + (\Delta F)\bar{A}^{(n)}. \tag{5.27}$$

Similarly from (4.5) and (5.17) we have

$$\bar{\bar{E}}\bar{A}^{(n)} - \bar{\bar{D}}\bar{A}^{(2n-1)} = \bar{\bar{E}}(\nabla A) + (\nabla E)\bar{A}^{(2n-1)}, \tag{5.28}$$

and from (4.11) and (5.11) we have

$$\bar{\bar{D}}\bar{A}^{(2n-1)} - \bar{A}^{(2n)} = \bar{\bar{D}}(\delta A) + (\delta D)\bar{A}^{(2n)}. \tag{5.29}$$

Adding the last three equations and recalling that $\bar{A}^{(2n)} = I$ and $\delta A = 0$, we arrive at the required result in the form

$$\bar{\bar{F}}A^{(1)} = I + G, \tag{5.30}$$

where

$$G = \bar{\bar{F}}(\Delta A) + (\Delta F)\bar{A}^{(n)} + \bar{\bar{E}}(\nabla A) + (\nabla E)\bar{A}^{(2n-1)} + \delta D. \tag{5.31}$$

6. Error Bounds for the Computed Solution

If we combine (5.11), (5.17) and (5.24) with (3.30), (4.6) and (4.15) in a manner similar to that used to derive (5.30) and (5.31), and also recall that $\bar{b}^{(2n)} = \bar{x}$, then we obtain

$$\bar{\bar{F}}b^{(1)} = \bar{x} + h, \tag{6.1}$$

where

$$h = \bar{\bar{F}}(\Delta b) + (\Delta F)\bar{b}^{(n)} + \bar{\bar{E}}(\nabla b) + (\nabla E)\bar{b}^{(2n-1)} + \bar{\bar{D}}(\delta b) + (\delta D)\bar{x}. \tag{6.2}$$

Premultiplication of the original system (2.1) by $\bar{\bar{F}}$ yields

$$\bar{\bar{F}}A^{(1)}x = \bar{\bar{F}}b^{(1)}. \tag{6.3}$$

Substituting by means of (5.30) and (6.1), we find that

$$(I+G)x = \bar{x} + h. \tag{6.4}$$

This equation relates the true solution x to the computed solution $\bar{x}$.

In order to derive bounds for $|x-\bar{x}|$ from (6.4) we recast this identity in the form

$$(I+G)(x-\bar{x}) = h - G\bar{x}. \tag{6.5}$$

Henceforth we impose the condition

$$\|G\| < 1, \tag{6.6}$$

the norm being the infinity norm, as defined in Section 1. Then from (6.5) we have

$$x-\bar{x} = (I-G+G^2-\ldots)(h-G\bar{x}). \tag{6.7}$$

Therefore

$$\|x-\bar{x}\| \leqslant (1+\|G\|+\|G\|^2+\ldots)\|h-G\bar{x}\|,$$

that is,

$$\|x-\bar{x}\| \leqslant \frac{\|h-G\bar{x}\|}{1-\|G\|}; \tag{6.8}$$

compare, for example, Wilkinson (1963, Chapter 3, section 12). This inequality supplies a uniform bound for the absolute error in any component of the solution. Sharper bounds for individual components are furnished by

$$|x_i-\bar{x}_i| \leqslant |(h-G\bar{x})_i| + \frac{\|G\|\,\|h-G\bar{x}\|}{1-\|G\|}, \quad i = 1, 2, \ldots, n, \tag{6.9}$$

this result being another deduction from (6.7).

To apply (6.8) and (6.9) we need to bound $\|G\|$ and $|h-G\bar{x}|$. For the former we have, from (5.31),

$$\|G\| \leqslant \|\bar{\bar{F}}\|\,\|\Delta A\| + \|\Delta F\|\,\|\bar{A}^{(n)}\| + \|\bar{\bar{E}}\|\,\|\nabla A\| + \|\nabla E\|\,\|\bar{A}^{(2n-1)}\| + \|\delta D\|. \tag{6.10}$$

For the latter we have, from (5.31) and (6.2)

$$\begin{aligned} h-G\bar{x} = \bar{\bar{F}}\{(\Delta b)-(\Delta A)\bar{x}\} + \bar{\bar{E}}\{(\nabla b)-(\nabla A)\bar{x}\} + \bar{\bar{D}}(\delta b) + \\ (\Delta F)(\bar{b}^{(n)}-\bar{A}^{(n)}\bar{x}) + (\nabla E)(\bar{b}^{(2n-1)}-\bar{A}^{(2n-1)}\bar{x}). \end{aligned} \tag{6.11}$$

Hence

$$|h-G\bar{x}| \leqslant p+q, \tag{6.12}$$

where

$$p = |\bar{\bar{F}}|(|\Delta b| + |\Delta A|\,|\bar{x}|) + |\bar{\bar{E}}|(|\nabla b| + |\nabla A|\,|\bar{x}|) + |\bar{\bar{D}}|\,|\delta b|, \tag{6.13}$$

$$q = |\Delta F|\,|\bar{b}^{(n)}-\bar{A}^{(n)}\bar{x}| + |\nabla E|\,|\bar{b}^{(2n-1)}-\bar{A}^{(2n-1)}\bar{x}|. \tag{6.14}$$

Bounds for ΔA, Δb, ∇A, ∇b, δb, ΔF, ∇E and δD that are needed in (6.10), (6.12), (6.13) and (6.14) are supplied in Sections 3–5.

The inequalities (6.8) and (6.9) constitute the main result of this paper. The major task that remains is to convert these bounds into computable form: this is carried out in Section 7. In the rest of the present section we offer some general comments on the nature of the bounds.

(i) Equations (5.31), (6.5) and, especially, (6.11) enable us to identify clearly the contributions of individual errors to the final solution, as follows.

Suppose first that there are no inherent errors. Then the terms that appear in the first line of the right-hand side of (6.11) all contain a factor γ in their bounds (Sections 3 and 4). They are therefore $O(\gamma)$. Next, because $A^{(n)}x = b^{(n)}$ and $A^{(2n-1)}x = b^{(2n-1)}$ the vectors $\bar{b}^{(n)}-\bar{A}^{(n)}\bar{x}$ and $\bar{b}^{(2n-1)}-\bar{A}^{(2n-1)}\bar{x}$ are both $O(\gamma)$.

Furthermore, the bounds for ΔF and ∇E both contain γ_l as a factor (Section 5). Hence the contribution of the second line of (6.11) is $O(\gamma_l\gamma)$. In a similar way it is seen that the second term on the right-hand side of (6.9) is $O(\gamma_l\gamma)$. Accordingly, the dominant contribution to the bound (6.9) derives from the first line of (6.11).

Now suppose that there are inherent errors, as well as abbreviation errors. Then the statement made in the last sentence of the preceding paragraph still holds, because the inherent errors enter (6.10) and (6.11) only through the terms ΔA and Δb; compare (3.1), (3.29) and (3.31).

To appreciate the contributions of the individual dominant terms consider, for example, $\bar{\bar{F}}\{(\Delta b)-(\Delta A)\bar{x}\}$. This arises from the inherent errors $\Delta A^{(1)}$ and $\Delta b^{(1)}$ of the original system and the abbreviation errors $\Delta A^{(2)}, \ldots, \Delta A^{(n)}$ and $\Delta b^{(2)}, \ldots, \Delta b^{(n)}$ incurred during the forward elimination stage. Since $\bar{\bar{F}}$ agrees with $(\bar{A}^{(1)})^{-1}$ to within a factor $I+O(\gamma_l)$, the contributions $\bar{\bar{F}}(\Delta b^{(1)})$ and $-\bar{\bar{F}}(\Delta A^{(1)})\bar{x}$ agree with the linearized changes in the solution caused by admissible changes in the data. Next, from (3.10), (3.15), (3.24) and (3.25) it is clear that $\Delta A^{(k)}$ represents the absolute error in $\bar{A}^{(k)}$ stemming from the abbreviations made in forming the multipliers $\bar{m}_{i,k-1}$ and the elements $\bar{a}_{ij}^{(k)}$. Similarly $\Delta b^{(k)}$ represents the absolute error in $\bar{b}^{(k)}$ stemming from abbreviations made in forming the components $\bar{b}_i^{(k)}$. Furthermore, because the last $n-k+1$ columns of $(A^{(k)})^{-1}$ are the same as those of $(A^{(1)})^{-1}$,† and the first $k-1$ rows of $\Delta A^{(k)}$ and the first $k-1$ components of $\Delta b^{(k)}$ all vanish, it follows that

$$(A^{(k)})^{-1}\{(\Delta b^{(k)})-(\Delta A^{(k)})\bar{x}\} = (A^{(1)})^{-1}\{(\Delta b^{(k)})-(\Delta A^{(k)})\bar{x}\}.$$

Hence $\bar{\bar{F}}\{(\Delta b^{(k)})-(\Delta A^{(k)})\bar{x}\}$ agrees precisely with the linearized perturbations in the solution that are caused by the changes $\Delta A^{(k)}$ and $\Delta b^{(k)}$ in $A^{(k)}$ and $b^{(k)}$, respectively.

In a similar manner we may verify that the contributions from the terms $\bar{\bar{E}}\{(\nabla b)-(\nabla A)\bar{x}\}$ and $\bar{\bar{D}}(\delta b)$ in (6.11) agree with linearized perturbations in the solution that are caused by abbreviation errors introduced during the backward elimination and normalization stages, respectively.‡

(ii) It is easily seen that the agreement with linearized perturbation theory (for the propagation of individual errors) is preserved in the passage from the identity (6.11) to the bound (6.12). We now consider the effects of all the inherent and abbreviation errors when taken together, and enquire whether these errors can combine in such a way that the bound (6.12) is attained. In answering this question we shall ignore terms that are $O(\gamma_l\gamma)$; in particular, this means that in (6.12) we consider only the contribution of p.

First, on re-examining the analysis of Section 3 we soon perceive that apart from the factor $e^{(n+3)\gamma_l}$, that is, apart from a second-order perturbation, the bounds (3.34) for ΔA and Δb would be attained if all the inherent errors and all the abbreviation errors incurred in computing $\bar{A}^{(n)}$ and $\bar{b}^{(n)}$ were to attain their maximum values and have appropriate signs. Similarly, the bounds (4.8) and (4.16) for ∇A, ∇b and δb are attainable (in theory) except for second-order effects.

Now we enquire whether it is possible for the first error vector in (6.11), namely

† This can be seen from the identity $(A^{(k)})^{-1} = (A^{(1)})^{-1}L^{(1)}L^{(2)}\ldots L^{(k-1)}$, obtained from the first of (2.8).

‡ Error theories for Gaussian elimination based on linearized perturbation theory have been discussed by Miller & Spooner (1978) and Stummel (unpublished). These references are not concerned with strict error bounds, however.

$\bar{\bar{F}}(\Delta b)$, to attain its corresponding bound in (6.13), that is, $|\bar{\bar{F}}|\,|\Delta b|$ with $|\Delta b|$ assigned its maximum possible value. If we consider just one component of $\bar{\bar{F}}(\Delta b)$, say the ith, then the answer is affirmative. This is because the full expression for this component is given by

$$\sum_{k=1}^{n} (\bar{\bar{F}})_{ik}(\Delta b)_k;$$

hence it suffices for each component $(\Delta b)_k$ of Δb to attain its maximum possible absolute value, and to have the same sign as the corresponding element $(\bar{\bar{F}})_{ik}$ of $\bar{\bar{F}}$. In general, however, it will not be possible for $(\Delta b)_k$ to have the same sign as $(\bar{\bar{F}})_{ik}$, *for all values of* i. In other words, there may not exist a single sign pattern of the $(\Delta b)_k$, $k = 1, 2, \ldots, n$, that enables the maximum bound for each of the n components of $\bar{\bar{F}}(\Delta b)$ to be attained simultaneously. Similar observations apply to the error vectors involving ΔA, ∇b and ∇A on the right-hand sides of (6.11) and (6.13). Therefore, although the bound (6.9) is attainable (in theory) for any chosen value of i, usually it will be impossible for this bound to be attained simultaneously for all values of i. On the other hand, the bound represented by (6.8) is attainable (in theory) by at least one component of $|x-\bar{x}|$.†

(iii) The final topic to be discussed in this section is the condition (6.6). All of the error bounds we have constructed contain either γ or γ_l as a factor, except the bounds (3.3) for the inherent errors. Accordingly, if $\Delta A^{(1)} = 0$ and $\bar{A}^{(1)}$ is non-singular, then it is always possible to satisfy (6.6) by taking γ and γ_l to be small enough, that is, by working with enough significant figures in each computational mode. However, if $\Delta A^{(1)} \neq 0$, that is, if there are inherent errors in $\bar{A}^{(1)}$, then it is possible to satisfy (6.6) with sufficiently small values of γ and γ_l only if $\|(\bar{A}^{(1)})^{-1}(\Delta A^{(1)})\| < 1$. This is evident from (5.31) and the relation

$$\bar{\bar{F}} = (\bar{A}^{(1)})^{-1}\{I+O(\gamma_l)\}.$$

This conclusion is hardly surprising: in effect it informs us that the perturbations in the given matrix $\bar{A}^{(1)}$ that are permitted by the bounds for the inherent errors must not be so large as to allow the perturbed matrix to become singular.

7. Computable Forms of the Error Bounds; Cost of the Computations

The purpose of this section is to cast the bounds (6.8) and (6.9) into computable form. The only extra condition that we shall need to impose on the parameters of the computing facility is given by

$$(3n+15)\gamma_l \leqslant t_0, \tag{7.1}$$

where $t_0 = 1{\cdot}2564 \ldots$ is defined in Olver (1982, Section 3). As a preliminary we record the following (easily verified) matrix form of the exponential rule of Olver (1982, Section 3). *Suppose we are given vectors of order* $n \times 1$ *and matrices of order*

† In practice, unless n is quite small the possibility that *all* the individual abbreviation errors actually attain their maximum values and reinforce the effect of each other in the final solution is so remote as to be almost inconceivable. Nevertheless, with our present knowledge we must allow for the possibility in order to be able to guarantee that our bounds are strict.

$n\times n$, all of whose elements are non-negative and stored exactly in $\mathscr{L}$. Each time two such vectors, or two such matrices, are added in the lower mode, an upper bound for each element of the true sum is e^{γ_l} times the corresponding element of the stored sum. Also, each time one of these vectors or matrices is premultiplied by another of these matrices in the lower mode, an upper bound for each element of the true product is $e^{n\gamma_l}$ times the corresponding element of the stored product.

The first quantity to be treated is the vector p defined by (6.13). Substituting by means of (3.34), (4.8) and (4.16) we have

$$p \leqslant |\bar{\bar{F}}|(\overline{\overline{\phi b}}\, e^{(n+3)\gamma_l} + \overline{\overline{\phi A}}|\bar{x}|\, e^{(n+3)\gamma_l}) + |\bar{\bar{E}}|(\overline{\overline{\psi b}}\,\gamma\, e^{(n+1)\gamma_l} + \overline{\overline{\psi A}}|\bar{x}|\,\gamma\, e^{2\gamma_l}) + 2|\bar{\bar{D}}|\overline{\overline{\chi b}}\,\gamma\, e^{3\gamma_l}.$$

Then applying the matrix form of the exponential rule and the inequality $|\bar{x}| \leqslant |\bar{\bar{x}}|e^{\gamma_l}$ we derive

$$p \leqslant \bar{\bar{y}}\, e^{(3n+6)\gamma_l}, \tag{7.2}$$

where y is the vector defined by

$$y = |F|\{(\phi b) + (\phi A)|x|\} + [|E|\{(\psi b) + (\psi A)|x|\} + 2|D|(\chi b)]\gamma. \tag{7.3}$$

The next quantity to be treated is the vector q defined by (6.14). Because q is $O(\gamma_l\gamma)$ we shall use norms in constructing a bound; this will save computing time and storage without incurring significant loss of sharpness in the final bounds for $|x-\bar{x}|$. We proceed from the inequality

$$q \leqslant \|q\|\iota, \tag{7.4}$$

where ι denotes the vector whose elements are all unity. From (6.14) we have

$$\|q\| \leqslant \|\Delta F\|\,\|\bar{b}^{(n)} - \bar{A}^{(n)}\bar{x}\| + \|\nabla E\|\,\|\bar{b}^{(2n-1)} - \bar{A}^{(2n-1)}\bar{x}\|. \tag{7.5}$$

Substituting by means of (5.18) and (5.25) we obtain

$$\|q\| \leqslant (\|\overline{\overline{\phi F}}\|\,\|\bar{b}^{(n)} - \bar{A}^{(n)}\bar{x}\| + \|\overline{\overline{\psi E}}\|\,\|\bar{b}^{(2n-1)} - \bar{A}^{(2n-1)}\bar{x}\|)\gamma_l\, e^{(n+2)\gamma_l}. \tag{7.6}$$

We now majorize each term in this bound in turn.

The vectors $\bar{b}^{(n)} - \bar{A}^{(n)}\bar{x}$ and $\bar{b}^{(2n-1)} - \bar{A}^{(2n-1)}\bar{x}$ have to be computed in the main mode [otherwise the bound for q would not be $O(\gamma_l\gamma)$]. Referring to Olver [1982, (7.6) and (7.7)], and bearing in mind that $\bar{A}^{(n)}$ is upper triangular, we see that

$$(\bar{b}^{(n)} - \bar{A}^{(n)}\bar{x})_i \simeq \overline{(b^{(n)} - A^{(n)}x)}_i;$$

$$\mathrm{ap}\left\{\left(\sum_{s=i}^{n} \overline{|a_{is}^{(n)}x_s|} + \sum_{s=i}^{n} \overline{|b_i^{(n)} - a_{ii}^{(n)}x_i - \ldots - a_{is}^{(n)}x_s|}\right)(e^{\gamma}-1)\right\}.$$

Since the term for $s=n$ in the second sum equals $|\overline{(b^{(n)} - A^{(n)}x)}_i|$, we deduce that

$$|(\bar{b}^{(n)} - \bar{A}^{(n)}\bar{x})_i| \leqslant |\overline{(b^{(n)} - A^{(n)}x)}_i|\, e^{\gamma} + \left(\sum_{s=i}^{n} \overline{|a_{is}^{(n)}x_s|} + \sum_{s=i}^{n-1} \overline{|b_i^{(n)} - a_{ii}^{(n)}x_i - \ldots - a_{is}^{(n)}x_s|}\right)(e^{\gamma}-1).$$

After $b^{(n)} - A^{(n)}x$ has been formed in $\mathscr{M}$ it is abbreviated to $\mathscr{L}$. Applying the exponential rule and the inequalities $\gamma \leqslant \gamma_l$, $e^{\gamma}-1 \leqslant \gamma\, e^{\gamma_l}$, we conclude that

$$|\bar{b}^{(n)} - \bar{A}^{(n)}\bar{x}| \leqslant \bar{\bar{r}}^{(n)}\, e^{(n+4)\gamma_l}, \tag{7.7}$$

where

$$(r^{(n)})_i = |(b^{(n)} - A^{(n)}x)_i| + \left\{\left(\sum_{s=i}^{n} |a_{is}^{(n)}x_s|\right) + \left(\sum_{s=i}^{n-1} |b_i^{(n)} - a_{ii}^{(n)}x_i - a_{i,i+1}^{(n)}x_{i+1} - \ldots - a_{is}^{(n)}x_s|\right)\right\}\gamma. \quad (7.8)$$

Hence

$$\|\bar{b}^{(n)} - \bar{A}^{(n)}\bar{x}\| \leqslant \|\bar{\bar{r}}^{(n)}\|\, e^{(n+4)\gamma_l}. \quad (7.9)$$

Similarly we derive

$$\|\bar{b}^{(2n-1)} - \bar{A}^{(2n-1)}\bar{x}\| \leqslant \|\bar{\bar{r}}^{(2n-1)}\|\, e^{4\gamma_l}, \quad (7.10)$$

where

$$(r^{(2n-1)})_i = |(b^{(2n-1)} - A^{(2n-1)}x)_i| + |a_{ii}^{(2n-1)}x_i|\gamma. \quad (7.11)$$

Again, in computing $(r^{(n)})_i$ and $(r^{(2n-1)})_i$ from (7.8) and (7.11) the residuals $(b^{(n)} - A^{(n)}x)_i$ and $(b^{(2n-1)} - A^{(2n-1)}x)_i$ must be computed in $\mathscr{M}$, and subsequently abbreviated to $\mathscr{L}$. Furthermore the products $a_{is}^{(n)}x_s$, $a_{ii}^{(2n-1)}x_i$, and the partial sums $b_i^{(n)} - a_{ii}^{(n)}x_i - \ldots - a_{is}^{(n)}x_s$ are to be taken from the values already available in $\mathscr{M}$. The bounds (7.9) and (7.10) are valid whether the remaining computations are performed in $\mathscr{M}$ or $\mathscr{L}$, provided that the bracketing in (7.8) is obeyed.

The other norms needed in (7.6) are matrix norms. Care is needed in forming them, since the computed values may be less than the true values. However, because each matrix norm is computed by summing n non-negative scalars in $\mathscr{L}$, an upper bound for its true value is obtained by multiplying the computed value by $e^{(n-1)\gamma_l}$, or more sharply, $e^{(k-1)\gamma_l}$, where k is the maximum number of non-zero elements in any row. Hence from (7.6), (7.9), (7.10) and the exponential rule we conclude that

$$\|q\| \leqslant \bar{\bar{\eta}}\, e^{(3n+7)\gamma_l}, \quad (7.12)$$

where

$$\eta = (\|\phi F\|\, \|r^{(n)}\| + \|\psi E\|\, \|r^{(2n-1)}\|)\gamma_l. \quad (7.13)$$

This is the desired bound for q.

The bounds (7.2) and (7.12) may be combined to yield a bound for $h - G\bar{x}$. On referring to (6.12) and (7.4) we immediately derive

$$|h - G\bar{x}| \leqslant (\bar{y} + \bar{\bar{\eta}}\iota)\, e^{(3n+7)\gamma_l}, \quad (7.14)$$

and, as a corollary,

$$\|h - G\bar{x}\| \leqslant (\|\bar{y}\| + \bar{\bar{\eta}})\, e^{(3n+7)\gamma_l}. \quad (7.15)$$

The remaining quantity that is needed in (6.8) and (6.9) is $\|G\|$. As in the case of q, $\|G\|$ may be replaced by a comparatively crude bound. We proceed from the inequality

$$\|G\| \leqslant \|\bar{\bar{F}}\|\, \|\overline{\overline{\phi A}}\|\, e^{(n+3)\gamma_l} + \|\overline{\overline{\phi F}}\|\, \|\bar{A}^{(n)}\|\gamma_l\, e^{(n+2)\gamma_l} + \|\bar{\bar{E}}\|\, \|\overline{\overline{\psi A}}\|\gamma\, e^{2\gamma_l} + \|\overline{\overline{\psi E}}\|\, \|\bar{A}^{(2n-1)}\|\gamma_l\, e^{(n+2)\gamma_l} + 2\gamma_l\, e^{2\gamma_l},$$

which is obtained from (6.10) by substituting (3.34), (4.8), (5.12), (5.18) and (5.25).

Using analysis similar to that used to derive (7.12) and (7.13), we conclude that

$$\|G\| \leqslant \bar{\rho}\, e^{(3n+6)\gamma_l}, \tag{7.16}$$

where

$$\rho = \|F\|\,\|\phi A\| + \|E\|\,\|\psi A\|\gamma + (\|\phi F\|\,\|A^{(n)}\| + \|\psi E\|\,\|A^{(2n-1)}\| + 2)\gamma_l. \tag{7.17}$$

As usual, the bound (7.16) applies independently of the order of summation and multiplication used in (7.17) as long as the bracketing is obeyed.

We also need a lower bound for $1-\|G\|$. By applying lemma 3.1 of Olver (1982) to (7.16) we obtain

$$\|G\| \leqslant \bar{\sigma}, \tag{7.18}$$

where

$$\sigma = \rho\{1+(6n+18)\gamma_l\}, \tag{7.19}$$

provided that $(3n+9)\gamma_l \leqslant t_0$, which is satisfied in consequence of the assumption (7.1). In order to satisfy (6.6) we restrict $\bar{\sigma} < 1$. Since

$$\overline{1-\sigma} \simeq 1-\bar{\sigma}; \quad \mathrm{rp}\,(\gamma_l),$$

it follows that

$$1-\|G\| \geqslant 1-\bar{\sigma} \geqslant \overline{1-\sigma}\; e^{-\gamma_l}. \tag{7.20}$$

Substituting in (6.8) by means of (7.15) and (7.20) and applying the exponential rule, we obtain

$$\|x-\bar{x}\| \leqslant \overline{(\|y\|+\eta)/(1-\sigma)}\; e^{(3n+10)\gamma_l}. \tag{7.21}$$

Similarly, from (6.9), (7.14), (7.15) and (7.18) we obtain

$$|x-\bar{x}| \leqslant \left(\bar{y} + \frac{\bar{\sigma}\|\bar{y}\|+\bar{\eta}}{1-\bar{\sigma}}\,\iota\right) e^{(3n+7)\gamma_l},$$

and hence

$$|x-\bar{x}| \leqslant \overline{y + \left(\frac{\sigma\|y\|+\eta}{1-\sigma}\right)\iota}\; e^{(3n+12)\gamma_l}. \tag{7.22}$$

Further applications of lemma 3.1 of Olver (1982) yield the desired computable forms of the final error bounds, given by

$$\|x-\bar{x}\| \leqslant \bar{\zeta}, \tag{7.23}$$

$$|x-\bar{x}| \leqslant \bar{z}, \tag{7.24}$$

where ζ is the scalar

$$\zeta = \frac{\|y\|+\eta}{1-\sigma}\{1+(6n+26)\gamma_l\}, \tag{7.25}$$

and z is the vector

$$z = \left(y + \frac{\sigma\|y\|+\eta}{1-\sigma}\,\iota\right)\{1+(6n+30)\gamma_l\}. \tag{7.26}$$

The requisite conditions of the cited lemma are satisfied in both cases in consequence of the assumption (7.1).

Let us summarize the main results of this section so far. The relations (7.24) and (7.26) supply computable bounds for the absolute errors in the individual components of the solution. The relations (7.23) and (7.25) supply a slightly simpler bound for the greatest of these errors. The only conditions needed are given by (7.1) and $\bar{\sigma} < 1$. Here σ is defined by (7.19) and (7.17), y is defined by (7.3), and η is defined by (7.13), (7.8) and (7.11); all norms in these expressions are infinity norms. The matrix ϕA and vector ϕb are defined in Section 3, the matrix ψA and vectors ψb and χb are defined in Section 4, and the matrices $D, E, F, \psi E$ and ϕF are defined in Section 5. All other quantities that appear in the bounds are defined in Section 2. Further details will become clear in the numerical example given in the next section.

What is the cost of computing the error bounds (7.25) and (7.26) compared with the cost of computing $\bar{x}$? We answer this question by supplying asymptotic estimates, for large n, of the total number of scalar arithmetic operations needed in the two computations.

First, consider multiplications and divisions. The total number required in the computation of $\bar{x}$ is $\frac{1}{3}n^3 + O(n^2)$. For the error bounds the computations that involve the greatest number of multiplications are the evaluations of E and F. They require $\frac{1}{6}n^3 + O(n^2)$ and $\frac{1}{2}n^3 + O(n^2)$, respectively. In the formation of ϕA, ϕb, ψA, ψb, χb, ψE and ϕF only $O(n^2)$ extra multiplications are needed when the prescriptions we have supplied are followed. The remaining computations, described in the present section, require no more than $O(n^2)$ multiplications and divisions. Accordingly, the total number of multiplications and divisions required to compute the error bounds is $\frac{2}{3}n^3 + O(n^2)$.

Secondly, consider additions (or subtractions). The total number required in the computation of the original solution is $\frac{1}{3}n^3 + O(n^2)$. The numbers of additions required in the computations of E and F are asymptotically the same as the corresponding numbers of multiplications, that is, $\frac{1}{6}n^3 + O(n^2)$ and $\frac{1}{2}n^3 + O(n^2)$, respectively. Next, the computation of ϕA entails $\frac{2}{3}n^3 + O(n^2)$ additions; compare (3.10), (3.15), (3.25) and (3.32). The computation of ψE entails $\frac{1}{3}n^3 + O(n^2)$ additions above those required to form E; compare (5.14) and (5.19). Similarly, the computation of ϕF requires $n^3 + O(n^2)$ extra additions. No other computation requires more than $O(n^2)$ additions, hence the total number of additions required to compute the error bounds is $\frac{8}{3}n^3 + O(n^2)$.

Summarizing the results of the two preceding paragraphs, we have shown that for large n the evaluation of the error bounds requires approximately twice as many multiplications (or divisions) and eight times as many additions (or subtractions) as the original computations. However, it should be appreciated that virtually all of the error-bound computations take place in the lower mode; in fact, the only exceptions are the evaluations of the residuals $b^{(n)} - A^{(n)}x$ and $b^{(2n-1)} - A^{(2n-1)}x$ needed in the computations of $r^{(n)}$ and $r^{(2n-1)}$ from (7.8) and (7.11). On the other hand, all of the original computations are performed in the main mode. In consequence, the extra computing time that is actually needed for the error bounds may be appreciably less than is suggested by the ratio 2 for multiplications and divisions, and 8 for additions and subtractions.†

† It is not easy to quantify this saving in a general manner, however. For example, if the main mode $\mathscr{M}$ is double precision then it may not always suffice to take the lower mode $\mathscr{L}$ to be single precision owing to the condition $\bar{\sigma} < 1$.

8. Example

We consider the solution of the following system of equations:†

$$\left.\begin{aligned} 0{\cdot}4096608x_1+0{\cdot}1234265x_2+0{\cdot}3678354x_3+0{\cdot}2943515x_4 &= 0{\cdot}4043867,\\ 0{\cdot}1784105x_1+0{\cdot}4002118x_2+0{\cdot}2786511x_3+0{\cdot}3927417x_4 &= -0{\cdot}2557968,\\ 0{\cdot}2246098x_1+0{\cdot}3872052x_2+0{\cdot}4015243x_3+0{\cdot}1129821x_4 &= 0{\cdot}1550030,\\ 0{\cdot}3645250x_1+0{\cdot}1920087x_2+0{\cdot}3728525x_3+0{\cdot}0643756x_4 &= 0{\cdot}4240800. \end{aligned}\right\} \quad (8.1)$$

All numbers are assumed to be correctly rounded approximations to their true values. Thus if the true system is denoted by (1.1), then in the notation of Section 3

$$A = \bar{A}^{(1)} + \Delta A^{(1)}, \qquad b = \bar{b}^{(1)} + \Delta b^{(1)}, \tag{8.2}$$

where $\bar{A}^{(1)}$ is the matrix of numerical coefficients on the left-hand sides of (8.1), and $\bar{b}^{(1)}$ is the vector of numerical values on the right-hand sides. In the bounds (3.3) each element of the matrix $\phi A^{(1)}$ is $0{\cdot}5\times 10^{-7}$, as is each component of the vector $\phi b^{(1)}$.

Our first objective is to compute the solution $x = [x_1, x_2, x_3, x_4]^{\mathrm{T}}$ as accurately as the data warrant without undue effort. More precisely, the cumulative contribution to $x-\bar{x}$ resulting from abbreviation errors introduced during the process of solution is to be comparable in magnitude with the perturbations in x that stem from the terms $\Delta A^{(1)}$ and $\Delta b^{(1)}$ in (8.2). As a guide to the optimum value of γ needed to achieve this objective, we observe that for a full system of n equations, the total number of inherent errors is n^2+n, and the total number of abbreviation errors is $\frac{2}{3}n^3+O(n^2)$ (in fact, all but $O(n^2)$ are made in the forward elimination stage). Provided that the system is solved in a stable manner—and we shall endeavour to ensure this by partial pivoting—it is reasonable to assume that the effects of the two types of error on the solution are comparable. Hence the maximum individual abbreviation error should be about $3/(2n)$ times the maximum individual inherent error.‡ In the present example we have $n = 4$, and the maximum rp in each element of data ranges from about $0{\cdot}12\times 10^{-6}$ to $0{\cdot}78\times 10^{-6}$. Therefore the rp of our working precision should be in the range $0{\cdot}45\times 10^{-7}$ to $0{\cdot}29\times 10^{-6}$. With this in mind, we choose the main mode, $\mathscr{M}$, to be eight decimal figures with correct rounding. In other words, when we state that "we compute in $\mathscr{M}$" in what follows, we mean that each sum, difference, product, or quotient is rounded to eight significant decimal figures, *immediately* it is formed. The value of the working relative precision γ is then given by

$$\gamma = 0{\cdot}5\times 10^{-7}; \tag{8.3}$$

compare Olver [1978, (4.7)]. For the lower mode, $\mathscr{L}$, we adopt a working precision of four decimal figures, again with correct rounding, with a similar interpretation of the phrase "we compute in $\mathscr{L}$"; in consequence

$$\gamma_l = 0{\cdot}5\times 10^{-3}. \tag{8.4}$$

† Compare the example given in National Physical Laboratory (1961, Chapter 1, section 8). The numerical entries have been extended randomly to seven decimals, and to avoid organizational complications the equations have been reordered in such a way that the pivots emerge in their natural order during the forward elimination stage.

‡ Compare also National Physical Laboratory (1961, Chapter 5, section 14).

8.1 *Forward Elimination*

The first step is given by Equations (2.5), (2.6), (2.7) with $k = 1$. Computing in $\mathscr{M}$, we obtain the following entries:

$\bar{m}_{i1}$	$\bar{A}^{(2)}$				$\bar{b}^{(2)}$
	0·40966080	0·12342650	0·36783540	0·29435150	0·40438670
0·43550786	0	0·34645859	0·11845589	0·26454931	−0·43191039
0·54828238	0	0·31953263	0·19984663	−0·048405640	−0·066715100
0·88982153	0	0·082181140	0·045544640	−0·19754470	0·064248010

At the same time, we compute in $\mathscr{L}$ the matrix $\phi A^{(2)}$ and vector $\phi b^{(2)}$, the non-zero elements of which are defined by (3.10), (3.15), (3.21) with $k = 1$. No further multiplications are needed on this step, only additions. In the case of (3.15), for example, the numerical values of the product $m_{i1} a_{1j}^{(1)}$ and the coefficient $a_{ij}^{(2)}$ are abbreviated from $\mathscr{M}$ to $\mathscr{L}$, and afterwards their absolute values are added in $\mathscr{L}$.

$\overline{\overline{\phi A^{(2)}}}$				$\overline{\overline{\phi b^{(2)}}}$
0	0	0	0	0
0·1784	0·4003	0·2787	0·3927	0·6080
0·2246	0·3872	0·4015	0·2098	0·2884
0·3645	0·1920	0·3728	0·4594	0·4241

Subsequent steps are carried out in a similar manner and the results are as follows.

$\bar{m}_{i2}$	$\bar{A}^{(3)}$				$\bar{b}^{(3)}$
	0·40966080	0·12342650	0·36783540	0·29435150	0·40438670
	0	0·34645859	0·11845589	0·26454931	−0·43191039
0·92228231	0	0	0·090596860	−0·29239479	0·33162821
0·23720336	0	0	0·017446505	−0·26029669	0·16669861

$\overline{\overline{\phi A^{(3)}}}$				$\overline{\overline{\phi b^{(3)}}}$
0	0	0	0	0
0	0	0	0	0
0	0·3195	0·1998	0·5364	0·7299
0	0·08218	0·04555	0·3231	0·2692

$\bar{m}_{i3}$	$\bar{A}^{(4)}$				$\bar{b}^{(4)}$
	0·40966080	0·12342650	0·36783540	0·29435150	0·40438670
	0	0·34645859	0·11845589	0·26454931	−0·43191039
	0	0	0·090596860	−0·29239479	0·33162821
0·19257295	0	0	0	−0·20398936	0·10283599

$\overline{\overline{\phi A^{(4)}}}$				$\overline{\overline{\phi b^{(4)}}}$
0	0	0	0	0
0	0	0	0	0
0	0	0	0	0
0	0	0·01745	0·2603	0·1667

The main computations of the forward elimination are now complete. For the subsequent computation of error bounds we record, in the lower mode, the matrix L defined by (2.12)

$\bar{\bar{L}}$

1	0	0	0
0·4355	1	0	0
0·5483	0·9223	1	0
0·8898	0·2372	0·1926	1

We shall also need the matrix ϕA and vector ϕb defined by (3.32) and (3.33). Recalling that each element of $\overline{\overline{\phi A^{(1)}}}$ and $\overline{\overline{\phi b^{(1)}}}$ is $0{\cdot}5000 \times 10^{-7}$ and computing in $\mathscr{L}$, we arrive at the following entries:

$\overline{\overline{\phi A}} \times 10^7$				$\overline{\overline{\phi b}} \times 10^7$
0·5000	0·5000	0·5000	0·5000	0·5000
0·5892	0·7002	0·6394	0·6964	0·8040
0·6123	0·8534	0·8007	0·8731	1·009
0·6823	0·6371	0·7180	1·022	0·9300

8.2 *Backward Elimination*

For the main computations of this stage it suffices to record the multipliers and right-hand sides, since the matrices $\bar{A}^{(5)}$, $\bar{A}^{(6)}$ and $\bar{A}^{(7)}$ are obtained from $\bar{A}^{(4)}$ simply by replacing appropriate elements by zeros. As each vector $b^{(n+k)}$ is computed in $\mathscr{M}$ the corresponding vector $\psi b^{(n+k)}$ is formed in $\mathscr{L}$. The requisite formulae are supplied by (2.16), (2.17), (4.1) and (4.2), and the steps are as follows.

$\bar{m}_{i4}$	$\bar{b}^{(5)}$	$\overline{\overline{\psi b^{(5)}}}$	$\bar{m}_{i3}$	$\bar{b}^{(6)}$	$\overline{\overline{\psi b^{(6)}}}$
−1·4429748	0·55277644	0·7012	4·0601341	−0·19520132	0·9432
−1·2968780	−0·29854466	0·4319	1·3075055	−0·53941972	0·7803
1·4333826	0·18422489	0·3316		0·18422489	0
	0·10283599	0		0·10283599	0

$\bar{m}_{i2}$	$\bar{b}^{(7)}$	$\overline{\overline{\psi b^{(7)}}}$
0·35625181	−0·0030320700	0·1952
	−0·53941972	0
	0·18422489	0
	0·10283599	0

At the conclusion of the main computations the non-zero elements of $\bar{A}^{(7)}$ are the diagonal elements of $\bar{A}^{(4)}$; thus:

$\bar{A}^{(7)}$

0·40966080	0	0	0
0	0·34645859	0	0
0	0	0·090596860	0
0	0	0	−0·20398936

For the error bounds we record, in $\mathscr{L}$, the matrix U defined by (2.22).

$\bar{U}$

1	0·3563	4·060	−1·443
0	1	1·308	−1·297
0	0	1	1·433
0	0	0	1

We shall also need the matrix ψA and vector ψb defined by (4.9) and (4.10). Computing in $\mathscr{L}$ we obtain the following entries:

		$\overline{\overline{\psi A}}$		$\overline{\overline{\psi b}}$
0	0·1234	0·3678	0·2944	1·839
0	0	0·1185	0·2645	1·212
0	0	0	0·2924	0·3316
0	0	0	0	0

8.3 *Normalization*

The final stage in the main computation is the solution of the diagonal system $A^{(7)}x = b^{(7)}$. This yields the required solution:

$$\bar{x} = [-0{\cdot}0074014160,\ -1{\cdot}5569529,\ 2{\cdot}0334578,\ -0{\cdot}50412428]^{\mathrm{T}}. \tag{8.5}$$

We also record, in $\mathscr{L}$, the matrix $C \equiv A^{(7)}$ and the vector $\chi b \equiv |b^{(7)}|$.

		$\bar{C}$		$\overline{\overline{\chi b}}$
0·4097	0	0	0	0·003032
0	0·3465	0	0	0·5394
0	0	0·09060	0	0·1842
0	0	0	−0·2040	0·1028

8.4 *Error Bounds*

The first step in the completion of the computation of the error bounds is to compute the matrices D, E and F by solution of equations (5.1); compare (5.5) to (5.9). At the same time we form ψE and ϕF by means of (5.14) and (5.20). All of these computations are carried out in $\mathscr{L}$.

$\bar{D}$

2·441	0	0	0
0	2·886	0	0
0	0	11·04	0
0	0	0	−4·902

	$\bar{E}$				$\overline{\overline{\psi E}}$		
2·441	−0·8697	−8·772	14·96	0	1·739	30·87	51·79
0	2·886	−3·775	9·153	0	0	7·550	27·46
0	0	11·04	−15·82	0	0	0	31·64
0	0	0	−4·902	0	0	0	0

$\bar{F}$				$\overline{\overline{\phi F}}$			
−7·234	6·321	−11·65	14·96	58·52	44·77	17·41	0
−7·644	5·823	−5·538	9·153	35·58	28·38	9·064	0
10·38	−9·247	14·09	−15·82	65·74	42·75	20·18	0
3·717	0·2923	0·9441	−4·902	14·37	4·360	1·888	0

The second step is to compute the vector y defined by (7.3). These computations are carried out in $\mathscr{L}$, the value of x being abbreviated from $\mathscr{M}$ to $\mathscr{L}$ at the outset. Intermediate steps are as follows.†

(i) $\times 10^7$	(ii) $\times 10^7$	(iii)	(iv)	(v) $\times 10^7$	$\bar{y} \times 10^7$
2·551	150·6	2·927	12·73	6·370	157·0
3·549	100·3	1·586	6·385	4·749	105·0
4·411	183·2	0·4790	5·288	4·678	187·9
3·902	33·81	0	0	0·5040	34·31

$$\text{(i)} \underset{(l)}{=} (\phi b)+(\phi A)|x|, \qquad \text{(ii)} \underset{(l)}{=} |F| \times \text{(i)}, \qquad \text{(iii)} \underset{(l)}{=} (\psi b)+(\psi A)|x|,$$

$$\text{(iv)} \underset{(l)}{=} |E| \times \text{(iii)}, \qquad \text{(v)} \underset{(l)}{=} \{\text{(iv)}+2|D|(\chi b)\}\gamma, \qquad y \underset{(l)}{=} \text{(ii)}+\text{(v)}.$$

The third step is to compute the scalar η defined by (7.13). We first evaluate the residuals $b^{(4)}-A^{(4)}x$ and $b^{(7)}-A^{(7)}x$. These computations are carried out in $\mathscr{M}$, and the results abbreviated to $\mathscr{L}$. At the same time we form the vectors $r^{(4)}$ and $r^{(7)}$ defined by (7.8) and (7.11). All of the products and partial sums needed for the computation of $r^{(4)}$ and $r^{(7)}$ are available during the computations of $b^{(4)}-A^{(4)}x$ and $b^{(7)}-A^{(7)}x$, and are abbreviated from $\mathscr{M}$ to $\mathscr{L}$ before use.

$\overline{\overline{b^{(4)}-A^{(4)}x}} \times 10^7$	$\bar{r}^{(4)} \times 10^7$	$\overline{\overline{b^{(7)}-A^{(7)}x}} \times 10^7$	$\bar{r}^{(7)} \times 10^7$
0	1·124	0	0·001516
0	0·5775	−0·1000	0·3697
0·1000	0·3395	0	0·09210
0	0·05140	0	0·05140

From these results it is evident that

$$\|\bar{r}^{(4)}\| = 1{\cdot}124 \times 10^{-7}, \qquad \|\bar{r}^{(7)}\| = 0{\cdot}3697 \times 10^{-7}.$$

Matrix norms that are needed are found to be

$$\|\phi F\| \underset{(l)}{=} 128{\cdot}7, \qquad \|\psi E\| \underset{(l)}{=} 84{\cdot}40.$$

Hence

$$\eta \underset{(l)}{=} (144{\cdot}7 \times 10^{-7} + 31{\cdot}20 \times 10^{-7})\gamma_l \underset{(l)}{=} 0{\cdot}08795 \times 10^{-7}.$$

The fourth step is to compute the scalar ρ defined by (7.17). Further matrix norms that are needed are found to be

$$\|F\| \underset{(l)}{=} 49{\cdot}54, \qquad \|\phi A\| \underset{(l)}{=} 3{\cdot}140 \times 10^{-7}, \qquad \|E\| \underset{(l)}{=} 27{\cdot}04,$$

$$\|\psi A\| \underset{(l)}{=} 0{\cdot}7856, \qquad \|A^{(4)}\| \underset{(l)}{=} 1{\cdot}195, \qquad \|A^{(7)}\| \underset{(l)}{=} 0{\cdot}4097.$$

† As in Olver (1982), the symbol $\underset{(l)}{=}$ signifies the result that is obtained by computing in $\mathscr{L}$.

Hence

$$\rho \underset{(l)}{=} 155{\cdot}6\times 10^{-7}+10{\cdot}62\times 10^{-7}+95{\cdot}20\times 10^{-3} \underset{(l)}{=} 0{\cdot}09522.$$

We are now in a position to compute the desired bounds (7.23) and (7.24) from formulae (7.19), (7.25) and (7.26). The requisite compensating factors are found to be

$$1+42\gamma_l \underset{(l)}{=} 1{\cdot}021, \qquad 1+50\gamma_l \underset{(l)}{=} 1{\cdot}025, \qquad 1+54\gamma_l \underset{(l)}{=} 1{\cdot}027.$$

The remaining computations are given by

$$\sigma \underset{(l)}{=} 0{\cdot}09722, \qquad \|y\| \underset{(l)}{=} 187{\cdot}9\times 10^{-7}, \qquad (\sigma\|y\|+\eta)/(1-\sigma) \underset{(l)}{=} 20{\cdot}34\times 10^{-7},$$

$$\zeta = 213{\cdot}4\times 10^{-7}, \tag{8.6}$$

$$\bar{z} = [182{\cdot}1\times 10^{-7}, 128{\cdot}7\times 10^{-7}, 213{\cdot}8\times 10^{-7}, 56{\cdot}13\times 10^{-7}]^{\mathrm{T}}. \tag{8.7}$$

8.5 *Discussion*

One of the main questions of interest is how well the bounds (8.7) compare with the true values of the maximum possible errors. By hypothesis, the numerical entries given in Equations (8.1) are inexact representations of the true values. In order to estimate the true maximum errors in the computed solution (8.5), we follow the method of Hansen (1969) and solve the system (1.1) to a higher working precision, with the perturbations $\Delta A^{(1)}$ and $\Delta b^{(1)}$ in (8.2) assigned their maximum values and their signs chosen in such a way that each perturbation reinforces the others in its effect on the final solution. This choice depends on the signs of the components of $\bar{x}$ and of the elements of the inverse matrix $(\bar{A}^{(1)})^{-1}$. Since $(A^{(1)})^{-1} = F$ [compare (5.2)] the signs of the elements of $(\bar{A}^{(1)})^{-1}$ are those of the corresponding numerical entries for F given above. Proceeding in this manner, we see that the maximum perturbations occur among the solutions that are obtained by setting

$$\Delta A^{(1)} = \pm X_i, \qquad \Delta b^{(1)} = \pm \xi_i, \quad i = 1, 2, 3, 4,$$

where

$$X_1 = X_2 = X_3 = \tfrac{1}{2}\times 10^{-7}\begin{bmatrix} -1 & -1 & 1 & -1 \\ 1 & 1 & -1 & 1 \\ -1 & -1 & 1 & -1 \\ 1 & 1 & -1 & 1 \end{bmatrix},$$

$$X_4 = \tfrac{1}{2}\times 10^{-7}\begin{bmatrix} 1 & 1 & -1 & 1 \\ 1 & 1 & -1 & 1 \\ 1 & 1 & -1 & 1 \\ -1 & -1 & 1 & -1 \end{bmatrix},$$

and

$$\xi_1 = \xi_2 = \xi_3 = \tfrac{1}{2}\times 10^{-7}[-1 \quad 1 \quad -1 \quad 1]^{\mathrm{T}}, \qquad \xi_4 = \tfrac{1}{2}\times 10^{-7}[1 \quad 1 \quad 1 \quad -1]^{\mathrm{T}}.$$

The solutions of these systems were computed on a Univac 1108 Computer at the University of Maryland using double precision (approximately 18 decimal digits).

TABLE 1

	$\Delta A^{(1)}=X_1$, $\Delta b^{(1)}=\xi_1$	$\Delta A^{(1)}=-X_1$, $\Delta b^{(1)}=-\xi_1$	$\Delta A^{(1)}=X_4$, $\Delta b^{(1)}=\xi_4$	$\Delta A^{(1)}=-X_4$, $\Delta b^{(1)}=-\xi_4$
x_1	−0·00739 13321 19 ...	−0·00741 18439 79 ...	−0·00740 86143 24 ...	−0·00739 45617 09 ...
x_2	−1·55694 5838 ...	−1·55696 0203 ...	−1·55695 7233 ...	−1·55694 8808 ...
x_3	2·03344 5341 ...	2·03347 0607 ...	2·03346 5895 ...	2·03345 0054 ...
x_4	−0·50412 66010 ...	−0·50412 18708 ...	−0·50412 17217 ...	−0·50412 67500 ...

Table 1 lists the first 10 digits of the results.

On comparing these results with (8.5), we see that the true maximum errors in the various components of the computed solution are estimated by

$$|x_1-\bar{x}_1| = 104{\cdot}2\ldots\times 10^{-7}, \qquad |x_2-\bar{x}_2| = 73{\cdot}03\ldots\times 10^{-7},$$

$$|x_3-\bar{x}_3| = 128{\cdot}0\ldots\times 10^{-7}, \qquad |x_4-\bar{x}_4| = 25{\cdot}58\ldots\times 10^{-7}.$$

Therefore the components of $\bar{z}$, given by (8.7), overestimate the actual maxima by factors of about 1·7, 1·8, 1·7 and 2·2, respectively. As noted in comment (ii) of Section 6, it is not possible for the maximum values of $|x_i-\bar{x}_i|$ to be attained simultaneously for all values of i, as a rule, but in this particular example it transpires that with the perturbations $\Delta A^{(1)}=-X_1$ and $\Delta b^{(1)}=-\xi_1$ the maxima are attained by the first three components and closely approached ($24{\cdot}09\ldots\times 10^{-7}$) by the fourth component.

The bounds (8.6) and (8.7) can be reduced slightly by increasing the working precision of the lower-mode computations. For example, had we used five significant decimal figures, with correct rounding, thereby reducing γ_l to $0{\cdot}5\times 10^{-4}$, then by reviewing the computations we easily see that the first-order contribution y is virtually unchanged, but the scalars η and σ are reduced by a factor of about 10, thereby reducing the second-order contribution $(\sigma\|y\|+\eta)/(1-\sigma)$ to each component of $\bar{z}$ from $20{\cdot}34\times 10^{-7}$ to about $1{\cdot}85\times 10^{-7}$. This reduces $\bar{z}$ to about $[163{\cdot}1\times 10^{-7}, 109{\cdot}7\times 10^{-7}, 194{\cdot}9\times 10^{-7}, 37{\cdot}14\times 10^{-7}]^{\mathrm{T}}$, representing a reduction of about 9% in the norm. Clearly any further diminution in the value of γ_l would yield very little improvement. These comparisons serve to illustrate the trade-off between the sharpness of the bounds and the computational effort as γ_l is varied.

Another way of reducing the error bounds would be to reduce the value of γ, that is, to increase the working precision of the main computations. This would also increase accuracy of the computed solutions. However, because we have assumed the presence of inherent errors in the data (which is a common situation in practice), there is a limit to the extent of these improvements. On setting $\Delta A^{(1)}=\Delta b^{(1)}=0$ in (8.2) and solving the system (1.1) to double precision on the Univac 1108, we obtain

$$x = [-0{\cdot}00740\,15879\,93\ldots, -1{\cdot}55695\,3020\ldots, 2{\cdot}03345\,7974\ldots, -0{\cdot}50412\,42359\ldots]^{\mathrm{T}}. \quad (8.8)$$

Consequently, for all values of γ that are low enough to ensure that the effect of the abbreviation errors is dominated completely by that of the inherent errors, the maximum errors in the components of the solution are estimated by

$$102{\cdot}5\ldots\times 10^{-7},\quad 71{\cdot}83\ldots\times 10^{-7},\quad 126{\cdot}3\ldots\times 10^{-7},\quad 25{\cdot}14\ldots\times 10^{-7}, \tag{8.9}$$

respectively, these values being obtained by comparing (8.8) with Table 1.

It will be recalled that at the beginning of this section we aimed at a value of γ that would render the cumulative effect of the abbreviation errors comparable with that of the inherent errors. We cannot judge whether we succeeded by comparing the actual errors, since the actual inherent errors are assumed to be unknown. However, if we compare (8.9) with (8.7), then we see that we succeeded inasmuch as the bounds for the inherent errors represent about 56%, 56%, 59% and 45%, respectively, of our total bound for each component.

8.6 *Remark*

The computations in Subsections 8.1 to 8.4 were carried out on a hand calculator. Subsequently all of the results were reproduced *exactly* by use of R. P. Brent's multiple-precision arithmetic package (Brent, 1978*a*, *b*) operating in rounding decimal modes.

9. Conclusions

We have described a method for constructing strict error bounds for the solution of a system of linear algebraic equations

$$Ax = b,$$

of arbitrary order n, by Gaussian elimination using floating-point arithmetic. The bounds take account of the inherent errors in the data, and all abbreviation errors incurred during the process of solution. The bounds agree with estimates for the maximum error obtained by linearized perturbation theory. They would therefore be attainable, except for second-order discrepancies, if each error, inherent or abbreviation, were to assume its maximum value and be of appropriate sign. Other features of the results are as follows:

(i) The bounds apply whether or not pivoting or scaling strategies are used, and whether or not the equations are well-conditioned. (Of course, however, the *actual size* of the bounds will be affected by pivoting, scaling and the nature of the conditioning.)

(ii) The bounds are expressed in a form that avoids the need for special hardware or software devices such as directed rounding. In consequence they are evaluable on most existing computers, and programs based on the analysis will enjoy a high degree of portability.

An extension to computers that have no form of guard digit in the accumulator register will be described in a separate paper (Olver, unpublished).

(iii) For large n, the evaluation of the error bounds requires $\frac{2}{3}n^3+O(n^2)$ multiplications and $\frac{8}{3}n^3+O(n^2)$ additions. This is to be compared with the $\frac{1}{3}n^3+O(n^2)$ multiplications and $\frac{1}{3}n^3+O(n^2)$ additions that are needed to compute the original solution. Often, however, almost all of the error-bound computations can be carried out in a lower mode, that is, with fewer digits in the mantissae of the floating-point representations.

(iv) The approach used is not confined to Gaussian elimination. Similar error bounds can be constructed for solutions of linear algebraic equations obtained by other direct methods. Indeed, in the case of methods based on triangular decomposition of the original matrix the error analysis is slightly easier: all of the derivation from (3.4) to (3.28), for example, can be replaced by a straightforward application of the error bound for computed inner products supplied by (7.6) and (7.7) of Olver (1982).

The present theory could also be used in combination with iterative refinement of Gaussian elimination (Wilkinson, 1963, Chapter 3, section 37; Stewart, 1973, Chapter 4, section 5) to construct *a posteriori* error bounds for the refined solutions obtained by this procedure; indeed, an efficient computing program ought to include such a combination as one of its options.

(v) Another method† for constructing *a posteriori* error bounds, applicable in the absence of inherent errors and based on the use of residuals, has been described by several writers, including Householder (1964, section 4.0.1), Hansen (1965), Hansen & Smith (1967), Aird & Lynch (1975), Thieler (1978) and Rump & Kaucher (1980). This procedure requires an approximate value of A^{-1} and the formation of the product of the approximate inverse and A. It, too, could be implemented by the rp–ap approach, without the need for hardware or software having directed roundings, and it could also be extended to allow for inherent errors in A and b. However, *even if an approximate value of A^{-1} is available this method is likely to be costlier than the method we propose*. This is because for large n the formation of the product of A and its approximate inverse, together with error bounds on the computed product, requires (asymptotically) n^3 lower-mode multiplications and $3n^3$ lower-mode additions. This is to be compared with $\frac{2}{3}n^3$ lower-mode multiplications and $\frac{8}{3}n^3$ lower-mode additions in our method (which includes the evaluation of A^{-1}). This conclusion remains valid even if directed rounding is available in the hardware or software, because this facility would not affect the number of multiplications in either method.

The writers are pleased to acknowledge helpful discussions with C. W. Clenshaw, D. W. Lozier and G. W. Stewart, computational assistance by R. E. Kaylor and J. M. Knapp-Cordes, and helpful suggestions by a referee.

This work was supported in part by the U.S. Army Research Office, Durham, under Contract DAAG 29–80–C–0032, and by the National Science Foundation under Grants MCS 78–02111 and MCS 78–11985.

References

Aird, T. J. & Lynch, R. E. 1975 Computable accurate upper and lower error bounds for approximate solutions of linear algebraic systems. *Ass. comput. Mach. Trans. Math. Software* **1**, 217–231.

Brent, R. P. 1978*a* A Fortran multiple-precision arithmetic package. *Ass. comput. Mach. Trans. Math. Software* **4**, 57–70.

Brent, R. P. 1978*b* Algorithm 524 MP, A Fortran multiple-precision arithmetic package. *Ass. comput. Mach. Trans. Math. Software* **4**, 71–81.

† This is not to be confused with the process of iterative refinement mentioned in (iv).

FOX, L. 1964 *Introduction to Numerical Linear Algebra.* Oxford: Clarendon Press.

HANSEN, E. 1965 Interval arithmetic in matrix computations, Part I. *SIAM J. Num. Analysis Ser. B* **2,** 308–320.

HANSEN, E. 1969 On the solution of linear algebraic equations with interval coefficients. *Linear Algebra Appl.* **2,** 153–165.

HANSEN, E. & SMITH, R. 1967 Interval arithmetic in matrix computations, Part II. *SIAM J. Num. Analysis* **4,** 1–9.

HOUSEHOLDER, A. S. 1964 *The Theory of Matrices in Numerical Analysis.* New York: Blaisdell (Ginn).

MILLER, W. & SPOONER, D. 1978 Software for roundoff analysis, II. *Ass. comput. Mach. Trans. Math Software* **4,** 369–387.

NATIONAL PHYSICAL LABORATORY 1961 Modern computing methods. *Notes on Applied Science* No. 16, 2nd ed. London: H.M.S.O.

NEWMAN, M. 1967 Solving equations exactly. *J. Res. natn. Bur. Stand.* **71B,** 171–179.

OLVER, F. W. J. 1978 A new approach to error arithmetic. *SIAM J. Num. Analysis* **15,** 368–393.

OLVER, F. W. J. 1982 Further developments of rp and ap error analysis. *IMA J. Num. Analysis* **2,** 249–274.

OLVER, F. W. J. (unpublished) Error bounds for arithmetic operations on computers without guard digits.

RUMP, S. M. & KAUCHER, E. 1980 Small bounds for the solution of systems of linear equations. In *Fundamentals of Numerical Computation* (*Computer-oriented Numerical Analysis*) (Alefeld, G. & Grigorieff, R. D., Eds). *Computing, Suppl.* **2,** 157–164.

STEWART, G. W. 1973 *Introduction to Matrix Computations.* London: Academic Press.

STUMMEL, F. (unpublished) Forward error analysis of Gaussian elimination. Part II: General linear algebraic systems.

THIELER, P. 1978 On componentwise error estimates for inverse matrices.*Computing* **19,** 303–312.

WILKINSON, J. H. 1961 Error analysis of direct methods of matrix inversion. *J. Ass. comput. Mach.* **8,** 281–330.

WILKINSON, J. H. 1963 Rounding errors in algebraic processes. *National Physical Laboratory Notes on Applied Science* No. 32. London: H.M.S.O.

Beyond Floating Point

C. W. CLENSHAW

University of Lancaster, Lancaster, England

AND

F. W. J. OLVER

University of Maryland, College Park, Maryland and National Bureau of Standards

Abstract. A new number system is proposed for computer arithmetic based on iterated exponential functions. The main advantage is to eradicate overflow and underflow, but there are several other advantages and these are described and discussed.

Categories and Subject Descriptors: G.1.0 [**Numerical Analysis**]: General—*computer arithmetic*

General Terms: Design, Theory

Additional Key Words and Phrases: Error analysis, fixed point, floating point, generalized distance, generalized exponentials, generalized logarithms, generalized precision, level-index form, local precision, overflow, underflow, wobbling precision

1. *Introduction*

The simplest system of number representation in computers is fixed point, but unfortunately the range of numbers that can be represented in fixed-point arithmetic is severely limited. Sometimes, and particularly in computations arising in linear algebra, the limitations may be circumvented by judicious scaling procedures; see, for example, [18, p. 99]. For most types of computation, however, it is difficult or even impossible to devise satisfactory scaling procedures. In consequence, at an early stage in computer development, fixed-point systems largely yielded to floating-point systems. In floating point each real number x is represented in the form

$$x = r^l \times a,$$

where r is the radix, l is a signed integer, and a is a signed rational fraction; often l and a are called the *exponent* and *mantissa*, respectively. If the floating-point representation is normalized (and this is usually the case), then a has to satisfy

$$\frac{1}{r} \le |a| < 1,$$

This work was supported, in part, by the U.S. Army Research Office, Durham under contract DAAG 29-80-C-0032, the U.S. National Science Foundation under Grant MCS 81-11725, and grants from the U.K. Science and Engineering Research Council.

Authors' addresses: C. W. Clenshaw, Department of Mathematics, Cartmel College, University of Lancaster, Bailrigg, Lancaster, LA1 4YL, England; F. W. J. Olver, Institute for Physical Science and Technology, University of Maryland, College Park, MD 20742.

Journal of the Association for Computing Machinery, Vol. 31, No. 2, April 1984, pp. 319–328.

except when $x = 0$. Obviously the normalized floating-point form of each representable nonzero number x is unique once r has been specified.

For a given word length, numbers of much greater magnitude can be accommodated in floating-point form than in fixed-point form. This gain is achieved at some cost, however. First, arithmetic operations are more complicated and take somewhat longer to perform. Second, the very ability to represent larger numbers implies that some precision must be sacrificed: some digits of each word are allocated to the exponent and are thus not available to the mantissa.

Failures caused by overflow or underflow are rarer with floating-point systems than they are with fixed-point systems. Nevertheless, they are not sufficiently rare to be negligible; indeed the possibility of overflow or underflow is of continuing concern to designers of mathematical software.[1] To overcome such failures, it may be necessary to disturb the original mathematical analysis of a problem by scaling or other artifices. For example, one might compute the ratios of successive members of a rapidly growing sequence rather than the actual members.

Because of continued rapid advances in computer technology, it is opportune to pose the following question. Is it possible to devise a number system for use in computers in which problems of overflow and underflow are abolished, thereby avoiding the need to tamper with the mathematical analysis of a problem? Naturally we would expect such a system to be achievable only at some cost, just as the floating-point system costs in speed and precision compared with the fixed-point system. One answer is to increase the amount of storage allocated to the exponent to one or more words, as in multiple-precision packages [1, 2] or extended-range packages [11, 17]. However, this is only a partial answer; furthermore, it is inefficient to allocate a great deal of storage to the exponent when it will be used only occasionally.

In this paper we propose another answer based on the representation of numbers as generalized exponential functions, and we shall show that such a system enjoys several mathematical advantages in addition to freedom from overflow and underflow. Generalized exponentials are not new to mathematicians; they have been discussed by Hardy [7], and Littlewood [10] briefly discussed similar functions with base e replaced by 10. However, the present paper may be the first in which generalized exponentials have been proposed seriously as a basis for computation.[2] The feasibility of such a system will depend on the development of satisfactory algorithms for addition and subtraction, including error analysis, and ultimately on the construction of hardware chips for implementing these processes in a fast and accurate manner.

2. *Generalized Exponentials and Logarithms*

Let x be any real number and

$$x = \pm e^{e^{e^{\cdot^{\cdot^{\cdot^{e^{a}}}}}}} \tag{1}$$

[1] See, for example, detailed discussions of very large and very small numbers in [15].

[2] The possibility of using ordinary exponentials, as opposed to generalized exponentials, as a basis is mentioned in [8, secs. 2 and 14].

where the process of exponentiation is performed l times, l being a nonnegative integer. (When $l = 0$, we have $x = \pm a$.) Then we call the right-hand side a *generalized exponential function* and denote it more concisely as

$$x = \pm[l/a]. \tag{2}$$

The integer l is called the *level* of x and the fractional part a the *index* of x, and we refer to $[l/a]$ as a *level-index* (li) form. If we restrict a by

$$0 \le a < 1, \tag{3}$$

then the li form is *normalized.* By repeatedly taking logarithms, we can see that the normalized li form of any nonzero real number is unique. *Henceforth we shall suppose that every number in li form is normalized, except where stated otherwise.*

The range of absolute values of all numbers that can be accommodated at level l is the interval $[e_l, e_{l+1})$, where the sequence $\{e_l\}$ is defined by $e_0 = 0$ and

$$e_l = e^{e_{l-1}}, \qquad l \ge 1.$$

Approximate values of the first few members of this sequence are given by

$$\begin{aligned}
&e_0 = 0, \qquad e_1 = 1, \qquad e_2 \risingdotseq 2.72, \qquad e_3 \risingdotseq 15.2,\\
&e_4 \risingdotseq 3{,}810{,}000 \risingdotseq 10^{6.58} \risingdotseq 2^{21.9},\\
&e_5 \risingdotseq 10^{1{,}660{,}000} \risingdotseq 2^{5{,}500{,}000} \risingdotseq 2^{2^{22.4}},\\
&e_6 \risingdotseq 10^{10^{1{,}660{,}000}} \risingdotseq 2^{2^{5{,}500{,}000}}.
\end{aligned}$$

From these numbers it is evident that we need not pass beyond level 4 to include all floating-point numbers that are representable on existing computers in single- or double-precision form. These levels also include a substantial fraction of the numbers that are representable in existing multiple-precision packages [1, 2] or extended-range packages [11, 17]. Certainly if we proceed to level 5, then all such numbers are included. And if we proceed to level 6, then we are able to represent numbers that exceed those representable by multiple-precision floating-point packages currently under construction that permit the use of a variable number of words for the exponent.

Of course, it can be argued that because only a finite number of levels can be assigned for use with a given word length, overflow is still possible in the li system. However, the only way to generate numbers of arbitrarily high levels is to perform operations that are equivalent to iterated exponentiation, and this is not often performed in ordinary computations. By assigning three bits to represent the level, thereby permitting the use of levels 0 to 7, *we would virtually abolish overflow from everyday work.*

From an analytical standpoint, a more satisfactory notation for generalized exponentials is as follows. Let $\phi(y)$ be defined by the relations

$$\phi(y) = y, \qquad 0 \le y < 1, \tag{4}$$

$$\phi(y) = e^{\phi(y-1)}, \qquad y \ge 1, \tag{5}$$

or equivalently,

$$\phi(y) = e^{e^{e^{\cdot^{\cdot^{\cdot^{e^{y-l}}}}}}} \tag{6}$$

where $l = \text{int}[y]$ and the exponentiations are carried out l times. This determines $\phi(y)$ for all nonnegative values of y. It is easily verified that $\phi(y)$ and $\phi'(y)$ are continuous, that is, $\phi(y) \in C^1[0, \infty)$. The function that is inverse to $x = \phi(y)$ we call a *generalized logarithm* and denote it by $y = \psi(x)$. From (4) and (5) it is seen that

$$\psi(x) = x, \qquad 0 \leq x < 1, \tag{7}$$

and

$$\psi(x) = \psi(\ln x) + 1, \qquad x \geq 1; \tag{8}$$

furthermore $\psi(x) \in C^1[0, \infty)$.[3] Explicitly,

$$\psi(x) = l + \ln^{(l)} x, \qquad x \geq 0, \tag{9}$$

where $\ln^{(l)} x$ denotes the lth iterated logarithm of x and the nonnegative integer l is determined (uniquely) by

$$0 \leq \ln^{(l)} x < 1. \tag{10}$$

When x is nonnegative and expressed in level-index form (2), we have

$$\psi(x) = l + a. \tag{11}$$

3. *Advantages of the li System*

In this section we show that the li system offers several advantages in addition to overcoming the problem of overflow.

3.1 Redistributed Precision. For a given word length the total number of representable numbers is the same, whether the system used be fixed point, floating point, level index, or any other that has been proposed.[4] The interval between consecutive representable numbers is an inverse measure of the *local precision* of the system.

In the fixed-point system all nonnegative real representable numbers lie in the interval $[0, 1)$ and they are equispaced. Since the li system covers a larger interval, its precision in the interval $[0, 1)$ is necessarily less. If, as suggested in Section 2, the number of bits assigned to the level is 3, then the spacing between representable numbers in the interval $[0, 1)$ is eight times larger than in the fixed-point system.

In the floating-point system we need to distinguish between the intervals $[0, 1/r)$ and $[1/r, \infty)$ where r again denotes the internal radix. The former is covered by use of negative exponents; this is discussed and compared with the li system in Section 4 below. In the interval $[1/r, \infty)$ the spacing between representable numbers jumps by a factor r each time the exponent increases by unity, then remains constant until the next change in the exponent. In the li system, however, because the generalized logarithm is a C^1 function, the spacing increases in a smooth manner as we proceed from one level to the next. To begin with, the spacing in the li system is less than in the floating-point system, but eventually the situation is reversed. Again, this is because the set of representable numbers is spread over a larger interval in the li system.

[3] P. L. Walker has drawn our attention to the fact that H. Kneser [9] has shown that there exists a real analytic function with the property (8); furthermore, Walker has computed numerical values of this function at the University of Lancaster. For present purposes, however, it is more convenient to adhere to the C^1 functions just defined because of the simplicity of the representations (4) and (7).

[4] For example, the fixed-slash and floating-slash rational arithmetic described in [12]. These systems, also, suffer from overflow problems.

As a typical example, consider the UNIVAC 1100 series computers, for which $r = 2$. In single precision seven bits are allocated to the exponent and 27 to the mantissa;[5] consequently, except at the jumps, the spacing between consecutive representable numbers is 2^{p-27}, where $p \in [0, 127]$ is the local exponent. In li form, three bits would be allocated to the level, leaving 31 bits for the index. By differentiating formula (1) we see that the spacing between one representable positive number x and the next is 2^{-31} when $0 < x \leq 1$, and approximately

$$2^{-31}x \ln x \ln^{(2)}x \ln^{(3)}x \cdots$$

when $x > 1$, where the product terminates at the iterated logarithm in the interval $[1, e)$. Since $p = \text{int}[\log_2 x] + 1$, the local spacings in the two systems become equal approximately when

$$2^{\text{int}[\log_2 x]-26} = 2^{-31}x \ln x \ln^{(2)}x \ln^{(3)}x \cdots. \tag{12}$$

Solving this equation we find that $x \fallingdotseq 2^{18}$, or in li form, $x \fallingdotseq [3/0.93]$. Thus for values of x in the interval $\frac{1}{2} \leq x < 2^{18}$ the local precision of the li system exceeds that of the floating-point system, whereas when $2^{18} < x < 2^{127}$ the situation is reversed.

The extent of the gain or loss can be assessed from the ratio of the two sides of eq. (12). In the present example, for numbers in the range $\frac{1}{2}$ to 2^{18} the maximum gain in local precision of the li system over the floating-point system is a factor of 16; for numbers in the range 2^{18} to 2^{127} there is a maximum loss of a factor of about 37; for numbers exceeding 2^{127} the floating-point system fails completely, while the li system is still effective.[6]

Is the gain in local precision of the smaller numbers at the expense of that of the larger numbers an asset? The answer depends on the nature of the computations being carried out. In linear algebra, for example, the answer would usually be affirmative since computed numbers are not unduly large as a rule. *Consequently the li system would recover much of the advantage of the fixed-point system without the disadvantage of requiring scaling procedures.* On the other hand, the smooth behavior of the local precision of the li system would always be an advantage, because it eliminates the undesirable phenomenon known as "wobbling precision" or "radix effect" introduced by the steplike behavior of the local precision of the floating-point system; compare [4, p. 7] or [14, sec. 5].

3.2 TRANSITIONS BETWEEN SYSTEMS. As we saw in Section 2, fixed-point numbers that are less than unity in magnitude are level-0 numbers, and all floating-point numbers having nonnegative exponents that can be represented on existing computers lie within the ranges covered by levels 0 to 5. However, a major advantage of the li system is that in effect it uses the fixed- and floating-point systems, and permits passage from one to the other, and beyond, in an automatic manner.

For example, all the while numbers generated by an algorithm are less than unity in magnitude, the li system may compute exclusively with level-0 numbers; in this case the system operates in a fixed-point mode. However, as soon as a number in excess of unity appears, the li system moves to level 1, in effect changing the operating mode from fixed point to floating point (in base e). Similarly, when a number in excess of e appears, the li system moves to level 2, and so on.

[5] The bits allocated to the signs of the exponent and mantissa are not taken into consideration here because two bits may be used in an analogous manner in the li system; compare again Section 4 below.

[6] In double precision on the UNIVAC 1100 series computers, there is a gain factor of up to 128 for numbers in the range 1/2 to 2^{70} and a loss factor of up to 68 for numbers in the range 2^{70} to 2^{1023}.

Incidentally, by analogy with the floating-point system it might be thought that a more suitable definition for an li number would involve logarithms to base r rather than base e. This would replace (1) by

$$\pm r^{r^{r^{\cdot^{\cdot^{\cdot^{r^a}}}}}} \tag{13}$$

However, it is not clear that any real advantage would accrue. There would be a loss of portability introduced by changes in r. (This is an argument for standardization, rather than any particular choice of base.) More seriously, the undesirable phenomenon of wobbling precision reappears if a base other than e is used. This is because the generalized logarithm $l + \log_r^{(l)} x$ is a C^1 function if $r = e$, but only a C^0 function if $r \neq e$.

3.3 Generalized Measures of Precision. The error measures commonly used for fixed- and floating-point arithmetic are absolute error and relative error, respectively. Recently, Olver [13, 14] has described advantages of using absolute precision and relative precision instead. Absolute precision is merely another name for maximum absolute error. Thus if x and $\bar{x}$ are real or complex numbers and α is a nonnegative real number such that

$$x = \bar{x} + u, \qquad \text{where} \quad |u| \leq \alpha, \tag{14}$$

then $\bar{x}$ is said to be *an approximation to x of absolute precision α*, and (14) is written equivalently as

$$x \simeq \bar{x}; \quad \mathrm{ap}(\alpha). \tag{15}$$

Relative precision, however, differs from maximum relative error: it is a logarithmic form of absolute precision. Thus if $x \neq 0$ and

$$x = \bar{x}e^v, \qquad \text{where} \quad |v| \leq \alpha, \tag{16}$$

then $\bar{x}$ is said to be *an approximation to x of relative precision α*, and (16) is written equivalently[7]

$$x \simeq \bar{x}; \quad \mathrm{rp}(\alpha). \tag{17}$$

Since

$$e^v = 1 + v + O(v^2), \qquad v \to 0,$$

it is clear that although relative precision differs from maximum relative error, the difference amounts only to quantities of the second order.

In the li system, absolute precision and relative precision are to be regarded as special cases of *generalized precision* (gp), defined as follows. Let x and $\bar{x}$ be nonnegative numbers such that

$$|\psi(x) - \psi(\bar{x})| \leq \alpha, \tag{18}$$

where $\psi(\cdot)$ again denotes the generalized logarithm defined in Section 2. Then we say that

$$x \simeq \bar{x}; \quad \mathrm{gp}(\alpha). \tag{19}$$

[7] Another notation that is sometimes useful is $x = 1(\alpha)\bar{x}$. Here $1(\alpha)$ means some number that approximates 1 to $\mathrm{rp}(\alpha)$. This is due to Pryce [16].

Consequently if $x = [l/a]$ and $\bar{x} = [\bar{l}/\bar{a}]$, then α is an upper bound for $|(l + a) - (\bar{l} + \bar{a})|$. *In the common case* $l = \bar{l}$ we have $|a - \bar{a}| \leq \alpha$.

The quantity $|\psi(x) - \psi(\bar{x})|$ is a metric and may be regarded as a *generalized distance*. Thus if (19) holds and

$$\bar{x} \simeq \bar{\bar{x}}; \quad \mathrm{gp}(\beta), \tag{20}$$

then

$$x \simeq \bar{\bar{x}}; \quad \mathrm{gp}(\alpha + \beta). \tag{21}$$

This is a natural generalization of a well-known property of absolute errors.

An advantage of the gp concept is that it enables precision requirements to be specified in a more satisfactory manner. For example, suppose that we wish to construct a general-purpose algorithm for generating a mathematical function such as a Bessel function. In the floating-point system we might specify a certain overall maximum relative error (or relative precision). However, this would lead to difficulties in the neighborhoods of zeros of the wanted function. An improvement would be to replace maximum relative error by maximum absolute error in the neighborhoods of the zeros. But the relation of the appropriate bound for the absolute error to that for the relative error is not obvious, and the extent of the "neighborhoods" of the zeros is also vague. Generalized precision would ease—if not completely resolve—the problem in a purely arithmetic and automatic manner. By specifying an overall generalized precision we automatically bound the absolute error when the computed approximation is of level 0, the relative error when the computed approximation is of level 1, and the natural generalization of these errors at higher levels.

3.4 Representation of Large Numbers. Dirac has estimated the ratio M, say, of the mass of the universe to that of a single proton to be about 10^{78} (cf. [6, p. 76]). The last digit of the exponent is quite uncertain; in consequence it would be impossible to express M in fixed-point form in a meaningful manner since there are no significant digits. Even decimal floating-point form $10^l \times a$ is not really sensible: although there is perhaps one significant digit available in the exponent l, there are none in the mantissa a. Representation in li form presents no difficulty, however. For example, we might write M in the form

$$M \simeq [4/0.500]; \quad \mathrm{gp}(0.003).$$

This will be a correct statement if

$$5.75 \times 10^{76} \leq M \leq 6.47 \times 10^{80}.$$

More impressively, the li system enables this idea to be taken much further. It is easy to record numbers in li form for which neither the mantissa nor the exponent of the floating-point form has any significant figures: even the *number* of digits in the exponent may not be specifiable. An example is furnished by

$$[5/0.87654].$$

If the index is correctly rounded, that is, if we assume the true value x is given by

$$x \simeq [5/0.87654]; \quad \mathrm{gp}(\tfrac{1}{2} \times 10^{-5}), \tag{22}$$

then it is impossible to record x in either fixed- or floating-point form. Nevertheless the relation (22) specifies a precise interval that contains the true value of x.

As Littlewood [10, p. 103] has pointed out, very large numbers enjoy some interesting arithmetical properties; our li notation proves convenient for their display. For example, the best approximation, with the same number of decimals in the index, to twice [5/0.87654] is still [5/0.87654]; more precisely

$$2 \times [5/0.87654] \simeq [5/0.87654]; \quad \mathrm{gp}(\tfrac{1}{2} \times 10^{-5}).$$

Even more remarkably, raising [5/0.87654] to a substantial power makes no difference. Thus we have

$$[5/0.87654]^n \simeq [5/0.87654]; \quad \mathrm{gp}(\tfrac{1}{2} \times 10^{-5}),$$

for any real value of n in the interval [1/4000,4000]. Obviously these relations simulate accepted "properties" $2 \times \infty = \infty$ and $\infty^n = \infty$ of the "number" ∞.

4. *Other Distinguished Points*

In framing the definition of li form given in Section 2, our object was to introduce a set of machine-representable numbers that approach the point at infinity much more closely than is possible by machine-representable numbers of other systems. Borrowing from the terminology of asymptotic analysis, we say that ∞ is the *distinguished point* associated with our definition. Sometimes, however, we may wish to use a finite distinguished point, say, ξ. By this we mean that we may wish to employ a set of machine-representable numbers that approach ξ extremely closely.

In the floating-point system this requirement is met by introducing negative exponents, possibly augmented, also, by the device known as gradual underflow [5]. This solves the problem when 0 is the distinguished point. For any other finite distinguished point ξ we translate ξ to the origin and again use negative exponents.

Similar extensions may be made in the li system by the simple device of using reciprocals. A very small number x may be represented as

$$x = [l/a]^{-1}.$$

This extension yields a set of numbers that approaches the origin much more closely than the corresponding set of floating-point numbers. It also overcomes the problem of underflow, just as the direct li system overcomes the problem of overflow. For any other finite distinguished point ξ, we would use the representation

$$x = \xi + [l/a]^{-1}.$$

It needs to be stressed that reciprocal li numbers are to be introduced only when there is a special reason for having a dense set of representable numbers in the neighborhood of the origin (or other distinguished point). For many purposes the set of representable numbers at level 0 will be quite appropriate. In this way, the li system differs significantly from the floating-point system, because without the use of negative exponents or gradual underflow, the nonzero representable floating-point numbers that are closest to the origin are $\pm 1/r$.

5. *Needs*

In order to forge the li system into a practicable tool for computer arithmetic, we need satisfactory algorithms for addition and subtraction. These will also permit multiplication and division (at the next higher level), and powering (at a higher level still).

At high levels addition or subtraction can be accomplished trivially. For example, if x is any positive number of level 5 and y is any nonnegative number not exceeding x, then

$$x + y \simeq x; \quad \mathrm{gp}(2^{-27}). \tag{23}$$

In consequence if not more than 26 bits are assigned to represent the index, then x is the appropriate approximation to $x + y$. At the next level, that is when x is of level 6 and again $0 \le y \le x$, (23) is replaceable by

$$x + y \simeq x; \quad \text{gp}(2^{-5502869}), \tag{24}$$

showing that x would be an acceptable approximation to $x + y$ on most computers, even if something like 100,000 words were employed to represent the index.

At lower levels proper algorithms for addition and subtraction, based on recurrence relations, are needed. For example, if we wish to form $[l/a] - [l/b]$, where $a > b$, we set

$$c_j = [j/a] - [j/b], \qquad j = 0, 1, \ldots, l. \tag{25}$$

Then $c_0 = a - b$, and higher members of the sequence $\{c_j\}$ satisfy

$$c_{j+1} = [(j + 1)/a](1 - e^{-c_j}). \tag{26}$$

The level and index of c_{j+1} are found from (26) by taking logarithms as often as necessary.

Evidently these algorithms will require subroutines, and ultimately hardware chips, for the fast and accurate computation of exponential and logarithmic functions. Some of the analysis developed in [3] may be applicable. Also, since it is envisaged that the use of li forms will be confined mainly to internal machine representations, the same subroutines will be needed in input and output.

A second need is to extend the error analysis of [13] and [14]. Suppose, for example, that $\bar{x}_1$ and $\bar{x}_2$ are stored values of exact numbers x_1 and x_2, such that

$$x_1 \simeq \bar{x}_1; \quad \text{gp}(\alpha_1), \qquad x_2 \simeq \bar{x}_2; \quad \text{gp}(\alpha_2).$$

How do we assign a value to α in the relation

$$x_1 + x_2 \simeq \bar{x}_1 + \bar{x}_2; \quad \text{gp}(\alpha)?$$

This is a problem of propagation of inherent errors. Next, if $\overline{\bar{x}_1 + \bar{x}_2}$ denotes the stored value of $\bar{x}_1 + \bar{x}_2$, how can we determine γ in the relation

$$\bar{x}_1 + \bar{x}_2 \simeq \overline{\bar{x}_1 + \bar{x}_2}; \quad \text{gp}(\gamma)?$$

This is a problem of propagation of abbreviation errors.[8]

Satisfactory solutions to the foregoing problems are being sought by the authors.

6. *Conclusions*

We have described a number system for use as a basis for computer arithmetic that appears to offer several advantages over existing systems. First, overflow and underflow are virtually abolished. Second, local precision is redistributed. Third, fixed-point and floating-point systems are included as special cases. Fourth, measures of precision can be generalized in a natural manner. Fifth, it is possible to define, and to operate with, numbers that cannot be represented in fixed-point or floating-point form. The disadvantage of the proposed system is that many (but not all) arithmetic operations will be more complicated and slower to implement because of the need to compute exponentials and logarithms. With the increasing speeds of modern computers this loss may be a reasonable price to pay for the advantages, just as some loss of speed and precision was an acceptable price for the adoption of the floating-point system in place of the fixed-point system.

[8] That is, chopping or rounding errors.

ACKNOWLEDGMENTS. The authors are pleased to acknowledge valuable comments by Dr. D. W. Lozier, Dr. P. L. Walker, and the referees.

REFERENCES

1. BRENT, R.P. A Fortran multiple-precision arithmetic package. *ACM Trans. Math. Softw. 4*, 1 (Mar. 1978), 57–70.
2. BRENT, R.P. Algorithm 524. MP, A Fortran multiple-precision arithmetic package. *ACM Trans. Math. Softw. 4*, 1 (Mar. 1978), 71–81.
3. CLENSHAW, C.W., AND OLVER, F.W.J. An unrestricted algorithm for the exponential function. *SIAM J. Numer. Anal. 17* (Apr. 1980), 310–331.
4. CODY, W.J., JR., AND WAITE, W. *Software Manual for the Elementary Functions.* Prentice-Hall, Englewood Cliffs, N.J., 1980.
5. COONEN, J.T. Underflow and the denormalized numbers. *Computer 14* (Mar. 1981), 75–87.
6. DIRAC, P.A.M. *Directions in Physics.* Wiley-Interscience, New York, 1978.
7. HARDY, G.H. *Orders of Infinity.* Cambridge University Press, New York, 1924.
8. KAHAN, W. *Implementation of Algorithms.* Parts I and II. National Technical Information Service, U.S. Department of Commerce, Springfield, Va., 1973.
9. KNESER, H. Reelle analytische Lösungen der Gleichung $\phi(\phi(x)) = e^x$ und verwandter Funktionalgleichung. *J. Reine Angew. Math. 187* (1948), 56–67.
10. LITTLEWOOD, J.E. *A Mathematician's Miscellany.* Methuen, London, 1953.
11. LOZIER, D.W., AND SMITH, J.M. Algorithm 567. Extended-range arithmetic and normalized Legendre polynomials. *ACM Trans. Math. Softw. 7*, 1 (Mar. 1981), 141–146.
12. MATULA, D.W., AND KORNERUP, P. Foundations of finite precision rational arithmetic. In Fundamentals of Numerical Computation (Computer-Oriented Numerical Analysis), G. Alefeld and R.D. Grigorieff, Eds. *Computing*, Suppl. 2 (1980), 85–111.
13. OLVER, F.W.J. A new approach to error arithmetic. *SIAM J. Numer. Anal. 15* (Apr. 1978), 368–393.
14. OLVER, F.W.J. Further developments of rp and ap error analysis. *IMA J. Numer. Anal. 2* (1982), 249–274.
15. PARLETT, B., ED. Special Issue on the Proposed IEEE Floating-Point Standard. *ACM SIGNUM Newsletter* (Oct. 1979), 1–32.
16. PRYCE, J.D. Round-off error analysis with fewer tears. *Bull. Inst. Math. Appl. 17* (Feb./Mar. 1981), 40–47.
17. SMITH, J.M., OLVER, F.W.J., AND LOZIER, D.W. Extended-range arithmetic and normalized Legendre polynomials. *ACM Trans. Math. Softw. 7*, 1 (Mar. 1981), 93–105.
18. WILKINSON, J.H. Rounding errors in algebraic processes. National Physical Laboratory, Notes on Applied Science No. 32. H. M. Stationery Office, London, 1963.

RECEIVED NOVEMBER 1982; REVISED JULY 1983; ACCEPTED AUGUST 1983

Comp. & Maths. with Appls. Vol. 12B, No. 5/6, pp. 1091–1101, 1986
Pergamon Journals Ltd

GENERALIZED EXPONENTIAL AND LOGARITHMIC FUNCTIONS

C. W. Clenshaw,[1] D. W. Lozier,[2] F. W. J. Olver[3] and P. R. Turner[1]
[1]Department of Mathematics, University of Lancaster, Lancaster LA1 4YL, England
[2]Mathematical Analysis Division, National Bureau of Standards, Gaithersburg, MD 20899, U.S.A.
[3]Institute for Physical Science and Technology, University of Maryland, College Park, MD 20742, U.S.A.

(*Received* 10 *March* 1985; *revised* 29 *April* 1985)

Abstract—Generalizations of the exponential and logarithmic functions are defined and an investigation is made of two possible versions of these functions. Some applications are described, including computer arithmetic, properties of very large and very small numbers, and the determination of functional roots.

1. INTRODUCTION

In a volume dedicated to the memory of Yudell Luke, it seems appropriate to discuss the properties of particular special functions. The present paper explores some of the properties and uses of two such functions, the *generalized exponential function* (g.e.f) and the *generalized logarithm* (g.l). Neither has, as yet, received a great deal of attention in the literature. Indeed, at the present time it is the case that we cannot offer definitions of these functions with the confidence that they will be accepted for the long-term future. It seems likely that there will be at least two functions competing for the title of "the generalized exponential function", and it is possible that each will be the subject of increasing interest. Similarly at least two functions will be competing for the title of "the generalized logarithm".

We begin by defining a *class* of g.e.f's. We say that ϕ is a g.e.f if it satisfies the following three conditions

$$\phi(x+1) = e^{\phi(x)} \quad \text{for} \quad -1 < x < \infty \tag{1.1}$$

$$\phi(0) = 0 \tag{1.2}$$

$$\phi(x) \text{ is strictly increasing for } 0 \leqslant x \leqslant 1. \tag{1.3}$$

It follows that $\phi(x)$ is strictly increasing from $-\infty$ to ∞ as x increases from -1 to ∞. Therefore ϕ has an inverse, ψ say, on $(-\infty, \infty)$. This inverse is the g.l corresponding to ϕ, and its properties that correspond to (1.1), (1.2) and (1.3) are given by

$$\psi(e^x) = 1 + \psi(x) \quad \text{for} \quad -\infty < x < \infty \tag{1.4}$$

$$\psi(0) = 0 \tag{1.5}$$

$$\psi(x) \text{ is strictly increasing for } 0 \leqslant x \leqslant 1. \tag{1.6}$$

In addition $\psi(x)$ is strictly increasing from -1 to ∞ as x increases from $-\infty$ to ∞.

All g.e.f's take the same values at the positive integers, namely $\phi(1) = 1$, $\phi(2) = e$, $\phi(3) = e^e$ and so on. The problem of defining "the g.e.f" is analogous to that of defining the gamma function, once the factorial function has been defined on the positive integers.

The interest of the authors in the g.e.f and g.l was aroused by the possibilities and advantages of their use for the representation and manipulation of real numbers within a computer. This application was described and discussed in [1], and it gives rise to what is now known as *level-index* (li) arithmetic, in which any positive real number X, however large, is represented in the computer by its g.l $x = \psi(X)$, so that $X = \phi(x)$. For this practical purpose it is obviously desirable to complete the definitions of ϕ and ψ in such a way as to make computation in the li system as simple as possible. This is described in Section 2. In Section 3 we consider other possible choices for the g.e.f and g.l. In the remaining sections we discuss various applications.

2. C^1 GENERALIZED EXPONENTIAL AND LOGARITHMIC FUNCTIONS

The simplest admissible choice of $\phi(x)$ on the interval [0, 1] is given by

$$\phi(x) = x, \quad 0 \leqslant x \leqslant 1. \tag{2.1}$$

Application of (1.1) then yields

$$\phi(x) = \ln(x+1), \quad -1 < x \leqslant 0; \quad \phi(x) = e^{x-1}, \quad 1 \leqslant x \leqslant 2 \tag{2.2}$$

and generally

$$\phi(x) = e^{e^{e^{\cdot^{\cdot^{\cdot^{e^{x-l}}}}}}}, \quad l \leqslant x \leqslant l+1 \tag{2.3}$$

where l is a positive integer and the process of exponentiation is performed l times.

Correspondingly, we have

$$\psi(x) = x, \quad 0 \leqslant x \leqslant 1 \tag{2.4}$$

$$\psi(x) = e^x - 1, \quad -\infty < x \leqslant 0; \quad \psi(x) = 1 + \ln x, \quad 1 \leqslant x \leqslant e \tag{2.5}$$

and generally

$$\psi(x) = l + \ln^{(l)} x, \quad 1 \leqslant x \tag{2.6}$$

where $\ln^{(l)} x$ is the lth repeated logarithm of x and l is determined by the condition

$$0 \leqslant \ln^{(l)} x < 1. \tag{2.7}$$

Next on differentiating (1.1) and replacing x by $x - 1$, we obtain

$$\phi'(x) = \phi(x)\phi'(x-1), \quad \phi''(x) = \phi'(x)\phi'(x-1) + \phi(x)\phi''(x-1). \tag{2.8}$$

From these equations and (2.1) we see that $\phi'(x)$ is continuous at $x = 1$, while $\phi''(x)$ jumps from 0 to 1 at this point. Since this behaviour is propagated to all positive integer values of the argument, it is apparent that

$$\phi(x) \in C^1(-1, \infty), \quad \psi(x) \in C^1(-\infty, \infty). \tag{2.9}$$

These smoothness properties are valuable for the efficient performance of li arithmetic; for example, they eliminate the phenomenon of "wobbling precision" [1].

The salient property of the function ϕ is its ability to represent large numbers with an appropriate balance between precision and economy. A simple example suffices to illustrate the point: $\phi(4.5) = 5.64 \times 10^{78}$, rounded to three significant figures, while if $\phi(5.5)$ is written similarly in floating-point decimal form, then its *exponent* exceeds 10^{78}, and it is scarcely sensible to attempt to represent its precision by specifying a certain number of significant figures. In these circumstances a new measure of precision is demanded: such a measure was proposed in [1]. This derives from the idea of regarding the distance between two real numbers X and Y as being the metric given by the difference between their g.l's $\psi(X)$ and $\psi(Y)$. This means of course that if X and Y both lie in [0, 1], then this distance is simply the familiar absolute distance $|X - Y|$, while if X and Y both lie in [1, e] then it is $|\ln(X/Y)|$. The latter is precisely the relative distance measure proposed by Olver [7] for floating-point arithmetic; it is similar to the more conventional notion of relative distance given by $|(X/Y) - 1|$ or $|(Y/X) - 1|$, but is more satisfactory because it is a metric. When X and Y lie in other intervals, the new metric is simply a natural generalization of these familiar concepts.

In brief, we say that $\bar{X} = \phi(\bar{x})$ represents $X = \phi(x)$ with a *generalized precision* α if

$$|\bar{x} - x| \leqslant \alpha. \tag{2.10}$$

Equivalent ways of expressing this relationship are

$$\bar{x} \simeq x; \quad \mathrm{ap}(\alpha) \tag{2.11}$$

in which "ap" denotes absolute precision, or absolute error, and

$$\bar{X} \simeq X; \quad \mathrm{gp}(\alpha) \tag{2.12}$$

in which "gp" denotes generalized precision.

To illustrate the significance of this notation numerically we now give examples, together with conventional equivalents, at increasing levels of magnitude. In each case we give "almost equivalent" statements: we are prevented from using the equivalence symbol $\Leftrightarrow$ by the fact that the numbers following the colons are rounded in all cases except (i).

(i) $x \simeq \phi(0.526)$; $\mathrm{gp}(\frac{1}{2} \times 10^{-3})$: $0.5255 \leqslant x \leqslant 0.5265$.

(ii) $x \simeq \phi(1.526)$; $\mathrm{gp}(\frac{1}{2} \times 10^{-3})$: $1.691 \leqslant x \leqslant 1.693$.

(iii) $x \simeq \phi(2.526)$; $\mathrm{gp}(\frac{1}{2} \times 10^{-3})$: $5.427 \leqslant x \leqslant 5.436$.

(iv) $x \simeq \phi(3.526)$; $\mathrm{gp}(\frac{1}{2} \times 10^{-3})$: $227.4 \leqslant x \leqslant 229.5$.

(v) $x \simeq \phi(4.526)$; $\mathrm{gp}(\frac{1}{2} \times 10^{-3})$: $5.535 \times 10^{98} \leqslant x \leqslant 4.516 \times 10^{99}$.

Case (v) illustrates once more the limitations of conventional measures of precision for large numbers: here there are no common significant figures in the endpoints of the interval in which x is known to lie. We conclude that a new measure is needed and that the notion of generalized precision is sufficient to meet this need in practical and theoretical situations. A more complete justification, based upon the arithmetic considerations which arise in the use of li arithmetic, will be found in [1].

3. ANALYTIC GENERALIZED EXPONENTIAL AND LOGARITHMIC FUNCTIONS

By modifying the choices (2.1) and (2.4) it is possible to consruct g.e.f's and g.l's that belong to $C^2(-1, \infty)$ and $C^2(-\infty, \infty)$, respectively, or are even smoother. For example, on replacing (2.1) by

$$\phi(x) = ax - \tfrac{1}{4}a^2x^2 + \tfrac{1}{6}a^2x^3, \quad 0 \leqslant x \leqslant 1 \tag{3.1}$$

where $a = 6 - 2\sqrt{6}$, we obtain a g.e.f in $C^2(-1, \infty)$. The question naturally arises: can we construct a g.e.f that is C^∞ on $(-1, \infty)$ or even analytic on a complex domain that contains this interval? [Of course, this analytic function must be real on $(-1, \infty)$]. The corresponding question for the g.l was answered affirmatively in 1948 by Kneser [6]. He showed that there is an analytic g.l that is real on the interval $(-\infty, \infty)$. He also constructed regions in the complex plane on which this g.l is analytic and indicated the location and nature of some of its singularities.

More recently, Walker [8] computed numerical values of an analytic g.l. His procedure is to assume the existence of a series expansion of the form

$$\psi(x) = c_1x + c_2x^2 + c_3x^3 + \cdots. \tag{3.2}$$

This enables $\psi(\mathrm{e}^x)$ to be expanded in powers of x, and by substituting in equation (1.4) we obtain an infinite set of simultaneous linear equations for the unknowns $\{c_j\}$. Taking the first n such equations and neglecting c_j for $j > n$, we have a set of n equations in n unknowns. These equations may be solved numerically to give a vector $\{c_j^{(n)}\}$, say. Interest in the results is enhanced by the apparent convergence of the sequence of solution vectors for increasing n, though we know of no proof of actual convergence.

The existence and computability of an analytic g.l prompts the next question. Is there a *unique* analytic g.l and a corresponding unique analytic g.e.f? This is easy to answer; if there is one analytic g.l, then there are infinitely many. We have only to add a suitable periodic analytic function of any g.l to itself to obtain another g.l. For example, if ψ is an analytic g.l and k is a constant in the interval $(-1, 1)$, then another analytic g.l is supplied by

$$\psi + (2\pi)^{-1}k \sin 2\pi\psi. \tag{3.3}$$

Accordingly, we have attempted to compute other analytic g.e.f's and the corresponding g.l's by applying an iterative scheme that relies on the essential equivalence of two forms of numerical approximation of a function on a given interval $[a, b]$, say. Let

$$f(x) = F(\xi) = {\sum_{r=0}^{n}}' a_r T_r(\xi) \tag{3.4}$$

where

$$2x = (b - a)\xi + (a + b) \tag{3.5}$$

T_r being the Chebyshev polynomial of the first kind, and the prime in (3.4) implying, as usual, that the first term in the sum is to be halved. Then the representation of f by the *coefficient-vector* $\{a_r\}_{r=0}^{n}$ is equivalent to its representation by the *value-vector* $\{F(\cos r\pi/n)\}_{r=0}^{n}$. That is to say, either vector may be computed from the other without loss of precision; see, for example, [3], [4].

We now suppose that we have an initial approximation to $\phi(x + 1)$ on the interval $[-1, 0]$ in the form of a coefficient-vector. We can use this to find the value-vector for $\phi(x + 1)$ on $[-1, 1]$: values on $[-1, 0]$ may be found directly by summation of series, while those on $[0, 1]$ require the application of the recursion relation (1.1). This value-vector yields a coefficient-vector for $\phi(x + 1)$ on $[-1, 1]$, and this in turn is used to compute a value-vector for $\phi(x + 1)$ on $[-1, 0]$, and hence a coefficient-vector for this interval. This completes one cycle of the iterative procedure.†

This procedure, initiated with various starting values and values of n, does indeed appear to suggest new g.e.f's; however, none of them is clearly preferable to that formed by rearranging and inverting Walker's power series. We give in Table 1 the coefficients in such a rearrangement, together with those of the inverse function. [In this table $T_r^*(x)$ denotes $T_r(2x - 1)$ as usual; cf. equations (3.4) and (3.5).] It is not easy to assess the accuracy of the entries in Table 1; the existence of a multiplicity of analytic g.e.f's is reflected in the conditioning of Walker's equations, which deteriorates rapidly as n increases. However, our values serve to indicate the nature of the solution obtained, and in particular its close proximity to the C^1 g.e.f of Section 2, whose Chebyshev series expansion has coefficients $a_0 = 1$, $a_1 = 1/2$, $a_j = 0\ (j \geqslant 2)$.

The next question is whether, from this multiplicity of g.l's, it is possible to select a *canonical* or *distinguished* function that alone enjoys an additional desirable property. If, for example, this property is that the g.l should have the most rapidly convergent Chebyshev-series expansion on the interval [0, 1], then so far the numerical evidence points in the direction of the function computed by Walker. However, we are unaware of any analytical investigation on these lines.

†In practice, certain modifications are implemented. On each computation of a value-vector, the known values of ϕ at integer arguments are inserted whenever possible. Moreover, convergence properties of the algorithm are often improved by starting each iterative cycle with a linear combination of the latest two approximations, rather than merely the most recent. Other refinements may be applied with practical advantage, but these details do not concern us here.

Table 1

r	a_r	b_r
0	0.99889 731	1.00109 464
1	0.49443 379	0.50544 366
2	0.00072 417	−0.00074 230
3	0.00548 385	−0.00554 163
4	−0.00016 650	0.00020 286
5	0.00008 089	0.00009 992
6	−0.00000 617	−0.00000 814
7	0.00000 146	−0.00000 200
8	−0.00000 016	0.00000 027
9	0.00000 002	0.00000 005
10	0.00000 000	0.00000 000
11	0.00000 000	0.00000 000
12		

$\phi(x) = \Sigma' a_r T_r^*(x)$ $\psi(x) = \Sigma' b_r T_r^*(x)$

4. li ARITHMETIC VIA SURFACE FITTING

In Section 2 we implied that the C^1 g.e.f and g.l that were constructed there are the most suitable functions for implementing li arithmetic. This statement is made on the assumption that li arithmetic operations are carried out directly, based on recursion relations given in [2]. We now describe another possible procedure.

The li operation of addition, for example, consists of finding the value of z that satisfies the equation

$$\phi(z) = \phi(x) + \phi(y) \tag{4.1}$$

for given positive values of x and y. This equation defines a surface $z = z(x, y)$. If this surface can be fitted economically, for example, by polynomials or rational functions, then li addition can be implemented by computing the value of z on the surface that corresponds to given values of x and y. Similar observations apply to the other li arithmetic operations, although because multiplication and division of two g.e.f's $\phi(x)$ and $\phi(y)$ are equivalent to addition and subtraction, respectively, of $\phi(x-1)$ and $\phi(y-1)$ when $x, y \geqslant 1$, the surface fitting need be undertaken only for the processes of addition and subtraction. Here emerges a possible use for analytic g.e.f's and g.l's. Because of their inherently greater smoothness, they may lead to less complicated and more economical surface fits than the C^1 functions of Section 2.

Figure 1 indicates the nature of the surface $z(x, y)$ for li addition within the cube $0 \leqslant x, y, z \leqslant 6$. Figure 2 provides a similar indication for subtraction. These surfaces were computed using the algorithms for addition and subtraction given in [2] for the g.e.f determined by (2.1).†

In Fig. 1 it will be observed that the surface develops a crease close to the plane $y = x$, a crease that becomes increasingly sharp as we move up the cube. Indeed by the time the top of the cube is approached the surface has effectively degenerated into two intersecting planes. This is a consequence of the fact that for large values of x, or y, or both quantities, the addition formula (4.1) effectively reduces to

$$z = \max(x, y); \tag{4.2}$$

compare Lemma 4.1 below.

The surface for the li subtraction operation is derivable from that for addition by change of axes: we have only to interchange x and z in (4.1) to convert this equation into the form

$$\phi(z) = \phi(x) - \phi(y). \tag{4.3}$$

†The surfaces have also been computed and plotted using the analytic g.l and the corresponding g.e.f generated from Walker's series expansion (3.2) in place of the C^1 g.l and g.e.f of Section 2. The resulting changes in the diagrams are imperceptible.

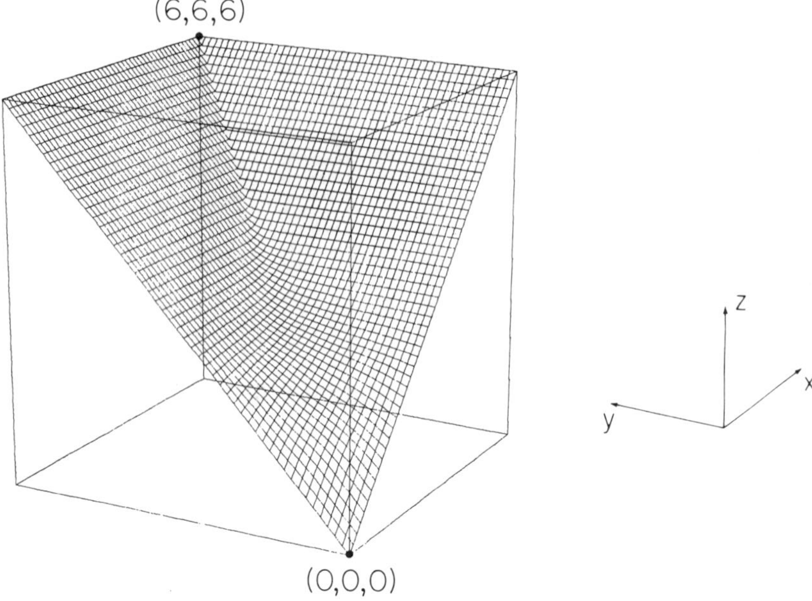

Fig. 1: li addition. $\phi(z) = \phi(x) + \phi(y)$.

The surface-fitting problem is quite different, however. As shown in Fig. 2, a crease again develops in the surface as we move up the cube near $y = x$, but on one side of this crease there is a precipitous drop or "cliff" to the plane $z = 0$.

The surface-fitting problems appear to be difficult both for addition and subtraction, owing to the rapidly changing nature of the surfaces near the plane $y = x$. Of the two, that

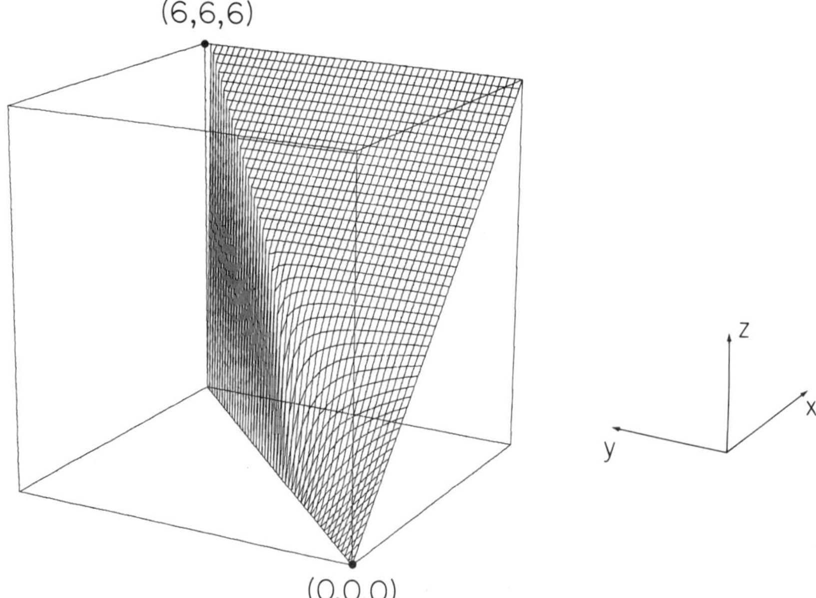

Fig. 2. li subtraction. $\phi(z) = \phi(z) - \phi(y)$.

for subtraction seems the more difficult because of the existence of the cliff. Initial attempts to fit each surface economically by double Chebyshev series expansions have proved to be unsuccessful.

We conclude this section with an analytic assessment of the approximate result (4.2).

Lemma 4.1

If ϕ *is the g.e.f determined by* (2.1), *then*

$$\phi(x) + \phi(y) \simeq \phi(x); \quad \text{gp}(\alpha) \tag{4.4}$$

provided that

$$x \geqslant 1, \quad x \geqslant y \geqslant 0, \quad \phi'(x-1) \geqslant (\ln 2)/\alpha. \tag{4.5}$$

Proof. Since ϕ' is nondecreasing on $[0, \infty)$, it follows from the given conditions and the mean-value theorem that

$$\phi(x-1+\alpha) \geqslant \phi(x-1) + \alpha\phi'(x-1) \geqslant \phi(x-1) + \ln 2.$$

Exponentiation then yields

$$\phi(x+\alpha) \geqslant 2\phi(x) \geqslant \phi(x) + \phi(y).$$

This is the required result.

An analogous result for subtraction follows. It is provable in a similar manner.

Lemma 4.2

If ϕ *is the g.e.f determined by* (2.1), *then*

$$\phi(x) - \phi(y) \simeq \phi(x); \quad \text{gp}(\alpha) \tag{4.6}$$

provided that

$$x-\alpha \geqslant 1, \quad x-\alpha \geqslant y \geqslant 0, \quad \phi'(x-\alpha-1) \geqslant (\ln 2)/\alpha. \tag{4.7}$$

Lemmas 4.1 and 4.2 need modification for other g.e.f's because in general it is not true that ϕ' is nondecreasing on $[0, \infty]$. However, the effective results for addition, subtraction, multiplication and division of large numbers—as typified by the approximate relation (4.2)—remain valid for all g.e.f's.

5. POWERS

The g.e.f and g.l can be used to study the approach to certain indeterminate limits. In the present section we consider the behaviour of the function

$$Z = X^Y. \tag{5.1}$$

We shall restrict $X \geqslant 1$ and $Y \geqslant 0$.

On setting

$$X = \phi(x), \quad Y = \phi(y), \quad Z = \phi(z) \tag{5.2}$$

in (5.1) and taking logarithms, we obtain

$$\phi(z-1) = \phi(x-1)\phi(y). \tag{5.3}$$

Figure 3 depicts the surface $z = z(x, y)$ defined by this equation within the cube

$$1 \leqslant x \leqslant 6, \quad 0 \leqslant y \leqslant 5, \quad 1 \leqslant z \leqslant 6. \tag{5.4}$$

This surface was computed from formula (5.3) by means of the algorithm for multiplication given in [2].

Within the region $x \geqslant 2$, $y \geqslant 1$ the surface in Fig. 3 is the same as that in Fig. 1, except for translations of 2, 1 and 2 units parallel to the axes of x, y and z, respectively. This

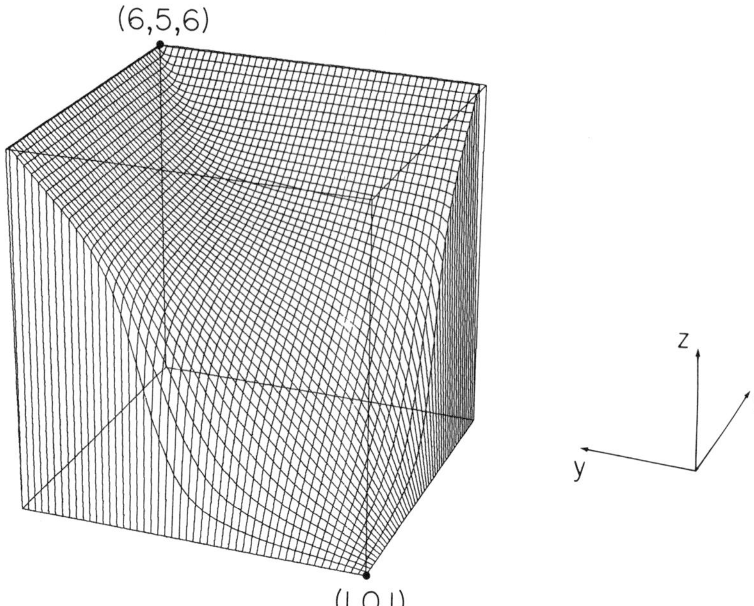

Fig. 3. Powers. $\phi(z) = \{\phi(x)\}^{\phi(y)}$.

is obvious on taking logarithms in (5.3)

$$\phi(z-2) = \phi(x-2) + \phi(y-1). \tag{5.5}$$

The character of the surface changes more rapidly between the planes $x = 1$ and $x = 2$, and also between the planes $y = 0$ and $y = 1$. For large values of $y\,(>x-1)$ the value of z is indistinguishable from that of $y+1$, except in the vicinity of $x = 1$ where there is a precipitous drop to the plane $z = 1$. Similarly, for large values of x the value of z is indistinguishable from that of x when $y < x-1$, except near $y = 0$ where there is a cliff to the plane $z = 1$. This case is examined more carefully below.

In order to obtain a closer look at the behaviour of Z when Y is small, that is, when we are in the vicinity of the right-hand cliff of Fig. 3, set

$$X = \phi(x), \quad Y = 1/\phi(y), \quad Z = \phi(z). \tag{5.6}$$

Then (5.3) is replaced by

$$\phi(z-1) = \phi(x-1)/\phi(y). \tag{5.7}$$

Figure 4 depicts the surface defined by this equation within the cube (5.4). It was computed from formula (5.7) by means of the algorithm for division given in [2].

Again, since

$$\phi(z-2) = \phi(x-2) - \phi(y-1), \tag{5.8}$$

it follows that within the region $x \geqslant 2$, $y \geqslant 1$, $z \geqslant 2$ the surface in Fig. 4 is the same as that in Fig. 2, except for translations of 2, 1 and 2 units parallel to the axes of x, y and z, respectively. The two most interesting parts of the surface occur near the planes $y = x-1$ and $y = 0$. First, the surface develops two creases near its intersection with $y = x-1$ as x increases, and it eventually degenerates into three planes. Secondly, as y approaches zero with x fixed the surface changes abruptly upwards into an almost vertical plane.

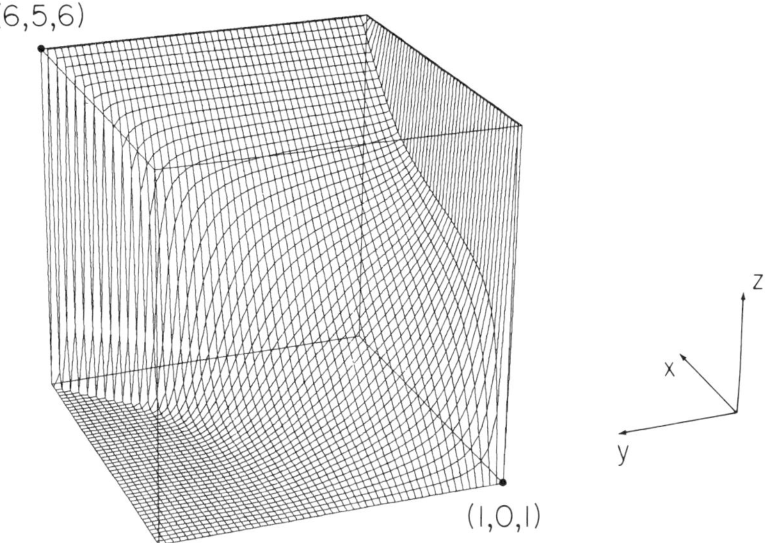

Fig. 4. Powers. $\phi(z) = \{\phi(x)\}^{1/\phi(y)}$.

Next, to examine the behaviour of Z when X is near to unity, that is, when we are in the vicinity of the left-hand cliff of Fig. 3 set

$$X = \phi\left[1 + \frac{1}{\phi(x-1)}\right], \quad Y = \phi(y), \quad Z = \phi(z), \quad \text{for } x \geqslant 2. \tag{5.9}$$

On taking logarithms we obtain†

$$\phi(z-1) = \phi(y)/\phi(x-1). \tag{5.10}$$

Comparison with (5.7) shows that the surface $z = z(x, y)$ defined by (5.1) and (5.9) is obtainable from that depicted in Fig. 4 by interchange of $x - 1$ and y.

Figure 5 draws together and presents, in a simple manner, some of the striking features of the power surfaces shown in Fig. 3 and 4. It consists of curves of z against y for selected constant values of X.

To produce these curves representing $Z = X^Y$, values of $z = \psi(Z)$ were plotted at equal intervals of $\psi(Y)$ for $Y \geqslant 1$ and at equal intervals of $\psi(1/Y)$ for $Y \leqslant 1$. The curve labelled n represents the case $x = n$, while that labelled n' represents its "dual", for which $x = 1 + 1/\phi(n-1)$.

The case $n = 2$ is self-dual, since the (unique) solution of

$$x = 1 + \frac{1}{\phi(x-1)}$$

is $x = 2$; the corresponding curve has no points of inflexion.

6. FUNCTIONAL ROOTS

Hammersley [5] investigated the problem of finding a function f that satisfies

$$f\{f(x)\} = e^x \tag{6.1}$$

†We continue to assume that we are using the g.e.f determined by (2.1). For other g.e.f's (5.9) would need to be modified by replacing $1/\phi(x-1)$ with $\psi\{1/\phi(x-1)\}$; then (5.10) remains valid.

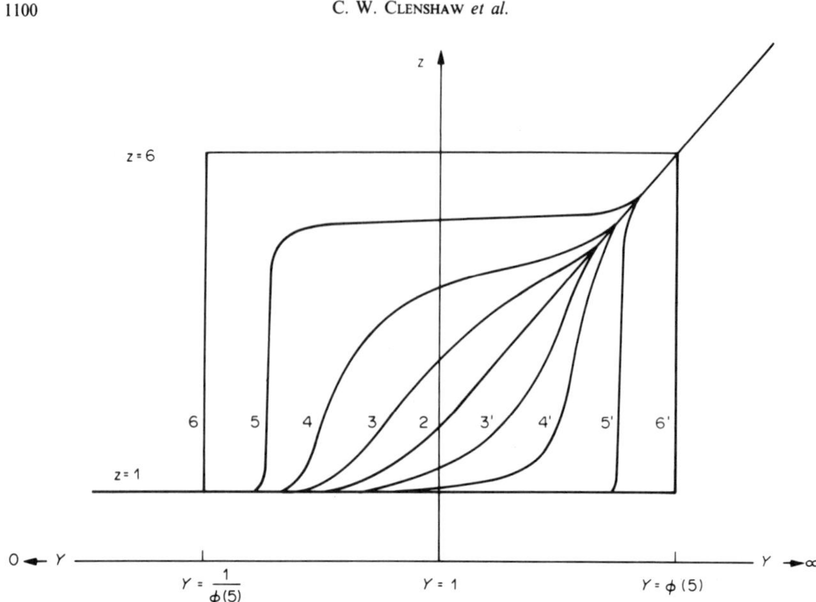

Fig. 5. Sections of power surfaces.

or, more generally

$$f\{f[f \cdots f(x)]\} = \mathrm{e}^x \tag{6.2}$$

where the functional operation is applied k times. Hammersley showed that for real variables and any integer value of k exceeding unity, there is an infinity of solutions belonging to $C^1(-\infty, \infty)$, and gave a method for constructing these solutions. He also discussed briefly whether there are analytic solutions of (6.1), and stated that there are no solutions that are meromorphic on the whole complex plane.

As pointed out by Kneser [6] the solution to (6.1) can be expressed in terms of the g.e.f and g.l; thus

$$f(x) = \phi\,\{\psi(x) + \tfrac{1}{2}\}. \tag{6.3}$$

Similarly

$$f(x) = \phi\left\{\psi(x) + \frac{1}{k}\right\} \tag{6.4}$$

satisfies (6.2). These results may be verified with the aid of the recurrence formula (1.4). If ϕ and ψ belong, respectively, to the classes of g.e.f's and g.l's discussed in Section 3, then the functions $f(x)$ defined by (6.3) and (6.4) are analytic on a domain that includes the real line. They are also real on this line.

7. CONCLUSION

We have outlined some of the properties of a generalized exponential function, and its inverse, a generalized logarithm. We have shown how to construct both C^1 and analytic versions of these functions; in particular we have drawn attention to some of the problems implicit in the definition of the analytic versions. We have indicated how the functions are useful in developing a new form of computer arithmetic, and also in the exploration of properties of very large and very small numbers. Lastly we have noted a connection between this work and the determination of certain functional roots.

Acknowledgements—The authors thank P. L. Walker for drawing their attention to Kneser's paper, and also for providing the numerical values of the coefficients in the series expansion (3.2). The surfaces shown in Figs 1–4 were computed at the University of Maryland and the National Bureau of Standards, and plotted by use of an Evans and Sutherland Picture System 300 at the National Bureau of Standards. The authors are pleased to acknowledge the assistance of R. E. Kaylor and S. Cramer, respectively, with these parts of the work, and also the assistance of Mr Kaylor with the attempts to fit double Chebyshev series expansions to the surfaces for li addition and li subtraction mentioned in Section 4. The research of one of us (F.W.J.O.) has been supported by the U.S. Army Research Office, Durham under Contract DAAG 29-84-K-0022, and the U.S. National Science Foundation under Grants MCS 81-11725 and DMS 84-19820.

REFERENCES

1. C. W. Clenshaw and F. W. J. Olver, Beyond floating point. *J. Assoc. Comp. Mach.* **31,** 319–328 (1984).
2. C. W. Clenshaw and F. W. J. Olver, Level-index arithmetic operations. *SIAM Jl numer. Analysis.* In press.
3. C. W. Clenshaw, Chebyshev series for mathematical functions. *NPL Mathematical Tables*, Vol. 5. H.M.S.O., London (1962).
4. L. Fox and I. B. Parker, *Chebyshev Polynomials in Numerical Analysis.* Oxford Univ. Press (1968).
5. J. M. Hammersley, Functional roots and indicial semigroups. *Bull. Inst. Math. Appl.* **19,** 194–196 (1983).
6. H. Kneser, Reelle analytische Lösungen der Gleichung $\phi\,[\phi\,(x)] = e^x$ und verwandter Funktionalgleichung. *J. Reine Angew. Math.* **187,** 56–67 (1948).
7. F. W. J. Olver, A new approach to error arithmetic. *SIAM J. Numer. Anal.* **15,** 368–393 (1978).
8. P. L. Walker, private communication.

SIAM J. NUMER. ANAL.
Vol. 24, No. 2, April 1987

LEVEL-INDEX ARITHMETIC OPERATIONS*

C. W. CLENSHAW† AND F. W. J. OLVER‡

Abstract. In a recent paper the authors described a system for the internal representation of numbers in a computer, based on repeated exponentiations. The main objective in introducing this system is to eradicate the problems of overflow and underflow. The present paper supplies algorithms for performing the four basic arithmetical operations in the new system. The algorithms are accompanied by error analyses, which show that the algorithms can be executed with fixed-point arithmetic. Illustrative examples are included.

Key words. binomial probability distribution, computer arithmetic, Euclidean norm, generalized exponential, generalized logarithm, generalized precision, overflow, underflow

AMS(MOS) subject classifications. 65-04, 65G99

1. Introduction. Recently the authors introduced a way of representing numbers internally in a computer, based on the idea of repeated exponentiation [2]. If F is any nonnegative real number, then we write

$$F = e^{e^{\cdot^{\cdot^{\cdot^{e^f}}}}}, \tag{1.1}$$

where $0 \leqq f < 1$ and the process of exponentiation is performed l times, l being a nonnegative integer. In particular, when $l = 0$, $F = f$. For a given value of F the numbers l and f are determined uniquely. They are called the *level* and *index* of F, respectively, and (1.1) is referred to as the *level-index* (li) form of F.

The level l and index f are somewhat analogous to the exponent ε and mantissa (or fractional part) μ in the standard floating-point representation

$$F = r^{\varepsilon}\mu, \tag{1.2}$$

in which $1/r \leqq \mu < 1$ and r is the internal arithmetic base of the computer. The main advantage of the representation (1.1) over (1.2) is the abolition of underflow and the virtual abolition of overflow. Other advantages discussed in [2] include the ability of the li system to function as a fixed-point system (when $l = 0$) or a floating-point system (when $l = 1$), the elimination of "wobbling precision" and the adoption of the absolute error in the index f as a generalized measure of precision.

In the present paper we show how to carry out arithmetic operations in the li system. Given the levels and indices of two nonnegative numbers F and G, say, we supply algorithms to find the level and index of the difference, sum, product and quotient of F and G. Except at low levels this computation cannot be done simply by finding the explicit fixed- or floating-point forms of F and G by repeated exponentiations, performing the required arithmetic operation and then converting the answer back to li form by repeatedly taking logarithms. The numbers involved may be too large. (Furthermore, if it were always possible to proceed in this manner then there would be little point in introducing the li system.) Instead, we shall construct algorithms that involve only ordinary arithmetic (in fact, fixed-point arithmetic).

* Received by the editors December 27, 1984; accepted for publication (in revised form) March 31, 1986.

† Department of Mathematics, The University of Lancaster, Lancaster, LA1 4YL, England.

‡ Institute for Physical Science and Technology, The University of Maryland, College Park, Maryland 20742. The research of this author has been supported, in part, by the U.S. Army Research Office, Durham, under contract DAAG 29-84-K-0022, the U.S. National Science Foundation under grant MCS 81-11725, and the United Kingdom Science and Engineering Research Council.

In the concluding sections we show, by means of two well-known examples, that the use of the new number system can lead to considerable simplifications in the construction of robust computing algorithms.

2. Arithmetic operations: algorithms.

2.1. Notation. As in [2], when $F \geqq 0$ we may express the li representation (1.1) concisely in either of the forms

$$F = [l/f] = \phi(l+f), \tag{2.1}$$

where $\phi(x)$ is the *generalized exponential function* defined by

$$\phi(x) = x, \quad 0 \leqq x < 1; \qquad \phi(x) = e^{\phi(x-1)}, \quad x \geqq 1. \tag{2.2}$$

Thus if $F = \phi(x)$, then l and f are, respectively, the integer and fractional parts of x.

The function that is inverse to $F = \phi(x)$ is the *generalized logarithm* $x = \psi(F)$, defined by

$$\psi(F) = F, \quad 0 \leqq F < 1; \qquad \psi(F) = \psi(\ln F) + 1, \quad F \geqq 1. \tag{2.3}$$

Explicitly

$$\psi(F) = l + \ln^{(l)} F, \qquad F \geqq 0, \tag{2.4}$$

where $\ln^{(l)} F$ denotes the lth repeated logarithm of F and the nonnegative integer l is determined uniquely by the condition

$$0 \leqq \ln^{(l)} F < 1. \tag{2.5}$$

Both $\phi(\cdot)$ and $\psi(\cdot)$ are increasing C^1 functions in the interval $[0, \infty)$.

Now let F and G be two numbers such that $F \geqq G \geqq 0$. We suppose that they are given in li form

$$F = [l/f] = \phi(x), \qquad x = l + f, \tag{2.6}$$

$$G = [m/g] = \phi(y), \qquad y = m + g, \tag{2.7}$$

and we seek their difference, sum, product or quotient H, say, also in li form

$$H = [n/h] = \phi(z), \qquad z = n + h. \tag{2.8}$$

We note that because $\psi(\cdot)$ is an increasing function we have $x \geqq y$, and hence $l \geqq m$.

2.2. Subtraction. Here $H = F - G$, so that

$$\phi(x) - \phi(y) = \phi(z). \tag{2.9}$$

Suppose first that $l = 0$. Then $m = 0$ and

$$n = 0, \qquad h = f - g. \tag{2.10}$$

Otherwise, we proceed as follows.

We compute three sequences $\{a_j\}$, $\{b_j\}$ and $\{c_j\}$, the members of which are defined by

$$1 = a_j \phi(x - j), \quad b_j = a_j \phi(y - j), \quad c_j = a_j \phi(z - j). \tag{2.11}$$

The a_j's are required for $j = l-1, l-2, \cdots, 0$. The b_j's are required for $j = m-1, m-2, \cdots, 0$, except that we need b_0 also when $m = 0$. The sequence c_j, $j = 0, 1, \cdots$, is terminated as soon as $c_j < a_j$ or $j = l-1$, whichever comes first.

Recurrence relations and initial values for generating the sequences are given by

(2.12) $$a_{j-1}=e^{-1/a_j}, \qquad a_{l-1}=e^{-f},$$

(2.13) $$b_{j-1}=e^{-(1-b_j)/a_j}, \quad b_{m-1}=a_{m-1}\,e^{g} \quad (m\geqq 1), \quad b_0=a_0 g \quad (m=0),$$

(2.14) $$c_j=1+a_j \ln c_{j-1}, \qquad c_0=1-b_0.$$

If c_j $(0\leqq j\leqq l-1)$ is the first member of its sequence to satisfy $c_j<a_j$, then

(2.15) $$n=j, \qquad h=\frac{c_j}{a_j}.$$

However, if $c_j\geqq a_j$ for $j=0, 1, \cdots, l-1$, then

(2.16) $$n=l, \qquad h=f+\ln c_{l-1}.$$

The relations (2.12) to (2.16) are readily derivable from (2.2), (2.11) and (2.6) to (2.9). It should be noted that the recurrence relations for the b_j and c_j are the same but they are applied in opposite directions.

2.3. Addition. Here $H=F+G$,

(2.17) $$\phi(x)+\phi(y)=\phi(z).$$

Suppose first that $l=0$. We compute $h_0=f+g$. Then

(2.18) $$n=0, \quad h=h_0 \quad \text{if } h_0<1,$$

or

(2.19) $$n=1, \quad h=\ln h_0 \quad \text{if } h_0\geqq 1.$$

When $l>0$ we again define a_j, b_j and c_j by (2.11). The only modifications to the procedure of § 2.2 are as follows. First, a_0 is not needed when $m>1$. Second, the second equation in (2.14) is replaced by $c_0=1+b_0$; this is the consequence of the replacement of (2.9) by (2.17). Third, the computation of the c_j's always proceeds to $j=l-1$. Subsequently we form h_l, where

(2.20) $$h_l=f+\ln c_{l-1};$$

then

(2.21) $$n=l, \qquad h=h_l \quad \text{if } h_l<1,$$

or

(2.22) $$n=l+1, \qquad h=\ln h_l \quad \text{if } h_l\geqq 1.$$

2.4. Multiplication and division. For multiplication $H=FG$ and

(2.23) $$\phi(x)\phi(y)=\phi(z).$$

First, if $m>0$ then $n>0$ and on taking logarithms in (2.23) we obtain

(2.24) $$\phi(x-1)+\phi(y-1)=\phi(z-1).$$

The values of n and h are found by applying the addition algorithm to the sum on the left-hand side and increasing the level of the answer by unity.

Secondly, if $l>0$ and $m=0$ then $\phi(y)=g$. The sequences $\{a_j\}$ and $\{c_j\}$ are computed exactly as in § 2.2, except that the starting value for $\{c_j\}$ is $c_0=g$. The values of n and h are as in (2.15) or (2.16). (The sequence $\{b_j\}$ is not required here.)

Thirdly, if $l=m=0$ then $n=0$ and $h\equiv fg$ is found by ordinary fixed-point multiplication.

For division the procedures are similar. The first case to consider is given by $H=F/G$, with $F\geqq G>0$. If $m>0$ then we take logarithms and use the subtraction algorithm. Secondly, if $l>0$ and $m=0$ then

$$\phi(z-1)=\phi(x-1)+\ln(1/g). \tag{2.25}$$

Since z necessarily exceeds unity in this case, we may start the computation of the c_j's from

$$c_1=1+a_1\ln(1/g).$$

Thirdly, if $l=m=0$ then

$$\phi(z-1)=\ln f+\ln(1/g) \tag{2.26}$$

and is nonnegative. If necessary, we continue taking logarithms until we obtain a number in the interval $[0,1)$.

The other case of division is given by $H=G/F$, with $F>G\geqq 0$. Necessarily $n=0$. When $m>0$ we compute $\phi(x-1)-\phi(y-1)$ by the subtraction algorithm, stopping at c_0; then $h=e^{-c_0/a_0}$. When $l>0$ and $m=0$ we compute $a_0\equiv 1/\phi(x)$ as in the subtraction (or addition) algorithm and then form $h=a_0g$. When $l=m=0$ we compute $h=g/f$ by ordinary fixed-point division.

It will be observed that some available precision may be lost in multiplication and division when the result is at level zero, just as in fixed-point multiplication and division. Often, of course, this loss is undesirable, and a natural way to avoid it is to represent level-zero numbers by the li forms of their reciprocals. This modification is discussed briefly in § 5 and more fully in [3].

2.5. Extensions. The subtraction/addition algorithm may be adapted to calculations involving several li numbers. Suppose, for example, that we wish to find z, where

$$\phi(x_1)\pm\phi(x_2)\pm\cdots\pm\phi(x_p)=\pm\phi(z), \tag{2.27}$$

and $x_1\geqq x_s\geqq 0$ for $s=2,3,\cdots,p$. We first compute the sequence $\{a_j\}$ defined by the first of (2.11) with $x=x_1$. Secondly, for each $s=2,3,\cdots,p$ we compute the sequence $\{b_j^{(s)}\}$ defined by

$$b_j^{(s)}=a_j\phi(x_s-j).$$

Thirdly, we generate the sequence $\{c_j\}$ defined by the third of (2.11). The recurrence relations for the a_j, $b_j^{(s)}$ and c_j are just as in (2.12), (2.13) and (2.14), with[1] $f=\text{fr}[x_1]$ and $g=\text{fr}[x_s]$, but with the starting value c_0 replaced by

$$\pm c_0=1\pm b_0^{(2)}\pm b_0^{(3)}\pm\cdots\pm b_0^{(p)},\qquad c_0\geqq 0. \tag{2.28}$$

It may happen that $c_{l-1}\geqq a_{l-1}$, as is always the case in the original addition algorithm. In this event we proceed as in (2.20), (2.21) and (2.22), except that it might also happen that $\ln h_l\geqq 1$; if so, we would compute the generalized logarithm of h_l and adjust the level accordingly.

[1] fr ≡ fractional part.

The advantage of this procedure is that we need only one sequence $\{a_j\}$ and, especially, only one sequence $\{c_j\}$. If parallel processing facilities are available, then the sequences $\{a_j\}$ and $\{b_j^{(s)}\}$ may all be computed simultaneously. In these circumstances the total computing time will be almost independent of p: only the comparatively rapid fixed-point summation (2.28) will be affected by the actual value of p.

Similar considerations apply to the computation of rational fractions of the form

$$\frac{\phi(x_1)\phi(x_2)\cdots\phi(x_p)}{\phi(y_1)\phi(y_2)\cdots\phi(y_q)}$$

and it is unnecessary to supply details.

3. Arithmetic operations: error analysis.

3.1. Effects of inherent errors. The object of this section is to ascertain how many guard digits need be retained in the implementation of the subtraction algorithm of § 2.2 and the addition algorithm of § 2.3 in order that the cumulative effect of the abbreviation errors[2] on the final result z be comparable with the unavoidable error in z stemming from abbreviations in the data x and y. In order to arrive at a solution to this problem we shall use linearized perturbation theory. In terms of this theory, the change δz in z caused by inherent errors δx in x and δy in y is given by

$$\delta z = \frac{\phi'(x)}{\phi'(z)}\delta x \mp \frac{\phi'(y)}{\phi'(z)}\delta y, \tag{3.1}$$

the upper sign being taken for subtraction and the lower sign for addition; compare (2.9) and (2.17).

The derivatives in (3.1) may be found with the aid of the chain rule

$$\phi'(x) = \phi(x)\phi(x-1)\cdots\phi(x-l+1), \tag{3.2}$$

with similar expressions for $\phi'(y)$ and $\phi'(z)$. *Here and elsewhere we follow the usual convention that empty products are assigned the value unity and empty sums are assigned the value zero.* Thus when $l=0$ we have $\phi'(x)=1$.

In the subtraction algorithm, as the value of y approaches that of x, the value of z tends to zero, which may cause the quotients $\phi'(x)/\phi'(z)$ and $\phi'(y)/\phi'(z)$ to become large. (This is of course, simply a manifestation of the inevitable loss of precision on subtracting two nearly equal numbers.) Furthermore, $\phi'(x) \geqq \phi'(y)$, since $x \geqq y$. In consequence, we shall seek to express the change in z stemming from the abbreviation errors as a multiple of $\phi'(x)/\phi'(z)$.

In the addition algorithm, we have[3]

$$1 \geqq \phi'(x)/\phi'(z) \geqq \{2(1+\ln 2)\}^{-1} = 0.2953\cdots. \tag{3.3}$$

In this case there is no need to include the factor $\phi'(x)/\phi'(z)$ in the bound for the change in z.

3.2. Working precisions; computed values. We first note that the members of the sequences $\{a_j\}$, $\{b_j\}$ and $\{c_j\}$ satisfy the following relations:

$$0 < a_0 < a_1 < \cdots < a_{l-1} \leqq 1, \tag{3.4}$$

$$0 \leqq b_0 \leqq b_1 \leqq \cdots \leqq b_{m-1} \leqq 1 \quad (m \geqq 1), \quad 0 \leqq b_0 \leqq 1 \quad (m=0), \tag{3.5}$$

$$0 \leqq c_0 \leqq c_1 \leqq \cdots \leqq c_{n-1} \leqq 1 \quad \text{(subtraction)}, \tag{3.6}$$

$$1 \leqq c_{l-1} \leqq c_{l-2} \leqq \cdots \leqq c_0 \leqq 2 \quad \text{(addition)}. \tag{3.7}$$

[2] That is, rounding or chopping errors [10].

[3] The lower bound in (3.3) is attained when $x = y = 2$.

(We also have $0 \leqq c_n \leqq 1$ when $n \leqq l-1$ in the case of subtraction.) Inequalities (3.4) follow from (2.12) and the fact that $e^{-1/t} < t$ when $t > 0$. To prove (3.5) in the case $m \geqq 1$, we observe from (2.11) and the assumption $x \geqq y$ that each b_j is bounded by unity. Furthermore,

$$\frac{b_{j-1}}{b_j} = \left(\frac{e^{t_1}}{t_1}\right) \Big/ \left(\frac{e^{t_2}}{t_2}\right), \quad t_1 = \phi(y-j), \quad t_2 = \phi(x-j),$$

and e^t/t is increasing when $t > 1$. The proof of (3.6) and (3.7) is similar.

Let r continue to denote the internal arithmetic base of the computer, and d_0 be the number of r-nary places to which f and g are stored. Bearing in mind (3.4) to (3.7), we assume that each member of the sequence $\{a_j\}$ is stored to d_1 r-nary places, and each member of the sequences $\{b_j\}$ and $\{c_j\}$ is stored to d r-nary places, where

$$d_0 < d \leqq d_1. \tag{3.8}$$

(The reason for the distinction in the number of places to which $\{a_j\}$, $\{b_j\}$ and $\{c_j\}$ are stored will become clear in § 3.6.) For brevity we write

$$\gamma_0 = r^{-d_0}, \quad \gamma = r^{-d}, \quad \gamma_1 = r^{-d_1}, \tag{3.9}$$

so that $\gamma_0 \geqq 2\gamma \geqq \gamma_1$.

In this section we distinguish computed values of quantities from their true values by adding overbars. In general, of course, $\bar{a}_j \neq a_j$, $\bar{b}_j \neq b_j$ and $\bar{c}_j \neq c_j$. Again, bearing in mind (3.4) to (3.7) we require the computed values to satisfy the following inequalities in order to avoid failure of the algorithms:

(i) $0 \leqq \bar{a}_j \leqq 1$, $0 \leqq \bar{b}_j \leqq 1$, $0 \leqq \bar{c}_j \leqq 1$ (subtraction), $1 \leqq \bar{c}_j \leqq 2$ (addition), $\bar{c}_0 = 1 - \bar{b}_0$ (subtraction), $\bar{c}_0 = 1 + \bar{b}_0$ (addition).

(ii) If $m = l$ and $\bar{b}_{l-1} = 1$, then $\bar{b}_j = 1$, for every j. Furthermore, in the case of subtraction $\bar{c}_0 = 0$, $\bar{n} = 0$ and $\bar{h} = 0$.

(iii) If (ii) does not apply, then $\bar{b}_j < 1$, for every j, $\bar{c}_0 > 0$, and $\bar{c}_j > 0$, $1 \leqq j \leqq n-1$. If, also, $\bar{a}_j = 0$ when $j \geqq 1$, then $\bar{a}_{j-1} = \bar{a}_{j-2} = \cdots = \bar{a}_0 = 0$ and $\bar{b}_0 = 0$.

3.3. Computation of a_j, b_j and c_j. Since we are considering the effects of abbreviation errors, we may suppose in the remainder of this section that x and y are exact.

We assume that for given values of a_j, b_j and c_{j-1} the quantities $\exp(-1/a_j)$, $\exp\{-(1-b_j)/a_j\}$ and $1 + a_j \ln c_{j-1}$ in equations (2.12), (2.13) and (2.14) are generated correct to absolute precisions γ_1, γ and γ, respectively. Accordingly, if δa_j, δb_j and δc_j are the errors in the computed values of a_j, b_j and c_j, respectively, then on neglecting terms of the second and higher orders in the Taylor-series expansions, we have[4]

$$|\delta a_{j-1}| \leqq a_j^{-2} e^{-1/a_j} |\delta a_j| + \gamma_1, \tag{3.10}$$

$$|\delta b_{j-1}| \leqq e^{-(1-b_j)/a_j} \left(\frac{|\delta b_j|}{a_j} + \frac{1-b_j}{a_j^2} |\delta a_j| \right) + \gamma, \tag{3.11}$$

$$|\delta c_j| \leqq (a_j / c_{j-1}) |\delta c_{j-1}| + |\ln c_{j-1}| \, |\delta a_j| + \gamma. \tag{3.12}$$

We assume also that e^{-f} and $a_{m-1} e^g$ or $a_0 g$ in (2.12) and (2.13) are evaluated to absolute precisions γ_1 and γ, respectively. In consequence of this assumption, and

[4] In (3.10)–(3.12) it needs to be emphasized that the symbols a_j, b_j and c_{j-1} denote the true values. Thus in case (iii) of § 3.2 if $\bar{a}_j = 0$ with $j \geqq 1$, then $\bar{a}_{j-1}(=0)$ and $\bar{b}_{j-1}(=0)$ are obtained exactly from (2.12) and (2.13); hence (3.10) and (3.11) would also apply without the terms γ_1 and γ on their right-hand sides.

also § 3.2(i), the starting values for the recurrences (3.10), (3.11) and (3.12) are subject to the conditions

(3.13) $|\delta a_{l-1}| \leqq \gamma_1;\qquad |\delta b_{m-1}| \leqq \gamma,\quad m \geqq 1;\qquad |\delta b_0| \leqq \gamma,\quad m=0;\qquad \delta c_0 = \delta b_0.$

Consider first the δa_j. The function $t^{-2}e^{-1/t}$ vanishes as $t \to 0$, rises to a maximum value of $4e^{-2} = 0.5413\cdots$ at $t = \frac{1}{2}$, then decreases to zero as $t \to \infty$. Setting $j = l-2$ in (3.10) and using the first of (3.13), we obtain

$$|\delta a_{l-2}| \leqq (4e^{-2}+1)\gamma_1.$$

Next, because $a_{l-1} \leqq 1$ it follows from (2.12) that $a_{l-2} \leqq e^{-1}$ $(<\frac{1}{2})$. Hence

$$a_{l-2}^{-2}\, e^{-1/a_{l-2}} \leqq e^2 e^{-e}.$$

Setting $j = l-3$ in (3.10) and substituting by means of the last two results, we find that $|\delta a_{l-3}|$ is bounded by $\lambda\gamma_1$, where

$$\lambda = (4+e^2)\, e^{-e} + 1 = 1.7515\cdots. \tag{3.14}$$

This argument may be continued, but it is easy to see (and also to prove by induction) that the bounds obtained for $|\delta a_{l-4}|, |\delta a_{l-5}|, \cdots$, are all smaller than that obtained for $|\delta a_{l-3}|$. Thus

$$|\delta a_j| \leqq \lambda\gamma_1, \qquad j = 0, 1, \cdots, l-1. \tag{3.15}$$

In the case of the δb_j suppose first that $m \geqq 1$. Using (3.15) and observing that the functions e^{-t} and te^{-t} are bounded by 1 and e^{-1}, respectively, when $t \geqq 0$, we see that (3.11) may be replaced by

$$|\delta b_{j-1}| \leqq \frac{1}{a_j}\left(|\delta b_j| + \frac{\lambda\gamma_1}{e}\right) + \gamma.$$

Applying this inequality recursively, beginning with the second of (3.13), we derive

$$|\delta b_j| \leqq \left(\frac{1}{a_{j+1}a_{j+2}\cdots a_{m-1}} + \frac{1}{a_{j+1}a_{j+2}\cdots a_{m-2}} + \cdots + \frac{1}{a_{j+1}}\right)\left(\gamma + \frac{\lambda\gamma_1}{e}\right) + \gamma.$$

Setting $j = 0$ and using the fact that $m \leqq l$, we obtain

$$|\delta b_0| \leqq \left(\frac{1}{a_1 a_2\cdots a_{l-1}} + \frac{1}{a_1 a_2 \cdots a_{l-2}} + \cdots + \frac{1}{a_1}\right)\left(\gamma + \frac{\lambda\gamma_1}{e}\right) + \gamma.$$

This inequality may be rewritten in the form

$$|\delta b_0| \leqq \frac{\phi'(x)}{\phi(x)}\left\{1 + \frac{1}{\phi'(x-l+1)} + \frac{1}{\phi'(x-l+2)} + \cdots + \frac{1}{\phi'(x-2)} + \frac{1}{\phi'(x-1)}\,\frac{\gamma}{\gamma + e^{-1}\lambda\gamma_1}\right\} \times (\gamma + e^{-1}\lambda\gamma_1);$$

compare (2.11) and (3.2). Hence

$$|\delta b_0| < \{\phi'(x)/\phi(x)\}\rho(\gamma + e^{-1}\lambda\gamma_1), \tag{3.16}$$

where

$$\rho = 1 + \sum_{j=1}^{\infty} \frac{1}{\phi'(j)} = 2.3921\cdots. \tag{3.17}$$

The result (3.16) has been derived on the assumption that $m \geqq 1$, but from the third of (3.13) it is true trivially when $m = 0$.

Lastly, consider the c_j. In the subtraction algorithm, if we set aside the trivial case $y=x$ (compare § 3.2 (ii)) we have $y \leqq x-\gamma_0$. From (2.11) it follows that $b_0 \leqq \phi(x-\gamma_0)/\phi(x)$. Since $l \neq 0$ we have $x \geqq 1$, and it is easily verified that with this condition the maximum value of $\phi(x-\gamma_0)/\phi(x)$ is $\exp(-\gamma_0)$. Therefore

$$c_0 \equiv 1-b_0 \geqq 1-e^{-\gamma_0} \geqq \gamma_0 - \tfrac{1}{2}\gamma_0^2 \geqq \gamma.$$

From (3.6) it now follows that $\gamma \leqq c_j \leqq 1, 1 \leqq j \leqq n-1$. Hence in (2.14) and (3.12) we have

$$|\ln c_{j-1}| \leqq \ln(1/\gamma). \tag{3.18}$$

And obviously, from (3.7), this inequality also holds for the addition algorithm.

Substituting in (3.12) by means of (3.15) and (3.18) we arrive at

$$|\delta c_j| \leqq (a_j/c_{j-1})|\delta c_{j-1}| + \gamma_2, \tag{3.19}$$

where we have written (temporarily)

$$\gamma_2 = \gamma + \lambda\gamma_1 \ln(1/\gamma). \tag{3.20}$$

Recursive use of (3.19) and reference to (3.13) then yields the required bound in the form

$$|\delta c_j| \leqq \left(1+\frac{a_j}{c_{j-1}}+\frac{a_j a_{j-1}}{c_{j-1}c_{j-2}}+\cdots+\frac{a_j a_{j-1}\cdots a_2}{c_{j-1}c_{j-2}\cdots c_1}\right)\gamma_2+\frac{a_j a_{j-1}\cdots a_1}{c_{j-1}c_{j-2}\cdots c_0}|\delta b_0|, \tag{3.21}$$

valid for all admissible j (that is, for $0 \leqq j \leqq \min(n, l-1)$).

3.4. Error bounds for subtraction. On multiplying each side of the inequality (3.21) by $c_0 c_1 \cdots c_{j-1} a_{j+1} a_{j+2} \cdots a_{l-1}$ and using the fact that each c_j is bounded by unity, we obtain

$$\begin{aligned} &c_0 c_1 \cdots c_{j-1} a_{j+1} a_{j+2} \cdots a_{l-1} |\delta c_j| \\ &\quad \leqq (a_{j+1}a_{j+2}\cdots a_{l-1} + a_j a_{j+1}\cdots a_{l-1} + \cdots + a_2 a_3 \cdots a_{l-1})\gamma_2 \\ &\qquad + a_1 a_2 \cdots a_{l-1}|\delta b_0|. \end{aligned}$$

From (2.11) and (3.2) it is seen that the left-hand side of this inequality equals $\phi'(z)|\delta c_j|/\{\phi'(z-j)\phi'(x)a_j\}$. Next, since $j \leqq l-1$ the right-hand side is bounded by

$$(1+a_{l-1}+a_{l-2}a_{l-1}+\cdots+a_2 a_3\cdots a_{l-1})\gamma_2 + a_1 a_2 \cdots a_{l-1}|\delta b_0|, \tag{3.22}$$

and therefore by $\rho\gamma_2 + \{\phi(x)/\phi'(x)\}|\delta b_0|$, where ρ is again defined by (3.17). Thus we have

$$\frac{|\delta c_j|}{a_j} \leqq \frac{\phi'(z-j)}{\phi'(z)}\{\phi'(x)\rho\gamma_2 + \phi(x)|\delta b_0|\},$$

or, on substituting by means of (3.16),

$$\frac{|\delta c_j|}{a_j} < \frac{\phi'(z-j)}{\phi'(z)}\phi'(x)\rho(\gamma_2+\gamma+e^{-1}\lambda\gamma_1). \tag{3.23}$$

Suppose first that $n \leqq l-1$. Then from (2.15) $h = c_n/a_n$. Assuming that this quotient is computed to absolute precision γ, we obtain

$$|\delta z| = |\delta h| \leqq (|\delta c_n|/a_n) + (c_n/a_n^2)|\delta a_n| + \gamma. \tag{3.24}$$

For the first term on the right-hand side we set $j=n$ in (3.23) and use the identity $\phi'(z-n)=1$. For the second term,

$$\frac{c_n}{a_n^2}|\delta a_n| < \frac{|\delta a_n|}{a_n} \leqq \phi(x-n)\lambda\gamma_1 \leqq \frac{\phi'(x)}{\phi'(z)}\lambda\gamma_1,$$

where we have used (2.11), (3.15) and the fact that

$$\frac{\phi'(z)}{\phi'(x)}\phi(x-n)$$
$$=\frac{\phi(z)\phi(z-1)\cdots\phi(z-n+1)}{\phi(x)\phi(x-1)\cdots\phi(x-n+1)}\frac{1}{\phi(x-n-1)\phi(x-n-2)\cdots\phi(x-l+1)}\leqq 1.$$

Substituting in (3.24) by means of these results and (3.20), we arrive at the required bound in the form

$$|\delta z|\leqq\frac{\phi'(x)}{\phi'(z)}\left\{(2\rho+1)\gamma+\left(e^{-1}\rho+1+\rho\ln\frac{1}{\gamma}\right)\lambda\gamma_1\right\}. \tag{3.25}$$

Alternatively suppose that $n=l$. Assuming that the expression (2.16) for h is computed to absolute precision γ, we have

$$|\delta z|=|\delta h|\leqq(|\delta c_{l-1}|/c_{l-1})+\gamma.$$

Then applying (3.23), with $j=l-1$, we see that (3.25) holds a fortiori in this case.

3.5. Error bounds for addition. In the addition algorithm the c_j are bounded below by unity. Hence from (3.21), with $j=l-1$, we see that $|\delta c_{l-1}|$ is bounded by the quantity (3.22), and hence

$$|\delta c_{l-1}|\leqq\rho(\gamma_2+\gamma+e^{-1}\lambda\gamma_1).$$

In (2.20) and (2.22) assume that $f+\ln c_{l-1}$ and $\ln h_l$ are evaluated to absolute precision γ. Then

$$|\delta h|=|\delta h_l|\leqq(|\delta c_{l-1}|/c_{l-1})+\gamma\leqq|\delta c_{l-1}|+\gamma\quad\text{if } n=l,$$

or

$$|\delta h|\leqq(|\delta h_l|/h_l)+\gamma\leqq|\delta h_l|+\gamma\leqq|\delta c_{l-1}|+2\gamma\quad\text{if } n=l+1.$$

On combining the above results and substituting for γ_2 by means of (3.20), we find that in all cases δz satisfies

$$|\delta z|=|\delta h|\leqq(2\rho+2)\gamma+\left(e^{-1}\rho+\rho\ln\frac{1}{\gamma}\right)\lambda\gamma_1. \tag{3.26}$$

3.6. Guard digits. At this stage we need to specify the relation between γ and γ_1; compare § 3.2. Inspection of (3.25) and (3.26) suggests that one advantageous way would be to restrict γ_1 to be bounded by a constant multiple of $\gamma/\ln(1/\gamma)$. Suppose, for example, we choose this multiple to be unity, that is, suppose that we require γ_1 to satisfy

$$\gamma_1\leqq\gamma/\ln(1/\gamma). \tag{3.27}$$

On substituting by means of this bound and replacing λ, ρ and e by their numerical values (see (3.14), (3.17)), we find that the results (3.25) and (3.26) reduce to

$$|\delta z|\leqq\{\phi'(x)/\phi'(z)\}[9.98+3.30\{\ln(1/\gamma)\}^{-1}]\gamma\quad\text{(subtraction)}, \tag{3.28}$$

$$|\delta z|\leqq[10.98+1.55\{\ln(1/\gamma)\}^{-1}]\gamma\quad\text{(addition)}. \tag{3.29}$$

In practice, the contributions of the terms involving $\{\ln(1/\gamma)\}^{-1}$ here will be quite small. With the modest assumption that we are working with at least 8 bits, so that $\gamma\leqq 2^{-8}$, we have

$$|\delta z|\leqq\{\phi'(x)/\phi'(z)\}\times 10.58\gamma\ \text{(subtraction)},\qquad |\delta z|\leqq 11.26\gamma\ \text{(addition)}. \tag{3.30}$$

The results just obtained show that if f and g are stored to d_0 digits in base r, then we should retain $\log_r 12$ guard digits in the sequences $\{b_j\}$ and $\{c_j\}$ and $\log_r 12+\log_r \{(d_0+\log_r 12) \ln r\}$ guard digits in the sequence $\{a_j\}$ to render the cumulative effects of the abbreviation errors comparable to the propagated effects of the inherent errors. Sample values of the smallest integers that are not less than $\log_r 12$ and $\log_r 12+\log_r \{(d_0+\log_r 12) \ln r\}$ are 4 and 9 for $r=2$, $d_0=32$; 4 and 10 for $r=2$, $d_0=64$; 2 and 8 for $r=10$, $d_0=1{,}000{,}000$. However, in designing a hardware processor for implementing the algorithms, extra guard digits should be included to ensure that the effect of the abbreviation errors is quite negligible compared with that of the inherent errors—apart from, of course, the final rounding or chopping of the guard digits themselves. This precaution is analogous to the use of guard digits in the accumulator register for ordinary floating-point arithmetic operations.

4. Arithmetic operations: numerical examples.

4.1. Example 1. We compute $F-G$ and $F+G$, where

$$F=\phi(3.4546), \qquad G=\phi(1.9999).$$

In the notation of § 2.1

$$l=3, \quad f=0.4546, \quad m=1, \quad g=0.9999.$$

We shall compute the sequences $\{b_j\}$ and $\{c_j\}$ to eight decimal places, using the rounding mode of abbreviation. In the notation of § 3.2 we have $r=10$, $d=8$.

$$\gamma=10^{-8}, \qquad \gamma/\ln(1/\gamma)=0.5428\cdots\times 10^{-9}.$$

Accordingly, it is ample to compute the sequence $\{a_j\}$ to ten decimal places.

For $F-G$ the computations in the subtraction algorithm proceed as follows. From (2.12) we find that[5]

$$a_2=0.63470\,17979, \quad a_1=0.20689\,51699, \quad a_0=0.00795\,96869.$$

From the second of (2.13) we obtain $b_0=0.02163\,451$. Lastly, from (2.14) we obtain

$$c_0=0.97836\,549, \quad c_1=0.99547\,480, \quad c_2=0.99712\,133.$$

Since $c_2>a_2$, we apply (2.16). Thus $n=3$, $h=0.45171\,718$, and the required result is given by

$$F-G=\phi(\mathbf{3.45171\,718}).$$

In the addition algorithm, the sequences $\{a_j\}$ and $\{b_j\}$ are the same but the starting value for $\{c_j\}$ is given by $c_0=1+b_0$. We find that

$$c_0=1.02163\,451, \quad c_1=1.00442\,834, \quad c_2=1.00280\,447.$$

From (2.20) we obtain $h_3=0.45740\,054$. Since $h_3<1$ equations (2.21) apply. Therefore

$$F+G=\phi(\mathbf{3.45740\,054}).$$

In this example it is possible to check the results by "unwinding," that is, by computing F and G in fixed-point or floating-point form. Repeated exponentiations yield

$$F=125.63308\,252\cdots, \qquad G=2.71801\,001\cdots.$$

[5] For simplicity we omit overbars from symbols in this section; compare § 3.2.

Hence

$$F-G=122.91507\,251\cdots,\qquad F+G=128.35109\,254\cdots,$$

$$\ln^{(3)}(F-G)=0.45171\,71752\cdots,\qquad \ln^{(3)}(F+G)=0.45740\,05475\cdots,$$

in adequate agreement with the results given above.

4.2. Example 2. We compute $F-G$ in the cases (i) $F=\phi(3.70001)$, $G=\phi(3.70000)$; (ii) $F=\phi(4.70001)$, $G=\phi(4.70000)$; (iii) $F=\phi(5.70001)$, $G=\phi(5.70000)$.

We use the same working precisions as in Example 1. In all three cases $f=0.70001$, $g=0.70000$. The computations are as follows.

(i) Here $l=m=3$, $a_2=0.49658\,03380$, $a_1=0.13348\,41086$, $a_0=0.00055\,77897$; $b_2=0.99999\,000$, $b_1=0.99997\,986$, $b_0=0.99984\,913$; $c_0=0.00015\,087$. Since $c_0<a_0$ we apply (2.15). Thus $n=0$, $h=0.27047\,828$ and

$$F-G=\phi(\mathbf{0.27047\,828}).$$

(ii) Here $l=m=4$, $a_3=0.49658\,03380$, $a_2=0.13348\,41086$, $a_1=0.00055\,77897$, $a_0=0.00000\,00000$; $b_3=0.99999\,000$, $b_2=0.99997\,986$, $b_1=0.99984\,913$, $b_0=0.76301\,447$; $c_0=0.23698\,553$, $c_1=0.99919\,692$, $c_2=0.99989\,276$, $c_3=0.99994\,674$. Since $c_3>a_3$ we apply (2.16). Thus $n=4$, $h=0.69995\,674$ and

$$F-G=\phi(\mathbf{4.69995\,674}).$$

(iii) Here $l=m=5$. On computing the a_j we find that $a_1=0.00000\,00000$. Also, $b_4=0.99999\,000$. Hence § 3.2 (iii) applies, and we have immediately $b_0=0$, $c_0=c_1=c_2=c_3=c_4=1$, $n=5$, $h=f$ and

$$F-G=\phi(\mathbf{5.70001\,000}).$$

The results in Cases (i) and (ii) may be checked by unwinding as in Example 1. In Case (i) we find that

$$F=1792.79022\,880\cdots,\qquad G=1792.51978\,870\cdots,\qquad F-G=0.27044\,010\cdots.$$

In Case (ii),

$$F=3.97103\,375\cdots\times10^{778},\qquad G=3.03007\,191\cdots\times10^{778},$$

$$F-G=0.94096\,184\cdots\times10^{778},\qquad \ln^{(4)}(F-G)=0.69995\,6737\cdots.$$

The only significant discrepancy occurs in Case (i). It is accounted for by the sensitivity of the answer z to the data x and y, and therefore, also, to abbreviation errors introduced during the computation. With the aid of (3.2), we find the following values for the coefficient of δx in (3.1):

$$\phi'(x)/\phi'(z)=2.704\cdots\times10^{4}\quad\text{in Case (i)},$$

$$\phi'(x)/\phi'(z)=4.224\cdots\quad\text{in Case (ii)}.$$

Therefore the actual discrepancies lie well within the projections of the error analysis of § 3.

In Case (iii) F and G are too large to be handled by unwinding in ordinary floating-point form.

4.3. Remark. In each example we computed the sequences $\{a_j\}$, $\{b_j\}$ and $\{c_j\}$ in order. In a software or hardware implementation, execution time could be saved by computing the a_j and b_j in parallel; compare § 2.5.

5. The symmetric level-index system. As we have noted in § 1, the li system functions as a fixed-point system for numbers in the interval $[0, 1]$: this is in the sense that the set of machine-representable numbers in this interval is equispaced. However, many algorithms entail the formation of products of very large and very small numbers, and if we wish to preserve relative precision in these cases then we need a set of machine-representable numbers that is increasingly dense as the origin is approached. The floating-point system achieves this by introduction of negative exponents. A corresponding modification of the li system is the *symmetric level-index* (sli) system, one notation for which is as follows.

In place of the mapping $F = \phi(x)$ and its inverse $x = \psi(F)$, we use $F = \Phi(x)$ and $x = \Psi(F)$, where

$$\Phi(x) = 1/\phi(1-x), \quad x < 0; \qquad \Phi(x) = \phi(1+x), \quad x \geqq 0; \tag{5.1}$$

$$\Psi(F) = 1 - \psi(1/F), \quad 0 < F < 1; \qquad \Psi(F) = \psi(F) - 1, \quad F \geqq 1. \tag{5.2}$$

Since $\phi(x)$ is an increasing C^1 function on the interval $[0, \infty)$ and $\phi(1) = \phi'(1) = 1$, it follows that $\Phi(x)$ is an increasing C^1 function on the interval $(-\infty, \infty)$. Similarly $\Psi(F)$ is an increasing C^1 function on the interval $(0, \infty)$.

Clearly arithmetic operations in the sli system can be constructed either by direct combination, or by modification, of the arithmetic operations given in § 2 for the li system. These procedures are examined in [3] and will not be discussed further here.

6. Applications. In this section we show, by means of two examples, that by eliminating overflow and underflow the li and sli systems not only make computing algorithms more robust, but may simplify their construction considerably.[6] These simplifications will save human effort in devising and programming algorithms, and they may recover some of the extra machine time that is needed to implement li or sli arithmetic.

6.1. Binomial probability distribution. The first example is the evaluation of the binomial probability distribution defined by

$$I(n, r, p) = \sum_{s=0}^{r} \binom{n}{s} p^s q^{n-s},$$

where $q = 1 - p$, $0 \leqq p \leqq 1$ and $0 \leqq r \leqq n$. This distribution has been tabulated by the National Bureau of Standards [9] for $p = 0.00(0.01)0.50$ and n up to 49.[7] In his well-known book on floating-point computation Sterbenz [12] devotes over six pages to the difficulties caused by overflow and underflow in programming the computation of $I(n, r, p)$. The problem has also been considered by Matsui and Iri [8]. The numerator $n(n-1) \cdots (n-s+1)$ and denominator $s!$ of the binomial coefficient overflow, and the powers p^s and q^{n-s} underflow, for quite moderate values of n, s and p. Of course, the final sum $I(n, r, p)$ always lies in the interval $[0, 1]$.

Sterbenz shows how to overcome these difficulties by careful rescaling and includes two programs for implementing his modified algorithms. In contrast, virtually any algorithm can be executed in sli arithmetic. This includes, for example, the following

[6] That overflow and underflow problems may be more common than is generally assumed has been demonstrated recently by Feldstein and Turner [4].

[7] Actually reference [9] tabulates $\sum_{s=r}^{n} \binom{n}{s} p^s q^{n-s}$, that is, $1 - I(n, r-1, p)$. Individual terms of the sum are also tabulated.

naïve algorithm:

$$
\begin{aligned}
&q=1-p,\ u=1,\ v=1,\ w=1,\ x=1\\
&\text{for } s=1 \text{ through } n\\
&\qquad x \leftarrow qx\\
&y=x\\
&z=y\\
&\text{for } s=1 \text{ through } r\\
&\qquad u \leftarrow (n+1-s)u\\
&\qquad v \leftarrow sv\\
&\qquad w \leftarrow pw\\
&\qquad x \leftarrow x/q\\
&\qquad y \leftarrow (u/v)wx\\
&\qquad z \leftarrow y+z\\
&I(n, r, p)=z.
\end{aligned}
$$

Thus at the close of the computations we have

$$u=n(n-1)\cdots(n-r+1), \quad v=r!, \quad w=p^r, \quad x=q^{n-r},$$

$$y=\binom{n}{r}p^r q^{n-r}, \qquad z=I(n, r, p).$$

The algorithm just given has been programmed and executed in sli arithmetic. Indices were rounded to 27 binary places at the conclusion of each arithmetic operation: this corresponds to $8\frac{1}{2}$ decimal places, approximately. Results for $p=0.1$, $n=2000$, $r=200$ (the case considered by Sterbenz) are as follows:

$$u=[3.68842667], \quad v=[3.64769156], \quad w=[-3.59530170],$$

$$x=[-3.50519488], \quad y=[-2.22893471], \quad z=[-0.65619393].$$

The square brackets signify that the numbers within are the sli images of the corresponding variables; for example,

$$u=\exp\exp\exp\exp(0.68842667), \qquad w=1/\exp\exp\exp\exp(0.59530170).$$

(This use of square brackets differs from that of § 2.1.) Approximate values of the corresponding floating-point (flp) numbers are given by

$$u=0.54144\times 10^{656}, \quad v=0.78879\times 10^{375}, \quad w=0.99996\times 10^{-200},$$

$$x=0.433058\times 10^{-82}, \quad y=0.29724761\times 10^{-1}, \quad z=0.51882226.$$

Accordingly, only the final results y and z are representable in single-precision IEEE standard floating-point arithmetic [6]. The intermediate quantities u and v would overflow, and w and x would underflow. (In fact, u and v also overflow in the double-precision version of the IEEE standard.)

It needs to be observed that although sli arithmetic cannot fail because of overflow or underflow, there is some loss of accuracy because of the naïveté of the algorithm. On recomputation with double precision in the sli images, the following results were obtained:

$$u=[3.68842666], \quad v=[3.64769155], \quad w=[-3.59530169],$$

$$x=[-3.50519492], \quad y=[-2.22894905], \quad z=[-0.65619750].$$

The loss of one decimal place in the original value of x stems from the large number of recurrence steps: 2200. The more severe loss of $3\frac{1}{2}$ decimal places in the value of y and 3 decimal places in the value of z stem from cancellation in the computation of y from the formula $y=(u/v)wx$. In effect, a very large number is being divided by another very large, and almost equal, number.[8] It is important to realize, however, that if higher accuracy is needed, then it could be achieved quite simply by executing the sli program in double, or higher, precision: *there is no need to recode the algorithm.* In contrast, when flp arithmetic fails, as it does in the present example, the algorithm being used may need to be modified extensively, or even abandoned.

6.2. Euclidean norm. Our second example is the evaluation of the Euclidean norm of a vector:

$$\|x\|=(x_1^2+x_2^2+\cdots+x_n^2)^{1/2}.$$

The direct algorithm proceeds as follows:

$$\begin{aligned}&y=0\\&\text{for } i=1 \text{ through } n\\&\qquad y\leftarrow y+x_i^2\\&\|x\|=y^{1/2}.\end{aligned}$$

When executed in floating-point arithmetic the algorithm fails when any of the squares x_i^2, or their sum, overflows or underflows, even though the required answer $\|x\|$ may lie between the smallest and largest machine-representable numbers. To avoid these failures careful rescalings are needed, and Blue [1] has devised a fairly robust, but rather complicated, algorithm on these lines. The kernel of Blue's algorithm consists of 19 lines of FORTRAN, including 6 machine-dependent constants.

With sli arithmetic there is no need for Blue's algorithm. The direct algorithm will always yield accurate answers with no possibility of overflow or underflow.

A numerical illustration is supplied in Tables 1 and 2. In Table 1 the x_i, their squares x_i^2 and partial sums $\sum x_i^2$ are represented as normalized decimal floating-point numbers with five decimal places in the mantissae; for example

$$x_1=0.51515\times10^{19},\qquad x_6=0.22261\times10^{-22}.$$

TABLE 1
Euclidean norm in flp.

i	x_i	x_i^2	$\sum x_i^2$
1	0.51515 +19	0.26538 +38	0.26538 +38
2	0.31416 +17	0.98697 +33	0.26539 +38
3	0.26658 +2	0.71065 +3	0.26539 +38
4	0.14142 +23	0.20000 +45	0.20000 +45
5	0.98765 +22	0.97545 +44	0.29755 +45
6	0.22261 −22	0.49555 −45	0.29755 +45
7	0.12345 +23	0.15240 +45	0.44995 +45
8	0.88088 +11	0.77595 +22	0.44995 +45

$\|x\|=0.21212\ +23.$

[8] The same kind of cancellation occurs, but in more subtle manner, in flp arithmetic; see [7]. This reference also contains a further discussion of the present example.

TABLE 2
Euclidean norm in sli.

i	x_i	x_i^2	$\sum x_i^2$
1	[3.2816147]	[3.4016766]	[3.4016766]
2	[3.2555873]	[3.3823005]	[3.4016767]
3	[2.1729316]	[2.6322989]	[3.4016767]
4	[3.3141689]	[3.4262379]	[3.4262379]
5	[3.3128548]	[3.4252394]	[3.4267863]
6	[−3.3183110]	[−3.4293888]	[3.4267863]
7	[3.3136730]	[3.4258610]	[3.4273541]
8	[3.1583057]	[3.3119641]	[3.4273541]

$\|x\| = [3.3156371]$.

In forming the squares and their partial sums each mantissa has been rounded to five decimal places immediately after computation. For computers that adhere to the IEEE floating-point standard, in single-precision the value of x_i^2 overflows for $i = 4, 5, 7$ and underflows for $i = 6$; furthermore, the partial sums overflow for $i \geqq 4$.

In Table 2 the x_i, x_i^2 and $\sum x_i^2$ are represented by their sli images to seven decimal places.[9] In forming the squares and their partial sums each sli entry has been rounded to seven decimal places immediately after computation. For comparison of the final results we have

$$\Phi(3.3156371) = 0.21211 \cdots \times 10^{23}.$$

This example would run successfully with Blue's program. However, if we were to increase the flp exponents of any or all the x_i's by 500, say, then this would no longer be the case. This is because these x_i's would be too large to be accommodated even in double-precision IEEE standard arithmetic.

7. Summary and conclusions. In § 2 we constructed algorithms for the operations of subtraction, addition, multiplication and division in the level-index number system. In § 3 we showed, by linearized perturbation analysis, that these algorithms can be implemented in fixed-point arithmetic. In § 4 we illustrated the algorithms by numerical examples in base 10. In § 5 we described briefly the symmetric level-index number system. In § 6 we showed how the use of the li and sli systems can simplify programming by means of two examples: the binomial probability distribution and the Euclidean norm.

The next stages in the development of the li and sli systems will include the following. (i) Fast processes are needed for evaluating the requisite exponentials and logarithms. Given numbers a, b and c in fixed-point form, we need to be able to form e^{-a}, $e^{-1/a}$, $e^{-(1-b)/a}$ and $\ln c$, for example, to fixed-point precision. On microcomputers or programmable calculators algorithms of the CORDIC type originated by J. E. Volder might be useful for this purpose; see, for example, [11], [14]. For mainframe computers, however, digital parallel algorithms of the kind used for fixed- and floating-point arithmetic operations will probably be more effective; see, for example, [5, § 3.2]. Considerable progress on these lines has been made by P. R. Turner [13]. (ii) The

[9] As in the previous example, it would take us too far afield to give a complete error analysis. As one might expect, however, an flp number with l digits in its exponent and d decimals in its mantissa, and an li or sli number with $l+d$ decimals in its fractional part are roughly to comparable precision [7].

linearized perturbation theory of § 3 needs to be strengthened by analysis that will yield strict (as well as realistic) error bounds.

Acknowledgments. The authors are pleased to acknowledge valuable criticisms of earlier versions of this paper by A. Feldstein, D. W. Lozier, P. R. Turner and the referees. Dr. Lozier also undertook the task of programming li and sli arithmetic and the algorithm of § 6.1.

REFERENCES

[1] J. L. BLUE, *A portable Fortran program to find the Euclidean norm of a vector*, ACM Trans. Math. Software, 4 (1978), pp. 15-23.

[2] C. W. CLENSHAW AND F. W. J. OLVER, *Beyond floating point*, J. Assoc. Comput. Mach., 31 (1984), pp. 319-328.

[3] C. W. CLENSHAW AND P. R. TURNER, *The symmetric level-index system*, manuscript.

[4] A. FELDSTEIN AND P. R. TURNER, *Overflow, underflow, and severe loss of significance in floating-point addition and subtraction*, IMA J. Numer. Anal., 6 (1986), pp. 241-251.

[5] K. HWANG AND F. A. BRIGGS, *Computer Architecture and Parallel Processing*, McGraw-Hill, New York, 1984.

[6] IEEE STANDARD 754, *Binary floating-point arithmetic*, The Institute of Electrical and Electronics Engineers, New York, 1985.

[7] D. W. LOZIER AND F. W. J. OLVER, *Closure and precision in computer arithmetic*, manuscript.

[8] S. MATSUI AND M. IRI, *An overflow/underflow-free floating-point representation of numbers*, J. Inform. Process., 4 (1981), pp. 123-133.

[9] NATIONAL BUREAU OF STANDARDS, *Tables of the Binomial Probability Distribution*, Applied Mathematics Series No. 6, U.S. Government Printing Office, Washington, D.C., 1950.

[10] F. W. J. OLVER, *Further developments of rp and ap error analysis*, IMA J. Numer. Anal., 2 (1982), pp. 249-274.

[11] C. W. SCHELIN, *Calculator function approximation*, Amer. Math. Monthly, 90 (1983), pp. 317-325.

[12] P. H. STERBENZ, *Floating-Point Computation*, Prentice-Hall, Englewood Cliffs, NJ, 1974.

[13] P. R. TURNER, *Towards a fast implementation of level-index arithmetic*, manuscript.

[14] J. S. WALTHER, *A unified algorithm for elementary functions*, AFIPS Conference Proc., 38 (1971), pp. 379-385.

MATHEMATICS OF COMPUTATION
VOLUME 50, NUMBER 182
APRIL 1988, PAGES 481-499

Error Bounds for Linear Recurrence Relations*

By F. W. J. Olver

Abstract. Recurrence relations of the form

$$a_r p_{r+1} = b_r p_r + c_r p_{r-1}$$

are examined in two cases: (A) oscillatory systems, for which $b_r^2 + 4a_r c_r < 0$; (B) monotonic systems, for which $b_r^2 + 4a_r c_r \geq 0$. In both cases, a posteriori methods are supplied for constructing strict and realistic error bounds in $O(r)$ arithmetic operations. A priori bounds, also requiring $O(r)$ arithmetic operations, are supplied in Case B. Several illustrative numerical examples are included.

1. Introduction. The application of mth order linear recurrence relations

$$a_{r0}p_r + a_{r1}p_{r-1} + a_{r2}p_{r-2} + \cdots + a_{rm}p_{r-m} + d_r = 0, \tag{1.1}$$

in which $a_{r0} \neq 0$, all r, to generate a sequence of values $p_m, p_{m+1}, \ldots$ from prescribed values of $p_0, p_1, \ldots, p_{m-1}$ is a well-understood procedure in numerical analysis. See, for example, [1], [2], [3], [4] and, most recently, the monograph of Wimp [19]. If the corresponding homogeneous equation is regarded as a difference equation, then it has m linearly independent solutions—the so-called complementary functions of (1.1). Each rounding error introduced in the recurrence process contaminates the wanted solution of (1.1) by small multiples of the complementary functions. This is of no concern if the wanted solution grows in size at least as fast as any of the complementary functions, that is, if it is a dominant solution. In other cases the process may fail, indeed fail disastrously, and in order to achieve stability it is necessary to apply the recurrence relation in a backward direction, or to solve a boundary value problem.

Perhaps because stability conditions are so well understood, comparatively little attention has been paid to the problem of constructing strict error bounds for the computed results. These bounds are to cover the effects of rounding errors introduced during the recurrence steps as well as inherent errors in the coefficients a_{rj} and d_r and the initial values $p_0, p_1, \ldots, p_{m-1}$. This is the problem treated in the present investigation. One obvious application is to the development of robust software for the generation of transcendental mathematical functions by recurrence.

The only relevant published work appears to be that for Miller's algorithm; see [7], [9], [16]. In fact, some results for the present problem could be found simply by specializing results given in these references, especially [7]. This approach leads to unnecessary complications, however, and a more direct attack is called for.

Received October 30, 1986, revised July 6, 1987.
1980 *Mathematics Subject Classification* (1985 *Revision*). Primary 65Q05; Secondary 65G05.
*This research has been supported by the U. S. Army Research Office, Durham under Contract DAAG-29-84-K-0022, the U. S. National Science Foundation under Grant DMS-84-19820 and the U. K. Science and Engineering Research Council.

We first observe that the evaluation of p_r for the range $r = m, m+1, \ldots, m+n-1$, say, is equivalent to the solution of a system of n linear algebraic equations. Hence the required error bounds can be found by available algorithms in matrix algebra; see, for example, [13], [14]. A drawback to this approach is that it requires the inversion of a lower triangular band matrix. The number of arithmetic operations needed for the inversion is $O(n^2)$, for large n, compared with only $O(n)$ operations for the computation of the solution p_r. It can be argued that it suffices to have the norm of the inverse matrix. However, it is an upper bound for the norm that is really needed, and this is tantamount to the original problem.[1]

Another drawback to the matrix approach is that it usually fails to provide insight into the nature of the error bounds; in particular, it will not yield realistic bounds of a priori type unless, of course, bounds for the elements or norm of the inverse matrix are known.

A second general approach is to apply rounded interval arithmetic [8, Section 2.4]. Often this procedure is quite successful. In many cases, however, the computed intervals are absurdly unrealistic. We illustrate this observation by two simple examples.

Example 1.1.

$$12p_{r+1} = 25p_r - 13p_{r-1}; \qquad p_0 = 1,\ p_1 = 13/12. \tag{1.2}$$

Computed interval values of $p_2, p_3, \ldots, p_{16}$ are given in Table 1.1. For example, the entries for $r = 2$ mean that

$$1.17360 \le p_2 \le 1.17363.$$

Six-figure decimal arithmetic was employed, with directed rounding[2] applied immediately following each arithmetic operation at each recurrence step.

Clearly the interval widths grow rapidly as r increases. After $r = 12$ the left endpoint begins to decrease and actually becomes negative at $r = 16$, even though the true solution $p_r = (13/12)^r$ is positive, increasing and dominant.

Example 1.2.

$$3p_{r+1} - \sqrt{22}p_r + 2p_{r-1} - 1 = 0; \qquad p_0 = p_1 = 1. \tag{1.3}$$

An interval solution was computed in the same manner as Example 1.1, and the results are presented in Table 1.2. Again the interval widths grow rapidly with r, even though the wanted solution is dominant and tends to the constant value $3.23013\ldots$ as $r \to \infty$. The actual solution is given by

$$p_r = \tfrac{1}{3}(5 + \sqrt{22}) - 2^{r/2}3^{-(r+2)/2}\{(2 + \sqrt{22})\cos r\omega + (\sqrt{176} - \sqrt{50})\sin r\omega\},$$

with $\omega = \tan^{-1}(1/\sqrt{11})$.

[1]Compare [5]. Here algorithms are supplied for computing the norm of the inverse of a tridiagonal matrix of order n in $O(n)$ operations. The algorithms entail the application of three-term homogeneous recurrence relations.

[2]That is, towards $-\infty$ for left endpoints and towards $+\infty$ for right endpoints.

TABLE 1.1

Interval solution of (1.2)

r	p_r		Ip_{r+1}/Ip_r
0	1	1	–
1	1.08333	1.08334	3.0
2	1.17360	1.17363	3.333...
3	1.27137	1.27147	2.5
4	1.37725	1.37750	2.6
5	1.49183	1.49248	2.523...
6	1.61568	1.61732	2.524...
7	1.74914	1.75328	2.514...
8	1.89194	1.90235	2.515...
9	2.04215	2.06834	2.514...
10	2.19359	2.25945	2.514...
11	2.32926	2.49487	2.514...
12	2.40488	2.82127	2.514...
13	2.30738	3.35430	2.514...
14	1.75065	4.38285	2.514...
15	0.0133583	6.63135	2.514...
16	– 4.72027	11.9189	

TABLE 1.2

Interval solution of (1.3)

r	p_r		Ip_{r+1}/Ip_r
0	1	1	–
1	1	1	–
2	1.23013	1.23014	3.0
3	1.58993	1.58996	2.333...
4	1.99904	1.99911	2.142...
5	2.39879	2.39894	2.133...
6	2.75102	2.75134	2.0
7	3.03517	3.03581	2.015...
8	3.24447	3.24576	1.968...
9	3.38203	3.38457	1.933...
10	3.45716	3.46207	1.930...
11	3.48206	3.49154	1.916...
12	3.46933	3.48750	1.915...
13	3.42980	3.46460	1.913...
14	3.37070	3.43730	1.912...
15	3.29356	3.42094	1.912...
16	3.19116	3.43477	

The explanation of the failure of interval arithmetic in these examples is the usual one: the process takes no account of the interdependence of errors at successive steps. In fact, in Example 1.1 the interval widths Ip_r, say, eventually grow in proportion to α^r, where $\alpha = 2.514\ldots$ is the largest zero of the polynomial $12z^2 - 25z - 13$. This is confirmed by the numerical values of the ratio Ip_{r+1}/Ip_r given in the final column of Table 1.1. Similarly in Example 1.2 the interval widths eventually grow in proportion to α^r, where $\alpha = 1.912\ldots$ is the largest zero of $3z^2 - \sqrt{22}z - 2$.

To construct methods that entail no more than $O(r)$ arithmetic operations and yield realistic error bounds, we have to impose restrictions on the nature of the recurrence relation. Without such restrictions, we have only the general matrix approach, with its $O(r^2)$ operations, to fall back on for realistic bounds. The present paper treats only real second-order relations. We also restrict ourselves to homogeneous systems, mainly because inhomogeneous problems often require error bounds for the associated complementary functions as a necessary preliminary [1], [10], [19]. In some cases, however, our methods carry over straightforwardly to inhomogeneous systems. Admittedly, the problems that fall within our scope amount to only a small subclass of the general problem of solving linear difference equations; nevertheless, this subclass includes many important recurrence relations satisfied by the higher transcendental functions.

We standardize (1.1) for homogeneous second-order systems in the form

$$a_r p_{r+1} = b_r p_r + c_r p_{r-1}, \tag{1.4}$$

with p_0 and p_1 prescribed and $a_r \neq 0$, all r. We distinguish two cases: *oscillatory systems* in which $b_r^2 + 4a_r c_r$ is negative for all r, and *monotonic systems* in which $b_r^2 + 4a_r c_r$ is nonnegative for all r. This classification is suggested, of course, by the nature of the solutions when the a_r, b_r and c_r are constants. Oscillatory systems are treated in Section 2, and monotonic systems in Sections 3, 4 and 5. In both cases we provide methods for constructing error bounds of a posteriori type. For monotonic systems we also furnish a priori bounds. Some numerical examples are supplied in Section 6, and brief conclusions are drawn in Section 7.

2. Oscillatory Systems. In (1.4) we replace c_r by $-c_r$ for convenience. The oscillatory case is then given by

$$a_r p_{r+1} = b_r p_r - c_r p_{r-1}, \tag{2.1}$$

with $b_r^2 < 4a_r c_r$, all r. Without loss of generality we may suppose that a_r and c_r are positive.

Example 1.2 is typical for systems of this kind in that interval arithmetic will generally yield unsatisfactory results. The error bounds, or interval widths, eventually grow at the same rate as the dominant solution of the equation

$$a_r p_{r+1} = |b_r| p_r + c_r p_{r-1}.$$

That this solution grows faster than the solutions of (2.1) can be inferred from the case in which the coefficients are constants.

In order to proceed, let q_r be a solution of (2.1) that is independent of p_r and (like p_r) is computed by forward recurrence from given values at $r = 0$ and 1. Denote the stored values of p_r, q_r and other quantities by the addition of overbars. Also, let ϕ_r and ψ_r be the aggregate errors introduced on the $(r-1)$st step in the computation of p_r and q_r, as expressed by the formulae

$$a_{r-1}\bar{p}_r = b_{r-1}\bar{p}_{r-1} - c_{r-1}\bar{p}_{r-2} + \phi_r, \qquad a_{r-1}\bar{q}_r = b_{r-1}\bar{q}_{r-1} - c_{r-1}\bar{q}_{r-2} + \psi_r. \tag{2.2}$$

Thus ϕ_r includes the effects of all abbreviation errors[3] introduced in the computation of $\bar{p}_r$ from $\bar{p}_{r-1}$ and $\bar{p}_{r-2}$ as well as the effects of inherent errors in the given values of the coefficients a_{r-1}, b_{r-1} and c_{r-1}. Similarly for ψ_r.

Bounds for $|\phi_r|$ and $|\psi_r|$ can be computed by standard methods of round-off error analysis, see for example [12], [18], or by interval arithmetic. For the initial values we set

$$\bar{p}_0 = p_0 + \phi_0, \quad \bar{p}_1 = p_1 + \phi_1, \quad \bar{q}_0 = q_0 + \psi_0, \quad \bar{q}_1 = q_1 + \psi_1. \tag{2.3}$$

The relationship of the stored values $\bar{p}_r$ and $\bar{q}_r$ to the true values p_r and q_r is easily verified to be

$$\bar{p}_r = p_r + B_r p_r - A_r q_r, \qquad \bar{q}_r = q_r + D_r p_r - C_r q_r, \tag{2.4}$$

where

$$A_r = -w_1 p_1 \phi_0 + \sum_{j=1}^{r} w_j p_{j-1}\phi_j, \qquad B_r = -w_1 q_1 \phi_0 + \sum_{j=1}^{r} w_j q_{j-1}\phi_j, \tag{2.5}$$

$$C_r = -w_1 p_1 \psi_0 + \sum_{j=1}^{r} w_j p_{j-1}\psi_j, \qquad D_r = -w_1 q_1 \psi_0 + \sum_{j=1}^{r} w_j q_{j-1}\psi_j, \tag{2.6}$$

and

$$w_1 = \frac{1}{p_1 q_0 - p_0 q_1}, \qquad w_r = \frac{1}{a_{r-1}(p_r q_{r-1} - p_{r-1} q_r)}, \qquad r \geq 2. \tag{2.7}$$

[3] By "abbreviation errors" we mean chopping or rounding errors.

The w_r are finite since p_r and q_r are assumed to be independent solutions. We also have the recurrence relation

$$w_r = (a_{r-2}/c_{r-1})w_{r-1}, \qquad r \geq 3, \tag{2.8}$$

and $w_2 = w_1/c_1$. Let us denote the wanted errors by

$$\varepsilon_r = p_r - \bar{p}_r, \qquad \eta_r = q_r - \bar{q}_r. \tag{2.9}$$

Suppose that we have computed $\bar{p}_r$ and $\bar{q}_r$, together with bounds on $|p_j|$, $|q_j|$, $|\varepsilon_j|$, $|\eta_j|$, $|A_j|$, $|B_j|$, $|C_j|$, $|D_j|$ and $|w_j|$, for all $j \leq r-1$. We first compute bounds on $|\phi_r|$, $|\psi_r|$ and $|w_r|$; compare (2.2) and (2.8). Next, from (2.5) and (2.6) we have

$$A_r = A_{r-1} + w_r p_{r-1}\phi_r, \qquad B_r = B_{r-1} + w_r q_{r-1}\phi_r, \tag{2.10}$$

$$C_r = C_{r-1} + w_r p_{r-1}\psi_r, \qquad D_r = D_{r-1} + w_r q_{r-1}\psi_r, \tag{2.11}$$

provided that $r \geq 1$. Using these relations we compute bounds on $|A_r|$, $|B_r|$, $|C_r|$ and $|D_r|$. Then by substituting the results obtained so far into the identities

$$E_r\varepsilon_r = -\{B_r(1 - C_r) + A_r D_r\}\bar{p}_r + A_r\bar{q}_r, \tag{2.12}$$

$$E_r\eta_r = -D_r\bar{p}_r + \{(1 + B_r)C_r - A_r D_r\}\bar{q}_r, \tag{2.13}$$

in which

$$E_r = (1 + B_r)(1 - C_r) + A_r D_r, \tag{2.14}$$

we arrive at bounds for $|\varepsilon_r|$ and $|\eta_r|$. (These identities are obtained by solving Eqs. (2.4) for p_r and q_r, and using (2.9).) Bounds for p_r and q_r follow from (2.9), and after computing $\bar{p}_{r+1}$ and $\bar{q}_{r+1}$ from (2.1) we are ready to repeat the cycle.

This is our method for constructing a posteriori error bounds. The magnitudes of the solutions p_r and q_r may rise or fall as r increases, depending on whether $c_r \gtrless a_r$. However, provided that the rate of growth of the magnitudes of the solutions does not differ significantly from that of $(c_r/a_r)^{1/2}$, all terms in the sums in (2.5) and (2.6) will remain of comparable magnitude, owing to the presence of the factors w_j. That this growth condition is not unreasonable can be seen by analogy with the case in which the difference equation has constant coefficients. Nevertheless, the condition will not always be satisfied in the general case, and it may need to be examined by asymptotic analysis or other independent means.

When the growth condition just discussed is satisfied, the bounds for $|A_r|$, $|B_r|$, $|C_r|$ and $|D_r|$ may be expected to grow approximately linearly with r, which is an essential requirement for the bounds for $|\varepsilon_r|$ and $|\eta_r|$ to be realistic. The number of arithmetic operations needed is several times that required to compute the $\bar{p}_r$, of course, but is still only $O(r)$ for large r. Moreover, many of these computations could be performed in parallel: if this is arranged, then the total execution time will not greatly exceed that needed for the computation of the $\bar{p}_r$ alone. Lastly, the method can be extended easily to inhomogeneous oscillatory systems, as long as the wanted solution is not dominated by the complementary functions as r increases.

3. Monotonic Systems (i). We now consider Eq. (1.4), that is,

$$a_r p_{r+1} = b_r p_r + c_r p_{r-1}, \tag{3.1}$$

with the condition $b_r^2 + 4a_r c_r \geq 0$, all r. We may suppose that $a_r > 0$, and we shall also suppose that $b_r \geq 0$.[4] In the present section we require $c_r \geq 0$, deferring the more difficult case of negative c_r until Sections 4 and 5.

The essential behavior in this case is that for appropriately chosen solutions the relative errors are simply additive. To express this result precisely and conveniently, we use relative precision (rp) in place of relative error, that is, we work in terms of the absolute errors of the logarithms of approximations [12].

We assume that the stored values $\bar{a}_r$, $\bar{b}_r$ and $\bar{c}_r$ of a_r, b_r and c_r, respectively, are correct to rp(δ), say, and the computations are performed in floating-point arithmetic with a working relative precision (wrp) of γ. (In other words, each arithmetic operation is accompanied by a chopping or rounding error not exceeding rp(γ).) We also assume that the initial values satisfy

$$(3.2) \qquad p_0 \simeq \bar{p}_0; \quad \mathrm{rp}(\varpi), \qquad p_1 \simeq \bar{p}_1; \quad \mathrm{rp}(\varpi),$$

where $\bar{p}_0$ and $\bar{p}_1$ are nonnegative, and ϖ, like δ and γ, is given. (Without these assumptions, p_r might be recessive as $r \to \infty$.) By application of the rules of rp error analysis and a simple inductive argument we deduce that

$$(3.3) \qquad p_r \simeq \bar{p}_r; \quad \mathrm{rp}\{\varpi + (2r-2)\delta + (3r-3)\gamma\}, \qquad r \geq 1.$$

This is the required result. Often it is improvable in minor ways. For example, if $a_r = 1$, all r, then the coefficients of δ and γ can be reduced to $r-1$ and $2r-2$, respectively.

It should also be noted that if interval arithmetic is applied directly to (3.1), then it will yield realistic a posteriori bounds. However, in view of the simplicity and effectiveness of the a priori bounds just given, the extra computations entailed by use of interval arithmetic can be avoided.

4. Monotonic Systems (ii). In this and the next section we consider the equation

$$(4.1) \qquad a_r p_{r+1} = b_r p_r - c_r p_{r-1},$$

in which $b_r^2 \geq 4a_r c_r$, $a_r > 0$, $b_r > 0$ and $c_r \geq 0$, for all r. We seek a solution p_r such that $p_r \geq 0$, for all r.

For reasons similar to those given in the oscillatory case (Section 2), interval arithmetic applied directly to (4.1) will yield unsatisfactory results. The method of Section 2 also fails. If p_r is dominant and q_r is recessive as $r \to \infty$, then in the second of (2.4) the term $D_r p_r$ soon overwhelms q_r. If p_r and q_r are both dominant, then the situation is even worse.

One way to proceed is to transform (4.1) into the nonlinear equation

$$(4.2) \qquad a_r h_{r+1} = b_r - (c_r/h_r)$$

satisfied by the ratio $h_r = p_r/p_{r-1}$. Then interval arithmetic, or a running error analysis [12], [18], can be applied to the computation of the sequence $\{h_r\}$ by recurrence, and also to the subsequent recovery of the wanted solution from the product

$$(4.3) \qquad p_r = h_r h_{r-1} \cdots h_1 p_0.$$

[4] Systems in which a_r and b_r have opposite signs for all r are accommodated by replacing p_r by $(-1)^r p_r$.

The reason these procedures are now more successful is that they make appropriate allowance for interactions of errors. In contrast, when (4.1) is computed in interval form, the upper (say) endpoint of p_{r+1} depends on the upper endpoint of p_r and the *lower* endpoint of p_{r-1}.

Another approach is to replace (4.1) by a pair of first-order linear equations with nonnegative coefficients; compare Section 3. For example, we can introduce a new variable u_r defined by

$$u_r = p_{r+1} - \lambda_r p_r,$$

where λ_r is a positive function of r at our disposal, subject to the condition $u_r \geq 0$. Then (4.1) is equivalent to

$$a_r u_r = \nu_r p_r + \mu_{r-1} u_{r-1}, \qquad p_{r+1} = \lambda_r p_r + u_r, \tag{4.4}$$

where

$$\mu_{r-1} = c_r/\lambda_{r-1}, \qquad \nu_r = b_r - a_r\lambda_r - \mu_{r-1}. \tag{4.5}$$

By hypothesis, $\lambda_{r-1} > 0$, hence μ_{r-1} is finite and nonnegative. The remaining coefficient ν_r is nonnegative as long as λ_r and λ_{r-1} also satisfy

$$a_r\lambda_{r-1}\lambda_r - b_r\lambda_{r-1} + c_r \leq 0. \tag{4.6}$$

If the coefficients a_r, b_r and c_r are slowly-varying functions of r such that $b_r^2 > 4a_r c_r$ and the starting values p_0, p_1 are chosen appropriately, then it will usually be possible to satisfy (4.6). This is because the zeros of the local characteristic polynomial $a_r z^2 - b_r z + c_r$ are real and distinct, and in effect (4.6) requires λ_{r-1} and λ_r to lie between them. For example, we might choose λ_r to be the arithmetic mean of the zeros, given by

$$\lambda_r = b_r/(2a_r).$$

Then (4.6) is satisfied as long as

$$b_{r-1}b_r \geq 4a_{r-1}c_r, \quad \text{all } r.$$

Solutions of (4.4) may be generated by interval arithmetic or with a running error analysis. Considerable cancellation may occur in the computation of ν_r from the second of (4.5); in consequence, it may be necessary to employ higher precision on this step.

In the next section we describe a semianalytical method. This method provides greater insight into the actual error propagation, and leads to useful a priori bounds. It has some features in common with the valuable method used by Mattheij and van der Sluis for obtaining error bounds for Miller's algorithm [7].

5. Monotonic Systems (iii). As in Section 4 we consider the equation

$$a_r p_{r+1} = b_r p_r - c_r p_{r-1}, \tag{5.1}$$

but with the conditions on the coefficients modified to $b_r^2 > 4a_r c_r$, $a_r > 0$, $b_r > 0$ and $c_r > 0$, for all r. Again, we wish to compute a solution p_r that is dominant as $r \to \infty$. We suppose that p_r is positive when $r > 0$ and nonnegative when $r = 0$. To begin with, we denote by q_r any positive solution that is independent of p_r.

As in earlier sections, we use overbars to indicate stored values. We first investigate the actual propagation of the aggregate abbreviation error ϕ_j, say, introduced on the $(j-1)$st application of (5.1) according to the formula

$$a_{j-1}\bar{p}_j = b_{j-1}\bar{p}_{j-1} - c_{j-1}\bar{p}_{j-2} + \phi_j, \qquad j \geq 2; \tag{5.2}$$

compare (2.2). The solution $p_r^{(j)}$, say, of (5.1) that satisfies

$$p_{j-1}^{(j)} = 0, \qquad p_j^{(j)} = \phi_j / a_{j-1}, \qquad j \geq 2,$$

is expressible in the form

$$p_r^{(j)} = \left(1 - \frac{p_{j-1}q_r}{q_{j-1}p_r}\right) \frac{t_j \phi_j}{a_{j-1}p_j} p_r, \tag{5.3}$$

where

$$t_j = \left(1 - \frac{p_{j-1}q_j}{q_{j-1}p_j}\right)^{-1}, \qquad j \geq 1. \tag{5.4}$$

With the assumed conditions, t_j is always finite.

Now suppose that q_r is the recessive solution of (5.1), so that $q_r/p_r \to 0$ as $r \to \infty$. Although q_r is unique only up to a constant factor, obviously from (5.4) the coefficients t_j in (5.3) do not depend on this factor. Furthermore, from (5.3) we have

$$\frac{p_r^{(j)}}{p_r} \to \frac{t_j \phi_j}{a_{j-1}p_j}, \qquad r \to \infty, \quad j \text{ fixed}. \tag{5.5}$$

This means that the relative error $\phi_j/(a_{j-1}p_j)$ introduced on the $(j-1)$st application of (5.1) is magnified ultimately by the factor t_j. If it happens that q_r/p_r is decreasing for all r, then we have, in addition,

$$\frac{|p_r^{(j)}|}{p_r} \leq \frac{t_j|\phi_j|}{a_{j-1}p_j}, \qquad r \geq j. \tag{5.6}$$

In other words, the actual propagated error is bounded by its limiting form. It also has the same sign.

For our purposes, it is not essential for q_r to be the recessive solution. Suppose that we are computing p_r over the range $r = 2, 3, \ldots, n$, where n is arbitrary. Let q_r now denote any solution of (5.1) that is positive when $0 \leq r \leq n-1$, nonnegative when $r = n$ and also has the property that q_r/p_r is decreasing for $0 \leq r \leq n$. Then q_r is independent of p_r; furthermore, if t_j is defined by (5.4) in terms of the present q_r, then (5.6) applies for $j = 2, 3, \ldots, n$.

To investigate the effect of inherent errors in the starting values at $r = 0$ and 1, let

$$p_0 = \bar{p}_0 - \phi_0, \qquad p_1 = \bar{p}_1 - \phi_1, \tag{5.7}$$

as in (2.3). Then the solution $p_r^{(0)}$, say, of (5.1) that satisfies

$$p_0^{(0)} = -\phi_0, \qquad p_1^{(0)} = -\phi_1, \tag{5.8}$$

is given by

$$p_r^{(0)} = \left(1 - \frac{p_1 q_r}{q_1 p_r}\right) \frac{t_0 \phi_0}{p_0} p_r - \left(1 - \frac{p_0 q_r}{q_0 p_r}\right) \frac{t_1 \phi_1}{p_1} p_r, \tag{5.9}$$

where t_1 is defined as in (5.4) and

$$t_0 = \left(\frac{q_0 p_1}{p_0 q_1} - 1\right)^{-1}. \tag{5.10}$$

With the assumed conditions we have

$$\frac{|p_r^{(0)}|}{p_r} \le \frac{t_0|\phi_0|}{p_0} + \frac{t_1|\phi_1|}{p_1}, \qquad r \ge 1. \tag{5.11}$$

On combining the effects of all the errors $\phi_0, \phi_1, \dots, \phi_r$ we arrive at

$$\frac{|p_r - \bar{p}_r|}{p_r} \le t_0\frac{|\phi_0|}{p_0} + t_1\frac{|\phi_1|}{p_1} + \sum_{j=2}^{r} t_j\frac{|\phi_j|}{a_{j-1}p_j}, \qquad 2 \le r \le n. \tag{5.12}$$

In the relations (5.9) to (5.12) we have supposed that $p_0 \ne 0$. If $p_0 = 0$, then we suppose that $\bar{p}_0 = 0$. The inequalities (5.11) and (5.12) then apply without the term $t_0|\phi_0|/p_0$ on their right-hand sides.[5]

In order to proceed, we need bounds on the coefficients t_j defined by (5.4) and (5.10). In turn, this necessitates bounds on p_{j-1}/p_j and q_j/q_{j-1}. Results of this kind have been supplied by the present writer [11], Mattheij [6] and van der Sluis [15]. For present purposes a simple and convenient result is provided by the following theorem. This result is included in that given by Theorem 4.1 of [6], but for simplicity we give a proof using our present notation.

THEOREM 5.1. *Let α_r and β_r denote the (positive) zeros of the quadratic $a_r z^2 - b_r z + c_r$, chosen so that $\alpha_r > \beta_r$. Write*

$$\alpha = \min(\alpha_1, \alpha_2, \dots, \alpha_{n-1}), \quad \mathrm{A} = \max(\alpha_1, \alpha_2, \dots, \alpha_{n-1}), \\ \mathrm{B} = \max(\beta_1, \beta_2, \dots, \beta_{n-1}), \tag{5.13}$$

and assume that $\alpha \ge \mathrm{B}$. Also, let v_r be any solution of (5.1) that is nonnegative when $r = 0$ and satisfies $v_1/v_0 \ge \mathrm{B}$. Then

$$\hat{\alpha} \le v_r/v_{r-1} \le \hat{\mathrm{A}}, \qquad r = 1, 2, \dots, n, \tag{5.14}$$

where

$$\hat{\alpha} = \min(\alpha, v_1/v_0), \qquad \hat{\mathrm{A}} = \max(\mathrm{A}, v_1/v_0). \tag{5.15}$$

(In the case $v_0 = 0$ the condition $v_1/v_0 \ge \mathrm{B}$ becomes $v_1 > 0$, $\hat{\alpha} = \alpha$ and $\hat{\mathrm{A}} = \infty$.)

To prove the theorem, write

$$f_r(z) = \frac{b_r}{a_r} - \frac{c_r}{a_r z},$$

so that

$$v_{r+1}/v_r = f_r(v_r/v_{r-1}).$$

We observe that for fixed r, $f_r(z)$ is increasing when $z > 0$ and

$$f_r(z) \le z, \quad \text{if } z \ge \alpha_r; \quad f_r(z) \ge z, \quad \text{if } \beta_r \le z \le \alpha_r.$$

[5] An appropriate modification could be made, however, if $p_0 = 0$ but $\bar{p}_0 \ne 0$.

From these results and the identity $f_r(\alpha_r) = \alpha_r$ it follows that:

(a) if $\alpha_r \le v_r/v_{r-1}$, then $\alpha_r \le v_{r+1}/v_r \le v_r/v_{r-1}$;
(b) if $\beta_r \le v_r/v_{r-1} \le \alpha_r$, then $v_r/v_{r-1} \le v_{r+1}/v_r \le \alpha_r$.

The result (5.14) is now proved by induction. Suppose that $v_r/v_{r-1} \ge \mathrm{B}$ and $\hat{\alpha} \le v_r/v_{r-1} \le \hat{\mathrm{A}}$, as is certainly the case when $r = 1$. Then $v_r/v_{r-1} \ge \beta_r$. Hence (a) or (b) applies. In either event we have $v_{r+1}/v_r \ge \mathrm{B}$ and $\hat{\alpha} \le v_{r+1}/v_r \le \hat{\mathrm{A}}$. □

Let us return to the bound (5.12). Defining α and B by (5.13) and applying Theorem 5.1, we find that

$$p_{r-1}/p_r \le 1/\rho, \qquad r = 1, 2, \ldots, n, \tag{5.16}$$

where

$$\rho = \min(\alpha, p_1/p_0), \tag{5.17}$$

provided that $\alpha \ge \mathrm{B}$ and $p_1/p_0 \ge \mathrm{B}$. To arrive at a similar bound for q_r/q_{r-1}, we now define q_r to be the solution of (5.1) that satisfies

$$q_{n-1} = 1, \qquad q_n = 0.$$

This solution can be generated by backward recurrence:

$$c_r q_{r-1} = b_r q_r - a_r q_{r+1}, \qquad r = n-1, n-2, \ldots, 1.$$

By applying Theorem 5.1 to this form of the difference equation, we deduce that

$$q_r/q_{r-1} \le \mathrm{B}, \qquad r = 1, 2, \ldots, n. \tag{5.18}$$

If we now restrict $\alpha > \mathrm{B}$ and $p_1/p_0 > \mathrm{B}$, then $\rho > \mathrm{B}$, implying that q_r/p_r is decreasing for $r = 0, 1, \ldots, n$. Accordingly, we may substitute in (5.4) and (5.10) by means of (5.16) and (5.18). This yields the required bounds in the form

$$t_0 \le \frac{\mathrm{B}}{\rho - \mathrm{B}}; \qquad t_j \le \frac{\rho}{\rho - \mathrm{B}}, \quad 1 \le j \le n. \tag{5.19}$$

It is now easy to see how to compute a posteriori bounds for $|p_r - \bar{p}_r|$ successively for $r = 2, 3, \ldots, n$. Write

$$T_r = t_0 \frac{|\phi_0|}{p_0} + t_1 \frac{|\phi_1|}{p_1} + \sum_{j=2}^{r} t_j \frac{|\phi_j|}{a_{j-1} p_j}, \qquad r \ge 1, \tag{5.20}$$

with the understanding that the term $t_0|\phi_0|/p_0$ is omitted in the case $p_0 = \bar{p}_0 = 0$ and the empty sum is zero in the case $r = 1$. From (5.12) we derive

$$p_r - \bar{p}_r = \vartheta_r T_{r-1} p_r + \vartheta_r t_r \frac{|\phi_r|}{a_{r-1}}, \qquad 2 \le r \le n,$$

where ϑ_r is some number in the interval $[-1, 1]$. Solving for p_r we deduce that

$$|p_r - \bar{p}_r| \le \frac{1}{1 - T_{r-1}} \left(T_{r-1} \bar{p}_r + t_r \frac{|\phi_r|}{a_{r-1}} \right), \tag{5.21}$$

provided that $T_{r-1} < 1$. As in Section 2 write $\varepsilon_r = p_r - \bar{p}_r$, and suppose that we have arrived at a lower bound for p_{r-1} and upper bounds for $|\varepsilon_{r-1}|$ and $|T_{r-1}|$, with $r \ge 2$. Inequalities (5.19) and (5.21) immediately yield an upper bound for $|\varepsilon_r|$. A lower bound for p_r can then be obtained, for example, from the inequality

$$p_r \ge \bar{p}_r - |\varepsilon_r| \tag{5.22}$$

(as long as $|\varepsilon_r| < \bar{p}_r$). And since

$$T_r = T_{r-1} + \frac{t_r|\phi_r|}{a_{r-1}p_r}, \qquad r \geq 2, \tag{5.23}$$

we can also find an upper bound for T_r. The cycle is now ready to be repeated.

A more interesting problem is to extend the foregoing analysis to yield a priori bounds. As in Section 3, we suppose that the stored values of the coefficients $\bar{a}_r$, $\bar{b}_r$ and $\bar{c}_r$ are correct to $\mathrm{rp}(\delta)$, the initial values $\bar{p}_0$ and $\bar{p}_1$ are correct to $\mathrm{rp}(\varpi)$ and the computations are carried out in floating-point arithmetic with $\mathrm{wrp}(\gamma)$.

THEOREM 5.2. *Let p_r and q_r be solutions of* (5.1) *such that $p_0 \geq 0$, $p_r > 0$ when $r > 0$, $q_r > 0$ when $0 \leq r \leq n-1$, $q_n \geq 0$, and q_r/p_r is decreasing for $0 \leq r \leq n$. Assume also the conditions of the preceding paragraph, and let $\varpi_0 = \varpi_1 = \varpi$ and*

$$\varpi_r = 2\left[(t_0+t_1)\varpi + \sum_{j=2}^{r} t_j\left\{\delta + 2\gamma + \left(\frac{b_{j-1}}{a_{j-1}}\frac{p_{j-1}}{p_j} + \frac{c_{j-1}}{a_{j-1}}\frac{p_{j-2}}{p_j}\right)(\delta+\gamma)\right\}\right], \tag{5.24}$$

$r \geq 2$, with t_j defined by (5.4) *and* (5.10).[6] *Then*

$$p_r \simeq \bar{p}_r; \qquad \mathrm{rp}(\varpi_r), \tag{5.25}$$

provided that $\varpi_r \leq \varsigma$, where $\varsigma = 0.265\ldots$ is the positive root of the equation

$$-\ln\left(1 - \frac{ze^{3z/2}}{2 - ze^{z/2}}\right) = z. \tag{5.26}$$

Proof. We first need an upper bound for the error term ϕ_j in (5.2). Since each arithmetic operation is accompanied by an abbreviation error of $\mathrm{rp}(\gamma)$, we apply the rules of rp error analysis [12] to obtain

$$|\phi_j| \leq \{a_{j-1}\bar{p}_j(\delta+2\gamma) + (b_{j-1}\bar{p}_{j-1} + c_{j-1}\bar{p}_{j-2})(\delta+\gamma)\}e^{\delta+2\gamma}, \qquad j \geq 2.$$

Next, on comparing (5.7) with the given conditions we have

$$|\phi_0| \leq p_0\varpi e^{\varpi}, \qquad |\phi_1| \leq p_1\varpi e^{\varpi}.$$

Substituting in (5.12) by means of these inequalities, we derive

$$\frac{|p_r - \bar{p}_r|}{p_r} \leq \left[(t_0+t_1)\varpi + \sum_{j=2}^{r} t_j\left\{\frac{\bar{p}_j}{p_j}(\delta+2\gamma) + \left(\frac{b_{j-1}}{a_{j-1}}\frac{\bar{p}_{j-1}}{p_j} + \frac{c_{j-1}}{a_{j-1}}\frac{\bar{p}_{j-2}}{p_j}\right)(\delta+\gamma)\right\}\right]e^{\hat{\delta}+2\gamma}, \tag{5.27}$$

where

$$\hat{\delta} = \max(\varpi, \delta). \tag{5.28}$$

We shall establish (5.25) by induction. Suppose that

$$p_j \simeq \bar{p}_j; \qquad \mathrm{rp}(\varpi_j), \qquad j = 0, 1, \ldots, r-1, \tag{5.29}$$

[6] Again, when $p_0 = \bar{p}_0 = 0$ we set $t_0 = 0$.

as is certainly the case when $r = 1$ and 2. If we extract the term $t_r(\bar{p}_r/p_r)(\delta + 2\gamma)$ from within the square brackets of the right member of (5.27) and express it in the form

$$t_r\left(\frac{\bar{p}_r}{p_r} - 1\right)(\delta + 2\gamma) + t_r(\delta + 2\gamma),$$

then with the aid of (5.29) and the fact that each of $\varpi_0, \varpi_1, \ldots, \varpi_{r-1}$ is bounded by ϖ_r,[7] we see that

$$\frac{|p_r - \bar{p}_r|}{p_r} \le \left\{t_r(\delta + 2\gamma)\frac{|p_r - \bar{p}_r|}{p_r} + \frac{1}{2}\varpi_r e^{\varpi_r}\right\} e^{\hat{\delta}+2\gamma}.$$

Next, from (5.24), (5.28) and the inequalities $t_1 > 1$, $t_2 > 1$ it is easily seen that $t_r(\delta + 2\gamma)$ and $\hat{\delta} + 2\gamma$ are both bounded by $\frac{1}{2}\varpi_r$ when $r \ge 2$. It follows that

$$\frac{|p_r - \bar{p}_r|}{p_r} \le \frac{1}{2}\varpi_r \frac{|p_r - \bar{p}_r|}{p_r} e^{\varpi_r/2} + \frac{1}{2}\varpi_r e^{3\varpi_r/2},$$

and hence that

$$-\ln\left(1 - \frac{|p_r - \bar{p}_r|}{p_r}\right) \le -\ln\left(1 - \frac{\varpi_r e^{3\varpi_r/2}}{2 - \varpi_r e^{\varpi_r/2}}\right) \le \varpi_r,$$

the last step being a consequence of the assumption $\varpi_r \le \varsigma$; compare (5.26). Thus (5.29) holds when $j = r$. □

For the purpose of constructing a priori bounds, Theorem 5.2 possesses the essential feature that the error bound for $\bar{p}_r$ is expressed in terms of the true solution p_r rather than the computed solution $\bar{p}_r$. With the notation of Theorem 5.1, and the assumptions $\alpha > \mathrm{B}$, $p_1/p_0 > \mathrm{B}$, the conditions of Theorem 5.2 on the solution q_r are satisfied, and we may apply (5.16) and (5.19). From (5.1) we have

$$\frac{b_{j-1}p_{j-1}}{a_{j-1}p_j} = 1 + \frac{c_{j-1}p_{j-2}}{a_{j-1}p_j};$$

accordingly, (5.24) may be simplified into

$$\varpi_r = 2\left[(t_0 + t_1)\varpi + \sum_{j=2}^{r} t_j\left\{2\delta + 3\gamma + \frac{c_{j-1}}{a_{j-1}}\frac{p_{j-2}}{p_j}(2\delta + 2\gamma)\right\}\right]. \tag{5.30}$$

Then by making the indicated substitutions we arrive at

$$\varpi_r \le \frac{2}{\rho - \mathrm{B}}\left[(\mathrm{B} + \rho)\varpi + \rho\sum_{j=2}^{r}\left\{2\delta + 3\gamma + \frac{c_{j-1}}{a_{j-1}}\frac{1}{\rho^2}(2\delta + 2\gamma)\right\}\right].$$

If we now introduce the quantity

$$C = \max_{j\in[1,n-1]}(c_j/a_j),$$

[7] This follows from the definition (5.24) and the inequality $t_1 > 1$.

then we are led to the further simplification

$$\varpi_r \leq \frac{2}{\rho - \mathrm{B}}\left[(\mathrm{B}+\rho)\varpi + (r-1)\left\{(2\delta+3\gamma)\rho + \frac{2C}{\rho}(\delta+\gamma)\right\}\right]. \tag{5.31}$$

Remarks. (a) The coefficient 2 outside the square brackets in the definition (5.24) of ϖ_r is arbitrary, to some extent. In fact any constant in excess of unity could be used instead, provided that an appropriate change is made in the definition of ς.

(b) By referring to the analysis in this section leading up to (5.12), it is easy to relate the terms on the right-hand side of (5.24) to the various errors introduced during the computations. Thus, the terms $(t_0+t_1)\varpi$ are contributed by the inherent errors in $\bar{p}_0$ and $\bar{p}_1$. In $\sum_{j=2}^{r}$ the terms $t_j(\delta+2\gamma)$ stem from the inherent error in $\bar{a}_{j-1}$ and the two errors introduced on abbreviating the difference $\overline{b_{j-1}p_{j-1}} - \overline{c_{j-1}p_{j-2}}$ and the quotient $\overline{b_{j-1}p_{j-1} - c_{j-1}p_{j-2}/\bar{a}_{j-1}}$. The remaining terms in $\sum_{j=2}^{r}$ stem from the inherent errors in $\bar{b}_{j-1}$ and $\bar{c}_{j-1}$, and the errors made in abbreviating the products $\bar{b}_{j-1}\bar{p}_{j-1}$ and $\bar{c}_{j-1}\bar{p}_{j-2}$.

(c) The bound (5.31) grows linearly with r, which is a necessary condition for it to be realistic. Moreover, if the coefficients a_r, b_r and c_r in the original equation are constants and $p_1/p_0 \geq \alpha$ (now the largest root of the characteristic equation), then $\rho = \alpha$ and the right-hand side of (5.31) becomes exactly twice the limiting value of the combined maximum effects of the inherent and abbreviation errors.

6. Numerical Examples.

Example 6.1. We compute the Legendre functions $P_r(x)$ and $Q_r(x)$ from the recurrence relation

$$(r+1)p_{r+1} = (2r+1)xp_r - rp_{r-1},$$

with the initial values

$$P_0(x) = 1, \quad P_1(x) = x, \quad Q_0(x) = \frac{1}{2}\ln\frac{1+x}{1-x}, \quad Q_1(x) = \frac{x}{2}\ln\frac{1+x}{1-x} - 1. \tag{6.1}$$

We take $x = 0.95$, with the understanding that this value may be in error by as much as ± 0.000001, and use six-decimal floating-point arithmetic, with chopping, for the calculation of $p_r \equiv P_r(x)$ and $q_r \equiv Q_r(x)$. The computed values $\bar{p}_r$ and $\bar{q}_r$ are given for $r = 0, 1, \ldots, 16$ in the second and third columns of Table 6.1(i).

Error bounds have been computed from the formulae given in Section 2. It transpires, for example, that $w_r = 1$, all r. Upper bounds $|\varepsilon_r|^{\mathcal{A}}$ and $|\eta_r|^{\mathcal{A}}$ for the absolute errors $|\varepsilon_r|$ and $|\eta_r|$ in $\bar{p}_r$ and $\bar{q}_r$, respectively, appear in the fourth and fifth columns of Table 6.1(i). Some of the intermediate computations are shown in Table 6.1(ii). Here, and in subsequent examples, the superscript $\mathcal{A}$ ("above") is again used to signify upper bounds of the designated quantities, whereas in the final column the superscript $\mathcal{B}$ ("below") on E_r indicates that entries in this column are lower bounds for E_r. These calculations were carried out by the methods of [12] using four-decimal floating-point arithmetic with chopping, except that in the cases $r = 0$ and 1 the values of $|\psi_r|^{\mathcal{A}}$ were found from Formulae (6.1) with the aid of high-precision values of the logarithmic function.

TABLE 6.1(i)

Legendre functions $P_r(x)$ and $Q_r(x)$

r	$\bar{p}_r$	$\bar{q}_r$	$10^6\|\varepsilon_r\|^A$	$10^6\|\eta_r\|^A$	$10^6\|\varepsilon_r\|$	$10^6\|\eta_r\|$
0	1	1.83178	0	11.09	0	11.0...
1	0.950000	0.740192	1	11.80	1	11.7...
2	0.853750	0.138880	83.19	84.93	2.8...	15.3...
3	0.718436	− 0.273566	138.8	102.8	6.7...	14.9...
4	0.554085	− 0.558962	291.3	178.2	12.7...	11.4...
5	0.372736	− 0.736972	441.6	315.9	17.8...	8.1...
6	0.187445	− 0.817756	500.4	437.7	20.6...	6.6...
7	0.0112185	− 0.811052	451.9	422.6	21.4...	22.9...
8	− 0.144030	− 0.729138	475.2	546.6	18.6...	52.7...
9	− 0.268424	− 0.587454	489.5	748.1	12.4...	84.1...
10	− 0.354878	− 0.404126	498.8	902.4	9.3...	109.8...
11	− 0.399597	− 0.198888	467.3	913.2	9.7...	123.9...
12	− 0.402295	0.00830666	359.4	784.8	12.4...	125.1...
13	− 0.366103	0.198763	535.5	903.5	19.8...	112.6...
14	− 0.297193	0.356448	716.4	970.4	25.9...	88.9...
15	− 0.204148	0.469164	834.4	994.6	29.9...	57.4...
16	− 0.0971412	0.529380	839.7	924.6	31.5...	16.4...

TABLE 6.1(ii)

Legendre functions (continued)

r	$10^6\|\phi_r\|^A$	$10^6\|\psi_r\|^A$	$10^6\|A_r\|^A$	$10^6\|B_r\|^A$	$10^6\|C_r\|^A$	$10^6\|D_r\|^A$	E_r^B
0	0	11.09	0	0	10.63	8.289	–
1	1	11.80	1.014	1.856	22.74	30.29	–
2	103.3	69.77	100.5	79.39	90.26	83.06	0.9998
3	150.6	46.09	232.2	101.6	131.4	90.70	0.9997
4	174.2	89.07	362.3	151.2	198.0	116.6	0.9996
5	169.3	189.2	462.4	249.2	307.0	225.4	0.9994
6	135.1	294.4	519.9	353.5	422.6	448.5	0.9992
7	74.25	378.2	541.2	419.9	500.5	768.5	0.9990
8	40.38	426.1	549.1	458.9	512.4	1129	0.9990
9	100.3	427.5	571.3	539.4	582.1	1460	0.9988
10	189.9	377.7	631.0	660.1	693.1	1705	0.9986
11	269.5	278.0	736.8	779.9	802.8	1842	0.9983
12	326.3	140.9	879.3	856.8	871.1	1896	0.9982
13	351.8	81.42	1034	871.9	916.4	1922	0.9981
14	340.4	212.6	1174	952.9	1008	1991	0.9980
15	291.0	383.5	1277	1070	1137	2157	0.9977
16	206.6	524.8	1337	1183	1261	2436	0.9975

Each of the quantities $|A_r|^A$, $|B_r|^A$, $|C_r|^A$ and $|D_r|^A$ appearing in Eqs. (2.4) grows monotonically with r, and very roughly in a linear fashion. The final error bounds $|\varepsilon_r|^A$ and $|\eta_r|^A$ exhibit some of the oscillatory character of the solutions p_r and q_r. The overall sizes of $|\varepsilon_r|^A$ and $|\eta_r|^A$ are linked directly to the sizes of the bounds $|\phi_r|^A$ and $|\psi_r|^A$ for the abbreviation errors ϕ_r and ψ_r in Eqs. (2.2).

Because of the uncertainty in the assumed value of x, the actual errors ε_r and η_r in $\bar{p}_r$ and $\bar{q}_r$ are unknown. However, their maximum absolute values can be found by taking $x = 0.95 \pm 0.000001$ in turn, and recalculating p_r and q_r using higher precision. The results are shown in the last two columns of Table 6.1(i). Of course, the bounds $|\varepsilon_r|^A$ and $|\eta_r|^A$ overestimate the actual values of $|\varepsilon_r|$ and $|\eta_r|$ considerably. This is caused partly by the stochastic nature of the actual abbreviation errors, and partly by the "radix effect". Had the computations been carried out in base 2, for example, instead of base 10, then the overestimation of the actual errors would be reduced by a factor of about 2 or 3 [12], [17].

Example 6.2. Let us solve the system (1.2) of Example 1.1 by the first method of Section 4, that is, by using the recurrence relation satisfied by the ratios $h_r \equiv p_r/p_{r-1}$. However, instead of assuming that the coefficients a_r, b_r and c_r in Eq. (4.1) are exactly 12, 25 and 13, respectively, we suppose that they are given in interval form $a_r = a$, $b_r = b$, $c_r = c$, all r, where

$$a = [11.9999, 12.0001], \quad b = [24.9998, 25.0002], \quad c = [12.9999, 13.0001].$$

The initial values $p_0 = 1$, $p_1 = 13/12$, are unchanged. (Of course, the method used in Example 1.1 would be just as unsuccessful with this modification.)

The recurrence formulae are given by

$$ah_r = b - (c/h_{r-1}), \qquad p_r = h_r p_{r-1}, \qquad r \geq 2. \tag{6.2}$$

Interval values of p_r and h_r, computed with six-figure decimal arithmetic, are given in Table 6.2. These results obviously represent a considerable improvement on those found on Table 1.1. However, they are not entirely satisfactory for the following reason. The interval width Ih_r of h_r grows roughly in proportion to r: this can be seen from the entries in the penultimate column of Table 6.2. This linear growth in Ih_r leads to an almost quadratic rate of growth in the corresponding relative errors of the p_r. This phenomenon is illustrated by the values of $Ip_r/(r^2\bar{p}_r)$ supplied in the last column of Table 6.2; here $\bar{p}_r$ denotes the midpoint of the interval value of p_r.

TABLE 6.2

Interval solution of Eqs. (6.2)

r	h_r		p_r		Ih_r	$Ip_r/(r^2\bar{p}_r)$
0	–	–	1	1	–	–
1	1.08333	1.08334	1.08333	1.08334	0.00001	0.000009...
2	1.08329	1.08338	1.17356	1.17367	0.00009	0.000023...
3	1.08325	1.08342	1.27125	1.27158	0.00017	0.000028...
4	1.08321	1.08346	1.37703	1.37771	0.00025	0.000030...
5	1.08318	1.08349	1.49157	1.49274	0.00031	0.000031...
6	1.08315	1.08352	1.61559	1.61742	0.00037	0.000031...
7	1.08312	1.08355	1.74987	1.75256	0.00043	0.000031...
8	1.08309	1.08357	1.89526	1.89903	0.00048	0.000031...
9	1.08307	1.08360	2.05269	2.05779	0.00053	0.000030...
10	1.08304	1.08362	2.22314	2.22987	0.00058	0.000030...
11	1.08302	1.08364	2.40770	2.41638	0.00062	0.000029...
12	1.08300	1.08366	2.60753	2.61854	0.00066	0.000029...
13	1.08299	1.08368	2.82392	2.83766	0.00069	0.000028...
14	1.08298	1.08370	3.05824	3.07518	0.00072	0.000028...
15	1.08296	1.08371	3.31195	3.33261	0.00075	0.000027...
16	1.08294	1.08372	3.58664	3.61162	0.00078	0.000027...

Example 6.3. We solve the problem posed in Example 6.2 by the second method of Section 4. On omitting the suffix r from the coefficients a_r, b_r, c_r, λ_r, μ_r and

ν_r, we obtain the recurrence relations

(6.3) $$au_r = \nu p_r + \mu u_{r-1}, \qquad p_{r+1} = u_r + \lambda p_r, \qquad r \geq 1,$$

in which

$$\lambda = b/(2a), \quad \mu = c/\lambda, \quad \nu = b - a\lambda - \mu.$$

The initial member of the sequence $\{u_r\}$ is given by $u_0 = p_1 - \lambda p_0$. Interval values of λ, μ and ν are found to be

$$\lambda = [1.04164, 1.04169], \quad \mu = [12.4797, 12.4803], \quad \nu = [0.0196000, 0.0204000],$$

and using six-figure decimal arithmetic we arrive at the interval values of p_r and u_r displayed in Table 6.3.

For large r, the intervals containing p_r are narrower than those obtained in Table 6.2 but from the last column, in which $\bar{p}_r$ again denotes the mean value of p_r, it is evident that the growth of the relative error is still not linear in r.

TABLE 6.3

Interval solution of Eqs. (6.3)

r	u_r		p_r		$Ip_r/(r\bar{p}_r)$
0	0.0416400	0.0417000	1	1	–
1	0.0450735	0.0452113	1.08333	1.08334	0.00000...
2	0.0487915	0.0490168	1.17350	1.17373	0.00009...
3	0.0528176	0.0531412	1.27115	1.27169	0.00014...
4	0.0571773	0.0576112	1.37689	1.37786	0.00017...
5	0.0618983	0.0624557	1.49139	1.49293	0.00020...
6	0.0670105	0.0677061	1.61538	1.61764	0.00023...
7	0.0725463	0.0733965	1.74965	1.75279	0.00025...
8	0.0785408	0.0795638	1.89504	1.89927	0.00027...
9	0.0850317	0.0862483	2.05248	2.05803	0.00030...
10	0.0920608	0.0934933	2.22297	2.23008	0.00031...
11	0.0996716	0.101346	2.40759	2.41656	0.00033...
12	0.107913	0.109856	2.60751	2.61866	0.00035...
13	0.116838	0.119079	2.82399	2.83770	0.00037...
14	0.126502	0.129076	3.05841	3.07509	0.00038...
15	0.136967	0.139910	3.31226	3.33238	0.00040...
16	–	–	3.58714	3.61122	0.00041...

Example 6.4. We compute the absolute value of the Bessel function $Y_r(x)$ by forward recurrence from the relation

(6.4) $$p_{r+1} = (2r/x)p_r - p_{r-1}.$$

We take $x = 100$ and the initial values

(6.5) $$p_{100} = -Y_{100}(100) = 0.166921\ldots, \qquad p_{101} = -Y_{101}(100) = 0.200285\ldots.$$

Using six-decimal floating-point arithmetic, with chopping, we obtain the values $\bar{p}_r$ given in the second column of Table 6.4.

We shall compute both a posteriori and a priori error bounds by the methods of Section 5. These computations are carried out in four-decimal floating-point arithmetic with chopping. In the terminology of [12] this is the lower mode of computation ($\mathcal{L}$), and its associated wrp is $\gamma_\ell = 10^{-3}$. For the computation of the $\bar{p}_r$, the wrp is $\gamma = 10^{-5}$.

Both types of error bound require the evaluation of the bounds (5.19) for the coefficients t_j. The zeros of the local characteristic polynomial $z^2 - (2r/x)z + 1$ are given by

$$\alpha_r = (r/x) + \{(r/x)^2 - 1\}^{1/2}, \qquad \beta_r = (r/x) - \{(r/x)^2 - 1\}^{1/2}.$$

Consequently, for any n exceeding 100, we have

$$\alpha = \alpha_{101} = 1.15177\ldots, \qquad \mathrm{B} = \beta_{101} = 0.868225\ldots;$$

compare (5.13). Also, from (5.17) and (6.5) we see that $\rho = \alpha$. From (5.19) we derive

(6.6) $$t_{100} \leq 3.061\ldots; \qquad t_j \leq 4.061\ldots, \qquad j \geq 101.$$

For simplicity, however, we use the same bound for all j:

(6.7) $$t_j < 4.062, \qquad j \geq 100.$$

For a posteriori error bounds we need to compute bounds for the quantities ϕ_r defined by

$$\bar{p}_r = \{(2r-2)/x\}\bar{p}_{r-1} - \bar{p}_{r-2} + \phi_r, \qquad r \geq 102;$$

compare (5.2). Since the coefficient $(2r-2)/x$ is exact, only two chopping errors are introduced at each recurrence step. Applying the methods of [12] we find that

$$|\phi_r| \leq \bar{\bar{\chi}}_r \gamma e^{3\gamma\iota}, \qquad r \geq 102,$$

where

$$\chi_r = p_r + \{(2r-2)/x\}p_{r-1},$$

and the double bar signifies the value computed in $\mathcal{L}$. The rest of the computation proceeds in accordance with the relations (5.21), (5.22) and (5.23), as described in Section 5. The main steps are shown in columns 3, 4, 5 and 6 of Table 6.4: As in Example 6.1, the superscripts $\mathcal{A}$ and $\mathcal{B}$ signify upper and lower bounds respectively. Again, these bounds were computed using the methods of [12].

TABLE 6.4

Bessel function $-Y_r(x)$

r	$\bar{p}_r$	$\bar{\bar{\chi}}_r$	$10^5 T_r^{\mathcal{A}}$	$p_r^{\mathcal{B}}$	$10^5\lvert\varepsilon_r\rvert^{\mathcal{A}}$	$\lvert\varepsilon_r/\bar{p}_r\rvert^{\mathcal{A}}$	$\varepsilon_r/\bar{p}_r$	$\varpi_r^{\mathcal{A}}$
100	0.166921	–	–	–	–	–	–	–
101	0.200285	–	4.531	–	–	–	–	–
102	0.237654	0.6421	15.70	0.2375	3.755	0.00016	0.000004...	0.00037
103	0.284529	0.7693	26.94	0.2844	7.710	0.00028	0.000007...	0.00060
104	0.348475	0.9345	38.14	0.3482	13.35	0.00039	0.000011...	0.00082
105	0.440299	1.165	49.20	0.4399	21.78	0.00050	0.000013...	0.00104
106	0.576152	1.500	60.13	0.5757	34.86	0.00061	0.000016...	0.00127
107	0.781141	2.002	70.94	0.7805	55.76	0.00072	0.000021...	0.00149
108	1.09548	2.766	81.61	1.094	89.94	0.00083	0.000032...	0.00172
109	1.58508	3.951	92.21	1.583	147.0	0.00093	0.000048...	0.00194
110	2.35999	5.814	102.7	2.356	243.8	0.00104	0.000057...	0.00216
111	3.60689	8.797	113.1	3.601	410.8	0.00114	0.000063...	0.00239
112	5.64730	13.65	123.5	5.639	702.6	0.00125	0.000067...	0.00261
113	9.04301	21.68	133.9	9.030	1218	0.00135	0.000074...	0.00284
114	14.7899	35.21	144.3	14.75	2147	0.00146	0.000077...	0.00306
115	24.6778	58.39	154.6	24.63	3840	0.00156	0.000084...	0.00328
116	41.9690	98.71	164.8	41.89	6966	0.00166	0.000088...	0.00351
117	72.6902	170.0	175.1	72.56	12810	0.00177	0.000090...	0.00373
118	128.126	298.1	–	–	23920	0.00187	0.000092...	0.00396

By way of comparison, the seventh column of Table 6.4 gives an upper bound $|\varepsilon_r/\bar{p}_r|^{\mathcal{A}}$ for the relative error. This is derived from the entries in the second and sixth columns. The next column gives the value of the actual relative error $\varepsilon_r/\bar{p}_r$ computed by use of high-precision values of $Y_r(100)$. Our bound overestimates the true error by a factor that ranges from about 35 at the beginning of the recurrences down to about 20 at $r = 118$. Two sources contribute to this factor. First, there is the radix effect associated with base 10. As we observed in Example 6.1, use of base 2 instead might save a factor of about 2 or 3. Secondly, we have used a uniform bound, given by (6.7), for the t_j. In fact, most of these coefficients are considerably less than 4.062. If desired, smaller bounds could be used without changing the $O(r)$ estimate of the total computing effort. For example, since the sequence β_r is decreasing, it is easy to see that the second of the bounds (5.19) can be replaced by

$$t_j \le \alpha/(\alpha - \beta_j), \qquad 101 \le j \le n.$$

The quantity $\alpha/(\alpha - \beta_j)$ has the values $2.258\ldots$ and $1.925\ldots$ at $j = 110$ and 118, respectively. Further sharpening is possible by application of the theorems given in [6, Section 5].

The final column of Table 6.4 gives a priori bounds $\varpi_r^{\mathcal{A}}$ for the relative precision of the approximation $\bar{p}_r$ to p_r. These were found as follows. Since the coefficients in (6.4) are exact, we have $\delta = 0$. Also, since $c_{j-1} = a_{j-1}$, all j, and only two chopping errors are made at each recurrence step, Eq. (5.24) may be replaced by

$$\varpi_r = 2\left\{(t_{100} + t_{101})\varpi + \gamma \sum_{j=102}^{r} t_j \left(2 + \frac{p_{j-2}}{p_j}\right)\right\}, \qquad j \ge 102.$$

On taking $\varpi = \gamma = 10^{-5}$, substituting for the t_j by means of (6.6) and using the fact that $p_{j-2}/p_j \le 1/\rho^2$, all j, we arrive at the numerical form

$$\varpi_r \le \{14.25 + (22.40)(r - 101)\} \times 10^{-5}, \qquad r \ge 102.$$

As expected, the values of $\varpi_r^{\mathcal{A}}$ are approximately twice the size of the a posteriori relative error bounds $|\varepsilon_r/\bar{p}_r|^{\mathcal{A}}$.

7. Conclusions. We have described various methods for computing error bounds for solutions of difference equations of the form

$$a_r p_{r+1} = b_r p_r + c_r p_{r-1}$$

that are generated by forward recurrence. Two cases are considered: (A) oscillatory systems, in which $b_r^2 + 4a_r c_r < 0$, all r; (B) monotonic systems, in which $b_r^2 + 4a_r c_r \ge 0$, all r. In Case B methods have been provided for finding bounds of both a posteriori and a priori types. In Case A, only an a posteriori method is available, and there is a need for a method for constructing a priori bounds analogous to that of Section 5.

Acknowledgments. Helpful comments on this work have been made by J. R. Cash, E. Kaucher and D. W. Lozier, and especially the referee. I am also pleased to acknowledge the assistance of Dr. Lozier with the generation of high-precision values of the Legendre and Bessel functions needed in Examples 6.1 and 6.4.

University of Maryland
Institute for Physical Science and Technology
College Park, Maryland 20742

National Bureau of Standards
Mathematical Analysis Division
Gaithersburg, Maryland 20899

1. J. R. CASH, *Stable Recursions*, Academic Press, London, 1979.

2. W. GAUTSCHI, "Computational aspects of three-term recurrence relations," *SIAM Rev.*, v. 9, 1967, pp. 24–82.

3. W. GAUTSCHI, "Zur Numerik rekurrenter Relationen," *Computing*, v. 9, 1972, pp. 107–126. [Translated as Report ARL 73-0005, Aerospace Research Laboratories, Wright-Patterson Air Force Base, Ohio, 1973.]

4. W. GAUTSCHI, "Computational methods in special functions—a survey," in *Theory and Application of Special Functions* (R. A. Askey, ed.), Academic Press, New York, 1975, pp. 1–98.

5. N. J. HIGHAM, "Efficient algorithms for computing the condition number of a tridiagonal matrix," *SIAM J. Sci. Statist. Comput.*, v. 7, 1986, pp. 150–165.

6. R. M. M. MATTHEIJ, "Accurate estimates of solutions of second order recursions," *Linear Algebra Appl.*, v. 12, 1975, pp. 29–54.

7. R. M. M. MATTHEIJ & A. VAN DER SLUIS, "Error estimates for Miller's algorithm," *Numer. Math.*, v. 26, 1976, pp. 61–78.

8. R. E. MOORE, *Methods and Applications of Interval Analysis*, Society for Industrial and Applied Mathematics, Philadelphia, 1979.

9. F. W. J. OLVER, "Error analysis of Miller's recurrence algorithm," *Math. Comp.*, v. 18, 1964, pp. 65–74.

10. F. W. J. OLVER, "Numerical solution of second-order linear difference equations," *J. Res. Nat. Bur. Standards Sect. B*, v. 71, 1967, pp. 111–129.

11. F. W. J. OLVER, "Bounds for the solutions of second-order linear difference equations," *J. Res. Nat. Bur. Standards Sect. B*, v. 71, 1967, pp. 161–166.

12. F. W. J. OLVER, "Further developments of rp and ap error analysis, " *IMA J. Numer. Anal.*, v. 2, 1982, pp. 249–274.

13. F. W. J. OLVER & J. H. WILKINSON, "A posteriori error bounds for Gaussian elimination," *IMA J. Numer. Anal.*, v. 2, 1982, pp. 377–406.

14. S. M. RUMP, "Solving algebraic problems with high accuracy," in *A New Approach to Scientific Computation* (U. W. Kulisch and W. L. Miranker, eds.), Academic Press, New York, 1983, pp. 51–120.

15. A. VAN DER SLUIS, "Estimating the solutions of slowly varying recursions," *SIAM J. Math. Anal.*, v. 7, 1976, pp. 662–695.

16. R. TAIT, "Error analysis of recurrence relations," *Math. Comp.*, v. 21, 1967, pp. 629–638.

17. P. R. TURNER, "The distribution of leading significant digits," *IMA J. Numer. Anal.*, v. 2, 1982, pp. 407–412.

18. J. H. WILKINSON, *Rounding Errors in Algebraic Processes*, National Physical Laboratory Notes on Applied Science No. 32, Her Majesty's Stationery Office, London, 1963.

19. J. WIMP, *Computation with Recurrence Relations*, Pitman, Boston, 1984.

SIAM J. NUMER. ANAL.
Vol. 27, No. 5, pp. 1295-1304, October 1990

CLOSURE AND PRECISION IN LEVEL-INDEX ARITHMETIC*

D. W. LOZIER† AND F. W. J. OLVER‡

Abstract. First it is proved that two recently introduced systems of computer arithmetic, the level-index (li) and symmetric level-index (sli) systems are closed under the four basic arithmetic operations, provided that division by zero is excluded and the operations are executed in finite precision. In consequence, the li and sli systems are free from the defects of overflow and underflow.

Second, measures of precision are discussed and compared. Third, the ranges and local precisions of numbers stored in the li and sli systems are compared with corresponding ranges and local precisions of numbers stored in the floating-point system.

Key words. closure, computer arithmetic, error analysis, floating-point system, generalized precision, level-index system, local precision, overflow, symmetric level-index system, underflow

AMS(MOS) subject classifications. 65-04, 65G99

1. Introduction. The floating-point (flp) system emerged as the standard form of computer arithmetic once it became clear that the effort of scaling computations to stay within representable ranges of the fixed-point system would place an intolerable burden on programmers. The flp system has served the computing community remarkably well, and it is difficult to imagine a more satisfactory number system with the technology that has been available hitherto. However, the flp system suffers from a major disadvantage: it is not closed under the basic arithmetic operations of addition, subtraction, multiplication, and division (excluding division by zero). In consequence, there will always be computations that cannot be executed because of overflow or underflow failure.[1] Discussions of these problems abound in the literature (see, for example, [6], [9]). Does a naturally closed system of arithmetic[2] exist and if so, could it be executed in a reasonably economic manner with today's computer technology? In [3] Clenshaw and Olver describe a new arithmetic system based on repeated exponentiations, which they call the level-index (li) system. They indicate, by means of an example, that this system is closed, and they also describe other advantages, including the introduction of a uniform metric measure of precision that includes absolute precision and relative precision as special cases. Subsequently, the same authors [4] have constructed and analysed algorithms for carrying out arithmetic operations in the li system, and they also have described briefly a modification, called the symmetric level-index (sli) system, that offers advantages over the li system in certain circumstances. Further details concerning the sli system will be found in [5].

The first purpose of the present paper is to prove that the li and sli systems are closed under the four basic arithmetic operations, excluding division by zero.

* Received by the editors December 30, 1987; accepted for publication (in revised form) September 28, 1989.

† National Institute of Standards and Technology, Gaithersburg, Maryland 20899.

‡ Institute for Physical Science and Technology, University of Maryland, College Park, Maryland 20742.
The research of this author was partially supported by the Army Research Office, Durham, under contract DAAG 29-84-K0022 and the National Science Foundation under grant DMS 84-19820.

[1] This is also true of modifications of the flp system that have been developed recently, including, for example, those described in [10], [11], and [14].

[2] By a "naturally closed system" we mean one that maintains a uniform measure of precision. This rules out the kind of "closure" achieved by adding NaN's ("not-a-numbers") to the flp system [12].

The second purpose is to compare the range and precision of numbers represented in the sli and flp systems. As a preliminary we discuss the natural error measures of these systems. Since these measures are fundamentally different we must interpret one in terms of the other in order to make a comparison.

Let us introduce our notation. The li system is based on the mapping

$$X=\phi(x), \tag{1.1}$$

and its inverse

$$x=\psi(X). \tag{1.2}$$

Here X is any real number, and its image (or "li image") x is stored internally in the computer to represent X. The functions ϕ and ψ are generalized exponentials and logarithms, defined by

$$\phi(x)=x, \quad 0\leqq x<1, \qquad \psi(X)=X, \quad 0\leqq X<1, \tag{1.3}$$

$$\phi(x)=e^{\phi(x-1)}, \quad x\geqq 1, \qquad \psi(X)=\psi(\ln X)+1, \quad X\geqq 1, \tag{1.4}$$

$$\phi(-x)=-\phi(x), \qquad \psi(-X)=-\psi(X). \tag{1.5}$$

Both $\phi(x)$ and $\psi(X)$ are increasing functions, with continuous first derivatives, for all x, $X\in\mathbb{R}$. The integer part l and fractional part f, say, of $|x|$ comprise the *level* and *index* of X, respectively. Other properties will be found in [2], [3], and [4].[3]

The main difference between the sli system and the li system is that numbers in the interval $(0, 1)$ are represented by the li images of their reciprocals. One way to formulate it is the invertible mapping

$$X=\pm\Phi(x), \qquad x=\Psi(|X|), \tag{1.6}$$

where the sign in the first equation is the same as the sign of X and the functions Φ and Ψ are defined by

$$\Phi(x)=e^{\phi(x)}, \quad -\infty<x<\infty, \qquad \Psi(X)=\psi(\ln X), \quad X>0. \tag{1.7}$$

Like $\phi(x)$ and $\psi(X)$, $\Phi(x)$ and $\Psi(X)$ are increasing C^1 functions on their intervals of definition, given by $-\infty<x<\infty$ and $0<X<\infty$.

2. Closure.

2.1. Proof of closure of the li system. In both the li and sli systems the image x is stored in fixed absolute precision. In this and subsequent sections we suppose that the internal arithmetic base (or radix) of the computer is r, the fractional part of x is stored to d r-nary places, where $d\geqq 1$, and the abbreviation mode is either chopping or rounding.

If we add any positive representable number $\phi(x)$ to itself, then the stored li image of the sum will not exceed x as long as

$$\phi(x+cr^{-d})>2\phi(x), \tag{2.1}$$

where c is a positive constant. If the li arithmetic processor computed to infinite precision, then we would have $c=1$ for chopping and $c=\frac{1}{2}$ for rounding; furthermore, by employing a sufficient number of guard digits in the processor we can approach these values (from below) arbitrarily closely. The only condition we will actually impose on c is given by

$$c\leqq 2\ln 2(=1.386\cdots), \tag{2.2}$$

[3] In [2], different definitions of $\phi(x)$ and $\psi(X)$ were employed for negative arguments.

which is always satisfied in practice. On taking logarithms, the inequality (2.1) becomes

$$\phi(x-1+cr^{-d}) > \phi(x-1) + \ln 2. \tag{2.3}$$

As long as $x \in [2, \infty)$, $\phi'(x-1)$ is increasing. Hence by application of the Mean Value Theorem it follows that (2.3) is satisfied when

$$cr^{-d}\phi'(x-1) \geqq \ln 2 \quad \text{and} \quad x \geqq 2. \tag{2.4}$$

Let $x = \chi(t)$ denote the inverse function to $t = \phi'(x)$, with the understanding that $\chi(1) = 1$. Then $\chi(t)$ is increasing when $t \geqq 1$. In consequence of (2.2) and the fact that $r \geqq 2$ and $d \geqq 1$, we have $c^{-1}r^d \ln 2 \geqq 1$. Hence both conditions (2.4) are satisfied when

$$x \geqq \chi(c^{-1}r^d \ln 2) + 1. \tag{2.5}$$

Consider now the set $\mathscr{A}$ of all numbers whose li images are exact to d r-nary places and whose magnitudes are bounded by M, where M is an arbitrary constant not less than $\phi\{\chi(c^{-1}r^d \ln 2) + 1\}$. If the sum or difference of any two members of $\mathscr{A}$ is computed by forming the corresponding li image followed by chopping or rounding, then as a consequence of the foregoing analysis the sum or difference is also a member of $\mathscr{A}$. Accordingly, the set $\mathscr{A}$ is closed under the li operations of addition and subtraction, provided that these operations are carried out in the manner just described.

If we extend the arithmetic operations to include multiplication, then the same conclusion applies, provided that the lower bound for M is increased to $\phi\{\chi(c^{-1}r^d \ln 2) + 2\}$. This is an immediate consequence of the equivalence of the relations

$$\phi(x) + \phi(y) = \phi(z), \qquad \phi(x+1)\phi(y+1) = \phi(z+1),$$

valid when $x, y \geqq 0$.

To show that the last result also applies when the arithmetic operations include division, other than by zero, we need to investigate the effect of dividing any positive representable number $\phi(x)$ by the smallest representable number $\phi(r^{-d}) \equiv r^{-d}$. The stored li image of the quotient will not exceed x as long as

$$\phi(x + cr^{-d}) > r^d\phi(x). \tag{2.6}$$

On using analysis similar to that given in the opening paragraph of this section, we see that (2.6) is satisfied when

$$x \geqq \chi(c^{-1}r^d d \ln r) + 1.$$

We therefore need to show that

$$\chi(c^{-1}r^d d \ln r) \leqq \chi(c^{-1}r^d \ln 2) + 1,$$

or, equivalently,

$$c^{-1}r^d d \ln r \leqq \phi'\{\chi(c^{-1}r^d \ln 2) + 1\}.$$

It is easily verified that $\phi'(x+1) \geqq e\{\phi'(x)\}^2$ when $x \geqq 1$; accordingly, it is sufficient to show that

$$d \ln r \leqq ec^{-1}r^d(\ln 2)^2. \tag{2.7}$$

From (2.2) we have $\frac{1}{2} \leqq c^{-1} \ln 2$. And since $2t < e^{1+t} \ln 2$ for all t, it follows that (2.7) *is* valid. This completes the proof.

In summary, we have shown that when the li system is used with any finite-precision arithmetic, the subset of its set of representable numbers that intersects an interval $[-M, M]$ is closed under the operations of addition, subtraction, multiplication, and division, excluding division by zero, provided that the arbitrary constant M is large enough.

2.2. Overflow and underflow. The function $\chi(t)$ is increasing, although only very slowly when t is large. Sample values, computed with the aid of Newton's rule, are as follows:

$$\chi(2^{32}) = 4.06\cdots, \quad \chi(2^{64}) = 4.26\cdots, \quad \chi(2^{1,024}) = 4.63\cdots,$$
$$\chi(2^{5,502,868}) < 5 < \chi(2^{5,502,869}).$$

Suppose, for example, $r = 2$, $d = 31$, and $c = \frac{1}{2}\ln 2$, that is, we are assigning 31 bits to storage of the fractional part of the li image and employing an appropriate number of guard digits in the arithmetic processing unit. Then $c^{-1}r^d \ln 2 = 2^{32}$; hence a lower bound for M for all four arithmetic operations, other than division by zero, is $\phi(6.06\cdots)$. (This result applies whether the abbreviation mode be chopping or rounding.) To increase the lower bound for M from $\phi(6.06\cdots)$ to $\phi(7)$, or more, we would need an aggregate wordlength in excess of 5,500,000 bits. Thus in practice it will always suffice to allocate three bits to storage of the integer part of the li image. This will admit levels zero through seven; indeed, level seven is redundant for the four basic arithmetic operations.

Similar conclusions hold for the sli system. In particular, four bits will always suffice for storage of the sign and integer part of the sli image x defined by (1.6) and (1.7).

With the allocation of three bits to storage of the integer part of the li image, or four bits to storage of the integer part and extra sign (or equivalently a biased integer part) of the sli image, problems of overflow and underflow will disappear in practice. In contrast, in the conventional flp system overflow and underflow can always occur, no matter how many bits of each word are allocated to storage of the exponent.

It has been claimed that overflow and, to a lesser extent, underflow serve as useful programming diagnostics. The same kind of diagnostic may be introduced into the li and sli systems by providing an interrupt whenever the arithmetic processor generates li, or sli, images that exceed thresholds specified by the programmer. Indeed, such a system would enjoy greater flexibility, inasmuch as it would not be tied directly to the hardware characteristics of the computer being used.

3. Measures of precision; error analysis.

3.1. Measures of precision. Owing to the structure of a floating-point number, the natural error measure associated with the floating-point system is relative error, or more elegantly, relative precision.[4] Because automatic computers have been in operation for a generation or so, there is a tendency among today's users to regard relative error as the only legitimate way to specify precision. Yet there are circumstances where it is entirely inappropriate.

Consider, for example, the Bessel functions $J_n(x)$ and $Y_n(x)$ for integer values of the order n and positive real values of the argument x. In the interval $0 < x \leqq n$ these functions exhibit monotonic behavior, and in constructing a software package

[4] The relative precision of a number is the absolute error in the logarithm of the absolute value of the number [15]. When both are small, relative precision and relative error are very nearly equal.

it would be quite natural and satisfactory to specify a given tolerance in relative precision there. However, in the interval $n \leqq x < \infty$ both functions are oscillatory, and a more appropriate error measure is absolute precision. This can be seen from typical physical applications in which a solution of a partial differential equation is expressed as an infinite series or infinite integral of Bessel functions (see, for example, [1], [13]). To use relative precision in setting a tolerance in this range would result in burdensome analytical and programming effort in the neighborhoods of zeros—effort that would be wasted in applications.

Relative precision can also be an inappropriate measure for very large numbers. For example, physicists have estimated the mass of the universe to be about 10^{78} times that of a single proton [8]. It would make as much sense to assert that this estimate is meaningless because its relative error is unassessable, as it would to assert that the approximate flp number 1.2345×10^{10} is useless because it has no accurate decimal places.

In the li system the natural error measure is the absolute error in the li image; it is called *generalized precision* [3]. It reduces to absolute precision at level zero and relative precision at level one, and therefore has the advantage of combining these two measures in an elegant manner. It also conforms to the kind of intuitive assessment for large numbers that is appropriate for the example discussed in the preceding paragraph.

3.2. Error analysis. Eventually, if the li and sli systems come to be widely adopted for internal computer arithmetic, then they will need an associated theory of roundoff error analysis. The way to proceed here will be to develop a theory that applies *directly* to li and sli arithmetic operations, and not simply to try to interpret everything in terms of relative precision and then rely on flp error analyses.[5] Some preliminary general results, together with a brief application to Gaussian elimination, will be found in [16].

We note that as we pass into the realms of larger and larger numbers, adherence to constant generalized precision will imply less and less relative precision in stored numbers (see § 4 below). However, this does not necessarily mean that the final results of a computation will be devoid of any "normal" precision, any more than a heavy loss of absolute precision, or even relative precision, during the course of an flp computation automatically renders the final answer useless.

4. Range and precision in the flp and sli systems.

4.1. Preliminaries. In the previous section we pointed out that the error measures and error analyses needed for the li and sli systems differ fundamentally from the corresponding measure and analysis associated with the flp system, just as the flp system differs in this respect from the fixed-point system. Naturally, however, we need to be able to compare in some general manner accuracies that will be achieved in everyday computations. With this in mind, we now proceed to make a detailed comparison of local precision, that is, the separation of neighboring representable numbers. We could do this either by transforming the error measure for the flp system into generalized-precision form, or by transforming the error measure for the sli system into relative-precision form. Since most readers are more accustomed to relative precision we adopt the latter course. The results extend considerably those of [3].

4.2. 32-bit word. Suppose, for example, that the internal arithmetic base r is two and the computer word has 32 bits. According to the IEEE standard [12], one of these

[5] Compare, for example, [7].

bits is allocated to the sign of the represented number X, one is allocated to the sign (or bias) of the exponent, and seven are allocated to the exponent itself. This leaves 24 for the mantissa (after allowing for the redundant first bit). This arrangement is indicated schematically by the trapezium OABC in Fig. 1. In this diagram, the vertical scale is $\xi \equiv \log_2 \log_2 X$. Since $\xi \geqq 0$ this means we are considering values of X such that $X \geqq 2$. The horizontal distance from the $3\pi/4$ ray OCJ to the ξ-axis represents the bits required for the exponent of X; overflow takes place for $\xi \geqq 7$ because only seven bits are available for storing the exponent. The distance from the ξ-axis to the vertical line segment AB represents the bits assigned to the mantissa.

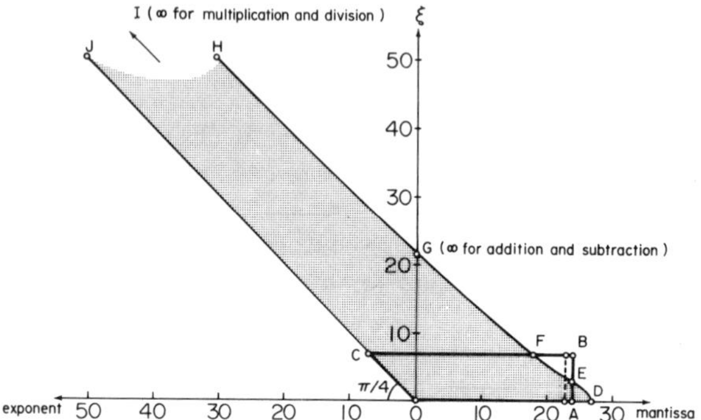

FIG. 1. *Accurate bits, in floating-point form, of the* IEEE *standard single-length word and the corresponding* sli *word. (Approximately to scale.)*

With a 32-bit word in the sli system we allocate one bit to the sign of X and four bits to the integer part and sign (or bias) of the sli image $x = \Psi(X)$. This leaves 27 bits for the fractional part of x. The absolute change δX, say, in X resulting from an increase of one unit in the last place of x is therefore given by

$$\delta X = \Phi(x+2^{-27}) - \Phi(x) = \phi(x+1+2^{-27}) - \phi(x+1). \tag{4.1}$$

Provided that $\delta X \leqq X$, we will take

$$m \equiv -\log_2 (\delta X/X) \tag{4.2}$$

as our measure of the number of correct bits in the mantissa of X. To compute m from ξ we first find x from one of the relations

$$x = \psi(2^{2^\xi}) - 1 = \psi(2^\xi \ln 2) = \psi(\xi \ln 2 + \ln\ln 2) + 1 \tag{4.3}$$

(the last equality applying when $\xi \ln 2 + \ln\ln 2 \geqq 0$). Then

$$\frac{\delta X}{X} = \frac{\phi(x+1+2^{-27})}{\phi(x+1)} - 1 = \exp\{\phi(x+2^{-27}) - \phi(x)\} - 1,$$

and on taking the logarithm, to base 2, of the last quantity we obtain $-m$. The value of m is represented in Fig. 1 by the horizontal distance of points on the continuous curve DEFG from the ξ-axis. By comparison, for the IEEE standard word the value of m (as defined by (4.2)) lies between 23 and 24, that is, between AB and the broken line immediately to its left.

At the intersection G of the curve DEFG with the ξ-axis we have $\delta X = X$ and $\xi = 21.70$, approximately. At this stage no correct bits remain in the mantissa of the equivalent flp form; in other words, all of the information afforded by the sli representation has passed into the exponent. G is also indistinguishable from the point on the ξ-axis that corresponds to $X=\phi\{\chi(2^{27}\ln 2)+1\}$, where $x=\chi(t)$ again denotes the inverse function to $t=\phi'(x)$. Thus in the notation of § 2.1, G corresponds to a lower bound for the constant M for the li operations of addition and subtraction with the chopping mode of abbreviation, that is, with $c=1$. We might say that G represents "infinity" for these operations.

When ξ exceeds 21.70 only part of the exponent is meaningful. In fact, the number of correct bits in the exponent is measured by

$$n \equiv -\log_2\{\delta(\log_2 X)/\log_2 X\}. \tag{4.4}$$

In terms of the image x, given by (4.3), we have

$$\frac{\delta(\log_2 X)}{\log_2 X}=\frac{\phi(x+2^{-27})}{\phi(x)}-1=\exp\{\phi(x+2^{-27}-1)-\phi(x-1)\}-1.$$

These formulae enable n to be computed as a function of ξ. The values of n are represented by the horizontal distance between the ray OCJ and the extrapolated curve GH.

The ray OCJ and the curve GH intersect eventually at a point I (off the diagram). At I we have $\xi=3{,}405{,}000$, approximately, and at this point no correct bits would remain in the exponent. Point I is also on almost exactly the same horizontal level as the point on the ξ-axis that corresponds to "infinity" for the li operations of multiplication and division, given by $X=\phi\{\chi(2^{27}\ln 2)+2\}$ (again compare § 2.1 with $c=1$).

Finally, if we proceed to still higher values of ξ, then there are no correct figures in the exponent. This does not mean that the sli representation is meaningless, only that the equivalent flp form is no longer appropriate.

Part of the enormous increase in representation range afforded by the sli system over the flp system can be seen by comparing the shaded area of Fig. 1, and its extension to the point I, with the trapezium OABC. The only part of the trapezium that is not contained in the shaded region is the curvilinear triangle EBF, corresponding to $2.85 \leqq \xi \leqq 7$, approximately. In this region the flp system generally gains and since the value of m at F is 17.78, approximately, the maximum gain amounts to five or six bits in the mantissa. Elsewhere the sli system gains: for $0 \leqq \xi \leqq 2.85$ there are up to four extra accurate bits in the mantissa, and for $\xi \geqq 7$ there is no overflow failure.

4.3. 64-bit word. With a 64-bit word the IEEE standard allocates one bit to the sign of the represented number X, and 11 bits to the biased exponent. Thus the increase in mantissa length from the single-precision version is from 24 to 53 bits. In the sli system, the whole increased allocation of 32 bits enters the fractional part of the image x, making a total of 59.

The comparison is illustrated in Fig. 2, which corresponds exactly in its lettering to Fig. 1. The values of ξ at the points E, G, and I are 4.83, 51.67, and 3.583×10^{15}, approximately. The abscissa of F is 45.90, approximately.

Comparing with Fig. 1, and allowing for the different scales, we compute that the area of the unshaded region EBF has increased by about 40 percent, whereas the area of the shaded region ADE has increased threefold and is now about 80 percent that of EBF. Thus compared with the 32-bit word, the relative-precision gains of flp over sli have increased slightly, but the relative-precision losses have increased substantially.

4.4. Other wordlengths and bases. In §§ 4.2 and 4.3 we concentrated on base 2 and wordlengths of 32 and 64 bits. However, the essential features of Figs. 1 and 2

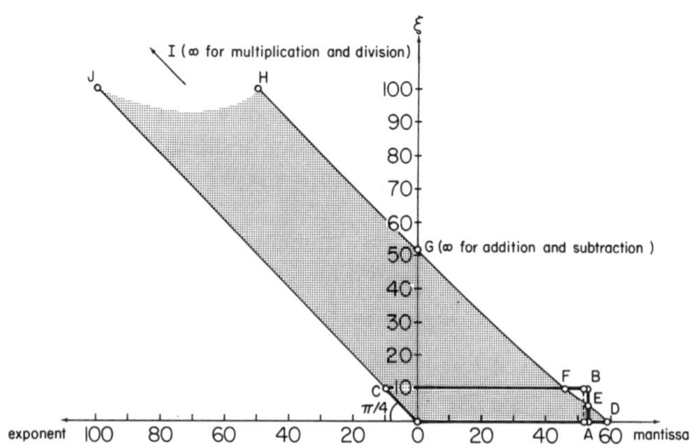

FIG. 2. *Accurate bits, in floating-point form, of the* IEEE *standard double-length word and the corresponding* sli *word. (Approximately to scale.)*

remain the same for other wordlengths, or multiple wordlengths, and other bases. In place of (4.1)-(4.4), we have

$$\delta X=\phi(x+1+r^{-d})-\phi(x+1), \tag{4.5}$$

$$x=\psi(r^{\xi}\ln r)=\psi(\xi\ln r+\ln\ln r)+1, \tag{4.6}$$

$$m=-\log_r(\delta X/X),\qquad n=-\log_r\{\delta(\log_r X)/(\log_r X)\}, \tag{4.7}$$

where $\xi=\log_r\log_r X$ and, as in § 2.1, d is the number of r-nary places assigned to represent the fractional part of the sli image.

An approximation $\hat{m}$, say, to m is obtained on linearizing (4.5); thus

$$\hat{m}=d-\log_r\phi'(x).$$

On using (4.6) we find that this becomes

$$\hat{m}=d-\log_r e\cdot(\Xi+\ln\Xi+\ln\ln\Xi+\cdots), \tag{4.8}$$

where $\Xi=\xi\ln r+\ln\ln r$ and the sum within the parentheses terminates at the repeated logarithm of Ξ in the interval $[0,1)$. And since the number of digits in the exponent of X is approximately ξ, it follows that *the total number of correct digits in the* flp *form of* X (*the number in the exponent plus the number in the mantissa*) *is equal to the number of correct places in the fractional part of the* sli *image of* X, *with an error* $O(\log_r\xi)$, *that is*, $O(\log_r^{(3)}X)$.

The approximate rule just given applies up to the stage at which all digits are lost in the mantissa. The rule means simply that, in Figs. 1 and 2, the curve DEFG is approximately parallel to the ray OCJ.

In a similar way, an approximation $\hat{n}$ to n is given by

$$\hat{n}=d-\log_r e\cdot(\ln\Xi+\ln\ln\Xi+\cdots), \tag{4.9}$$

the sum being terminated as in (4.8).

4.5. Conclusions. For the range of numbers that lie between the limits of underflow and overflow in the flp system, the results of §§ 4.2 and 4.3 indicate that there is essentially little difference between the local precisions of the IEEE standard flp system and the sli system. As a consequence, we expect that when we carry out computations in which all intermediate and final results lie within this range, the accuracies in the final results achieved by the two systems will be comparable. Sometimes the sli system will gain slightly, and sometimes the flp system will gain slightly. The former event is likely to occur when all computed values have moderate magnitudes, the latter when some of the computed numbers approach the limits imposed by overflow and underflow.

However, as soon as computed numbers pass beyond the overflow and underflow limits in the flp system, they are replaced by ∞ symbols or zero and *all* local precision disappears.[6] In contrast, computed numbers in the sli system maintain their local generalized precision, *and they may also retain a high degree of relative precision.* For example, suppose that the number of largest magnitude that occurs is $10^{1,000,000}$, which is well beyond the IEEE standard limit for overflow even in double precision. In double-precision sli form this number has local relative precision of about 1.6×10^{-10}, which is ample for many purposes.

A general remedy for overflow or underflow in the flp system is to rescale the algorithm being used to bring all computed numbers within the representable range (assuming this is possible). It should be realized, however, that if the same rescaled program were to be used with the sli system, then the accuracy of the final results would be increased and rendered comparable with that derived from the flp system. To put this another way, the role of scaling in the two systems is different. When overflow/underflow occurs in flp, scaling is *essential* in order to achieve any results. In sli, scaling can be used to improve the accuracy of final results, but its use is *optional.*

5. General conclusions. The main results established in this paper are as follows. First, we proved that the level-index (li) and symmetric level-index (sli) systems are closed under the four basic arithmetic operations, other than division by zero, when these operations are carried out in finite-precision arithmetic. In consequence, these systems are free from overflow and underflow.

Second, we showed that the range of magnitudes of representable numbers in the sli system is vastly greater than the corresponding range for the floating-point (flp) system.

Third, we demonstrated that the sli system is more accurate than the flp system in the following sense. On average, numbers that lie within the representable range of the flp system have comparable local precision in the two systems. But numbers outside this range are devoid of any precision in the flp system.

We have not touched on the question of execution speeds of the new systems in this paper. In their present form the algorithms for the implementation of arithmetic operations described in [4] and [5] are more complicated than their flp counterparts and slower to execute. It should be appreciated, however, that a similar (though less acute) situation existed when flp system was being introduced. At that time few computer specialists would have predicted that the day would arrive when flp arithmetic operations are implemented in hardware at speeds that differ little from those for fixed-point arithmetic operations. With this in mind, methods for speeding up the execution of li and sli arithmetics are being actively pursued.[7]

Furthermore, in many types of computations, including, for example, those of exploratory type, some reduction in execution speed would be acceptable if the tradeoff included reduced effort in the mathematical development of algorithms and programs,

[6] This is not quite the case when denormalized numbers [12] are being employed, but the main conclusions of this section are unaffected.

[7] See, for example, [17] and [18]. A surface-fitting approach is also being explored.

and increased portability. Conceivably, there could even be a *reduction* in overall running time in cases where much simpler programs can be used in the new systems.[8]

Acknowledgments. The authors are pleased to acknowledge helpful criticisms by C. W. Clenshaw, A. Feldstein, P. R. Turner, and the referees.

REFERENCES

[1] H. S. CARSLAW AND J. C. JAEGER, *Operational Methods in Applied Mathematics*, Second ed., Oxford University Press, London, 1948.

[2] C. W. CLENSHAW, D. W. LOZIER, F. W. J. OLVER, AND P. R. TURNER, *Generalized exponential and logarithmic functions*, Comput. Math. Appl. Part B, 12 (1986), pp. 1091-1101.

[3] C. W. CLENSHAW AND F. W. J. OLVER, *Beyond floating point*, J. Assoc. Comput. Mach., 31 (1984), pp. 319-328.

[4] ———, *Level-index arithmetic operations*, SIAM J. Numer. Anal., 24 (1987), pp. 470-485.

[5] C. W. CLENSHAW AND P. R. TURNER, *The symmetric level-index system*, IMA J. Numer. Anal., 8 (1988), pp. 517-526.

[6] W. J. CODY, *SPECFUN—a portable special function package*, in New Computing Environments, A. Wouk, ed., Society for Industrial and Applied Mathematics, Philadelphia, PA, 1987.

[7] J. W. DEMMEL, *On error analysis in arithmetic with varying relative precision*, in Proc. Eighth Symposium on Computer Arithmetic, M. J. Irwin and R. Stefanelli, eds., IEEE Computer Society Press, Washington, DC, 1987, pp. 148-152.

[8] P. A. M. DIRAC, *Directions in Physics*, Wiley-Interscience, New York, 1978.

[9] A. FELDSTEIN AND P. R. TURNER, *Overflow, underflow, and severe loss of significance in floating-point addition and subtraction*, IMA J. Numer. Anal., 6 (1986), pp. 241-251.

[10] H. HAMADA, *URR: Universal representation of real numbers*, New Generation Computing, OHM-Sha, Springer-Verlag, Berlin, New York, 1983, pp. 205-209.

[11] T. E. HULL, A. ABRHAM, M. S. COHEN, A. F. X. CURLEY, C. B. HALL, D. A. PENNY, AND J. T. M. SAWCHUK, *Numerical turing*, ACM SIGNUM Newsletter 20 (1985), pp. 26-32.

[12] IEEE STANDARD 754, *Binary floating-point arithmetic*, Institute of Electrical and Electronics Engineers, New York, 1985.

[13] A. G. MACKIE, *Boundary Value Problems*, Oliver and Boyd, Edinburgh, 1965.

[14] S. MATSUI AND M. IRI, *An overflow/underflow-free floating-point representation of numbers*, J. Inform. Process., 4 (1981), pp. 123-133.

[15] F. W. J. OLVER, *Further developments of rp and ap error analysis*, IMA J. Numer. Anal., 2 (1982), pp. 249-274.

[16] ———, *Rounding errors in algebraic processes—in level-index arithmetic*, in Reliable Numerical Computation, M. G. Cox and S. Hammarling, eds., Oxford University Press, London, 1990, pp. 197-205.

[17] F. W. J. OLVER AND P. R. TURNER, *Implementation of level-index arithmetic using partial table look-up*, in Proc. Eighth Symposium on Computer Arithmetic, M. J. Irwin and R. Stefanelli, eds., IEEE Computer Society Press, Washington, DC, 1987, pp. 144-147.

[18] P. R. TURNER, *Towards a fast implementation of level-index arithmetic*, Bull. Inst. Math. Appl., 22 (1986), pp. 188-191.

[19] ———, *Algorithms for the elementary functions in level-index arithmetic*, in Scientific Software Systems, J. C. Mason and M. G. Cox, eds., Chapman and Hall, London, 1990, pp. 123-134.

[8] This possibility is discussed in [19].

Asymptotic and Computational Analysis
(R. Wong, ed.)
Lecture Notes in Pure and Applied Mathematics,
124, Marcel Dekker, New York, 1990, 329-355

ON STOKES' PHENOMENON AND CONVERGING FACTORS

Dedicated to my friends and fellow workers in asymptotic analysis, numerical analysis and special functions.

F. W. J. Olver*

Institute for Physical Science and Technology,
University of Maryland, College Park, MD 20742

ABSTRACT

Recently M. V. Berry has provided a new interpretation of Stokes' phenomenon in which the change in form of a compound asymptotic expansion occurs smoothly, albeit very rapidly, as a Stokes line is crossed. Berry's analysis is based on R. B. Dingle's theory of terminants, and is therefore quite formal. In this paper new analysis is developed to place the theories of both Dingle and Berry on rigorous mathematical foundations. The analysis is illustrated by application to Macdonald's modified Bessel function, the generalized exponential integral and one of the confluent hypergeometric functions, but the method, like the methods of Dingle and Berry, is quite general.

*This research has been supported by the U.S. National Science Foundation under Grant DMS 87-23039.

1. INTRODUCTION AND SUMMARY

Discontinuities in compound asymptotic expansions in the neighbourhood of an irregular singular point were first explored and described in a series of papers by Sir George Stokes, beginning with [12]. The need for discontinuities in the representation of analytic and *a fortiori* smooth functions was hard to accept,[1] especially because there is no single line or curve in the complex plane that can be identified as the exact place where the discontinuities occur. In consequence, there has always been an element of mystery associated with this "phenomenon" of Stokes, whether one approaches the subject from the standpoint of rigorous mathematical analysis or formal physical applications.

With a view to arriving at a fuller understanding of the phenomenon, I applied a theory of error bounds in a paper presented at the 1978 SIAM Spring Meeting, held at the University of Wisconsin [11]. The example chosen was Macdonald's modified Bessel function $K_\nu(z)$ with fixed real or complex values of the order ν, and large absolute values of the complex argument z. Let us use the symbols $\sum_1$ and $\sum_2$ to denote the formal series

$$\sum_1 = \left(\frac{\pi}{2z}\right)^{\frac{1}{2}} e^{-z} \sum_{s=0}^{\infty} \frac{A_s(\nu)}{z^s}, \qquad \sum_2 = \left(\frac{\pi}{2z}\right)^{\frac{1}{2}} e^{z} \sum_{s=0}^{\infty} (-)^s \frac{A_s(\nu)}{z^s}, \tag{1.1}$$

where

$$A_0(\nu) = 1, \; A_s(\nu) = \frac{(4\nu^2-1^2)(4\nu^2-3^2)\cdots\{4\nu^2-(2s-1)^2\}}{s!\;8^s}, \quad s \ge 1. \tag{1.2}$$

Also, let δ denote an arbitrarily small positive constant. Then in the sense of Poincaré

$$K_\nu(z) \sim \sum_1 \tag{1.3}$$

[1]Not least by Stokes himself; compare a letter to his fiancée, dated March 19, 1857 and reprinted in [13].

as $|z| \to \infty$, uniformly with respect to ph z in the sector $|\text{ph } z| \le \frac{3}{2}\pi - \delta$. On the other hand, as $z \to \infty$ in the sector $\frac{1}{2}\pi + \delta \le \text{ph } z \le \frac{5}{2}\pi - \delta$ we have the compound expansion

$$K_\nu(z) \sim \sum_1 + 2i \cos(\nu\pi) \sum_2, \tag{1.4}$$

again uniformly valid (in Poincaré's sense) with respect to ph z. In this example the discontinuity occurs in the coefficient of $\sum_2$. In the common sector of validity, given by $\frac{1}{2}\pi + \delta \le \text{ph } z \le \frac{3}{2}\pi - \delta$, either (1.3) or (1.4) may be used on the grounds that the contribution of $\sum_2$ is uniformly exponentially small compared with that of $\sum_1$. However, in the sector $|\text{ph } z| \le \frac{1}{2}\pi - \delta$, $\sum_2$ dominates $\sum_1$; hence the omission of $\sum_2$ from the asymptotic expansion of $K_\nu(z)$ is mandatory. $\sum_2$ is also dominant in the sector $\frac{3}{2}\pi + \delta \le \text{ph } z \le \frac{5}{2}\pi - \delta$; consequently it is mandatory here to have the coefficient $2i \cos(\nu\pi)$ associated with $\sum_2$.

In which part of the common sector $\frac{1}{2}\pi + \delta \le \text{ph } z \le \frac{3}{2}\pi - \delta$ should we prefer the expansion (1.3), and in which part the expansion (1.4)? This was the question addressed in [11]. Except for a region **P** that is bounded by the imaginary axis and a parabola having the real axis as axis, I showed that for all sufficiently large $|z|$ the optimum form of (1.3) will yield greater or lesser accuracy than the optimum form of (1.4), according as ph $z \lessgtr \pi$; see Fig. 1. As a corollary, if it is decided that the change from (1.3) to (1.4) is to take place along a ray emanating from the origin, then this ray has to be the "Stokes line" ph $z = \pi$, since this is the only ray that is completely contained in **P**.

Combined with the error bounds given in [11], the result just stated is fully satisfactory for the purpose of constructing a computing algorithm for generating $K_\nu(z)$ for large values of $|z|$. However, it leaves unresolved the actual situation inside the region **P**. We know that just before we enter **P** from the second quadrant the coefficient of the series $\sum_2$ should be zero, whereas when we emerge from **P** into the third quadrant this coefficient needs to be $2i\cos(\nu\pi)$.

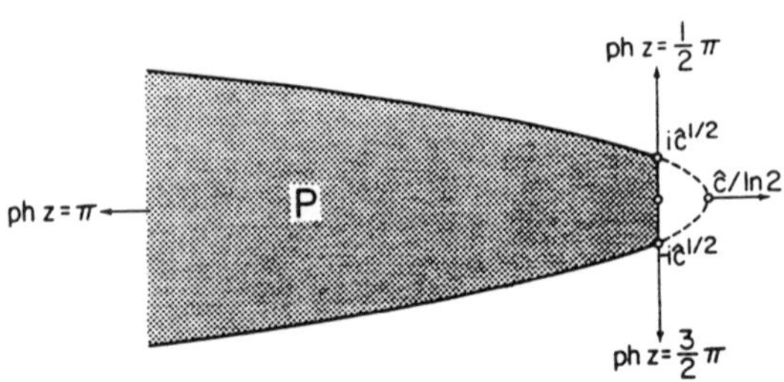

FIG. 1 *Region of uncertainty in the z-plane.*
$\hat{c} = (\frac{1}{2}\ln 2)^2 + \frac{1}{16} + \frac{1}{2}(\pi+1)|\nu^2 - \frac{1}{4}| + \frac{1}{2}|\nu^2 + \frac{1}{12}|$.
Reproduced with permission from Reference [11]. (Copyright 1980 by the Society for Industrial and Applied Mathematics. All rights reserved.)

In a recent paper [2], M. V. Berry has adopted the view that the coefficient of $\sum_2$ should be regarded as continuous function of ph z, rather than a discontinuous constant. This is achieved by terminating the series in equations (1.1): $\sum_1$ is truncated at its optimum number of terms, given by $n = \mathrm{int}[2|z|] + 1$,[2] and $\sum_2$ is truncated at its first term. The required coefficient S_n, say, is defined *exactly* by the equation

$$K_\nu(z) = \left(\frac{\pi}{2z}\right)^{\frac{1}{2}} e^{-z} \sum_{s=0}^{n-1} \frac{A_s(\nu)}{z^s} + S_n \times 2i\cos(\nu\pi)\left(\frac{\pi}{2z}\right)^{\frac{1}{2}} e^{z}. \qquad (1.5)$$

Berry calls S_n the *Stokes multiplier*. Clearly S_n is a piecewise

[2] "int" means "integer part of".

continuous function of $|z|$, owing to the relation between n and $|z|$, and a continuous function of $\text{ph}\, z$. Berry claims that if $|z|$ is large and fixed and $\text{ph}\, z$ increases from values somewhat below π to values somewhat above π, then S_n changes rapidly, *and of course continuously*, from 0 to 1. This interesting result is obviously consistent with the results of [11], as described above.

Section 2 of the present paper describes in detail Berry's method, as applied to the function $K_\nu(z)$. The required approximation to the Stokes multiplier S_n for large $|z|$ is derived by application of R. B. Dingle's theory of terminants. This theory is well-known to physicists, but is quite formal. In §§3 and 4 I indicate how to put Berry's method, and therefore incidentally Dingle's theory, on a rigorous analytical foundation. At the same time I show how to improve Berry's approximation for S_n, and also indicate briefly how to link the new results with the rigorous theory of converging factors that was presented in [10], Chapter 14. Some conclusions are drawn in the final section, §5.

The full proofs of the results of §§3 and 4 are quite long. In consequence, only the main steps are sketched; further details will be furnished elsewhere.

2. BERRY'S THEORY

Hankel's integral representation for Macdonald's function can be expressed in the form

$$K_\nu(z) = \frac{\sqrt{\pi}\left(\frac{1}{2}z\right)^\nu}{\Gamma\left(\nu+\frac{1}{2}\right)} \int_1^\infty e^{-zt}(t^2-1)^{\nu-\frac{1}{2}}\, dt, \tag{2.1}$$

valid when

$$\text{Re}\,\nu > -\frac{1}{2}, \qquad |\text{ph}\, z| < \frac{1}{2}\pi;$$

see, for example, [10], p. 254. On replacing t by $1 + 2t$ we have

$$K_\nu(z) = \sqrt{\pi}\,\frac{(2z)^\nu e^{-z}}{\Gamma\left(\nu+\frac{1}{2}\right)} \int_0^\infty e^{-2zt}t^{\nu-\frac{1}{2}}(1+t)^{\nu-\frac{1}{2}}dt. \tag{2.2}$$

Then rotating the integration path through an angle $-\pi$ and replacing t by $te^{-\pi i}$ we obtain the analytic continuation of $K_\nu(z)$ to the sector $\frac{1}{2}\pi < \text{ph}\, z < \frac{3}{2}\pi$, given by

$$K_\nu(z) = -i\sqrt{\pi}\, e^{-\nu\pi i} \frac{(2z)^\nu e^{-z}}{\Gamma\left(\nu+\frac{1}{2}\right)} \int_{\mathscr{C}} e^{2zt} t^{\nu-\frac{1}{2}} (1-t)^{\nu-\frac{1}{2}} dt. \tag{2.3}$$

The integration path $\mathscr{C}$ is from $t = 0$ to $t = +\infty$, but unless $\nu - \frac{1}{2}$ is a nonnegative integer $\mathscr{C}$ has to pass above the singularity at $t = 1$; see Fig. 2. The branches of $t^{\nu-\frac{1}{2}}$ and $(1-t)^{\nu-\frac{1}{2}}$ are continuous along $\mathscr{C}$ and take their principal values in the neighbourhood of $t = 0$.

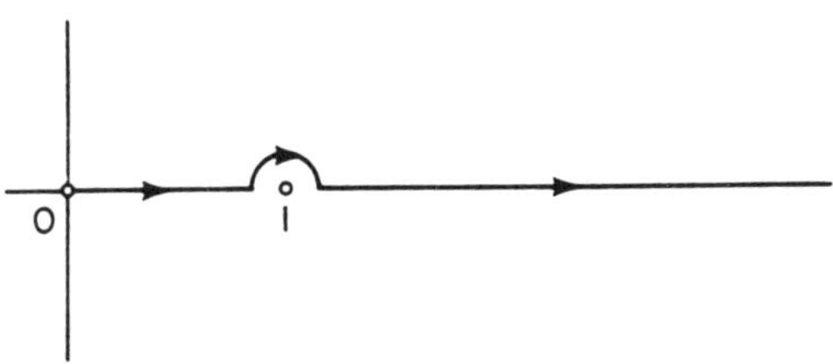

FIG. 2 *t-plane. Contour* $\mathscr{C}$.

The Maclaurin expansion of $(1-t)^{\nu-\frac{1}{2}}$ is given by

$$(1-t)^{\nu-\frac{1}{2}} = \sum_{s=0}^{\infty} (-)^s \binom{\nu-\frac{1}{2}}{s} t^s, \qquad |t| < 1.$$

Substituting this series in (2.3) and integrating term by term, as in Laplace's method, we derive

$$K_\nu(z) \sim -i\sqrt{\pi}\, e^{-\nu\pi i} \frac{(2z)^\nu e^{-z}}{\Gamma\left(\nu+\frac{1}{2}\right)} \sum_{s=0}^{\infty} (-)^s \binom{\nu - \frac{1}{2}}{s} \frac{\Gamma\left(s+\nu+\frac{1}{2}\right)}{(2ze^{-\pi i})^{s+\nu+\frac{1}{2}}} \tag{2.4}$$

as $z \to \infty$, valid when $\frac{1}{2}\pi + \delta \le \text{ph } z \le \frac{3}{2}\pi - \delta$.[3] This expansion is, of course, simply a rewritten form of (1.3) for this range of ph z.

Now for large s

$$(-)^s \binom{\nu - \frac{1}{2}}{s} \Gamma\left(s+\nu+\frac{1}{2}\right) = \frac{\Gamma(s)}{\Gamma\left(\frac{1}{2} - \nu\right)} \left\{1+O\left(\frac{1}{s}\right)\right\}. \tag{2.5}$$

Hence if $s \ge n$,

$$(-)^s \binom{\nu - \frac{1}{2}}{s} \Gamma\left(s+\nu+\frac{1}{2}\right) = \frac{\Gamma(s)}{\Gamma\left(\frac{1}{2} - \nu\right)} \left\{1+O\left(\frac{1}{n}\right)\right\} \tag{2.6}$$

as $n \to \infty$, uniformly with respect to s. Following Dingle [4], [5] and [6], Chapter 21, Berry terminates the divergent series (2.4) at its n th term, replaces the coefficients in the remainder by the right-hand side of (2.6) and then interprets the remainder by Borel summation. This yields (1.5), with

$$S_n = \left\{1 + O\left(\frac{1}{n}\right)\right\} \hat{S}_n \tag{2.7}$$

and

$$\hat{S}_n = \frac{\sec(\nu\pi) e^{-2z}}{2i\Gamma\left(\nu+\frac{1}{2}\right)\Gamma\left(\frac{1}{2} - \nu\right)} \int_{\mathscr{C}} e^{2zt} \frac{t^{n-1}}{1-t}\, dt = \frac{e^{-2z}}{2\pi i} \int_{\mathscr{C}} e^{2zt} \frac{t^{n-1}}{1-t}\, dt. \tag{2.8}$$

Again, these equations are valid when $\frac{1}{2}\pi + \delta \le \text{ph } z \le \frac{3}{2}\pi - \delta$.

---

[3]Compare [10], Chapter 4, Theorem 6.1. For each choice of δ the indentation of $\mathscr{C}$ at $t = 1$ has to be sufficiently small. Observe that we cannot use Watson's lemma here because $\mathscr{C}$ does not coincide with the positive real axis.

Another way of viewing the result just obtained is to apply Laplace's method to the last integral and insert the result in (1.5) by means of (2.7). This reproduces the asymptotic expansion (2.4), except that in the terms beyond the n th the coefficients $(-)^s\binom{\nu-\frac{1}{2}}{s}\Gamma\left(s+\nu+\frac{1}{2}\right)$ are replaced by the right-hand side of (2.6). This is exactly what we expect, since Borel summation is formally equivalent to the inversion of Watson's lemma, or in the present case Laplace's method.

The next step is to approximate S_n, or equivalently, $\hat{S}_n$. As in the theory of converging factors it is crucial to choose n to be either at, or close to, its optimum value. The optimum situation occurs when the infinite series $\sum_1$ is truncated just before its numerically smallest term: from (1.1), (1.2) and (1.5) we see that for large $|z|$ this corresponds to $n = \mathrm{int}[2|z|] + 1$. Berry sets

$$2z = -A - iB, \qquad n - 1 = A + \mu, \tag{2.9}$$

where A, B and μ are real, A being large and positive and $|\mu|$ being bounded. Since

$$\mu = \mathrm{int}\left[\sqrt{A^2+B^2}\,\right] - A = \mathrm{int}\left[A + \frac{B^2}{2A} - \frac{B^4}{8A^3} + \cdots\right] - A,$$

this assumption on μ implies $B^2/(2A)$ is bounded. Thus we are working in a region of the z-plane similar to that indicated in Fig. 1. On substituting in (2.8) by means of (2.9) we have

$$\hat{S}_n = \frac{e^{A+iB}}{2\pi i}\int_{\mathscr{C}} e^{-(A+iB)t}\,\frac{t^{A+\mu}}{1-t}\,dt.$$

To obtain an approximation for large A we first shift the singularity of the integrand to the origin by the change of variable $t = 1 + \tau$. This gives

$$\hat{S}_n = -\frac{1}{2\pi i}\int_{-1}^{\infty} e^{-A\{\tau-\ell n(1+\tau)\}}(1+\tau)^{\mu}e^{-iB\tau}\,\frac{d\tau}{\tau},$$

where the path passes above the origin. Again, following Laplace's method we expect that as $A \to \infty$ the major contribution to this integral derives from the neighbourhood of $\tau = 0$. We therefore expand locally in powers of τ, and extend the lower limit of integration to $-\infty$. This leads to the approximation

$$\hat{S}_n \sim -\frac{1}{2\pi i}\int_{-\infty}^{\infty} e^{-\frac{1}{2}A\tau^2}\left(1+\mu\tau+\frac{1}{3}A\tau^3\right)e^{-iB\tau}\,\frac{d\tau}{\tau}. \qquad (2.10)$$

By taking the indentation of the path above the origin to be a semicircle and then letting the radius tend to zero, we see that

$$-\frac{1}{2\pi i}\int_{-\infty}^{\infty} e^{-\frac{1}{2}A\tau^2}\cos(B\tau)\frac{d\tau}{\tau} = \frac{1}{2}.$$

In the remaining contributions the singularity at the origin is removable, and again on discarding the odd parts of the integrand we see that (2.10) is exactly equivalent to

$$\hat{S}_n \sim \frac{1}{2} + \frac{1}{2\pi}\int_{-\infty}^{\infty} e^{-\frac{1}{2}A\tau^2}\,\frac{\sin(B\tau)}{\tau}\,d\tau + \frac{i}{2\pi}\int_{-\infty}^{\infty} e^{-\frac{1}{2}A\tau^2}\left(\mu+\frac{1}{3}A\tau^2\right)\cos(B\tau)d\tau,$$

where the integration paths are now along the real axis. Evaluating the last two integrals, we arrive at the desired approximation in the form

$$\hat{S}_n \sim \frac{1}{2} + \frac{1}{2}\,\mathrm{erf}\left(\frac{B}{\sqrt{2A}}\right) + i\,\frac{e^{-B^2/(2A)}}{\sqrt{2\pi A}}\left(\mu + \frac{1}{3} - \frac{B^2}{3A}\right), \qquad (2.11)$$

where, as usual, erf denotes the error function:

$$\mathrm{erf}(\zeta) = \frac{2}{\sqrt{\pi}}\int_0^{\zeta} e^{-t^2}dt. \qquad (2.12)$$

This is, essentially, Berry's approximation to the Stokes multiplier for the present problem. He goes on to observe that owing to the factor $(2\pi A)^{-1/2}$ the first two terms dominate, and hence, in consequence of (2.7),

$$S_n \sim \frac{1}{2} + \frac{1}{2}\,\mathrm{erf}\left(\frac{B}{\sqrt{2A}}\right). \tag{2.13}$$

The extreme values of the error function are given by

$$\mathrm{erf}(-\infty) = -1, \qquad \mathrm{erf}(+\infty) = 1,$$

and as the following table shows these extremes are approached rapidly:

ζ	$-\infty$	-2	-1	0	1	2	∞
$\mathrm{erf}(\zeta)$	-1	-0.995	-0.843	0	0.843	0.995	1

Hence even though we have assumed $|B|\sqrt{2A}$ to be bounded, the approximation (2.13) indicates that S_n increases smoothly from the value 0 when $B/\sqrt{2A}$ is moderately large and negative, to $\frac{1}{2}$ when $B/\sqrt{2A} = 0$, and finally to 1 when $B/\sqrt{2A}$ is moderately large and positive. This is exactly what we expect, because the corresponding change in $\mathrm{ph}\, z$ is from values just less than π to values just greater than π; compare the first of equations (2.9). The importance of Berry's result is that it quantifies the change in S_n as $\mathrm{ph}\, z$ varies with $|z|$ fixed. Firstly, the change is continuous. Secondly, it is very rapid because $|\arctan(B/A)|$ is vanishingly small when $A \to \infty$ with $|B|/\sqrt{2A}$ bounded. Berry calls the quantity $B/\sqrt{2A}$ the ***Stokes variable*** because of its key role in the approximation of S_n.

Although we have shown how to treat Stokes' phenomenon only in the vicinity of $\mathrm{ph}\, z = \pi$ for Macdonald's function, the method is quite general. For example, Berry applies it to the asymptotic expansion of Dawson's integral $e^{-z^2}\int_0^z e^{t^2}dt$ and the Airy function of the second kind $\mathrm{Bi}(z)$, near $\mathrm{ph}\, z = 0$ in both cases. Furthermore, in both cases he computes S_n directly from its defining equation (compare (1.5)) for various values of z, and demonstrates that the numerical results agree well with the corresponding values derived from his approximation (compare (2.13)). The essential requirement for the method to succeed for a given asymptotic expansion is that for large s the s th term can be approximated by an expression of the form $M\Gamma(s-\beta+1)F^{\beta-1-s}$, where M, F and β are independent of s; compare (2.4) and (2.5). When this condition is fulfilled, Dingle's theory is applicable and yields an integral for the Stokes multiplier similar to (2.8), from which approximations of the forms (2.11) and (2.13) again follow.

From the mathematical standpoint there are two major problems in putting this valuable formal analysis on a rigorous basis. Firstly, there is the justification of Dingle's theory used in the construction of an appropriate integral representation of the Stokes multiplier. Secondly, there is the approximation to this multiplier in terms of the error function. Had we considered the generalized exponential integral in place of Macdonald's function, the first problem would not have arisen. Because of this, and also because the results for the generalized exponential integral play a fundamental role in the other cases, we begin with the generalized exponential integral, deferring the more difficult problem of justifying Dingle's theory until §4.

3. GENERALIZED EXPONENTIAL INTEGRAL

For real or complex values of p and z, other than $z = 0$, the function $E_p(z)$ is defined by

$$E_p(z) = z^{p-1} \int_z^{\infty} \frac{e^{-t}}{t^p}\, dt, \tag{3.1}$$

with appropriate choices of integration path and branches of the multivalued functions. In the sector $|\mathrm{ph}\, z| < \frac{1}{2}\pi$, this definition is equivalent to

$$E_p(z) = e^{-z} \int_0^\infty \frac{e^{-zt}}{(1+t)^p}\, dt, \qquad (3.2)$$

where the integration path is now the positive real axis, and $(1+t)^p$ assumes its principal value. Our concern in this section is the asymptotic behaviour of $E_p(z)$ for large $|z|$ and fixed p. By applying Watson's lemma to the last integral and extending the region of validity of the result by analytic continuation,[4] we obtain

$$E_p(z) \sim \frac{e^{-z}}{z} \sum_{s=0}^{\infty} (-)^s \frac{(p)_s}{z^s}, \qquad |\mathrm{ph}\, z| \le \tfrac{3}{2}\pi - \delta, \qquad (3.3)$$

where $(p)_s$ is Pochhammer's notation for $p(p+1)\cdots(p+s-1)$ and δ is again an arbitrarily small positive constant.

To derive asymptotic expansions of $E_p(z)$ for other ranges of ph z, we may use the continuation formula[5]

$$E_p(z) = \frac{2\pi i e^{-p\pi i}}{\Gamma(p)} z^{p-1} + E_p(ze^{-2\pi i}). \qquad (3.4)$$

Thus for the sector $\frac{1}{2}\pi + \delta \le \mathrm{ph}\, z \le \frac{7}{2}\pi - \delta$ we have

$$E_p(z) \sim \frac{2\pi i e^{-p\pi i}}{\Gamma(p)} z^{p-1} + \frac{e^{-z}}{z} \sum_{s=0}^{\infty} (-)^s \frac{(p)_s}{z^s}. \qquad (3.5)$$

Comparison of (3.3) and (3.5) shows that Stokes' phenomenon occurs in the vicinity of $\mathrm{ph}\, z = \pi$. We now investigate this region in detail.[6]

We shall need an alternative integral representation, given by

---

[4] See, for example, [10], Chapter 4, §3.

[5] Provable by use of (3.6) below.

[6] Stokes' phenomenon also occurs in the vicinities of the other Stokes lines $\mathrm{ph}\, z = -\pi,\ \pm 3\pi,\ \pm 5\pi, \ldots,$ and similar methods can be used in these cases.

$$E_p(z) = \frac{z^{p-1}e^{-z}}{\Gamma(p)} \int_0^\infty \frac{e^{-zt}t^{p-1}}{1+t}\,dt, \qquad |\mathrm{ph}\, z| < \tfrac{1}{2}\pi. \tag{3.6}$$

When p is a positive integer this formula can be obtained from the integral (3.2) by repeated integration by parts; see, for example, [9], §3.[7] However, as long as z^{p-1} and t^{p-1} have their principal values it follows by application of the convolution theorem for the Laplace transform that formula (3.6) is valid in the half-plane $\mathrm{Re}\, p > 0$. Next, if n denotes an arbitrary nonnegative integer, we have identically

$$\frac{1}{1+t} = 1 - t + t^2 - \cdots + (-)^{n-1}t^{n-1} + \frac{(-)^n t^n}{1+t}, \qquad t \neq -1.$$

The result of substituting in (3.6) by means of this expansion and then integrating term by term can be expressed in the form

$$E_p(z) = \frac{e^{-z}}{z} \sum_{s=0}^{n-1} (-)^s \frac{(p)_s}{z^s} + \frac{2\pi i e^{-p\pi i}}{\Gamma(p)} z^{p-1} T_{n+p}(z), \tag{3.7}$$

where

$$T_q(z) = \frac{e^{q\pi i}\Gamma(q)}{2\pi i} \frac{E_q(z)}{z^{q-1}}. \tag{3.8}$$

Although we have assumed that $\mathrm{Re}\, p > 0$ and $|\mathrm{ph}\, z| < \frac{1}{2}\pi$ in deriving (3.7), analytic continuation with respect to p and z removes both of these restrictions, other than $z \neq 0$. Accordingly, we now have an explicit formula for the n th remainder term in the asymptotic expansion (3.3) expressed as a multiple $T_{n+p}(z)$ of the "extra term" $2\pi i e^{-p\pi i} z^{p-1}/\Gamma(p)$ in the expansion (3.5). In Berry's

---

[7] The integral (3.6), with p a positive integer, plays a fundamental role in Dingle's theory [4] and [6], Chapter 21: his converging factor $\Lambda_s(z)$ is defined by

$$\Lambda_s(z) = \frac{1}{s!} \int_0^\infty \frac{\varepsilon^s e^{-\varepsilon}}{1+(\varepsilon/z)}\,d\varepsilon, \quad |\mathrm{ph}\, z| < \pi, \quad s = 0,1,2,\ldots .$$

In our present notation $\Lambda_s(z) = z e^z E_{s+1}(z)$.

terminology, $T_{n+p}(z)$ is the Stokes multiplier.

From (3.8) and (3.6) it is seen that

$$T_q(z) = \frac{e^{q\pi i}}{2\pi i} e^{-z} \int_0^\infty \frac{e^{-zt} t^{q-1}}{1+t} dt, \tag{3.9}$$

valid when $|\text{ph } z| < \frac{1}{2}\pi$ and $\text{Re } q > 0$. As in the case of the integral (2.2) we rotate the path of integration in (3.9) through an angle $-\pi$, and then replace t by $te^{-\pi i}$. This yields

$$T_q(z) = \frac{e^{-z}}{2\pi i} \int_{\mathscr{C}} \frac{e^{zt} t^{q-1}}{1-t} dt, \tag{3.10}$$

where the contour $\mathscr{C}$ is again as indicated in Fig. 2. This formula is valid when $\text{Re } q > 0$ and z lies in the sector of interest, given by $\frac{1}{2}\pi < \text{ph } z < \frac{3}{2}\pi$.

As in §§1 and 2, we consider the multiplier $T_{n+p}(z)$ when the infinite series in (3.7) is truncated just before its numerically smallest term. The corresponding value of n is given by $n = \text{int}[\hat{n}] + 1$, where $|p + \hat{n}| = |z|$. Accordingly, we set

$$z = \rho e^{i(\theta+\pi)}, \qquad n = \rho - p + \alpha, \tag{3.11}$$

where ρ is a large positive parameter and $|\theta|$ and $|\alpha|$ are bounded, θ being real. This gives

$$T_{n+p}(z) = T_{\rho+\alpha}(\rho e^{i(\theta+\pi)}) = \frac{\exp(\rho e^{i\theta})}{2\pi i} \int_{\mathscr{C}} \exp(-\rho e^{i\theta} t) \frac{t^{\rho+\alpha-1}}{1-t} dt. \tag{3.12}$$

For large ρ, the integrand in (3.12) has a saddle-point at $t = e^{-i\theta}$ that coalesces with the simple pole at $t = 1$ when $\theta = 0$. Problems of this type have been considered by several writers, especially van der Waerden [14], Bleistein [3] and Jones [8]. To construct an asymptotic expansion for $T_{n+p}(z)$ when ρ is large that is uniform with respect to θ in a closed interval containing $\theta = 0$, we follow these authors and employ a quadratic change of integration variable of the form

$$e^{i\theta}t - \ln t \quad = \quad \frac{1}{2}w^2 + icw + d, \tag{3.13}$$

where c and d are chosen in such a way that the singularity $t = 1$ corresponds to $w = 0$, and the saddle-point $t = e^{-i\theta}$ corresponds to $w = -ic$. Accordingly, we have

$$d = e^{i\theta}, \quad \frac{1}{2}c^2 \quad = \quad 1 + i\theta - e^{i\theta}. \tag{3.14}$$

In solving the last equation for c as a function of θ we choose the continuous branch with the Maclaurin expansion that begins

$$c \quad = \quad \theta + \frac{1}{6}i\theta^2 - \frac{1}{36}\theta^3 + \cdots . \tag{3.15}$$

Values of $\frac{1}{2}c^2$ and c for $\theta \in [-\frac{1}{2}\pi, \frac{1}{2}\pi]$ are indicated on Figs. 3 and 4.

By carrying out the conformal mapping from the t-plane to the w-plane, and making appropriate deformations of integration path, we find that

$$T_{n+p}(z) \quad = \quad \frac{\exp(\rho e^{i\theta})}{2\pi i} \int_{-ic-\infty}^{-ic+\infty} e^{-\rho(\frac{1}{2}w^2+icw+d)} \frac{f(\theta,\alpha,w)}{w} dw, \tag{3.16}$$

where

$$f(\theta,\alpha,w) \quad = \quad t^{\alpha-1} \frac{w}{1-t} \frac{dt}{dw}, \tag{3.17}$$

and the integration path is parallel to the real axis, indented if necessary with a loop to pass above the origin; see Fig. 5. This result is valid in a θ-interval that includes $\left[-\frac{1}{2}\pi, \frac{1}{2}\pi\right]$.

The function $f(\theta,\alpha,w)$ is free from singularity at $w = 0$, and we may therefore set

$$f(\theta,\alpha,w) \quad = \quad f(\theta,\alpha,0) + wg(\theta,\alpha,w), \tag{3.18}$$

where $g(\theta,\alpha,w)$ is analytic at $w = 0$. On substituting in (3.16) by means of this equation and observing that $\exp(\rho e^{i\theta}) = e^{\rho d}$, we obtain

$$T_{n+p}(z) \quad = \quad \frac{f(\theta,\alpha,0)}{2\pi i} \int_{-ic-\infty}^{-ic+\infty} e^{-\rho(\frac{1}{2}w^2+icw)} \frac{dw}{w} +$$

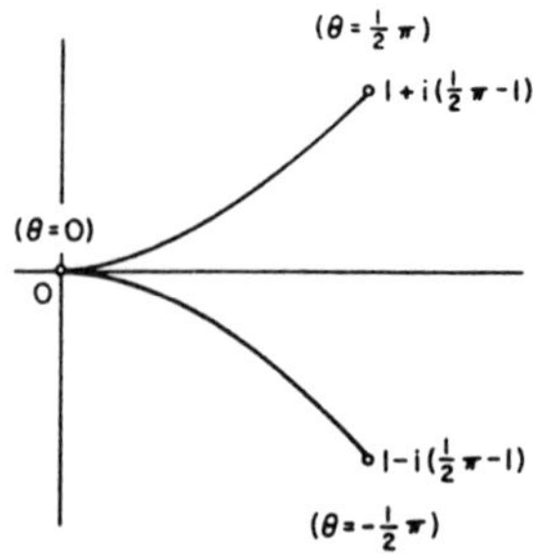

FIG. 3 $\frac{1}{2}c^2$-plane.

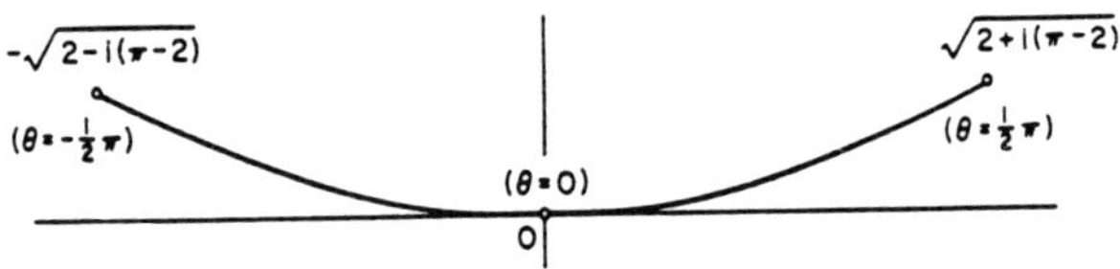

FIG. 4 *c-plane.*

FIG. 5 *w-plane. Path for the integrals in equations (3.16) and (3.19).*

$$+\frac{1}{2\pi i}\int_{-ic-\infty}^{-ic+\infty} e^{-\rho(\frac{1}{2}w^2+icw)} g(\theta,\alpha,w)dw. \tag{3.19}$$

In the first term in the right member of (3.19) the value of $f(\theta,\alpha,0)$ is found by letting $w \to 0$ in (3.17) and using L'Hospital's rule:

$$f(\theta,\alpha,0) = -1. \tag{3.20}$$

Furthermore, the contour integral can be evaluated in terms of the error function; thus

$$\int_{-ic-\infty}^{-ic+\infty} e^{-\rho(\frac{1}{2}w^2+icw)} \frac{dw}{w} = -\pi i\left\{1 + \operatorname{erf}\left(c\sqrt{\tfrac{1}{2}\rho}\right)\right\}. \tag{3.21}$$

In the remaining contribution to $T_{n+p}(z)$ in (3.19), the indentation of the integration path is no longer necessary, because the integrand is analytic at $w = 0$. The Taylor-series expansion of $g(\theta,\alpha,w)$ at the new saddle-point $w = -ic$ has the form

$$g(\theta,\alpha,w) = \sum_{s=0}^{\infty} g_s(\theta,\alpha)(w+ic)^s, \tag{3.22}$$

in which the coefficients $g_s(\theta,\alpha)$ are continuous functions of θ and α. Multiplying by $\exp\{-\rho(\frac{1}{2}w^2+icw)\}$ and integrating term by term, we find that

$$\int_{-ic-\infty}^{-ic+\infty} e^{-\rho(\frac{1}{2}w^2+icw)} g(\theta,\alpha,w)dw \sim e^{-\frac{1}{2}\rho c^2} \sum_{s=0}^{\infty} \Gamma\left(s+\frac{1}{2}\right) g_{2s}(\theta,\alpha)\left(\frac{2}{\rho}\right)^{s+\frac{1}{2}}, \tag{3.23}$$

as $\rho \to \infty$ uniformly with respect to $\theta \in \left[-\frac{1}{2}\pi,\frac{1}{2}\pi\right]$ and bounded values of $|\alpha|$.

Combination of (3.19), (3.20), (3.21) and (3.23) yields

$$T_{n+p}(z) \sim \frac{1}{2} + \frac{1}{2}\,\mathrm{erf}\left(c\sqrt{\tfrac{1}{2}\rho}\,\right) - i\,\frac{e^{-\frac{1}{2}\rho c^2}}{\sqrt{2\pi\rho}} \sum_{s=0}^{\infty} \left(\frac{1}{2}\right)_s g_{2s}(\theta,\alpha)\left(\frac{2}{\rho}\right)^s. \tag{3.24}$$

In combination with (3.7), this is the desired result.

We observe that when $\theta = 0$ we have $c = 0$. Accordingly (3.24) reduces to

$$T_{n+p}(z) \sim \frac{1}{2} - \frac{i}{\sqrt{2\pi\rho}} \sum_{s=0}^{\infty} \left(\frac{1}{2}\right)_s g_{2s}(0,\alpha)\left(\frac{2}{\rho}\right)^s. \tag{3.25}$$

Thus the error in the commonly-used mean value $\frac{1}{2}$ for the multiplier $T_{n+p}(z)$ in these circumstances is $O\left(\rho^{-\frac{1}{2}}\right)$, that is, $O\left(|z|^{-\frac{1}{2}}\right)$.

Next, from Figs. 3 and 4 we see that if ρ is large and fixed and θ increases from 0 to $\frac{1}{2}\pi$, then the real parts of both c and $\frac{1}{2}c^2$ are positive and increasing. In consequence, $e^{-\frac{1}{2}\rho c^2}$ becomes very small, $\mathrm{erf}\left(c\sqrt{\frac{1}{2}\rho}\,\right) \to 1 + O\left(e^{-\frac{1}{2}\rho c^2}\Big/\sqrt{\frac{1}{2}\pi\rho c^2}\,\right)$, and the multiplier $T_{n+p}(z)$ tends towards 1 rapidly. Similarly as θ decreases from 0 to $-\frac{1}{2}\pi$, $T_{n+p}(z)$ tends towards zero rapidly. This is exactly the kind of behaviour described by Berry; indeed, in the present circumstances his formal approximation to the Stokes multiplier is given by

$$T_{n+p}(z) \sim \frac{1}{2} + \frac{1}{2}\,\mathrm{erf}\left(\sin\theta\sqrt{\tfrac{1}{2}\rho\sec\theta}\,\right);$$

compare (2.13) with $A + iB = \rho e^{i\theta}$. Since

$$c = \theta + \frac{1}{6}i\theta^2 - \frac{1}{36}\theta^3 + \cdots,$$

$$\sin\theta\sqrt{\sec\theta} = \theta + \frac{1}{12}\theta^3 + \cdots,$$

our "Stokes variable" $c\sqrt{\frac{1}{2}\rho}$ is approximated by $\sin\theta\sqrt{\frac{1}{2}\rho\sec\theta}$ when θ is small. An advantage of our result, however, is that it furnishes a uniform asymptotic expansion for $T_{n+p}(z)$ in a

θ-interval that includes $\left[-\frac{1}{2}\pi, \frac{1}{2}\pi\right]$. *Inter alia* we no longer need assume that $|B|/\sqrt{2A}$ is bounded.

The coefficients $g_{2s}(\theta,\alpha)$ in the infinite series in (3.24) can be calculated from formulae (3.13), (3.17), (3.18), (3.20) and (3.22) in the usual manner; see, for example, [10], Chapter 9, §§10.1 and 12.2. The first one is found to be

$$g_0(\theta,\alpha) \quad = \quad \frac{i}{c} + \frac{e^{-i\alpha\theta}}{1-e^{-i\theta}}, \tag{3.26}$$

this expression being replaced by its limiting value

$$g_0(0,\alpha) \quad = \quad \frac{2}{3} - \alpha \tag{3.27}$$

at $\theta = 0$.

In the case $p = 1$ the last result can be confirmed by means of the asymptotic expansion of the converging factor for $E_1(xe^{\pi i})$, with x large and positive, that was derived in [10], Chapter 14, §4. In the notation of this reference we have

$$-e^{-x}E_1(xe^{\pi i}) \quad = \quad i\pi e^{-x} + \sum_{s=0}^{n-1} \frac{s!}{x^{s+1}} + C_n(x)\,\frac{n!}{x^{n+1}}, \tag{3.28}$$

where

$$C_n(x) \quad = \quad x - n - \frac{1}{3} + O(n^{-1}) \tag{3.29}$$

as $n \to \infty$, uniformly with respect to bounded values of $|x - n|$. Comparing this result with (3.7) and setting $z = xe^{\pi i}$, $p = 1$, we see that

$$T_{n+1}(xe^{\pi i}) \quad = \quad \frac{1}{2} + \frac{n!}{2\pi i}\,\frac{e^x}{x^{n+1}}\,C_n(x).$$

Then on substituting $x = \rho$ and $n = \rho - 1 + \alpha$ (compare (3.11)), and using (3.29) and Stirling's formula, we obtain

$$T_{n+1}(z) \quad = \quad \frac{1}{2} + \frac{i(\alpha-\frac{2}{3})}{(2\pi\rho)^{\frac{1}{2}}} + O\left(\frac{1}{\rho^{\frac{3}{2}}}\right).$$

in agreement with (3.25) and (3.27).

4. CONFLUENT HYPERGEOMETRIC FUNCTION

Instead of proceeding now to Macdonald's function, we shall consider one of the confluent hypergeometric functions:

$$U(a,a-b+1,z) = \frac{1}{\Gamma(a)} \int_0^\infty e^{-zt} t^{a-1} (1+t)^{-b} dt, \tag{4.1}$$

where the integration path is along the real axis and t^{a-1} and $(1+t)^{-b}$ assume their principal values. This integral converges when $\operatorname{Re} a > 0$ and $|\operatorname{ph} z| < \frac{1}{2}\pi$; elsewhere $U(a,a-b+1,z)$ is defined by analytic continuation. Since

$$K_\nu(z) = \sqrt{\pi}(2z)^\nu e^{-z} U(\nu+\tfrac{1}{2}, 2\nu+1, 2z),$$

results for Macdonald's function will follow as a special case; see below.[8]

By application of Watson's lemma we have

$$U(a,a-b+1,z) \sim z^{-a} \sum_{s=0}^{\infty} (-)^s \frac{(a)_s (b)_s}{s! z^s} \tag{4.2}$$

as $z \to \infty$ in the sector $|\operatorname{ph} z| \le \frac{3}{2}\pi - \delta$ $\left(< \frac{3}{2}\pi\right)$, for any fixed values of a and b.[9] The relevant continuation formula is supplied by

$$U(a,a-b+1,z) = e^{-2a\pi i} U(a,a-b+1,ze^{-2\pi i})$$

$$+ \frac{2\pi i e^{-a\pi i}}{\Gamma(a)\Gamma(b)} e^z U(1-b,a-b+1,ze^{-\pi i}). \tag{4.3}$$

Hence we derive

---

[8] Also included as special cases are Dawson's integral and the Airy function of the second kind. As noted in §2, these functions were used as examples in Berry's paper [2]. Dawson's integral is also included as a special case of the generalized exponential integral treated in §3.

[9] The restriction $\operatorname{Re} a > 0$ is removed in the usual way; compare, for example, [10], Chapter 4, §§3, 5.

$$U(a,a-b+1,z) \sim z^{-a} \sum_{s=0}^{\infty} (-)^s \frac{(a)_s(b)_s}{s!z^s}$$

$$-2\pi i \frac{e^{-(a+b)\pi i}}{\Gamma(a)\Gamma(b)} z^{b-1}e^z \sum_{s=0}^{\infty} \frac{(1-a)_s(1-b)_s}{s!z^s} \tag{4.4}$$

as $z \to \infty$ in the sector $\frac{1}{2}\pi + \delta \le \text{ph } z \le \frac{5}{2}\pi - \delta$.

Stokes' phenomenon occurs in the vicinity of $\text{ph } z = \pi$. We first seek a suitable representation for the remainder term in the asymptotic expansion (4.2). In [7] and [10], Chapter 14, this representation was obtained by use of the form of Taylor's theorem that is obtained by repeated integration by parts. This approach does not succeed for the present problem and the first step is to use instead Cauchy's integral formula.

On rotating the path of integration in (4.1) through an angle $-(\pi-\gamma)$, where γ is an arbitrary constant that satisfies $0 < \gamma \le \frac{1}{2}\pi$, and replacing t by $te^{-\pi i}$, we obtain

$$U(a,a-b+1,z) = \frac{e^{-a\pi i}}{\Gamma(a)} \int_0^{\infty e^{i\gamma}} e^{zt}t^{a-1}(1-t)^{-b}dt, \tag{4.5}$$

valid when $\frac{1}{2}\pi - \gamma < \text{ph } z < \frac{3}{2}\pi - \gamma$. We apply Taylor's theorem in the form

$$(1-t)^{-b} = \sum_{s=0}^{n-1} \frac{(b)_s}{s!} t^s + \chi_n(t), \tag{4.6}$$

in which n is an arbitrary nonnegative integer and

$$\chi_n(t) = \frac{t^n}{2\pi i} \int_{\mathscr{L}} \frac{(1-w)^{-b}}{w^n(w-t)} dw.$$

Here $\mathscr{L}$ is a simple closed contour that encloses $w = 0$ and $w = t$, but not $w = 1$; see, for example [1], Chapter 4, §3.1. Now suppose that $\mathrm{Re}\, b > 0$. Then the integral of $(1-w)^{-b} w^{-n} (w-t)^{-1}$ around any large circle vanishes as the radius of the circle tends to infinity. Accordingly, $\mathscr{L}$ may be deformed into the loop integral depicted in Fig. 6, giving

$$\chi_n(t) = \frac{t^n}{2\pi i} \int_{\infty}^{(1-)} \frac{(1-w)^{-b}}{w^n (w-t)} \, dw. \tag{4.7}$$

On the upper side of the loop $(1-w)^{-b} = e^{b\pi i}(w-1)^{-b}$, where $(w-1)^{-b}$ has its principal value. Similarly, on the lower side of the loop $(1-w)^{-b} = e^{-b\pi i}(w-1)^{-b}$. Hence if, also, $\mathrm{Re}\, b < 1$, we may collapse the loop on to the interval $[1,\infty)$. This yields

$$\chi_n(t) = \frac{\sin(b\pi)}{\pi} t^n \int_1^{\infty} \frac{(w-1)^{-b}}{w^n (w-t)} \, dw. \tag{4.8}$$

We now substitute in (4.5) by means of (4.6) and (4.8), and then integrate term by term to obtain

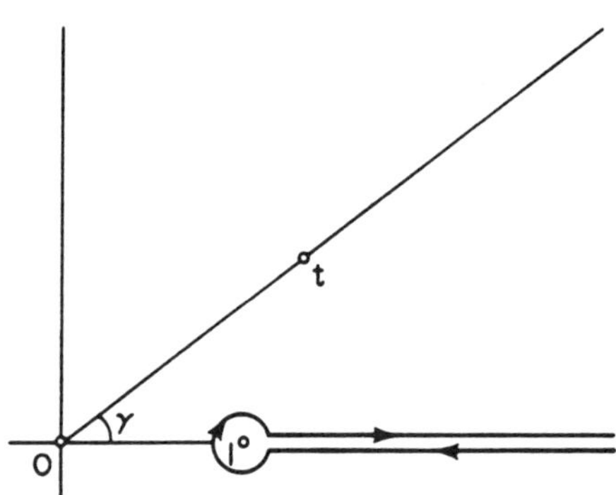

FIG. 6 *w-plane. Path for the integral (4.7).*

$$U(a,a-b+1,z) = z^{-a} \sum_{s=0}^{n-1} (-)^s \frac{(a)_s (b)_s}{s! z^s} + R_n(z), \tag{4.9}$$

where

$$R_n(z) = \frac{e^{-a\pi i}\sin(b\pi)}{\pi\Gamma(a)} \int_0^{\infty e^{i\gamma}} e^{zt} t^{n+a-1} dt \int_1^{\infty} \frac{(w-1)^{-b}}{w^n(w-t)} dw, \tag{4.10}$$

valid when $\frac{1}{2}\pi - \gamma < \operatorname{ph} z < \frac{3}{2}\pi - \gamma$, $\operatorname{Re} a > 0$ and $0 < \operatorname{Re} b < 1$. This is the desired explicit representation of the n th remainder term in the expansion (4.2). Our objective now is to determine the asymptotic behaviour of this remainder term when the asymptotic expansion (4.2) is truncated at or near its numerically smallest term. Corresponding to (3.11) we set

$$z = \rho e^{i(\theta+\pi)}, \qquad n = \rho - a - b + 1 + \alpha, \tag{4.11}$$

where θ is real, and seek the asymptotic behaviour of $R_n(z)$ as $\rho \to \infty$ for fixed values of a and b, and bounded values of $|\theta|$ and $|\alpha|$.

Provided that $\operatorname{Re} a < \operatorname{Re} b$ we may convert the repeated integral (4.10) into a double integral, and then take new variables $\tau = t/w$, $v = w - 1$. This leads to

$$R_n(z) = \frac{e^{-a\pi i}\sin(b\pi)}{\pi\Gamma(a)} \int_0^{\infty e^{i\gamma}} \frac{\tau^{n+a-1}}{1-\tau} e^{z\tau} d\tau \int_0^{\infty} v^{-b}(1+v)^{a-1} e^{z\tau v} dv.$$

The last major step is to substitute for $(1+v)^{a-1}$ by means of the binomial expansion

$$(1+v)^{a-1} = \sum_{s=0}^{\infty} (-)^s \frac{(1-a)_s}{s!} v^s,$$

and then integrate term by term. This yields

$$R_n(z) \sim \frac{e^{-a\pi i}\sin(b\pi)}{\pi\Gamma(a)} \sum_{s=0}^{\infty} (-)^s \frac{(1-a)_s\Gamma(s+1-b)}{s!}$$

$$\times \int_0^{\infty e^{i\gamma}} \frac{\tau^{n+a-1}e^{z\tau}}{(1-\tau)(z\tau e^{-\pi i})^{s-b+1}}\, d\tau.$$

The integrals in this expansion may be identified in terms of the function $T_q(z)$ introduced in §3; compare equation (3.10). Using also the recurrence and reflection formulae for the Gamma function, we arrive at

$$R_n(z) \sim -2\pi i \frac{e^{-(a+b)\pi i}}{\Gamma(a)\Gamma(b)} z^{b-1}e^z \sum_{s=0}^{\infty} \frac{(1-a)_s(1-b)_s}{s!} \frac{T_{n-s+a+b-1}(z)}{z^s} \tag{4.12}$$

as $\rho \to \infty$, where z and n are related to ρ by (4.11). This is a uniform asymptotic expansion in the sense that if a and b are fixed and the infinite sum is truncated at its m th term, then the error in the resulting approximation to $R_n(z)$ is $z^{b-1}e^zO(\rho^{-m})$, that is, $z^{b-m-1}e^zO(1)$, uniformly with respect to $\theta \in \left[-\frac{1}{2}\pi, \frac{1}{2}\pi\right]$ and bounded values of $|\alpha|$. All of the restrictions on a and b that were introduced during the analysis, given by $0 < \text{Re } a < \text{Re } b < 1$ are removable by analytic continuation. This elegant expansion is the desired result; compare (4.4) and (4.9). In particular, we note that except for the presence of the functions $T_{n-s+a+b-1}(z)$, the right-hand side of (4.12) is identical with the second line of (4.4).

To compare our result with that of Berry in the same circumstances, we truncate (4.12) at its first term, given by

$$R_n(z) = -2\pi i \frac{e^{-(a+b)\pi i}}{\Gamma(a)\Gamma(b)} z^{b-1}e^z\left\{T_{n+a+b-1}(z) + O\left(\frac{1}{z}\right)\right\}.$$

If we now set $p = a + b - 1$, then equations (4.11) become identical with (3.11); hence we may replace $T_{n+a+b-1}(z)$ by the uniform asymptotic expansion (3.24). Again, on taking only the dominant terms we arrive at

$$R_n(z) = -2\pi i \frac{e^{-(a+b)\pi i}}{\Gamma(a)\Gamma(b)} z^{b-1} e^z \left\{ \frac{1}{2} + \frac{1}{2}\mathrm{erf}\left(c\sqrt{\frac{1}{2}\rho}\right) + e^{-\frac{1}{2}\rho c^2} O\left(\rho^{-\frac{1}{2}}\right) \right\},$$

where c is defined as in §3; see equations (3.14) and (3.15). Berry's approximation has the same form, except that c is replaced by $\sin\theta\sqrt{\sec\theta}$. Similar comments to those made towards the end of §3 again apply.

Lastly, on specializing the main results of this section to the case of Macdonald's function we find that the Stokes multiplier S_n defined by (1.5) has the uniform expansion

$$S_n \sim \sum_{s=0}^{\infty} (-)^s \frac{A_s(\nu)}{z^s} T_{n-s}(2z),$$

as $z \to \infty$ in the sector $\frac{1}{2}\pi \le \mathrm{ph}\, z \le \frac{3}{2}\pi$. Here n and z are related by $n = 2|z| + \alpha$, where $|\alpha|$ is bounded. This is a rigorous, and more precise, version of Berry's result (2.13).

5. CONCLUSIONS

The purpose of this paper has been to provide a rigorous mathematical basis both for R. B. Dingle's well-established theory of terminants and a recent new interpretation of Stokes' phenomenon by M.V. Berry. The theories of these authors were outlined in §2 by means of an application to Macdonald's modified Bessel function $K_\nu(z)$ of large argument.

In §3 we investigated the asymptotic expansion of the generalized exponential integral $E_p(z)$ for large $|z|$ in the vicinity of $\mathrm{ph}\, z = \pi$ by constructing an integral representation for a so-called Stokes multiplier. The integrand has a coalescing saddle-point and simple pole, and by employing a quadratic change of integration variable we were able to construct a uniform asymptotic expansion for the Stokes multiplier in terms of the error function. This analysis corresponds to the steps in Berry's method that led from the integral representation (2.8) to the approximations (2.11) and (2.13). We also noted briefly the connection of the new results to the theory of Airey's converging factors.

In §4 we considered the asymptotic expansion of the confluent hypergeometric function $U(a,a-b+1,z)$ for fixed a and b and large $|z|$ in the vicinity of $\text{ph } z = \pi$. By employing Cauchy's integral formula for the remainder term in Taylor's theorem, we constructed a double integral for the n th remainder term $R_n(z)$ in the asymptotic expansion of $U(a,a-b+1,z)$. Then by a change of integration variables we were able to derive a uniform asymptotic expansion for $R_n(z)$ in a series of generalized exponential integrals. This analysis corresponds to the steps in the Dingle-Berry theory that led from the expansion (2.4) to the representations (2.7) and (2.8). Subsequently, we observed that if we restrict ourselves to the dominant term and substitute the approximations that were found in §3 for the generalized exponential integral, then we obtain an approximation for $R_n(z)$ in terms of the error function similar to that of Berry.

Although we used the confluent hypergeometric function in §4 to illustrate our analysis, the method is quite general and indeed is applicable in the same circumstances that the methods of Dingle and Berry can be used.

Full details of the proofs outlined in §§3, 4 are too lengthy to include in the present paper, and will appear elsewhere.

ACKNOWLEDGMENT

I am indebted to Dr. M. V. Berry for permission to make use of his results before they were published.

REFERENCES

1. L. V. Ahlfors, *Complex analysis*, Second edition, McGraw-Hill, New York, 1966.

2. M. V. Berry, "Uniform asymptotic smoothing of Stokes's discontinuities", *Proc. Roy. Soc. London Ser. A* 422: 7-21 (1989).

3. N. Bleistein, "Uniform asymptotic expansions of integrals with stationary point near algebraic singularity", *Comm. Pure Appl. Math.* 19: 353-370 (1966).

4. R. B. Dingle, "Asymptotic expansions and converging factors I. General theory and basic converging factors", *Proc. Roy. Soc. London Ser. A* 244: 456-475 (1958).

5. R. B. Dingle, "Asymptotic expansion and converging factors IV. Confluent hypergeometric, parabolic cylinder, modified Bessel, and ordinary Bessel functions", *Proc. Roy. Soc. London Ser. A* 249: 270-283 (1958).

6. R. B. Dingle, *Asymptotic expansions: their derivation and interpretation*, Academic Press, London, 1973.

7. H. Jeffreys, "The remainder in Watson's lemma", *Proc. Roy. Soc. London Ser. A* 248: 88-92 (1958).

8. D. S. Jones, "Asymptotic behavior of integrals", *SIAM Rev.* 14: 286-317 (1972).

9. G. F. Miller, *Tables of generalized exponential integrals*, N.P.L. Math. Tables, Vol. 3, H. M. Stationery Office, London, 1960.

10. F. W. J. Olver, *Asymptotics and special functions*, Academic Press, New York, 1974.

11. F. W. J. Olver, "Asymptotic approximations and error bounds", *SIAM Review* 22: 188-203 (1980).

12. G. G. Stokes, "On the discontinuity of arbitrary constants which appear in divergent developments", *Trans. Cambridge Philos. Soc.* 10: 105-128 (1857). Reprinted in *Mathematical and Physical Papers*, Vol. 4, 77-109, Cambridge University Press, London, 1904.

13. G. G. Stokes, *Memoir and scientific correspondence*, selected and arranged by J. Larmor, Vol. I, 62 (1907), Cambridge University Press, London.

14. B. L. van der Waerden, "On the method of saddle points", *Appl. Sci. Res. Ser. B* 2: 33-45 (1951).

SIAM J. MATH. ANAL.
Vol. 22, No. 5, pp. 1460-1474, September 1991

UNIFORM, EXPONENTIALLY IMPROVED, ASYMPTOTIC EXPANSIONS FOR THE GENERALIZED EXPONENTIAL INTEGRAL*

F. W. J. OLVER†

Abstract. By allowing the number of terms in an asymptotic expansion to depend on the asymptotic variable, it is possible to obtain an error term that is exponentially small as the asymptotic variable tends to its limit. This procedure is called "exponential improvement." It is shown how to improve exponentially the well-known Poincaré expansions for the generalized exponential integral (or incomplete Gamma function) of large argument. New uniform expansions are derived in terms of elementary functions, and also in terms of the error function.

Inter alia, the results supply a rigorous foundation for some of the recent work of M. V. Berry on a smooth interpretation of the Stokes phenomenon.

Key words. coalescing critical points, converging factors, Dingle's terminants, error function, incomplete Gamma function, Stokes' phenomenon

AMS(MOS) subject classifications. primary 41A60; secondary 33A70

1. Introduction. Suppose that a function $f(z)$ has an asymptotic expansion of the form

$$f(z) \sim f_0 + \frac{f_1}{z} + \frac{f_2}{z^2} + \cdots,$$

as $z \to \infty$ in a certain region $\mathbf{R}$, say, of the complex plane. By definition, if the series is truncated at the term f_{n-1}/z^{n-1}, where n is an arbitrary fixed integer, then the error in representing $f(z)$ by the truncated series is $O(z^{-n})$ as $z \to \infty$ in $\mathbf{R}$. For some time, however, it has been known that if we permit the number of terms in the truncated series to depend on $|z|$, then it is possible to make the truncation error *exponentially* small as $z \to \infty$ in $\mathbf{R}$.

Consider, for example, the exponential integral defined by

$$E_1(z) = e^{-z} \int_0^\infty \frac{e^{-zt}}{1+t}\,dt$$

when $|\text{ph } z| < \pi/2$, and by analytic continuation elsewhere. This has the well-known expansion.

$$e^z E_1(z) \sim \sum_{s=0}^{\infty} (-)^s \frac{s!}{z^{s+1}}, \qquad z \to \infty \quad \text{in } |\text{ph } z| \leqq \frac{3}{2}\pi - \delta, \tag{1.1}$$

where δ is an arbitrary positive constant. Let $R_n(z)$ denote the nth remainder term in this expansion, given by

$$e^z E_1(z) = \sum_{s=0}^{n-1} (-)^s \frac{s!}{z^{s+1}} + R_n(z). \tag{1.2}$$

In [9, Chap. 14, § 3.1] it was shown that if ζ is a real or complex variable and θ is real, then

$$R_n\{(n+\zeta)\, e^{i\theta}\} = O(n^{-1/2}\, e^{-n-\zeta}), \tag{1.3}$$

* Received by the editors February 9, 1990; accepted for publication September 19, 1990.

† Institute for Physical Science and Technology, University of Maryland, College Park, Maryland 20742.
This research was supported by the National Science Foundation under grant DMS 87-23039.

as $n \to \infty$, uniformly with respect to $\theta \in [-\pi+\delta, \pi-\delta]$ and bounded values of $|\zeta|$. Let us now restrict ζ to be real, set $z=(n+\zeta)\,e^{i\theta}$, and regard z as the asymptotic variable instead of n. Then we have

$$R_n(z) = O(z^{-1/2}\,e^{-|z|}), \qquad |z| \to \infty, \tag{1.4}$$

uniformly with respect to ph $z \in [-\pi+\delta, \pi-\delta]$ and bounded values of $||z|-n|$. For example, (1.4) would apply if $n = \operatorname{int}[|z|]$, the integer part of $|z|$. When the approximation given by (1.2) is modified in this way, that is, by taking

$$n = |z| - \zeta \tag{1.5}$$

with $|\zeta|$ bounded, we shall say that the resulting partial sum is *uniformly exponentially accurate* in the sector $|\text{ph}\, z| \leqq \pi - \delta$.

The results in [9, Chap. 14, § 3] actually go much further. The object in this reference was to provide a rigorous basis for the theory of "converging factors." In the case of the asymptotic expansion (1.1) of $E_1(z)$ it was shown that

$$R_n(z) = (-)^n \frac{n!}{z^{n+1}} C_n(z), \tag{1.6}$$

where the converging factor $C_n(z)$ possesses an asymptotic expansion of the form

$$C_n\{(n+\zeta)\,e^{i\theta}\} \sim \sum_{s=0}^{\infty} \frac{P_s(\alpha,\zeta)}{n^s}, \qquad n \to \infty, \tag{1.7}$$

in which the $P_s(\alpha,\zeta)$ are polynomials in $\alpha \equiv (1+e^{i\theta})^{-1}$ and ζ. Again, (1.7) is uniformly valid for $\theta \in [-\pi+\delta, \pi-\delta]$ and bounded $|\zeta|$. As before, we restrict ζ to be real and set $z=(n+\zeta)\,e^{i\theta}$. Then (1.5) applies and the combination of (1.6) and (1.7) yields

$$R_n(z) \sim (-)^n \frac{\Gamma(|z|-\zeta+1)}{z^{|z|-\zeta+1}} \sum_{s=0}^{\infty} \frac{P_s(\alpha,\zeta)}{(|z|-\zeta)^s}, \qquad |z| \to \infty.$$

On replacing the Gamma function by Stirling's series and setting $|z| = z\,e^{-i\theta}$, we see that this expansion can be rearranged as an asymptotic expansion in descending powers of z; thus

$$R_n(z) \sim (-)^n\, e^{-|z|} z^{-1/2}\, e^{(\zeta-|z|-1/2)i\theta} \sum_{s=0}^{\infty} \frac{Q_s(\theta,\zeta)}{z^s}, \qquad |z| \to \infty, \tag{1.8}$$

where the coefficients $Q_s(\theta,\zeta)$ are rational functions of $e^{i\theta}$ and polynomials in ζ. Again, this expansion is uniformly valid for ph $z \in [-\pi+\delta, \pi-\delta]$ and bounded $|\zeta|$. We call the combination of (1.2) and (1.8) a ***uniform, exponentially improved*** ("UEI"), or more precisely, a ***uniform, $e^{-|z|}$-improved, asymptotic expansion.***

Recently, Ursell [11] has considered functions $f(z)$ representable as Laplace transforms

$$f(z) = \int_0^\infty e^{-zt}\, \psi(t)\, dt,$$

in which $\psi(t)$ is analytic in a neighborhood of the origin. He has shown that the asymptotic expansion of $f(z)$ obtained by straightforward application of Watson's lemma can always be rendered exponentially accurate, in the sense described above. Ursell's analysis applies only to positive real values of z, but it could be extended easily to the complex plane.

The purpose of the present investigation is to show how to construct UEI expansions for a wide class of functions. The new theory goes beyond that presented in [9, Chap. 14] in three ways: (i) the number of functions that can be treated successfully is greatly increased; (ii) nonelementary functions may be used in constructing the expansions; (iii) as a consequence of (ii), regions of validity are extended considerably.

One of the theoretical and practical consequences of this investigation is to provide a rigorous basis for a recent powerful interpretation of the Stokes phenomenon that has been developed by Berry [1]. Indeed, it was this aspect that motivated this work. This is explained fully in [10], and inter alia we shall supply proofs, and significant extensions, of all results that were stated in [10].

In the present paper we confine our attention to the construction of UEI expansions for the generalized exponential integral $E_p(z)$, when p is fixed and $|z|$ is large, both p and z being real or complex. This is because the generalized exponential integral plays a fundamental role in other cases—an observation first made by Dingle [4].

Another investigation of the generalized exponential integral (or incomplete Gamma function) has been provided by Jones. Jones' paper [6] was presented independently of and at the same time as [10]. There is substantial overlap of [6] with the present investigation, but there are significant differences in the method of proof and results achieved.

2. UEI expansions in terms of elementary functions.

2.1. General properties of the generalized exponential integral. For real or complex values of p and z, other than $z=0$, the generalized exponential integral $E_p(z)$ is defined by

$$E_p(z)=z^{p-1}\Gamma(1-p,z)=z^{p-1}\int_z^\infty \frac{e^{-t}}{t^p}\,dt. \tag{2.1}$$

The only restriction on the integration path is that it must not intersect the origin. Accordingly, unless p is a nonpositive integer, $E_p(z)$ is a multiple-valued function of z. On the other hand, $E_p(z)$ is a single-valued function of p; indeed from (2.1) it is clear that for fixed nonzero values of z each branch of $E_p(z)$ is an entire function of p.[1]

On replacing t by $z(1+t)$ we find that $E_p(z)$ is also given by

$$E_p(z)=e^{-z}\int_0^\infty \frac{e^{-zt}}{(1+t)^p}\,dt, \qquad |\mathrm{ph}\, z|<\frac{1}{2}\pi, \tag{2.2}$$

where the integration path now runs along the real axis, and $(1+t)^p$ has its principal value.

An integral representation that we shall find particularly useful is given by

$$E_p(z)=\frac{z^{p-1}e^{-z}}{\Gamma(p)}\int_0^\infty \frac{e^{-zt}t^{p-1}}{1+t}\,dt, \qquad \mathrm{Re}\, p>0, \quad |\mathrm{ph}\, z|<\frac{1}{2}\pi. \tag{2.3}$$

Again the integration path is along the real axis, and t^{p-1} and z^{p-1} assume their principal values. This result may be derived from (2.2) with the aid of the convolution formula for the Laplace transform. The integral on the right-hand side can be regarded as either a Laplace transform or a Stieltjes transform.

Other branches of $E_p(z)$ can be related to the principal branch (for which $-\pi<\mathrm{ph}\, z\leqq\pi$) by rotation of the integration path in (2.3), and analytic continuation with

[1] For the case in which p is a positive integer, various properties and some numerical tables of $E_p(z)$ will be found in [7] and [8].

respect to z. Each time the path crosses the simple pole at $t=-1$ a contribution is made by the residue. Thus we find that

$$E_p(z)=\frac{2\pi i\,e^{-kp\pi i}}{\Gamma(p)}\frac{\sin(kp\pi)}{\sin(p\pi)}z^{p-1}+E_p(z\,e^{-2k\pi i}), \tag{2.4}$$

where k is any integer. Analytic continuation removes all restrictions on p and z, other than $z=0$, from this result.

2.2. Poincaré expansions for large $|z|$. Let p be fixed and $z\to\infty$. Then by applying the extended form of Watson's lemma, as given by Theorem 3.3 of [9, Chap. 4], to the integral representation (2.2), we find that

$$E_p(z)\sim\frac{e^{-z}}{z}\sum_{s=0}^{\infty}(-)^s\frac{(p)_s}{z^s},\qquad |\text{ph } z|\leqq\frac{3}{2}\pi-\delta, \tag{2.5}$$

where $(p)_s$ is Pochhammer's symbol for the ascending factorial $p(p+1)\cdots(p+s-1)$, and δ continues to denote an arbitrary positive constant. Corresponding expansions in other phase ranges are obtainable by combination of (2.4) and (2.5). For example, by taking $k=1$ in (2.4) we derive

$$E_p(z)\sim\frac{2\pi i\,e^{-p\pi i}}{\Gamma(p)}z^{p-1}+\frac{e^{-z}}{z}\sum_{s=0}^{\infty}(-)^s\frac{(p)_s}{z^s},\qquad \frac{1}{2}\pi+\delta\leqq\text{ph } z\leqq\frac{7}{2}\pi-\delta. \tag{2.6}$$

In the common sector $\pi/2+\delta\leqq\text{ph } z\leqq\frac{3}{2}\pi-\delta$, both (2.5) and (2.6) apply. Their apparent discrepancy is a term that is exponentially small compared with the main contribution; hence there is no anomaly. This is, of course, simply a manifestation of Stokes' phenomenon. On the ray $\text{ph } z=\pi$, the dominance of one contribution in (2.6) over the other is maximal, and for this reason we call $\text{ph } z=\pi$ a *Stokes line.*[2] The other Stokes lines for $E_p(z)$ for large $|z|$ occur at $\text{ph } z=k\pi$, where k is any integer.

2.3. UEI expansions for the sector $|\text{ph } z|\leqq\pi-\delta$. If n is an arbitrary nonnegative integer, then we have identically

$$\frac{1}{1+t}=1-t+t^2-\cdots+(-)^{n-1}t^{n-1}+(-)^n\frac{t^n}{1+t},\qquad t\neq-1. \tag{2.7}$$

On substituting this expansion in (2.3) and integrating term by term, we obtain the following explicit representation of the remainder term in (2.5):

$$E_p(z)=\frac{e^{-z}}{z}\sum_{s=0}^{n-1}(-)^s\frac{(p)_s}{z^s}+(-)^n\frac{2\pi}{\Gamma(p)}z^{p-1}F_{n+p}(z), \tag{2.8}$$

where

$$F_{n+p}(z)=\frac{e^{-z}}{2\pi}\int_0^{\infty}\frac{e^{-zt}t^{n+p-1}}{1+t}\,dt=\frac{\Gamma(n+p)}{2\pi}\frac{E_{n+p}(z)}{z^{n+p-1}}. \tag{2.9}$$

In deriving this result we have assumed that $\text{Re } p>0$ and $|\text{ph } z|<\pi/2$. However, by analytic continuation with respect to p the first condition is replaceable by $\text{Re } p>-n$. To ease the second restriction, we rotate the path of integration through an angle $-\gamma$,

[2] Sometimes the name anti-Stokes line is used instead; see the discussion on p. 518 of [9].

where $-\pi<\gamma<\pi$, and set $t=\tau e^{-i\gamma}$. Then by analytic continuation with respect to z we have

$$F_{n+p}(z)=\frac{e^{-i(n+p)\gamma}e^{-z}}{2\pi}\int_0^\infty \frac{\exp(-z\tau e^{-i\gamma})\tau^{n+p-1}}{1+\tau e^{-i\gamma}}\,d\tau, \tag{2.10}$$

valid when $\operatorname{Re} p>-n$ and $|\operatorname{ph}(z e^{-i\gamma})|<\pi/2$.

For future reference we also record here the continuation formula for $F_{n+p}(z)$ corresponding to (2.4). This is given by

$$F_{n+p}(z)=(-)^n i e^{-kp\pi i}\frac{\sin(kp\pi)}{\sin(p\pi)}+e^{-2kp\pi i}F_{n+p}(z e^{-2k\pi i}), \tag{2.11}$$

$k=0, \pm 1, +2, \cdots$.

The ratio of the $(s+1)$st term to the sth term in (2.5) is $(1-p-s)/z$. In consequence, when $|z|$ is large compared with $|p|$, the optimum number of terms (that is, the number of terms preceding the numerically smallest term) is $\operatorname{int}[\hat{n}]+1$, where $\hat{n}$ is the positive number satisfying $|p+\hat{n}|=|z|$. Accordingly, we set

$$z=\rho e^{i\theta}, \qquad n=\rho-p+\alpha, \tag{2.12}$$

where ρ is a large positive parameter, θ is real and $|\alpha|$ is bounded.[3] With $\gamma=\theta$ in (2.10), we have

$$F_{n+p}(z)=\frac{e^{-i(\rho+\alpha)\theta}e^{-z}}{2\pi}\int_0^\infty \frac{e^{-\rho\tau}\tau^{\rho+\alpha-1}}{1+\tau e^{-i\theta}}\,d\tau, \tag{2.13}$$

valid when $-\pi<\theta<\pi$ and $\operatorname{Re}(\rho+\alpha)>0$.

For large ρ the integrand has a saddlepoint at $\tau=1$. By application of Theorem 7.1 of [9, Chap. 4] (Laplace's method) and use of the second of (2.12) we find that

$$F_{n+p}(z)\sim\frac{e^{-i(\rho+\alpha)\theta}}{1+e^{-i\theta}}\frac{e^{-\rho-z}}{(2\pi\rho)^{1/2}}\sum_{s=0}^{\infty}\frac{a_{2s}(\theta,\alpha)}{\rho^s}, \qquad \rho\to\infty, \tag{2.14}$$

where the coefficients $a_{2s}(\theta,\alpha)$ are continuous functions of θ and α. Moreover, by means of a straightforward extension of the proof of the cited theorem, we can prove that the expansion (2.14) holds uniformly with respect to θ and α, when $\theta\in[-\pi+\delta, \pi-\delta]$ and $|\alpha|$ is bounded.

The combination of (2.8), (2.12), and (2.14) is the required expansion. It is a UEI expansion throughout its sector of validity $|\operatorname{ph} z|\leqq\pi-\delta$, because if the series in (2.14) is truncated at its mth term, where m is arbitrary, but fixed, then the relative error in the resulting approximation to $E_p(z)$ is uniformly $O(z^{p-m-1/2}e^{-|z|})$.

The coefficients $a_{2s}(\theta,\alpha)$ are calculable in the usual manner (see, for example, [9, Chap. 3, § 8.1]). One way to express them is found to be

$$a_{2s}(\theta,\alpha)=1\cdot 3\cdot 5\cdots(2s-1)\sum_{j=0}^{2s}\lambda_{2s-1,j-1}A_j(\theta,\alpha), \tag{2.15}$$

where

$$A_s(\theta,\alpha)=\sum_{j=0}^{s}(-)^j\binom{\alpha}{s-j}\frac{1}{(1+e^{i\theta})^j}, \tag{2.16}$$

[3] This α is unrelated to the α of § 1.

and $\lambda_{s,j}$ is the coefficient of x^s in the expansion of t^j, t being related to x via

$$\tfrac{1}{2}x^2 = t - \ln(1+t) = \tfrac{1}{2}t^2 - \tfrac{1}{3}t^3 + \tfrac{1}{4}t^4 - \cdots,$$

with $x \sim t$ as $t \to 0$. Reversion of the last expansion yields

$$t = x + \tfrac{1}{3}x^2 + \tfrac{1}{36}x^3 - \tfrac{1}{270}x^4 + \tfrac{1}{4320}x^5 + \cdots, \tag{2.17}$$

and with the aid of this result we arrive at the following explicit expressions for the first three coefficients:

$$\begin{aligned} &a_0(\theta, \alpha) = 1, \qquad a_2(\theta, \alpha) = \tfrac{1}{12} + A_2(\theta, \alpha), \\ &a_4(\theta, \alpha) = \tfrac{1}{288} + \tfrac{1}{12}A_2(\theta, \alpha) + 2A_3(\theta, \alpha) + 3A_4(\theta, \alpha). \end{aligned} \tag{2.18}$$

2.4. Remarks. (i) From (2.15), (2.16), and (2.18) we observe that the coefficients $a_{2s}(\theta, \alpha)$ become unbounded as $\theta \to \pm\pi$; in consequence, the interval of validity $|\theta| \leqq \pi - \delta$ of (2.14) is maximal.

(ii) The expansion (2.14) can be rearranged as an expansion for the converging factor in descending powers of n, as indicated in § 1. The writer has verified that in the case where $p = 1$ the first three coefficients in the resulting expansion agree with those found in [9, Chap. 14, § 3.2] by quite different methods. (They are also simpler in form than their counterparts in (2.14).)

(iii) In [10] the function

$$T_{n+p}(z) = e^{(n+p)\pi i} \frac{\Gamma(n+p)}{2\pi i} \frac{E_{n+p}(z)}{z^{n+p-1}}$$

played the role of $F_{n+p}(z)$. An advantage of using $F_{n+p}(z)$ in the present paper is that it leads to a symmetric form for the main result; compare (5.10) and (5.11) below.

3. Nonelementary UEI expansions: formal derivation.

3.1. Approach. The region of validity of the UEI expansion of § 2 falls short of the Stokes lines at ph $z = \pm\pi$. We now seek UEI expansions that hold uniformly in sectors containing these lines. To begin with, we concentrate on the sector $0 <$ ph $z < 2\pi$.

The essential difficulty is that the integrand in (2.13) has a saddlepoint at $\tau = 1$ and a simple pole at $\tau = -e^{i\theta}$, and these points coincide as $\theta \to \pi$. To overcome this difficulty we use a modification of Laplace's method introduced by van der Waerden [12] and developed subsequently by Jones [5] and Bleistein [2]. This yields an expansion involving a nonelementary function, namely, the complementary error function.

3.2. Transformation of integration variable. We employ a quadratic change of integration variable, given by

$$\tfrac{1}{2}w^2 = \tau - \ln\tau - 1. \tag{3.1}$$

The saddlepoint at $\tau = 1$ then corresponds to $w = 0$. We resolve the ambiguity in the choice of branch of $(2\tau - 2\ln\tau - 2)^{1/2}$ by requiring

$$w \sim \tau - 1 \quad \text{as } \tau \to 1. \tag{3.2}$$

Let $\mathbf{\Delta}$ denote the sector $|\text{ph}\,\tau| < \pi$ and $\mathbf{W}$ be its map in the w-plane. The mapping is easily determined by passage through the intermediate variable v, given by

$$v = \tau - \ln\tau - 1, \qquad w = \sqrt{2v}.$$

Corresponding points in the τ and w planes are indicated in Figs. 1 and 2. $\mathbf{W}$ is the unshaded region shown in Fig. 2; its boundaries are the curves C_1D_1 and C_2D_2 defined parametrically by

$$\tfrac{1}{2}w^2 = -\sigma - \ln\sigma \mp i\pi - 1, \qquad 0 \leqq \sigma < \infty.$$

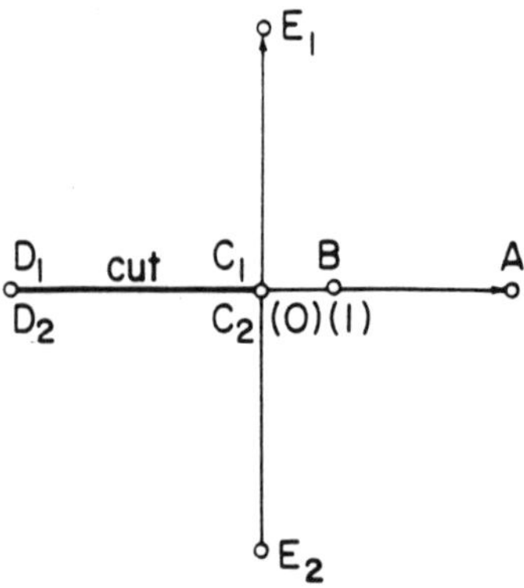

FIG. 1. *τ-plane: domain* $\mathbf{\Delta}$.

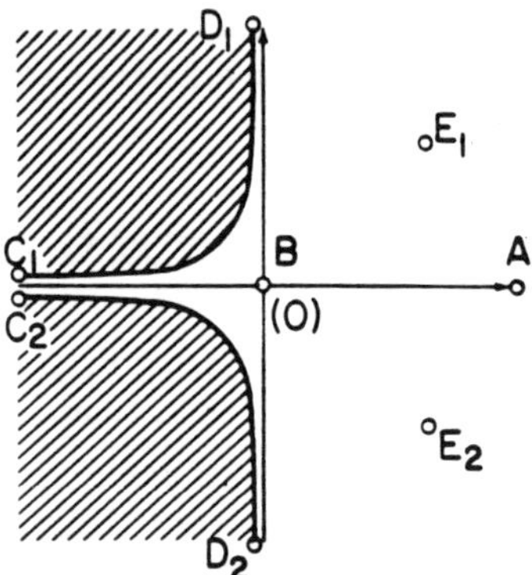

FIG. 2. *w-plane: domain* $\mathbf{W}$.

From these diagrams and the corresponding map in the v-plane (not illustrated), it is clear that the mapping between the domains $\mathbf{\Delta}$ and $\mathbf{W}$ is one-to-one, and that τ and w are analytic functions of each other when $\tau \in \mathbf{\Delta}$ and $w \in \mathbf{W}$.

In the w-plane, the pole at $\tau = e^{i(\theta-\pi)}$ corresponds to $w = -ic(\theta)$, say, where

$$\tfrac{1}{2}\{c(\theta)\}^2 = -e^{i(\theta-\pi)} + i(\theta-\pi) + 1. \tag{3.3}$$

In consequence of (3.2) we have

$$c(\theta) \sim -(\theta-\pi) \quad \text{as } \theta \to \pi; \tag{3.4}$$

in fact, the Taylor series expansion of $c(\theta)$ at $\theta = \pi$ begins

$$c(\theta) = -(\theta-\pi) - \frac{i}{6}(\theta-\pi)^2 + \frac{1}{36}(\theta-\pi)^3 + \cdots. \tag{3.5}$$

Graphs of $\frac{1}{2}\{c(\theta)\}^2$ and $c(\theta)$ are indicated in Figs. 3 and 4.[4]

Now consider formula (2.13). This was obtained by rotation of the path of integration in (2.9) and analytic continuation with respect to z, and is valid when

[4] Although in this section we consider only values of θ in the interval $(0, 2\pi)$, the graphs of $\frac{1}{2}\{c(\theta)\}^2$ and $c(\theta)$ are shown for the more extensive range $[-\pi, 3\pi]$ for subsequent reference. The reader should also note that the scales of Figs. 2, 3, and 4 are not the same.

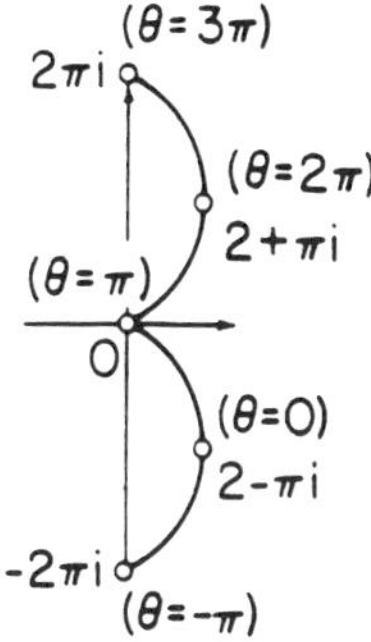

FIG. 3. $\frac{1}{2}\{c(\theta)\}^2$-*plane.*

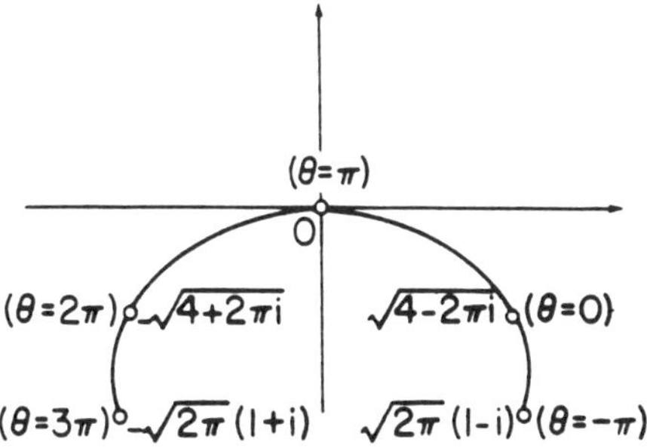

FIG. 4. $c(\theta)$-*plane.*

$-\pi<\theta<\pi$. However, an extension of this process shows that (2.13) continues to be valid when $\pi\leqq\theta<2\pi$, as long as the integration path in (2.13) is deformed to pass above the pole at $\tau=e^{i(\theta-\pi)}$. In the w-plane this pole is mapped onto the point $w=-ic(\theta)$. In consequence, on transforming variables from τ to w in (2.13), we obtain

$$F_{n+p}(z)=\frac{e^{-i(\rho+\alpha)\theta}\,e^{-\rho-z}}{2\pi}\int_{-\infty}^{\infty}\exp\left(-\frac{1}{2}\rho w^2\right)\frac{f(\theta,\alpha,w)}{w+ic(\theta)}\,dw,\qquad 0<\theta<2\pi, \tag{3.6}$$

where[5]

$$f(\theta,\alpha,w)=\frac{w+ic(\theta)}{1+\tau e^{-i\theta}}\,\tau^{\alpha-1}\,\frac{d\tau}{dw}, \tag{3.7}$$

and the path is indented to pass above the point $w=-ic(\theta)$ when $\theta\geqq\pi$.

3.3. Formal expansion of the transformed integral. The function $f(\theta,\alpha,w)$ is analytic at $w=-ic(\theta)$, and we may therefore set

$$f(\theta,\alpha,w)=f\{\theta,\alpha,-ic(\theta)\}[1-\{w+ic(\theta)\}g(\theta,\alpha,w)], \tag{3.8}$$

where $g(\theta,\alpha,w)$ is analytic throughout $\mathbf{W}$, including $w=-ic(\theta)$. On substituting this

[5] The reader is cautioned that several notational changes have been made from the earlier paper [10]. For example, c has become $-c(\theta)$, and to obtain the new $f(\theta,\alpha,w)$ from that of [10] it is necessary to replace θ and w by $\theta-\pi$ and $w+ic(\theta)$, respectively, and then multiply the result by $e^{i\alpha(\theta-\pi)}$.

expression for $f(\theta, \alpha, w)$ into (3.6), we obtain

$$F_{n+p}(z) = \frac{e^{-i(\rho+\alpha)\theta}\, e^{-\rho-z}}{2\pi} f\{\theta, \alpha, -ic(\theta)\} \cdot \left\{ \int_{-\infty}^{\infty} \frac{\exp(-\frac{1}{2}\rho w^2)}{w + ic(\theta)}\, dw - \int_{-\infty}^{\infty} \exp\left(-\frac{1}{2}\rho w^2\right) g(\theta, \alpha, w)\, dw \right\}. \tag{3.9}$$

The first integral in the right-hand side of the last equation is evaluable in terms of the complementary error function:

$$\int_{-\infty}^{\infty} \frac{\exp(-\frac{1}{2}\rho w^2)}{w + ic(\theta)}\, dw = -\pi i \exp\left(\frac{1}{2}\rho\{c(\theta)\}^2\right) \operatorname{erfc}\left\{c(\theta)\sqrt{\frac{1}{2}\rho}\right\}. \tag{3.10}$$

In the second integral the path may be taken to be a straight line, since the integrand is analytic in **W**. We may expand $g(\theta, \alpha, w)$ in a Taylor series centered on the transformed saddlepoint at the origin, in the form

$$g(\theta, \alpha, w) = \sum_{s=0}^{\infty} g_s(\theta, \alpha) w^s, \tag{3.11}$$

and on multiplying by $\exp(-\frac{1}{2}\rho w^2)$ and integrating formally term by term, we arrive at

$$\int_{-\infty}^{\infty} \exp\left(-\frac{1}{2}\rho w^2\right) g(\theta, \alpha, w)\, dw \sim \sum_{s=0}^{\infty} \Gamma\left(s + \frac{1}{2}\right) g_{2s}(\theta, \alpha) \left(\frac{2}{\rho}\right)^{s+1/2}. \tag{3.12}$$

Lastly, the value of $f\{\theta, \alpha, -ic(\theta)\}$ is found by letting $\tau \to e^{i(\theta-\pi)}$ in (3.7); thus

$$f\{\theta, \alpha, -ic(\theta)\} = -e^{i\alpha(\theta-\pi)}. \tag{3.13}$$

Combination of (3.9), (3.10), (3.12), and (3.13), followed by use of (3.3) and (2.12) yields the desired expansion in the form

$$F_{n+p}(z) \sim (-)^n i\, e^{-p\pi i} \left[\frac{1}{2} \operatorname{erfc}\left\{c(\theta)\sqrt{\frac{1}{2}\rho}\right\} - i \frac{\exp(-\frac{1}{2}\rho\{c(\theta)\}^2)}{(2\pi\rho)^{1/2}} \sum_{s=0}^{\infty} \left(\frac{1}{2}\right)_s g_{2s}(\theta, \alpha) \left(\frac{2}{\rho}\right)^s \right]. \tag{3.14}$$

To evaluate the coefficients $g_{2s}(\theta, \alpha)$, we find by reversion of (3.1)

$$\tau = 1 + w + \frac{1}{3} w^2 + \frac{1}{36} w^3 - \frac{1}{270} w^4 + \frac{1}{4320} w^5 + \cdots;$$

compare (2.17). We now substitute this Maclaurin expansion into the formula

$$g(\theta, \alpha, w) = e^{i\alpha(\pi-\theta)} \frac{\tau^{\alpha-1}}{1 + \tau e^{-i\theta}} \frac{d\tau}{dw} + \frac{1}{w + ic(\theta)} \tag{3.15}$$

obtained from (3.7), (3.8), and (3.13), and identify the coefficient of w^{2s} on the right-hand side of (3.11). For example, the first one is found to be

$$g_0(\theta, \alpha) = \frac{e^{i\alpha(\pi-\theta)}}{1 + e^{-i\theta}} - \frac{i}{c(\theta)}, \tag{3.16}$$

the right-hand side being replaced by its limiting value

$$g_0(\pi, \alpha) = \tfrac{2}{3} - \alpha, \tag{3.17}$$

when $\theta = \pi$.

In the next two sections we shall establish the asymptotic nature of the formal series (3.14), and determine its maximum region of validity in the z-plane. At the same time, we shall supply another way of calculating the coefficients $g_{2s}(\theta, \alpha)$.

4. Proof of the validity of the expansion (3.14) when $\delta \leqq \text{ph}\, z \leqq 2\pi - \delta$.

4.1. Objective. In this section we shall show that if the infinite series in the expansion (3.14) is truncated at the term $s = m-1$, say, where m is any fixed integer, then the difference between the resulting approximation and $F_{n+p}(z)$ is $\exp[-\frac{1}{2}\rho\{c(\theta)\}^2]O(\rho^{-m-1/2})$ as $\rho \to \infty$, uniformly with respect to θ and α. The method of proof is similar to that used in [9, Chap. 9, §§ 9-13].

4.2. Bounds for the coefficients $g_s(\theta, \alpha)$. A preliminary step is to prove that as s increases, the rate of growth of the coefficients $g_s(\theta, \alpha)$ is uniformly algebraic.

Referring to (3.11) and applying Cauchy's integral formula for the derivatives of an analytic function, we have

$$g_s(\theta, \alpha) = \frac{1}{s!}\left[\frac{d^s g(\theta, \alpha, w)}{dw^s}\right]_{w=0} = \frac{1}{2\pi i}\int_{\mathscr{W}} \frac{g(\theta, \alpha, w)}{w^{s+1}}\, dw,$$

where $\mathscr{W}$ is any simple closed contour that encloses the origin and lies within $\mathbf{W}$ (Fig. 2). Let us also require $\mathscr{W}$ to enclose the point $-ic(\theta)$. Then we may substitute in the last integral by means of (3.15) to obtain

$$g_s(\theta, \alpha) = \frac{e^{i\alpha(\pi-\theta)}}{2\pi i}\int_{\mathscr{T}} \frac{1}{w^{s+1}} \frac{\tau^{\alpha-1}}{1+\tau e^{-i\theta}}\, d\tau + \frac{1}{2\pi i}\int_{\mathscr{W}} \frac{dw}{w^{s+1}\{w+ic(\theta)\}}, \tag{4.1}$$

where $\mathscr{T}$ is the map of $\mathscr{W}$ in the τ-plane.

By hypothesis, $\theta \in [\delta, 2\pi-\delta]$. In consequence, we can construct a simple closed contour that (i) lies in the domain $\mathbf{\Delta}$ (Fig. 1); (ii) is independent of θ; (iii) has the arc $\tau = e^{i(\theta-\pi)}$, $\delta \leqq \theta \leqq 2\pi - \delta$, in its interior. We take $\mathscr{T}$ to be this contour and $\mathscr{W}$ its w-map. Let (i) $2\pi l_1$ and $2\pi l_2$ denote the lengths of $\mathscr{T}$ and $\mathscr{W}$, respectively; (ii) M be the maximum value of $|\tau^{\alpha-1}/(1+\tau e^{-i\theta})|$ when $\tau \in \mathscr{T}$, $\theta \in [\delta, 2\pi-\delta]$ and α ranges over its (bounded) set of values; (iii) d be the minimum value of $|w+ic(\theta)|$ when $w \in \mathscr{W}$ and $\theta \in [\delta, 2\pi-\delta]$. Clearly, l_1, l_2, M are finite, and $d>0$. Since $c(\pi)=0$, it is also clear that $|w| \geqq d$ when $w \in \mathscr{W}$. Majorizing the two integrals on the right-hand side of (4.1) by use of these bounds, we find that

$$|g_s(\theta, \alpha)| \leqq \frac{l_1 M e^{(\pi-\delta)|\text{Im}\,\alpha|}}{d^{s+1}} + \frac{l_2}{d^{s+2}} \leqq \frac{A}{d^s}, \tag{4.2}$$

where A is assignable independently of θ and α.

4.3. Bounding the error term. Let m be an arbitrary nonnegative integer, and define $\phi_{2m}(\theta, \alpha, w)$ by the equation

$$g(\theta, \alpha, w) = \sum_{s=0}^{2m-1} g_s(\theta, \alpha) w^s + w^{2m}\phi_{2m}(\theta, \alpha, w); \tag{4.3}$$

compare (3.11). Correspondingly, in (3.14) we have

$$F_{n+p}(z) = (-)^n i e^{-p\pi i}\left[\frac{1}{2}\,\text{erfc}\left\{c(\theta)\sqrt{\frac{1}{2}\rho}\right\} - i\frac{\exp(-\frac{1}{2}\rho\{c(\theta)\}^2)}{(2\pi\rho)^{1/2}} \cdot \left\{\sum_{s=0}^{m-1}\left(\frac{1}{2}\right)_s g_{2s}(\theta, \alpha)\left(\frac{2}{\rho}\right)^s + \Phi_m(\theta, \alpha, \rho)\right\}\right], \tag{4.4}$$

where

$$\Phi_m(\theta, \alpha, \rho) = \sqrt{\frac{\rho}{2\pi}} \int_{-\infty}^{\infty} \exp\left(-\frac{1}{2}\rho w^2\right) w^{2m} \phi_{2m}(\theta, \alpha, w)\, dw. \tag{4.5}$$

Suppose first that $-d/2 \leqq w \leqq d/2$, where d is defined in § 4.2. Then using (4.2) we see that

$$|\phi_{2m}(\theta, \alpha, w)| = \left| \sum_{s=2m}^{\infty} g_s(\theta, \alpha) w^{s-2m} \right| \leqq \frac{2A}{d^{2m}}.$$

Hence

$$\begin{aligned} &\left| \int_{-d/2}^{d/2} \exp\left(-\frac{1}{2}\rho w^2\right) w^{2m} \phi_{2m}(\theta, \alpha, w)\, dw \right| \\ &\qquad < \frac{2A}{d^{2m}} \int_{-\infty}^{\infty} \exp\left(-\frac{1}{2}\rho w^2\right) w^{2m}\, dw = O\left(\frac{1}{\rho^{m+1/2}}\right). \end{aligned} \tag{4.6}$$

Second, suppose that $d/2 \leqq w < \infty$. From (3.1) we see that as $w \to +\infty$ we have $\tau \sim w^2/2$ and $d\tau/dw \sim w$. Hence

$$\frac{\tau^{\alpha-1}}{1+\tau e^{-i\theta}} \frac{d\tau}{dw} \sim 2^{2-\alpha} e^{i\theta} w^{2\alpha-3} \quad \text{uniformly as } w \to +\infty.$$

We now refer to (3.15) and bear in mind that $|1+\tau e^{-i\theta}|$ and $|w+ic(\theta)|$ each have positive lower bounds when $w \in [d/2, \infty)$ and $\theta \in [\delta, 2\pi-\delta]$; compare Figs. 1, 2, and 4. In this way we may verify that

$$|g(\theta, \alpha, w)| \leqq A w^a, \qquad \tfrac{1}{2}d \leqq w < \infty,$$

where

$$a = \max_{\forall \alpha} (2 \operatorname{Re} \alpha - 3, -1), \tag{4.7}$$

and we are now using the symbol A generically to denote a finite constant that is independent of θ and α. Substituting into (4.3) by means of this result and (4.2), we conclude that when $m \geqq a/2$ we have

$$|\phi_{2m}(\theta, \alpha, w)| \leqq A, \qquad \tfrac{1}{2}d \leqq w < \infty.$$

Hence

$$\begin{aligned} &\left| \int_{d/2}^{\infty} \exp\left(-\frac{1}{2}\rho w^2\right) w^{2m} \phi_{2m}(\theta, \alpha, w)\, dw \right| \\ &\qquad \leqq A \int_{0}^{\infty} \exp\left(-\frac{1}{2}\rho w^2\right) w^{2m}\, dw = O\left(\frac{1}{\rho^{m+1/2}}\right). \end{aligned} \tag{4.8}$$

Lastly, suppose that $-\infty < w \leqq -d/2$. From (3.1) we see that if $w \to -\infty$, then $\tau \sim \exp(-w^2/2-1)$ and $d\tau/dw \sim -w\tau$. Hence

$$\frac{\tau^{\alpha-1}}{1+\tau e^{-i\theta}} \frac{d\tau}{dw} \sim -w\tau^{\alpha} \sim -w \exp\left\{-\alpha\left(\frac{1}{2}w^2+1\right)\right\},$$

uniformly, and therefore from (3.15) we have

$$|g(\theta, \alpha, w)| \leqq A|w|\, e^{bw^2}, \qquad -\infty < w \leqq -\tfrac{1}{2}d,$$

where

$$b = \max_{\forall \alpha} (-\tfrac{1}{2} \operatorname{Re} \alpha, 0); \tag{4.9}$$

compare (4.7). Substituting in (4.3) by means of this result and (4.2), we conclude that when $m \geqq 1$ we have

$$|\phi_{2m}(\theta, \alpha, w)| \leqq A\, e^{bw^2}, \qquad -\infty < w \leqq -\tfrac{1}{2} d.$$

Hence if, also, $\rho > 2b$ we have

$$\begin{aligned} &\left| \int_{-\infty}^{-d/2} \exp\left(-\frac{1}{2}\rho w^2\right) w^{2m} \phi_{2m}(\theta, \alpha, w)\, dw \right| \\ &\qquad \leqq A \int_{-\infty}^{0} \exp\left\{-\left(\frac{1}{2}\rho - b\right) w^2\right\} w^{2m}\, dw = O\left(\frac{1}{\rho^{m+1/2}}\right). \end{aligned} \tag{4.10}$$

On combining (4.5), (4.6), (4.8), and (4.10), we conclude that the error term in the expansion (4.4) satisfies

$$\Phi_m(\theta, \alpha, \rho) = O(\rho^{-m}), \qquad \rho \to \infty, \tag{4.11}$$

uniformly with respect to $\theta \in [\delta, 2\pi - \delta]$ and bounded values of $|\alpha|$. This is the desired result.

4.4. Remark. The significance of the results established in this section apropos the Stokes phenomenon is as follows. From Fig. 4 it is seen that $\xi \equiv c(\theta)\sqrt{\rho/2}$ lies in the sector $-\pi/4 \leqq \text{ph}\, \xi \leqq 0$ when $-\pi \leqq \theta \leqq \pi$, and in the sector $0 \leqq \text{ph}\,(-\xi) \leqq \pi/4$ when $\pi \leqq \theta \leqq 3\pi$. It is well known that $\text{erfc}\,(\xi) = O(e^{-\xi^2})$ uniformly throughout the first sector, and $\text{erfc}\,(\xi) = 2 + O(e^{-\xi^2})$ uniformly throughout the second sector (see, for example, [9, Chaps. 2-4]). In consequence, if ρ is large and fixed and θ increases continuously from values just below π to values just above π, then $\frac{1}{2}\text{erfc}\,\{c(\theta)\sqrt{\rho/2}\}$ changes rapidly, but smoothly, from being exponentially small to being exponentially close to 1. From (4.2) and (4.11) it is easily seen that the same conclusion also applies to the whole content of the square brackets in (4.4). On substituting into (2.8) by means of this result we perceive that if $|z|$ is large and the asymptotic expansion (2.5) is truncated at its optimum number of terms, then there is a rapid, *but smooth*, transition to the form (2.6) in the neighborhood of $\text{ph}\, z = \pi$. Berry described the Stokes phenomenon in this illuminating manner in [1], but his analysis was purely formal. The present investigation serves to place Berry's conclusions on a rigorous basis—in the case of the generalized exponential integral. For further details concerning this aspect see [10].

5. Main results and conclusions.

5.1. Comparison of the expansions of §§ 2 and 4; formulae for the coefficients $g_{2s}(\theta, \alpha)$. Let us summarize the results obtained so far. Setting $z = \rho\, e^{i\theta}$, $n = \rho - p + \alpha$ and defining $F_{n+p}(z)$ by (2.8), we proved in § 2 that

$$F_{n+p}(z) \sim \frac{e^{-i(\rho+\alpha)\theta}}{1+e^{-i\theta}} \frac{e^{-\rho-z}}{(2\pi\rho)^{1/2}} \sum_{s=0}^{\infty} \frac{a_{2s}(\theta, \alpha)}{\rho^s}, \qquad \rho \to \infty, \tag{5.1}$$

uniformly with respect to bounded $|\alpha|$ and $\theta \in [-\pi + \delta, \pi - \delta]$, δ being an arbitrary positive constant. In §§ 3 and 4, we proved that

$$\begin{aligned} F_{n+p}(z) \sim (-)^n i\, e^{-p\pi i} \Bigg[&\frac{1}{2} \text{erfc} \left\{ c(\theta) \sqrt{\frac{1}{2}\rho} \right\} \\ &- i \frac{\exp(-\frac{1}{2}\rho\{c(\theta)\}^2)}{(2\pi\rho)^{1/2}} \sum_{s=0}^{\infty} \left(\frac{1}{2}\right)_s g_{2s}(\theta, \alpha) \left(\frac{2}{\rho}\right)^s \Bigg] \end{aligned} \tag{5.2}$$

as $\rho \to \infty$, uniformly with respect to bounded $|\alpha|$ and $\theta \in [\delta, 2\pi - \delta]$; here $c(\theta)$ is defined as in § 3.2.

Now consider the common sector of validity, given by $\delta \leqq \theta \leqq \pi - \delta$. From Fig. 4 we see that $c(\theta)$ lies in the fourth quadrant of $\mathbb{C}$ and is bounded away from the origin. We may therefore replace $\frac{1}{2}$ erfc $\{c(\theta)\sqrt{\rho/2}\}$ by an asymptotic expansion in descending powers of $c(\theta)\sqrt{\rho/2}$ that is appropriate for this region. This is given by[6]

$$\frac{1}{2}\operatorname{erfc}\left\{c(\theta)\sqrt{\frac{1}{2}\rho}\right\} \sim \frac{\exp(-\frac{1}{2}\rho\{c(\theta)\}^2)}{c(\theta)(2\pi\rho)^{1/2}} \sum_{s=0}^{\infty} (-)^s \frac{(\frac{1}{2})_s}{\{c(\theta)\}^{2s}} \left(\frac{2}{\rho}\right)^s, \tag{5.3}$$

this result being uniformly valid with respect to θ in an interval that includes $[\delta, \pi - \delta]$. Substitution into (5.2) yields

$$\begin{aligned} F_{n+p}(z) \sim (-)^n i\, e^{-p\pi i} \frac{\exp(-\frac{1}{2}\rho\{c(\theta)\}^2)}{(2\pi\rho)^{1/2}} \\ \cdot \left\{ \sum_{s=0}^{\infty} (-)^s \frac{(\frac{1}{2})_s}{\{c(\theta)\}^{2s+1}} \left(\frac{2}{\rho}\right)^s - i \sum_{s=0}^{\infty} \left(\frac{1}{2}\right)_s g_{2s}(\theta, \alpha) \left(\frac{2}{\rho}\right)^s \right\}. \end{aligned} \tag{5.4}$$

We also observe from (2.12) and (3.3) that (5.1) may be recast in the form

$$F_{n+p}(z) \sim (-)^n e^{-p\pi i} \frac{e^{i\alpha(\pi-\theta)}}{1+e^{-i\theta}} \frac{\exp(-\frac{1}{2}\rho\{c(\theta)\}^2)}{(2\pi\rho)^{1/2}} \sum_{s=0}^{\infty} \frac{a_{2s}(\theta, \alpha)}{\rho^s}. \tag{5.5}$$

We now have two uniform asymptotic expansions of the same function in descending powers of ρ. They must therefore be identical. Equating coefficients, we conclude that

$$g_{2s}(\theta, \alpha) = \frac{e^{i\alpha(\pi-\theta)}}{1+e^{-i\theta}} \frac{a_{2s}(\theta, \alpha)}{1 \cdot 3 \cdots (2s-1)} + \frac{(-)^{s-1} i}{\{c(\theta)\}^{2s+1}}, \qquad s = 0, 1, 2, \cdots. \tag{5.6}$$

Analytic continuation extends this formula to all values of θ, other than odd multiples of π; furthermore, at $\theta = \pi$ we may replace the right-hand side by its limiting value.

With the aid of the formula $a_0(\theta, \alpha) = 1$ given at the end of § 2.3, we immediately perceive that (5.6) agrees with (3.16) in the case $s = 0$. For other values of s, formula (5.6) provides a convenient way of evaluating $g_{2s}(\theta, \alpha)$.

5.2. Extending the sector of validity. In expanding the error function that appears in (5.2) in the form (5.3), we considered only values of θ in the interval $[\delta, \pi - \delta]$. However, from Figs. 3 and 4 it is clear that (5.3) continues to be uniformly valid in an interval that includes $[-\pi + \delta, \pi - \delta]$. Since this again leads to an expansion, namely (5.5), that is known to be valid in this larger interval, it follows that (5.2) itself must be uniformly valid in this interval.

By symmetry, we also expect (5.2) to be valid in the interval $[\pi + \delta, 3\pi - \delta]$. And this can be verified by expanding the complementary error function in (5.2) in a form appropriate for this sector, and comparing the result with the expansion

$$F_{n+p}(z) \sim (-)^n i\, e^{-p\pi i} + \frac{e^{-i(\rho+\alpha)\theta}}{1+e^{-i\theta}} \frac{e^{-\rho-z}}{(2\pi\rho)^{1/2}} \sum_{s=0}^{\infty} \frac{a_{2s}(\theta, \alpha)}{\rho^s}, \qquad \pi + \delta \leqq \theta \leqq 3\pi - \delta, \tag{5.7}$$

obtained from (2.11), with $k = 1$, and (5.1).[7]

5.3. Main theorem. Another expansion for $F_{n+p}(z)$ can be obtained from (5.2) by replacing p and z by their complex conjugates, and then taking the conjugate of the whole result. On combining all the expansions obtained so far we arrive at the following theorem.

[6] See, for example, [9, pp. 67, 112].

[7] In deriving (5.7), we also need to use (2.12) and the fact that $a_{2s}(\theta, \alpha)$ is periodic in θ, with period 2π.

THEOREM 1. *Let*

$$z=\rho e^{i\theta}, \qquad n=\rho-p+\alpha, \tag{5.8}$$

and define $c(\theta)$ *by* (3.3), (3.4), *and* $g_{2s}(\theta,\alpha)$ *by* (5.6), (2.15), (2.16). *Then*

$$E_p(z)=\frac{e^{-z}}{z}\sum_{s=0}^{n-1}(-)^s\frac{(p)_s}{z^s}+(-)^n\frac{2\pi}{\Gamma(p)}z^{p-1}F_{n+p}(z), \tag{5.9}$$

where for fixed p and large $|z|$

$$F_{n+p}(z)\sim(-)^n i\,e^{-p\pi i}\left[\frac{1}{2}\operatorname{erfc}\left\{c(\theta)\sqrt{\frac{1}{2}\rho}\right\}\right.\\ \left.-i\frac{\exp(-\frac{1}{2}\rho\{c(\theta)\}^2)}{(2\pi\rho)^{1/2}}\sum_{s=0}^{\infty}\left(\frac{1}{2}\right)_s g_{2s}(\theta,\alpha)\left(\frac{2}{\rho}\right)^s\right], \tag{5.10}$$

valid when $-\pi+\delta\leqq\theta\leqq3\pi-\delta$, *and*

$$F_{n+p}(z)\sim(-)^{n-1}i\,e^{p\pi i}\left[\frac{1}{2}\operatorname{erfc}\left\{\overline{c(-\theta)}\sqrt{\frac{1}{2}\rho}\right\}\right.\\ \left.+i\frac{\exp(-\frac{1}{2}\rho\{\overline{c(-\theta)}\}^2)}{(2\pi\rho)^{1/2}}\sum_{s=0}^{\infty}\left(\frac{1}{2}\right)_s\overline{g_{2s}(-\theta,\bar\alpha)}\left(\frac{2}{\rho}\right)^s\right], \tag{5.11}$$

valid when $-3\pi+\delta\leqq\theta\leqq\pi-\delta$. *These expansions are uniform with respect to* θ *and bounded values of* $|\alpha|$; *furthermore, the* θ*-intervals of validity are maximal.*

The only part of this theorem we have not established already is the maximality of the θ-intervals of validity. However, this is an immediate consequence of the fact that the coefficients $g_{2s}(\theta,\alpha)$ become infinite as $\theta\to-\pi$ or $\theta\to3\pi$; compare (5.6) and (2.15).

5.4. Remarks. (i) If we truncate the infinite series in (5.10) at the term $s=m-1$, where m is an arbitrary fixed nonnegative integer, then the error in the resulting approximation to $F_{n+p}(z)$ is $\exp[-\frac{1}{2}\rho\{c(\theta)\}^2]z^{-m-1/2}O(1)$, that is, $e^{-z-|z|}z^{-m-1/2}O(1)$; compare (3.3) (again). On referring to the expansions (2.5) and (2.6) we see that the combination of (5.9) and (5.10) is a uniform, $e^{-|z|}$-improved, expansion (in the sense of § 1) throughout the region of validity of (5.10). Similarly, the combination of (5.9) and (5.11) is a uniform, $e^{-|z|}$-improved, expansion throughout the region of validity of (5.11).

(ii) In applications, the use of (5.10) and (5.11) can be confined to the sectors $0\leqq\operatorname{ph}z\leqq\pi$ and $-\pi\leqq\operatorname{ph}z\leqq0$, respectively, and the continuation formula (2.11) (or equivalently (2.4)) used elsewhere. Indeed, this procedure is consistent with maximum accuracy; compare the observations made in [9, Chap. 14, § 1]. However, there are two reasons we sought the maximal regions of validity of these expansions. First, these extensions show that, for example, the combination of (5.9) and (5.10) includes both (2.5) and (2.6) within most of their regions of validity. Second, the extensions complete the proof of results stated in [10, § 3] in connection with Berry's interpretation of the Stokes phenomenon.

(iii) The expansions (5.10) and (5.11) have the common interval of validity $|\operatorname{ph}z|\leqq\pi-\delta$. The two expansions are not the same here, but their discrepancy is absorbable in the implied error terms. Thus there is also a Stokes phenomenon associated with these expansions in the neighborhood of $\operatorname{ph}z=0$, and it would appear to be possible to extend the whole process to construct UEI expansions of the UEI expansions.[8]

[8] For further comments on this possibility see [3, § 4].

(iv) The most serious deficiency in the present results is a set of realistic error bounds for the expansions (5.10) and (5.11). Unfortunately, at this time this remains a general drawback to asymptotic expansions obtained from integral representations with coalescing critical points.

Acknowledgements. The author is pleased to acknowledge helpful suggestions by the referees.

REFERENCES

[1] M. V. BERRY, *Uniform asymptotic smoothing of Stokes's discontinuities*, Proc. Roy. Soc. London Ser. A, 422 (1989), pp. 7-21.
[2] N. BLEISTEIN, *Uniform asymptotic expansions of integrals with stationary point near algebraic singularity*. Comm. Pure Appl. Math., 19 (1966), pp. 353-370.
[3] W. G. C. BOYD, *Stieltjes transforms and the Stokes phenomenon*, Proc. Roy. Soc. London Ser. A, 429 (1990), pp. 227-246.
[4] R. B. DINGLE, *Asymptotic expansions and converging factors* I. *General theory and basic converging factors*, Proc. Roy. Soc. London Ser. A, 244 (1958), pp. 456-475.
[5] D. S. JONES, *Asymptotic behavior of integrals*, SIAM Rev., 14 (1972), pp. 286-317.
[6] ———, *Uniform asymptotic remainders*, in Asymptotic and Computational Analysis, R. Wong, ed., Marcel Dekker, New York, 1990, pp. 241-264.
[7] G. F. MILLER, *Tables of Generalized Exponential Integrals*, N. P. L. Mathematical Tables, Vol. 3, H.M. Stationery Office, London, 1960.
[8] National Bureau of Standards, *Handbook of Mathematical Functions*, Applied Mathematical Series No. 55, M. Abramowitz and I. A. Stegun, eds., U.S. Government Printing Office, Washington, DC, 1964.
[9] F. W. J. OLVER, *Asymptotics and Special Functions*, Academic, Press, New York, 1974.
[10] ———, *On Stokes' phenomenon and converging factors*, in Asymptotic and Computational Analysis, R. Wong, ed., Marcel Dekker, New York, 1990, pp. 329-355.
[11] F. URSELL, *Integrals with a large parameter. A strong form of Watson's lemma*, in Elasticity: Mathematical Methods and Applications, R. W. Ogden and G. Eason, eds., Ellis Horwood,Chichester, 1990, pp. 391-395.
[12] B. L. VAN DER WAERDEN, *On the method of saddle points*, Appl. Sci. Res. Ser. B, 2 (1951), pp. 33-45.

SIAM J. MATH. ANAL.
Vol. 22, No. 5, pp. 1475-1489, September 1991

UNIFORM, EXPONENTIALLY IMPROVED, ASYMPTOTIC EXPANSIONS FOR THE CONFLUENT HYPERGEOMETRIC FUNCTION AND OTHER INTEGRAL TRANSFORMS*

F. W. J. OLVER†

Abstract. A new generalized asymptotic expansion is constructed for the confluent hypergeometric function $U(a, a-b+1, z)$ in which the parameters a and b are real or complex constants, and z is a large complex variable. The expansion is expressed in terms of generalized exponential integrals (or, equivalently, incomplete Gamma functions). It has a larger region of validity and greater accuracy than the conventional expansions of Poincaré type; moreover, it provides insight into the manner in which the Poincaré expansions change smoothly, albeit rapidly, from one to the other in the vicinity of the so-called Stokes lines. The expansion is accompanied by strict error bounds in the most important part of its region of validity.

The method used is quite general and can be applied to other functions that are representable as transforms of Laplace or Stieltjes type.

Key words. coalescing critical points, error bounds, generalized exponential integral, incomplete Gamma function, Laplace transform, Stieltjes transform, Stokes' phenomenon

AMS(MOS) subject classifications. primary 41A60; secondary 33A30

1. Introduction and summary. In the preceding paper [10] we investigated the generalized exponential integral $E_p(z)$, in which p and z are unrestricted real or complex variables. We began with the identity

$$E_p(z)=\frac{e^{-z}}{z}\sum_{s=0}^{n-1}(-)^s\frac{(p)_s}{z^s}+(-)^n\frac{2\pi}{\Gamma(p)}z^{p-1}F_{n+p}(z), \tag{1.1}$$

in which n is an arbitrary nonnegative integer, $(p)_s$ denotes the ascending factorial $p(p+1)\cdots(p+s-1)$, and

$$F_p(z)=\frac{\Gamma(p)}{2\pi}\frac{E_p(z)}{z^{p-1}}. \tag{1.2}$$

Writing z in polar form $z=\rho e^{i\theta}$, we were able to prove that if $\rho\to\infty$, with p fixed, then

$$\begin{aligned}F_{n+p}(z)\sim(-)^n i\,e^{-p\pi i}\Bigg[&\frac{1}{2}\operatorname{erfc}\left\{c(\theta)\sqrt{\frac{1}{2}\rho}\right\}\\&-i\frac{\exp(-\frac{1}{2}\rho\{c(\theta)\}^2)}{(2\pi\rho)^{1/2}}\sum_{s=0}^{\infty}\left(\frac{1}{2}\right)_s g_{2s}(\theta,\alpha)\left(\frac{2}{\rho}\right)^s\Bigg],\end{aligned} \tag{1.3}$$

uniformly with respect to $\theta\in[-\pi+\delta, 3\pi-\delta]$ and bounded values of $|\alpha|$, where $\alpha=n-\rho+p$. Here (and elsewhere) δ denotes an arbitrarily small positive constant; furthermore,

$$c(\theta)=\sqrt{2\{e^{i\theta}+i(\theta-\pi)+1\}},$$

with an appropriate choice of branch of the square root, and the coefficients $g_{2s}(\theta,\alpha)$ are continuous functions of θ and α. We also supplied a similar expansion for $F_{n+p}(z)$ when $\theta\in[-3\pi+\delta, \pi-\delta]$.

The importance of the expansion (1.3) is threefold.

---

* Received by the editors February 9, 1990; accepted for publication September 19, 1990.

† Institute for Physical Science and Technology, University of Maryland, College Park, Maryland 20742.
This research was supported by the National Science Foundation under grant DMS 87-23039.

First, the combination of (1.1) and (1.3) unifies the Poincaré-type expansion

$$E_p(z) \sim \frac{e^{-z}}{z} \sum_{s=0}^{\infty} (-)^s \frac{(p)_s}{z^s}, \qquad \theta \in \left[-\frac{3}{2}\pi + \delta, \frac{3}{2}\pi - \delta\right], \tag{1.4}$$

and the compound expansion

$$E_p(z) \sim \frac{2\pi i\, e^{-p\pi i}}{\Gamma(p)} z^{p-1} + \frac{e^{-z}}{z} \sum_{s=0}^{\infty} (-)^s \frac{(p)_s}{z^s}, \qquad \theta \in \left[\frac{1}{2}\pi + \delta, \frac{7}{2}\pi - \delta\right], \tag{1.5}$$

since these expansions can be derived from (1.1) and (1.3) by appropriate re-expansion in the common regions of validity.

Second, as a consequence of this unification, the combination of (1.1) and (1.3) accurately quantifies the Stokes phenomenon, that is, the rapid but smooth change in form from (1.4) to (1.5) as θ passes through the common interval of validity $[\pi/2+\delta, \frac{3}{2}\pi - \delta]$.

Third, in much of its region of validity the combination of (1.1) and (1.3) is more accurate than either (1.4) or (1.5), owing to the fact that it contains an extra factor $e^{-|z|}$ in its uniform error estimates. For this reason, we called the combination of (1.1) and (1.3) a *uniform, exponentially improved* (UEI), *asymptotic expansion.*

The purpose of the present paper is to furnish a general method for constructing generalized asymptotic expansions that enjoy similar properties, especially uniform exponential improvement. The functions we shall consider are representable as Laplace or Stieltjes transforms. We illustrate the method by detailed treatment of the confluent hypergeometric function defined by

$$U(a, a-b+1, z) = \frac{1}{\Gamma(a)} \int_0^{\infty} e^{-zt} t^{a-1} (1+t)^{-b}\, dt, \tag{1.6}$$

when Re $a>0$ and $|\text{ph } z| < \pi/2$, and by analytic continuation elsewhere. Special cases of this function include Bessel and modified Bessel functions, parabolic cylinder functions, and Airy functions. However, our method applies to a broader class of functions than those of confluent hypergeometric type.

Instead of expressing the generalized asymptotic expansions in terms of the complementary error function, as was done for the function $E_p(z)$, we find it more convenient, and elegant, to express these expansions in terms of the F_p functions. Our main result is as follows:

THEOREM 1. *Define* $R_n(a, b, z)$ *by*

$$U(a, a-b+1, z) = z^{-a} \sum_{s=0}^{n-1} (-)^s \frac{(a)_s (b)_s}{s!\, z^s} + R_n(a, b, z), \tag{1.7}$$

where

$$n = |z| - a - b + 1 + \alpha, \tag{1.8}$$

$|z|$ *being large, a and b being fixed real or complex parameters, and* $|\alpha|$ *being bounded. Then*

$$\begin{aligned} R_n(a, b, z) = (-)^n 2\pi \frac{z^{b-1} e^z}{\Gamma(a)\Gamma(b)} \Bigg\{ &\sum_{s=0}^{m-1} (-)^s \frac{(1-a)_s (1-b)_s}{s!} \frac{F_{n-s+a+b-1}(z)}{z^s} \\ &+ (1-a)_m (1-b)_m R_{m,n}(a, b, z) \Bigg\}, \end{aligned} \tag{1.9}$$

where m is an arbitrary fixed integer, and

$$R_{m,n}(a, b, z) = O(e^{-z-|z|} z^{-m}), \qquad |\text{ph } z| \leq \pi, \tag{1.10}$$

$$R_{m,n}(a, b, z) = O(z^{-m}), \qquad \pi \leq |\text{ph } z| \leq \tfrac{5}{2}\pi - \delta. \tag{1.11}$$

Furthermore, these sectors of validity are maximal.

Theorem 1 is proved in the next four sections. In § 6 we derive a strict and realistic bound for $R_{m,n}(a, b, z)$ in the sector $|\text{ph } z| \leqq \pi$. Some general conclusions are drawn in § 7.

To conclude this Introduction we make the following observations:

(i) From (1.10) and (1.11) it is seen that the combination of (1.7) and (1.9) furnishes a uniform exponentially improved expansion in a sector that includes $|\text{ph } z| \leqq \pi$. For other phase ranges improved expansions can be constructed immediately by combining (1.7) and (1.9) with the connection formulae [4, p. 27]

$$\begin{aligned} e^{k(a-b)\pi i} U(a, a-b+1, z\,e^{2k\pi i}) &\\ = \pm \frac{e^{\mp(a+b)\pi i} \sin k(a-b)\pi - \sin(k \mp 1)(a-b)\pi}{\sin(a-b)\pi} U(a, a-b+1, z) &\\ + \frac{2\pi i \sin k(a-b)\pi}{\sin(a-b)\pi} \frac{e^{\mp b\pi i}}{\Gamma(a)\Gamma(b)} e^z U(1-b, a-b+1, z\,e^{\pm\pi i}), & \end{aligned} \tag{1.12}$$

in which k is an arbitrary integer and either upper signs, or lower signs, are taken throughout.

(ii) The well-known Poincaré-type expansion

$$U(a, a-b+1, z) \sim z^{-a} \sum_{s=0}^{\infty} (-)^s \frac{(a)_s(b)_s}{s!\,z^s}, \qquad |\text{ph } z| \leqq \tfrac{3}{2}\pi - \delta, \tag{1.13}$$

and the two compound expansions

$$\begin{aligned} U(a, a-b+1, z) \sim z^{-a} \sum_{s=0}^{\infty} (-)^s \frac{(a)_s(b)_s}{s!\,z^s} &\\ \mp 2\pi i \frac{e^{\mp(a+b)\pi i}}{\Gamma(a)\Gamma(b)} z^{b-1} e^z \sum_{s=0}^{\infty} \frac{(1-a)_s(1-b)_s}{s!\,z^s}, &\\ |\text{ph}\{z \exp(\mp\tfrac{3}{2}\pi i)\}| \leqq \pi - \delta, & \end{aligned} \tag{1.14}$$

obtained by substitution of (1.13) into (1.12), with $k = \pm 1$, can be recovered from (1.7) and (1.9) by appropriate re-expansion.

(iii) Owing to the presence of the factors $(1-a)_m$ and $(1-b)_m$ in (1.9), $R_n(a, b, z)$ can be expressed exactly as a finite combination of F_p functions when a or b is a positive integer, by taking m to be sufficiently large. Furthermore, the estimates (1.10) and (1.11) enjoy certain uniformity properties with respect to the parameters a and b. In the case of the sector $|\text{ph } z| \leqq \pi$ the last statement is verifiable by inspection of the error bound for $R_{m,n}(a, b, z)$ that is supplied in § 6 below.

(iv) The original purpose of the present paper was to supply proofs of results that were stated in [9, § 4]. In turn, the main purpose of [9] was to provide a rigorous basis for the formal researches of Berry on Stokes' phenomenon [2]. These objectives are achieved, but we go well beyond them, especially with respect to regions of validity and exponential improvement.

(v) A formal expansion of $R_n(a, b, z)$ in terms of the function $z^{n+b} e^z F_{n+b}(z)$ and its derivatives was found by Dingle [5]. This expansion is not equivalent to (1.9) and Dingle was concerned only with the sector $|\text{ph } z| < \pi$. Whether his expansion is valid in a larger sector has not been investigated, but perhaps this question is moot since our new expansion is of a simpler and more revealing form.

(vi) For work on the modified Bessel function $K_\nu(z)$ that is closely related to [9, § 4] and the present paper, see [3] and [6].

2. Representation of the remainder term as a Stieltjes transform. If, in (1.6), we rotate the path of integration through an angle $-\gamma$, γ being an arbitrary number in the interval $(-\pi, \pi)$, then we obtain the analytic continuation of $U(a, a-b+1, z)$ in the sector $|\text{ph}\,(z e^{-i\gamma})| < \pi/2$, given by

$$U(a, a-b+1, z) = \frac{1}{\Gamma(a)} \int_0^{\infty e^{-i\gamma}} e^{-zt} t^{a-1} (1+t)^{-b}\, dt. \tag{2.1}$$

We now expand the factor $(1+t)^{-b}$ by Taylor's theorem, in the form

$$(1+t)^{-b} = \sum_{s=0}^{n-1} (-)^s \frac{(b)_s}{s!} t^s + \chi_n(b, t), \tag{2.2}$$

where n is an arbitrary nonnegative integer,

$$\chi_n(b, t) = \frac{t^n}{2\pi i} \int_{\mathscr{L}} \frac{(1+w)^{-b}}{w^n (w-t)}\, dw, \tag{2.3}$$

and $\mathscr{L}$ is a simple closed contour that encloses $w = 0$ and $w = t$, but not $w = -1$ (see, for example, [1, Chap. 4, § 3.1]). On substituting into (2.1) by means of (2.2) we obtain (1.7) with the following representation of the remainder term:

$$R_n(a, b, z) = \frac{1}{\Gamma(a)} \int_0^{\infty e^{-i\gamma}} e^{-zt} t^{a-1} \chi_n(b, t)\, dt. \tag{2.4}$$

Now suppose that $\text{Re}\, b + n > 0$. Then the integral of $(1+w)^{-b} w^{-n} (w-t)^{-1}$ around any large circle in the w-plane vanishes as the radius of the circle tends to infinity. Accordingly, the contour $\mathscr{L}$ in (2.3) may be deformed into the loop contour depicted in Fig. 1, giving

$$\chi_n(b, t) = \frac{t^n}{2\pi i} \int_{-\infty}^{(-1-)} \frac{(1+w)^{-b}}{w^n (w-t)}\, dw.$$

If, also, $\text{Re}\, b < 1$, then the loop may be collapsed on to the interval $(-\infty, -1]$ in the usual way. Subsequent replacement of w by $-w$ yields

$$\chi_n(b, t) = (-)^n \frac{\sin(\pi b)}{\pi} t^n \int_1^{\infty} \frac{(w-1)^{-b}}{w^n (w+t)}\, dw, \tag{2.5}$$

where $(w-1)^{-b}$ has its principal value.

We now substitute in (2.4) by means of (2.5), to obtain

$$R_n(a, b, z) = (-)^n \frac{\sin(\pi b)}{\pi \Gamma(a)} \int_0^{\infty e^{-i\gamma}} e^{-zt} t^{n+a-1}\, dt \int_1^{\infty} \frac{(w-1)^{-b}}{w^n (w+t)}\, dw, \tag{2.6}$$

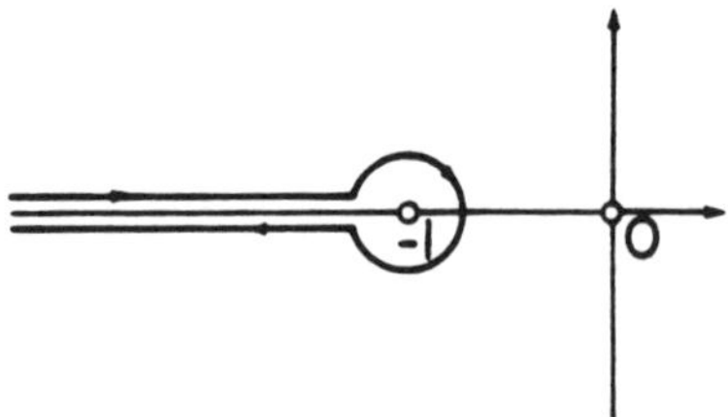

FIG. 1. *w-plane.*

where the fractional powers continue to assume their principal values. The assumptions made so far are given by $0<\operatorname{Re} a$, $-n<\operatorname{Re} b<1$, $|\operatorname{ph}(z e^{-i\gamma})|<\pi/2$. However, by analytic continuation with respect to a, we see that (2.4) and (2.6) remain valid when the first condition is relaxed to $-n<\operatorname{Re} a$. By absolute convergence of the repeated integrals we may interchange the order of integration (see, for example, [7, Thm. 1]). Then by replacing t by $w\tau$, we arrive at

$$R_n(a, b, z)=\frac{(-)^n \sin(\pi b)}{\pi\Gamma(a)}\int_1^\infty (w-1)^{-b} w^{a-1}\,dw \int_0^{\infty e^{-i\gamma}} \frac{e^{-zw\tau}\tau^{n+a-1}}{1+\tau}\,d\tau.$$

Provided that $\operatorname{Re} a<\operatorname{Re} b$ the order of integration may again be reversed, and on replacing w by $1+v$, we obtain the desired integral representation for the remainder term, given by

$$R_n(a, b, z)=(-)^n \frac{\sin(\pi b)}{\pi\Gamma(a)}\int_0^{\infty e^{-i\gamma}} \frac{e^{-z\tau}\tau^{n+a-1}}{1+\tau}\,d\tau \int_0^\infty e^{-z\tau v} v^{-b}(1+v)^{a-1}\,dv, \tag{2.7}$$

valid with the conditions

$$-n<\operatorname{Re} a<\operatorname{Re} b<1, \qquad |\operatorname{ph}(z e^{-i\gamma})|<\tfrac{1}{2}\pi. \tag{2.8}$$

Remark. A key step in the foregoing analysis is the use of Cauchy's integral formula for the remainder term in a Taylor-series expansion. Since the objective is to represent the remainder term $R_n(a, b, z)$ in the expansion (1.7) as a Stieltjes transform, applicable methods based on properties of Laplace or Stieltjes transforms, given, for example, in [11] and [12], can be used instead. This approach was used by Boyd [3] and Jones [6].

3. Proof of Theorem 1 when $|\operatorname{ph} z|\leqq\pi-\delta$. Throughout this section we continue to assume that all fractional powers take their principal values and that γ is an arbitrary constant in the interval $(-\pi, \pi)$.

Let m be an arbitrary nonnegative integer and $v\in[0, \infty)$. By Taylor's theorem we have

$$(1+v)^{a-1}=\sum_{s=0}^{m-1}(-)^s\frac{(1-a)_s}{s!}v^s+(1-a)_m v^m\phi_m(a, v), \tag{3.1}$$

where $\phi_0(a, v)=(1+v)^{a-1}$ and

$$\phi_m(a, v)=\frac{(-)^m}{(m-1)!}\int_0^1 (1-t)^{m-1}(1+vt)^{a-m-1}\,dt, \qquad m\geqq 1. \tag{3.2}$$

Next, if we refer to the definition of $F_p(z)$, given by [10, (2.9)] and then apply analytic continuation with respect to z, we see that

$$F_p(z)=\frac{e^{-z}}{2\pi}\int_0^{\infty e^{-i\gamma}}\frac{e^{-zt}t^{p-1}}{1+t}\,dt, \quad \operatorname{Re} p>0, \quad |\operatorname{ph}(z e^{-i\gamma})|<\tfrac{1}{2}\pi. \tag{3.3}$$

Provided that $m<n+\operatorname{Re} a+\operatorname{Re} b$ we may substitute for $(1+v)^{a-1}$ by means of (3.1) in the inner integral in (2.7) and integrate term by term. On referring to (3.3) and using the reflection and recurrence formulae for the Gamma function, we arrive at (1.9) with

$$R_{m,n}(a, b, z)=\frac{z^{1-b}e^{-z}}{2\pi\Gamma(m+1-b)}\int_0^{\infty e^{-i\gamma}}\frac{e^{-z\tau}\tau^{n+a-1}}{1+\tau}\,d\tau\int_0^\infty e^{-z\tau v}v^{m-b}\phi_m(a, v)\,dv. \tag{3.4}$$

The last result has been established with the conditions $\operatorname{Re} a+\operatorname{Re} b>m-n$ and (2.8). From its definition we see that $\phi_m(a, v)$ is a continuous function of a and v and an entire function of a. Also, if $m > \text{Re}\, a - 1$, then $|(1+vt)^{a-m-1}| \leqq 1$, and in consequence

(3.5) $$|\phi_m(a, v)| \leqq 1/m!, \qquad v \in [0, \infty), \quad m > \text{Re}\, a - 1.$$

Hence by analytic continuation with respect to a and b we see that if $|\text{ph}\,(z\,e^{-i\gamma})| < \pi/2$ and $n > m$, then (1.9) and (3.4) hold in the region defined by

(3.6) $$\text{Re}\, a < m+1, \quad \text{Re}\, b < m+1, \quad \text{Re}\, a + \text{Re}\, b > m + 1 - n.$$

We now seek to majorize $|R_{m,n}(a, b, z)|$ for fixed values of a, b, and m, bounded values of $|\alpha|$, and large values of $\rho \equiv |z|$. Here α is defined (1.8) and m exceeds both $\text{Re}\, a - 1$ and $\text{Re}\, b - 1$. (The other two conditions, $n > m$ and $\text{Re}\, a + \text{Re}\, b > m + 1 - n$, are satisfied automatically when $\rho \to \infty$ with $|\alpha|$ bounded.) Also, since we are assuming throughout this section that $\text{ph}\, z \in [-\pi + \delta, \pi - \delta]$, we may set $\gamma = \text{ph}\, z = \theta$ without violating the condition $|\text{ph}\,(z\,e^{-i\gamma})| < \pi/2$.

With $\gamma = \theta$ we have $\tau = t\,e^{-i\theta}$, where $0 \leqq t < \infty$. Hence (3.4) may be recast as

(3.7) $$R_{m,n}(a, b, z) = \frac{e^{-(n+a)i\theta} z^{1-b} e^{-z}}{2\pi\Gamma(m+1-b)} \int_0^\infty \frac{e^{-\rho t} t^{n+a-1}}{1+t\,e^{-i\theta}}\, dt \int_0^\infty e^{-\rho t v} v^{m-b} \phi_m(a, v)\, dv.$$

By use of (3.5) we see that the inner integral satisfies

(3.8) $$\left| \int_0^\infty e^{-\rho t v} v^{m-b} \phi_m(a, v)\, dv \right| \leqq \frac{\Gamma(m+1-\text{Re}\, b)}{m!(\rho t)^{m+1-\text{Re}\, b}}.$$

For the outer integral we have

(3.9) $$|1 + t\,e^{-i\theta}|^{-1} \leqq \text{cosec}\, \delta.$$

Hence

(3.10) $$|R_{m,n}(a, b, z)| \leqq \frac{e^{\pi(|\text{Im}\, a| + |\text{Im}\, b|)}\Gamma(m+1-\text{Re}\, b)}{2\pi \sin\delta\, m!|\Gamma(m+1-b)|} \frac{\Gamma(n-m+\text{Re}\, a + \text{Re}\, b - 1)|e^{-z}|}{\rho^{n+\text{Re}\, a + \text{Re}\, b - 1}}.$$

Substituting for n by means of (the real part of) (1.8) and using Stirling's formula, we conclude that as $\rho \to \infty$ the right member of this inequality is $O\{e^{-z-|z|}/z^{m+1/2}\}$ uniformly for bounded $|\alpha|$; compare (1.10).

Lastly, the conditions $m > \text{Re}\, a - 1$ and $m > \text{Re}\, b - 1$ may be removed in the usual way by replacing m in (1.9) by a sufficiently large integer and referring to [10, (2.14)].[1] This completes the proof of Theorem 1 in the case where $|\text{ph}\, z| \leqq \pi - \delta$; indeed, we have a slightly stronger asymptotic estimate for $R_{m,n}(a, b, z)$—by a factor $|z|^{-1/2}$—for this sector.

4. Proof of Theorem 1 when $\delta \leqq \text{ph}\, z \leqq 2\pi - \delta$. We return to the representation of $R_n(a, b, z)$ furnished by (1.9) and (3.4), and valid with the conditions $|\gamma| < \pi$, $|\text{ph}\,(z\,e^{-i\gamma})| < \pi/2$, $n > m$, and (3.6). The natural way to try to extend the proof of § 3 to larger values of ph z would be to rotate further the path of the outer integral in (3.4), that is, to take values of γ equaling or exceeding π. The difficulty is that as $\gamma \to \pi$, the integration path approaches the singularity of the integrand at $\tau = -1$. To overcome this difficulty we adopt, temporarily, the extra conditions $0 < \gamma < \pi$, $\pi/2 < \text{ph}\, z < \frac{3}{2}\pi$, and decompose $R_{m,n}(a, b, z)$ as follows:

(4.1) $$R_{m,n}(a, b, z) = R^{(1)}_{m,n}(a, b, z) + R^{(2)}_{m,n}(a, b, z),$$

[1] Compare also (4.5) below.

where

$$R_{m,n}^{(1)}(a, b, z) = \frac{z^{1-b}e^{-z}}{2\pi\Gamma(m+1-b)} \int_0^{\infty e^{-i\gamma}} \frac{e^{-z\tau}\tau^{n+a-1}}{1+\tau}\, d\tau \times \int_0^{\infty} e^{zv}v^{m-b}\phi_m(a, v)\, dv, \tag{4.2}$$

$$R_{m,n}^{(2)}(a, b, z) = \frac{z^{1-b}e^{-z}}{2\pi\Gamma(m+1-b)} \int_0^{\infty e^{-i\gamma}} e^{-z\tau}\tau^{n+a-1}\, d\tau \times \int_0^{\infty} \frac{e^{-z\tau v} - e^{zv}}{1+\tau} v^{m-b}\phi_m(a, v)\, dv. \tag{4.3}$$

The right member of (4.2) may be regarded as the product of two single integrals, instead of as a double integral. The first of these is identifiable as an F_p function; the second may be continued analytically by rotating the path of integration through an arbitrary angle $-\hat{\gamma}$, say, where $\hat{\gamma} \in (-\pi, \pi)$. With the aid of (3.3) we obtain

$$R_{m,n}^{(1)}(a, b, z) = \frac{z^{1-b}}{\Gamma(m+1-b)} F_{n+a}(z) \int_0^{\infty e^{-i\hat{\gamma}}} e^{zv}v^{m-b}\phi_m(a, v)\, dv, \tag{4.4}$$

valid with the conditions $\pi/2 < |\mathrm{ph}\,(z e^{-i\hat{\gamma}})| < \frac{3}{2}\pi$ and (3.6). (The conditions $|\mathrm{ph}\,(z e^{-i\gamma})| < \pi/2$ and $\pi/2 < \mathrm{ph}\, z < \frac{3}{2}\pi$ disappear.) From Theorem 1 of [10], we obtain[2]

$$F_{n+a}(z) = O(e^{-z-|z|}), \qquad |\mathrm{ph}\, z| \leqq \pi, \tag{4.5}$$

$$F_{n+a}(z) = O(1), \qquad \pi \leqq |\mathrm{ph}\, z| \leqq 3\pi - \delta. \tag{4.6}$$

Next, in this section we consider only the sector $\delta \leqq \mathrm{ph}\, z \leqq 2\pi - \delta$; hence we may set $\hat{\gamma} = \theta - \pi$. On replacing v by $v e^{i(\pi-\theta)}$ we derive

$$\int_0^{\infty e^{-i\hat{\gamma}}} e^{zv}v^{m-b}\phi_m(a, v)\, dv = e^{i(\pi-\theta)(m-b+1)} \int_0^{\infty} e^{-|z|v}v^{m-b}\phi_m(a, v e^{i(\pi-\theta)})\, dv. \tag{4.7}$$

One of our assumptions is that $\mathrm{Re}\, a < m+1$; accordingly, from (3.2) we perceive that

$$|\phi_m(a, v e^{i(\pi-\theta)})| \leqq A_m, \tag{4.8}$$

where A_m is assignable independently of $\theta \in [\delta, 2\pi - \delta]$ and $v \in [0, \infty)$. In consequence, also, of the second condition of (3.6) it follows that

$$\int_0^{\infty e^{-i\hat{\gamma}}} e^{zv}v^{m-b}\phi_m(a, v)\, dv = O(z^{b-m-1}).$$

Then combining this result with (4.4)-(4.6), we arrive at

$$R_{m,n}^{(1)}(a, b, z) = \begin{cases} O(e^{-z-|z|}z^{-m}), & \delta \leqq \mathrm{ph}\, z \leqq \pi, \\ O(z^{-m}), & \pi \leqq \mathrm{ph}\, z \leqq 2\pi - \delta. \end{cases} \tag{4.9}$$

For the contribution of $R_{m,n}^{(2)}(a, b, z)$, we first rotate the path for the inner integral in (4.3) through an angle $(\pi - \gamma)/2$. This yields

$$R_{m,n}^{(2)}(a, b, z) = \frac{z^{1-b}e^{-z}}{2\pi\Gamma(m+1-b)} \int_0^{\infty e^{-i\gamma}} e^{-z\tau}\tau^{n+a-1}\, d\tau \times \int_0^{\infty e^{i(\pi-\gamma)/2}} \frac{e^{-z\tau v} - e^{zv}}{1+\tau} v^{m-b}\phi_m(a, v)\, dv, \tag{4.10}$$

[2] In deriving (4.5) and (4.6) from the cited theorem, we have used the following facts: $\mathrm{erfc}\,(\xi) = O(e^{-\xi^2})$ throughout the sector $|\mathrm{ph}\, \xi| \leqq \pi/4$; $\mathrm{erfc}\,(\xi) = O(1)$ throughout the sector $|\mathrm{ph}\,(-\xi)| \leqq \pi/4$ (compare [10, § 4.4]).

valid when $0<\gamma<\pi$, $|\mathrm{ph}\,(z\,e^{-i\gamma})|<\pi/2$, $|\mathrm{ph}\,(z\,e^{i(\pi-3\gamma)/2})|<\pi/2$, and $|\mathrm{ph}\,(z\,e^{-i(\pi+\gamma)/2})|<\pi/2$, that is, when

$$0<\gamma<\pi \quad \text{and} \quad \tfrac{1}{2}\gamma<\mathrm{ph}\,z<\tfrac{3}{2}\gamma. \tag{4.11}$$

Furthermore, because the integrand is now free from singularity at $\tau=-1$ we may extend the rotation of each integration path by increasing γ. Thus (4.10) is also valid with the conditions

$$\pi\leqq\gamma<2\pi \quad \text{and} \quad \tfrac{3}{2}\gamma-\pi<\mathrm{ph}\,z<\pi+\tfrac{1}{2}\gamma. \tag{4.12}$$

In accordance with (4.11) we may set $\gamma=\theta$ $(=\mathrm{ph}\,z)$ in (4.10) when $\delta\leqq\mathrm{ph}\,z<\pi$. Alternatively, if $\pi\leqq\mathrm{ph}\,z\leqq 2\pi-\delta$, then we may set $\gamma=\theta$ in (4.10) in accordance with (4.12). In either event we find that

$$\begin{aligned} R^{(2)}_{m,n}(a,b,z)=&\frac{z^{1-b}e^{-z}}{2\pi\Gamma(m+1-b)}\int_0^{\infty e^{-i\theta}} e^{-z\tau}\tau^{n+a-1}\,d\tau \\ &\times\int_0^{\infty e^{i(\pi-\theta)/2}}\frac{e^{-z\tau v}-e^{zv}}{1+\tau}\,v^{m-b}\phi_m(a,v)\,dv, \end{aligned} \tag{4.13}$$

valid when $\delta\leqq\mathrm{ph}\,z\leqq 2\pi-\delta$.

Once again, subject to (3.6) we seek to estimate $R^{(2)}_{m,n}(a,b,z)$ for fixed values of a, b, and m, bounded values of $|\alpha|$, and large values of $\rho\equiv|z|$.

We first observe that the integration variable of the inner integral in (4.13) lies within the sector $|\mathrm{ph}\,v|<\pi/2$. Hence

$$|\phi_m(a,v)|\leqq e^{\pi|\mathrm{Im}\,a|/2}/m!; \tag{4.14}$$

compare (3.5) and (4.8).

Next, we have identically

$$\frac{e^{-z\tau v}-e^{zv}}{1+\tau}=zv\,e^{-z\tau v}\frac{1-e^{zv(1+\tau)}}{zv(1+\tau)}=zv\,e^{zv}\frac{e^{-zv(1+\tau)}-1}{zv(1+\tau)}.$$

Furthermore, by application of the maximum-modulus theorem it is easily verified that

$$\left|\frac{1-e^{-\zeta}}{\zeta}\right|\leqq 1, \qquad \mathrm{Re}\,\zeta\geqq 0. \tag{4.15}$$

Combination of the last two results yields

$$\left|\frac{e^{-z\tau v}-e^{zv}}{1+\tau}\right|\leqq\begin{cases}|zv\,e^{-z\tau v}|, & \mathrm{Re}\,\{zv(1+\tau)\}\leqq 0,\\ |zv\,e^{zv}|, & \mathrm{Re}\,\{zv(1+\tau)\}\geqq 0.\end{cases}$$

With $\mathrm{ph}\,\tau=-\theta$ and $\mathrm{ph}\,v=\pi/2-\theta/2$, we have

$$\mathrm{Re}\,\{zv(1+\tau)\}=\rho|v|(|\tau|-1)\sin\tfrac{1}{2}\theta.$$

Accordingly,

$$\mathrm{Re}\,\{zv(1+\tau)\}\lesseqqgtr 0 \quad \text{according as } |\tau|\lesseqqgtr 1.$$

Therefore when $0<|\tau|\leqq 1$ we have

$$\begin{aligned} &\left|\int_0^{\infty e^{i(\pi-\theta)/2}}\frac{e^{-z\tau v}-e^{zv}}{1+\tau}\,v^{m-b}\phi_m(a,v)\,dv\right| \\ &\leqq\frac{e^{\pi|\mathrm{Im}\,a|/2}\,e^{(\pi-\theta)\mathrm{Im}\,b/2}\rho}{m!}\int_0^{\infty}e^{-\rho|\tau v|\sin\theta/2}|v|^{m-\mathrm{Re}\,b+1}\,d|v| \\ &\leqq\frac{e^{\pi(|\mathrm{Im}\,a|+|\mathrm{Im}\,b|)/2}\rho}{m!}\,\frac{\Gamma(m+2-\mathrm{Re}\,b)}{(\rho|\tau|\sin\frac{1}{2}\delta)^{m+2-\mathrm{Re}\,b}}. \end{aligned} \tag{4.16}$$

Similarly, when $|\tau| \geqq 1$ we find that

(4.17)
$$\left| \int_0^{\infty e^{i(\pi-\theta)/2}} \frac{e^{-z\tau v} - e^{zv}}{1+\tau} v^{m-b} \phi_m(a, v)\, dv \right| \leqq \frac{e^{\pi(|\mathrm{Im}\, a| + |\mathrm{Im}\, b|)/2} \rho}{m!} \frac{\Gamma(m+2-\mathrm{Re}\, b)}{(\rho \sin \frac{1}{2}\delta)^{m+2-\mathrm{Re}\, b}}.$$

We now prepare to substitute in (4.13) by means of the inequalities just obtained. At this stage it is convenient to use the symbol A_m generically to denote a quantity that may depend on m, a, and b, but is independent of n, z and (bounded values of) α; compare, also, (4.8). In (4.13) we have

$$|\tau^{n+a-1}| \leqq A_m |\tau|^{\rho + \mathrm{Re}\, \alpha - \mathrm{Re}\, b};$$

compare (1.8). Hence

$$|R^{(2)}_{m,n}(a, b, z)| \leqq A_m \frac{|e^{-z}|}{\rho^m} \left\{ \int_0^1 e^{-\rho|\tau|} |\tau|^{\rho + \mathrm{Re}\, \alpha - m - 2}\, d|\tau| + \int_1^\infty e^{-\rho|\tau|} |\tau|^{\rho + \mathrm{Re}\, \alpha - \mathrm{Re}\, b}\, d|\tau| \right\}.$$

Replacing both integration ranges by $(0, \infty)$ and subsequently using Stirling's formula, we derive

(4.18)
$$|R^{(2)}_{m,n}(a, b, z)| \leqq A_m \frac{|e^{-z}|}{\rho^m} \left\{ \frac{\Gamma(\rho + \mathrm{Re}\, \alpha - m - 1)}{\rho^{\rho + \mathrm{Re}\, \alpha - m - 1}} + \frac{\Gamma(\rho + \mathrm{Re}\, \alpha + 1 - \mathrm{Re}\, b)}{\rho^{\rho + \mathrm{Re}\, \alpha + 1 - \mathrm{Re}\, b}} \right\} = O\left(\frac{e^{-z-|z|}}{z^{m+1/2}} \right).$$

This result is valid when $\delta \leqq \mathrm{ph}\, z \leqq 2\pi - \delta$, and on combining it with (4.1) and (4.9) we arrive at

$$R_{m,n}(a, b, z) = \begin{cases} O(e^{-z-|z|} z^{-m}), & \delta \leqq \mathrm{ph}\, z \leqq \pi, \\ O(z^{-m}), & \pi \leqq \mathrm{ph}\, z \leqq 2\pi - \delta. \end{cases}$$

After removing the restrictions (3.6) on m in the same manner as that used at the end of § 3 (compare (4.5) and (4.6)), we see that the proof of Theorem 1 is complete for the sector $\delta \leqq \mathrm{ph}\, z \leqq 2\pi - \delta$.

5. Completion of the proof of Theorem 1. The next extension is to the sector $\frac{3}{2}\pi + \delta \leqq \mathrm{ph}\, z \leqq \frac{5}{2}\pi - \delta$. Rather than attempting to extend the method of proof introduced in § 4, we appeal to the connection formulae (1.12). An advantage of this approach is that it also determines the maximum regions of validity.

From (1.12) with $k = 1$, z replaced by $z e^{-2\pi i}$ and upper signs taken, we have

(5.1)
$$U(a, a-b+1, z) = e^{-2a\pi i} U(a, a-b+1, z e^{-2\pi i}) + 2\pi i \frac{e^{-a\pi i}}{\Gamma(a)\Gamma(b)} e^z U(1-b, a-b+1, z e^{-\pi i}).$$

Substituting in each side of this equation by means of (1.7) and (1.9), then using the identity

(5.2)
$$F_{n-s+a+b-1}(z e^{-2\pi i}) = (-)^{n+s} i\, e^{(a+b)\pi i} + e^{2(a+b)\pi i} F_{n-s+a+b-1}(z)$$

obtained from [10], (2.11), and carrying out some reduction, we eventually arrive at

(5.3) $$R_{m,n}(a,b,z)=e^{-2(a+b)\pi i}R_{m,n}(a,b,z\,e^{-2\pi i})+R^{(3)}_{m,n}(a,b,z)+R^{(4)}_{m,n}(a,b,z),$$

where

(5.4) $$R^{(3)}_{m,n}(a,b,z)=(-)^{n-1}i\,e^{-(a+b)\pi i}\sum_{s=m}^{n-1}\frac{(m+1-a)_{s-m}(m+1-b)_{s-m}}{s!\,z^s},$$

and

(5.5) $$\begin{aligned}R^{(4)}_{m,n}(a,b,z)=2\pi i&\frac{z^{1-a-b}\,e^{-z}}{\Gamma(m+1-a)\Gamma(m+1-b)}\\&\cdot\left\{\sum_{s=0}^{m-1}\frac{(a)_s(b)_s}{s!}\frac{F_{n-s-a-b+1}(z\,e^{-\pi i})}{z^s}\right.\\&\qquad\left.+(a)_m(b)_mR_{m,n}(1-b,1-a,z\,e^{-\pi i})\right\}.\end{aligned}$$

Since $\frac{3}{2}\pi+\delta\leqq \operatorname{ph} z\leqq\frac{5}{2}\pi-\delta$, we have $|\operatorname{ph}(z\,e^{-2\pi i})|\leqq\pi/2-\delta$; hence from the results of § 3 it follows that

(5.6) $$R_{m,n}(a,b,z\,e^{-2\pi i})=O(e^{-z-|z|}z^{-m-1/2}).$$

Next, although the number of terms in the sum in (5.4) increases with $|z|$, it is routine to verify that

(5.7) $$R^{(3)}_{m,n}(a,b,z)=(-)^{n-1}\frac{i\,e^{-(a+b)\pi i}}{m!\,z^m}+O\left(\frac{1}{z^{m+1}}\right).$$

For $R^{(4)}_{m,n}(a,b,z)$ we have $\frac{1}{2}\pi+\delta\leqq\operatorname{ph}(z\,e^{-\pi i})\leqq\frac{3}{2}\pi-\delta$; accordingly, from the results of § 4 it follows that

$$R_{m,n}(1-b,1-a,z\,e^{-\pi i})=O(z^{-m}),$$

and

$$F_{n-s-a-b+1}(z\,e^{-\pi i})=O(1),$$

for each s. Hence

(5.8) $$R^{(4)}_{m,n}(a,b,z)=O(z^{1-a-b}\,e^{-z}).$$

On subst[illegible]ting in (5.3) by means of (5.6), (5.7), and (5.8) we conclude that

(5.9) $$R_{m,n}(a,b,z)=O(z^{-m}),$$

as required. Then combining this estimate with the results of §§ 3 and 4 we establish (1.10) in the sector $-\pi+\delta\leqq\operatorname{ph} z\leqq\pi$, and (1.11) in the sector $\pi\leqq\operatorname{ph} z\leqq\frac{5}{2}\pi-\delta$. A similar proof holds for the conjugate sector, or we can appeal to symmetry.

To complete the proof of Theorem 1, we have only to demonstrate that the estimate (1.10) breaks down after we cross the rays $\operatorname{ph} z=\pm\pi$, and the estimate (1.11) breaks down after we cross $\operatorname{ph} z=\pm\frac{5}{2}\pi$.

In the case where $\operatorname{ph} z=\pi$, we observe from (4.4) and (4.7) that as $z\to\infty$ in the sector $\delta\leqq\operatorname{ph} z\leqq 2\pi-\sigma$, we have

$$R^{(1)}_{m,n}(a,b,z)\sim(-)^{m-1}e^{-b\pi i}\phi_m(a,0)\frac{F_{n+a}(z)}{z^m}=-\frac{e^{-b\pi i}F_{n+a}(z)}{m!\,z^m};$$

compare also (3.2). And when $\pi+\delta\leqq\operatorname{ph} z\leqq 2\pi-\delta$, $(-)^nF_{n+a}(z)$ tends to the constant $i\,e^{-a\pi i}$ (compare Theorem 1 of [10]), giving $R^{(1)}_{m,n}(a,b,z)\sim(\text{constant})z^{-m}$. Obviously from (4.18) this algebraic behavior cannot be cancelled in (4.1) by the contribution of $R^{(2)}_{m,n}(a,b,z)$. A similar argument applies to the ray $\operatorname{ph} z=-\pi$.

Lastly, after we cross $\operatorname{ph} z=\frac{5}{2}\pi$, the contribution of $R^{(4)}_{m,n}(a,b,z)$ in (5.3) is no longer absorbable in the estimate $O(z^{-m})$ because it becomes exponentially large. On the other hand, the term $e^{-2(a+b)\pi i}R_{m,n}(a, b, z\,e^{-2\pi i})$ remains exponentially small and $R^{(3)}_{m,n}(a, b, z)$ remains $O(z^{-m})$. Similarly for the ray $\text{ph}\, z = -\frac{5}{2}\pi$.

6. Error bounds. For computational purposes the use of (1.7) and (1.9) should be confined to the sector $|\text{ph}\, z| \leqq \pi$ in which the error term has undergone maximum exponential improvement; elsewhere continuation formulae are to be applied. As always, it is highly desirable to supply a rigorous and realistic bound for the error term in any asymptotic approximation. The analyses supplied in §§ 3-5 lend themselves only in part to achieving this objective.

In § 3, for example, the bound (3.10) breaks down as $\delta \to 0$. However, a slight modification of the analysis leading to this result yields a satisfactory bound when $|\text{ph}\, z| \leqq \pi/2$: in this sector the right-hand side of (3.9) is replaceable by unity, thus eliminating the factor $(\sin \delta)^{-1}$ from (3.10). Similarly, if we restrict $\text{ph}\, z \in [\pi/2, \pi]$, then the bounds derived in § 4 can be tightened; however, the factor $(\operatorname{cosec} \delta/2)^{m+2-\text{Re}\, b}$ that appears in (4.16) and (4.17) can be replaced only by $(\sqrt{2})^{m+2-\text{Re}\, b}$, which is a drawback.

In this section, we modify the analysis of § 4 in a more substantial manner in order to arrive at a sharper bound for $R_{m,n}(a, b, z)$ in the sector $|\text{ph}\, z| \leqq \pi$. This modification is based partly on the analysis of Boyd [3] for constructing error bounds for a similar expansion for the modified Bessel function $K_\nu(z)$. The bounds we shall derive are similar to, but not the same as, those of Boyd when the parameters a and b (and ipso facto ν) are real, and they are more readily computable when a, b (and ν) are complex.

As before, we set $z = \rho\, e^{i\theta}$. Throughout the following analysis we restrict $|\theta| < \pi$, relaxing this condition to $|\theta| \leqq \pi$ at the close by appeal to continuity.

In (3.4) we take $\gamma = \theta$, and decompose $R_{m,n}(a, b, z)$ in a manner slightly different from that given by (4.1)-(4.3). We write

$$R_{m,n}(a, b, z) = S^{(1)}_{m,n}(a, b, z) + S^{(2)}_{m,n}(a, b, z), \tag{6.1}$$

where

$$S^{(1)}_{m,n}(a, b, z) = \frac{z^{1-b}\, e^{-z}}{2\pi\Gamma(m+1-b)} \int_0^{\infty e^{-i\theta}} \frac{e^{-z\tau}\tau^{n+a-1}}{1+\tau}\, d\tau \int_0^\infty e^{-\rho v} v^{m-b} \phi_m(a, v)\, dv, \tag{6.2}$$

$$\begin{aligned} S^{(2)}_{m,n}(a, b, z) = {}& \frac{z^{1-b}\, e^{-z}}{2\pi\Gamma(m+1-b)} \int_0^{\infty e^{-i\theta}} e^{-z\tau}\tau^{n+a-1}\, d\tau \\ & \cdot \int_0^\infty \frac{e^{-z\tau v} - e^{-\rho v}}{1+\tau} v^{m-b} \phi_m(a, v)\, dv, \end{aligned} \tag{6.3}$$

these equations being valid with the conditions $|\theta| < \pi$ and (3.6).

As in § 4, the first integral in (6.2) may be identified in terms of $F_{n+a}(z)$. For the second integral, we utilize the bound (3.5) for $\phi_m(a, v)$. Thus we derive

$$|S^{(1)}_{m,n}(a, b, z)| \leqq \frac{e^{\theta\, \text{Im}\, b}\Gamma(m+1-\text{Re}\, b)}{m!\,|\Gamma(m+1-b)|} \frac{|F_{n+a}(z)|}{\rho^m}. \tag{6.4}$$

In (6.3) we set $\tau = t\, e^{-i\theta}$; thus

$$\begin{aligned} S^{(2)}_{m,n}(a, b, z) = {}& \frac{e^{-(n+a)i\theta}}{2\pi\Gamma(m+1-b)} z^{1-b}\, e^{-z} \int_0^\infty e^{-\rho t} t^{n+a-1}\, dt \\ & \cdot \int_0^\infty \frac{e^{-\rho t v} - e^{-\rho v}}{1+t\, e^{-i\theta}} v^{m-b} \phi_m(a, v)\, dv. \end{aligned} \tag{6.5}$$

To bound the inner integral, the inequalities

$$0 \leqq \frac{e^{-\rho t v} - e^{-\rho v}}{1-t} \leqq \begin{cases} \rho v\, e^{-\rho t v}, & 0 \leqq t \leqq 1, \\ \rho v\, e^{-\rho v}, & t \geqq 1, \end{cases} \tag{6.6}$$

and

$$\left| \frac{1-t}{1+t\, e^{-i\theta}} \right| \leqq 1 \tag{6.7}$$

are applied: (6.6) is easily verified with the aid of (4.15), and (6.7) is verifiable by considering the bilinear transformation $T = (1-t)/(1+t\,e^{-i\theta})$; compare [3, § 4]. Referring again to (3.5), we conclude that

$$\left| \int_0^\infty \frac{e^{-\rho t v} - e^{-\rho v}}{1+t\, e^{-i\theta}} v^{m-b} \phi_m(a, v)\, dv \right| \leqq \frac{\rho}{m!} \frac{\Gamma(m+2-\operatorname{Re} b)}{(\rho t_1)^{m+2-\operatorname{Re} b}},$$

where $t_1 = \min(t, 1)$. If we further restrict $\operatorname{Re} a + \operatorname{Re} b > m+2-n$ (compare (3.6)), then we may substitute this bound in (6.5). Referring once again to (1.8), we find that

$$\begin{aligned} |S^{(2)}_{m,n}(a, b, z)| \leqq {} & \frac{e^{\theta(\operatorname{Im} a + \operatorname{Im} b)} \Gamma(m+2-\operatorname{Re} b)}{2\pi\, m!\, |\Gamma(m+1-b)|} \frac{|e^{-z}|}{\rho^m} \\ & \cdot \left\{ \int_0^1 e^{-\rho t} t^{\rho-m+\operatorname{Re} a-2}\, dt + \int_1^\infty e^{-\rho t} t^{\rho-\operatorname{Re} b+\operatorname{Re} a}\, dt \right\}. \end{aligned} \tag{6.8}$$

Inequalities (6.4) and (6.8) furnish the desired upper bound on $|R_{m,n}(a, b, z)|$ via (6.1). The condition $|\theta| < \pi$ may now be eased by continuity considerations. Thus the aggregate conditions on (6.4) and (6.8) are given by $|\theta| \leqq \pi$ and

$$\operatorname{Re} a < m+1, \quad \operatorname{Re} b < m+1, \quad \operatorname{Re} a + \operatorname{Re} b > m+2-n. \tag{6.9}$$

It remains to bound the integrals that appear in (6.8). A simple approach is to extend each integration range to $[0, \infty)$. This immediately yields

$$\int_0^1 e^{-\rho t} t^{\rho-m+\operatorname{Re} a-2}\, dt < \frac{\Gamma(\rho - m + \operatorname{Re} \alpha - 1)}{\rho^{\rho-m+\operatorname{Re} a-1}},$$

$$\int_1^\infty e^{-\rho t} t^{\rho-\operatorname{Re} b+\operatorname{Re} a}\, dt < \frac{\Gamma(\rho - \operatorname{Re} b + \operatorname{Re} \alpha + 1)}{\rho^{\rho-\operatorname{Re} b+\operatorname{Re} a+1}}.$$

However, each of these bounds overestimates the actual value of the corresponding left-hand side by a factor that approaches two as $\rho \to \infty$. More sophisticated bounds that are free from this defect are supplied in the Appendix.

7. Conclusions. We have constructed a uniform generalized asymptotic expansion for the confluent hypergeometric function $U(a, a-b+1, z)$, valid when the parameters a and b are fixed and z tends to infinity in the sector $|\operatorname{ph} z| \leqq \frac{5}{2}\pi - \delta$, where δ is an arbitrarily small positive constant. This expansion is in terms of generalized exponential integrals (or equivalently incomplete Gamma functions) and it includes as special cases three well-known expansions of Poincaré type valid in the ph z intervals $[-\frac{5}{2}\pi + \delta, -\frac{1}{2}\pi - \delta]$, $[-\frac{3}{2}\pi + \delta, \frac{3}{2}\pi - \delta]$, $[\frac{1}{2}\pi + \delta, \frac{5}{2}\pi - \delta]$. It also quantifies accurately the rapid, but smooth, transitions between these expansions in the neighborhoods of the Stokes lines ph $z = \pm\pi$. These smooth transitions were first described by M. V. Berry using formal analysis and error functions as approximants. The present results serve to place

Berry's conclusions on a rigorous foundation in the case of the confluent hypergeometric function. However, it should be noted that Berry's analysis applied only in the neighborhoods of the Stokes lines, whereas our result is uniformly valid in a sector of total angle $5\pi-2\delta$.

Our new expansion enjoys the important property that it is a uniform, exponentially improved expansion throughout the sector $|\text{ph } z|\leqq \pi$, in the sense described in [10, § 1]. Furthermore, we have derived strict and realistic bounds for the error term in this sector. Uniform, exponentially improved expansions in other sectors can be easily constructed with the aid of standard connection formulae, and normally we need not compute the new expansion outside the sector $|\text{ph } z|\leqq \pi$.

Although we have treated only the confluent hypergeometric function in the present paper, our method is applicable to a large class of functions that can be represented by Laplace transforms.[3] The basic steps are as follows: (i) The remainder term of the Maclaurin expansion of the kernel of the transform is represented as a contour integral by means of Cauchy's integral formula. (ii) The integral obtained in step (i) is used to construct a Stieltjes transform in the form of a double integral for the remainder term associated with the desired asymptotic expansion. (iii) The double integral is expanded in a series of generalized exponential integrals. (iv) The region of validity is extended by suitable rotations of integration paths and use of continuation formulae. The only step in which we made use of special properties of the confluent hypergeometric function was (iv), where we relied on continuation formulae. However, this was largely a matter of convenience, and in any case this step is the least important.

In Berry's theory the conditions adopted ensure that the function whose asymptotic expansions are under investigation is representable as a Laplace transform of the type admitted above. The scope of the present method therefore appears to be essentially the same as that of Berry.

Appendix. Bounds for some incomplete Gamma functions. In this appendix we construct bounds for the incomplete Gamma functions

$$I_\lambda^{(1)}(\rho)=\int_1^\infty e^{-\rho t}t^{\rho+\lambda-1}\,dt,\qquad I_\lambda^{(2)}(\rho)=\int_0^1 e^{-\rho t}t^{\rho+\lambda-1}\,dt, \tag{A1}$$

that have the same asymptotic forms as the functions themselves when $\rho\to\infty$ with λ positive and fixed. These results were referred to at the end of § 6.

LEMMA. *When λ and ρ are positive*

$$I_\lambda^{(1)}(\rho)\leqq\sqrt{\frac{\pi}{2\rho}}\,e^{-\rho}\exp\left(\frac{\kappa_1^2}{2\rho}\right)\left\{1+\operatorname{erf}\left(\frac{\kappa_1}{\sqrt{2\rho}}\right)\right\}, \tag{A2}$$

$$I_\lambda^{(2)}(\rho)\leqq\sqrt{\frac{\pi}{2\rho}}\,e^{-\rho}\exp\left(\frac{\kappa_2^2}{2\rho}\right)\left\{1+\operatorname{erf}\left(\frac{\kappa_2}{\sqrt{2\rho}}\right)\right\}, \tag{A3}$$

where

$$\kappa_1=\sup_{\tau\in(0,\infty)}\omega(\tau),\qquad \kappa_2=\sup_{\tau\in(-1,0)}\omega(\tau), \tag{A4}$$

[3] This includes, for example, the integral $\int_0^\infty e^{-zt}t^{d-1}F(a,b;c;-t)\,dt$, in which a, b, c, d are parameters. This is a generalized hypergeometric function of ${}_2F_2$ type.

and[4]

$$\omega(\tau)=\frac{1}{\sqrt{2\tau-2\ln(1+\tau)}}\ln\left\{\frac{(1+\tau)^{\lambda}}{|\tau|}\sqrt{2\tau-2\ln(1+\tau)}\right\}. \tag{A5}$$

To establish this result, we first observe that

$$\omega(\tau)\to 0,\quad \tau\to+\infty;\qquad \omega(\tau)\to\lambda-\tfrac{1}{3},\quad \tau\to 0+;$$
$$\omega(\tau)\to-\infty,\quad \tau\to-1+;\qquad \omega(\tau)\to\tfrac{1}{3}-\lambda,\quad \tau\to 0-.$$

Hence κ_1 and κ_2 are both finite; furthermore, $\kappa_1\geqq\max(\lambda-\frac{1}{3},0)$ and $\kappa_2\geqq\frac{1}{3}-\lambda$.

In the definition (A1) of $I_\lambda^{(1)}(\rho)$ let us replace t by $1+\tau$, and then set

$$\tfrac{1}{2}v^2=\tau-\ln(1+\tau), \tag{A6}$$

with $v\sim\tau$ when $\tau\to 0+$. We find that

$$I_\lambda^{(1)}(\rho)=e^{-\rho}\int_0^\infty \exp\left(-\frac{1}{2}\rho v^2\right)f(v)\,dv, \tag{A7}$$

where

$$f(v)=(1+\tau)^{\lambda-1}\frac{d\tau}{dv}=(1+\tau)^{\lambda}\frac{v}{\tau}.$$

Clearly, $f(v)$ is positive when $v\in(0,\infty)$, and tends to unity when $v\to 0+$. Furthermore, from (A4), (A5), and (A6) we see that

$$f(v)\leqq e^{\kappa_1 v},\qquad 0<v<\infty. \tag{A8}$$

Substitution of this bound into (A7) leads to (A2).

The proof of (A3) is similar.

We note that by applying Laplace's method [8, Chap. 3], to the integrals in the definitions (A1) we derive

$$I_\lambda^{(1)}(\rho),\, I_\lambda^{(2)}(\rho)\sim\sqrt{\frac{\pi}{2\rho}}\,e^{-\rho},\quad \rho\to\infty.$$

Obviously, the right-hand sides of (A2) and (A3) also have this asymptotic form.

We also observe that for computational purposes the bounds (A2) and (A3) are simplifiable, with an insignificant loss of sharpness when ρ is large. This is achieved via the inequality $\operatorname{erf}(t)\leqq 2t/\sqrt{\pi}$, which is valid for all nonnegative values of t. In this way we derive

$$\begin{aligned} I_\lambda^{(1)}(\rho)&\leqq\sqrt{\frac{\pi}{2\rho}}\,e^{-\rho}\exp\left(\frac{\kappa_1^2}{2\rho}\right)\left(1+\sqrt{\frac{2}{\pi\rho}}\,\kappa_1\right)\\ &<\sqrt{\frac{\pi}{2\rho}}\,e^{-\rho}\exp\left(\frac{2\kappa_1^2}{\pi\rho}\right)\left(1+\sqrt{\frac{2}{\pi\rho}}\,\kappa_1\right)<\frac{\pi e^{-\rho}}{\sqrt{2\pi\rho}-2\kappa_1}, \end{aligned} \tag{A9}$$

provided that $\rho>2\kappa_1^2/\pi$. (The last step is a consequence of the inequality $(1+t)\,e^{t^2}<(1-t)^{-1}$, $0<t<1$.) The corresponding simplification for $I_\lambda^{(2)}(\rho)$ is found to be

$$I_\lambda^{(2)}(\rho)<\frac{\pi e^{-\rho}}{\sqrt{2\pi\rho}-2\kappa_2},\qquad \rho>\frac{2\kappa_2^2}{\pi}, \tag{A10}$$

[4] In (A5) the positive square root must be taken in both instances. Thus $\sqrt{2\tau-2\ln(1+\tau)}\sim|\tau|$ as $\tau\to 0$ from above or below.

provided that $\kappa_2 > 0$. If $\kappa_2 \leqq 0$, then we have

$$I_\lambda^{(2)}(\rho) \leqq \sqrt{\frac{\pi}{2\rho}}\, e^{-\rho}; \tag{A11}$$

compare (A7) and (A8).

Remark. The method that we have used in this Appendix may also be applied to the general problem of bounding error terms that arise with Watson's lemma and the method of steepest descents. It enjoys some advantages over that described in [8, Chap. 3, § 9; Chap. 4, § 10].

Acknowledgment. The writer is pleased to acknowledge helpful discussions with W. G. C. Boyd.

REFERENCES

[1] L. V. AHLFORS, *Complex Analysis*, Second ed., McGraw-Hill, New York, 1966.

[2] M. V. BERRY, *Uniform asymptotic smoothing of Stokes' discontinuities*, Proc. Roy. Soc. London Ser. A, 422 (1989), pp. 7-21.

[3] W. G. C. BOYD, *Stieltjes transforms and the Stokes phenomenon*, Proc. Roy. Soc. London Ser. A, 429 (1990), pp. 227-246.

[4] H. BUCHHOLZ, *The Confluent Hypergeometric Function* (translated by H. Lichtblau and K. Wetzel from 1953 German ed.), Springer Tracts in Natural Philosophy, Vol. 15, Springer-Verlag, Berlin, New York, 1969.

[5] R. B. DINGLE, *Asymptotic expansions and converging factors* IV. *Confluent hypergeometric, parabolic cylinder, modified Bessel, and ordinary Bessel functions*, Proc. Roy. Soc. London Ser. A, 249 (1958), pp. 270-283.

[6] D. S. JONES, *Uniform asymptotic remainders*, in Asymptotic and Computational Analysis, R. Wong, ed., Marcel Dekker, New York, 1990, pp. 241-264.

[7] E. R. LOVE, *Changing the order of integration*, J. Austral. Math. Soc. 9 (1970), pp. 421-432.

[8] F. W. J. OLVER, *Asymptotics and Special Functions*, Academic Press, New York, 1974.

[9] ———, *On Stokes' phenomenon and converging factors*, in Asymptotic and Computational Analysis, R. Wong, ed., Marcel Dekker, New York, 1990, pp. 329-355.

[10] ———, *Uniform, exponentially improved, asymptotic expansions for the generalized exponential integral*, SIAM J. Math. Anal., this issue (1991), pp. 1460-1474.

[11] E. C. TITCHMARSH, *Introduction to the Theory of Fourier Integrals*, Second ed., Oxford University Press, London, New York, 1948.

[12] D. V. WIDDER, *The Laplace Transform*, Princeton University Press, Princeton, NJ, 1941.

SIAM J. MATH. ANAL.
Vol. 24, No 3, pp. 756–767, May 1993

EXPONENTIALLY-IMPROVED ASYMPTOTIC SOLUTIONS OF ORDINARY DIFFERENTIAL EQUATIONS I: THE CONFLUENT HYPERGEOMETRIC FUNCTION*

F. W. J. OLVER†

Abstract. There has been renewed interest in both formal and rigorous theories of exponentially-small contributions to asymptotic expansions. In particular, a generalized asymptotic expansion was obtained for the confluent hypergeometric function $U(a, a-b+1, z)$ in which the parameters a and b are complex constants, and z is a large complex variable. This expansion is expressed in terms of generalized exponential integrals and has a larger region of validity and greater accuracy than conventional expansions of Poincaré type. The expansion was established by transformations and a re-expansion of an integral representation of $U(a, a-b+1, z)$. In this paper it is shown how the same result can be achieved by a direct differential-equation approach, thereby laying the foundation for a rigorous theory of generalized asymptotic solutions of linear differential equations.

Key words. factorial series, Gamma function, generalized asymptotic expansion, generalized exponential integral, incomplete Gamma function, superasymptotics

AMS subject classifications. primary 34E05; secondary 33C15

1. Introduction. The confluent hypergeometric function $U(a, a-b+1, z)$ has the well-known asymptotic expansion

$$U(a, a-b+1, z) \sim z^{-a} \sum_{s=0}^{\infty} (-)^s \frac{(a)_s (b)_s}{s!\, z^s}, \tag{1.1}$$

valid when the real or complex parameters a and b are fixed, and the argument $z \to \infty$ in the sector $|\mathrm{ph}\, z| \leqq \frac{3}{2}\pi - \delta$. Here $(a)_s$ and $(b)_s$ denote the ascending factorials $a(a+1)\cdots(a+s-1)$ and $b(b+1)\cdots(b+s-1)$, respectively, and δ is an arbitrary positive constant. If either a or b is a nonpositive integer, then the expansion (1.1) terminates and furnishes an exact representation of $U(a, a-b+1, z)$. In other cases, for given values of a, b, and z, $|z|$ being sufficiently large, the terms decrease numerically to a minimum; thereafter they increase unboundedly. The accuracy obtainable from (1.1) is limited, and greatest when the summation ceases close to the numerically smallest term. Approximately, this term is given by $s = \mathrm{int}\,[|z|]$, the integer part of $|z|$, or somewhat more exactly by $s = \mathrm{int}\,[|z| - \mathrm{Re}\, a - \mathrm{Re}\, b + 2]$.

In a recent paper [7] the author established the following result.

THEOREM 1.1. *Define $R_n(a, b, z)$ by*

$$U(a, a-b+1, z) = z^{-a} \sum_{s=0}^{n-1} (-)^s \frac{(a)_s (b)_s}{s!\, z^s} + R_n(a, b, z), \tag{1.2}$$

where

$$n = |z| - a - b + 1 + \alpha, \tag{1.3}$$

$|z|$ being large, a and b being fixed real or complex parameters, and $|\alpha|$ being bounded.

* Received by the editors April 15, 1992; accepted for publication (in revised form) August 19, 1992.

† Institute for Physical Science and Technology, University of Maryland, College Park, Maryland 20742.
This research was supported by National Science Foundation grant DMS 87-23039 and by a Senior Visiting Fellowship from the Royal Irish Academy.

Then

$$R_n(a,b,z)=(-)^n 2\pi\frac{e^z z^{b-1}}{\Gamma(a)\Gamma(b)}\left\{\sum_{s=0}^{m-1}(-)^s\frac{(1-a)_s(1-b)_s}{s!}\frac{F_{n+a+b-s-1}(z)}{z^s}\right. \tag{1.4}$$
$$\left.+(1-a)_m(1-b)_m R_{m,n}(a,b,z)\right\},$$

where m is an arbitrary fixed nonnegative integer,

$$R_{m,n}(a,b,z)=O(e^{-z-|z|}z^{-m}),\qquad |\text{ph } z|\leqq\pi, \tag{1.5}$$

$$R_{m,n}(a,b,z)=O(z^{-m}),\qquad \pi\leqq|\text{ph } z|\leqq\tfrac{5}{2}\pi-\delta, \tag{1.6}$$

and δ denotes an arbitrary positive constant.

In this result F denotes the function defined by

$$F_p(z)=\frac{e^{-z}}{2\pi}\int_0^\infty\frac{e^{-zt}t^{p-1}}{1+t}\,dt, \tag{1.7}$$

when $\text{Re } p>0$ and $|\text{ph } z|<\frac{1}{2}\pi$, and by analytic continuation elsewhere.

It will be observed that Theorem 1.1 provides a re-expansion of the remainder term $R_n(a,b,z)$ when the original expansion (1.1) is truncated at or near its optimal stage; compare (1.3). In applications there are two advantages of the expansion given by (1.2) and (1.4), compared with (1.1). First, the total sector of validity $|\text{ph } z|\leqq\frac{5}{2}\pi-\delta$ is greater. Secondly, the attainable accuracy is considerably improved.

Another important feature of Theorem 1.1 is that it leads to a very clear understanding of the Stokes phenomenon: indeed, it was the insightful formal researches of Berry [1] on this aspect that motivated the research leading to Theorem 1.1. In brief, the explanation is that if n and $|z|$ are large, fixed, and approximately equal, then the functions $F_{n+a+b-s-1}(z)$ that appear in (1.4) change very rapidly, but *smoothly*, from being exponentially small to being almost constant as ph z passes continuously through either of the values $\pm\pi$.

The proof of Theorem 1.1 was based on an integral representation of the function $U(a,a-b+1,z)$. By suitable expansion of this representation, the remainder term $R_n(a,b,z)$ was expressed as a double integral, from which (1.4) was generated by appropriate transformations and re-expansion. Now the expansion (1.1) can also be obtained by direct application of the asymptotic theory of linear differential equations; see, for example, [5, Chap. 7, § 10]. Two questions naturally arise. Can the expansion (1.4) also be derived by a purely differential-equation approach? If so, can a more general theory be constructed, indeed, a theory that would be applicable in cases where no suitable integral representation of the wanted solution exists? Again, the formal researches of Berry [2] indicate that the answers to both questions are in the affirmative. The purpose of the present paper is to provide a rigorous proof of Theorem 1.1 based on differential-equation theory. The analysis we shall develop serves as a valuable preliminary to the more general case, treated in [10]. Other relevant references are [4] and [11].

In proving Theorem 1.1 we shall concentrate on the result (1.5) for the central sector $|\text{ph } z|\leqq\pi$. The result (1.6) in the abutting sectors $\pi\leqq|\text{ph } z|\leqq\frac{5}{2}\pi-\delta$ may then be derived by application of well-known connection formulae for $U(a,a-b+1,z)$; compare [7, § 5].

2. Properties of the function $F_p(z)$. We collect here results pertaining to the function $F_p(z)$ that will be needed in the present paper and its sequel [10]. In each result p and z may be real or complex.

In terms of the generalized exponential integral $E_p(z)$ and the incomplete Gamma function $\Gamma(1-p, z)$, $F_p(z)$ is given by

$$F_p(z)=\frac{\Gamma(p)}{2\pi}\frac{E_p(z)}{z^{p-1}}=\frac{\Gamma(p)}{2\pi}\Gamma(1-p, z). \tag{2.1}$$

From the definition (1.7) we easily derive the following identities:

$$F_{p+1}(z)+F_p(z)=\frac{\Gamma(p)}{2\pi}\frac{e^{-z}}{z^p}, \tag{2.2}$$

$$F_{p+2}(z)+F_{p+1}(z)=\frac{p}{z}\{F_{p+1}(z)+F_p(z)\}, \tag{2.3}$$

$$F_p'(z)=-F_{p+1}(z)-F_p(z), \qquad \frac{d}{dz}\{e^zF_p(z)\}=-e^zF_{p+1}(z). \tag{2.4}$$

By rotation of the integration path we derive the following continuation formula in which k denotes any integer:

$$F_p(ze^{2k\pi i})=ie^{-kp\pi i}\frac{\sin(kp\pi)}{\sin(p\pi)}+e^{-2kp\pi i}F_p(z), \qquad z\neq 0. \tag{2.5}$$

When $|z|$ is large and p is fixed, or bounded, we find by application of Watson's lemma [5, Chap. 4, § 3],

$$F_p(z)\sim\frac{e^{-z}}{2\pi}\sum_{s=0}^{\infty}(-)^s\frac{\Gamma(p+s)}{z^{p+s}}, \qquad |\mathrm{ph}\, z|\leqq\tfrac{3}{2}\pi-\delta\,(<\tfrac{3}{2}\pi). \tag{2.6}$$

Next, when $|p|$ and $|z|$ are both large,

$$F_p(z)=\tfrac{1}{2}i\,e^{-p\pi i}[\mathrm{erfc}\,\{c(\theta)\sqrt{\tfrac{1}{2}|z|}\}+e^{-|z|\{c(\theta)\}^2/2}O(z^{-1/2})], \tag{2.7}$$

the O-term being uniform with respect to $\theta\equiv\mathrm{ph}\, z$ in the interval $[-\pi+\delta, 3\pi-\delta]$, and also uniform with respect to bounded values of $|p-|z||$. Here $c(\theta)$ is the continuous branch of the function

$$c(\theta)=\{2\,e^{i\theta}+2i(\theta-\pi)+2\}^{1/2} \tag{2.8}$$

that is asymptotic to $\pi-\theta$ as $\theta\to\pi$. The approximation (2.7) is derived in [6], and a graph of $c(\theta)$ is also included in this reference.[1] As a consequence of these results, the corresponding approximation for the sector $-3\pi+\delta\leq\mathrm{ph}\, z\leqq\pi-\delta$, and the well-known asymptotic estimates

$$\mathrm{erfc}\,(\zeta)=O(e^{-\zeta^2}\zeta^{-1}), \qquad \zeta\to\infty \text{ in } |\mathrm{ph}\,\zeta|\leqq\tfrac{3}{4}\pi-\delta,$$
$$\mathrm{erfc}\,(\zeta)=2+O(e^{-\zeta^2}\zeta^{-1}), \qquad \zeta\to\infty \text{ in } |\mathrm{ph}\,(-\zeta)|\leqq\tfrac{3}{4}\pi-\delta,$$

we derive the following uniform estimates, again valid when $|z|$ is large and $|p-|z||$ is bounded:

$$F_p(z)=e^{-z-|z|}O(1), \qquad |\mathrm{ph}\, z|\leqq\pi, \tag{2.9}$$

$$F_p(z)=e^{-z-|z|}O(z^{-1/2}), \qquad |\mathrm{ph}\, z|\leqq\pi-\delta, \tag{2.10}$$

$$F_p(z)=\pm i\,e^{\mp p\pi i}+e^{-z-|z|}O(1), \qquad \pi\leqq\pm\mathrm{ph}\, z\leqq 3\pi-\delta, \tag{2.11}$$

$$F_p(z)=\pm i\,e^{\mp p\pi i}+e^{-z-|z|}O(z^{-1/2}), \qquad \pi+\delta\leqq\pm\mathrm{ph}\, z\leqq 3\pi-\delta. \tag{2.12}$$

In (2.11) either all upper signs are taken, or all lower signs; (2.12) is similar.

[1] The result (2.7) is contained in the proof of Theorem 1 of [6], rather than in the actual statement of this theorem.

3. Matching of the remainder term by a series of F-functions. The function $U(a, a-b+1, z)$ satisfies the equation

$$Lw=0, \tag{3.1}$$

in which L denotes the differential operator

$$\frac{d^2}{dz^2}+\left(\frac{a-b+1}{z}-1\right)\frac{d}{dz}-\frac{a}{z}.$$

If n is an arbitrary nonnegative integer and we apply the operator L to the nth partial sum of the series (1.1), then we find that

$$L\left\{z^{-a}\sum_{s=0}^{n-1}(-)^s\frac{(a)_s(b)_s}{s!\,z^s}\right\}=(-)^{n-1}\frac{A_n}{z^{n+a+1}}, \tag{3.2}$$

where

$$A_n=\frac{(a)_n(b)_n}{(n-1)!}=\frac{\Gamma(n+a)\Gamma(n+b)}{\Gamma(a)\Gamma(b)(n-1)!}. \tag{3.3}$$

Hence from (3.1) it follows that the remainder term in (1.2) satisfies

$$LR_n(a,b,z)=(-)^n\frac{A_n}{z^{n+a+1}}. \tag{3.4}$$

Our objective is to show that $R_n(a, b, z)$ can be expanded in the form (1.4) in which m is an arbitrary nonnegative integer, and the new remainder $R_{m,n}(a, b, z)$ is estimated by (1.5) and (1.6). We shall approach this problem by constructing a finite series of F-functions which, when operated upon by L, will match the right-hand side of (3.4) except for an asymptotically small term.

Consider first $L\{e^zF_p(z)/z^q\}$, where p and q are arbitrary constants. With the aid of (2.4) we find that

$$\frac{d}{dz}\left\{\frac{e^zF_p(z)}{z^q}\right\}=-\frac{e^zF_{p+1}(z)}{z^q}-q\frac{e^zF_p(z)}{z^{q+1}},$$

and hence

$$\frac{d^2}{dz^2}\left\{\frac{e^zF_p(z)}{z^q}\right\}=\frac{e^zF_{p+2}(z)}{z^q}+2q\frac{e^zF_{p+1}(z)}{z^{q+1}}+q(q+1)\frac{e^zF_p(z)}{z^{q+2}}.$$

As a consequence,

$$L\left\{\frac{e^zF_p(z)}{z^q}\right\}=\frac{e^zF_{p+2}(z)}{z^q}+(2q-a+b-1+z)\frac{e^zF_{p+1}(z)}{z^{q+1}}$$
$$+\{q(q-a+b)+(q-a)z\}\frac{e^zF_p(z)}{z^{q+2}}.$$

The term in $F_{p+2}(z)$ can be eliminated with the aid of (2.3); thus

$$L\left\{\frac{e^zF_p(z)}{z^q}\right\}=(p+2q-a+b-1)\frac{e^zF_{p+1}(z)}{z^{q+1}}+\{q(q-a+b)+(p+q-a)z\}\frac{e^zF_p(z)}{z^{q+2}}.$$

This equation may be rearranged in the form

$$L\left\{\frac{e^zF_p(z)}{z^q}\right\}=(p+q-a)\left\{\frac{e^zF_{p+1}(z)}{z^{q+1}}+\frac{e^zF_p(z)}{z^{q+1}}\right\}+(q+b-1)\frac{e^zF_{p+1}(z)}{z^{q+1}}$$
$$+q(q-a+b)\frac{e^zF_p(z)}{z^{q+2}}.$$

Then by use of (2.2) we arrive at

$$L\left\{\frac{e^zF_p(z)}{z^q}\right\}=\frac{p+q-a}{2\pi}\frac{\Gamma(p)}{z^{p+q+1}}+(q+b-1)\frac{e^zF_{p+1}(z)}{z^{q+1}}+q(q-a+b)\frac{e^zF_p(z)}{z^{q+2}}. \tag{3.5}$$

In order to make the asymptotic behaviour of the first term on the right-hand side of (3.5) match that of the right-hand side of (3.4), we must first arrange that the powers of z agree; thus

$$p+q=n+a. \tag{3.6}$$

From (3.3) and Stirling's formula, we derive

$$A_n \sim (\text{constant})\times e^{-n}n^{n+a+b-(1/2)}, \qquad n\to\infty.$$

Also, with $q=n+a-p$,

$$(p+q-a)\Gamma(p)\sim(\text{constant})\times n\, e^{-p}p^{p-(1/2)}, \qquad p\to\infty.$$

Evidently, apart from the constant factors, the asymptotic behaviour of these two expressions will be the same if we choose $p=n+a+b-1$ and, correspondingly, $q=1-b$. With these choices (3.5) becomes

$$L\left\{\frac{e^zF_{n+a+b-1}(z)}{z^{1-b}}\right\}=\frac{n}{2\pi}\frac{\Gamma(n+a+b-1)}{z^{n+a+1}}+(1-a)(1-b)\frac{e^zF_{n+a+b-1}(z)}{z^{3-b}}. \tag{3.7}$$

The second term on the right-hand side of the last equation is to be regarded as a residual, and to drive it into another residual, but with a higher power of z in the denominator, we consider (3.5) with q increased by unity, to $2-b$. At the same time, to preserve the asymptotic form of the other contribution, we decrease p by unity, to $n+a+b-2$; compare (3.6). Thus we have

$$\begin{aligned}L\left\{\frac{e^zF_{n+a+b-2}(z)}{z^{2-b}}\right\}&=\frac{n}{2\pi}\frac{\Gamma(n+a+b-2)}{z^{n+a+1}}+\frac{e^zF_{n+a+b-1}(z)}{z^{3-b}}\\&\quad+(2-a)(2-b)\frac{e^zF_{n+a+b-2}(z)}{z^{4-b}}.\end{aligned}$$

Then by eliminating the final term from (3.7), we arrive at

$$\begin{aligned}&L\left\{\frac{e^zF_{n+a+b-1}(z)}{z^{1-b}}-(1-a)(1-b)\frac{e^zF_{n+a+b-2}(z)}{z^{2-b}}\right\}\\&=\frac{n}{2\pi z^{n+a+1}}\{\Gamma(n+a+b-1)-(1-a)(1-b)\Gamma(n+a+b-2)\}\\&\quad-(1-a)_2(1-b)_2\frac{e^zF_{n+a+b-2}(z)}{z^{4-b}}.\end{aligned} \tag{3.8}$$

The procedure may be repeated. The last term of the right member of (3.8) is now regarded as the residual, and we drive it into another residual with yet a higher power of z in the denominator by use of (3.5) with $p=n+a+b-3$ and $q=3-b$. Continuing in this manner we readily establish, by induction, the general result

$$\begin{aligned}&L\left\{\sum_{s=0}^{m-1}(-)^s\frac{(1-a)_s(1-b)_s}{s!}\frac{e^zF_{n+a+b-s-1}(z)}{z^{s-b+1}}\right\}\\&=\frac{nB_{m,n}}{2\pi z^{n+a+1}}+(-)^{m-1}\frac{(1-a)_m(1-b)_m}{(m-1)!}\frac{e^zF_{n+a+b-m}(z)}{z^{m-b+2}},\end{aligned} \tag{3.9}$$

in which m is arbitrary, and

$$B_{m,n}=\sum_{s=0}^{m-1}(-)^s\frac{(1-a)_s(1-b)_s}{s!}\Gamma(n+a+b-s-1). \tag{3.10}$$

On comparing (3.4) and (3.9) we perceive that the desired matching is representable in the form

$$L\left\{R_n(a,b,z)+(-)^{n-1}\frac{2\pi A_n}{nB_{m,n}}\sum_{s=0}^{m-1}(-)^s\frac{(1-a)_s(1-b)_s}{s!}\frac{e^zF_{n+a+b-s-1}(z)}{z^{s-b+1}}\right\}$$
$$=(-)^{m+n}\frac{2\pi A_n}{nB_{m,n}}\frac{(1-a)_m(1-b)_m}{(m-1)!}\frac{e^zF_{n+a+b-m}(z)}{z^{m-b+2}}.$$

In § 4 we shall, in effect, invert the operator L in the last equation in order to estimate asymptotically the content of the braces in the left member. However, by comparison with the known result (1.4) we suspect that a simplifying approximation can be made for the ratio $A_n/(nB_{m,n})$. This is indeed the case, and the required result is as follows.

LEMMA 3.1. *Let a and b be fixed (or bounded) complex numbers and m be a fixed nonnegative integer. Then as $n\to\infty$*

$$\frac{\Gamma(n+a)\Gamma(n+b)}{\Gamma(n+1)}=\sum_{s=0}^{m-1}(-)^s\frac{(1-a)_s(1-b)_s}{s!}\Gamma(n+a+b-s-1)$$
$$+(1-a)_m(1-b)_m\Gamma(n+a+b-m-1)O(1).$$

This result is proved in [12, Appendix]. See also [8], [9].

4. Estimation of $R_{m,n}(a,b,z)$. Throughout this section it will be understood that the parameters a and b are fixed (or bounded).

Let us return to (3.4) and (3.9). By combination, we obtain

$$LR_n(a,b,z)-L\left\{(-)^n\frac{2\pi}{\Gamma(a)\Gamma(b)}\sum_{s=0}^{m-1}(-)^s\frac{(1-a)_s(1-b)_s}{s!}\frac{e^zF_{n+a+b-s-1}(z)}{z^{s-b+1}}\right\}$$
$$=(-)^n\left\{A_n-\frac{n}{\Gamma(a)\Gamma(b)}B_{m,n}\right\}\frac{1}{z^{n+a+1}}$$
$$+(-)^{m+n}\frac{2\pi(1-a)_m(1-b)_m}{(m-1)!\,\Gamma(a)\Gamma(b)}\frac{e^zF_{n+a+b-m}(z)}{z^{m-b+2}}.$$

Hence, with $R_{m,n}(a,b,z)$ defined as in (1.4), we have

$$L\{e^zz^{b-1}R_{m,n}(a,b,z)\}=\frac{C_{m,n}}{z^{n+a+1}}+\frac{(-)^m}{(m-1)!}\frac{e^zF_{n+a+b-m}(z)}{z^{m-b+2}}, \tag{4.1}$$

where

$$C_{m,n}=\frac{\Gamma(a)\Gamma(b)}{2\pi(1-a)_m(1-b)_m}\left\{A_n-\frac{n}{\Gamma(a)\Gamma(b)}B_{m,n}\right\}. \tag{4.2}$$

And as a consequence of (3.3), (3.10), and Lemma 3.1 we note that as $n\to\infty$, with m fixed,

$$C_{m,n}=n\Gamma(n+a+b-m-1)O(1)=n^{n+a+b-m-(1/2)}e^{-n}O(1). \tag{4.3}$$

In order to invert the operator L in (4.1) we need two linearly independent solutions of the equation $Lw=0$. One of these has to be the solution that is recessive at infinity in the sector $|\text{ph } z|<\frac{1}{2}\pi$, that is, $U(a, a-b+1, z)$. As a second solution we select $V(a, a-b+1, z)$, the solution that is recessive at infinity in the sector $|\text{ph } (-z)|<\frac{1}{2}\pi$. For brevity, we shall denote these solutions by $U(z)$ and $V(z)$, respectively. Then their defining properties are expressed by

$$U(z)=z^{-a}\{1+O(z^{-1})\}, \qquad z\to\infty \text{ in } |\text{ph } z|\leqq\tfrac{3}{2}\pi-\delta; \tag{4.4}$$

$$V(z)=e^{z}(-z)^{b-1}\{1+O(z^{-1})\}, \qquad z\to\infty \text{ in } |\text{ph } (-z)|\leqq\tfrac{3}{2}\pi-\delta; \tag{4.5}$$

compare [5, Chap. 7, § 10.1].

Until the end of this section, we shall restrict $0\leqq\text{ph } z\leqq\pi$. The branch of z^{-a} in (4.4) is then the principal value, and the choice of branch of $(-z)^{b-1}$ in (4.5) is given by

$$V(z)=e^{\pi i(1-b)}e^{z}z^{b-1}\{1+O(z^{-1})\}, \qquad z\to\infty \text{ in } 0\leqq\text{ph } z\leqq\pi, \tag{4.6}$$

where z^{b-1} has its principal value. The Wronskian of the two solutions is

$$\mathscr{W}\{U(z), V(z)\}=e^{\pi i(1-b)}e^{z}z^{b-a-1}. \tag{4.7}$$

By the method of variation of parameters, using (4.7), we find that one solution of (4.1) is given by

$$R_{m,n}(a, b, z)=R^{(1)}_{m,n}(a, b, z)+R^{(2)}_{m,n}(a, b, z), \tag{4.8}$$

where

$$e^{z}z^{b-1}R^{(1)}_{m,n}(a, b, z)=C_{m,n}\int_{z}^{\infty}\frac{K(z, t)}{t^{n+a+1}}\,dt, \tag{4.9}$$

$$e^{z}z^{b-1}R^{(2)}_{m,n}(a, b, z)=\frac{(-)^{m}}{(m-1)!}\int_{z}^{\infty}\frac{K(z, t)}{t^{m-b+2}}\,e^{t}F_{n+a+b-m}(t)\,dt, \tag{4.10}$$

and

$$K(z, t)=e^{\pi i(b-1)}\,e^{-t}t^{a-b+1}\{U(z)V(t)-V(z)U(t)\}. \tag{4.11}$$

From (2.6), (4.4), and (4.6) we may verify that as $z\to\infty$, the right members of (4.9) and (4.10) are $O(z^{-n-a})$ and $O(z^{-n-a-1})$, respectively. Hence with $R_{m,n}(a, b, z)$ defined by (4.8) it follows that $e^{z}z^{b-1}R_{m,n}(a, b, z)$ is $O(z^{-n-a})$. Again, with the aid also of (2.6) we see that the right-hand side of (1.4) becomes $O(z^{-n-a})$. This is precisely what is required by (1.2), and since there is only one solution of (3.4) that is $O(z^{-n-a})$ as $z\to\infty$, it follows that (4.8) *is* the correct choice of solution of (4.1) when $R_{m,n}(a, b, z)$ is defined by (1.2) and (1.4).

In order to estimate $R_{m,n}(a, b, z)$ from (4.8), (4.9), and (4.10), we need a uniform estimate of $K(z, t)$ when $|z|$ is large. This estimate will depend on the integration paths used in (4.9) and (4.10). We shall employ the same path for each integral, and our first restrictions are that $0\leqq\text{ph } t\leqq\pi$ and $|t|\geqq|z|$ everywhere on this path. Then from (4.4) and (4.6) we conclude that

$$U(z)V(t)=z^{-a}\,e^{t}t^{b-1}O(1) \tag{4.12}$$

when $|z|$ is large in the sector $0\leqq\text{ph } z\leqq\pi$, uniformly for t on the path. As is customary in proofs of this nature, we now try to arrange that the same estimate applies to the other constituent $V(z)U(t)$ in the kernel $K(z, t)$. With this in view we prescribe the integration path in (4.9) and (4.10) to consist of: (i) a circular arc from $t=z$ to $t=|z|$, centered at the origin and described in the positive sense; (ii) the real axis from $t=|z|$

to $t=\infty$. This path is illustrated in Fig. 4.1. If z is real and positive, the circular arc is absent.

LEMMA 4.1. *Assume that*

$$|z| \geqq \tfrac{1}{2}\pi|a+b-1| \quad \textit{and} \quad 0 \leqq \operatorname{ph} z \leqq \pi.$$

Then on the integration path depicted in Fig. 4.1.

$$\left| e^{z-t}\left(\frac{z}{t}\right)^{a+b-1} \right| \leqq \exp\left\{\frac{\pi^2|\operatorname{Im}(a+b)|^2}{8|z|}\right\},$$

provided that $(z/t)^{a+b-1}$ *has its principal value.*

This result is proved in the Appendix. We note, in passing, that the bound is unity when $a+b$ is real, and is $1+O(z^{-1})$ in other circumstances.

Corresponding to (4.12), we have

$$V(z)U(t) = e^z z^{b-1} t^{-a} O(1),$$

and hence, by Lemma 4.1,

$$V(z)U(t) = z^{-a} e^t t^{b-1} O(1). \tag{4.13}$$

On substituting into (4.11) by means of (4.12) and (4.13) we obtain the desired estimate

$$K(z,t) = z^{-a} t^a O(1), \tag{4.14}$$

uniformly valid when t lies in the path depicted in Fig. 4.1 and $|z|$ is large.

Next, on substituting into (4.9) by means of (4.14), we obtain

$$e^z z^{b-1} R_{m,n}^{(1)}(a,b,z) = C_{m,n} z^{-a} O(1) \int_z^\infty \left| \frac{dt}{t^{n+1}} \right|.$$

On the chosen path

$$\int_z^\infty \left| \frac{dt}{t^{n+1}} \right| \leqq \frac{\pi}{|z|^n} + \frac{1}{n|z|^n}. \tag{4.15}$$

Hence we have

$$R_{m,n}^{(1)}(a,b,z) = C_{m,n} \frac{e^{-z}}{z^{n+a+b-1}} \left(\pi + \frac{1}{n}\right) O(1). \tag{4.16}$$

So far in the analysis we have not assumed any relationship between $|z|$ and n. It is at this stage that we introduce the condition (1.3) in which a, b, and α are bounded. Since $n \to \infty$ as $|z| \to \infty$, we may substitute for $C_{m,n}$ in (4.16) by means of (4.3). We obtain

$$R_{m,n}^{(1)}(a,b,z) = n^{n+a+b-m-(1/2)} e^{-n} \frac{e^{-z}}{z^{n+a+b-1}} O(1) = e^{-z-|z|} z^{-m+(1/2)} O(1). \tag{4.17}$$

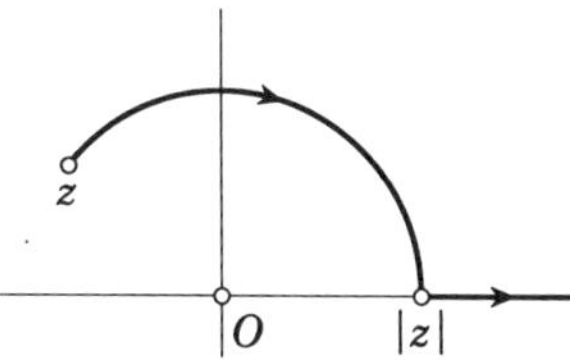

FIG. 4.1. *t-plane. Path for the integrals* (4.9) *and* (4.10). *Sector* $0 \leqq \operatorname{ph} z \leqq \pi$.

The corresponding estimation of $R^{(2)}_{m,n}(a, b, z)$ from (4.10) is more complicated. Consider first the circular arc from z to $|z|$. On this part of the path $|n+a+b-m-|t||$ is bounded; compare (1.3). Hence from (2.9) we obtain

$$F_{n+a+b-m}(t)=e^{-t-|t|}O(1).$$

Using this result and (4.14) we derive

$$\int_z^{|z|}\frac{K(z,t)}{t^{m-b+2}}e^tF_{n+a+b-m}(t)\,dt=z^{-a}O(1)\int_z^{|z|}\frac{e^{-|t|}|dt|}{|t^{m-a-b+2}|}=\frac{e^{-|z|}}{z^{m-b+1}}O(1).\tag{4.18}$$

Now consider the straight line segment from $|z|$ to ∞. On referring to (1.7) and (4.14) we perceive that

$$\int_{|z|}^{\infty}\frac{K(z,t)}{t^{m-b+2}}e^tF_{n+a+b-m}(t)\,dt$$
$$=O(z^{-a})\int_{|z|}^{\infty}\frac{dt}{t^{m-\operatorname{Re}a-\operatorname{Re}b+2}}\int_0^{\infty}\frac{e^{-t\tau}\tau^{n+\operatorname{Re}a+\operatorname{Re}b-m-1}}{1+\tau}\,d\tau.$$

Provided that $m>\operatorname{Re}a+\operatorname{Re}b-1$, the integration order may be interchanged [3, Thm. 1]; thus

$$\int_{|z|}^{\infty}\frac{K(z,t)}{t^{m-b+2}}e^tF_{n+a+b-m}(t)\,dt$$
$$=O(z^{-a})\int_0^{\infty}\frac{\tau^{n+\operatorname{Re}a+\operatorname{Re}b-m-1}}{1+\tau}\,d\tau\int_{|z|}^{\infty}\frac{e^{-t\tau}}{t^{m-\operatorname{Re}a-\operatorname{Re}b+2}}\,dt.$$

In terms of the incomplete Gamma function the inner integral on the right-hand side of the last equation is

$$\tau^{m-\operatorname{Re}a-\operatorname{Re}b+1}\Gamma(\operatorname{Re}a+\operatorname{Re}b-m-1,|z|\tau).$$

Since we are assuming that $m>\operatorname{Re}a+\operatorname{Re}b-1$, this quantity is bounded by

$$e^{-|z|\tau}|z|^{\operatorname{Re}a+\operatorname{Re}b-m-2}\tau^{-1};$$

compare [5, Chap. 3, eq. (1.05)]. Hence we see that

$$\int_{|z|}^{\infty}\frac{K(z,t)}{t^{m-b+2}}e^tF_{n+a+b-m}(t)\,dt=\frac{O(1)}{z^{m-b+2}}\int_0^{\infty}\frac{e^{-|z|\tau}\tau^{n+\operatorname{Re}a+\operatorname{Re}b-m-2}}{1+\tau}\,d\tau$$
$$=e^{|z|}z^{b-m-2}F_{n+\operatorname{Re}a+\operatorname{Re}b-m-1}(|z|)O(1)=e^{-|z|}z^{b-m-2}O(1);\tag{4.19}$$

compare (1.7) and (2.9).

We may now substitute into (4.10) by means of (4.18) and (4.19) to obtain

$$R^{(2)}_{m,n}(a,b,z)=e^{-z-|z|}z^{-m}O(1).\tag{4.20}$$

Then from (4.8), (4.17), and (4.20) we arrive at

$$R_{m,n}(a,b,z)=e^{-z-|z|}O(z^{-m+(1/2)})\tag{4.21}$$

as $z\to\infty$ in the sector $0\leqq\operatorname{ph}z\leqq\pi$. A similar proof applies when $-\pi\leqq\operatorname{ph}z\leqq0$.

To complete the proof of (1.5) we need to show that: (i) the order term in (4.21) can be strengthened to $O(z^{-m})$; (ii) the condition $m>\operatorname{Re}a+\operatorname{Re}b-1$ can be removed. Both steps are easily achieved simply by increasing m in (1.4) and using the estimate

$$F_{n+a+b-s-1}(z)=e^{-z-|z|}O(1)$$

as necessary for $s\leqq m-1$; compare, again, (2.9).

5. Conclusions. We have developed a new form of asymptotic analysis for the study of solutions of linear differential equations in order to establish an exponentially-improved asymptotic expansion of the confluent hypergeometric function $U(a, a-b+1, z)$ in the neighbourhood of the irregular singularity at $z=\infty$. This expansion was derived previously from an integral representation of $U(a, a-b+1, z)$. Our proof applies directly to the sector $|\text{ph } z| \leqq \pi$, which is the region of maximum exponential improvement. The corresponding results for the sectors $\pi \leqq |\text{ph } z| \leqq \frac{5}{2}\pi - \delta$ can be obtained by application of connection formulae.

The integral-representation approach also led to strict and realistic error bounds for the exponentially-improved asymptotic expansion of $U(a, a-b+1, z)$ in the sector $|\text{ph } z| \leqq \pi$. It may be feasible to obtain similar error bounds via our differential-equation approach, but this has not been explored in the present paper.

Appendix. Proof of Lemma 4.1. Write

$$\Phi(t) = \text{Re}\{t + (a+b-1) \ln t\},$$

where the logarithm assumes its principal value. Then on the path depicted in Fig. 4.1 we have

$$\left| e^{z-t} \left(\frac{z}{t}\right)^{a+b-1} \right| = e^{\Phi(z) - \Phi(t)}.$$

Let us consider the behaviour of $\Phi(t)$ at t passes along the contour $ABCD$ shown in Fig. A.1. Here ABC is the semicircle $t = \rho\, e^{i\chi}$, where $\rho = |z|$ and $\pi \geqq \chi \geqq 0$; CD is the segment of the real axis from $t = \rho$ to $t = \infty$. We shall also write

$$a + b - 1 = \kappa_R + i\kappa_I,$$

where κ_R and κ_I are real.

On CD we have

$$\Phi(t) = t + \kappa_R \ln t, \qquad \Phi'(t) = 1 + (\kappa_R/t).$$

Hence $\Phi(t)$ is nondecreasing, provided that $t \geqq -\kappa_R$ in the case $\kappa_R < 0$.

Now suppose that t lies on ABC and $\kappa_I \geqq 0$. Then

$$\Phi(t) = \rho \cos \chi + \kappa_R \ln \rho - \kappa_I \chi, \qquad \frac{d\Phi}{d\chi} = -\rho \sin \chi - \kappa_I.$$

Hence $\Phi(t)$ is nondecreasing.

Lastly, suppose that t lies on ABC and $\kappa_I = -\kappa_I'$, where $\kappa_I' > 0$. Then

$$\Phi(t) = \rho \cos \chi + \kappa_R \ln \rho + \kappa_I' \chi, \quad \frac{d\Phi}{d\chi} = -\rho \sin \chi + \kappa_I', \quad \frac{d^2\Phi}{d\chi^2} = -\rho \cos \chi.$$

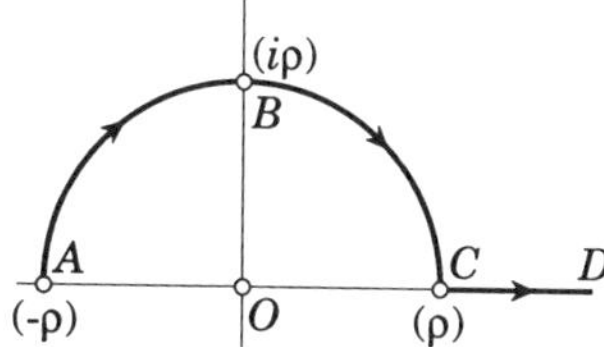

FIG. A.1. *t-plane.*

Suppose also that $\rho > \kappa_I'$. Then $d\Phi/d\chi$ vanishes at $\chi=\chi_0$ and $\chi=\pi-\chi_0$, where $\chi_0=\sin^{-1}(\kappa_I'/\rho)$. The graph of $\Phi(t)$ plotted against χ is illustrated in Fig. A.2.

At C, $t=\rho$, $\chi=0$, and $\Phi(t)=\Phi(\rho)=\rho+\kappa_R \ln \rho$.

At $t=\rho\, e^{i\chi_0}$, $\Phi(t)$ is at a maximum, and we find that

$$\Phi(\rho\, e^{i\chi_0})-\Phi(\rho)=\rho \cos \chi_0-\rho+\kappa_I'\chi_0=h,$$

say. Similarly, at $t=\rho\, e^{i(\pi-\chi_0)}$, $\Phi(t)$ is at a minimum, and we find that

$$\Phi(\rho\, e^{i\pi})-\Phi(\rho\, e^{i(\pi-\chi_0)})=h,$$

with the same h. Also, because $\chi_0=\sin^{-1}(\kappa_I'/\rho)$, we have

$$h=\rho(\cos \chi_0-1+\chi_0 \sin \chi_0).$$

Since $0\leqq \chi_0 \leqq \frac{1}{2}\pi$, we have by an elementary inequality $0\leqq h\leqq \frac{1}{2}\rho\chi_0^2$, and hence by Jordan's inequality

$$0\leqq h\leqq \tfrac{1}{2}\rho\left(\frac{\pi\kappa_I'}{2\rho}\right)^2=\frac{\pi^2\kappa_I'^2}{8\rho}.$$

We require one further condition, given by $\rho\geqq\frac{1}{2}\pi\kappa_I'$. The purpose of this condition is to ensure that $\Phi(\rho)\geqq\Phi(\rho\, e^{i\pi})$ and, in consequence, that the point C in Fig. A.2 does not lie below A.[2]

On combining the foregoing results we see that we can assert that if z and t are any two points on the path depicted in Fig. A.1, t being to the right of z, then in all cases

$$\Phi(z)-\Phi(t)\leqq h\leqq \frac{\pi^2\kappa_I^2}{8\rho},$$

provided that $|z|\geqq-\kappa_R$ when κ_R is negative, and $|z|\geqq-\frac{1}{2}\pi\kappa_I$ when κ_I is negative. The last two conditions are certainly fulfilled when $|z|\geqq\frac{1}{2}\pi|\kappa_R+i\kappa_I|=\frac{1}{2}\pi|a+b-1|$, and Lemma 4.1 follows.

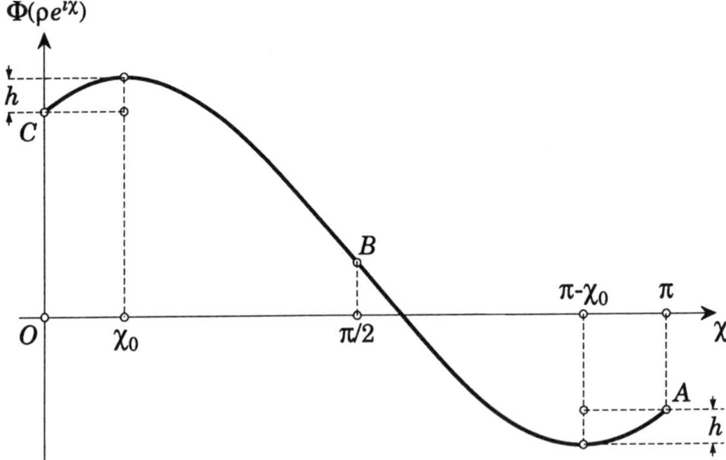

FIG. A.2. *Graph of $\Phi(\rho e^{i\chi})$ when κ_I is negative.*

[2] Actually, it would suffice for C to be no lower than the local minimum at $\chi=\pi-\chi_0$.

Acknowledgment. The writer is pleased to acknowledge helpful discussions with R.B. Paris and A. D. Wood.

REFERENCES

[1] M. V. BERRY, *Uniform asymptotic smoothing of Stokes's discontinuities*, Proc. Roy. Soc. London Ser. A, 422 (1989), pp. 7-21.

[2] ———, *Waves near Stokes lines*, Proc. Roy. Soc. London Ser. A, 427 (1990), pp. 265-280.

[3] E. R. LOVE, *Changing the order of integration*, J. Austral. Math. Soc., 11 (1970), pp. 421-432.

[4] J. B. MCLEOD, *Smoothing of Stokes discontinuities*, Proc. Roy. Soc. London Ser. A, 437 (1992), pp. 343-354.

[5] F. W. J. OLVER, Asymptotics and Special Functions, Academic Press, New York, 1974.

[6] ———, *Uniform, exponentially improved, asymptotic expansions for the generalized exponential integral*, SIAM J. Math. Anal., 22 (1991), pp. 1460-1474.

[7] ———, *Uniform, exponentially improved, asymptotic expansions for the confluent hypergeometric function and other integral transforms*, SIAM J. Math. Anal., 22 (1991), pp. 1475-1489.

[8] ———, *Asymptotic expansions of the coefficients in asymptotic series solutions of linear differential equations*, manuscript.

[9] ———, *On an asymptotic expansion of a ratio of Gamma functions*, manuscript.

[10] ———, *Exponentially-improved asymptotic solutions of ordinary differential equations* II: *Irregular singularities of rank one*, manuscript.

[11] R. B. PARIS, *Smoothing of the Stokes phenomenon for high-order differential equations*, Proc. Roy. Soc. London Ser. A, 436 (1992), pp. 165-186.

[12] ———, *Smoothing of the Stokes phenomenon using Mellin-Barnes integrals*, J. Comput. Appl. Math., 41 (1992), pp. 117-133.

Proc. Sixth SIAM Conference on Parallel Processing for Scientific Computing, **v. 2,** (R. F. Sincovec et al., eds.) 1993

Airy and Bessel Functions by Parallel Integration of ODEs *

D. W. Lozier[†] F. W. J. Olver[‡]

Abstract

The computation of mathematical functions is a part of the scientific computing infrastructure that has not benefited very much from parallel and vector hardware. Special functions with complex variables and parameters are needed in many scientific and engineering calculations but the availability of good software, even for serial computers, is limited. The approaches used heretofore include power series, asymptotic series, and recurrence relations. To these we add the defining differential equation which we integrate numerically in parallel. Our method and its implementation in Fortran software for the Airy function will be described. Accuracy and speedup due to parallelism will be discussed. Important in themselves, Airy functions are needed also in the application of the new approach to Bessel functions.

1 Introduction

Special functions occur in a great variety of calculations in the physical sciences. Excellent codes are available in standard software libraries, including IMSL, NAG, SLATEC (the nonproprietary library of DOE), Mathematica and Matlab for most functions involving only a single real variable. Many gaps remain, however, for functions with real argument and one or more real parameters, and there are much larger gaps for functions with complex arguments and/or parameters. One of the main reasons for this state of affairs is that because of the very varied analytical behavior of these functions, the choice of efficient algorithms in a serial computing environment changes frequently from region to region. As a result, the final code for any given function is apt to draw upon a substantial collection of intricate methods of computation. In contrast, a parallel environment favors relatively simple algorithms that can be applied over very large regions.

We propose to take advantage of the development of parallel and vector computing machines to reduce the number of algorithms that are needed for each function, and at the same time to achieve substantial reductions in execution times. In particular, we shall develop and test parallel methods for solving the differential and difference equations satisfied by the special functions. Our ultimate objective is the creation of highly-tested, robust, fast, transportable software covering almost all conceivable ranges of complex values of the argument and real or complex values of the parameters, for some of the more commonly encountered special functions.

*The research of the second author has been supported by NSF Grant CCR-89-14933.

[†]Applied and Computational Mathematics Division, National Institute of Standards and Technology, Gaithersburg, MD 20899

[‡]Institute for Physical Science and Technology, University of Maryland, College Park, MD 20742

2 General Algorithms for Special Functions

Suppose that we wish to compute a solution $w(z)$ of a homogeneous linear second-order differential equation of the form

$$\frac{d^2w}{dz^2} + f(z)\frac{dw}{dz} + g(z)w = 0 \tag{1}$$

along a path $\mathcal{P}$ from $z = a$ to $z = b$ in the complex plane; see Fig. 1.

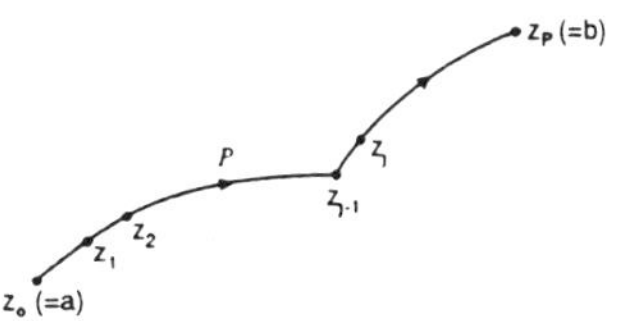

FIG. 1. *A typical integration path in the complex plane.*

Initial values of $w(z)$ and $w'(z)$ are known at $z = a$, and we seek the corresponding values of $w(z)$ and $w'(z)$ at $z = b$. It is assumed that numerical integration from a to b along $\mathcal{P}$ is stable for the wanted solution. $\mathcal{P}$ is subdivided at the points $z_0, z_1, z_2, \ldots, z_P$ in order from $a(= z_0)$ to $b(= z_P)$. Two independent solutions $p_j(z)$ and $q_j(z)$ are constructed for each segment $z_{j-1}z_j$ of $\mathcal{P}$. Then it is easily verified that the wanted solution $w(z)$ satisfies

$$\begin{bmatrix} w(z_j) \\ w'(z_j) \end{bmatrix} = A_j B_j \begin{bmatrix} w(z_{j-1}) \\ w'(z_{j-1}) \end{bmatrix}, \tag{2}$$

where A_j, B_j are the matrices

$$A_j = \begin{bmatrix} p_j(z_j) & q_j(z_j) \\ p_j'(z_j) & q_j'(z_j) \end{bmatrix}, \quad B_j = \begin{bmatrix} p_j(z_{j-1}) & q_j(z_{j-1}) \\ p_j'(z_{j-1}) & q_j'(z_{j-1}) \end{bmatrix}^{-1}. \tag{3}$$

Thus we have

$$\begin{bmatrix} w(z_P) \\ w'(z_P) \end{bmatrix} = A_P B_P A_{P-1} B_{P-1} \ldots A_1 B_1 \begin{bmatrix} w(z_0) \\ w'(z_0) \end{bmatrix}. \tag{4}$$

All pairs of solutions $p_j(z)$ and $q_j(z)$ are to be computed simultaneously, enabling the matrices $A_1, B_1, A_2, B_2, \ldots, A_P, B_P$ to be formed in parallel. And of course parallelization, in the form of cascading, can be used to compute the product $A_P B_P A_{P-1} \ldots A_1 B_1$.

Error analysis indicates that as long as we are integrating in a stable direction everywhere along $\mathcal{P}$ for the wanted solution $w(z)$, the initial values for the solutions $p_j(z)$ and $q_j(z)$ may be prescribed safely at $z = z_{j-1}$; thus

$$p_j(z_{j-1}) = 1, \; p_j'(z_{j-1}) = 0, \; q_j(z_{j-1}) = 0, \; q_j'(z_{j-1}) = 1. \tag{5}$$

With this choice B_j becomes the unit matrix, and the relation between the initial and final values of $w(z)$ and its derivative simplifies to

$$\begin{bmatrix} w(z_P) \\ w'(z_P) \end{bmatrix} = A_P A_{P-1} \ldots A_1 \begin{bmatrix} w(z_0) \\ w'(z_0) \end{bmatrix}. \tag{6}$$

In choosing the method for integrating $p_j(z)$ and $q_j(z)$ over the segment $z_{j-1}z_j$ it is not sufficient that it be numerically efficient. It also needs to be analytically tractable, especially for complex variables. This is in order to control the global error and to optimize the segment lengths and other parameters. In the case of Bessel's equation (and many other differential equations satisfied by the special functions) the coefficients $f(z)$ and $g(z)$ are simple rational functions that can be differentiated easily any number of times. A natural method to use is therefore the Taylor-series method. In other words, to proceed from $z = z_{j-1}$ to $z = z_j$ we simply expand $p_j(z)$ and $q_j(z)$ in their Taylor series centered at $z = z_{j-1}$.

For homogeneous linear second-order difference equations of the form

$$w_{j+1} + f_j w_j + g_j w_{j-1} = 0 \tag{7}$$

parallelization is carried out in an analogous (and in fact simpler) manner.

3 Algorithms for the Airy Functions

For background information on Airy functions, see [1,3,4]. For the purpose of computation, we subdivide the complex z-plane into four regions: I, II, III, IV as indicated in Fig. 2.

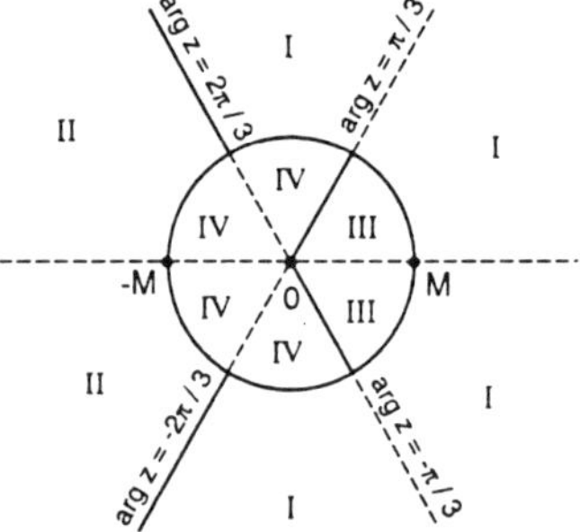

FIG. 2. *Subdivision of the complex plane for the Airy functions* Ai(z) *and* Ai′(z).

In Region I, given by $|z| \geq M$ and $|\arg z| \leq 2\pi/3$, Ai(z) and Ai′(z) are computed from their asymptotic expansions

$$\mathrm{Ai}(z) \sim \frac{e^{-\xi}}{2\sqrt{\pi}z^{1/4}} \sum_{s=0}^{\infty} (-)^s \frac{u_s}{\xi^s}, \quad \mathrm{Ai}'(z) \sim -\frac{z^{1/4}e^{-\xi}}{2\sqrt{\pi}} \sum_{s=0}^{\infty} (-)^s \frac{v_s}{\xi^s}, \tag{8}$$

where $\xi = \frac{2}{3}z^{3/2}$ and

$$u_s = \frac{(2s+1)(2s+3)(2s+5)\dots(6s-1)}{(216)^s s!}, \quad v_s = -\frac{6s+1}{6s-1}u_s. \tag{9}$$

In Region II, given by $|z| \geq M$ and $|\arg(-z)| \leq \pi/3$, we use the compound asymptotic expansions

$$\mathrm{Ai}(-z) \sim \frac{1}{\sqrt{\pi}z^{1/4}} \left\{ \cos(\xi - \frac{1}{4}\pi) \sum_{s=0}^{\infty} (-)^s \frac{u_{2s}}{\xi^{2s}} + \sin(\xi - \frac{1}{4}\pi) \sum_{s=0}^{\infty} (-)^s \frac{u_{2s+1}}{\xi^{2s+1}} \right\}, \tag{10}$$

$$\text{(11)} \qquad \mathrm{Ai}'(-z) \sim \frac{z^{1/4}}{\sqrt{\pi}} \left\{ \sin(\xi - \frac{1}{4}\pi) \sum_{s=0}^{\infty} (-)^s \frac{v_{2s}}{\xi^{2s}} - \cos(\xi - \frac{1}{4}\pi) \sum_{s=0}^{\infty} (-)^s \frac{v_{2s+1}}{\xi^{2s+1}} \right\},$$

Region III, given by $|z| \leq M$ and $|\arg z| \leq \pi/3$, is covered by integration of Airy's equation

$$\text{(12)} \qquad \frac{d^2 w}{dz^2} = zw$$

using the parallelized form (Sec. 2 above) of the Taylor-series method along rays towards the origin.

Lastly, Region IV, given by $|z| \leq M$ and $|\arg(-z)| \leq 2\pi/3$, is covered by integration of Airy's equation, again by the parallelized form of the Taylor-series method, but now along rays that proceed away from the origin.

Comprehensive error analyses have been carried out for all four regions. Also, a general optimizing procedure has been devised to determine: (i) the number of terms (m) to be used in the asymptotic expansions; (ii) the number of processors (P) to be used in the parallelization of the integration of the differential equations; (iii) the number of terms (n) to be used in the Taylor series for each of the P segments $z_{j-1}z_j$; (iv) the value of M, that is, the radius of the circular boundary separating Regions I and II from Regions III and IV. Of course, the four parameters m, P, n and M are interrelated, and they are constrained by the desired global precision and available hardware facilities (vector or parallel, maximum number of processors, etc.).

4 Programs for the Airy Functions

The algorithms described in the previous section need further consideration to obtain programs that are robust and efficient.

The first concern is underflow and overflow. These phenomena are likely to occur only in Regions I and II, where $|z|$ is large. In Region I, the exponential factor $\exp(-\xi)$ in the expansions (8) decays when $|\arg z| < \pi/3$ and grows when $\pi/3 < |\arg z| < 2\pi/3$. In Region II, the right-hand side of the connection formula

$$\text{(13)} \qquad \mathrm{Ai}(z) = e^{-\pi i/3}\mathrm{Ai}(ze^{2\pi i/3}) + e^{\pi i/3}\mathrm{Ai}(ze^{-2\pi i/3})$$

always has one term that increases exponentially while the other decreases exponentially.

Therefore, complete loss of significance can be caused by either underflow or overflow in Region I and by overflow in Region II. Accordingly, a computer program should be designed to compute the scaled Airy functions

$$\text{(14)} \qquad \overline{\mathrm{Ai}}(z) = e^{\xi}\mathrm{Ai}(z), \ \overline{\mathrm{Ai}'}(z) = e^{\xi}\mathrm{Ai}'(z)$$

The original functions can then be obtained by multiplication by $\exp(-\xi)$, provided the latter quantity is within the floating-point range.

In Region I, an efficient procedure for the summation of asymptotic series is needed. For the series (8) we generate the polynomials

$$\text{(15)} \qquad \sum_{s=0}^{m-1} (-)^s \frac{u_s}{\xi^s}, \ \sum_{s=0}^{m-1} (-)^s \frac{v_s}{\xi^s}$$

by nested multiplication, then multiply by the appropriate factors to obtain $\overline{\mathrm{Ai}}(z)$ and $\overline{\mathrm{Ai}'}(z)$. In our program, m, u_s and v_s are stored as data and we use the same value of m for all arguments z.

The computation of the expansions (10) and (11) in Region II is simplified by using the connection formula (13). When z is in Region II, the rotated arguments $z\exp(\pm 2\pi i/3)$ lie in Region I. The result of substituting the original asymptotic expansion (8) into the connection formula is equivalent to using the compound asymptotic expansion. Furthermore, on taking proper account of the phase angles, we find that

$$\overline{\mathrm{Ai}}(z) \sim \frac{1}{2\sqrt{\pi}z^{1/4}}\left\{\sum_{s=0}^{\infty}(-)^s\frac{u_s}{\xi^s} \pm ie^{2\xi}\sum_{s=0}^{\infty}\frac{u_s}{\xi^s}\right\}, \tag{16}$$

$$\overline{\mathrm{Ai}'}(z) \sim -\frac{z^{1/4}}{2\sqrt{\pi}}\left\{\sum_{s=0}^{\infty}(-)^s\frac{v_s}{\xi^s} \mp ie^{2\xi}\sum_{s=0}^{\infty}\frac{v_s}{\xi^s}\right\} \tag{17}$$

where the upper sign is taken when $2\pi/3 < \arg z < \pi$ and the lower sign is taken when $-\pi < \arg z < -2\pi/3$. Here, as before, $\xi = \frac{2}{3}z^{3/2}$ and principal values are taken throughout.

In Regions III and IV, the task is to compute $\overline{\mathrm{Ai}}(z)$ and $\overline{\mathrm{Ai}'}(z)$ at $z = b$ where $0 < |b| < M$. This is done by evaluating

$$\begin{bmatrix}\overline{\mathrm{Ai}}(b)\\ \overline{\mathrm{Ai}'}(b)\end{bmatrix} = e^{\beta-\alpha}A_P A_{P-1}\dots A_1\begin{bmatrix}\overline{\mathrm{Ai}}(a)\\ \overline{\mathrm{Ai}'}(a)\end{bmatrix} \tag{18}$$

where $\alpha = \frac{2}{3}a^{3/2}$, $\beta = \frac{2}{3}b^{3/2}$, and

$$a = \begin{cases} Mb/|b| & (b \text{ in Region III}),\\ 0 & (b \text{ in Region IV}).\end{cases} \tag{19}$$

When b is in Region III, $\overline{\mathrm{Ai}}(a)$ and $\overline{\mathrm{Ai}'}(a)$ are computed by the algorithm for Region I. For Region IV, $\overline{\mathrm{Ai}}(0)$ and $\overline{\mathrm{Ai}'}(0)$ are stored program constants.

The 2×2 matrices

$$A_j = \begin{bmatrix} p_j(z_j) & q_j(z_j)\\ p_j'(z_j) & q_j'(z_j)\end{bmatrix} \tag{20}$$

are formed by evaluating the first n terms of the Taylor series

$$p_j(z_j) = \sum_{s=0}^{\infty} h_j^s\frac{p_j^{(s)}(z_{j-1})}{s!},\quad q_j(z_j) = \sum_{s=0}^{\infty} h_j^s\frac{q_j^{(s)}(z_{j-1})}{s!} \tag{21}$$

where $h_j = z_j - z_{j-1}$. The functions $p_j(z)$ and $q_j(z)$ are solutions of Airy's differential equation (12) with initial values given by Eq. (5). The higher derivatives are generated by the recurrence relation

$$w^{(s+2)} = zw^{(s)} + sw^{(s-1)}, \tag{22}$$

which is obtained from Eq. (12) by differentiation. The points $a = z_0, z_1, z_2, \dots, z_P = b$ lie on the ray through b and the direction of numerical integration is as required for numerical stability.

The optimizing procedure mentioned at the end of Sec. 3 determines the parameters m, P, n and M so as to minimize a theoretical measure of the runtime under the assumptions that $|b-a| = M$, the number of segments $z_{j-1}z_j$ is equal to P, and the segments are equal in length. The resulting segment length M/P is the maximum allowable Taylor step. However, instead of taking P segments of length $|b-a|/P$ when $|b-a| < M$, we take N segments of length $|b-a|/N$ where

$$N = \begin{cases} \text{int}[P(M-|b|)/M]) + 1 & (b \text{ in Region III}), \\ \text{int}[P|b|/M]) + 1 & (b \text{ in Region IV}). \end{cases} \tag{23}$$

With this modification, $z_N = z_{N+1} = \cdots = z_P = b$, the identity matrix is substituted for $A_{N+1}, \ldots, A_P$ in Eq. (18), and the integration is carried out with the minimum number of (nonzero) Taylor steps.

The linear algebra in Eq. (18) involves $N-1$ 2×2 matrix products, one matrix-vector product, and one scalar multiplication. The rearrangement

$$\begin{bmatrix} \overline{\text{Ai}}(b) & 0 \\ \overline{\text{Ai}'}(b) & 0 \end{bmatrix} = A_N A_{N-1} \cdots A_1 A_0 \tag{24}$$

with

$$A_0 = \begin{bmatrix} e^{\beta-\alpha}\overline{\text{Ai}}(a) & 0 \\ e^{\beta-\alpha}\overline{\text{Ai}'}(a) & 0 \end{bmatrix} \tag{25}$$

may be better for parallel processing. Then the N 2×2 matrix products are formed in a binary tree-structured cascade. If there are $N+1$ processors, the computing load is balanced among the processors computing $A_1, A_2, \ldots, A_N$ because the work of each is exactly the same, and the load on the processor computing A_0 is balanced approximately with the load on the other processors by the parameters set in the optimizing procedure. Refinements could be made on particular hardware by carefully timing the different tasks and adjusting the parameters.

At present, the optimizing procedure neglects all communication times while taking into account an estimate of the computing time of the cascading process (as well as estimates of the computing time of the other components of the algorithm). The influence of communication times could be taken into account during the hardware-specific refinement process or, possibly, by a modification of the optimizing procedure.

In the not unlikely event that there are fewer than $P+1$ processors, each processor may need to compute the product of several 2×2 matrices. The modifications needed to handle this case are not hard to envision, at least if $P+1$ and the available number of processors are integral powers of two. Load balancing remains possible if Eq. (24) is being evaluated but for Eq. (18) it is increasingly unlikely to be successful as the disparity increases between $P+1$ and the available number of processors.

If the processors are vector processors, very likely there will be fewer than $P+1$ of them. In this case evaluation of Eq. (18) is probably better. One processor evaluates $\overline{\text{Ai}}(a)$ and $\overline{\text{Ai}'}(a)$, and each of the remaining processors is apportioned the task of computing a product of several 2×2 matrices. With appropriate coding, the construction of these matrices vectorizes. The vector length is the number of matrices in the product. Also with appropriate coding, the vectorized cascading of matrix products is possible. With just one or two processors, vectorization undoubtedly improves the computational efficiency but as the number of processors increases, the average vector length necessarily decreases. Eventually a point is reached at which little gain will result from the vector capability of the processors.

5 Algorithms for Bessel Functions

We propose two main methods. First, the uniform expansions in terms of Airy functions when $|\nu|$ is large: these are typified by

$$J_\nu(\nu z) \sim \frac{1}{\nu^{1/3}}\left(\frac{4\zeta}{1-z^2}\right)^{1/4}\left\{\mathrm{Ai}(\nu^{2/3}\zeta)\sum_{s=0}^{\infty}\frac{A_s(\zeta)}{\nu^{2s}} + \frac{\mathrm{Ai}'(\nu^{2/3}\zeta)}{\nu^{4/3}}\sum_{s=0}^{\infty}\frac{B_s(\zeta)}{\nu^{2s}}\right\} \tag{26}$$

in which ζ is related to z by

$$\frac{2}{3}\zeta^{3/2} = \ln\frac{1+(1-z^2)^{1/2}}{z} - (1-z^2)^{1/2}, \tag{27}$$

and the coefficients $A_s(\zeta)$ and $B_s(\zeta)$ are defined by integro-recurrence relations. Because of their uniformity, the expansions enable the Bessel functions to be computed when $|\nu| \geq \nu_N$, say, where ν_N depends on the working precision but can be assigned independently of z in appropriate regions. Furthermore, because of their doubly asymptotic nature the same expansions can be used when $|z| \geq Z_L$, say, where Z_L is assignable independently of ν in the disk $|\nu| \leq \nu_N$.

Second, in the complementary region $|z| \leq Z_L$ and $|\nu| \leq \nu_N$, we shall use the parallel method described in Sec. 2 for solving Bessel's differential equation, coupled with the power-series expansions for the solutions when $|z|$ is small.

Compared with existing software, we expect to reduce the number, and simplify the nature, of the algorithms as well as to increase the execution speeds.

6 Conclusions

We have written and tested the accuracy of Fortran software to compute $\overline{\mathrm{Ai}}(z)$ and $\overline{\mathrm{Ai}'}(z)$ according to the algorithms described in this paper. The tests, performed on a Convex 3820 with a single vector processor, show that the accuracy is very acceptable in comparison with the published software [2] of D. E. Amos. We expect this conclusion to hold true on other computer hardware as well.

Table 1 provides the results of tests that were made just inside and outside the circular boundary $|z| = M$ and to either side of the rays $z = \exp(k\pi/6), k = 1, 2, \ldots, 12$. The 48 test arguments fall into all four computational regions. The Wronskian tests are based on the verification of the Wronskian identities

$$\mathcal{W}\{\mathrm{Ai}(z), \mathrm{Ai}(ze^{\pm 2\pi i/3})\} = \frac{e^{\mp\pi i/6}}{2\pi}. \tag{28}$$

TABLE 1

Maximum absolute values of the complex relative error in units of the rounding unit in double precision (row 1) and single precision (rows 2-4). All four computational regions were tested with 48 arguments very close to the circular boundary $|z| = M$.

	New Software	Amos's Software
DP Wronskian Test	38	71
SP Wronskian Test	26	68
$\overline{\mathrm{Ai}}(z)$ Comparison Test	38	93
$\overline{\mathrm{Ai}'}(z)$ Comparison Test	25	180

TABLE 2

Parameters used for a vector computer with IEEE arithmetic. η = machine rounding unit, M = radius of circular boundary, m = number of terms in asymptotic series, n = number of terms in Taylor series, P = maximum vector length.

	Single Precision	Double Precision
η	1.2×10^{-7}	2.2×10^{-16}
M	5.38021	9.1226
m	17	37
n	7	19
P	64	32

in single and double precision. The comparison tests compare the new software, and also Amos's software, in single precision against Amos's software in double precision. The errors reported in Table 1 are the absolute values of the complex relative error, measured in units of the machine rounding unit.

The comparison tests were repeated with the test arguments moved from the circular boundary $|z| = M$ to the circles $|z| = 1, 2, \ldots, 12$. The resulting maximum error for $\overline{\mathrm{Ai}}(z)$ was 163 for the new software and 658 for Amos's software; for $\overline{\mathrm{Ai}'}(z)$, the maximum errors were 18 and 147. The large error for $\overline{\mathrm{Ai}}(z)$ is due to the proximity of one of the test arguments to the zero of $\overline{\mathrm{Ai}}(z)$ at $z = 11.00852\ldots$. If the test arguments around the circle $|z| = 11$ are ignored, the error for $\overline{\mathrm{Ai}}(z)$ drops to 65 for the new software and 359 for Amos's software; for $\overline{\mathrm{Ai}'}(z)$, the errors remain unchanged.

Table 2 shows the algorithmic parameters used in our Convex program. The precisions quoted are appropriate for any computer that adheres to the IEEE standard for floating-point arithmetic.

Preliminary timing studies indicate that the vector capabilities of the Convex produce a twofold speedup in comparison with the same tests run with Convex unvectorized code. This compares favorably with Amos's software which exhibits no benefit from vectorization. Our software appears to be faster than Amos's in Regions I and II where only the asymptotic series needs to be evaluated. The observed speed ratio is approximately 3:1. In Regions III and IV where many Taylor series need to be evaluated, our software appears to be slower by a ratio of approximately 2:3. This gap could perhaps be closed by adjusting the parameters of the algorithm and improving the coding of our program. Amos's software computes the Airy functions as a special case of the modified Bessel functions $K_{1/3}(z)$ and $K_{2/3}(z)$.

We are modifying the software for a true multiprocessor, an iWarp computer with 8 scalar processors. When this is completed, we will conduct more detailed timing studies. Based on the results obtained on the Convex and the substantially improved performance the algorithms are designed to produce when multiple processors are being used, we are confident that the results will be favorable.

References

[1] M. Abramowitz and I. A. Stegun. *Handbook of Mathematical Functions*. National Bureau of Standards Applied Mathematics Series 55, December 1972, U. S. Government Printing Office, Washington, DC 20402.

[2] D. E. Amos. *Algorithm 644, A portable package for Bessel functions of a complex variable and nonnegative order*. ACM Trans. on Math Software 12 (1986), pp. 265-273.

[3] J. C. P. Miller. *The Airy Integral.* British Association for the Advancement of Science Mathematical Tables, The University Press, Cambridge, 1946.
[4] F. W. J. Olver. *Asymptotics and Special Functions.* Academic Press, 1974.

Methods and Applications of Analysis
1 (1) 1994, pp. 1–13

Asymptotic expansions of the coefficients in asymptotic series solutions of linear differential equations

F. W. J. Olver

Abstract. In the neighborhood of an irregular singularity of rank one at infinity, a differential equation of the form

$$\frac{d^2w}{dz^2} + f(z)\frac{dw}{dz} + g(z)w = 0$$

has well-known asymptotic solutions of the form

$$e^{\lambda_1 z} z^{\mu_1} \sum_{n=0}^{\infty} \frac{a_{n,1}}{z^n}, \quad e^{\lambda_2 z} z^{\mu_2} \sum_{n=0}^{\infty} \frac{a_{n,2}}{z^n},$$

in which λ_1, λ_2, μ_1, and μ_2 are constants. It is proved that for large n, the coefficients $a_{n,1}$, and $a_{n,2}$ can be expanded in asymptotic series of inverse factorials with explicit coefficients.

1. Introduction

It is well known that the Gamma function has an asymptotic expansion of the form

$$\Gamma(n) \sim \sqrt{2\pi} n^{n-(1/2)} e^{-n} \left\{1 + \frac{1}{12n} + \frac{1}{288n^2} + \cdots\right\} \tag{1.1}$$

as $n \to \infty$ in the sector $|\operatorname{ph} n| \leq \pi - \delta$, where δ is an arbitrary positive constant. Now suppose that a and b are fixed (or bounded) real or complex parameters. Then from (1.1) it follows that

$$\frac{\Gamma(n+a)\Gamma(n+b)}{\Gamma(n+1)} \sim \sqrt{2\pi} n^{n+a+b-(3/2)} e^{-n} \sum_{j=0}^{\infty} \frac{u_j}{n^j} \tag{1.2}$$

in the same circumstances, where $u_0 = 1$ and higher coefficients are polynomials in a and b. It is not difficult to find explicit expressions for the first few, for example,

$$\begin{aligned} u_1 =& \frac{1}{2}(a^2 + b^2 - a - b) + \frac{1}{12}, \\ u_2 =& \frac{1}{24}\{3(a^2+b^2)^2 - 2(5a^3 + 3a^2b + 3ab^2 + 5b^3) \\ & \qquad + 2(5a^2 + 3ab + 5b^2) - 3(a+b)\} + \frac{1}{288}, \end{aligned}$$

Received December 18, 1992, revised May 12, 1993.
1991 *Mathematics Subject Classification.* Primary: 34E05; secondary: 33B15.
Key words and phrases. Asymptotic expansions, differential equations, exponential improvement, factorial series, Gamma function, Gevrey properties, irregular singularity.
This research was supported by the National Science Foundation under grants DMS 87-23039 and DMS 92-08690.

but a general formula for u_j is unavailable.

In consequence of Stirling's formula, the expansion (1.2) can be rearranged as a series of inverse factorials:

$$\frac{\Gamma(n+a)\Gamma(n+b)}{\Gamma(n+1)} \sim \sum_{j=0}^{\infty} v_j \Gamma(n+a+b-j-1), \tag{1.3}$$

again valid when $n \to \infty$ in $|\operatorname{ph} n| \leq \pi - \delta$. The interesting feature of this rearrangement is that in contrast to (1.2), the coefficients enjoy a simple general form given by

$$v_j = (-)^j \frac{(1-a)_j(1-b)_j}{j!}. \tag{1.4}$$

Here we have employed Pochhammer's notation for ascending factorials, given by $(z)_0 = 1$ and

$$(z)_j = z(z+1)(z+2)\cdots(z+j-1), \quad j \geq 1.$$

The results (1.3) and (1.4) are stated without proof by R. B. Dingle on p. 15 (and elsewhere) in [2].

An elegant proof of (1.4) has been supplied recently by R. B. Paris in the Appendix of [9]. Paris' proof is based on the identity

$$\frac{\Gamma(n+a)\Gamma(n+b)}{\Gamma(n+1)\Gamma(n+a+b-1)} = \{1-\chi(n)\}{}_2F_1(1-a, 1-b; 2-a-b-n; 1), \tag{1.5}$$

in which

$$\chi(n) = \sin(\pi a)\sin(\pi b)\operatorname{cosec}(\pi n + \pi a)\operatorname{cosec}(\pi n + \pi b).$$

This result is valid when neither $n + a$ nor $n + b$ is a nonpositive integer. If we let $|\operatorname{Im} n| \to \infty$ with $\operatorname{Re} n$ fixed, then $\chi(n)$ becomes exponentially small and can be neglected. The coefficients in the required asymptotic expansion are then obtainable from the power-series expansion for the hypergeometric function in (1.5).[1]

Paris needed the expansion (1.3) in the construction of exponentially-improved asymptotic expansions for the confluent hypergeometric function $U(a, a-b+1, z)$, with large $|z|$, via Mellin-Barnes integral representations. It was also needed by the present writer [7] in solving the same problem via the confluent hypergeometric differential equation.

The first purpose of the present paper is to supply an alternative, and quite simple, proof of (1.4). This proof serves as a preliminary for the main problem considered in the paper: the asymptotic nature of the coefficients in asymptotic series solutions of second-order linear differential equations in the neighborhood of an irregular singularity of unit rank. It transpires that the same method of proof yields some elegant, and apparently new, results for this more general problem.

---

[1]Another proof of (1.3) and (1.4) will be found in [8]. This proof is based on contour integration.

Let n be a nonnegative integer, and for $n > -\operatorname{Re} a$ and $n > -\operatorname{Re} b$ define

$$a_n = \frac{\Gamma(n+a)\Gamma(n+b)}{n!}. \tag{2.1}$$

Then a_n satisfies the recurrence relation

$$na_n = (n+a-1)(n+b-1)a_{n-1}. \tag{2.2}$$

Motivated by (1.3), we substitute the following generalized asymptotic expansions into this relation

$$\begin{aligned} a_n &\sim \sum_{j=0}^{\infty} v_j \Gamma(n+a+b-j-1), \\ a_{n-1} &\sim \sum_{j=0}^{\infty} v_j \Gamma(n+a+b-j-2). \end{aligned} \tag{2.3}$$

We seek to determine the unknown coefficients v_j. As a preliminary, we rearrange the coefficients in (2.2) as linear combinations of descending factorials; thus

$$n = (n+a+b-j-1) + (j+1-a-b),$$

and

$$\begin{aligned} (n+a-1)(n+b-1) =&(n+a+b-j-1)(n+a+b-j-2) \\ &+ (2j+1-a-b)(n+a+b-j-2) \\ &+ (j+1-a)(j+1-b). \end{aligned}$$

On substituting (2.3) into (2.2), we derive

$$\begin{aligned} &\sum_{j=0}^{\infty} v_j \Gamma(n+a+b-j) + \sum_{j=0}^{\infty} (j+1-a-b) v_j \Gamma(n+a+b-j-1) \\ &\quad \sim \sum_{j=0}^{\infty} v_j \Gamma(n+a+b-j) + \sum_{j=0}^{\infty} (2j+1-a-b) v_j \Gamma(n+a+b-j-1) \\ &\qquad + \sum_{j=0}^{\infty} (j+1-a)(j+1-b) v_j \Gamma(n+a+b-j-2). \end{aligned}$$

Upon reduction, this asymptotic identity becomes

$$\sum_{j=1}^{\infty} j v_j \Gamma(n+a+b-j-1) \sim -\sum_{j=1}^{\infty} (j-a)(j-b) v_{j-1} \Gamma(n+a+b-j-1),$$

and, equating coefficients, we find that

$$v_j = -\frac{(j-a)(j-b)}{j} v_{j-1}.$$

For the first coefficient we have, from (2.1) and (2.3),

$$v_0 = \lim_{n\to\infty} \frac{\Gamma(n+a)\Gamma(n+b)}{n!\,\Gamma(n+a+b-1)} = 1.$$

The required result (1.4) follows immediately.[2]

3. Linear differential equations

The asymptotic theory of the general homogeneous linear differential equation of the second order with an irregular singularity of rank one is given in [6], Chapter 7. Without loss of generality we may suppose the singularity is at infinity. The main features of the theory are as follows. The differential equation has the form

$$\frac{d^2w}{dz^2} + f(z)\frac{dw}{dz} + g(z)w = 0, \tag{3.1}$$

in which the functions $f(z)$ and $g(z)$ can be expanded in power series

$$f(z) = \sum_{s=0}^{\infty} \frac{f_s}{z^s}, \quad g(z) = \sum_{s=0}^{\infty} \frac{g_s}{z^s}, \tag{3.2}$$

that converge in a neighborhood of $z = \infty$. Furthermore, not all of the coefficients f_0, g_0, and g_1 vanish (otherwise, infinity would be a regular singularity). We may also suppose, without loss of generality, that

$$f_0^2 \neq 4g_0; \tag{3.3}$$

cf. [6], Chapter 7, §1.3. Let λ_1 and λ_2 be the roots of the characteristic equation

$$\lambda^2 + f_0\lambda + g_0 = 0. \tag{3.4}$$

In consequence of (3.3), we have $\lambda_1 \neq \lambda_2$. Also define

$$\mu_1 = \frac{f_1\lambda_1 + g_1}{\lambda_2 - \lambda_1}, \quad \mu_2 = \frac{f_1\lambda_2 + g_1}{\lambda_1 - \lambda_2}. \tag{3.5}$$

Then (3.1) has unique solutions $w_1(z)$ and $w_2(z)$ such that

$$w_1(z) \sim e^{\lambda_1 z}\{(\lambda_2 - \lambda_1)z\}^{\mu_1} \sum_{n=0}^{\infty} \frac{a_{n,1}}{z^n} \tag{3.6}$$

as $z \to \infty$ in the sector $|\,\mathrm{ph}(\lambda_2 - \lambda_1)z| \leq \frac{3}{2}\pi - \delta$, and

$$w_2(z) \sim e^{\lambda_2 z}\{(\lambda_2 - \lambda_1)z\}^{\mu_2} \sum_{n=0}^{\infty} \frac{a_{n,2}}{z^n} \tag{3.7}$$

as $z \to \infty$ in the sector $-\frac{1}{2}\pi + \delta \leq \mathrm{ph}(\lambda_2 - \lambda_1)z \leq \frac{5}{2}\pi - \delta$. Here δ again denotes an arbitrary positive constant, and the coefficients are given by $a_{0,1} = a_{0,2} = 1$ and, for $n \geq 1$,

$$\begin{aligned}(\lambda_1 - \lambda_2)na_{n,1} =& (n - \mu_1)(n - 1 - \mu_1)a_{n-1,1} \\ &+ \sum_{s=1}^{n}\{\lambda_1 f_{s+1} + g_{s+1} - (n - s - \mu_1)f_s\}a_{n-s,1},\end{aligned} \tag{3.8}$$

[2] It is only the formula for v_j that is at issue. By restricting n to be a nonnegative integer in the present section, we do not impair the overall region of validity $|\,\mathrm{ph}\, n| \leq \pi - \delta$ of (1.3).

$$(\lambda_2 - \lambda_1)na_{n,2} = (n-\mu_2)(n-1-\mu_2)a_{n-1,2} + \sum_{s=1}^{n}\{\lambda_2 f_{s+1} + g_{s+1} - (n-s-\mu_2)f_s\}a_{n-s,2}. \tag{3.9}$$

The main objective of this paper is to derive asymptotic expansions for $a_{n,1}$ and $a_{n,2}$ as $n \to \infty$. This type of problem has been studied before. Indeed, the asymptotic forms of the coefficients in formal series solutions of more general differential equations are well known; see [1], [3], [4], [10] and [11]. In the case of (3.1) itself, it is known how to construct asymptotic expansions for $a_{n,1}$ and $a_{n,2}$ in descending powers of n. However, the determination of the coefficients of the successive powers is cumbersome and no general formula is available. We shall show that by employing inverse factorial series instead, the coefficients can be expressed in simple explicit forms. It should be noted that Dingle [2, Chapters 13 and 24] also used inverse factorial series for expanding the late coefficients of asymptotic series. However, he did not consider the present problem (except in the special case mentioned in §1); furthermore, his analyses are of a formal character.

As in §2, our derivation of the new expansions for $a_{n,1}$ and $a_{n,2}$ is based directly on the recurrence relations satisfied by these coefficients and we employ only elementary analysis. An alternative, and somewhat shorter, proof based on some new integral representations for $a_{n,1}$ and $a_{n,2}$ will be found in [5]. An advantage of the present approach is that it is applicable to more general recurrence relations for which an integral representation of the solution may be unavailable.

4. Main result

Theorem 4.1. *Let J be an arbitrary nonnegative fixed integer. Then as $n \to \infty$*

$$a_{n,1} = \frac{1}{(\lambda_1 - \lambda_2)^n}\left[\Lambda_1 \sum_{j=0}^{J-1} a_{j,2}(\lambda_1-\lambda_2)^j \Gamma(n+\mu_2-\mu_1-j) + O\{\Gamma(n+\mu_2-\mu_1-J)\}\right], \tag{4.1}$$

$$a_{n,2} = \frac{1}{(\lambda_2 - \lambda_1)^n}\left[\Lambda_2 \sum_{j=0}^{J-1} a_{j,1}(\lambda_2-\lambda_1)^j \Gamma(n+\mu_1-\mu_2-j) + O\{\Gamma(n+\mu_1-\mu_2-J)\}\right], \tag{4.2}$$

where Λ_1 and Λ_2 are constants.

This theorem is proved in the next two sections. At this stage we make the following observations:

(i) Actual values of the constants Λ_1 and Λ_2 are not derived in the present paper for the general case.[3] However, in [5] it is shown that

$$\Lambda_1 = -ie^{(\mu_2-\mu_1)\pi i}C_1/(2\pi), \quad \Lambda_2 = iC_2/(2\pi),$$

[3]In [5] it is assumed that (3.1) has been normalized in such a way that $\lambda_2 - \lambda_1 = 1$. This normalization is not assumed in the formulas given here.

where C_1, C_2 are the coefficients in the connection formulas

$$w_1(z) = e^{2\pi i\mu_1} w_1(ze^{-2\pi i}) + C_1 w_2(z),$$
$$w_2(z) = e^{-2\pi i\mu_2} w_2(ze^{2\pi i}) + C_2 w_1(z).$$

See also [1], [3].

(ii) As in the case of (1.3), the expansions (4.1) and (4.2) are generalized asymptotic expansions. Numerically their character resembles that of ordinary Poincaré expansions, since the successive Gamma functions decrease asymptotically by a factor n.

5. Proof of Theorem 4.1: The first approximation

Our objective in this section is to prove that

$$a_{n,1} = (\lambda_1 - \lambda_2)^{-n}\Gamma(n + \mu_2 - \mu_1)\{\Lambda_1 + O(n^{-1})\} \tag{5.1}$$

as $n \to \infty$. This result is a special case of known results; see, for example, [4]. However, for the sake of completeness and simplicity, we furnish a direct and elementary proof.

The underlying idea of the proof is as follows. In the recurrence relation (3.8), the first term on the right-hand side and the term in the sum for $s = 1$ can be combined. In this way we obtain

$$(\lambda_1 - \lambda_2)na_{n,1} = (n - 1 - c_1)(n - 1 - c_2)a_{n-1,1} + \sum_{s=2}^{n}\{\lambda_1 f_{s+1} + g_{s+1} - (n - s - \mu_1)f_s\}a_{n-s,1}, \tag{5.2}$$

again valid when $n \geq 1$.[4] Here c_1, c_2 are constants that satisfy

$$c_1 + c_2 = 2\mu_1 + f_1 - 1, \quad c_1c_2 = \mu_1(\mu_1 + f_1 - 1) + \lambda_1 f_2 + g_2. \tag{5.3}$$

We note that, in passing,

$$\mu_1 + \mu_2 = -f_1 \tag{5.4}$$

(cf. (3.5)); in consequence, the first of (5.3) is equivalent to

$$c_1 + c_2 = \mu_1 - \mu_2 - 1. \tag{5.5}$$

If we neglect the sum on the right-hand side of (5.2), we obtain

$$(\lambda_1 - \lambda_2)na_{n,1} = (n - 1 - c_1)(n - 1 - c_2)a_{n-1,1}.$$

Since $a_{0,1} = 1$, this recurrence relation has the exact solution

$$a_{n,1} = \frac{1}{\Gamma(-c_1)\Gamma(-c_2)}\frac{\Gamma(n - c_1)\Gamma(n - c_2)}{(\lambda_1 - \lambda_2)^n n!}. \tag{5.6}$$

In consequence of (5.5) and Stirling's formula, the right-hand sides of (5.1) and (5.6) share the same asymptotic form; more precisely

$$\frac{\Gamma(n - c_1)\Gamma(n - c_2)}{(\lambda_1 - \lambda_2)^n n!} = \frac{\Gamma(n + \mu_2 - \mu_1)}{(\lambda_1 - \lambda_2)^n}\{1 + O(n^{-1})\}, \quad n \to \infty. \tag{5.7}$$

[4] As usual, empty sums are interpreted as zero.

Thus our essential object in this section is to show that the sum in (5.2) can be treated as a perturbation, whose effect is absorbable in the error term $O(n^{-1})$ in (5.1).

Since the series (3.2) are assumed to converge in a neighborhood of $z = \infty$, there exist constants F and ρ such that

$$|f_s| \leq F\rho^s, \quad |g_s| \leq F\rho^s, \tag{5.8}$$

for all s. Without loss of generality, we may suppose that $\rho \geq 1$. From these inequalities, it follows that for all positive values of the integer n and all s such that $1 \leq s \leq n$, we have

$$|\lambda_1 f_{s+1} + g_{s+1} - (n - s - \mu_1) f_s| \leq G(n + \rho)\rho^s, \tag{5.9}$$

where G is another assignable constant.

Let $\gamma_1 = \operatorname{Re} c_1$, $\gamma_2 = \operatorname{Re} c_2$, and take N to be a fixed positive integer that satisfies all of the following inequalities:

$$N > \gamma_1, \quad N > \gamma_2, \quad \frac{\rho|\lambda_1 - \lambda_2|(N+1)}{(N-\gamma_1)(N-\gamma_2)} \leq \frac{1}{2}, \tag{5.10}$$

and

$$N \geq \sqrt{(1+\gamma_1)(1+\gamma_2)} - 1 \qquad \text{when} \qquad (1+\gamma_1)(1+\gamma_2) > 0. \tag{5.11}$$

(Obviously such an integer always exists.) When $n \geq N$, we substitute into (5.2) by means of the equation

$$a_{n,1} = \frac{\Gamma(n - c_1)\Gamma(n - c_2)}{(\lambda_1 - \lambda_2)^n \, n!} \alpha_n. \tag{5.12}$$

This leads to the following recurrence relation for the quantities α_n:

$$\alpha_n = \alpha_{n-1} + \sum_{s=2}^{n-N} h_s(n) \alpha_{n-s} + K(n), \quad n \geq N+1, \tag{5.13}$$

in which

$$\begin{aligned} h_s(n) = & \frac{\{\lambda_1 f_{s+1} + g_{s+1} - (n - s - \mu_1) f_s\}(\lambda_1 - \lambda_2)^{s-1}}{(n - 1 - c_1)(n - 2 - c_1) \cdots (n - s - c_1)} \\ & \times \frac{(n-1)(n-2)\cdots(n-s+1)}{(n - 1 - c_2)(n - 2 - c_2) \cdots (n - s - c_2)}, \end{aligned} \tag{5.14}$$

and

$$\begin{aligned} K(n) = & \frac{(\lambda_1 - \lambda_2)^{n-1}(n-1)!}{\Gamma(n - c_1)\Gamma(n - c_2)} \\ & \times \sum_{s=n-N+1}^{n} \{\lambda_1 f_{s+1} + g_{s+1} - (n - s - \mu_1) f_s\} a_{n-s,1}. \end{aligned} \tag{5.15}$$

In consequence of (5.9) and (5.10), we have

$$|h_s(n)| \leq H_s(n), \quad 2 \leq s \leq n - N, \tag{5.16}$$

where

$$H_s(n) = \frac{G(n+\rho)\rho^s|\lambda_1-\lambda_2|^{s-1}}{(n-1-\gamma_1)(n-2-\gamma_1)\cdots(n-s-\gamma_1)} \times \frac{(n-1)(n-2)\cdots(n-s+1)}{(n-1-\gamma_2)(n-2-\gamma_2)\cdots(n-s-\gamma_2)}. \tag{5.17}$$

We now introduce a majorizing sequence $\{\beta_n\}$ for $\{\alpha_n\}$, defined by

$$\beta_N = \max(|\alpha_N|, 1) \tag{5.18}$$

and

$$\beta_n = \beta_{n-1} + \sum_{s=2}^{n-N} H_s(n)\beta_{n-s} + |K(n)|, \quad n \geq N+1. \tag{5.19}$$

Obviously

$$|\alpha_n| \leq \beta_n, \quad n \geq N. \tag{5.20}$$

The next step is to prove that β_n tends to a limit as $n \to \infty$. Suppose now that $n \geq N+3$. From the definition (5.17), we have

$$\frac{H_{s+1}(n)}{H_s(n)} = \frac{\rho|\lambda_1-\lambda_2|(n-s)}{(n-s-1-\gamma_1)(n-s-1-\gamma_2)}, \quad 2 \leq s \leq n-N-1.$$

Let

$$\phi(\nu) = \frac{\nu}{(\nu-1-\gamma_1)(\nu-1-\gamma_2)}, \quad \nu \geq N+1.$$

Then

$$\frac{\phi'(\nu)}{\phi(\nu)} = \frac{(1+\gamma_1)(1+\gamma_2)-\nu^2}{\nu(\nu-1-\gamma_1)(\nu-1-\gamma_2)}.$$

In consequence of the assumed conditions (5.10), (5.11), we see that $\phi'(\nu) \leq 0$ when $\nu \geq N+1$. Thus as s increases the sequence of ratios $\{H_{s+1}(n)/H_s(n)\}$ is nondecreasing; accordingly

$$\frac{H_{s+1}(n)}{H_s(n)} \leq \frac{H_{n-N}(n)}{H_{n-N-1}(n)} = \frac{\rho|\lambda_1-\lambda_2|(N+1)}{(N-\gamma_1)(N-\gamma_2)} \leq \frac{1}{2}; \tag{5.21}$$

cf. again (5.10). Hence

$$H_s(n) \leq 2^{2-s}H_2(n), \quad 2 \leq s \leq n-N. \tag{5.22}$$

From (5.19), it is obvious that the sequence $\beta_N, \beta_{N+1}, \beta_{N+2}, \ldots$ is increasing. With the aid of (5.18), (5.19), and (5.22) we derive

$$\beta_n = \beta_{n-1}(1+\theta_n),$$

where

$$|\theta_n| \leq \sum_{s=2}^{n-N} H_s(n) + \frac{|K(n)|}{\beta_{n-1}} \leq 2H_2(n) + |K(n)|.$$

From (5.17) with $s = 2$, we see that $H_2(n) = O(n^{-2})$ as $n \to \infty$. Furthermore, since the only unknown coefficients that appear in the sum in (5.15) are $a_{0,1}, a_{1,1}, \ldots, a_{N-1,1}$, it follows from Stirling's approximation and (5.9) that

$$|K(n)| = \frac{(|\lambda_1 - \lambda_2|e\rho)^n}{n^{n-\gamma_1-\gamma_2-(3/2)}} O(1), \quad n \to \infty. \tag{5.23}$$

Thus $\theta_n = O(n^{-2})$. In consequence, the infinite product

$$\prod_{n=N+1}^{\infty} (1 + \theta_n)$$

converges, and so β_n tends to a finite limit β, say, as $n \to \infty$.

Finally, from (5.13), (5.16), (5.20), and (5.22), we see that

$$|\alpha_n - \alpha_{n-1}| \le \beta \sum_{s=2}^{n-N} 2^{2-s} H_2(n) + |K(n)| = O\Big(\frac{1}{n^2}\Big), \tag{5.24}$$

as before. Hence α_n approaches a finite limit Λ_1, say; furthermore

$$\alpha_n = \Lambda_1 + O(n^{-1}), \quad n \to \infty. \tag{5.25}$$

In combination with (5.12) and (5.7), this establishes (5.1).

6. Proof of Theorem 4.1: Higher approximations

We now propose to extend the asymptotic approximation (5.1) into the desired asymptotic expansion (4.1). We first observe from (5.14) that in the relation (5.13), the functions $h_s(n)$ can be expanded in convergent series of the form

$$h_s(n) = \frac{1}{n^s} \sum_{j=0}^{\infty} \frac{h_{j,s}}{n^j} \tag{6.1}$$

when n is large; the coefficients $h_{j,s}$ depend on $f_s, f_{s+1}, g_{s+1}, \lambda_1, \lambda_2, \mu_1, c_1$, and c_2.

Assume that $n \ge N + 3$. Then we have

$$\left|\sum_{s=3}^{n-N} h_s(n)\alpha_{n-s} + K(n)\right| \le \beta \sum_{s=3}^{n-N} 2^{3-s} H_3(n) + |K(n)| = O\Big(\frac{1}{n^3}\Big);$$

cf. (5.16), (5.17) (with $s = 3$), (5.21) and (5.23). Hence from (5.13) we have

$$\alpha_n - \alpha_{n-1} = h_2(n)\alpha_{n-2} + O\Big(\frac{1}{n^3}\Big) = \frac{h_{0,2}\Lambda_1}{n^2} + O\Big(\frac{1}{n^3}\Big);$$

cf. (5.25) and (6.1) (with $s = 2$). Accordingly, from the expansion

$$\alpha_n = \Lambda_1 + \sum_{s=n}^{\infty} (\alpha_s - \alpha_{s+1}),$$

we derive

$$\alpha_n = \Lambda_1 - \frac{h_{0,2}\Lambda_1}{n} + O\Big(\frac{1}{n^2}\Big), \quad n \to \infty.$$

Continuing the resubstitutions, we easily see that

$$a_n \sim \sum_{j=0}^{\infty} \frac{u_j}{n^j},$$

where the coefficients u_j are constants that depend on Λ_1, the coefficients in the expansions (3.2) for $f(z)$ and $g(z)$, and the Bernoulli numbers.[5]

In consequence, from (5.12) we have

$$a_{n,1} \sim \frac{\Gamma(n-c_1)\Gamma(n-c_2)}{(\lambda_1-\lambda_2)^n\, n!} \sum_{j=0}^{\infty} \frac{u_j}{n^j}, \qquad n \to \infty. \tag{6.2}$$

In turn, this expansion may be rearranged in the form

$$a_{n,1} \sim \frac{1}{(\lambda_1-\lambda_2)^n} \sum_{j=0}^{\infty} v_j \Gamma(n+\mu_2-\mu_1-j), \qquad n \to \infty, \tag{6.3}$$

where $v_0, v_1, v_2, \ldots$ comprise another sequence of constants; cf. again (5.7).

In (6.3) it is clear that $v_0 = u_0 = \Lambda_1$. We shall find $v_1, v_2, \ldots$ by substituting into (3.8) by means of (6.3) and equating coefficients. We first need to overcome a difficulty stemming from the fact that the number of terms in the sum in (3.8) increases with n. This is achieved by truncating the sum at a fixed number of terms and estimating the remainder, as follows:

Lemma 6.1. *If M is any fixed nonnegative integer, then as $n \to \infty$*

$$\sum_{s=M+1}^{n} \{\lambda_1 f_{s+1} + g_{s+1} - (n-s-\mu_1) f_s\} a_{n-s,1} = O\left\{\frac{\Gamma(n+\mu_2-\mu_1-M)}{(\lambda_1-\lambda_2)^n}\right\}. \tag{6.4}$$

Proof. Define M_0 to be the least nonnegative integer such that

$$\mathrm{Re}(M_0+\mu_2-\mu_1) > 0 \text{ and } |M_0+\mu_2-\mu_1| \geq 2\rho|\lambda_1-\lambda_2|, \tag{6.5}$$

where ρ is defined as in (5.8). From (5.1) it follows that

$$|a_{s,1}| \leq A|(\lambda_1-\lambda_2)^{-s}\Gamma(s+\mu_2-\mu_1)|, \qquad s \geq M_0, \tag{6.6}$$

where A is assignable independently of s.

From (5.9) and (6.6), we derive

$$|\{\lambda_1 f_{s+1} + g_{s+1} - (n-s-\mu_1) f_s\} a_{n-s,1}| \leq K_s(n), \qquad 1 \leq s \leq n - M_0,$$

where

$$K_s(n) = AG(n+\rho)\rho^s |(\lambda_1-\lambda_2)^{s-n}\Gamma(n-s+\mu_2-\mu_1)|.$$

When $1 \leq s \leq n - M_0 - 1$, we have

$$\frac{K_{s+1}(n)}{K_s(n)} = \frac{\rho|\lambda_1-\lambda_2|}{|n-s+\mu_2-\mu_1-1|} \leq \frac{\rho|\lambda_1-\lambda_2|}{|M_0+\mu_2-\mu_1|} \leq \frac{1}{2};$$

[5]Compare [6], p. 292, Example 3.2.

cf. (6.5). Hence

$$\begin{aligned}\sum_{s=M+1}^{n-M_0} \left|\{\lambda_1 f_{s+1} + g_{s+1} - (n-s-\mu_1)f_s\}a_{n-s,1}\right| &\le \sum_{s=M+1}^{n-M_0} 2^{M+1-s}K_{M+1}(n)\\ &\le 2K_{M+1}(n)\\ &= O\left\{\frac{\Gamma(n+\mu_2-\mu_1-M)}{(\lambda_1-\lambda_2)^n}\right\}. \end{aligned} \tag{6.7}$$

In the remaining part of the sum in (6.4), the only a's that appear are $a_{0,1}, a_{1,1}, \dots, a_{M_0-1,1}$. With the aid, again, of (5.9), we see that

$$\begin{aligned}&\sum_{s=n-M_0+1}^{n} |\{\lambda_1 f_{s+1}+g_{s+1} - (n-s-\mu_1)f_s\}a_{n-s,1}|\\ &\qquad = O(n\rho^n) = O\left\{\frac{\Gamma(n+\mu_2-\mu_1-M)}{(\lambda_1-\lambda_2)^n}\right\}\end{aligned} \tag{6.8}$$

(cf. also (5.15) and (5.23).) Combination of (6.7) and (6.8) completes the proof of the lemma.

To continue the preparation of (3.8) for substitution by means of (6.3), we rearrange the coefficients as descending factorials (as in §2). Thus we set

$$\begin{aligned} n &= (n+\mu_2-\mu_1-j)+(\mu_1-\mu_2+j),\\ (n-\mu_1)(n-1-\mu_1) &= (n+\mu_2-\mu_1-j)(n+\mu_2-\mu_1-j-1)\\ &\quad +2(j-\mu_2)(n+\mu_2-\mu_1-j-1)\\ &\quad +\mu_2(\mu_2-1)+(1-2\mu_2)j+j^2, \end{aligned}$$

and

$$\lambda_1 f_{s+1}+g_{s+1}-(n-s-\mu_1)f_s = -f_s(n+\mu_2-\mu_1-j-s)+(\mu_2-j)f_s+\lambda_1 f_{s+1}+g_{s+1}.$$

We then find that

$$\begin{aligned}&(\lambda_1-\lambda_2)^{n-1}\{(\lambda_1-\lambda_2)na_{n,1}-(n-\mu_1)(n-1-\mu_1)a_{n-1,1}\}\\ &\quad\sim \sum_{j=0}^{\infty}(\mu_1+\mu_2-j)v_j\Gamma(n+\mu_2-\mu_1-j)\\ &\qquad -\sum_{j=0}^{\infty}\{\mu_2(\mu_2-1)+(1-2\mu_2)j+j^2\}v_j\Gamma(n+\mu_2-\mu_1-j-1),\end{aligned} \tag{6.9}$$

and

$$\begin{aligned}&(\lambda_1-\lambda_2)^{n-1}\sum_{s=1}^{M}\{\lambda_1 f_{s+1}+g_{s+1}-(n-s-\mu_1)f_s\}a_{n-s,1}\\ &\sim -\sum_{s=1}^{M} f_s(\lambda_1-\lambda_2)^{s-1}\sum_{j=0}^{\infty} v_j\Gamma(n+\mu_2-\mu_1-j-s+1)\\ &\quad +\sum_{s=1}^{M}(\lambda_1-\lambda_2)^{s-1}\sum_{j=0}^{\infty}\{(\mu_2-j)f_s+\lambda_1 f_{s+1}+g_{s+1}\}v_j\Gamma(n+\mu_2-\mu_1-j-s).\end{aligned} \tag{6.10}$$

Bearing in mind Lemma 6.1, we may equate coefficients in the right members in (6.9) and (6.10) up to (but excluding) the terms in $\Gamma(n+\mu_2-\mu_1-M)$. From the leading terms, we derive

$$(\mu_1+\mu_2)v_0=-f_1v_0,$$

in agreement with (5.4).

Next, on equating coefficients of $\Gamma(n+\mu_2-\mu_1-m)$, with $1\le m\le M-1$, we have

$$\begin{aligned}(\mu_1+\mu_2-m)v_m-\{\mu_2(\mu_2-1)+(1-2\mu_2)(m-1)+(m-1)^2\}v_{m-1}\\ =-\sum_{s=1}^{m+1} f_s(\lambda_1-\lambda_2)^{s-1}v_{m-s+1}\\ +\sum_{s=1}^{m}\{(\mu_2-m+s)f_s+\lambda_1 f_{s+1}+g_{s+1}\}(\lambda_1-\lambda_2)^{s-1}v_{m-s}.\end{aligned}$$

Upon rearrangement and use once again of (5.4), the last equation reduces to

$$\begin{aligned}-mv_m=&(m-\mu_2)(m-1-\mu_2)v_{m-1}\\ &+\sum_{s=1}^{m}\{\lambda_2 f_{s+1}+g_{s+1}-(m-s-\mu_2)f_s\}(\lambda_1-\lambda_2)^{s-1}v_{m-s}.\end{aligned}$$

From (3.9) it is easily verified that this is exactly the same as the recurrence relation satisfied by $(\lambda_1-\lambda_2)^m a_{m,2}$. And since $a_{0,2}=1$, we conclude that

$$v_m=(\lambda_1-\lambda_2)^m a_{m,2}v_0.$$

This result has been derived on the assumption that $m\le M-1$, but since M is arbitrary it becomes valid for all m. Substituting this result into (6.3), and recalling that $v_0=\Lambda_1$, we derive the required result (4.1).

The companion result (4.2) is proved in a similar manner, or we can appeal to symmetry. This completes the proof of Theorem 4.1.

7. Summary

In §§1 and 2, we discussed the problem of constructing asymptotic expansions for a ratio of Gamma functions, and gave a new proof of the expansion

$$\frac{\Gamma(n+a)\Gamma(n+b)}{\Gamma(n+1)}\sim\sum_{j=0}^{\infty}(-)^j\frac{(1-a)_j(1-b)_j}{j!}\Gamma(n+a+b-j-1) \qquad (7.1)$$

as $n\to\infty$ in $|\operatorname{ph} n|\le\pi-\delta$ $(<\pi)$.

In §§3 to 6, we used a similar method of proof to obtain new asymptotic expansions, again in series of inverse factorials, for the coefficients in asymptotic series solutions of homogeneous linear differential equations of the second order in the neighborhood of an irregular singularity of rank one. The results are summarized by Theorem 4.1.

It is easily verified that if Theorem 4.1 is applied to the following form of the confluent hypergeometric differential equation:

$$\frac{d^2w}{dz^2}+\left(\frac{a-b+1}{z}-1\right)\frac{dw}{dz}-\frac{a}{z}w=0,$$

then the expansion (7.1) results. Thus (7.1) may be regarded as a special case of Theorem 4.1. Apart from obvious analytical and computational interests, the new expansions are of importance in the general theory of exponentially-improved asymptotic solutions of ordinary linear differential equations [5], just as the expansion (7.1) arises in the corresponding theory for the confluent hypergeometric equation [7], [9].

Acknowledgement. The writer is indebted to A. D. Wood for improvements in the presentation of this paper, and to the referees for helpful suggestions.

References

1. W. Balser, W. B. Jurkat and D. A. Lutz, *On the reduction of connection problems for differential equations with an irregular singular point to ones with only regular singularities,* II, SIAM J. Math. Anal. **19** (1988), 398–443.
2. R. B. Dingle, *Asymptotic Expansions: Their Derivation and Interpretation*, Academic Press, London, 1973.
3. G. K. Immink, *A note on the relationship between Stokes multipliers and formal solutions of analytic differential equations*, SIAM J. Math. Anal. **21** (1990), 782–792.
4. W. Jurkat, D. Lutz and A. Peyerimhoff, *Birkhoff invariants and effective calculations for meromorphic linear differential equations.* I, J. Math. Anal. Appl. **53** (1976), 438–470.
5. A. B. Olde Daalhuis and F. W. J. Olver, *Exponentially-improved asymptotic solutions of ordinary differential equations* II*: Irregular singularities of rank one*, Proc. Roy. Soc. London, Ser. A, to appear.
6. F. W. J. Olver, *Asymptotics and Special Functions*, Academic Press, New York, 1974.
7. ———, *Exponentially-improved asymptotic solutions of ordinary differential equations* I*: The confluent hypergeometric function*, SIAM J. Math. Anal. **24** (1993), 756–767.
8. ———, *On an asymptotic expansion of a ratio of Gamma functions*, manuscript.
9. R. B. Paris, *Smoothing of the Stokes phenomenon using Mellin-Barnes integrals*, J. Comput. Appl. Math. **41** (1992), 117–133.
10. J. P. Ramis, *Les séries k-sommables et leur applications.* In: Lecture Notes in Physics **126**, (D. Iagolnitzer, ed.), Springer-Verlag, Berlin, 1980, 178–199.
11. Y. Sibuya, *Gevrey property of formal solutions in a parameter.* In: Asymptotic and Computational Analysis, (R. Wong, ed.), Lecture Notes in Pure and Applied Mathematics **124**, Marcel Dekker, New York, 1990, 393–401.

Institute for Physical Science and Technology, University of Maryland, College Park, Maryland 20742, U. S. A.

International Series of Numerical Mathematics, Vol.119, © 1994 Birkhäuser, pp. 497-510.

THE GENERALIZED EXPONENTIAL INTEGRAL

F.W.J. Olver*

Dedicated, in friendship, to Walter Gautschi on the occasion of his 65th birthday, and in recognition of his numerous important contributions to the theory of special functions.

Abstract. This paper concerns the role of the generalized exponential integral in recently-developed theories of exponentially-improved asymptotic expansions and the Stokes phenomenon. The first part describes the asymptotic behavior of the integral when both the argument and order are large in absolute value. The second part shows how to increase the accuracy of asymptotic expansions of solutions of linear differential equations of the second order by re-expanding the remainder terms in series of generalized exponential integrals.

1 INTRODUCTION

For real or complex values of the variables p and z, the generalized exponential integral ("g.e.i.") is defined by

$$E_p(z) = z^{p-1}\Gamma(1-p,z) = z^{p-1}\int_z^{\infty} \frac{e^{-t}}{t^p}dt, \quad z \neq 0, \tag{1.1}$$

with the proviso that the integration path does not pass through the origin. Unless p is a nonpositive integer, $E_p(z)$ is a multiple-valued function of z with branch-points at $z = 0$ and ∞. As a function of p, each branch of $E_p(z)$ is entire. The ordinary exponential integral corresponds to the case $p = 1$.

Recently, the g.e.i. has assumed an important role in a branch of asymptotic analysis called "exponential asymptotics". To explain this subject, we turn to the asymptotic expansion of $E_p(z)$ itself. For fixed p and large $|z|$ we have the well-known expansion

$$E_p(z) \sim \frac{e^{-z}}{z}\sum_{s=0}^{\infty}(-)^s\frac{p(p+1)\cdots(p+s-1)}{z^s}, \quad |\mathrm{ph}\, z| \leq \frac{3}{2}\pi - \delta, \tag{1.2}$$

where δ is an arbitrary small positive constant. The meaning of this expansion is that assigned by Poincaré: for each fixed nonnegative integer n

$$E_p(z) = \frac{e^{-z}}{z}\left\{\sum_{s=0}^{n-1}(-)^s\frac{p(p+1)\cdots(p+s-1)}{z^s} + R_n(z)\right\}, \tag{1.3}$$

*Institute for Physical Science and Technology and Department of Mathematics, University of Maryland, College Park, MD 20742

where

$$R_n(z) = O(z^{-n}) \text{ uniformly as } z \to \infty \text{ in the sector } |\text{ph}\, z| \le \frac{3}{2}\pi - \delta. \quad (1.4)$$

This result is easily established, for example, by repeated integration of (1.1) by parts. The restriction of z to a sector in the final expansion is typical. Indeed, if a Poincaré-type asymptotic expansion of an analytic function is valid for all values of ph z, then it is necessarily a Laurent expansion and therefore converges for all sufficiently large $|z|$ [13, pp.18-19].

Another important standard feature of the expansion (1.2) is that for any given values of p and z the accuracy obtainable by summing this series is limited. Excluding the case in which p is a nonpositive integer, the best that we can do is to terminate the sum just prior to the numerically smallest term. After that, the incorporation of additional terms only makes matters worse. On the other hand, if we take fixed number of terms in the expansion and keep increasing the value of $|z|$, then because

$$R_n(z) \sim (-)^n p(p+1)\cdots(p+n-1)z^{-n}$$

the relative error decreases in an algebraic manner.

The object of exponential asymptotics is to increase the accuracy obtainable from asymptotic approximations or asymptotic expansions of Poincaré type. When successful, it generally leads to approximations in which the relative error is exponentially, rather than algebraically, small as the absolute value of the asymptotic variable z tends to infinity. The earliest work on the subject appears to be that of T.J. Stieltjes in 1886 [17]. The formal work on "converging factors" by J.R. Airey [1] and J.C.P. Miller [11] is also in this vein, as is R.B. Dingle's formal theory of "terminants" [8]. Outlines and comparisons of these investigations will be found in [16].

2 RE-EXPANSION IN SERIES OF ELEMENTARY FUNCTIONS

The general way in which greater accuracy is extracted from an asymptotic expansion is by appropriate re-expansion of the remainder term. In the case of the expansion (1.3) an explicit formula for $R_n(z)$ is available from the partial integration procedure, and is given by

$$R_n(z) = (-)^n \frac{p(p+1)\cdots(p+n-1)}{z^n} z e^z E_{n+p}(z). \quad (2.1)$$

The next step is to truncate the expansion either at or close to its optimal stage, that is, just before the numerically smallest term. Since the ratio of the $(n+1)^{th}$ term to the nth term is $-(p+n-1)/z$ this means that we choose n so that $|p+n-1| = |z|$, approximately. More precisely, if $\hat{n}$ is the positive real number

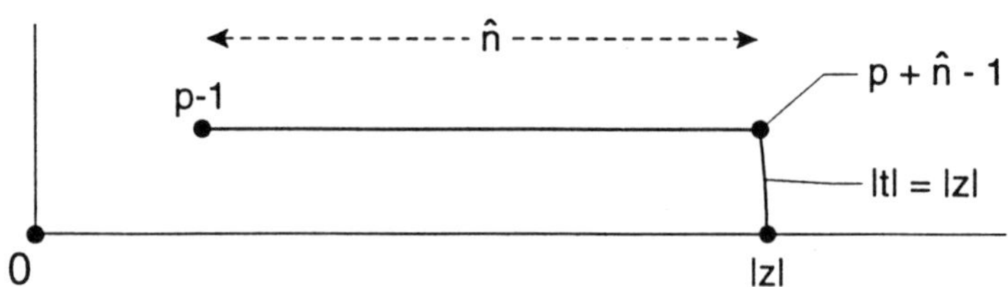

Figure 2.1: t-plane.

that satisfies $|p+\hat{n}-1| = |z|$, then we set $n = \text{int}[\hat{n}]$. Thus n is now a function of $|z|$, albeit discontinuous, that tends to infinity with $|z|$.

From Figure 2.1, it is clear that $|p+\hat{n}-1-|z||$ is bounded as $|z| \to \infty$ (in fact it tends to $|\text{Im}\, p|$). And since

$$|p+n-|z|| \leq |p+\hat{n}-1-|z||+1,$$

it follows that $|p+n-|z||$ is bounded, also. On replacing $p+n$ by p in (2.1) we see that the desired re-expansion of $R_n(z)$ can be found if we are able to expand $E_p(z)$ when $|z|$ and $|p|$ are both large and $|p-|z||$ is bounded.

Accordingly, we set

$$z = \rho e^{i\theta}, \quad p = \rho + \alpha, \tag{2.2}$$

where $\rho(>0)$ is large, and $|\alpha|$ is bounded. We also employ another well-known integral representation for the g.e.i., given by†

$$E_p(z) = \frac{z^{p-1}e^{-z}}{\Gamma(p)} \int_0^\infty \frac{e^{-zt}t^{p-1}}{1+t} dt, \quad \text{Re}\, p > 0, \quad |\text{ph}\, z| < \frac{1}{2}\pi, \tag{2.3}$$

and for later convenience we renormalize the definition of $E_p(z)$ in the following way:

$$E_p(z) = \frac{2\pi}{\Gamma(p)} z^{p-1} F_p(z). \tag{2.4}$$

With these notational changes we arrive that

$$F_p(z) = \frac{e^{-z}}{2\pi} \int_0^\infty \frac{e^{-zt}t^{p-1}}{1+t} dt = \frac{e^{-z}}{2\pi} \int_0^\infty \frac{\exp(-\rho e^{i\theta}t)t^{\rho+\alpha-1}}{1+t} dt. \tag{2.5}$$

For large ρ the last integral has a saddle-point at $t = e^{-i\theta}$. To apply Laplace's method, we rotate the integration path through an angle $-\theta$. We can do this directly when $-\frac{1}{2}\pi < \theta < \frac{1}{2}\pi$, and by analytic continuation beyond $\theta = \pm\frac{1}{2}\pi$,

†Formula (2.3) can be obtained from (1.1) with the aid of the convolution formula for the Laplace transform.

but because the integrand has a singularity at $t = -1$, of necessity we restrict $-\pi < \theta < \pi$. Setting $t = \tau e^{-i\theta}$ on the new path, we arrive at

$$F_p(z) = \frac{e^{-i(\rho+\alpha)\theta} e^{-z}}{2\pi} \int_0^\infty \frac{e^{-\rho\tau} \tau^{\rho+\alpha-1}}{1 + \tau e^{-i\theta}} d\tau.$$

The saddle-point is now located at $\tau = 1$, and expanding the integral about this point in the usual way, we arrive at

$$F_p(z) \sim \frac{e^{-i(\rho+\alpha)\theta}}{1 + e^{-i\theta}} \frac{e^{-\rho-z}}{(2\pi\rho)^{1/2}} \sum_{s=0}^{\infty} \frac{a_{2s}(\theta, \alpha)}{\rho^s} \tag{2.6}$$

as $\rho \to \infty$, uniformly with respect to bounded $|\alpha|$ and $\theta \in [-\pi + \delta, \pi - \delta]$, δ again denoting an arbitrary small positive constant. For this range of θ the coefficients $a_{2s}(\theta, \alpha)$ are continuous functions of θ and α. For example, we have

$$a_0(\theta, \alpha) = 1, \quad a_2(\theta, \alpha) = \frac{1}{12} + \frac{1}{2}\alpha(\alpha - 1) - \frac{\alpha}{1 + e^{i\theta}} + \frac{1}{(1 + e^{i\theta})^2}.$$

To return to the original remainder term, we have from (2.1) and (2.4)

$$R_n(z) = (-)^n \frac{2\pi}{\Gamma(p)} z^p e^z F_{n+p}(z). \tag{2.7}$$

To apply (2.6) we replace p by $n + p$. This simply has the effect of changing the second of (2.2) into

$$p + n = \rho + \alpha, \tag{2.8}$$

except that p is now fixed. In this way we arrive at

$$R_n(z) \sim (-)^n \frac{(2\pi)^{1/2}}{\Gamma(p)} \frac{e^{i(p-\rho-\alpha)\theta}}{1 + e^{-i\theta}} \rho^{p-(1/2)} e^{-\rho} \sum_{s=0}^{\infty} \frac{a_{2s}(\theta, \alpha)}{\rho^s} \tag{2.9}$$

as $z \to \infty$, uniformly with respect to ph $z \in [-\pi + \delta, \pi - \delta]$ and bounded $|\alpha|$ in (2.8). This is the desired expansion. It includes the optimal value of n, as defined earlier in this section.

The most interesting feature of the expansion (2.9) is the factor $e^{-\rho}$, that is, $e^{-|z|}$. This is indeed exponentially small as $|z| \to \infty$; furthermore, this applies uniformly in the sector $|\text{ph } z| \le \pi - \delta$. It is worth reflecting at this stage where the exponential smallness of $R_n(z)$ originates. It is essentially due to the increase of n with $|z|$; thus for each increase of a unit in the value of $|z|$ we take one more term in the expansion (1.3). Now the numerically smallest term of the sum in (1.2) is $(-)^n\Gamma(p + n)/\{\Gamma(p)z^n\}$, with $n = \text{int}[\hat{n}]$ and $\hat{n}$ determined by $|p + \hat{n} - 1| = |z|$; compare the opening paragraph of this section. For large n and fixed p this term is approximately

$$(-)^n \sqrt{2\pi} n^{n+p-(1/2)} e^{-n} z^{-n} / \Gamma(p),$$

and since (2.8) applies, with $|\alpha|$ bounded, the last expression is asymptotic to

$$(-)^n \sqrt{2\pi} e^{-|z|} |z|^{|z|+\alpha-(1/2)} z^{-|z|+p-\alpha} / \Gamma(p),$$

that is,

$$(-)^n \sqrt{2\pi} e^{i(p-\alpha-|z|)\theta} |z|^{p-(1/2)} e^{-|z|} / \Gamma(p). \tag{2.10}$$

This estimate of the numerically smallest term cannot be used for the remainder term, since in the present circumstances neighboring terms are comparable with the smallest term. However, there is obviously a strong link between (2.9) and (2.10). Indeed, the leading term of (2.9) differs from (2.10) only by the factor $1/(1+e^{-i\theta})$.

The previous paragraph points to the source of the exponential smallness of $R_n(z)$. But our actual analysis has taken us beyond this. We have not merely found the order of magnitude of $R_n(z)$ when (2.8) applies with $|\alpha|$ bounded, we have re-expanded $R_n(z)$ in another asymptotic series. If we truncate the sum in (2.9) after m terms, then for fixed m the absolute error in this approximation to $R_n(z)$ is uniformly $O(e^{-\rho}\rho^{p-(1/2)-m})$ as $\rho \to \infty$. We therefore say that the combination of (1.3) and (2.9) yields an *exponential improvement* over the original Poincaré form (1.2).

3 RE-EXPANSION IN TERMS OF THE ERROR FUNCTION

The analysis of §2 applies when $|\theta| \leq \pi - \delta$ $(< \pi)$. Everything breaks down as $\theta \to \pm\pi$. Thus in (2.6) and (2.9) the factor $1/(1+e^{-i\theta})$ and the coefficients $a_{2s}(\theta, \alpha)$, other than $a_0(\theta, \alpha)$, all become infinite. However, in applications that we shall be making and also because of interest in the g.e.i. itself, we seek approximations for $F_p(z)$, or equivalently $E_p(z)$ or $\Gamma(1-p, z)$, that are uniform with respect to θ in intervals containing $\theta = \pi$ or $-\pi$.

From the standpoint of Laplace's method for contour integrals, or the method of steepest descents, the basic problem is the coalescence of the saddle-point at $t = e^{-i\theta}$ in the integral in (2.5) with the simple pole at $t = -1$. Thanks to the researches of B.L. van der Waerden [19], N. Bleistein [7] and D.S. Jones [10], this is a well-understood problem in asymptotics, and it is possible to construct uniform asymptotic expansions with the aid of the error function.‡ We shall not enter into the details of the analysis: they can be found in [14] and [15] (together with the proofs of all results quoted in §2). The final result is expressible as follows.

As in §2, set

‡Asymptotic expansions for incomplete Gamma functions in terms of the error function have been provided by N.M. Temme [18]. However, they do not apply to the combination of variables p and z that we are considering here.

$$z = \rho e^{i\theta}, \quad p = \rho + \alpha, \tag{3.1}$$

Then as $\rho \to \infty$ we have

$$F_p(z) \sim ie^{-p\pi i}\left[\frac{1}{2}\text{erfc}\left\{c(\theta)\sqrt{\frac{1}{2}\rho}\right\} - i\frac{e^{-\rho\{c(\theta)\}^2/2}}{(2\pi\rho)^{1/2}}\sum_{s=0}^{\infty}\frac{h_{2s}(\theta,\alpha)}{\rho^s}\right], \tag{3.2}$$

uniformly with respect to $\theta \in [-\pi+\delta, 3\pi-\delta]$[§] and bounded values of $|\alpha|$. In this expansion erfc denotes the complementary error function and $c(\theta)$ is defined by

$$c(\theta) = \sqrt{2\{1 + e^{i\theta} + i(\theta - \pi)\}}, \tag{3.3}$$

the branch of the square root being chosen so that

$$c(\theta) \sim \pi - \theta \quad \text{as} \quad \theta \to \pi,$$

and determined by continuity elsewhere; see Figs.3.1 and 3.2. The coefficients $h_{2s}(\theta,\alpha)$ are continuous functions of θ and α throughout the region of validity of (3.2). Thus unlike the $a_{2s}(\theta,\alpha)$ they are continuous at $\theta = \pi$. However, the two sets of coefficients are related as follows:

$$h_{2s}(\theta,\alpha) = \frac{e^{i\alpha(\pi-\theta)}}{1+e^{-i\theta}}a_{2s}(\theta,\alpha) - (-)^s i\frac{1\cdot 3\cdot 5\cdots(2s-1)}{\{c(\theta)\}^{2s+1}}.$$

(At $\theta = \pi$ the singularities in the two terms on the right-hand side cancel each other.)

As in §2 the corresponding expansion for the original remainder term $R_n(z)$ is found on replacing n by $n+p$ in (3.2) and substituting into (2.7). We observe that owing to the factor

$$e^{-\rho\{c(\theta)\}^2/2} \equiv e^{-\rho - z - i\rho(\theta-\pi)}$$

exponential improvement of (1.2) is achieved throughout the interval $-\pi + \delta \leq \theta \leq \frac{3}{2}\pi - \delta$.

Next, the extent of the θ-interval of validity of (3.2) is noteworthy. In particular, it includes that of the expansion (2.6). In fact, (2.6) can be derived as a special case of (3.2), as follows. When $-\pi+\delta \leq \theta \leq \pi - \delta$ we see from Fig.3.2 that $c(\theta)$ lies in the right half-plane and is bounded away from the origin. Accordingly, the argument $c(\theta)\sqrt{\frac{1}{2}\rho}$ of the complementary error function also lies in the right half-plane and tends to infinity with ρ. We may therefore substitute for erfc by means of its own asymptotic expansion, given by

[§]A similar expansion applies when $\theta \in [-3\pi+\delta, \pi-\delta]$.

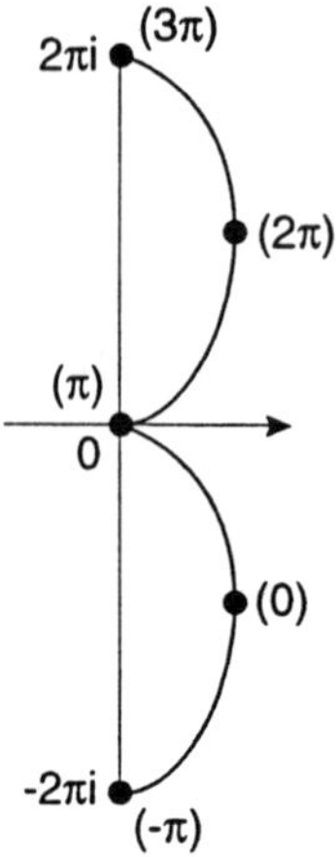

Figure 3.1: $\frac{1}{2}\{c(\theta)\}^2$-plane.(Values of θ in parentheses.)

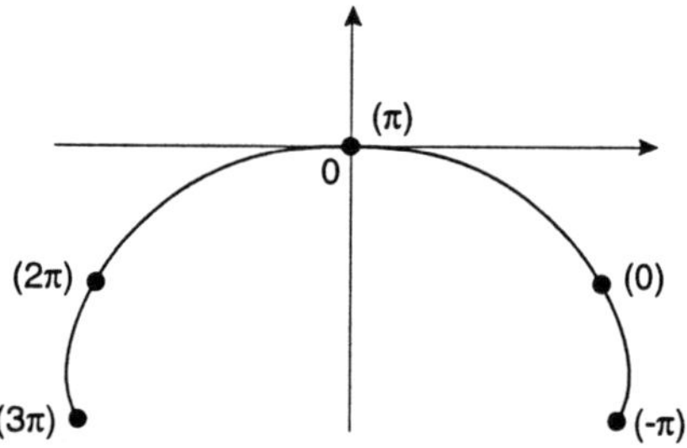

Figure 3.2: $c(\theta)$-plane.(Values of θ in parentheses.)

$$\operatorname{erfc}(\zeta) \sim \frac{e^{-\zeta^2}}{\sqrt{\pi}\zeta}\sum_{s=0}^{\infty}(-)^s\frac{1\cdot 3\cdots(2s-1)}{(2\zeta^2)^s}, \quad |\operatorname{ph}\zeta| \le \frac{3}{4}\pi-\delta, \tag{3.4}$$

with $\zeta = c(\theta)\sqrt{\frac{1}{2}\rho}$. Rearrangement of the result yields (2.6).

4 STOKES' PHENOMENON

Let us now consider the expansion (3.2) when $\theta \in [\pi+\delta, 3\pi-\delta]$. In this case $c(\theta)$ and ζ both lie in the left half-plane; compare again Fig.3.2. The expansion (3.4) is inapplicable, but because

$$\operatorname{erfc}(\zeta) = 2 - \operatorname{erfc}(-\zeta)$$

we have instead

$$\operatorname{erfc}(\zeta) \sim 2 + \frac{e^{-\zeta^2}}{\sqrt{\pi}\zeta}\sum_{s=0}^{\infty}(-)^s\frac{1\cdot 3\cdots(2s-1)}{(2\zeta^2)^s}, \quad |\operatorname{ph}(-\zeta)| \le \frac{3}{4}\pi-\delta. \tag{4.1}$$

On substituting into (3.2) we find that

$$F_p(z) = ie^{-ip\pi} + \text{something exponentially small ("ses")}, \ \pi+\delta \le \theta \le 3\pi-\delta,$$

and hence from (2.7)

$$R_n(z) = 2\pi i\frac{e^{-ip\pi}}{\Gamma(p)}z^p e^z\{1+(\text{ses})\},$$

valid when (2.8) holds with fixed p and bounded $|\alpha|$. Now consider (1.3). When $\theta \equiv \operatorname{ph} z = \pi+\delta$, $|e^z|$ is exponentially small. As θ increases, $|e^z|$ increases, but remains exponentially small until θ passes through $\frac{3}{2}\pi$, after which it becomes the *dominant* contribution to the right-hand side of (1.3). (This is not inconsistent with (1.2), however, because (1.2) requires $\operatorname{ph} z \le \frac{3}{2}\pi-\delta$.) In fact (1.3) has transformed into another well-known asymptotic expansion, given by*

$$E_p(z) \sim 2\pi i\frac{e^{-ip\pi}}{\Gamma(p)}z^{p-1} + \frac{e^{-z}}{z}\sum_{s=0}^{\infty}(-)^s\frac{p(p+1)\cdots(p+s-1)}{z^s},$$
$$\frac{1}{2}\pi+\delta \le \operatorname{ph} z \le \frac{7}{2}\pi-\delta. \tag{4.2}$$

There has long been an element of mystery concerning overlapping sectors of validity for differing asymptotic expansions of the same analytic function – in this case

*The expansion (4.2) is easily obtained by combining (1.2) with the connection formula $E_p(z) = \{2\pi i e^{-ip\pi}z^{p-1}/\Gamma(p)\} + E_p(ze^{-2\pi i})$.

the expansions (1.2) and (4.2). The mystery does not center on any inconsistency. In the common interval of validity $\frac{1}{2}\pi + \delta \le \operatorname{ph} z \le \frac{3}{2}\pi - \delta$ the contribution of the term in z^{p-1} is exponentially small compared with that of the infinite series and is therefore absorbable in any of the remainder terms associated with this series. The mystery is how the change from one form of expansion to the other ought to take place, because the change introduces a discontinuity in form whereas there is no discontinuity in $E_p(z)$ itself. This is of course an example of the celebrated Stokes phenomenon. A remarkable feature of the expansion (3.2) is that it furnishes a *smooth* transition from one asymptotic expansion to the other. When $\rho \equiv |z|$ is large, the change takes place rapidly as θ passes through the critical value π, because it stems almost entirely from the behavior of the term $\operatorname{erfc}\{c(\theta)\sqrt{\frac{1}{2}\rho}\}$; compare Figs.4.1 and 4.2. Nevertheless the change is smooth. To put the matter in a more colorful way, the contribution $2\pi i e^{-ip\pi} z^{p-1}/\Gamma(p)$ is born in a natural manner as θ approaches and then passes beyond the value π.

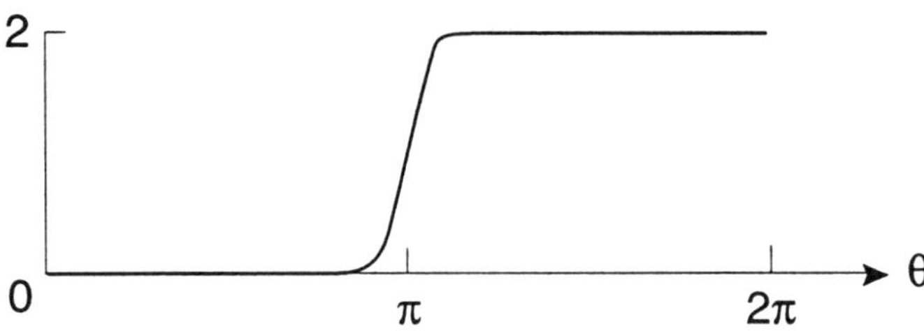

Figure 4.1: Graph of $|\operatorname{erfc}\{4c(\theta)\}|$.

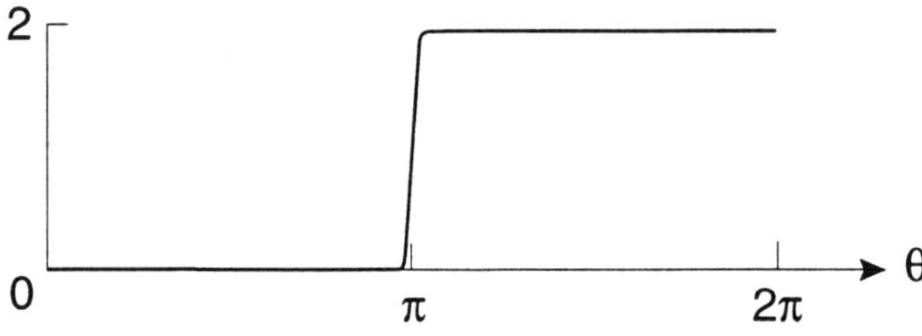

Figure 4.2: Graph of $|\operatorname{erfc}\{16c(\theta)\}|$.

It was a quest by M.V. Berry for a more satisfactory explanation of the Stokes phenomenon that has resurrected the subject of exponential asymptotics. In Berry's original paper in 1989 [2] he supplied a general analysis of the Stokes phenomenon, and proceeded to apply this to various functions, including the g.e.i. Besides providing a smooth interpretation of the phenomenon, Berry demonstrated the improvement in the accuracy of his new approximations by means of numerical examples. In the case of the g.e.i. the results we have derived in this section go beyond those of Berry. In the first place our results have been established rigorously. Secondly, Berry's approximation applies only in the immediate vicinity of the Stokes line (ph $z = \pi$). Thirdly, our re-expansion (3.2) is considerably more accurate than Berry's approximation, even near the Stokes line. However, these observations in no way detract from the immense value of Berry's pioneering work, both in [2] and in numerous papers published subsequently by him and his students on other aspects of exponential asymptotics, for example, [3] - [6] and [9].

5 APPLICATIONS TO OTHER FUNCTIONS

The analyses for the g.e.i. given in §§2 and 3 above were greatly facilitated by the availability of the simple explicit formulas (2.1) and (2.3) for the remainder term in the original asymptotic expansion (1.3). Asymptotic expansions of other functions invariably have more complicated remainder terms and it is often much more difficult to re-expand them. It is again possible to seek re-expansions in terms of the error function, and indeed this was Berry's approach. I have found it more elegant mathematically to follow an earlier lead of Dingle and employ series of g.e.i.'s as the basic form of approximation, leaving the connection to the error function as an implicit consequence of the known asymptotic behavior of the g.e.i. described in §3 above. As an illustration, I will describe the re-expansion of asymptotic solutions of ordinary linear differential equations of the second order in the neighborhood of an irregular singularity of rank one. Several important special functions satisfy such equations, including Bessel functions and, more generally, confluent hypergeometric functions.

Without loss of generality we may suppose that the singularity is located at $z = \infty$. Then the equations we are considering have the general form

$$\frac{d^2w}{dz^2} + f(z)\frac{dw}{dz} + g(z)w = 0, \tag{5.1}$$

where the coefficients $f(z)$ and $g(z)$ are analytic at infinity, that is, they can be expanded in power series

$$f(z) = \sum_{s=0}^{\infty} \frac{f_s}{z^s}, \quad g(z) = \sum_{s=0}^{\infty} \frac{g_s}{z^s},$$

that converge for all sufficiently large values of $|z|$. And again, without loss of generality, we may assume that the roots λ_1 and λ_2 of the characteristic equation

$$\lambda^2 + f_0\lambda + g_0 = 0$$

are distinct. For notational convenience we may then normalize equation (5.1) so that $\lambda_2 - \lambda_1 = 1$. (This simply means that we replace the original independent variable z by $z/(\lambda_2 - \lambda_1)$.)

Asymptotic solutions of (5.1) are well known in these circumstances, and are given by [13, Chap. 7]

$$w_1(z) = e^{\lambda_1 z} z^{\mu_1} \sum_{s=0}^{n-1} \frac{a_{s,1}}{z^s} + R_n^{(1)}(z), \tag{5.2}$$

$$w_2(z) = e^{\lambda_2 z} z^{\mu_2} \sum_{s=0}^{n-1} \frac{a_{s,2}}{z^s} + R_n^{(2)}(z), \tag{5.3}$$

where for fixed n and large $|z|$

$$R_n^{(1)}(z) = e^{\lambda_1 z} z^{\mu_1} O(z^{-n}), \quad |\mathrm{ph}\, z| \le \frac{3}{2}\pi - \delta, \tag{5.4}$$

$$R_n^{(2)}(z) = e^{\lambda_2 z} z^{\mu_2} O(z^{-n}), \quad -\frac{1}{2}\pi + \delta \le \mathrm{ph}\, z \le \frac{5}{2}\pi - \delta. \tag{5.5}$$

Here the indices μ_1 and μ_2 are given by

$$\mu_1 = f_1\lambda_1 + g_1, \quad \mu_2 = -(f_1\lambda_2 + g_1),$$

and the coefficients $a_{s,1}$ and $a_{s,2}$ are determined recursively by

$$-sa_{s,1} = (s - \mu_1)(s - 1 - \mu_1)a_{s-1,1} + \sum_{j=1}^{s} \{\lambda_1 f_{j+1} + g_{j+1} - (s - j - \mu_1)f_j\}\, a_{s-j,1},$$

$$sa_{s,2} = (s - \mu_2)(s - 1 - \mu_2)a_{s-1,2} + \sum_{j=1}^{s} \{\lambda_2 f_{j+1} + g_{j+1} - (s - j - \mu_2)f_j\}\, a_{s-j,2},$$

beginning with $a_{0,1} = a_{0,2} = 1$.

Theorem. *Let m be an arbitrary fixed nonnegative integer. Then*

$$R_n^{(1)}(z) = (-)^{n-1} i e^{(\mu_2-\mu_1)\pi i} e^{\lambda_2 z} z^{\mu_2} \left\{ C_1 \sum_{s=0}^{m-1} (-)^s a_{s,2} \frac{F_{n+\mu_2-\mu_1-s}(z)}{z^s} + R_{m,n}^{(1)}(z) \right\}, \tag{5.6}$$

$$R_n^{(2)}(z) = (-)^{n} i e^{(\mu_2-\mu_1)\pi i} e^{\lambda_1 z} z^{\mu_1} \left\{ C_2 \sum_{s=0}^{m-1} (-)^s a_{s,1} \frac{F_{n+\mu_1-\mu_2-s}(ze^{-\pi i})}{z^s} + R_{m,n}^{(2)}(z) \right\}, \tag{5.7}$$

where C_1 and C_2 are the coefficients in the connection formulas

$$w_1(z) = e^{2\pi\mu_1 i} w_1(ze^{-2\pi i}) + C_1 w_2(z), \tag{5.8}$$

$$w_2(z) = e^{-2\pi\mu_2 i} w_2(ze^{2\pi i}) + C_2 w_1(z), \tag{5.9}$$

and as $z \to \infty$ with $|n - |z||$ bounded

$$R_{m,n}^{(1)}(z) = O(e^{-|z|-z} z^{-m}), \quad |\mathrm{ph}\, z| \le \pi, \tag{5.10}$$

$$R_{m,n}^{(1)}(z) = O(z^{-m}), \quad \pi \le |\mathrm{ph}\, z| \le \frac{5}{2}\pi - \delta, \tag{5.11}$$

$$R_{m,n}^{(2)}(z) = O(e^{-|z|+z} z^{-m}), \quad 0 \le \mathrm{ph}\, z \le 2\pi, \tag{5.12}$$

$$R_{m,n}^{(2)}(z) = O(z^{-m}), \quad -\frac{3}{2}\pi + \delta \le \mathrm{ph}\, z \le 0 \quad \text{and} \quad 2\pi \le \mathrm{ph}\, z \le \frac{7}{2}\pi - \delta, \tag{5.13}$$

uniformly with respect to ph z *in each case.*

This result is proved by A.B. Olde Daalhuis and the present writer in [12]. Several observations may be made, as follows.

(i) The condition that $|n - |z||$ be bounded as $z \to \infty$ includes the situation in which n is chosen optimally in (5.2) or (5.3). This is a consequence of the asymptotic expansions

$$a_{s,1} \sim (-)^s \frac{e^{(\mu_2-\mu_1)\pi i}}{2\pi i} C_1 \sum_{j=0}^{\infty} (-)^j a_{j,2} \Gamma(s + \mu_2 - \mu_1 - j), \tag{5.14}$$

$$a_{s,2} \sim -\frac{1}{2\pi i} C_2 \sum_{j=0}^{\infty} a_{j,1} \Gamma(s + \mu_1 - \mu_2 - j), \tag{5.15}$$

also proved in [12].

(ii) The sector of validity in the z-plane for the expansion of each solution has a total angle $5\pi - 2\delta$, compared with $3\pi - 2\delta$ in the original Poincaré expansions (5.2) to (5.5). Furthermore, uniform exponential improvement is achieved in the central parts of these sectors, given by $|\mathrm{ph}\, z| \le \pi$ for the first solution, and $0 \le \mathrm{ph}\, z \le 2\pi$ for the second solution.

(iii) The Stokes phenomenon for the solution $w_1(z)$ in the vicinities of the Stokes lines $\mathrm{ph}\, z = \pm\pi$ is explained smoothly by the behavior of the F-functions in the expansion (5.6) in these regions (§§3,4). Similarly for the solution $w_2(z)$ in the vicinities of ph $z = 0$ and 2π.

(iv) The expansion given by (5.2), (5.6), (5.10) and (5.11) includes three expansion of Poincaré type as particular cases; compare the discussion in §4 leading up to the expansion (4.2). Similarly for the expansion of the solution $w_2(z)$.

(v) The coefficients $a_{s,1}$ in the original Poincaré expansion for the first solution appear as coefficients in the re-expansion of the remainder term for the second solution, and *vice versa*. This phenomenon is sometimes called *resurgence* [5]. The same phenomenon also occurs in the expansions (5.14) and (5.15).

6 SUMMARY

We have re-expanded the remainder term in the well-known asymptotic expansion for the generalized exponential integral, both in a series of elementary functions, and in series involving the complementary error function. Advantages of these re-expansions include increased accuracy, increased regions of validity, and a smooth interpretation of the Stokes phenomenon.

We have also considered the well-known asymptotic solutions of second-order linear differential equations in the neighborhood of an irregular singularity of rank one, and indicated how to re-expand the remainder terms in series of generalized exponential integrals. These re-expansions enjoy similar advantages to those of the re-expansions of the generalized exponential integral itself.

Acknowledgment. This research was supported by the National Science Foundation under Grant DMS 92-08690. The writer is pleased to acknowledge the assistance of M.A. McClain of the National Institute of Science and Technology in the computations for the diagrams.

REFERENCES

[1] Airey J.R. The "converging factor" in asymptotic series and the calculation of Bessel, Laguerre and other functions. *Philos. Mag.* [7], **24**:521–552, 1937.

[2] Berry M.V. Uniform asymptotic smoothing of Stokes's discontinuities. *Proc. Roy. Soc. London* Ser. A, **422**:7–21, 1989.

[3] Berry M.V. Waves near Stokes lines. *Proc. Roy. Soc. London* Ser. A, **427**:265–280, 1990.

[4] Berry M.V. Infinitely many Stokes smoothings in the gamma function. *Proc. Roy. Soc. London* Ser. A, **434**:465–472, 1991.

[5] Berry M.V., Howls C.J. Hyperasymptotics. *Proc. Roy. Soc. London* Ser. A, **430**:653–668, 1990.

[6] Berry M.V., Howls C.J. Hyperasymptotics for integrals with saddles. *Proc. Roy. Soc. London* Ser. A, **434**:657–675, 1991.

[7] Bleistein N. Uniform asymptotic expansions of integrals with stationary point near algebraic singularity. *Comm. Pure Appl. Math.*, **19**:353–370, 1966.

[8] Dingle R.B. *Asymptotic Expansions: Their Derivation and Interpretation.* Academic Press, London, 1973.

[9] Howls C.J. Hyperasymptotics for integrals with finite endpoints. *Proc. Roy. Soc. London* Ser. A, **439**:373–396, 1992.

[10] Jones D.S. Asymptotic behavior of integrals. *SIAM Rev.*, **14**:286–317, 1972.

[11] Miller J.C.P. A method for the determination of converging factors, applied to the asymptotic expansions for the parabolic cylinder functions. *Proc. Cambridge Philos. Soc.*, **48**:243–254, 1952.

[12] Olde Daalhuis A.B., Olver F.W.J. Exponentially-improved asymptotic solutions of ordinary differential equations II: irregular singularities of rank one. *Proc. Roy. Soc. London* Ser. A. (In press).

[13] Olver F.W.J. *Asymptotics and Special Functions.* Academic Press, New York, 1974.

[14] Olver F.W.J. On Stokes' phenomenon and converging factors. In *Asymptotic and Computational Analysis*, Lecture Notes in Pure and Applied Mathematics, **124**:329–355. Marcel Dekker, New York, 1990. R. Wong, ed.

[15] Olver F.W.J. Uniform, exponentially improved, asymptotic expansions for the generalized exponential integral. *SIAM J. Math. Anal.*, **22**:1460–1474, 1991.

[16] Olver F.W.J. Converging factors. In *Wave Asymptotics*, pages 54–68. Cambridge University Press, 1992. P.A. Martin and G.R. Wickham, eds.

[17] Stieltjes T.J. Recherches sur quelques séries semi-convergentes. *Ann. Sci. École Norm. Sup.* [3], **3**:201–258, 1886. Reprinted in *Complete Works.* Noordhoff, Groningen, **2**:2–58, 1918.

[18] Temme N.M. The asymptotic expansion of the incomplete Gamma functions. *SIAM J. Math. Anal.*, **10**:757–766, 1979.

[19] van der Waerden B.L. On the method of saddle points. *Appl. Sci. Res.* Ser. B, **2**:33–45, 1951.

Exponentially improved asymptotic solutions of ordinary differential equations. II Irregular singularities of rank one

By A. B. Olde Daalhuis[1] and F. W. J. Olver[2]

[1] *CWI, P.O. Box 4079, 1009 AB Amsterdam, The Netherlands*
[2] *Institute for Physical Science and Technology, University of Maryland, College Park, Maryland 20742, U.S.A.*

Re-expansions are found for the optimal remainder terms in the well-known asymptotic series solutions of homogeneous linear differential equations of the second order in the neighbourhood of an irregular singularity of rank one. The re-expansions are in terms of generalized exponential integrals and have greater regions of validity than the original expansions, as well being considerably more accurate and providing a smooth interpretation of the Stokes phenomenon. They are also of strikingly simple form. In addition, explicit asymptotic expansions for the higher coefficients of the original asymptotic solutions are obtained.

1. Introduction

The general homogeneous linear differential equation of the second order is given by

$$Lw = 0, \tag{1.1}$$

where the operator L is of the form

$$L = \frac{\mathrm{d}^2}{\mathrm{d}z^2} + f(z)\frac{\mathrm{d}}{\mathrm{d}z} + g(z). \tag{1.2}$$

If, as we shall suppose, the point at infinity is an irregular singularity of rank one, then the functions $f(z)$ and $g(z)$ can be expanded in power series

$$f(z) = \sum_{s=0}^{\infty} \frac{f_s}{z^s}, \quad g(z) = \sum_{s=0}^{\infty} \frac{g_s}{z^s}, \tag{1.3}$$

that converge in an unbounded open annulus $\boldsymbol{A}$ centred at the origin. Not all of the coefficients f_0, g_0 and g_1 vanish, otherwise infinity would be a regular singularity.

The asymptotic theory of solutions of (1.1) in these circumstances is well known and will be found, for example, in Olver (1974, ch. 7, §§ 1-2). Following the notations used in this reference, we shall assume, without loss of generality, that the

Proc. R. Soc. Lond. A (1994) **445**, 39–56

roots λ_1 and λ_2 of the characteristic equation

$$\lambda^2 + f_0\lambda + g_0 = 0 \tag{1.4}$$

are distinct.† Then equation (1.1) has unique solutions $w_1(z)$ and $w_2(z)$ such that

$$w_1(z) \sim e^{\lambda_1 z} z^{\mu_1} \sum_{s=0}^{\infty} \frac{a_{s,1}}{z^s}, \tag{1.5}$$

as $z \to \infty$ in the sector $|\operatorname{ph}\{(\lambda_2 - \lambda_1)z\}| \leqslant \frac{3}{2}\pi - \delta$, and

$$w_2(z) \sim e^{\lambda_2 z} z^{\mu_2} \sum_{s=0}^{\infty} \frac{a_{s,2}}{z^s}, \tag{1.6}$$

as $z \to \infty$ in the sector $|\operatorname{ph}\{(\lambda_1 - \lambda_2)z\}| \leqslant \frac{3}{2}\pi - \delta$. Here (and elsewhere in this paper) δ denotes an arbitrary small positive constant, and the exponents μ_1, μ_2 and the coefficients $a_{s,1}$, $a_{s,2}$ may be found by formal substitution in (1.1) (see § 2 below). Any branches may be taken for z^{μ_1} and z^{μ_2}, provided that they are continuous and used consistently throughout.

In the special case in which L is the confluent hypergeometric differential operator, it is known (Olver 1991*b*, 1993; Paris 1992*b*) that the remainder terms associated with the expansions (1.5) and (1.6) can be re-expanded in such a way that these expansions are *exponentially improved* in the sense defined in Olver (1991*a*, *b*); furthermore, the sectors of validity are increased. The purpose of this paper is to develop a similar theory for the more general case. Earlier work on this problem includes the formal research of Berry (1990) and the rigorous analysis of Paris (1992*a*). The latter applies to certain differential equations that can be solved exactly in terms of Mellin–Barnes integrals. The investigation whose aims are closest to those of this paper is that of McLeod (1992); however, McLeod's results are neither so general nor so powerful as the ones we shall develop.

As in the earlier references, the re-expansions of the remainder terms will be expressed in terms of generalized exponential integrals (or incomplete Gamma functions), defined by

$$F_p(z) = \frac{e^{-z}}{2\pi} \int_0^{\infty} \frac{e^{-zt} t^{p-1}}{1+t} \, dt, \tag{1.7}$$

when $\Re p > 0$ and $|\operatorname{ph} z| < \frac{1}{2}\pi$, and by analytic continuation elsewhere. Relevant properties of these functions will be found in Olver (1993, § 2).

The original intention was to use a direct differential-equation approach as in the special case treated in Olver (1993). However, significant difficulties appear in the analysis that are absent from the proofs in that reference. Thus it is necessary, at first, to match the optimal remainder terms by a double series of F-functions, rather than a single series; furthermore, the coefficients in the double series are unavailable in simple explicit form. To prove that the double series may be reduced to a single series, with explicit coefficients, elaborate indirect arguments based on limiting forms of the double series have to be used.

The approach in this paper is quite different. By using the connection formu-

† The case $\lambda_1 = \lambda_2$ can always be handled by application of a preliminary transformation due to Fabry (Olver 1974, ch. 7, § 1.3).

lae for the solutions and contour integration we construct Stieltjes-type transforms for the remainder terms, from which the desired re-expansions can be found directly.‡ Not only is the analysis considerably simpler; it will lend itself more readily to further developments and extensions. These include higher re-expansions of remainder terms (hyperasymptotics), and differential equations of other orders or with other types of singularity.

We should also add that if the theorems of this paper are applied to the confluent hypergeometric equation, then the results agree with those of Olver (1993).

2. Main results

If we replace the independent variable z by $z/(\lambda_2 - \lambda_1)$, then the essential form (1.2) of the differential operator L is unchanged, but the new characteristic values satisfy

$$\lambda_2 - \lambda_1 = 1. \tag{2.1}$$

The effect of this transformation is to simplify considerably the notation in subsequent analyses; *in consequence, throughout the rest of this paper we shall assume that the condition* (2.1) *is satisfied.*

The branches of the asymptotic solutions are chosen to be

$$w_1(z) \sim \mathrm{e}^{\lambda_1 z} z^{\mu_1} \sum_{s=0}^{\infty} \frac{a_{s,1}}{z^s}, \quad |\mathrm{ph} z| \leqslant \tfrac{3}{2}\pi - \delta, \tag{2.2}$$

and

$$w_2(z) \sim \mathrm{e}^{\lambda_2 z} z^{\mu_2} \sum_{s=0}^{\infty} \frac{a_{s,2}}{z^s}, \quad -\tfrac{1}{2}\pi + \delta \leqslant \mathrm{ph} z \leqslant \tfrac{5}{2}\pi - \delta; \tag{2.3}$$

compare (1.5) and (1.6). The characteristic values λ_1, λ_2 are the roots of the quadratic equation (1.4), and the exponents μ_1 and μ_2 are given by

$$\mu_1 = f_1\lambda_1 + g_1, \quad \mu_2 = -(f_1\lambda_2 + g_1). \tag{2.4}$$

The coefficients are determined by $a_{0,1} = a_{0,2} = 1$ and, when $s \geqslant 1$,

$$-sa_{s,1} = (s-\mu_1)(s-1-\mu_1)a_{s-1,1} + \sum_{j=1}^{s}\{\lambda_1 f_{j+1} + g_{j+1} - (s-j-\mu_1)f_j\}a_{s-j,1}, \tag{2.5}$$

$$sa_{s,2} = (s-\mu_2)(s-1-\mu_2)a_{s-1,2} + \sum_{j=1}^{s}\{\lambda_2 f_{j+1} + g_{j+1} - (s-j-\mu_2)f_j\}a_{s-j,2}. \tag{2.6}$$

A direct consequence of (1.3) is that $w_1(z\mathrm{e}^{-2\pi i})$ and $w_2(z\mathrm{e}^{2\pi i})$ are also solutions of (1.1). Note that $w_1(z)$ and $\mathrm{e}^{2\pi i\mu_1}w_1(z\mathrm{e}^{-2\pi i})$ are dominant solutions in the sector

‡ These transforms can be regarded as 'resurgence relations' in the terminology of Berry (1991) and Berry & Howls (1991). Perhaps it should be noted that Stieltjes transforms were used by Olver (1990) and Boyd (1990), respectively, in deriving exponentially improved asymptotic expansions for the confluent hypergeometric function and a modified Bessel function via integral-representation approaches.

$\frac{1}{2}\pi + \delta \leqslant \text{ph} z \leqslant \frac{3}{2}\pi - \delta$ and have exactly the same asymptotic expansion there. Similarly for $w_2(z)$ and $e^{-2\pi i \mu_2} w_2(z e^{2\pi i})$ in the sector $|\text{ph} z| \leqslant \frac{1}{2}\pi - \delta$. Thus there are constants C_1 and C_2 such that

$$w_1(z) = e^{2\pi i \mu_1} w_1(z e^{-2\pi i}) + C_1 w_2(z), \tag{2.7}$$

$$w_2(z) = e^{-2\pi i \mu_2} w_2(z e^{2\pi i}) + C_2 w_1(z). \tag{2.8}$$

Formulae (2.7) and (2.8) are called the connection formulae, and we assume the constants C_1 and C_2 to be known.

The remainder of this paper is devoted to the proof of the following theorems.

Theorem 2.1. *Let m be an arbitrary fixed non-negative integer. Then as $s \to \infty$*

$$a_{s,1} = (-)^s \frac{e^{(\mu_2 - \mu_1)\pi i}}{2\pi i} \times \left\{ C_1 \sum_{j=0}^{m-1} (-)^j a_{j,2} \Gamma(s + \mu_2 - \mu_1 - j) + \Gamma(s + \mu_2 - \mu_1 - m) \mathcal{O}(1) \right\}, \tag{2.9}$$

$$a_{s,2} = -\frac{1}{2\pi i} \left\{ C_2 \sum_{j=0}^{m-1} a_{j,1} \Gamma(s + \mu_1 - \mu_2 - j) + \Gamma(s + \mu_1 - \mu_2 - m) \mathcal{O}(1) \right\}. \tag{2.10}$$

Theorem 2.2. *Define $R_n^{(1)}(z)$ and $R_n^{(2)}(z)$ by*

$$w_1(z) = e^{\lambda_1 z} z^{\mu_1} \sum_{s=0}^{n-1} \frac{a_{s,1}}{z^s} + R_n^{(1)}(z), \tag{2.11}$$

$$w_2(z) = e^{\lambda_2 z} z^{\mu_2} \sum_{s=0}^{n-1} \frac{a_{s,2}}{z^s} + R_n^{(2)}(z), \tag{2.12}$$

where

$$n = |z| + \alpha, \tag{2.13}$$

and α is bounded as $|z| \to \infty$. Then

$$R_n^{(1)}(z) = (-)^{n-1} i e^{(\mu_2 - \mu_1)\pi i} e^{\lambda_2 z} z^{\mu_2} \times \left\{ C_1 \sum_{s=0}^{m-1} (-)^s a_{s,2} \frac{F_{n+\mu_2-\mu_1-s}(z)}{z^s} + R_{m,n}^{(1)}(z) \right\}, \tag{2.14}$$

$$R_n^{(2)}(z) = (-)^n i e^{(\mu_2 - \mu_1)\pi i} e^{\lambda_1 z} z^{\mu_1} \times \left\{ C_2 \sum_{s=0}^{m-1} (-)^s a_{s,1} \frac{F_{n+\mu_1-\mu_2-s}(z e^{-\pi i})}{z^s} + R_{m,n}^{(2)}(z) \right\}, \tag{2.15}$$

where m is an arbitrary fixed non-negative integer, and for large $|z|$

$$R_{m,n}^{(1)}(z) = \mathcal{O}(e^{-|z|-z} z^{-m}), \quad |\text{ph} z| \leqslant \pi, \tag{2.16}$$

$$R_{m,n}^{(1)}(z) = \mathcal{O}(z^{-m}), \quad \pi \leqslant |\text{ph} z| \leqslant \tfrac{5}{2}\pi - \delta, \tag{2.17}$$

$$R_{m,n}^{(2)}(z) = \mathcal{O}(e^{-|z|+z} z^{-m}), \quad 0 \leqslant \text{ph} z \leqslant 2\pi, \tag{2.18}$$

$$R_{m,n}^{(2)}(z) = \mathcal{O}(z^{-m}), \quad -\tfrac{3}{2}\pi + \delta \leqslant \text{ph} z \leqslant 0 \text{ and } 2\pi \leqslant \text{ph} z \leqslant \tfrac{7}{2}\pi - \delta, \tag{2.19}$$

uniformly with respect to ph$z$ *in each case.*

Furthermore if C_1 *and* C_2 *are both non-zero, then the sectors of validity are maximal.*

Remark (i). The results (2.9) and (2.10) are investigated in Olver (1994) using elementary analysis based on the recurrence relations (2.5) and (2.6).

Remark (ii). In consequence of (2.9) and (2.10), when C_1 and C_2 are non-zero the condition that α be bounded in equation (2.13) includes the situation in which the series in (2.11) and (2.12) are truncated at their optimal stages.

Remark (iii). At first sight it may seem remarkable that the coefficients $a_{s,2}$ that appear in the re-expansion (2.14) of the optimal remainder term in the expansion (2.2) for $w_1(z)$ are the same as those in the expansion (2.3) for $w_2(z)$. One way to understand this phenomenon is as follows. If an expansion of the form (2.14) holds throughout the sector $|\text{ph}z| \leqslant \frac{5}{2}\pi - \delta$, then from (2.17) and Olver (1993, eqn (2.11)), we see that in the outermost parts of this sector the contribution of (2.14) is dominant when compared with the finite sum in (2.11) and must therefore match the expansions for $w_1(z)$ in these outer regions obtained by use of connection formulae typified by (2.7). A similar observation applies to the coefficients $a_{s,1}$ in (2.15).

Remark (iv). Corresponding results for other phase ranges can be derived easily from the stated results. For example, since $w_2(ze^{2\pi i})$ is another solution of (1.1), on replacing z by $ze^{2\pi i}$ throughout (2.12), (2.15), (2.18) and (2.19), we obtain a similar expansion for a solution in the phase range $-\frac{7}{2}\pi + \delta \leqslant \text{ph}z \leqslant \frac{3}{2}\pi - \delta$.

Remark (v). If $C_1 = 0$, then equations (2.14), (2.16), (2.17) combine into

$$R_n^{(1)}(z) = O(e^{-|z|+\lambda_1 z} z^{\mu_2 - m}), \quad |\text{ph}z| \leqslant \pi,$$

and

$$R_n^{(1)}(z) = O(e^{\lambda_2 z} z^{\mu_2 - m}), \quad \pi \leqslant |\text{ph}z| \leqslant \tfrac{5}{2}\pi - \delta,$$

for any integer m; compare (2.1). Actually, a stronger result applies in this case and it can be derived directly as follows.

From (2.7) we see that when $C_1 = 0$ we have

$$w_1(z) = e^{2\pi i \mu_1} w_1(ze^{-2\pi i}).$$

Accordingly, the function $e^{-\lambda_1 z} z^{-\mu_1} w_1(z)$ is single-valued and analytic on $\boldsymbol{A}$. In consequence (Olver 1974, ch. 1, § 7.5) the expansion

$$w_1(z) = e^{\lambda_1 z} z^{\mu_1} \sum_{s=0}^{\infty} \frac{a_{s,1}}{z^s}$$

converges on $\boldsymbol{A}$. Let ρ be any constant that exceeds the radius of the boundary of $\boldsymbol{A}$. Since $a_{s,1}/\rho^s \to 0$ as $s \to \infty$, it follows that

$$|a_{s,1}| \leqslant H\rho^s,$$

where H is assignable independently of s. Hence if $|z| > \rho$ we have

$$|R_n^{(1)}(z)| = |e^{\lambda_1 z} z^{\mu_1} \sum_{s=n}^{\infty} \frac{a_{s,1}}{z^s}| \leqslant H|e^{\lambda_1 z} z^{\mu_1}| \left(\frac{\rho}{|z|}\right)^n \frac{|z|}{|z| - \rho}$$

$$= \left(\frac{\rho}{|z|}\right)^{|z|} e^{\lambda_1 z} z^{\mu_1 - \alpha} O(1);$$

compare (2.13). Furthermore, this estimate applies without restriction on ph$z$. Similarly, (2.18) and (2.19) may be strengthened when $C_2 = 0$.

3. Stieltjes-type transforms for the coefficients and remainder terms

Let us define

$$v_1(z) = \mathrm{e}^{-\lambda_1 z} z^{-\mu_1 - 1} w_1(z), \quad v_2(z) = \mathrm{e}^{-\lambda_1 z} z^{-\mu_1 - 1} w_2(z), \tag{3.1}$$

so that for large $|z|$

$$v_1(z) \sim \frac{1}{z} \sum_{s=0}^{\infty} \frac{a_{s,1}}{z^s}, \quad |\mathrm{ph} z| \leqslant \tfrac{3}{2}\pi - \delta, \tag{3.2}$$

$$v_2(z) \sim \mathrm{e}^z z^{\mu_2 - \mu_1 - 1} \sum_{s=0}^{\infty} \frac{a_{s,2}}{z^s}, \quad -\tfrac{1}{2}\pi + \delta \leqslant \mathrm{ph} z \leqslant \tfrac{5}{2}\pi - \delta; \tag{3.3}$$

compare (2.1), (2.2) and (2.3).

Lemma 3.1. *Let ρ be any constant such that $\rho - \delta$ exceeds the radius of the boundary of $\boldsymbol{A}$,† and $\mathcal{X}$ any constant in the closed interval $[-\frac{1}{2}\pi + \delta, \frac{1}{2}\pi - \delta]$. Then*

$$v_1(z) = -\frac{C_1}{2\pi i} \int_{\rho \mathrm{e}^{(\mathcal{X}+\pi)i}}^{\infty \mathrm{e}^{(\mathcal{X}+\pi)i}} \frac{v_2(t)}{t - z} \mathrm{d}t - \frac{1}{2\pi i} \int_{\rho \mathrm{e}^{(\mathcal{X}-\pi)i}}^{\rho \mathrm{e}^{(\mathcal{X}+\pi)i}} \frac{v_1(t)}{t - z} \mathrm{d}t, \tag{3.4}$$

valid when z lies in the annular sector

$$|z| > \rho, \quad \mathcal{X} - \pi < \mathrm{ph} z < \mathcal{X} + \pi. \tag{3.5}$$

In (3.4) the path in the first integral is a straight line, and in the second integral it is an arc of the circle $|t| = \rho$ described in the positive sense.

Proof. From (2.7) and (3.1) we have

$$C_1 v_2(t) = v_1(t) - v_1(t\mathrm{e}^{-2\pi i}).$$

Accordingly, if r is any positive number exceeding ρ and $|z|$, it follows that

$$\begin{aligned} C_1 \int_{\rho \mathrm{e}^{(\mathcal{X}+\pi)i}}^{r \mathrm{e}^{(\mathcal{X}+\pi)i}} \frac{v_2(t)}{t - z} \mathrm{d}t &= \int_{\rho \mathrm{e}^{(\mathcal{X}+\pi)i}}^{r \mathrm{e}^{(\mathcal{X}+\pi)i}} \frac{v_1(t)}{t - z} \mathrm{d}t - \int_{\rho \mathrm{e}^{(\mathcal{X}+\pi)i}}^{r \mathrm{e}^{(\mathcal{X}+\pi)i}} \frac{v_1(t\mathrm{e}^{-2\pi i})}{t - z} \mathrm{d}t \\ &= \int_{\rho \mathrm{e}^{(\mathcal{X}+\pi)i}}^{r \mathrm{e}^{(\mathcal{X}+\pi)i}} \frac{v_1(t)}{t - z} \mathrm{d}t - \int_{\rho \mathrm{e}^{(\mathcal{X}-\pi)i}}^{r \mathrm{e}^{(\mathcal{X}-\pi)i}} \frac{v_1(t)}{t - z} \mathrm{d}t. \end{aligned} \tag{3.6}$$

By application of Cauchy's theorem to the contour indicated in figure 1, we obtain

$$v_1(z) = -\frac{1}{2\pi i} \left(\int_{\rho \mathrm{e}^{(\mathcal{X}+\pi)i}}^{r \mathrm{e}^{(\mathcal{X}+\pi)i}} + \int_{r \mathrm{e}^{(\mathcal{X}+\pi)i}}^{r \mathrm{e}^{(\mathcal{X}-\pi)i}} + \int_{r \mathrm{e}^{(\mathcal{X}-\pi)i}}^{\rho \mathrm{e}^{(\mathcal{X}-\pi)i}} + \int_{\rho \mathrm{e}^{(\mathcal{X}-\pi)i}}^{\rho \mathrm{e}^{(\mathcal{X}+\pi)i}} \right) \frac{v_1(t)}{t - z} \mathrm{d}t. \tag{3.7}$$

Let $r \to \infty$. Since $\mathcal{X} - \pi \geqslant -\frac{3}{2}\pi + \delta$ and $\mathcal{X} + \pi \leqslant \frac{3}{2}\pi - \delta$, it follows from (3.2) that $v_1(t) = \mathcal{O}(1/r)$, uniformly on the circular arc of radius r. Hence the limiting

† Actually, until §4 it would suffice for ρ to exceed the radius of the boundary of $\boldsymbol{A}$.

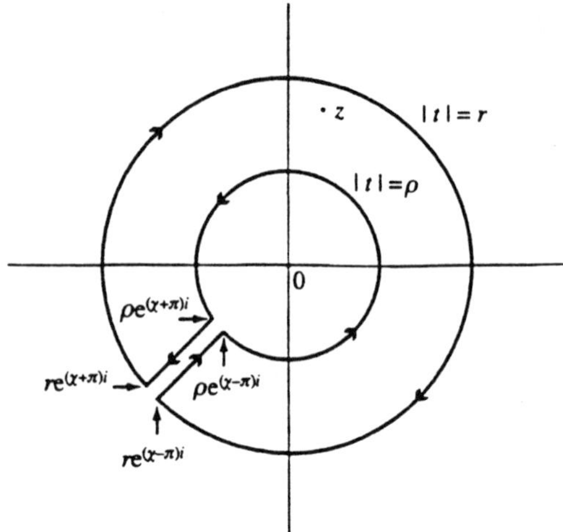

Figure 1. t-plane. Contour for equation (3.7).

value of the integral around this arc is zero. The desired result (3.4) is obtained by combining (3.6) and (3.7), and then taking the limit.

Lemma 3.2. *Assume the conditions of Lemma 3.1, and let n be an arbitrary non-negative integer. Then*

$$a_{s,1} = \frac{1}{2\pi i}\left\{(-)^{s-1}C_1 \int_{\rho e^{\chi i}}^{\infty e^{\chi i}} v_2(te^{\pi i})t^s\,\mathrm{d}t + \int_{\rho e^{(\chi-\pi)i}}^{\rho e^{(\chi+\pi)i}} v_1(t)t^s\,\mathrm{d}t\right\}, \tag{3.8}$$

and

$$R_n^{(1)}(z) = -\frac{\mathrm{e}^{\lambda_1 z}z^{\mu_1}}{2\pi i z^{n-1}}\left\{(-)^n C_1 \int_{\rho e^{\chi i}}^{\infty e^{\chi i}} \frac{v_2(te^{\pi i})t^n}{t+z}\,\mathrm{d}t + \int_{\rho e^{(\chi-\pi)i}}^{\rho e^{(\chi+\pi)i}} \frac{v_1(t)t^n}{t-z}\mathrm{d}t\right\}. \tag{3.9}$$

Proof. To prove this result, we substitute into (3.4) by means of the expansion

$$\frac{1}{t-z} = -\sum_{s=0}^{n-1}\frac{t^s}{z^{s+1}} + \frac{t^n}{z^n(t-z)},$$

and subsequently replace t by $te^{\pi i}$ in the integrals along the straight-line paths. We obtain

$$w_1(z) = \mathrm{e}^{\lambda_1 z}z^{\mu_1}\sum_{s=0}^{n-1}\frac{\tilde{a}_{s,1}}{z^s} + \tilde{R}_n^{(1)}(z), \tag{3.10}$$

where

$$\tilde{a}_{s,1} = \frac{1}{2\pi i}\left\{(-)^{s-1}C_1 \int_{\rho e^{\chi i}}^{\infty e^{\chi i}} v_2(te^{\pi i})t^s\,\mathrm{d}t + \int_{\rho e^{(\chi-\pi)i}}^{\rho e^{(\chi+\pi)i}} v_1(t)t^s\,\mathrm{d}t\right\}, \tag{3.11}$$

and

$$\tilde{R}_n^{(1)}(z) = -\frac{\mathrm{e}^{\lambda_1 z}z^{\mu_1}}{2\pi i z^{n-1}}\left\{(-)^n C_1 \int_{\rho e^{\chi i}}^{\infty e^{\chi i}} \frac{v_2(te^{\pi i})t^n}{t+z}\,\mathrm{d}t + \int_{\rho e^{(\chi-\pi)i}}^{\rho e^{(\chi+\pi)i}} \frac{v_1(t)t^n}{t-z}\,\mathrm{d}t\right\}. \tag{3.12}$$

Obviously, Lemma 3.2 will follow if we can show that $\tilde{a}_{s,1} = a_{s,1}$ and $\tilde{R}_n^{(1)}(z) = R_n^{(1)}(z)$. For this purpose we assume temporarily that n is fixed and z is large with $\mathrm{ph} z = 0$. With the aid of (3.3) we easily deduce from (3.12) that in these circumstances we have

$$\tilde{R}_n^{(1)}(z) = \mathrm{e}^{\lambda_1 z} z^{\mu_1} \mathcal{O}(z^{-n}). \tag{3.13}$$

On comparing (3.10) and (3.13) with (2.2) and recalling that asymptotic expansions of Poincaré type are unique, we deduce that $\tilde{a}_{s,1} = a_{s,1}$, $s = 0, 1, \ldots, n-1$, and hence from (2.11) and (3.10) that $\tilde{R}_n^{(1)}(z) = R_n^{(1)}(z)$, (if $\mathrm{ph} z = 0$ or not).

4. Proof of Theorem 2.1

Lemma 4.1. *Let m be an arbitrary fixed non-negative integer, and t lie in the annular sector*

$$|t| \geqslant \rho - \delta, \quad |\mathrm{ph} t| \leqslant \tfrac{3}{2}\pi - \delta. \tag{4.1}$$

Then

$$v_2(t\mathrm{e}^{\pi i}) = -\mathrm{e}^{(\mu_2 - \mu_1)\pi i} \mathrm{e}^{-t} t^{\mu_2 - \mu_1 - 1} \left\{ \sum_{j=0}^{m-1} (-)^j \frac{a_{j,2}}{t^j} + \frac{\phi_m(t)}{t^m} \right\}, \tag{4.2}$$

where

$$|\phi_m(t)| \leqslant \Phi_m, \tag{4.3}$$

and Φ_m is assignable independently of t.

This result is an immediate consequence of (3.3) and the fact that $v_2(t\mathrm{e}^{\pi i})$ is analytic on the annular sector (4.1).

To prove Theorem 2.1 we set $\mathcal{X} = 0$ in (3.8). We obtain

$$a_{s,1} = (-)^{s-1} \frac{C_1}{2\pi i} \int_\rho^\infty v_2(t\mathrm{e}^{\pi i}) t^s \,\mathrm{d}t + \frac{1}{2\pi i} \int_{\rho \mathrm{e}^{-\pi i}}^{\rho \mathrm{e}^{\pi i}} v_1(t) t^s \,\mathrm{d}t. \tag{4.4}$$

In the second integral, $v_1(t)$ is bounded on the path of integration; accordingly

$$\int_{\rho \mathrm{e}^{-\pi i}}^{\rho \mathrm{e}^{\pi i}} v_1(t) t^s \,\mathrm{d}t = \mathcal{O}(\rho^s), \quad s \to \infty.$$

In the first integral, we may substitute in the integrand by means of Lemma 4.1. This yields

$$\int_\rho^\infty v_2(t\mathrm{e}^{\pi i}) t^s \,\mathrm{d}t = -\mathrm{e}^{(\mu_2 - \mu_1)\pi i} \left\{ \sum_{j=0}^{m-1} (-)^j a_{j,2} \int_\rho^\infty \mathrm{e}^{-t} t^{s + \mu_2 - \mu_1 - j - 1} \,\mathrm{d}t \right.$$
$$\left. + \int_\rho^\infty \mathrm{e}^{-t} t^{s + \mu_2 - \mu_1 - m - 1} \phi_m(t) \mathrm{d}t \right\}. \tag{4.5}$$

Now,

$$\begin{aligned} \int_\rho^\infty \mathrm{e}^{-t} t^{s + \mu_2 - \mu_1 - j - 1} \mathrm{d}t &= \Gamma(s + \mu_2 - \mu_1 - j) - \gamma(s + \mu_2 - \mu_1 - j, \rho) \\ &= \Gamma(s + \mu_2 - \mu_1 - j) + s^{-1} \mathcal{O}(\rho^s), \quad s \to \infty. \end{aligned}$$

(This step follows from the well-known power-series expansion for the incomplete Gamma function, given for example in Olver (1974, ch. 2, § 5.1).) For the other integral in (4.5) we have

$$\left|\int_{\rho}^{\infty} \mathrm{e}^{-t} t^{s+\mu_2-\mu_1-m-1} \phi_m(t)\, \mathrm{d}t\right| \leqslant \Phi_m \int_{\rho}^{\infty} \mathrm{e}^{-t} t^{s+\Re\mu_2-\Re\mu_1-m-1}\, \mathrm{d}t$$
$$< \Phi_m \Gamma(s+\Re\mu_2-\Re\mu_1-m),$$

provided that $s > \Re\mu_1 - \Re\mu_2 + m$.

On combining the foregoing results we arrive at

$$a_{s,1} = (-)^s \frac{\mathrm{e}^{(\mu_2-\mu_1)\pi i}}{2\pi i}\left\{C_1 \sum_{j=0}^{m-1} (-)^j a_{j,2} \Gamma(s+\mu_2-\mu_1-j) + \epsilon_{m,s}\right\},$$

where, for large s,

$$\epsilon_{m,s} = \mathcal{O}(\rho^s) + C_1\Gamma(s+\Re\mu_2-\Re\mu_1-m)\mathcal{O}(1) \subseteq \Gamma(s+\mu_2-\mu_1-m)\mathcal{O}(1).$$

This establishes (2.9). The proof of (2.10) is similar.†

5. Proof of Theorem 2.2 for $w_1(z)$ when $|\mathrm{ph}\, z| \leqslant \pi - \delta$

From (3.9) with $\mathcal{X} = 0$ we obtain

$$R_n^{(1)}(z) = -\frac{\mathrm{e}^{\lambda_1 z} z^{\mu_1}}{2\pi i z^{n-1}}\left\{(-)^n C_1 \int_{\rho}^{\infty} \frac{v_2(t\mathrm{e}^{\pi i})t^n}{t+z}\,\mathrm{d}t + \int_{\rho \mathrm{e}^{-\pi i}}^{\rho \mathrm{e}^{\pi i}} \frac{v_1(t)t^n}{t-z}\,\mathrm{d}t\right\}, \tag{5.1}$$

valid when $|z| > \rho$ and $|\mathrm{ph} z| < \pi$. For the second integral we note that $|t-z| \geqslant |z| - \rho$ and that $|v_1(t)|$ is bounded on the integration path. In consequence, when $|z| \to \infty$ with $||z| - n|$ bounded (compare (2.13)), we derive

$$\int_{\rho \mathrm{e}^{-\pi i}}^{\rho \mathrm{e}^{\pi i}} \frac{v_1(t)t^n}{t-z}\mathrm{d}t = \frac{1}{z}\mathcal{O}(\rho^n), \tag{5.2}$$

uniformly for all values of ph$z$.

In the first integral in (5.1) we may substitute by means of Lemma 4.1. From (1.7) we see that when $n > \Re(\mu_1 - \mu_2) + m - 1$

$$\int_0^{\infty} \frac{\mathrm{e}^{-t} t^{n+\mu_2-\mu_1-j-1}}{t+z}\,\mathrm{d}t = 2\pi \mathrm{e}^z z^{n+\mu_2-\mu_1-j-1} F_{n+\mu_2-\mu_1-j}(z), \quad |\mathrm{ph} z| < \pi. \tag{5.3}$$

Accordingly,

$$\int_{\rho}^{\infty} \frac{v_2(t\mathrm{e}^{\pi i})t^n}{t+z}\mathrm{d}t = -\mathrm{e}^{(\mu_2-\mu_1)\pi i}\left\{2\pi \mathrm{e}^z z^{n+\mu_2-\mu_1-1} \sum_{j=0}^{m-1} (-)^j a_{j,2} \frac{F_{n+\mu_2-\mu_1-j}(z)}{z^j}\right.$$
$$\left. - S_{m,n}^{(1)}(z) + S_{m,n}^{(2)}(z)\right\}, \tag{5.4}$$

† Alternatively, we can interchange the roles of $w_1(z)$ and $w_2(z)$ as indicated in § 7 below.

where

$$S^{(1)}_{m,n}(z) = \sum_{j=0}^{m-1} (-)^j a_{j,2} \int_0^\rho \frac{e^{-t} t^{n+\mu_2-\mu_1-j-1}}{t+z}\, dt$$

and

$$S^{(2)}_{m,n}(z) = \int_\rho^\infty \frac{e^{-t} t^{n+\mu_2-\mu_1-m-1}}{t+z} \phi_m(t)\, dt.$$

In $S^{(1)}_{m,n}(z)$ we have $|t+z| \geqslant |z| - \rho$. Hence

$$\left|S^{(1)}_{m,n}(z)\right| \leqslant \frac{1}{|z|-\rho} \sum_{j=0}^{m-1} |a_{j,2}| \gamma(n + \Re\mu_2 - \Re\mu_1 - j, \rho) = \frac{1}{|z|n} O(\rho^n) \tag{5.5}$$

as $|z| \to \infty$ with $||z| - n|$ bounded, uniformly for all values of ph$z$; compare (4.6).

For $S^{(2)}_{m,n}(z)$ we restrict $|\text{ph} z| \leqslant \pi - \delta (< \pi)$. Then $|t+z| \geqslant |z| \sin\delta$ on the integration path. Using also the bound (4.3), we find that when $n > \Re(\mu_1 - \mu_2) + m$

$$\left|S^{(2)}_{m,n}(z)\right| \leqslant \frac{\Phi_m}{|z|\sin\delta} \int_\rho^\infty e^{-t} t^{n+\Re\mu_2-\Re\mu_1-m-1}\, dt < \frac{\Phi_m \Gamma(n + \Re\mu_2 - \Re\mu_1 - m)}{|z|\sin\delta}.$$

On combining the foregoing results and referring to (2.1) and (2.14), we perceive that

$$R^{(1)}_{m,n}(z) = e^{-z} z^{-n-\mu_2+\mu_1} \left\{ O(\rho^n) + \Gamma(n + \Re\mu_2 - \Re\mu_1 - m) O(1) \right\}.$$

Applying Stirling's formula and recalling again that $|z|$ and n are related by (2.13), with α bounded, we see that when $|\text{ph} z| \leqslant \pi - \delta$ we have

$$R^{(1)}_{m,n}(z) = e^{-z} z^{-n-\mu_2+\mu_1} e^{-n} n^{n+\Re\mu_2-\Re\mu_1-m-\frac{1}{2}} O(1) \subseteq e^{-z-|z|} O(z^{-m-\frac{1}{2}}). \tag{5.6}$$

This result agrees with (2.16); indeed, in the present circumstances it is stronger by a factor $O(z^{-\frac{1}{2}})$.

6. Proof of Theorem 2.2 for $w_1(z)$ when $|\text{ph} z| \leqslant \frac{3}{2}\pi - 3\delta$

Lemma 6.1. *Let A_1 and A_2 denote the closed annular sectors*

$$A_1 = \{\tau : |\tau| \geqslant \rho, \quad -\tfrac{3}{2}\pi + 2\delta \leqslant \text{ph}\tau \leqslant \tfrac{1}{2}\pi - 2\delta\},$$
$$A_2 = \{\tau : |\tau| \geqslant \rho + \delta, \quad -\tfrac{3}{2}\pi + 3\delta \leqslant \text{ph}\tau \leqslant \tfrac{1}{2}\pi - 3\delta\}.$$

Then

$$\left| \frac{\phi_m(t) - \phi_m(ze^{-\pi i})}{t+z} \right| \leqslant \Psi_m, \tag{6.1}$$

where $\phi_m(t)$ is defined as in Lemma 4.1 and Ψ_m is assignable independently of t and z, provided that $t \in A_1$ and $ze^{-\pi i} \in A_2$.

Proof. This result can be proved in various ways. We shall proceed as follows. Write $\zeta = ze^{-\pi i}$, so that

$$\frac{\phi_m(t) - \phi_m(ze^{-\pi i})}{t+z} = \frac{\phi_m(t) - \phi_m(\zeta)}{t - \zeta}. \tag{6.2}$$

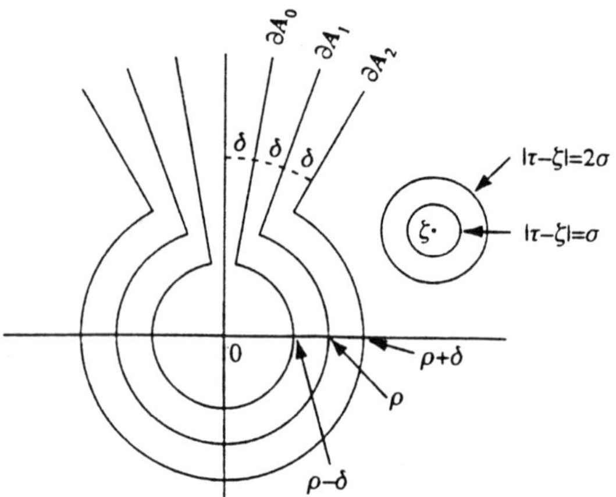

Figure 2. τ-plane. $\partial \boldsymbol{A}_0$ is the boundary of $\boldsymbol{A}_0$, etc.

Also define

$$\boldsymbol{A}_0 = \{\tau : |\tau| \geqslant \rho - \delta, \ -\tfrac{3}{2}\pi + \delta \leqslant \operatorname{ph}\tau \leqslant \tfrac{1}{2}\pi - \delta\}.$$

Because $\rho - \delta$ exceeds the radius of the boundary of $\boldsymbol{A}$ (Lemma 3.1), we have $\boldsymbol{A} \supset \boldsymbol{A}_0 \supset \boldsymbol{A}_1 \supset \boldsymbol{A}_2$.

From figure 2 it is clear that we can find a positive constant σ such that if $\zeta \in \boldsymbol{A}_2$, then the closed disc $|\tau - \zeta| \leqslant \sigma$ lies in $\boldsymbol{A}_1$ and the closed disc $|\tau - \zeta| \leqslant 2\sigma$ lies in $\boldsymbol{A}_0$.† Accordingly, if $\zeta \in \boldsymbol{A}_2$ and $0 < |t - \zeta| \leqslant \sigma$, then

$$\frac{\phi_m(t) - \phi_m(\zeta)}{t - \zeta} = \frac{1}{2\pi i} \int_{|\tau - \zeta| = 2\sigma} \frac{\phi_m(\tau)}{(\tau - t)(\tau - \zeta)} d\tau.$$

With the aid of Lemma 4.1 we then derive

$$\left| \frac{\phi_m(t) - \phi_m(\zeta)}{t - \zeta} \right| \leqslant 2\sigma \frac{\Phi_m}{\sigma \cdot 2\sigma} = \frac{\Phi_m}{\sigma}. \tag{6.3}$$

On the other hand, if $\zeta \in \boldsymbol{A}_2$ and $t \in \boldsymbol{A}_1$ with $|t - \zeta| > \sigma$, then we have directly

$$\left| \frac{\phi_m(t) - \phi_m(\zeta)}{t - \zeta} \right| \leqslant \frac{2\Phi_m}{\sigma}. \tag{6.4}$$

Combination of (6.2), (6.3) and (6.4) establishes (6.1) (with $\Psi_m = 2\Phi_m/\sigma$), provided that $t \neq z e^{-\pi i}$. The last condition is removed on replacing the left-hand side of (6.1) by its limiting value.

† In fact, it suffices that σ be bounded by δ and $(\frac{1}{2}\rho + \frac{1}{2}\delta)\sin 2\delta$.

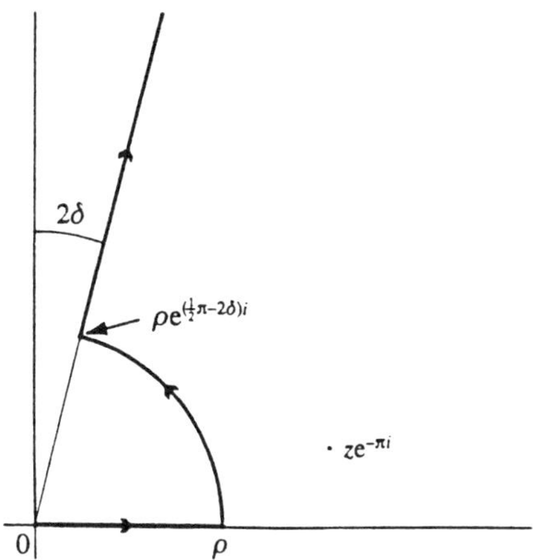

Figure 3. t-plane.

To continue the proof of Theorem 2.2 we set $\mathcal{X} = \frac{1}{2}\pi - 2\delta$ in (3.9). We obtain

$$R_n^{(1)}(z) = -\frac{e^{\lambda_1 z} z^{\mu_1}}{2\pi i z^{n-1}} \left\{ (-)^n C_1 \int_{\rho e^{(\frac{1}{2}\pi - 2\delta)i}}^{\infty e^{(\frac{1}{2}\pi - 2\delta)i}} \frac{v_2(te^{\pi i}) t^n}{t+z} \, dt + \int_{\rho e^{(-\frac{1}{2}\pi - 2\delta)i}}^{\rho e^{(\frac{3}{2}\pi - 2\delta)i}} \frac{v_1(t) t^n}{t-z} \, dt \right\}, \tag{6.5}$$

valid when $|z| > \rho$ and $-\frac{1}{2}\pi - 2\delta < \text{ph} z < \frac{3}{2}\pi - 2\delta$. As in (5.2) it follows that

$$\int_{\rho e^{(-\frac{1}{2}\pi - 2\delta)i}}^{\rho e^{(\frac{3}{2}\pi - 2\delta)i}} \frac{v_1(t) t^n}{t-z} dt = \frac{1}{z} \mathcal{O}(\rho^n) \tag{6.6}$$

as $|z| \to \infty$ with $||z| - n|$ bounded.

Next, by substitution of (4.2) we obtain

$$\int_{\rho e^{(\frac{1}{2}\pi - 2\delta)i}}^{\infty e^{(\frac{1}{2}\pi - 2\delta)i}} \frac{v_2(te^{\pi i}) t^n}{t+z} \, dt$$

$$= -e^{(\mu_2 - \mu_1)\pi i} \left\{ \sum_{j=0}^{m-1} (-)^j a_{j,2} \int_{\rho e^{(\frac{1}{2}\pi - 2\delta)i}}^{\infty e^{(\frac{1}{2}\pi - 2\delta)i}} \frac{e^{-t} t^{n+\mu_2-\mu_1-j-1}}{t+z} \, dt \right.$$

$$\left. + \int_{\rho e^{(\frac{1}{2}\pi - 2\delta)i}}^{\infty e^{(\frac{1}{2}\pi - 2\delta)i}} \frac{e^{-t} t^{n+\mu_2-\mu_1-m-1}}{t+z} \phi_m(t) \, dt \right\}. \tag{6.7}$$

Bearing in mind that $|ze^{-\pi i}| > \rho$ and $-\frac{3}{2}\pi - 2\delta < \text{ph}(ze^{-\pi i}) < \frac{1}{2}\pi - 2\delta$ we may deform the path for the integrals under the summation sign, as indicated in figure 3. Thus we have

$$\int_{\rho e^{(\frac{1}{2}\pi - 2\delta)i}}^{\infty e^{(\frac{1}{2}\pi - 2\delta)i}} \frac{e^{-t} t^{n+\mu_2-\mu_1-j-1}}{t+z} \, dt$$

$$= \left(\int_0^{\infty e^{(\frac{1}{2}\pi - 2\delta)i}} - \int_\rho^{\rho e^{(\frac{1}{2}\pi - 2\delta)i}} - \int_0^\rho \right) \frac{e^{-t} t^{n+\mu_2-\mu_1-j-1}}{t+z} \, dt. \tag{6.8}$$

By analytic continuation of (5.3) it follows that

$$\int_0^{\infty e^{(\frac{1}{2}\pi-2\delta)i}} \frac{e^{-t}t^{n+\mu_2-\mu_1-j-1}}{t+z}dt = 2\pi e^z z^{n+\mu_2-\mu_1-j-1}F_{n+\mu_2-\mu_1-j}(z).$$

And as in the derivation of (5.2) and (5.5) we see that the contributions of the second and third integrals in the right member of (6.8) are $z^{-1}\mathcal{O}(\rho^n)$ and $(zn)^{-1}\mathcal{O}(\rho^n)$ respectively. Hence we have

$$\sum_{j=0}^{m-1}(-)^j a_{j,2}\int_{\rho e^{(\frac{1}{2}\pi-2\delta)i}}^{\infty e^{(\frac{1}{2}\pi-2\delta)i}} \frac{e^{-t}t^{n+\mu_2-\mu_1-j-1}}{t+z}dt$$

$$= 2\pi e^z z^{n+\mu_2-\mu_1-1}\sum_{j=0}^{m-1}(-)^j a_{j,2}\frac{F_{n+\mu_2-\mu_1-j}(z)}{z^j}+\frac{1}{z}\mathcal{O}(\rho^n). \quad (6.9)$$

To estimate the remaining integral in (6.7) we decompose it as follows:

$$\int_{\rho e^{(\frac{1}{2}\pi-2\delta)i}}^{\infty e^{(\frac{1}{2}\pi-2\delta)i}} \frac{e^{-t}t^{n+\mu_2-\mu_1-m-1}}{t+z}\phi_m(t)dt = T^{(1)}_{m,n}(z)+T^{(2)}_{m,n}(z), \quad (6.10)$$

where

$$T^{(1)}_{m,n}(z) = \phi_m(ze^{-\pi i})\int_{\rho e^{(\frac{1}{2}\pi-2\delta)i}}^{\infty e^{(\frac{1}{2}\pi-2\delta)i}} \frac{e^{-t}t^{n+\mu_2-\mu_1-m-1}}{t+z}dt, \quad (6.11)$$

$$T^{(2)}_{m,n}(z) = \int_{\rho e^{(\frac{1}{2}\pi-2\delta)i}}^{\infty e^{(\frac{1}{2}\pi-2\delta)i}} e^{-t}t^{n+\mu_2-\mu_1-m-1}\frac{\phi_m(t)-\phi_m(ze^{-\pi i})}{t+z}dt, \quad (6.12)$$

and until the final paragraph of this section we restrict

$$|z| \geqslant \rho+\delta, \quad -\tfrac{1}{2}\pi+3\delta \leqslant \mathrm{ph}\, z \leqslant \tfrac{3}{2}\pi-3\delta, \quad (6.13)$$

or, equivalently, $ze^{-\pi i} \in \boldsymbol{A}_2$.

From Lemma 4.1 we know that $|\phi_m(ze^{-\pi i})| \leqslant \Phi_m$ when conditions (6.13) are satisfied. Hence we have

$$T^{(1)}_{m,n}(z) = e^z z^{n+\mu_2-\mu_1-m-1}F_{n+\mu_2-\mu_1-m}(z)\mathcal{O}(1)+\frac{1}{z}\mathcal{O}(\rho^n); \quad (6.14)$$

compare (6.8) and (6.9).

For $T^{(2)}_{m,n}(z)$ we observe that the integrand in (6.12) is analytic at $t = ze^{-\pi i}$. Therefore we may deform the integration path in the following way:

$$\int_{\rho e^{(\frac{1}{2}\pi-2\delta)i}}^{\infty e^{(\frac{1}{2}\pi-2\delta)i}} = \int_\rho^\infty - \int_\rho^{\rho e^{(\frac{1}{2}\pi-2\delta)i}};$$

again see figure 3. By application of Lemma 6.1 we have

$$\left|\int_\rho^\infty e^{-t}t^{n+\mu_2-\mu_1-m-1}\frac{\phi_m(t)-\phi_m(ze^{-\pi i})}{t+z}dt\right|$$

$$\leqslant \Psi_m\int_\rho^\infty e^{-t}t^{n+\Re\mu_2-\Re\mu_1-m-1}dt$$

$$< \Psi_m\Gamma(n+\Re\mu_2-\Re\mu_1-m),$$

and

$$\left|\int_{\rho}^{\rho e^{(\frac{1}{2}\pi-2\delta)i}} e^{-t}t^{n+\mu_2-\mu_1-m-1}\frac{\phi_m(t)-\phi_m(ze^{-\pi i})}{t+z}dt\right|$$

$$\leqslant \Psi_m\int_{\rho}^{\rho e^{(\frac{1}{2}\pi-2\delta)i}}\left|e^{-t}t^{n+\mu_2-\mu_1-m-1}dt\right| = \mathcal{O}(\rho^n).$$

On combining the foregoing results we obtain

$$T_{m,n}^{(2)}(z) = \Gamma(n+\mu_2-\mu_1-m)\mathcal{O}(1)+\mathcal{O}(\rho^n). \tag{6.15}$$

If we substitute into (6.10) by means of (6.14) and (6.15) and then combine the $\mathcal{O}$-terms, we derive

$$\int_{\rho e^{(\frac{1}{2}\pi-2\delta)i}}^{\infty e^{(\frac{1}{2}\pi-2\delta)i}} \frac{e^{-t}t^{n+\mu_2-\mu_1-m-1}}{t+z}\phi_m(t)\,dt = e^z z^{n+\mu_2-\mu_1-m-1}F_{n+\mu_2-\mu_1-m}(z)\mathcal{O}(1)$$
$$+\Gamma(n+\mu_2-\mu_1-m)\mathcal{O}(1). \tag{6.16}$$

The results (6.9) and (6.16) enable us to evaluate the right-hand side of (6.7). Thus we have

$$\int_{\rho e^{(\frac{1}{2}\pi-2\delta)i}}^{\infty e^{(\frac{1}{2}\pi-2\delta)i}} \frac{v_2(te^{\pi i})t^n}{t+z}\,dt = -2\pi e^{(\mu_2-\mu_1)\pi i}e^z z^{n+\mu_2-\mu_1-1}$$
$$\times\left\{\sum_{j=0}^{m-1}(-)^j a_{j,2}\frac{F_{n+\mu_2-\mu_1-j}(z)}{z^j}+\frac{F_{n+\mu_2-\mu_1-m}(z)}{z^m}\mathcal{O}(1)\right\}$$
$$+\Gamma(n+\mu_2-\mu_1-m)\mathcal{O}(1). \tag{6.17}$$

We now return to (6.5). On substituting by means of (6.6) and (6.17) we see that equation (2.14) applies with the estimate

$$R_{m,n}^{(1)}(z) = C_1 z^{-m}F_{n+\mu_2-\mu_1-m}(z)\mathcal{O}(1)$$
$$+C_1 e^{-z}z^{-n-\mu_2+\mu_1+1}\Gamma(n+\mu_2-\mu_1-m)\mathcal{O}(1)+e^{-z}z^{-n-\mu_2+\mu_1}\mathcal{O}(\rho^n). \tag{6.18}$$

From equations (2.9) and (2.11) of Olver (1993), we have

$$z^{-m}F_{n+\mu_2-\mu_1-m}(z) = \begin{cases}\mathcal{O}(e^{-z-|z|}z^{-m}), & -\frac{1}{2}\pi+3\delta\leqslant \operatorname{ph}z\leqslant\pi,\\ \mathcal{O}(z^{-m}), & \pi\leqslant\operatorname{ph}z\leqslant\frac{3}{2}\pi-3\delta.\end{cases}$$

Furthermore, from Stirling's formula we deduce that

$$e^{-z}z^{-n-\mu_2+\mu_1+1}\Gamma(n+\mu_2-\mu_1-m) = \mathcal{O}\left\{e^{-z-|z|}z^{\frac{1}{2}-m}\right\};$$

compare (5.6). And the remaining term in (6.18) is absorbable in these estimates. Accordingly, we arrive at

$$R_{m,n}^{(1)}(z) = \begin{cases}\mathcal{O}(e^{-z-|z|}z^{\frac{1}{2}-m}), & -\frac{1}{2}\pi+3\delta\leqslant\operatorname{ph}z\leqslant\pi,\\ \mathcal{O}(z^{\frac{1}{2}-m}), & \pi\leqslant\operatorname{ph}z\leqslant\frac{3}{2}\pi-3\delta.\end{cases}$$

These results agree with (2.16) and (2.17) in the corresponding phase ranges, except that z^{-m} is replaced by $z^{\frac{1}{2}-m}$. To strengthen the estimates into the required form we re-expand the remainder term in the usual manner; thus

$$R_{m,n}^{(1)}(z) = (-)^m C_1 a_{m,2} \frac{F_{n+\mu_2-\mu_1-m}(z)}{z^m} + R_{m+1,n}^{(1)}(z).$$

This completes the proof of Theorem 2.2 for the solution $w_1(z)$ in the phase range $-\frac{1}{2}\pi + 3\delta \leqslant \text{ph} z \leqslant \frac{3}{2}\pi - 3\delta$. The corresponding extension to the range $-\frac{3}{2}\pi + 3\delta \leqslant \text{ph} z \leqslant \frac{1}{2}\pi - 3\delta$ may be carried out in an analogous manner: for example, the integration paths everywhere are replaced by their conjugates, and $\phi_m(ze^{-\pi i})$ is replaced by $\phi_m(ze^{\pi i})$. Alternatively, we can appeal to symmetry.

7. Completion of the proof of Theorem 2.2

On replacing 3δ by δ in the results of §6, we see that equations (2.11), (2.14), (2.16) and (2.17) are established, except that the region of validity in (2.17) is restricted to $\pi \leqslant |\text{ph} z| \leqslant \frac{3}{2}\pi - \delta$.

The corresponding results for the solution $w_2(z)$ can be arrived at by replacing the independent variable in the original equations (1.1) and (1.2) with $\zeta = ze^{-\pi i}$. Thus we have

$$\frac{d^2w}{d\zeta^2} + f^*(\zeta)\frac{dw}{d\zeta} + g^*(\zeta)w = 0,$$

where

$$f^*(\zeta) = -f(-\zeta), \quad g^*(\zeta) = g(-\zeta).$$

Hence

$$f^*(\zeta) = \sum_{s=0}^{\infty} (-)^{s-1} \frac{f_s}{\zeta^s}, \quad g^*(\zeta) = \sum_{s=0}^{\infty} (-)^s \frac{g_s}{\zeta^s}, \quad \zeta \in \boldsymbol{A};$$

compare (1.3). In the expansions that correspond to (2.2) and (2.3) the characteristic values are λ_1^* and λ_2^*, where $\lambda_1^* = -\lambda_2$, $\lambda_2^* = -\lambda_1$. Accordingly, $\lambda_2^* - \lambda_1^* = 1$; compare (2.1). Similarly, the exponents are found to be $\mu_1^* = \mu_2$, $\mu_2^* = \mu_1$. If we apply the part of Theorem 2.2 that we have established so far and then restore the variable $z = \zeta e^{\pi i}$, we arrive at (2.12), (2.15), (2.18) and (2.19) except, again, the region of validity of (2.19) is restricted: in this case to the union of the sectors $-\frac{1}{2}\pi + \delta \leqslant \text{ph} z \leqslant 0$ and $2\pi \leqslant \text{ph} z \leqslant \frac{5}{2}\pi - \delta$. The analysis is straightforward and there is no need to record the details.

The remaining task is to attain the full regions of validity of (2.17) and (2.19). As in the case of the confluent hypergeometric function (Olver 1991*b*, 1993) we shall achieve this by use of connection formulae.

First, we consider the solution $w_1(z)$. From (2.5) of Olver (1993), with $k = -1$ and $p = n + \mu_2 - \mu_1 - s$, we obtain

$$F_{n+\mu_2-\mu_1-s}(ze^{-2\pi i}) = (-)^{n-s-1} i e^{(\mu_2-\mu_1)\pi i} + e^{2(\mu_2-\mu_1)\pi i} F_{n+\mu_2-\mu_1-s}(z). \tag{7.1}$$

Hence from (2.14) we have

$$e^{2\mu_1\pi i} R_n^{(1)}(ze^{-2\pi i}) = (-)^{n-1} i e^{(\mu_2-\mu_1)\pi i} C_1 e^{\lambda_2 z} z^{\mu_2} \sum_{s=0}^{m-1} (-)^s a_{s,2} \frac{F_{n+\mu_2-\mu_1-s}(z)}{z^s}$$
$$- C_1 e^{\lambda_2 z} z^{\mu_2} \sum_{s=0}^{m-1} \frac{a_{s,2}}{z^s} - (-)^n i e^{(\mu_1-\mu_2)\pi i} e^{\lambda_2 z} z^{\mu_2} R_{m,n}^{(1)}(ze^{-2\pi i}). \tag{7.2}$$

On substituting into (2.7) by means of (2.11) and (2.12) then referring to (2.14) and (7.2), we find that on reduction

$$R^{(1)}_{m,n}(z) = e^{2(\mu_1-\mu_2)\pi i} R^{(1)}_{m,n}(ze^{-2\pi i}) + \hat{R}^{(1)}_{m,n}(z) + \hat{R}^{(2)}_{n}(z), \tag{7.3}$$

where

$$\hat{R}^{(1)}_{m,n}(z) = (-)^n i e^{(\mu_1-\mu_2)\pi i} C_1 \sum_{s=m}^{n-1} \frac{a_{s,2}}{z^s},$$
$$\hat{R}^{(2)}_{n}(z) = (-)^n i e^{(\mu_1-\mu_2)\pi i} C_1 e^{-\lambda_2 z} z^{-\mu_2} R^{(2)}_{n}(z).$$

We now let $z \to \infty$ in the sector $\frac{3}{2}\pi - \delta \leqslant \text{ph} z \leqslant \frac{5}{2}\pi - \delta$ with $||z| - n|$ bounded. From (2.16) we immediately derive

$$e^{2(\mu_1-\mu_2)\pi i} R^{(1)}_{m,n}(ze^{-2\pi i}) = \mathcal{O}(e^{-|z|-z} z^{-m}) \subseteq \mathcal{O}(z^{-m}). \tag{7.4}$$

Next, consider $\hat{R}^{(1)}_{m,n}(z)$. If we write $\hat{\alpha} = \sup \alpha$, then we have $|z| \geqslant n - \hat{\alpha}$; see (2.13). From Theorem 2.1 we know that

$$a_{s,2} = \mathcal{O}\Big\{\Gamma(s+\mu_1-\mu_2)\Big\}, \quad s \to \infty.$$

Let M be the least positive integer that satisfies $M \geqslant m$ and $M \geqslant \hat{\alpha}$. Applying Stirling's formula, we see that there is an assignable constant A such that

$$|a_{s,2}| \leqslant A e^{-s} s^{s+\Re(\mu_1-\mu_2)-\frac{1}{2}}, \quad s \geqslant M.$$

Therefore when $n \geqslant M$ we have

$$\left|\sum_{s=m}^{n-1} \frac{a_{s,2}}{z^s}\right| \leqslant \sum_{s=m}^{M-1} \frac{|a_{s,2}|}{|z|^s} + \frac{A}{|z|^M} \sum_{s=M}^{n-1} \frac{e^{-s} s^{s+\Re(\mu_1-\mu_2)-\frac{1}{2}}}{(n-\hat{\alpha})^{s-M}}$$
$$\leqslant \sum_{s=m}^{M-1} \frac{|a_{s,2}|}{|z|^s} + \frac{A}{|z|^M} \sum_{s=M}^{\infty} \frac{e^{-s} s^{s+\Re(\mu_1-\mu_2)-\frac{1}{2}}}{(s+1-\hat{\alpha})^{s-M}}.$$

The infinite sum converges; hence we see that

$$\hat{R}^{(1)}_{m,n}(z) = \mathcal{O}(z^{-m}). \tag{7.5}$$

Lastly, in the second paragraph of this section we showed that the region of validity of (2.18) includes the sector $\frac{3}{2}\pi - \delta \leqslant \text{ph} z \leqslant 2\pi$, and that of (2.19) includes $2\pi \leqslant \text{ph} z \leqslant \frac{5}{2}\pi - \delta$. Substituting into (2.15) by means of these estimates and using also Olver (1993, eqns (2.9) and (2.11)) with z replaced by $ze^{-\pi i}$ and $p = n + \mu_1 - \mu_2 - s$, we arrive at

$$R^{(2)}_{n}(z) = \mathcal{O}(e^{\lambda_1 z} z^{\mu_1} e^{z-|z|}), \quad \tfrac{3}{2}\pi - \delta \leqslant \text{ph} z \leqslant 2\pi,$$
$$R^{(2)}_{n}(z) = \mathcal{O}(e^{\lambda_1 z} z^{\mu_1}), \quad 2\pi \leqslant \text{ph} z \leqslant \tfrac{5}{2}\pi - \delta.$$

Correspondingly,

$$\hat{R}^{(2)}_{n}(z) = \mathcal{O}(e^{-|z|} z^{\mu_1-\mu_2}), \quad \tfrac{3}{2}\pi - \delta \leqslant \text{ph} z \leqslant 2\pi,$$
$$\hat{R}^{(2)}_{n}(z) = \mathcal{O}(e^{-z} z^{\mu_1-\mu_2}), \quad 2\pi \leqslant \text{ph} z \leqslant \tfrac{5}{2}\pi - \delta.$$

Thus in both cases we may assert that

$$\hat{R}^{(2)}_{n}(z) = \mathcal{O}(z^{-m}). \tag{7.6}$$

On substituting into (7.3) by means of (7.4), (7.5) and (7.6), we obtain the required result

$$R^{(1)}_{m,n}(z) = O(z^{-m}), \quad \tfrac{3}{2}\pi - \delta \leqslant \mathrm{ph}\, z \leqslant \tfrac{5}{2}\pi - \delta. \tag{7.7}$$

The extension of the region of validity of (2.17) to the sector $-\frac{5}{2}\pi+\delta \leqslant \mathrm{ph}\, z \leqslant -\frac{3}{2}\pi + \delta$ may be carried out by similar analysis. And the extension of (2.19) to the sectors $-\frac{3}{2}\pi+\delta \leqslant \mathrm{ph}\, z \leqslant -\frac{1}{2}\pi+\delta$ and $\frac{5}{2}\pi-\delta \leqslant \mathrm{ph}\, z \leqslant \frac{7}{2}\pi-\delta$ is then achieved by the procedure outlined in the second paragraph of this section.

Another extension of the foregoing analysis shows that if $C_1C_2 \neq 0$, then (7.7) breaks down when $\mathrm{ph}\, z$ crosses $\frac{5}{2}\pi$. This is because (7.4) and (7.5) continue to hold, but in the vicinity of $\mathrm{ph}\, z = \frac{5}{2}\pi$ we have

$$R^{(2)}_n(z) = -e^{2(\mu_2-\mu_1)\pi i} e^{\lambda_1 z} z^{\mu_1}\{C_2 + O(z^{-1})\};$$

compare again (2.15), (2.19) and Olver (1993, eqn (2.11)). Hence

$$\hat{R}^{(2)}_n(z) = (-)^{n-1} i e^{(\mu_2-\mu_1)\pi i} C_1 e^{-z} z^{\mu_1-\mu_2}\{C_2 + O(z^{-1})\},$$

and this is exponentially large when $\mathrm{ph}\, z$ exceeds $\frac{5}{2}\pi$. A similar observation applies to the other boundary $\mathrm{ph}\, z = -\frac{5}{2}\pi+\delta$, and also to the boundaries $\mathrm{ph}\, z = -\frac{3}{2}\pi+\delta$ and $\mathrm{ph}\, z = \frac{7}{2}\pi - \delta$ in (2.19).

The proof of Theorem 2.2 is complete.

8. Conclusions

In this paper we have considered the asymptotic expansions of solutions of the general homogeneous linear differential equation of the second order in the neighbourhood of an irregular singularity of rank one. We have shown that if these expansions are truncated at (or near) their optimal stage, then the remainder term can be re-expanded as a series of F-functions (generalized exponential integrals), divided by rising powers of $-z$, z being the independent variable. Furthermore, the coefficients are the same as those in the original asymptotic expansion of the complementary solution.

The total sector of validity of each of the new expansions has an angle of $5\pi-2\delta$, compared with $3\pi-2\delta$ for the original Poincaré forms, δ being an arbitrary small positive constant. Moreover, the new expansions are considerably more accurate and also provide a smooth interpretation of the Stokes phenomenon.

We have also shown how to construct explicit asymptotic expansions for the higher coefficients in the original asymptotic solutions of the differential equation in terms of inverse factorials. Again, the coefficients are the lower coefficients of the complementary solution.

Our method of proof is to construct Stieltjes-type transforms for the remainder terms from the standard connection formulae for the solutions, and then to derive the required results by appropriate expansions of the integrands. Necessary extensions of the regions of validity are found by use, again, of the connection formulae. The method appears to be fairly general, and could be applied, for example, to linear differential equations of other orders or with other types of singularity.

We are indebted to the referees for several improvements in the presentation of the results. The research of F. W. J. O. has been supported by the U.S. National Science Foundation unde grants DMS 87-23039 and DMS 92-08690.

References

Berry, M. V. 1990 Waves near Stokes lines. *Proc. R. Soc. Lond.* A**427**, 265–280.

Berry, M. V. 1991 Asymptotics, superasymptotics, hyperasymptotics, ... In *Asymptotics beyon all orders* (ed. H. Segur, S. Tanveer & H. Levine), ser. B (Physics), vol. 284, pp. 1–14. Ne York: Plenum Press.

Berry, M. V. & Howls, C. J. 1991 Hyperasymptotics for integrals with saddles. *Proc. R. So Lond.* A**434**, 657–675.

Boyd, W. G. C. 1990 Stieltjes transforms and the Stokes phenomenon. *Proc. R. Soc. Lon* A**429**, 227–246.

McLeod, J. B. 1992 Smoothing of Stokes discontinuities. *Proc. R. Soc. Lond.* A**437**, 343–354.

Olver, F. W. J. 1974 *Asymptotics and special functions.* New York: Academic Press.

Olver, F. W. J. 1990 On Stokes' phenomenon and converging factors. In *Asymptotic and con putational analysis* (ed. R. Wong), pp. 329–355. New York: Marcel Dekker.

Olver, F. W. J. 1991*a* Uniform, exponentially improved, asymptotic expansions for the genera ized exponential integral. *SIAM J. math. Analysis* **22**, 1460–1474.

Olver, F. W. J. 1991*b* Uniform, exponentially improved, asymptotic expansions for the confluer hypergeometric function and other integral transforms. *SIAM J. math. Analysis* **22**, 1475 1489.

Olver, F. W. J. 1993 Exponentially-improved asymptotic solutions of ordinary differential equ tions I: The confluent hypergeometric function. *SIAM J. math. Analysis* **24**, 756–767.

Olver, F. W. J. 1994 Asymptotic expansions of the coefficients in asymptotic series solutions linear differential equations. *Methods appl. Analysis* **1**, 1–13.

Paris, R. B. 1992*a* Smoothing of the Stokes phenomenon for high-order differential equation *Proc. R. Soc. Lond.* A**436**, 165–186.

Paris, R. B. 1992*b* Smoothing of the Stokes phenomenon using Mellin–Barnes integrals. *J. Com appl. Math.* **41**, 117–133.

Received 20 April 1993; accepted 7 September 1993

ON AN ASYMPTOTIC EXPANSION OF A RATIO OF GAMMA FUNCTIONS

By F. W. J. Olver
Institute for Physical Science and Technology, University of Maryland

(Communicated by T. D. Spearman, M.R.I.A.)

[Received 6 January 1993. Read 3 October 1994. Published 31 August 1995.]

Abstract

An explicit integral representation is found for the remainder term in an asymptotic expansion of a ratio of Gamma functions in inverse factorial series. This result is required in the construction of exponentially-improved asymptotic solutions of the confluent hypergeometric differential equation.

1. Introduction

This paper is concerned with the generalised asymptotic expansion

$$\frac{\Gamma(n+a)\,\Gamma(n+b)}{\Gamma(n+1)} \sim \sum_{s=0}^{\infty} (-)^s \frac{(1-a)_s(1-b)_s}{s!}\Gamma(n+a+b-s-1), \; n \to \infty, \qquad (1.1)$$

in which a and b are fixed real or complex parameters, and $(1-a)_s$ and $(1-b)_s$ are the usual notations for ascending factorials, for example, $(1-a)_0 = 1$ and

$$(1-a)_s = (1-a)(2-a)\cdots(s-a).$$

The meaning of the '$\sim$' sign is that if the sum on the right-hand side of (1.1) is truncated at the term for $s = m-1$, say, then the remainder term is $O\{\Gamma(n+a+b-m-1)\}$ as $n \to \infty$. This result was stated, without proof, by Dingle [1, p. 15 and elsewhere]. Recently, Paris [5, appendix] furnished a proof based on the reflection formula for the Gamma function and properties of the hypergeometric function of argument 1. Paris also showed that the expansion applies uniformly as $n \to \infty$ in the sector $|\mathrm{ph}\, n| \leq \pi - \epsilon$, where ϵ is an arbitrary small positive constant. Subsequently [4], I supplied an alternative proof based on a difference equation satisfied by $\Gamma(n+a)\Gamma(n+b)/\Gamma(n+1)$.

The expansion (1.1) is of importance in the theory of exponentially-improved asymptotic solutions of linear differential equations, particularly the confluent hypergeometric equation ([3]; [5]). The purpose of the present paper is to supply a third proof, based on contour integration. More precisely, we shall prove the following theorem.

Theorem 1.1. *Let a and b be fixed (or bounded) complex numbers, m be a fixed non-negative integer and ϵ be an arbitrary small positive constant. Then as $n \to \infty$ in the* *sector* $|\text{ph}\, n| \leq \pi - \epsilon$,

$$\frac{\Gamma(n+a)\,\Gamma(n+b)}{\Gamma(n+1)} = \sum_{s=0}^{m-1} (-)^s \frac{(1-a)_s\,(1-b)_s}{s!}\Gamma(n+a+b-s-1)$$
$$+(1-a)_m(1-b)_m\,\Gamma(n+a+b-m-1)\,O(1). \tag{1.2}$$

An advantage of this new proof is that it furnishes an explicit integral representation for the remainder term, from which error bounds can be constructed.

2. Derivation of the expansion

Consider the meromorphic function

$$\phi(t) = \frac{\Gamma(t-a+1)\,\Gamma(t-b+1)\,\Gamma(n+a+b-t-1)\,\Gamma(-t)}{\Gamma(1-a)\,\Gamma(1-b)}. \tag{2.1}$$

Its only possible poles in the t-plane are located at the points

$$a-s-1, \quad b-s-1, \quad s, \quad n+a+b+s-1, \quad \text{for} \quad s = 0,\,1,\,2,\,\ldots; \tag{2.2}$$

see Fig. 1. Let δ be an arbitrary constant such that $0 < \delta < 1$, and m be an arbitrary non-negative integer such that

$$m > \text{Re}\, a - 1 + \delta, \quad m > \text{Re}\, b - 1 + \delta. \tag{2.3}$$

Also let n be a real or complex number such that

$$\text{Re}\,(n+a+b-1) > m. \tag{2.4}$$

Define C_m to be the infinite contour that runs upward along the line $\text{Re}\, t = m$, with a semicircular indentation of radius δ to pass to the left of the point $t = m$. Then, in consequence of the assumptions (2.3) and (2.4), C_m separates the poles $a-s-1$ and $b-s-1$ from the poles $n+a+b-s-1$ (see Fig. 1).

Now suppose temporarily that neither a nor b is a positive integer. Then we can construct an infinite contour $\mathscr{L}$ that runs upward along the imaginary axis, save for indentations to ensure that (i) the poles $0,\,1,\,\ldots,\,m-1$ lie in the right component of $\mathbb{C}\setminus\mathscr{L}$ and C_m lies in the closure of this component, and (ii) the poles $a-s-1$, $b-s-1$ lie in the left component of $\mathbb{C}\setminus\mathscr{L}$. Again see Fig. 1. Then by Barnes's lemma [6, §14.52] we have

$$\frac{1}{2\pi i}\int_{\mathscr{L}} \phi(t)\,dt = \frac{\Gamma(n+a)\,\Gamma(n+b)}{\Gamma(n+1)}. \tag{2.5}$$

The only poles of $\phi(t)$ that lie between $\mathscr{L}$ and C_m are those located at $t = 0,\,1,\,\ldots,\,m-1$. Since the residue of $\Gamma(-t)$ at $t = s$ is $(-1)^{s-1}/s!$ we deduce from the

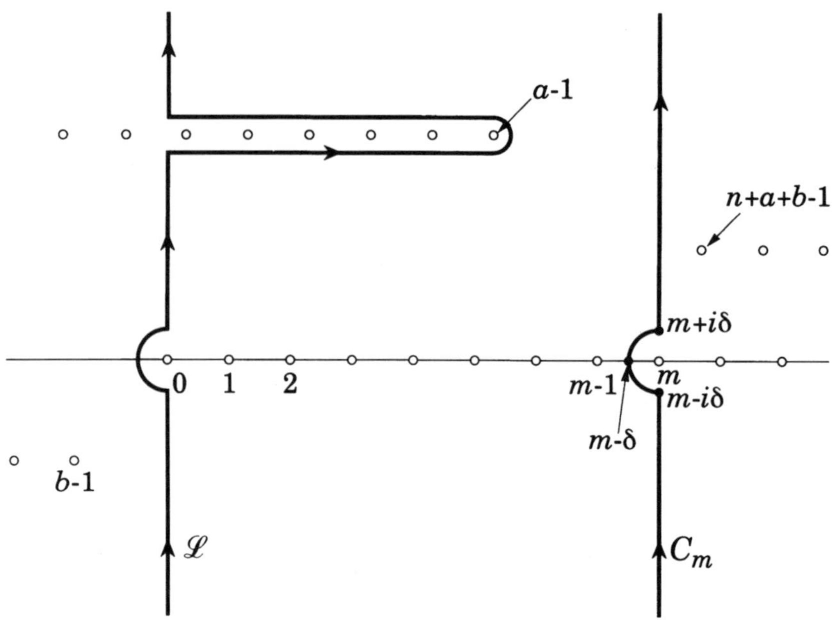

FIG. 1—t-plane. Poles ∘ ∘ ∘ of $\phi(t)$, and contours C_m, $\mathscr{L}$.

theory of residues, and equation (2.5), that

$$\frac{\Gamma(n+a)\,\Gamma(n+b)}{\Gamma(n+1)} = \sum_{s=0}^{m-1} (-)^s \frac{(1-a)_s\,(1-b)_s}{s!}\Gamma(n+a+b-s-1) + \frac{1}{2\pi i}\int_{C_m} \phi(t)\,dt. \tag{2.6}$$

Analytic continuation with respect to a and b removes the restriction that neither a nor b is a positive integer—provided that (2.3) and (2.4) still apply. This is the required expansion.

3. Proof of the asymptotic nature of the expansion

Equation (2.6) furnishes the mth remainder term in the original expansion (1.1). To confirm the asymptotic nature of this expansion we need to estimate the behaviour of the integral

$$\frac{1}{2\pi i}\int_{C_m} \phi(t)\,dt \equiv \frac{1}{2\pi i}\int_{C_m} \frac{\Gamma(t-a+1)\,\Gamma(t-b+1)\,\Gamma(n+a+b-t-1)\,\Gamma(-t)}{\Gamma(1-a)\,\Gamma(1-b)}\,dt.$$

We first suppose that $n \to \infty$ through positive real values. On C_m we have for all sufficiently large n

$$\left|\frac{\Gamma(n+a+b-t-1)}{\Gamma(n+a+b-m-1)}\right| \le \frac{\Gamma(n+\operatorname{Re}a+\operatorname{Re}b-\operatorname{Re}t-1)}{|\Gamma(n+a+b-m-1)|}$$
$$\le \frac{\Gamma(n+\operatorname{Re}a+\operatorname{Re}b-m+\delta-1)}{|\Gamma(n+a+b-m-1)|} = O(n^\delta);$$

compare [2, pp 38 and 119]. Secondly,

$$\int_{C_m} |\Gamma(t-a+1)\,\Gamma(t-b+1)\,\Gamma(-t)dt| < \infty;$$

compare [2, p. 300]. Thirdly,

$$\frac{1}{\Gamma(1-a)\,\Gamma(1-b)} = \frac{(1-a)_m\,(1-b)_m}{\Gamma(m-a+1)\,\Gamma(m-b+1)}.$$

Combination of these results yields

$$\frac{1}{2\pi i}\int_{C_m} \phi(t)\,dt = (1-a)_m\,(1-b)_m\,\Gamma(n+a+b-m-1)\,O(n^{\delta}),\ n \to \infty. \tag{3.1}$$

To strengthen the error estimate in (3.1) from $O(n^{\delta})$ to $O(1)$, we refer to (2.6) and re-expand the error term in the form

$$\frac{1}{2\pi i}\int_{C_m} \phi(t)\,dt = (-)^m\frac{(1-a)_m\,(1-b)_m}{m!}\Gamma(n+a+b-m-1) + \frac{1}{2\pi i}\int_{C_{m+1}} \phi(t)\,dt.$$

We then apply the result just obtained to the last integral.

Similarly, when m does not satisfy (2.3) we re-expand the remainder term in the form

$$\frac{1}{2\pi i}\int_{C_m} \phi(t)\,dt = \sum_{s=m}^{\hat{m}-1}(-)^s\frac{(1-a)_s\,(1-b)_s}{s!}\Gamma(n+a+b-s-1) + \frac{1}{2\pi i}\int_{C_{\hat{m}}} \phi(t)\,dt,$$

where $\hat{m}$ is chosen large enough to satisfy (2.3).

Lastly, to extend the region of validity of equation (1.2) to the sector $|\mathrm{ph}\, n| \le \pi - \epsilon$, we observe that in consequence of Stirling's series the left-hand side can be expanded in this sector as a Poincaré expansion in descending powers of n. This expansion can be rearranged in a descending factorial series, also uniformly valid in the same sector. And since such an expansion is unique, the coefficients must be the same as those in the expansion on the right-hand side.

This completes the proof of Theorem 1.1.

Remarks. (i) Interestingly, the infinite series

$$\sum_{s=0}^{\infty}(-)^s\frac{(1-a)_s\,(1-b)_s}{s!}\Gamma(n+a+b-s-1)$$

converges when $\mathrm{Re}\, n < 0$, provided that $n+a+b$ is not an integer. However, its sum is not $\Gamma(n+a)\,\Gamma(n+b)/\Gamma(n+1)$, but

$$\frac{\sin\pi(n+a)\,\sin\pi(n+b)}{\sin\pi n\,\sin\pi(n+a+b)}\,\frac{\Gamma(n+a)\,\Gamma(n+b)}{\Gamma(n+1)}.$$

This result can be extracted from the proof of Barnes's lemma given in [6]. Alternatively, it emerges from Paris's proof [5].

(ii) If either a or b is a positive integer, k, say, then the remainder term in (1.2) vanishes identically when $m \geq k$, and the result becomes an exact identity.

(iii) The integral representation for the remainder term, given by (2.1) and (2.6) with C_m indicated in Fig. 1, is valid with the conditions (2.3) and (2.4). However, by deforming C_m these conditions could be eased, provided that none of the quantities $1-a-n$, $1-b-n$ and $1-a-b+m-n$ is a positive integer.

ACKNOWLEDGEMENTS

This research was supported by a Senior Visiting Fellowship from the Royal Irish Academy during a visit to Dublin City University in 1991, and by the US National Science Foundation under Grants DMS 87-23039 and DMS 92-08690. The writer is indebted to R. B. Paris for improvements in the proof, and to A. D. Wood and the referee for improvements in the presentation.

REFERENCES

[1] Dingle, R. B. 1973 *Asymptotic expansions: their derivation and interpretation.* London. Academic Press.

[2] Olver, F. W. J. 1974 *Asymptotics and special functions.* New York. Academic Press.

[3] Olver, F. W. J. 1993 Exponentially-improved asymptotic solutions of ordinary differential equations I: The confluent hypergeometric function. *SIAM Journal on Mathematical Analysis* **24**, 756–67.

[4] Olver, F. W. J. 1994 Asymptotic expansions of the coefficients in asymptotic series solutions of linear differential equations. *Methods and Applications of Analysis* **1**, 1–13.

[5] Paris, R. B. 1992 Smoothing of the Stokes phenomenon using Mellin–Barnes integrals. *Journal of Computational and Applied Mathematics* **41**, 117–33.

[6] Whittaker, E. T. and Watson, G. N. 1927 *A course of modern analysis* (4th edn). London. Cambridge University Press.

Methods and Applications of Analysis
2 (2) 1995, pp. 173–197

HYPERASYMPTOTIC SOLUTIONS OF SECOND-ORDER LINEAR DIFFERENTIAL EQUATIONS I

A. B. Olde Daalhuis and F. W. J. Olver

ABSTRACT. A sequence of re-expansions is developed for the remainder terms in the well-known Poincaré series expansions of the solutions of homogeneous linear differential equations of the second order in the neighborhood of an irregular singularity of rank one. These re-expansions are in series of repeated integrals of the generalized exponential integral, and the coefficients in these series are the same as those of the original Poincaré expansions. Each step of the process reduces the estimate of the error term by the same exponentially-small factor, while increasing the region of validity.

It also is shown how to ensure that the process is numerically stable. A numerical example is included.

1. Introduction and summary

The general homogeneous linear differential equation of the second order is given by

$$\frac{d^2w}{dz^2}+f(z)\frac{dw}{dz}+g(z)w=0. \tag{1.1}$$

If, as we shall suppose, the point at infinity is an irregular singularity of rank one, then the functions $f(z)$ and $g(z)$ can be expanded in power series

$$f(z)=\sum_{s=0}^{\infty}\frac{f_s}{z^s},\quad g(z)=\sum_{s=0}^{\infty}\frac{g_s}{z^s},$$

that converge on an open annulus $|z|>a$. Not all of the coefficients f_0, g_0, and g_1 vanish, otherwise infinity would be a regular singularity.

In a recent paper [6], we showed how to improve the accuracy and extend the region of applicability of the well-known Poincaré asymptotic expansions of the solutions of (1.1) for large $|z|$. This was achieved by truncating the expansions at or near their optimal stage (that is, as a rule, at or near their smallest term) and re-expanding the remainder term in a series of generalized exponential integrals. In the present paper, we show how to achieve additional improvement, both in accuracy and in the region of validity, by further re-expansions of remainder terms.

We follow existing terminology [1, 2, 5, 9] for these new types of asymptotic expansions. Thus re-expansions in terms of generalized exponential integrals are called

Received June 2, 1994, revised November 3, 1994.

1991 *Mathematics Subject Classification.* Primary 34E05; Secondary 33B20, 33C10.

Key words and phrases: asymptotic expansions, Bessel functions, connection formulas, differential equations, exponential improvement, exponential integral, hyperasymptotics, hyperterminant, incomplete Gamma function, irregular singularity, remainder term, superasymptotics.

The research of the second author was supported by the National Science Foundation under Grant DMS 92-08690.

exponentially-improved or *superasymptotic expansions.* Further re-expansions are called *hyperasymptotic expansions.* The levels of improvement are enumerated in the following way. The original Poincaré expansions are regarded as being at level zero, the exponentially-improved expansions are at level one, and the hyperasymptotic expansions are at levels two and above.

The paper is arranged as follows. In §2, we define and describe properties of certain multiple integrals, the so-called "hyperterminants", that are needed in subsequent sections. In §§3, 4, we show how to optimize the remainder terms in the well-known Poincaré or "zeroth-level" asymptotic expansions for the solutions of the second-order linear differential equation in the neighborhood of an irregular singularity of rank one. This problem is well understood in the literature, but we introduce a somewhat different form of proof that is to be used in later sections.

In §5, we re-expand the remainder terms that appear in §4, to obtain "first-level" expansions. These expansions are in series of generalized exponential integrals, or first-level hyperterminants, and are the same as those found in [6]. However, we now are able to optimize this re-expansion and the outcome is perhaps somewhat surprising. By taking approximately $2|z|$ terms in the zeroth-level expansion — that is, *twice* the number used when we optimize at that level — and $|z|$ terms in the first-level expansion, the error estimate is improved from $e^{-|z|}$ times an arbitrary power of z^{-1} to $e^{-2|z|}|z|^{-\frac{1}{2}}$.

In §§6, 7, the process of re-expansion is continued to the second level and then generalized. At the lth level, l being arbitrary, the expansions of the solutions are in terms of hyperterminants at that level and all preceding levels, and the coefficients at each level alternate between the sets of coefficients for the original pair of Poincaré expansions. On optimizing, we find that the pattern described in the preceding paragraph continues. Thus we require approximately $(l+1)|z|$ terms at level zero, $l|z|$ terms at level one, and so on, finishing with $|z|$ terms at level l. The total number of terms is approximately $\frac{1}{2}(l+1)(l+2)|z|$, and the final error estimate is $e^{-(l+1)|z|}$ times a power of z. Since l is arbitrary, this means that, in theory, there is no limit on the attainable exponential improvement.

In §8, the numerical stability of the generalized asymptotic expansion is examined, and it is demonstrated that instability, in the form of cancellation, begins when level 2 is included, and becomes severe at higher levels. It also is shown how to overcome this difficulty by reducing the number of terms called for in the optimization process that is used in §7. With the numerically stable form of expansion, the optimal error estimate on stopping at the lth level ($l \geqslant 2$) is $(l+1)^{-e|z|}$ times a power of z. The number of terms required also is less.

In §9, a numerical example is provided. In §10, it is shown how to extend the sector of validity beyond $|\operatorname{ph} z| \leqslant \pi$ for the hyperasymptotic expansions of §7. This is achieved via continuation formulas for the remainder terms. The sector of validity can extend as far as $|\operatorname{ph} z| \leqslant (l+\frac{3}{2})\pi - \delta$, but as the sector widens the exponential improvement diminishes. A similar, but less extensive, continuation can also be made for the numerically stable hyperasymptotic expansions of §8.

In the concluding section, §11, comparisons of our new results are made with earlier results obtained in an important paper by Berry and Howls [1]. Comments also are made on the Stokes phenomenon and the numerical evaluation of the hyperterminants.

2. Auxiliary functions

In [6] our re-expansions for the solutions of (1.1) were expressed in terms of the function $F_p(z)$ defined by

$$F_p(z) = \frac{e^{-z}}{2\pi} \int_0^\infty \frac{e^{-zt} t^{p-1}}{1+t} dt, \tag{2.1}$$

when $\Re p > 0$ and $|\operatorname{ph} z| < \frac{1}{2}\pi$, and by analytic continuation elsewhere. This function is directly related to the generalized exponential integral and the incomplete Gamma function, and its relevant properties are summarized in §2 of [9].

In the present paper, we shall need the following generalizations of $F_p(z)$:

$$G_\omega^{(0)}(z) = \frac{1}{z}, \tag{2.2a}$$

$$G_\omega^{(1)}(z; M_0) = \int_0^\infty \frac{e^{-t} t^{M_0 - 1 + \omega}}{t+z} dt, \tag{2.2b}$$

and, in general,

$$G_\omega^{(l)}(z; M_0, M_1, \ldots, M_{l-1}) =$$

$$\int_0^\infty \cdots \int_0^\infty \frac{e^{-t-t_1-\cdots-t_{l-1}} t^{M_0+\omega} t_1^{M_1-\omega} \cdots t_{l-2}^{M_{l-2}+(-)^{l-2}\omega} t_{l-1}^{M_{l-1}-1+(-)^{l-1}\omega}}{(t+z)(t_1+t)(t_2+t_1)\cdots(t_{l-1}+t_{l-2})} dt_{l-1} \cdots dt_1 dt. \tag{2.2c}$$

Here, z and ω are real or complex parameters and l, M_0, $M_1, \ldots$ are nonnegative integers. By observing that

$$t_1 + t \geqslant t, \quad t_j + t_{j-1} \geqslant t_{j-1}, \quad 2 \leq j < l-1, \tag{2.3}$$

we see that these multiple integrals converge when $|\operatorname{ph} z| < \pi$ and

$$M_j + (-)^j \Re\omega > 0, \quad 0 \leq j < l-1. \tag{2.4}$$

Elsewhere, the $G_\omega^{(l)}$ are defined by analytic continuation with respect to z and ω. Clearly, when (2.4) applies the only singularities of $G_\omega^{(l)}(z; M_0, \ldots, M_{l-1})$ are branch-points or poles at $z = 0$ and ∞.

It will be observed that there is some degree of arbitrariness in the choice of the parameter ω and the integers $M_0, M_1, \ldots, M_{l-1}$. For example, from (2.1) we see that

$$F_{M_0+\omega}(z) = (2\pi)^{-1} e^{-z} z^{1-M_0-\omega} G_\omega^{(1)}(z; M_0), \tag{2.5a}$$

but we equally well could write

$$F_{M_0+\omega}(z) = (2\pi)^{-1} e^{-z} z^{1-M_0-\omega} G_{\omega-1}^{(1)}(z; M_0+1). \tag{2.5b}$$

In the present paper, this ambiguity is resolved by requiring that ω is always determined by

$$\omega = \mu_2 - \mu_1, \tag{2.6}$$

where μ_1 and μ_2 are defined in the next section. The functions $G_\omega^{(l)}$ are closely related to the "generalized terminants" or "hyperterminants" introduced in [1, 2], and some properties of the $G_\omega^{(l)}$ follow directly from those of the K_{rn} given in [1]. Other properties are as follows.

From (2.2) we have immediately

$$G_\omega^{(l)}(z; M_0, \ldots, M_{l-1}) = \int_0^\infty \frac{e^{-t} t^{M_0+\omega}}{t+z} G_{-\omega}^{(l-1)}(t; M_1, \ldots, M_{l-1}) dt, \tag{2.7}$$

when $l \geqslant 1$, and hence

$$G_\omega^{(l)}(z; M_0, \ldots, M_{l-1}) = z^{M_0+\omega} \int_0^\infty \frac{e^{-zt} t^{M_0+\omega}}{t+1} G_{-\omega}^{(l-1)}(zt; M_1, \ldots, M_{l-1}) dt, \tag{2.8}$$

provided that $|\operatorname{ph} z| < \frac{1}{2}\pi$. If we rotate the path in this integral through an angle 2π and subsequently replace z by $ze^{-2\pi i}$, then we obtain the continuation formula

$$\begin{aligned} &G_\omega^{(l)}(ze^{-2\pi i}; M_0, \ldots, M_{l-1}) - G_\omega^{(l)}(z; M_0, \ldots, M_{l-1}) \\ &\qquad = 2\pi i e^{-(M_0+\omega)\pi i} e^z z^{M_0+\omega} G_{-\omega}^{(l-1)}(ze^{-\pi i}; M_1, \ldots, M_{l-1}), \end{aligned} \tag{2.9}$$

again valid when $l \geqslant 1$.

An upper bound for $G_\omega^{(l)}$ can be found from (2.2c) by use of (2.3) and the inequality

$$|t+z| \geqslant |z| \mathcal{S}(z), \tag{2.10}$$

where $\mathcal{S}(z) = 1$ if $|\operatorname{ph} z| \leqslant \frac{1}{2}\pi$, and $\mathcal{S}(z) = |\sin(\operatorname{ph} z)|$ if $\frac{1}{2}\pi \leqslant |\operatorname{ph} z| < \pi$. Again, the integrals uncouple and we find that

$$\left|G_\omega^{(l)}(z; M_0, \ldots, M_{l-1})\right| \leqslant \frac{\Gamma(M_0 + \Re\omega)\Gamma(M_1 - \Re\omega) \cdots \Gamma(M_{l-1} + (-)^{l-1}\Re\omega)}{|z|\mathcal{S}(z)}, \tag{2.11}$$

valid when $|\operatorname{ph} z| < \pi$ and (2.4) applies.

For the closed sector $|\operatorname{ph} z| \leqslant \pi$ we give the following estimate.

Lemma 2.1. *If $M_0 = |z| + \mathcal{O}(1)$, then as $z \to \infty$ in $|\operatorname{ph} z| \leqslant \pi$*

$$\begin{aligned} &G_\omega^{(l)}(z; M_0, \ldots, M_{l-1}) \\ &\qquad = \Gamma(M_0 + \Re\omega)\Gamma(M_1 - \Re\omega) \cdots \Gamma\big(M_{l-1} + (-)^{l-1}\Re\omega\big)\mathcal{O}\big(z^{-\frac{1}{2}}\big), \end{aligned} \tag{2.12}$$

uniformly for all positive integers l.

Proof. Let δ be a constant such that $0 < \delta < \pi$. If $|\operatorname{ph} z| \leqslant \pi - \delta$, then $\mathcal{S}(z) \geqslant \sin\delta$, and (2.12) is simply a weaker form of (2.11).

Next, in consequence of (2.5a) and [9, (2.9)], we know that

$$G_\omega^{(1)}(z; M_0) = \mathcal{O}\big(e^{-|z|} z^{M_0 - 1 + \Re\omega}\big) = \Gamma(M_0 + \Re\omega)\mathcal{O}\big(z^{-\frac{1}{2}}\big), \tag{2.13}$$

which proves (2.12) for $l = 1$.

Now suppose that $l \geqslant 2$ and $0 < \operatorname{ph} z < \pi$. On substituting into (2.2c) by means of the identity

$$\frac{1}{(t+z)(t_1+t)} = \frac{1}{(t+z)(t_1+e^{-\pi i}z)} - \frac{1}{(t_1+e^{-\pi i}z)(t_1+t)} \tag{2.14}$$

and using (2.2*b*), we obtain

$$G^{(l)}_{\omega}(z;M_0,\ldots,M_{l-1}) = G^{(1)}_{\omega}(z;M_0+1)G^{(l-1)}_{-\omega}(e^{-\pi i}z;M_1,\ldots,M_{l-1})$$
$$-\int_0^\infty\cdots\int_0^\infty \frac{e^{-t-t_1-\cdots-t_{l-1}}t^{M_0+\omega}t_1^{M_1-\omega}\cdots t_{l-1}^{M_{l-1}-1+(-)^{l-1}\omega}}{(t_1+e^{-\pi i}z)(t_1+t)(t_2+t_1)\cdots(t_{l-1}+t_{l-2})}dt_{l-1}\cdots dt_1 dt. \tag{2.15}$$

Analytic continuation extends the validity of this result to the sector $0 < \operatorname{ph} z < 2\pi$. If we restrict $\delta \leqslant \operatorname{ph} z \leqslant \pi$, then from (2.11) and (2.13) we obtain

$$\begin{aligned} G^{(1)}_{\omega}&(z;M_0+1)G^{(l-1)}_{-\omega}(e^{-\pi i}z;M_1,\ldots,M_{l-1}) \\ &= \frac{\Gamma(M_0+1+\Re\omega)\Gamma(M_1-\Re\omega)\cdots\Gamma(M_{l-1}+(-)^{l-1}\Re\omega)}{z}\mathcal{O}(z^{-\frac{1}{2}}) \\ &= \Gamma(M_0+\Re\omega)\Gamma(M_1-\Re\omega)\cdots\Gamma(M_{l-1}+(-)^{l-1}\Re\omega)\mathcal{O}(z^{-\frac{1}{2}}). \end{aligned}$$

The multiple integral in (2.15) may be estimated by analysis similar to that used to establish (2.11). We find that

$$\begin{aligned} \int_0^\infty\cdots\int_0^\infty & \frac{e^{-t-t_1-\cdots-t_{l-1}}t^{M_0+\omega}t_1^{M_1-\omega}\cdots t_{l-1}^{M_{l-1}-1+(-)^{l-1}\omega}}{(t_1+e^{-\pi i}z)(t_1+t)(t_2+t_1)\cdots(t_{l-1}+t_{l-2})}dt_{l-1}\cdots dt_1 dt \\ &= \Gamma(M_0+\Re\omega)\Gamma(M_1-\Re\omega)\cdots\Gamma(M_{l-1}+(-)^{l-1}\Re\omega)\mathcal{O}(z^{-1}), \end{aligned}$$

as $z \to \infty$ in $\delta \leqslant \operatorname{ph} z \leqslant 2\pi-\delta$.

On substituting into (2.15) by means of the last two equations, we obtain (2.12) for $\delta \leqslant \operatorname{ph} z \leqslant \pi$. The proof of (2.12) for the sector $-\pi \leqslant \operatorname{ph} z \leqslant -\delta$ is similar. □

3. Integral representations for the original remainder terms

As in [6], we may assume, without loss of generality, that the roots λ_1, λ_2 of the characteristic equation

$$\lambda^2 + f_0\lambda + g_0 = 0 \tag{3.1}$$

satisfy

$$\lambda_2 - \lambda_1 = 1. \tag{3.2}$$

Then equation (1.1) has unique solutions $w_1(z)$ and $w_2(z)$ such that as $|z| \to \infty$

$$w_1(z) \sim e^{\lambda_1 z}z^{\mu_1}\sum_{s=0}^{\infty}\frac{a_{s,1}}{z^s}, \quad |\operatorname{ph} z| \leqslant \frac{3}{2}\pi-\delta, \tag{3.3a}$$

$$w_2(z) \sim e^{\lambda_2 z}z^{\mu_2}\sum_{s=0}^{\infty}(-)^s\frac{a_{s,2}}{z^s}, \quad -\frac{1}{2}\pi+\delta \leqslant \operatorname{ph} z \leqslant \frac{5}{2}\pi-\delta; \tag{3.3b}$$

here and subsequently, δ denotes an arbitrary small positive constant. The exponents μ_1 and μ_2 are given by

$$\mu_1 = f_1\lambda_1 + g_1, \tag{3.4a}$$
$$\mu_2 = -(f_1\lambda_2 + g_1). \tag{3.4b}$$

The coefficients are determined by $a_{0,1} = a_{0,2} = 1$ and, when $s \geqslant 1$,

$$-sa_{s,1} = (s-\mu_1)(s-1-\mu_1)a_{s-1,1} + \sum_{j=1}^{s} \{\lambda_1 f_{j+1} + g_{j+1} - (s-j-\mu_1)f_j\} a_{s-j,1}, \tag{3.5a}$$

$$-sa_{s,2} = (s-\mu_2)(s-1-\mu_2)a_{s-1,2} - \sum_{j=1}^{s} (-)^j \{\lambda_2 f_{j+1} + g_{j+1} - (s-j-\mu_2)f_j\} a_{s-j,2}. \tag{3.5b}$$

Other solutions of (1.1) include $w_1(ze^{-2\pi i})$ and $w_2(ze^{2\pi i})$. We assume that the coefficients C_1 and C_2 in the connection formulas

$$w_1(z) = e^{2\pi i\mu_1} w_1(ze^{-2\pi i}) + C_1 w_2(z), \tag{3.6a}$$

$$w_2(z) = e^{-2\pi i\mu_2} w_2(ze^{2\pi i}) + C_2 w_1(z), \tag{3.6b}$$

are known or can be calculated (see [7]). We also assume that C_1 and C_2 are nonzero.[1]

The foregoing notation agrees with that of [6], except that we have replaced $a_{s,2}$ by $(-)^s a_{s,2}$. In [6], we also found it convenient to work with the functions

$$v_1(z) = e^{-\lambda_1 z} z^{-\mu_1 - 1} w_1(z), \quad v_2(z) = e^{-\lambda_1 z} z^{-\mu_1 - 1} w_2(z),$$

in place of the actual solutions $w_1(z)$ and $w_2(z)$. For reasons of symmetry, we find it more convenient in the present paper to employ the pair

$$u_1(z) = e^{-\lambda_1 z} z^{-\mu_1} w_1(z), \tag{3.7a}$$

$$u_2(z) = e^{-\mu_2 \pi i} e^{\lambda_2 z} z^{-\mu_2} w_2(ze^{\pi i}), \tag{3.7b}$$

which we shall regard as the *basic functions* for equation (1.1).

From (3.3) we obtain

$$u_1(z) \sim \sum_{s=0}^{\infty} \frac{a_{s,1}}{z^s}, \tag{3.8a}$$

$$u_2(z) \sim \sum_{s=0}^{\infty} \frac{a_{s,2}}{z^s}, \tag{3.8b}$$

each of these expansions being valid when $z \to \infty$ in $|\operatorname{ph} z| \leqslant \frac{3}{2}\pi - \delta$. In place of (3.6) we now have

$$u_1(z) = u_1(ze^{-2\pi i}) + 2\pi i K_1 e^{-\omega\pi i} e^z z^{\omega} u_2(ze^{-\pi i}), \tag{3.9a}$$

$$u_2(z) = u_2(ze^{-2\pi i}) + 2\pi i K_2 e^{\omega\pi i} e^z z^{-\omega} u_1(ze^{-\pi i}), \tag{3.9b}$$

in which ω is defined as in (2.6) and

$$K_1 = (2\pi i)^{-1} e^{\omega\pi i} C_1, \tag{3.10a}$$

$$K_2 = -(2\pi i)^{-1} C_2. \tag{3.10b}$$

[1] If, for example, $C_1 = 0$, then the expansion (3.3a) converges and can be handled quite differently; compare [6], §2, Remark (v).

We shall need the following transforms of Stieltjes type:

$$u_1(z) = K_1 z \int_\rho^\infty \frac{e^{-t}t^{-1+\omega}}{t+z} u_2(t)dt - \frac{z}{2\pi i}\int_{\rho e^{-\pi i}}^{\rho e^{\pi i}} \frac{u_1(t)}{t(t-z)}dt, \tag{3.11a}$$

$$u_2(z) = K_2 z \int_\rho^\infty \frac{e^{-t}t^{-1-\omega}}{t+z} u_1(t)dt - \frac{z}{2\pi i}\int_{\rho e^{-\pi i}}^{\rho e^{\pi i}} \frac{u_2(t)}{t(t-z)}dt, \tag{3.11b}$$

valid when $|z| > \rho$ and $|\operatorname{ph} z| < \pi$. Here ρ is an arbitrary constant such that $\rho > a$, a being defined as in §1. In each of these equations, the path in the first integral is a straight line and in the second integral is an arc of the circle $|t| = \rho$ described in the positive sense. The proof is based on equations (3.9) and is similar to the proof of Lemma 3.1 of [6]. We omit the proof.

Let $R_1^{(0)}(z; N_0)$ and $R_2^{(0)}(z; N_0)$ denote the remainder terms when the expansions (3.8) are terminated after N_0 terms, N_0 being an arbitrary nonnegative integer; thus

$$u_1(z) = \sum_{s=0}^{N_0-1} \frac{a_{s,1}}{z^s} + R_1^{(0)}(z; N_0), \tag{3.12a}$$

$$u_2(z) = \sum_{s=0}^{N_0-1} \frac{a_{s,2}}{z^s} + R_2^{(0)}(z; N_0). \tag{3.12b}$$

If we substitute into (3.11) by means of the identities

$$\frac{1}{t+z} = \frac{1}{z}\sum_{s=0}^{N_0-1} (-)^s \left(\frac{t}{z}\right)^s + \frac{(-)^{N_0}}{t+z}\left(\frac{t}{z}\right)^{N_0}, \tag{3.13a}$$

$$\frac{1}{t-z} = -\frac{1}{z}\sum_{s=0}^{N_0-1} \left(\frac{t}{z}\right)^s + \frac{1}{t-z}\left(\frac{t}{z}\right)^{N_0}, \tag{3.13b}$$

then, as in the proof of Lemma 3.2 of [6], we obtain the following integral representations

$$R_1^{(0)}(z; N_0) = (-)^{N_0} \frac{K_1}{z^{N_0-1}} \int_\rho^\infty \frac{e^{-t}t^{N_0-1+\omega}}{t+z} u_2(t)dt + \varepsilon_1(z; \rho; N_0), \tag{3.14a}$$

$$R_2^{(0)}(z; N_0) = (-)^{N_0} \frac{K_2}{z^{N_0-1}} \int_\rho^\infty \frac{e^{-t}t^{N_0-1-\omega}}{t+z} u_1(t)dt + \varepsilon_2(z; \rho; N_0), \tag{3.14b}$$

when $|z| > \rho$ and $|\operatorname{ph} z| < \pi$, where

$$\varepsilon_1(z; \rho; N_0) = -\frac{z^{1-N_0}}{2\pi i}\int_{\rho e^{-\pi i}}^{\rho e^{\pi i}} \frac{t^{N_0-1}}{t-z} u_1(t)dt, \tag{3.15a}$$

$$\varepsilon_2(z; \rho; N_0) = -\frac{z^{1-N_0}}{2\pi i}\int_{\rho e^{-\pi i}}^{\rho e^{\pi i}} \frac{t^{N_0-1}}{t-z} u_2(t)dt. \tag{3.15b}$$

We note that the functions $\varepsilon_1(z; \rho; N_0)$ and $\varepsilon_2(z; \rho; N_0)$ are analytic on the annulus $|z| > \rho$. Furthermore, if $\mathbf{A}$ denotes the closed annulus $|z| \geqslant \rho + \delta$, then

$$\varepsilon_1(z; \rho; N_0),\ \varepsilon_2(z; \rho; N_0) = \mathcal{O}\big(\rho^{N_0} z^{-N_0}\big), \tag{3.16a, b}$$

where the $\mathcal{O}$-term is uniform with respect to $z \in \mathbf{A}$ and all nonnegative integers N_0.

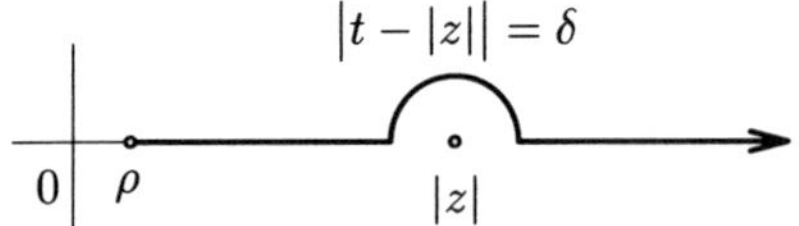

FIGURE 3.1. t-plane. Path $\mathcal{P}$ when $|z| \geqslant \rho + \delta$ and $0 \leqslant \operatorname{ph} z \leqslant \pi$.

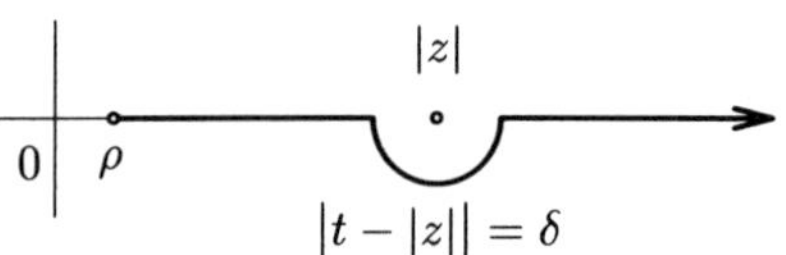

FIGURE 3.2. t-plane. Path $\mathcal{P}$ when $|z| \geqslant \rho + \delta$ and $-\pi \leqslant \operatorname{ph} z < 0$.

We further note that the process of substituting into (3.11) by means of (3.13) also yields integral representations for the coefficients $a_{s,1}$ and $a_{s,2}$. From these representations asymptotic expansions of $a_{s,1}$ and $a_{s,2}$ for large s can be constructed in inverse factorial series. This result appears as Theorem 2.1 in [6], and for later reference we record these expansions in the present notation:

$$a_{s,1} \sim (-)^s K_1 \sum_{j=0}^{\infty} a_{j,2} \Gamma(s - j + \omega), \tag{3.17a}$$

$$a_{s,2} \sim (-)^s K_2 \sum_{j=0}^{\infty} a_{j,1} \Gamma(s - j - \omega). \tag{3.17b}$$

The final step in this section is to modify the representations (3.14) in such a way that they include the phases $\operatorname{ph} z = \pm\pi$. This is achieved by restricting $z \in \mathbf{A}$ and deforming the integration path by a semicircular indentation of radius δ that is centered at $|z|$, and passes above $|z|$ when $0 \leqslant \operatorname{ph} z \leqslant \pi$ and below $|z|$ when $-\pi \leqslant \operatorname{ph} z < 0$; see Figures 3.1 and 3.2. We denote the deformed path by $\mathcal{P}$. Then by continuity we derive

$$R_1^{(0)}(z; N_0) = (-)^{N_0} \frac{K_1}{z^{N_0 - 1}} \int_{\mathcal{P}} \frac{e^{-t} t^{N_0 - 1 + \omega}}{t + z} u_2(t) dt + \varepsilon_1(z; \rho; N_0), \tag{3.18a}$$

$$R_2^{(0)}(z; N_0) = (-)^{N_0} \frac{K_2}{z^{N_0 - 1}} \int_{\mathcal{P}} \frac{e^{-t} t^{N_0 - 1 - \omega}}{t + z} u_1(t) dt + \varepsilon_2(z; \rho; N_0), \tag{3.18b}$$

valid when $z \in \mathbf{A}$ and $|\operatorname{ph} z| \leqslant \pi$.

4. Optimal expansions at level zero (Poincaré's expansions)

Throughout this section, we suppose that $|\operatorname{ph} z| \leqslant \pi$.

We seek to estimate and then optimize the remainder terms $R_1^{(0)}(z; N_0)$ and $R_2^{(0)}(z; N_0)$ that appear in (3.12) by permitting N_0 to be a linear function of $|z|$. More precisely, we assume that

$$N_0 = \beta_0 |z| + \alpha_0, \tag{4.1}$$

where β_0 is a positive constant at our disposal and α_0 is bounded.[2] Whatever the choice of β_0 and α_0, we assume throughout that $|z|$ is restricted in such a way that

$$N_0 \geqslant 1 + |\Re \omega|. \tag{4.2}$$

[2]Typically, $N_0 = \operatorname{int}[\beta_0 |z|]$, so that $-1 < \alpha_0 \leqslant 0$.

This is obviously achieved if we restrict $z \in \mathbf{A}_0$, where $\mathbf{A}_0$ is the closed annulus defined by

$$|z| \geqslant (1 + |\Re\omega| - \tilde{\alpha}_0)/\beta_0, \tag{4.3}$$

$\tilde{\alpha}_0$ being the lesser of $1 + |\Re\omega|$ and $\liminf \alpha_0$.

In the representation (3.18a), we observe that because $z \in \mathbf{A}$, we have $|t + z| \geqslant \delta$ everywhere on $\mathcal{P}$. Since also $u_2(t) = \mathcal{O}(1)$ as $t \to \infty$, it follows that the contribution of the straight-line segments of $\mathcal{P}$ is estimated by

$$\left(\int_{\rho}^{|z|-\delta} + \int_{|z|+\delta}^{\infty} \right) \frac{e^{-t} t^{N_0 - 1 + \omega}}{t + z} u_2(t) dt = \Gamma(N_0 + \Re\omega) \mathcal{O}(1), \tag{4.4}$$

uniformly with respect to $z \in \mathbf{A} \cap \mathbf{A}_0$. On the semicircular arc we have

$$\int_{|z|-\delta}^{|z|+\delta} \frac{e^{-t} t^{N_0 - 1 + \omega}}{t + z} u_2(t) dt = \mathcal{O}\{e^{-|z|}(|z| + \delta)^{N_0 - 1 + \Re\omega}\}, \tag{4.5}$$

also uniformly on $\mathbf{A} \cap \mathbf{A}_0$. On referring to (4.1) and applying Stirling's formula, we see that

$$\frac{e^{-|z|}(|z| + \delta)^{N_0 - 1 + \Re\omega}}{\Gamma(N_0 + \Re\omega)} = e^{-|z|}(\beta_0^{\beta_0} e^{-\beta_0})^{-|z|} z^{-\frac{1}{2}} \mathcal{O}(1) = \mathcal{O}(z^{-\frac{1}{2}}),$$

uniformly on $\mathbf{A} \cap \mathbf{A}_0$. The last step follows from the observation that $\beta_0^{\beta_0} e^{-\beta_0} \geqslant e^{-1}$ for all positive values of β_0. Accordingly, on combining (4.4) and (4.5) we have

$$(-)^{N_0} \frac{K_1}{z^{N_0 - 1}} \int_{\mathcal{P}} \frac{e^{-t} t^{N_0 - 1 + \omega}}{t + z} u_2(t) dt = \Gamma(N_0 + \Re\omega) \mathcal{O}(z^{1 - N_0}), \tag{4.6}$$

uniformly on $\mathbf{A} \cap \mathbf{A}_0$.

The other contribution to $R_1^{(0)}(z; N_0)$ in (3.18a), namely $\varepsilon_1(z; \rho; N_0)$, is estimated by (3.16). Obviously, this contribution, too, may be absorbed into the right-hand side of (4.6). We therefore have proved that

$$R_1^{(0)}(z; N_0) = \Gamma(N_0 + \Re\omega) \mathcal{O}(z^{1 - N_0}), \tag{4.7}$$

and, hence,

$$R_1^{(0)}(z; N_0) = (\beta_0^{\beta_0} e^{-\beta_0})^{|z|} \mathcal{O}(z^{\frac{1}{2} + \Re\omega}), \tag{4.8}$$

uniformly on $\mathbf{A} \cap \mathbf{A}_0$ in both instances. And, in the same circumstances, we have, by symmetry,

$$R_2^{(0)}(z; N_0) = \Gamma(N_0 - \Re\omega) \mathcal{O}(z^{1 - N_0}) = (\beta_0^{\beta_0} e^{-\beta_0})^{|z|} \mathcal{O}(z^{\frac{1}{2} - \Re\omega}). \tag{4.9}$$

The estimates (4.8) and (4.9) apply for any value of the positive constant β_0, but they are minimal when $\beta_0 = 1$. Then letting $z \to \infty$ we arrive at the main result of this section: *if* $z \to \infty$ *in* $|\operatorname{ph} z| \leqslant \pi$ *and* $N_0 = |z| + \mathcal{O}(1)$, *then*

$$R_1^{(0)}(z; N_0) = \mathcal{O}(e^{-|z|} z^{\frac{1}{2} + \Re\omega}), \tag{4.10a}$$

$$R_2^{(0)}(z; N_0) = \mathcal{O}(e^{-|z|} z^{\frac{1}{2} - \Re\omega}). \tag{4.10b}$$

Remark. The estimates (4.10) can also be obtained by setting $m = 0$ in Theorem 2.2 of [6]. Indeed, in this way we find that they can be improved to

$$R_1^{(0)}(z; N_0) = \mathcal{O}(e^{-|z|} z^{\Re\omega}), \tag{4.11a}$$

$$R_2^{(0)}(z; N_0) = \mathcal{O}(e^{-|z|} z^{-\Re\omega}). \tag{4.11b}$$

We have included the analysis of this section for the following reasons. First, we wanted to show that $\beta_0 = 1$ is optimal by analysis of the remainder terms instead of the more usual analysis of the actual terms. Secondly, we need some of the intermediate results later. Thirdly, with a method similar to the proof of Lemma 2.1, with $l = 2$, we can obtain (4.11) directly from the integral representations (3.18).

5. Level one (exponentially-improved expansions)

Throughout this section, we suppose that $|\operatorname{ph} z| \leqslant \pi$ and that ρ and δ are chosen to satisfy $\rho - \delta > a$.

In (3.12b), replace z by t and N_0 by another arbitrary nonnegative integer N_1. On substituting the result into (3.18a), we obtain

$$\begin{aligned} R_1^{(0)}(z; N_0) = (-)^{N_0} \frac{K_1}{z^{N_0-1}} \sum_{s=0}^{N_1-1} a_{s,2} \int_{\mathcal{P}} \frac{e^{-t} t^{N_0-s-1+\omega}}{t+z} dt \\ + (-)^{N_0} \frac{K_1}{z^{N_0-1}} \int_{\mathcal{P}} \frac{e^{-t} t^{N_0-1+\omega}}{t+z} R_2^{(0)}(t; N_1) dt + \varepsilon_1(z; \rho; N_0), \end{aligned} \tag{5.1}$$

valid when $z \in \mathbf{A}$. To ensure convergence of all integrals that appear below, we restrict the choice of N_0 and N_1 by condition (4.2) and also

$$N_1, N_0 - N_1 \geqslant 1 + |\Re\omega|. \tag{5.2a, b}$$

When $z \in \mathbf{A}$, we may deform the integration path in (2.2b) into the union of $\mathcal{P}$ and the interval $[0, \rho]$ (thereby making (2.2b) valid when $|\operatorname{ph} z| \leqslant \pi$). On substituting into (5.1) by means of this result, we obtain

$$R_1^{(0)}(z; N_0) = (-)^{N_0} \frac{K_1}{z^{N_0-1}} \sum_{s=0}^{N_1-1} a_{s,2} G_\omega^{(1)}(z; N_0 - s) + R_1^{(1)}(z; N_0, N_1), \tag{5.3}$$

where

$$\begin{aligned} R_1^{(1)}(z; N_0, N_1) = (-)^{N_0-1} \frac{K_1}{z^{N_0-1}} \sum_{s=0}^{N_1-1} a_{s,2} \int_0^\rho \frac{e^{-t} t^{N_0-s-1+\omega}}{t+z} dt \\ + (-)^{N_0} \frac{K_1}{z^{N_0-1}} \int_{\mathcal{P}} \frac{e^{-t} t^{N_0-1+\omega}}{t+z} R_2^{(0)}(t; N_1) dt + \varepsilon_1(z; \rho; N_0), \end{aligned} \tag{5.4}$$

again valid when $z \in \mathbf{A}$.

Equation (5.3) is the desired re-expansion of $R_1^{(0)}(z; N_0)$. We now seek to optimize the new remainder term $R_1^{(1)}(z; N_0, N_1)$ by assuming that (4.1) applies and also that

$$N_1 = \beta_1 |z| + \alpha_1, \tag{5.5}$$

where $\beta_1 \in (0, \beta_0)$ is another constant at our disposal and α_1 is bounded. The conditions (4.2) and (5.2) are satisfied when $z \in \mathbf{A}_1$, where $\mathbf{A}_1$ is an unbounded closed annulus centered at the origin and of sufficiently large radius; compare (4.3). Obviously, $\mathbf{A}_1 \subseteq \mathbf{A}_0$.

We first observe that we cannot use the uniform estimates (4.9) for $R_2^{(0)}(z; N_0)$ to estimate the integral along $\mathcal{P}$ on the right-hand side of (5.4). This is because (4.9), with $z = t$ and $N_0 = N_1$, does not apply to all values of t on $\mathcal{P}$. Instead, we substitute into this integral by means of (3.14b), with z, ρ, N_0, and t replaced by t, $\rho - \delta$, N_1, and t_1, respectively. This yields

$$R_1^{(1)}(z; N_0, N_1) = (-)^{N_0+N_1} \frac{K_1 K_2}{z^{N_0-1}} \int_{\mathcal{P}} \int_{\rho-\delta}^{\infty} \frac{e^{-t} t^{N_0-N_1+\omega}}{t+z} \frac{e^{-t_1} t_1^{N_1-1-\omega}}{t_1+t} u_1(t_1) dt_1 dt + S_1^{(1)}(z; N_0, N_1), \tag{5.6}$$

where

$$S_1^{(1)}(z; N_0, N_1) = (-)^{N_0-1} \frac{K_1}{z^{N_0-1}} \sum_{s=0}^{N_1-1} a_{s,2} \int_0^{\rho} \frac{e^{-t} t^{N_0-s-1+\omega}}{t+z} dt + (-)^{N_0} \frac{K_1}{z^{N_0-1}} \int_{\mathcal{P}} \frac{e^{-t} t^{N_0-1+\omega}}{t+z} \varepsilon_2(t; \rho-\delta; N_1) dt + \varepsilon_1(z; \rho; N_0), \tag{5.7}$$

again valid when $z \in \mathbf{A}_1$.

We first estimate $S_1^{(1)}(z; N_0, N_1)$. To begin with, we have from (3.17b)

$$a_{s,2} = N_1^{-1} \Gamma(N_1 - \Re\omega) \mathcal{O}(1),$$

uniformly for $s = 0, 1, \ldots, N_1 - 1$ and all integers N_1 that satisfy (5.2a). Next, since $N_0 - N_1 + \Re\omega \leqslant N_0 - s - 1 + \Re\omega \leqslant N_0 - 1 + \Re\omega$, it follows that

$$\int_0^{\rho} \frac{e^{-t} t^{N_0-s-1+\omega}}{t+z} dt = \mathcal{O}(\rho_1^{N_0} z^{-1}), \tag{5.8}$$

uniformly for $s = 0, 1, \ldots, N_1 - 1$ and $z \in \mathbf{A} \cap \mathbf{A}_1$, where $\rho_1 = \max(\rho, 1)$. Hence, for the sum on the right-hand side of (5.7), we have

$$(-)^{N_0-1} \frac{K_1}{z^{N_0-1}} \sum_{s=0}^{N_1-1} a_{s,2} \int_0^{\rho} \frac{e^{-t} t^{N_0-s-1+\omega}}{t+z} dt = \rho_1^{N_0} z^{-N_0} \Gamma(N_1 - \Re\omega) \mathcal{O}(1), \tag{5.9}$$

uniformly on $\mathbf{A} \cap \mathbf{A}_1$.

For the second term on the right-hand side of (5.7), we note that from (3.16b)

$$\varepsilon_2(t; \rho-\delta; N_1) = (\rho-\delta)^{N_1} t^{-N_1} \mathcal{O}(1) \subseteq \mathcal{O}(\rho^{N_1} t^{-N_1}), \tag{5.10}$$

uniformly for t in the annulus $|t| \geqslant \rho$ and all nonnegative integers N_1. Then, by use of analysis similar to that used to establish (4.6), we obtain

$$(-)^{N_0} \frac{K_1}{z^{N_0-1}} \int_{\mathcal{P}} \frac{e^{-t} t^{N_0-1+\omega}}{t+z} \varepsilon_2(t; \rho-\delta; N_1) dt = \rho^{N_1} z^{1-N_0} \Gamma(N_0 - N_1 + \Re\omega) \mathcal{O}(1), \tag{5.11}$$

uniformly on $\mathbf{A} \cap \mathbf{A}_1$.

The remaining term in (5.7) is estimated directly by (3.16a). In consequence, it may be absorbed into the right-hand side of (5.9). We may combine the foregoing results into the following form:

$$S_1^{(1)}(z;N_0,N_1)=\{\rho_1^{N_0}\Gamma(N_1-\Re\omega)+\rho^{N_1}\Gamma(N_0-N_1+\Re\omega)\}\mathcal{O}(z^{1-N_0}), \tag{5.12}$$

uniformly on $\mathbf{A}\cap\mathbf{A}_1$.

We now turn our attention to the double integral in (5.6). In the inner integral, we have $|t_1+t|\geqslant|t|$ when $t\in\mathcal{P}$; also $u_1(t_1)=\mathcal{O}(1)$. Hence,

$$\int_{\rho-\delta}^{\infty}\frac{e^{-t_1}t_1^{N_1-1-\omega}}{t_1+t}u_1(t_1)dt_1=t^{-1}\Gamma(N_1-\Re\omega)\mathcal{O}(1),$$

uniformly for $t\in\mathcal{P}$. Accordingly, we have

$$\begin{aligned}(-)^{N_0+N_1}\frac{K_1K_2}{z^{N_0-1}}\int_{\mathcal{P}}\int_{\rho-\delta}^{\infty}\frac{e^{-t}t^{N_0-N_1+\omega}}{t+z}\frac{e^{-t_1}t_1^{N_1-1-\omega}}{t_1+t}u_1(t_1)dt_1dt\\=\Gamma(N_0-N_1+\Re\omega)\Gamma(N_1-\Re\omega)\mathcal{O}(z^{1-N_0}),\end{aligned} \tag{5.13}$$

uniformly on $\mathbf{A}\cap\mathbf{A}_1$; compare again the derivation of (4.6).

Let us now compare (5.12) with (5.13). It easily is seen that as a consequence of (4.1), (5.2), and (5.5), each of the ratios

$$\frac{\rho_1^{N_0}}{\Gamma(N_0-N_1+\Re\omega)},\quad\frac{\rho^{N_1}}{\Gamma(N_1-\Re\omega)}, \tag{5.14}$$

is bounded on $\mathbf{A}\cap\mathbf{A}_1$. In consequence, the estimate (5.12) for $S_1^{(1)}(z;N_0,N_1)$ may be absorbed into (5.13). We therefore have proved that

$$R_1^{(1)}(z;N_0,N_1)=\Gamma(N_0-N_1+\Re\omega)\Gamma(N_1-\Re\omega)\mathcal{O}(z^{1-N_0}), \tag{5.15}$$

uniformly on $\mathbf{A}\cap\mathbf{A}_1$.

If we substitute into (5.15) by means of (4.1) and (5.5) and let $z\to\infty$, then with the aid once again of Stirling's formula, we find that

$$R_1^{(1)}(z;N_0,N_1)=\{(\beta_0-\beta_1)^{\beta_0-\beta_1}e^{-(\beta_0-\beta_1)}\}^{|z|}(\beta_1^{\beta_1}e^{-\beta_1})^{|z|}\mathcal{O}(1). \tag{5.16}$$

This estimate is minimal when $\beta_0-\beta_1=1$ and $\beta_1=1$, that is, when $N_0=2|z|+\mathcal{O}(1)$ and $N_1=|z|+\mathcal{O}(1)$, and it becomes

$$R_1^{(1)}(z;N_0,N_1)=\mathcal{O}(e^{-2|z|}). \tag{5.17}$$

By analysis similar to the proof of Lemma 2.1, we can sharpen the estimate (5.17) by a factor $z^{-\frac{1}{2}}$, as follows. When $|\operatorname{ph}z|\leqslant\pi-\delta$, we may use the inequality $|t+z|\geqslant|z|\sin\delta$ in place of $|t+z|\geqslant\delta$ in (5.13) to replace the term $\mathcal{O}(z^{1-N_0})$ on the right-hand side by $\mathcal{O}(z^{-N_0})$. When $\delta\leqslant\pm\operatorname{ph}z\leqslant\pi$, we substitute by means of (2.14) and the corresponding form of (2.14) when $e^{-\pi i}z$ is replaced by $e^{\pi i}z$. This yields

$$\begin{aligned}
&\int_{\mathcal{P}}\int_{\rho-\delta}^{\infty} \frac{e^{-t}t^{N_0-N_1+\omega}}{t+z}\frac{e^{-t_1}t_1^{N_1-1-\omega}}{t_1+t}u_1(t_1)dt_1dt \\
&\quad = G_{\omega}^{(1)}(z;N_0-N_1+1)\int_{\rho-\delta}^{\infty}\frac{e^{-t_1}t_1^{N_1-1-\omega}}{t_1+e^{\mp\pi i}z}u_1(t_1)dt_1 \\
&\qquad - \int_0^{\rho}\int_{\rho-\delta}^{\infty}\frac{e^{-t}t^{N_0-N_1+\omega}}{t+z}\frac{e^{-t_1}t_1^{N_1-1-\omega}}{t_1+e^{\mp\pi i}z}u_1(t_1)dt_1dt \\
&\qquad - \int_{\mathcal{P}}\int_{\rho-\delta}^{\infty}\frac{e^{-t}t^{N_0-N_1+\omega}}{t_1+e^{\mp\pi i}z}\frac{e^{-t_1}t_1^{N_1-1-\omega}}{t_1+t}u_1(t_1)dt_1dt.
\end{aligned}$$

The first term on the right-hand side can be estimated with the aid of (2.13). Moreover, the resulting estimate for this term is found to dominate those for the second and third terms. Thus, we have

$$\begin{aligned}
(-)^{N_0+N_1}\frac{K_1K_2}{z^{N_0-1}}&\int_{\mathcal{P}}\int_{\rho-\delta}^{\infty}\frac{e^{-t}t^{N_0-N_1+\omega}}{t+z}\frac{e^{-t_1}t_1^{N_1-1-\omega}}{t_1+t}u_1(t_1)dt_1dt \\
&= \Gamma(N_0-N_1+\Re\omega)\Gamma(N_1-\Re\omega)\mathcal{O}\big(z^{\frac{1}{2}-N_0}\big),
\end{aligned} \tag{5.18}$$

when $\delta \leqslant \pm\operatorname{ph} z \leqslant \pi$ and, hence, also when $|\operatorname{ph} z| \leqslant \pi$; compare the second sentence of this paragraph. The other term in (5.6), namely $S_1^{(1)}(z;N_0,N_1)$, is absorbable in this new estimate because the ratios (5.14) are certainly $\mathcal{O}(z^{-\frac{1}{2}})$ as $z\to\infty$. Accordingly, we arrive at the main result of this section: *if* $z\to\infty$ *in* $|\operatorname{ph} z|\leqslant\pi$ *and* $N_0 = 2|z|+\mathcal{O}(1)$, $N_1 = |z|+\mathcal{O}(1)$, *then*

$$R_1^{(1)}(z;N_0,N_1) = \mathcal{O}\big(e^{-2|z|}z^{-\frac{1}{2}}\big). \tag{5.19}$$

By symmetry, in the same circumstances, we have

$$R_2^{(0)}(z;N_0) = (-)^{N_0}\frac{K_2}{z^{N_0-1}}\sum_{s=0}^{N_1-1}a_{s,1}G_{-\omega}^{(1)}(z;N_0-s) + R_2^{(1)}(z;N_0,N_1), \tag{5.20}$$

where

$$R_2^{(1)}(z;N_0,N_1) = \mathcal{O}\big(e^{-2|z|}z^{-\frac{1}{2}}\big). \tag{5.21}$$

Remark (i). This result is similar to Theorem 2.2 of [6]. However, there is a significant difference. In [6], we truncated each of the expansions (3.12) at (or near) its smallest term and then re-expanded the remainder term in the form (5.3). In the present notation, this sets $\beta_0 = 1$. With this constraint, the error terms $R_1^{(1)}(z;N_0,N_1)$ and $R_2^{(1)}(z;N_0,N_1)$ are optimized when $\beta_1 = \frac{1}{2}$; compare (5.16). In full, we have $N_0 = |z|+\mathcal{O}(1)$, $N_1 = \frac{1}{2}|z|+\mathcal{O}(1)$ and

$$R_1^{(1)}(z;N_0,N_1),\quad R_2^{(1)}(z;N_0,N_1) = \mathcal{O}(2^{-|z|}e^{-|z|}). \tag{5.22a, b}$$

As expected, these estimates are weaker than (5.19) and (5.21). In other words, it is more accurate to continue the expansions (3.12) beyond their smallest terms, in fact, to take as many terms again and *then* re-expand the remainder in series of $G_{\pm\omega}^{(1)}$

functions (or equivalently F_p functions) until we reach the vicinity of the smallest term of the re-expanded series.

Remark (ii). It should be noted that in sharpening the estimate (5.17) into (5.19), we needed the condition $N_0 - N_1 = |z| + \mathcal{O}(1)$ in order to be able to estimate $G^{(1)}_\omega(z; N_0 - N_1 + 1)$ by means of (2.13). To put this another way, the sharpening does not become available until the original estimate (5.16) has been optimized.

6. Level two

Throughout this section, we suppose that $|\operatorname{ph} z| \leqslant \pi$ and $\rho - 2\delta > a$.

Our purpose is to re-expand $R_1^{(1)}(z; N_0, N_1)$ and $R_2^{(1)}(z; N_0, N_1)$, and we proceed in a manner analogous to the two preceding sections. We substitute into (5.6) by means of (3.12a) and (3.14a), with z, ρ, N_0, and t replaced by t_1, $\rho - 2\delta$, N_2, and t_2, respectively, and refer to (2.2c) with $l = 2$, $M_0 = N_0 - N_1$, $M_1 = N_1 - s$. Again, N_0, N_1, N_2 are arbitrary integers. These substitutions are certainly valid when (4.2) and (5.2) apply, and also

$$N_2,\ N_1 - N_2 \geqslant 1 + |\Re\omega|. \tag{6.1a, b}$$

We arrive at

$$R_1^{(1)}(z; N_0, N_1) = (-)^{N_0+N_1} \frac{K_1 K_2}{z^{N_0-1}} \sum_{s=0}^{N_2-1} a_{s,1} G^{(2)}_\omega(z; N_0 - N_1, N_1 - s) + R_1^{(2)}(z; N_0, N_1, N_2), \tag{6.2}$$

where

$$R_1^{(2)}(z; N_0, N_1, N_2) = (-)^{N_0+N_1+N_2} \frac{K_1^2 K_2}{z^{N_0-1}} \times \\ \times \int_{\mathcal{P}} \int_{\rho-\delta}^{\infty} \int_{\rho-2\delta}^{\infty} \frac{e^{-t-t_1-t_2} t^{N_0-N_1+\omega} t_1^{N_1-N_2-\omega} t_2^{N_2-1+\omega}}{(t+z)(t_1+t)(t_2+t_1)} u_2(t_2)\, dt_2\, dt_1\, dt \\ + S_1^{(2)}(z; N_0, N_1, N_2) \tag{6.3}$$

and

$$S_1^{(2)}(z; N_0, N_1, N_2) = (-)^{N_0+N_1-1} \frac{K_1 K_2}{z^{N_0-1}} \times \\ \times \sum_{s=0}^{N_2-1} a_{s,1} \left(\int_0^{\rho} \int_0^{\infty} + \int_{\mathcal{P}} \int_0^{\rho-\delta} \right) \frac{e^{-t-t_1} t^{N_0-N_1+\omega} t_1^{N_1-s-1-\omega}}{(t+z)(t_1+t)} dt_1\, dt \\ + (-)^{N_0+N_1} \frac{K_1 K_2}{z^{N_0-1}} \int_{\mathcal{P}} \int_{\rho-\delta}^{\infty} \frac{e^{-t-t_1} t^{N_0-N_1+\omega} t_1^{N_1-1-\omega}}{(t+z)(t_1+t)} \varepsilon_1(t_1; \rho - 2\delta; N_2)\, dt_1\, dt \\ + S_1^{(1)}(z; N_0, N_1), \tag{6.4}$$

valid when $z \in \mathbf{A}$; compare (5.6) and (5.7).

Again, following the analysis of §§4 and 5, we seek to estimate, and then optimize, the new remainder term $R_1^{(2)}(z; N_0, N_1, N_2)$, by setting

$$N_0 = \beta_0|z| + \alpha_0, \quad N_1 = \beta_1|z| + \alpha_1, \quad N_2 = \beta_2|z| + \alpha_2, \tag{6.5}$$

where $\beta_0, \beta_1, \beta_2$ are constants such that $0 < \beta_2 < \beta_1 < \beta_0$ and $\alpha_0, \alpha_1, \alpha_2$ are bounded. We restrict $z \in \mathbf{A}_2$, where $\mathbf{A}_2$ is an unbounded closed annulus centered at the origin and of radius sufficiently large to ensure that the conditions (4.2), (5.2), and (6.1) are fulfilled. Thus, $\mathbf{A}_2 \subseteq \mathbf{A}_1 \subseteq \mathbf{A}_0$.

We first observe that

$$a_{s,1}\int_0^\rho\int_0^\infty \frac{e^{-t-t_1}t^{N_0-N_1+\omega}t_1^{N_1-s-1-\omega}}{(t+z)(t_1+t)}dt_1dt \\ = \Gamma(s_1)\Gamma(N_1-s-1-\Re\omega)\rho^{N_0-N_1}\mathcal{O}(1), \tag{6.6}$$

where $s_1 = \max(s+\Re\omega, 1)$, uniformly for $z \in \mathbf{A}\cap\mathbf{A}_2$ and $s = 0, 1, \ldots, N_2-1$. If $s+\Re\omega < 1$, then

$$\Gamma(s_1)\Gamma(N_1-s-1-\Re\omega) \leqslant \Gamma(N_1-1-\Re\omega), \tag{6.7a}$$

whereas if $s+\Re\omega \geqslant 1$, then[3]

$$\Gamma(s_1)\Gamma(N_1-s-1-\Re\omega) \leqslant \Gamma(N_1-1). \tag{6.7b}$$

With the aid, also, of (6.1b), we conclude that

$$\sum_{s=0}^{N_2-1} a_{s,1}\int_0^\rho\int_0^\infty \frac{e^{-t-t_1}t^{N_0-N_1+\omega}t_1^{N_1-s-1-\omega}}{(t+z)(t_1+t)}dt_1dt = \rho^{N_0-N_1}\Gamma(N_1+|\Re\omega|)\mathcal{O}(1), \tag{6.8}$$

uniformly on $\mathbf{A}\cap\mathbf{A}_2$. The rest of the analysis is similar to that of §5, and there is no need to enter into all the details. Corresponding to (5.12) and (5.15), we find that

$$S_1^{(2)}(z;N_0,N_1,N_2) = \Big\{\rho^{N_0-N_1}\Gamma(N_1+|\Re\omega|) + \rho_1^{N_1}\Gamma(N_0-N_1+\Re\omega)\Gamma(N_2+\Re\omega) \\ + \rho^{N_2}\Gamma(N_0-N_1+\Re\omega)\Gamma(N_1-N_2-\Re\omega)\Big\}\mathcal{O}(z^{1-N_0}) + S_1^{(1)}(z;N_0,N_1), \tag{6.9}$$

and

$$R_1^{(2)}(z;N_0,N_1,N_2) \\ = \Gamma(N_0-N_1+\Re\omega)\Gamma(N_1-N_2-\Re\omega)\Gamma(N_2+\Re\omega)\mathcal{O}(z^{1-N_0}), \tag{6.10}$$

uniformly on $\mathbf{A}\cap\mathbf{A}_2$ in both equations.

On substituting into the last result by means of (6.5), we obtain

$$R_1^{(2)}(z;N_0,N_1,N_2) = \{(\beta_0-\beta_1)^{\beta_0-\beta_1}e^{\beta_1-\beta_0}\}^{|z|} \times \\ \times \{(\beta_1-\beta_2)^{\beta_1-\beta_2}e^{\beta_2-\beta_1}\}^{|z|}\big(\beta_2^{\beta_2}e^{-\beta_2}\big)^{|z|}\mathcal{O}\big(z^{-\frac{1}{2}+\Re\omega}\big), \tag{6.11}$$

uniformly on $\mathbf{A}\cap\mathbf{A}_2$ and, in particular, as $z\to\infty$. The minimizing choice is given by $\beta_0-\beta_1 = \beta_1-\beta_2 = \beta_2 = 1$, that is, $\beta_0 = 3$, $\beta_1 = 2$, $\beta_2 = 1$. The corresponding estimate for $R_2^{(2)}(z;N_0,N_1,N_2)$ is obtained by replacing $\Re\omega$ by $-\Re\omega$. Again, with

[3] In deriving (6.7b), we have used the inequality $\Gamma(x)\Gamma(y) \leqslant \Gamma(x+y)$ when $x, y \geqslant 1$; see, e.g., [8, Chapter 2, §1.6].

these choices for β_0, β_1, β_2, we can sharpen the minimal estimates with a factor $z^{-\frac{1}{2}}$; compare (5.17) and (5.19). Thus we have the main result of this section: *if* $z \to \infty$ *in* $|\operatorname{ph} z| \leqslant \pi$ *and* $N_0 = 3|z| + \mathcal{O}(1)$, $N_1 = 2|z| + \mathcal{O}(1)$, $N_2 = |z| + \mathcal{O}(1)$, *then*

$$R_1^{(2)}(z; N_0, N_1, N_2) = \mathcal{O}\big(e^{-3|z|} z^{-1+\Re\omega}\big) \tag{6.12a}$$

and

$$R_2^{(2)}(z; N_0, N_1, N_2) = \mathcal{O}\big(e^{-3|z|} z^{-1-\Re\omega}\big). \tag{6.12b}$$

7. General levels

The pattern of resubstituting into the successive remainder terms now is clear, and the general results can be written down by inspection and verified by induction. To facilitate the statement of the final theorems, we introduce the following notation pertaining to the parity of l: $\nu_l = 0$ or 1, according as l is even or odd.

Theorem 7.1. *Let l be an arbitrary nonnegative integer and N_0, N_1, ..., N_l be integers such that*

$$N_j = \beta_j |z| + \alpha_j, \quad j = 0, 1, \ldots, l, \tag{7.1}$$

in which the β's are constants that satisfy

$$0 < \beta_l < \beta_{l-1} < \cdots < \beta_0 \tag{7.2}$$

and the α's are bounded as $|z| \to \infty$. Then

$$\begin{aligned} u_1(z) = {} & \sum_{s=0}^{N_0-1} \frac{a_{s,1}}{z^s} + (-)^{N_0} \frac{K_1}{z^{N_0-1}} \sum_{s=0}^{N_1-1} a_{s,2} G_\omega^{(1)}(z; N_0 - s) + \ldots \\ & + (-)^{N_0+N_1+\cdots+N_{l-1}} \frac{K_1^{\frac{1}{2}(l+\nu_l)} K_2^{\frac{1}{2}(l-\nu_l)}}{z^{N_0-1}} \times \\ & \times \sum_{s=0}^{N_l-1} a_{s,1+\nu_l} G_\omega^{(l)}(z; N_0 - N_1, \ldots, N_{l-2} - N_{l-1}, N_{l-1} - s) \\ & + R_1^{(l)}(z; N_0, N_1, \ldots, N_l), \end{aligned} \tag{7.3a}$$

$$\begin{aligned} u_2(z) = {} & \sum_{s=0}^{N_0-1} \frac{a_{s,2}}{z^s} + (-)^{N_0} \frac{K_2}{z^{N_0-1}} \sum_{s=0}^{N_1-1} a_{s,1} G_{-\omega}^{(1)}(z; N_0 - s) + \ldots \\ & + (-)^{N_0+N_1+\cdots+N_{l-1}} \frac{K_1^{\frac{1}{2}(l-\nu_l)} K_2^{\frac{1}{2}(l+\nu_l)}}{z^{N_0-1}} \times \\ & \times \sum_{s=0}^{N_l-1} a_{s,2-\nu_l} G_{-\omega}^{(l)}(z; N_0 - N_1, \ldots, N_{l-2} - N_{l-1}, N_{l-1} - s) \\ & + R_2^{(l)}(z; N_0, N_1, \ldots, N_l) \end{aligned} \tag{7.3b}$$

and as $z \to \infty$ in $|\operatorname{ph} z| \leqslant \pi$,

$$R_1^{(l)}(z; N_0, N_1, \ldots, N_l) = \left[\prod_{j=0}^{l-1} \left\{(\beta_j - \beta_{j+1})^{\beta_j - \beta_{j+1}} e^{\beta_{j+1} - \beta_j}\right\}^{|z|}\right] \left(\beta_l^{\beta_l} e^{-\beta_l}\right)^{|z|} \mathcal{O}\left(z^{\frac{1}{2}(1-l)+\nu_{l+1}\Re\omega}\right), \tag{7.4a}$$

$$R_2^{(l)}(z; N_0, N_1, \ldots, N_l) = \left[\prod_{j=0}^{l-1} \left\{(\beta_j - \beta_{j+1})^{\beta_j - \beta_{j+1}} e^{\beta_{j+1} - \beta_j}\right\}^{|z|}\right] \left(\beta_l^{\beta_l} e^{-\beta_l}\right)^{|z|} \mathcal{O}\left(z^{\frac{1}{2}(1-l)-\nu_{l+1}\Re\omega}\right). \tag{7.4b}$$

In Theorem 7.1, the remainder terms $R_1^{(l)}$ and $R_2^{(l)}$ are not optimized. Optimization is achieved on setting $\beta_j = l+1-j$, $j = 0, 1, \ldots, l$ or, equivalently, $N_j = (l+1-j)N$, where $N = |z| + \mathcal{O}(1)$. This yields:

Theorem 7.2. *Let*

$$u_1(z) = \sum_{s=0}^{(l+1)N-1} \frac{a_{s,1}}{z^s} + \sum_{j=1}^{l} (-)^{\frac{1}{2}j(j+1+2l)N} \frac{K_1^{\frac{1}{2}(j+\nu_j)} K_2^{\frac{1}{2}(j-\nu_j)}}{z^{(l+1)N-1}} \times \sum_{s=0}^{(l+1-j)N-1} a_{s,1+\nu_j} G_\omega^{(j)}(z; N, \ldots, N, (l+2-j)N - s) + R_1^{(l)}(z; (l+1)N, lN, \ldots, N), \tag{7.5a}$$

$$u_2(z) = \sum_{s=0}^{(l+1)N-1} \frac{a_{s,2}}{z^s} + \sum_{j=1}^{l} (-)^{\frac{1}{2}j(j+1+2l)N} \frac{K_1^{\frac{1}{2}(j-\nu_j)} K_2^{\frac{1}{2}(j+\nu_j)}}{z^{(l+1)N-1}} \times \sum_{s=0}^{(l+1-j)N-1} a_{s,2-\nu_j} G_{-\omega}^{(j)}(z; N, \ldots, N, (l+2-j)N - s) + R_2^{(l)}(z; (l+1)N, lN, \ldots, N), \tag{7.5b}$$

where $N = |z| + \mathcal{O}(1)$. Then, as $z \to \infty$ in $|\operatorname{ph} z| \leqslant \pi$,

$$R_1^{(l)}(z; (l+1)N, lN, \ldots, N) = \mathcal{O}\left(e^{-(l+1)|z|} z^{-\frac{1}{2}l+\nu_{l+1}\Re\omega}\right), \tag{7.6a}$$

$$R_2^{(l)}(z; (l+1)N, lN, \ldots, N) = \mathcal{O}\left(e^{-(l+1)|z|} z^{-\frac{1}{2}l-\nu_{l+1}\Re\omega}\right). \tag{7.6b}$$

Remark (i). When $|\operatorname{ph} z| \leqslant \pi - \delta$, we can improve the estimates (7.6) by a factor $z^{-\frac{1}{2}}$ for all values of l: we have only to retrace the analysis with the contour $\mathcal{P}$ freed from the indentations indicated in Figures 3.1 and 3.2 and apply the inequality (2.10).

Remark (ii). Each time the level l increases by unity, the number of terms at each previous level in the expansions (7.3) increases by $|z|$ (approximately). In Remark (i) at the end of §5, we indicated how to optimize the remainder term at level 1 whilst constraining the number of terms at level 0 to be $|z|$. It transpired that $\frac{1}{2}|z|$ terms are needed at level 1. This process may be continued. If we leave unchanged the number of terms at levels 0 and 1, then $\frac{1}{4}|z|$ terms are needed at level 2 and so on, until we reach $2^{-l}|z|$ terms at level l. Furthermore, the remainder terms then satisfy

$$R_1^{(l)}(z; N_0, N_1, \ldots, N_l) = \mathcal{O}\left(2^{-L|z|}e^{-|z|}z^{\frac{1}{2}(1-l)+\nu_{l+1}\Re\omega}\right), \tag{7.7a}$$

$$R_2^{(l)}(z; N_0, N_1, \ldots, N_l) = \mathcal{O}\left(2^{-L|z|}e^{-|z|}z^{\frac{1}{2}(1-l)-\nu_{l+1}\Re\omega}\right), \tag{7.7b}$$

where $L = 2 - 2^{1-l}$. We observe immediately that $L < 2$ for all values of l; in consequence the overall exponential improvement is limited to a factor $e^{-\gamma|z|}$, where $\gamma = 1 + 2\ln 2 = 2.386\ldots$.

The pattern of remainder terms just described was discovered by Berry and Howls [1] in a related problem. Some further observations on their paper will be found in the concluding section §11.

8. Numerical stability

Theorem 7.2 is an elegant result. Its essential message is that we can generate a relative error term whose asymptotic estimate for large $|z|$ contains a factor $e^{-(l+1)|z|}$, l being an arbitrary nonnegative integer, by taking (approximately) $(l+1)|z|$ terms in the original Poincaré expansion, $l|z|$ terms in the first level re-expansion and so on, ending with $|z|$ terms at the lth level. Furthermore, the coefficients of the auxiliary functions $G_{\pm\omega}^{(l)}$ at successive levels alternate between the sets of coefficients in the original Poincaré expansions. In applications, however, there is a potential source of weakness. After we pass beyond the smallest term at any level, succeeding terms at that level grow rapidly. If any rises in absolute value well above unity (unity being the order of magnitude of $u_1(z)$ and $u_2(z)$), then severe cancellation will take place in summing the series (7.3) numerically, rendering the whole process unstable.

In order to demonstrate, and then overcome, this instability, we revert to Theorem 7.1 and permit the constants $\beta_0, \beta_1, \ldots, \beta_l$ to be arbitrary, subject to (7.2).

Consider first the sum at the zeroth level for $u_1(z)$. From (3.17a), we have

$$a_{s,1} \sim (-)^s K_1 \Gamma(s+\omega), \quad s \to \infty.$$

Accordingly (as we already know), as s increases, $|a_{s,1}z^{-s}|$ decreases until $s = |z|$, approximately, and it then increases unboundedly. For $s = N_0 - 1$ we have

$$a_{N_0-1,1} \sim (-)^{N_0-1} K_1 \Gamma(N_0 - 1 + \omega) \tag{8.1}$$

and, hence, by application of (7.1) and Stirling's formula,

$$|a_{N_0-1,1}z^{1-N_0}| \sim \text{constant} \times \left(\beta_0^{\beta_0}\right)^{|z|} e^{-\beta_0|z|} z^{-\frac{1}{2}+\Re\omega}. \tag{8.2}$$

This estimate obviously exceeds, or is less than, unity, according as $\beta_0^{\beta_0}e^{-\beta_0} \gtrless 1$, that is, $\beta_0 \gtrless e$.

Next, consider level 1. We have

$$G_\omega^{(1)}(z; M_0) = \Gamma(M_0 + \Re\omega)\mathcal{O}(1), \tag{8.3}$$

as $z \to \infty$ in $|\operatorname{ph} z| \leqslant \pi$, uniformly for all values of M_0 that satisfy $M_0 + |\Re\omega| \geqslant 1$. This result may be proved by the method used to establish (4.6). With the aid of (3.17b), we see that

$$a_{s,2}G_\omega^{(1)}(z; N_0 - s) = \Gamma\{\max(s - \Re\omega, 1)\}\Gamma(N_0 - s + \Re\omega)\mathcal{O}(1), \tag{8.4}$$

uniformly for $s = 0, 1, \ldots, N_1 - 1$. From (7.1) and (8.1), we observe that at $s = 0$ this estimate equals $a_{N_0-1,1}\mathcal{O}(z)$. As s increases, the right-hand side of (8.4) decreases until $s = \frac{1}{2}N_0$, approximately, and then grows. Moreover, at $s = N_1 - 1$ we obtain

$$a_{N_1-1,2}G_\omega^{(1)}(z; N_0 - N_1 + 1) = \Gamma(N_1 - 1 - \Re\omega)\Gamma(N_0 - N_1 + 1 + \Re\omega)\mathcal{O}(1)$$

and hence by use of (7.1) and Stirling's formula

$$a_{N_1-1,2}G_\omega^{(1)}(z; N_0 - N_1 + 1)z^{1-N_0} = b_1^{|z|}e^{-\beta_0|z|}\mathcal{O}(1), \tag{8.5}$$

where

$$b_1 = (\beta_0 - \beta_1)^{\beta_0-\beta_1}\beta_1^{\beta_1}.$$

Since $\beta_0 - \beta_1$ and β_1 are both less then β_0, we have $b_1 < \beta_0^{\beta_0}$. Accordingly, the estimate (8.5) is asymptotically small compared with (8.2).

At higher levels

$$\begin{aligned} G_\omega^{(l)}&(z; N_0 - N_1, \ldots, N_{l-2} - N_{l-1}, N_{l-1} - s) \\ &= \Gamma(N_0 - N_1 + \Re\omega)\cdots\Gamma(N_{l-2} - N_{l-1} + (-)^{l-2}\Re\omega) \times \\ &\quad \times \Gamma(N_{l-1} - s + (-)^{l-1}\Re\omega)\mathcal{O}(1), \end{aligned} \tag{8.6}$$

as $z \to \infty$ in $|\operatorname{ph} z| \leqslant \pi$, uniformly for $s \in [0, N_l - 1]$. As in the case of (8.3), this result may be proved by the method used to establish (4.6), (5.13), and (6.10). Armed with this estimate, we may show that the behavior of the terms at each level follows a similar pattern. The first term is within a factor $\mathcal{O}(z)$ of the last term at the previous level. As s increases the terms at level l decrease to a minimum at $s = \frac{1}{2}N_{l-1}$, approximately, and then grow in magnitude. Moreover, whether or not the series at this level is terminated at this minimum, as long as $0 < \beta_l < \beta_{l-1}$, the last term is asymptotically small compared with $|a_{N_0-1,1}z^{1-N_0}|$.

A similar analysis applies to the expansion (7.3b); basically we have only to replace $\Re\omega$ by $-\Re\omega$ throughout. We therefore conclude: *whatever the value of the constants* $\beta_1, \beta_2, \ldots, \beta_l$, *as long as* (7.2) *applies, the summation of the series* (7.3) *is numerically stable or unstable according as* $\beta_0 \lesseqgtr e$.

In the remaining case, given by $\beta_0 = e$, the growth (if any) of $a_{N_0-1,1}z^{1-N_0}$ and $a_{N_0-1,2}z^{1-N_0}$ is algebraic rather than exponential; compare (8.2). Accordingly, we may say that the summation of (7.3) is weakly unstable, in the sense that any numerical cancellation that takes place will not be catastrophic in nature.

On returning to Theorem 7.2, we note that $\beta_0 = l + 1$. Hence, Theorem 7.2 leads to a stable summation procedure only when $l = 0$ or 1, that is, when the series (7.3) are terminated at the zeroth or first level.

When $l \geqslant 2$ we need to modify the optimization of the remainder term in order to maintain stability. This means that with $\beta_0 = e$ we need to minimize

$$\left[\prod_{j=0}^{l-1}(\beta_j - \beta_{j+1})^{\beta_j-\beta_{j+1}}e^{\beta_{j+1}-\beta_j}\right]\left(\beta_l^{\beta_l}e^{-\beta_l}\right);$$

compare (7.4). It is easily verified that this minimum occurs when

$$\beta_j = \frac{l+1-j}{l+1}e, \quad j = 1, 2, \ldots, l,$$

and it equals $(l+1)^{-e}$.

We may summarize the findings of this section as follows:

Theorem 8.1 (Numerically stable expansion). *Assume the notation of Theorem* 7.1 *and that* $l \geqslant 2$. *If*

$$N_j = \frac{l+1-j}{l+1} e|z| + \mathcal{O}(1), \quad j = 0, 1, \ldots, l, \tag{8.7}$$

then as $z \to \infty$ *in* $|\mathrm{ph}\, z| \leqslant \pi$

$$R_1^{(l)}(z; N_0, N_1, \ldots, N_l) = \mathcal{O}\{(l+1)^{-e|z|} z^{\frac{1}{2}(1-l)+\nu_{l+1}\Re\omega}\}, \tag{8.8a}$$

$$R_2^{(l)}(z; N_0, N_1, \ldots, N_l) = \mathcal{O}\{(l+1)^{-e|z|} z^{\frac{1}{2}(1-l)-\nu_{l+1}\Re\omega}\}. \tag{8.8b}$$

Remark. When $l \geqslant 2$ the overall exponential improvement yielded by Theorem 8.1 is less than that yielded by Theorem 7.2, especially when $l \geqslant 3$. On the other hand, fewer terms are needed in the expansions (7.3).

9. Example

We take as example the differential equation

$$\frac{d^2w}{dz^2} + \left(\frac{1}{z} - 1\right)\frac{dw}{dz} - \frac{1}{2z} w = 0, \tag{9.1}$$

satisfied by $e^{\frac{1}{2}z} K_0(\frac{1}{2}z)$ and $e^{\frac{1}{2}z} K_0(\frac{1}{2}ze^{-\pi i})$, where K_0 is the modified Bessel function. The values of λ_1, λ_2, μ_1, μ_2, and ω are found to be $\lambda_1 = 0$, $\lambda_2 = 1$, $\mu_1 = \mu_2 = -\frac{1}{2}$, and $\omega = 0$. The basic functions $u_1(z)$, $u_2(z)$ and the coefficients $a_{s,1}$, $a_{s,2}$ are given by[4]

$$u_1(z) = u_2(z) = \pi^{-\frac{1}{2}} z^{\frac{1}{2}} e^{\frac{1}{2}z} K_0(z/2)$$

and

$$a_{s,1} = a_{s,2} = (-)^s \frac{1^2 \cdot 3^2 \cdots (2s-1)^2}{4^s s!}, \tag{9.2}$$

and the coefficients K_1 and K_2 in the connection formulas (3.10) are known to be

$$K_1 = K_2 = \pi^{-1};$$

see, for example, [8], Chapter 7, §§4, 8, or we can take the limit as $s \to \infty$ in (3.17) above, using (9.2).

For illustration, we take $z = 20$. The squares in Figure 9.1 are the plot of the logarithm to base 10 of the absolute value of each term in the expansions (7.3) against its ordinal number.[5]

For $l = 0$ we set $N_0 = 20$, which terminates the original asymptotic expansions (3.8) at (or very nearly at) their smallest term. For $l = 1$ we set $N_0 = 40$, $N_1 = 20$, and for $l = 2$ we set $N_0 = 60$, $N_1 = 40$, $N_2 = 20$. As expected, in the case $l = 2$ a few of the terms rise above unity in magnitude, indicating some instability in the summation. For $l = 3$ (not shown in the diagram) the instability would be much more severe.

---

[4]Another solution of (9.1) is $e^{\frac{1}{2}z} I_0(\frac{1}{2}z)$, where I_0 is the other modified Bessel function. Although $\pi^{\frac{1}{2}} e^{\frac{1}{2}z} I_0(\frac{1}{2}z)$ has the same form of asymptotic expansion as $-i\pi^{-\frac{1}{2}} e^{\frac{1}{2}z} K_0(\frac{1}{2}ze^{-\pi i})$, it should be noted that it cannot be taken as $w_2(z)$ because $\pi^{\frac{1}{2}} e^{\frac{1}{2}z} I_0(\frac{1}{2}z)$ is not a recessive solution of (9.1) in the sector $\frac{1}{2}\pi + \delta \leqslant \mathrm{ph}\, z \leqslant \frac{3}{2}\pi - \delta$ (or for that matter in any sector).

[5]The terms were computed by the methods given in the Appendix of [1].

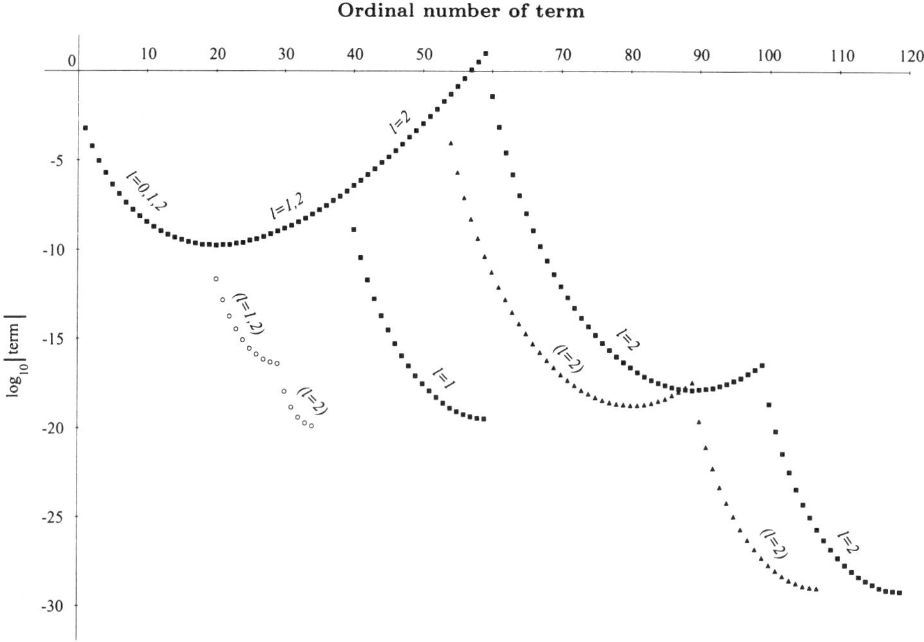

FIGURE 9.1. Magnitudes of the terms in the three hyperasymptotic expansions.

The curve indicated by the triangles shows the modification of the case $l = 2$ consequent upon using the numerically stable form of expansion furnished by Theorem 8.1. We take $N_0 = 54$, $N_1 = 36$, $N_2 = 18$. In this expansion all terms are below unity in magnitude, but as expected the final accuracy is slightly less; see Table 9.1.

Next, the curve indicated by the circles is for the case $l = 2$, with $N_0 = 20$, $N_1 = 10$, $N_2 = 5$. This corresponds to optimization with a fixed number of terms at each level.

level	approximation	exact−approx.	N_0	N_1	N_2
0	0.988139270254112817375114072700	1.8×10^{-10}	20		
1	0.988139270438649159234772899885	3.4×10^{-20}	40	20	
2	0.988139270438649159268429546441	6.1×10^{-30}	60	40	20
0	0.988139270254112817375114072700	1.8×10^{-10}	20		
1	0.988139270438649159234772899885	3.4×10^{-20}	40	20	
2	0.988139270438649159268429546437	1.0×10^{-29}	54	36	18
0	0.988139270254112817375114072700	1.8×10^{-10}	20		
1	0.988139270438649118161993331991	4.1×10^{-18}	20	10	
2	0.988139270438649159281542952765	-1.3×10^{-20}	20	10	5
exact	0.988139270438649159268429546447	0			

TABLE 9.1. Hyperasymptotic approximations to $\pi^{-\frac{1}{2}}z^{\frac{1}{2}}e^{\frac{1}{2}z}K_0(\frac{1}{2}z)$ for $z = 20$.

As we noted in Remark (ii) at the end of §7, when continued to higher levels the last term can never be less than about $e^{-20(1+2\ln 2)} \doteqdot 2\times 10^{-21}$. This is approximately 10^8 times as large as the last term in the other two expansions with $l=2$.

Lastly, we observe that the pattern of growth depicted by all the curves in Figure 9.1 is exactly that predicted in §8 for the general case.

10. Extensions of the regions of validity

The region of validity supplied by Theorems 7.1, 7.2, and 8.1 is the closed sector $|\operatorname{ph} z| \leqslant \pi$. Values of the analytic continuation of $w_1(z)$ and $w_2(ze^{\pi i})$ for any other value of $\operatorname{ph} z$ can be calculated by repeated application of the connection formulas (3.6) or (3.9). Nevertheless, it is of some interest to ascertain whether the region of validity in Theorems 7.2 and 8.1 can be extended beyond $\operatorname{ph} z = \pm\pi$, especially as an extension to $|\operatorname{ph} z| \leqslant \frac{5}{2}\pi - \delta$ was supplied in [6] for the unoptimized case at level 1. We shall show in this section that such extensions can be made at all levels, although at the cost of weakening the asymptotic estimates of the remainder terms. We shall achieve this by constructing continuation formulas for the remainder terms.

From (3.9) and (3.12) we derive

$$\begin{aligned} R_1^{(0)}(z;N_0) - R_1^{(0)}(ze^{-2\pi i};N_0) &= u_1(z) - u_1(ze^{-2\pi i}) \\ &= 2\pi i K_1 e^{-\omega\pi i} e^z z^\omega u_2(ze^{-\pi i}). \end{aligned} \tag{10.1}$$

If $\pi \leqslant \operatorname{ph} z \leqslant \frac{3}{2}\pi$ and $N_0 = |z| + \mathcal{O}(1)$, then from (4.11$a$) we have

$$R_1^{(0)}(ze^{-2\pi i};N_0) = \mathcal{O}\big(e^{-|z|} z^{\Re\omega}\big), \tag{10.2}$$

whereas from (3.8b)

$$2\pi i K_1 e^{-\omega\pi i} e^z z^\omega u_2(ze^{-\pi i}) = \mathcal{O}\big(e^z z^{\Re\omega}\big). \tag{10.3}$$

Hence,

$$R_1^{(0)}(z;N_0) = \mathcal{O}\big(e^z z^{\Re\omega}\big), \quad \pi \leqslant \operatorname{ph} z \leqslant \frac{3}{2}\pi - \delta. \tag{10.4a}$$

Similarly,

$$R_2^{(0)}(z;N_0) = \mathcal{O}\big(e^z z^{-\Re\omega}\big), \quad \pi \leqslant \operatorname{ph} z \leqslant \frac{3}{2}\pi - \delta. \tag{10.4b}$$

Accordingly, the exponential improvement supplied by (4.11) deteriorates gradually as we pass beyond $\operatorname{ph} z = \pi$ and disappears altogether as we approach $\operatorname{ph} z = \frac{3}{2}\pi$.

At the next level, we have from (5.3)

$$\begin{aligned} R_1^{(1)}(z;N_0,N_1) - R_1^{(1)}(ze^{-2\pi i};N_0,N_1) &= R_1^{(0)}(z;N_0) - R_1^{(0)}(ze^{-2\pi i};N_0) \\ &+ (-)^{N_0-1}\frac{K_1}{z^{N_0-1}}\sum_{s=0}^{N_1-1} a_{s,2}\big\{G_\omega^{(1)}(z;N_0-s) - G_\omega^{(1)}(ze^{-2\pi i};N_0-s)\big\}. \end{aligned} \tag{10.5}$$

From (10.1) and (3.12b), with z and N_0 replaced by $ze^{-\pi i}$ and N_1, respectively, we obtain

$$R_1^{(0)}(z;N_0) - R_1^{(0)}(ze^{-2\pi i};N_0) = 2\pi i K_1 e^{-\omega\pi i} e^z z^\omega \left\{ \sum_{s=0}^{N_1-1} (-)^s \frac{a_{s,2}}{z^s} + R_2^{(0)}(ze^{-\pi i};N_1) \right\}.$$

Also, from (2.9) with $l = 1$ and $M_0 = N_0 - s$, and using (2.2a), we have

$$\begin{aligned}(-)^{N_0} \frac{K_1}{z^{N_0-1}} &\sum_{s=0}^{N_1-1} a_{s,2}\{G_\omega^{(1)}(z;N_0-s) - G_\omega^{(1)}(ze^{-2\pi i};N_0-s)\} \\ &= 2\pi i K_1 e^{-\omega\pi i} e^z z^\omega \sum_{s=0}^{N_1-1} (-)^s \frac{a_{s,2}}{z^s}.\end{aligned}$$

On substituting into (10.5) by means of the last two equations, we find that

$$R_1^{(1)}(z;N_0,N_1) - R_1^{(1)}(ze^{-2\pi i};N_0,N_1) = 2\pi i K_1 e^{-\omega\pi i} e^z z^\omega R_2^{(0)}(ze^{-\pi i};N_1). \tag{10.6a}$$

Once again, by symmetry

$$R_2^{(1)}(z;N_0,N_1) - R_2^{(1)}(ze^{-2\pi i};N_0,N_1) = 2\pi i K_2 e^{\omega\pi i} e^z z^{-\omega} R_1^{(0)}(ze^{-\pi i};N_1). \tag{10.6b}$$

Suppose that $\pi \leqslant \operatorname{ph} z \leqslant 2\pi$, $N_0 = 2|z| + \mathcal{O}(1)$ and $N_1 = |z| + \mathcal{O}(1)$. Then from (5.19) we have

$$R_1^{(1)}(ze^{-2\pi i};N_0,N_1) = \mathcal{O}(e^{-2|z|}z^{-\frac{1}{2}}), \tag{10.7}$$

and from (4.11b)

$$2\pi i K_1 e^{-\omega\pi i} e^z z^\omega R_2^{(0)}(ze^{-\pi i};N_1) = \mathcal{O}(e^{z-|z|}). \tag{10.8}$$

Combination of (10.6a), (10.7), and (10.8) yields

$$R_1^{(1)}(z;N_0,N_1) = \mathcal{O}(e^{z-|z|}), \quad \pi \leqslant \operatorname{ph} z \leqslant 2\pi. \tag{10.9}$$

Next, if $2\pi \leqslant \operatorname{ph} z \leqslant \frac{5}{2}\pi - \delta$ and $N_0 = 2|z| + \mathcal{O}(1)$, $N_1 = |z| + \mathcal{O}(1)$, then (10.7) continues to apply, but from (10.4b) we see that the right-hand side of (10.8) is replaced by $\mathcal{O}(1)$. Accordingly,

$$R_1^{(1)}(z;N_0,N_1) = \mathcal{O}(1), \quad 2\pi \leqslant \operatorname{ph} z \leqslant \frac{5}{2}\pi - \delta. \tag{10.10}$$

By similar analysis we may show that the estimates (10.7), (10.9), and (10.10) also apply to the remainder term $R_2^{(1)}(z;N_0,N_1)$ in the same ranges of $\operatorname{ph} z$.

The process may be continued to higher levels and also to negative values of $\operatorname{ph} z$. With the aid of (2.9), (3.9), and (7.3), the generalizations of (10.6) may be verified to be

$$\begin{aligned}R_1^{(l)}(z;N_0,N_1,\ldots,N_l) &- R_1^{(l)}(ze^{-2\pi i};N_0,N_1,\ldots,N_l) \\ &= 2\pi i K_1 e^{-\omega\pi i} e^z z^\omega R_2^{(l-1)}(ze^{-\pi i};N_1,N_2,\ldots,N_l)\end{aligned} \tag{10.11a}$$

and

$$R_2^{(l)}(z;N_0,N_1,\ldots,N_l) - R_2^{(l)}(ze^{-2\pi i};N_0,N_1,\ldots,N_l)$$
$$= 2\pi i K_2 e^{\omega\pi i} e^z z^{-\omega} R_1^{(l-1)}(ze^{-\pi i};N_1,N_2,\ldots,N_l). \tag{10.11b}$$

Then by induction we may establish the following result.

Theorem 10.1. *If $k = 0,1,\ldots,l$, then as $z \to \infty$ in $k\pi \leqslant |\operatorname{ph} z| \leqslant (k+1)\pi$, the remainder terms in Theorem 7.2 satisfy*

$$R_1^{(l)}(z;(l+1)N,lN,\ldots,N) = \mathcal{O}\big(e^{\nu_k z+(k-l-1)|z|} z^{\frac{1}{2}(k-l)+\nu_{l+1}\Re\omega}\big), \tag{10.12a}$$
$$R_2^{(l)}(z;(l+1)N,lN,\ldots,N) = \mathcal{O}\big(e^{\nu_k z+(k-l-1)|z|} z^{\frac{1}{2}(k-l)-\nu_{l+1}\Re\omega}\big). \tag{10.12b}$$

Also, if $z \to \infty$ in $(l+1)\pi \leqslant |\operatorname{ph} z| \leqslant (l+\frac{3}{2})\pi - \delta$, then

$$R_1^{(l)}(z;(l+1)N,lN,\ldots,N) = \mathcal{O}\big(e^{\nu_{l+1} z} z^{\nu_{l+1}\Re\omega}\big), \tag{10.13a}$$
$$R_2^{(l)}(z;(l+1)N,lN,\ldots,N) = \mathcal{O}\big(e^{\nu_{l+1} z} z^{-\nu_{l+1}\Re\omega}\big). \tag{10.13b}$$

Remark. The sector of validity of Theorem 8.1 can also be extended in a similar manner. However, because the estimates (8.8) involve the factor $\exp\{-e|z|\ln(l+1)\}$ instead of the more powerful factor $\exp\{-(l+1)|z|\}$, the increase is more restrictive. We shall not enter into details.

11. Conclusions

There are several points of similarity between this paper and the paper of Berry and Howls [1]. Thus the same hyperterminants appear in the expansions, and the coefficients of these hyperterminants are related to the coefficients at the lowest level. There are significant differences, however. In the first place, the theory in [1] is purely formal: it is based on Dingle's re-expansions of remainder terms using Borel summation and a "resurgence formula", also due to Dingle [3]. Secondly, the asymptotic expansions that are re-expanded in [1] are the Liouville-Green expansions. Only in certain cases, for example, Airy's differential equation, are these the same as the Poincaré power-series expansions. Thirdly, the optimization process is carried out differently, in that the number of terms at a given level is constrained not to change when higher levels are incorporated into the expansion. As we saw in Remark (ii) of §7, this results in there being (approximately) $2^{-j}|z|$ terms at level j, and whatever the final level l happens to be the overall exponential improvement in the estimate for the error term is restricted to $e^{-(1+2\ln 2)|z|}$, that is, $e^{-(2.386\ldots)|z|}$ times a power of $|z|$. With our method of optimization, there is no limit on the attainable exponential improvement, even in the numerically stable form.

In earlier papers, for example [6], expansions at level 1 were regarded as providing a smooth interpretation of the Stokes phenomenon, because of the behavior and analytic nature of the individual terms in the neighborhoods of the Stokes lines. Since each branch of each $G_\omega^{(l)}$ function is analytic in its argument z (except at the origin), the hyperasymptotic expansions also furnish a smooth interpretation of the Stokes phenomenon. An added feature, however, is that these expansions apply to several

Stokes lines simultaneously. Thus, for example, $2l$ Stokes lines are covered in this way in the region of validity given by Theorem 10.1.

The practical implementation of the new expansions, in common with those of [1], depends on the ability to compute the necessary hyperterminants either by means of asymptotic approximations or by direct numerical methods. At the lth level, the hyperterminants are l-fold multiple integrals. The case $l = 0$ is trivial, and for $l = 1$, algorithms and software packages exist; see [4, §5.7].[6] Some progress on the problem of computing hyperterminants at level 2 in the case when ω is an integer is made in Appendix B of [1], and these results were used in the numerical example given in §9.

Acknowledgement. The authors are indebted to the referees for helpful suggestions in the presentation of this paper.

References

1. M. V. Berry and C. J. Howls, *Hyperasymptotics*, Proc. Roy. Soc. London, Ser. A **430** (1990), 653–668.
2. ———, *Hyperasymptotics for integrals with saddles*, Proc. Roy. Soc. London, Ser. A **434** (1991), 657–675.
3. R. B. Dingle, *Asymptotic Expansions: Their Derivation and Interpretation*, Academic Press, London, 1973.
4. D. W. Lozier and F. W. J. Olver, *Numerical evaluation of special functions.* In *Mathematics of Computation 1943–1993: A Half-Century of Computational Mathematics*, (W. Gautschi, ed.), Proceedings of Symposia in Applied Mathematics, Vol. 48, American Mathematical Society, Providence, Rhode Island, 1994.
5. A. B. Olde Daalhuis, *Hyperasymptotic expansions of confluent hypergeometric functions*, IMA J. Appl. Math. **49** (1992), 203–216.
6. A. B. Olde Daalhuis and F. W. J. Olver, *Exponentially-improved asymptotic solutions of ordinary differential equations. II: Irregular singularities of rank one*, Proc. Roy. Soc. London, Ser. A **445** (1994), 39–56.
7. ———, *On the calculation of Stokes multipliers for linear differential equations of the second order*, Methods Appl. Anal. (to appear).
8. F. W. J. Olver, *Asymptotics and Special Functions*, Academic Press, New York, 1974.
9. ———, *Exponentially-improved asymptotic solutions of ordinary differential equations* I: *The confluent hypergeometric function*, SIAM J. Math. Anal. **24** (1993), 756–767.

Institute for Physical Science and Technology, University of Maryland, College Park, Maryland 20742, U.S.A.
E-mail: aod@olgao.umd.edu, olver@bessel.umd.edu

[6]At least one existing software package is defective in the complex plane, however, especially near the Stokes lines ph $z = \pm\pi$.

Methods and Applications of Analysis
2 (3) 1995, pp. 348–367

ON THE CALCULATION OF STOKES MULTIPLIERS FOR LINEAR DIFFERENTIAL EQUATIONS OF THE SECOND ORDER

A. B. Olde Daalhuis and F. W. J. Olver

ABSTRACT. Two new methods are described for the computation of connection coefficients for the asymptotic solutions of linear second-order differential equations having an irregular singularity of arbitrary rank. The first method is based on new asymptotic expansions of the higher coefficients in the asymptotic solutions. The second method is based on direct numerical solution of the differential equation. Numerical examples are included.

1. Introduction

This paper is concerned with solutions of the homogeneous linear differential equation

$$\frac{d^2w}{dz^2} + f(z)\frac{dw}{dz} + g(z)w = 0, \tag{1.1}$$

in the neighborhood of an irregular singularity of positive integer rank r. Without loss of generality we may suppose that this singularity is located at $z = \infty$. Then $f(z)$ and $g(z)$ can be expanded in power series of the form

$$f(z) = z^{r-1}\sum_{s=0}^{\infty}\frac{f_s}{z^s}, \qquad g(z) = z^{2r-2}\sum_{s=0}^{\infty}\frac{g_s}{z^s}, \tag{1.2a,b}$$

that converge on an open annulus $|z| > a$. Moreover, at least one of the coefficients f_0, g_0, and g_1 is nonzero (otherwise the singularity would be of lower rank).

The nature and the existence of the asymptotic solutions of systems of homogeneous linear differential equations in the neighborhoods of irregular singularities has been the subject of many investigations; see, for example, [16,17]. In the present case, the construction of the asymptotic solutions proceeds as follows [15].[1]

Let

$$\phi(z) = \tfrac{1}{4}f^2(z) + \tfrac{1}{2}f'(z) - g(z), \tag{1.3}$$

so that

$$\phi(z) = z^{2r-2}\sum_{s=0}^{\infty}\frac{h_s}{z^s}, \qquad |z| > a, \tag{1.4}$$

where

$$h_s = \tfrac{1}{4}(f_0 f_s + f_1 f_{s-1} + \cdots + f_s f_0) + \tfrac{1}{2}(2r-1-s)f_{s-r} - g_s, \tag{1.5}$$

Received October 3, 1994, revised May 11, 1995.

1991 *Mathematics Subject Classification.* Primary: 34E05, Secondary: 65D30.

Key words and phrases: asymptotic expansions, connection formulas, irregular singularity, numerical integration, remainder term, singulant, Taylor-series method.

The research of the second author was supported by the National Science Foundation under Grant DMS 92-08690.

[1]The present notation differs slightly from that of [15].

with f_{s-r} interpreted as being zero when $s < r$. In particular, we have $h_0 = \frac{1}{4}f_0^2 - g_0$. If h_0 is nonzero, then we can expand the square root of $\phi(z)$ in the form

$$\{\phi(z)\}^{\frac{1}{2}} = z^{r-1}\sum_{s=0}^{\infty}\frac{\phi_s}{z^s}, \tag{1.6}$$

where

$$\phi_0 = \pm h_0^{\frac{1}{2}} = \pm\left(\tfrac{1}{4}f_0^2 - g_0\right)^{\frac{1}{2}}, \tag{1.7}$$

and higher coefficients can be computed by means of the recurrence relation

$$sh_0\phi_s = \sum_{j=1}^{s}\left(\tfrac{3}{2}j - s\right)h_j\phi_{s-j}, \qquad s \geq 1; \tag{1.8}$$

compare [13], Chapter 1, Exercise 8.4.

With the foregoing definitions, formal series solutions of (1.1) are given by

$$e^{\xi_1(z)}z^{\mu_1}\sum_{s=0}^{\infty}\frac{a_{s,1}}{z^s}, \qquad e^{\xi_2(z)}z^{\mu_2}\sum_{s=0}^{\infty}\frac{a_{s,2}}{z^s}, \tag{1.9a,b}$$

where

$$\xi_1(z) = -z^r\sum_{s=0}^{r-1}\frac{\phi_s + \frac{1}{2}f_s}{(r-s)z^s}, \qquad \xi_2(z) = z^r\sum_{s=0}^{r-1}\frac{\phi_s - \frac{1}{2}f_s}{(r-s)z^s}, \tag{1.10a,b}$$

$$\mu_1 = -\phi_r - \tfrac{1}{2}f_r - \tfrac{1}{2}r + \tfrac{1}{2}, \qquad \mu_2 = \phi_r - \tfrac{1}{2}f_r - \tfrac{1}{2}r + \tfrac{1}{2}, \tag{1.11a,b}$$

and the coefficients $a_{s,j}$, $j = 1, 2$, are given by $a_{0,j} = 1$ and

$$2sp_{0,j}a_{s,j} = \sum_{k=1}^{s}\{q_{k-1,j} - 2(s-k)p_{k,j}\}a_{s-k,j} + (s-r)(s-r+1)a_{s-r,j}, \tag{1.12}$$

the last term being absent when $s \leq r$. Here $p_{k,j}$ and $q_{k,j}$ are the coefficients in the expansions

$$p_j(z) = z^{r-1}\sum_{k=0}^{\infty}\frac{p_{k,j}}{z^k}, \qquad q_j(z) = z^{r-3}\sum_{k=0}^{\infty}\frac{q_{k,j}}{z^k}, \qquad |z| > a, \tag{1.13a,b}$$

of the functions

$$p_j(z) = \xi_j'(z) + \frac{\mu_j}{z} + \tfrac{1}{2}f(z), \tag{1.14a}$$

$$q_j(z) = \xi_j''(z) + {\xi_j'}^2(z) + \frac{2\mu_j}{z}\xi_j'(z) + \frac{\mu_j(\mu_j - 1)}{z^2} + f(z)\left\{\xi_j'(z) + \frac{\mu_j}{z}\right\} + g(z). \tag{1.14b}$$

In the exceptional case $\frac{1}{4}f_0^2 = g_0$ (which includes, of course, the commonly occurring case of $f_0 = g_0 = 0$), the dominant terms (for large $|z|$) in the polynomials $\xi_1(z)$ and $\xi_2(z)$ have the same coefficients. If we make the transformation [15]

$$W = \exp\left\{\tfrac{1}{2}\int\left(\sum_{s=0}^{r-1}f_s z^{r-s-1}\right)dz\right\}w, \qquad t = z^{\frac{1}{2}},$$

then it is readily verified that at $t = \infty$, the transformed differential equation has either a regular singularity or an irregular singularity of rank not exceeding $2r - 1$ with unequal dominant terms in the corresponding polynomials $\xi_1(z)$ and $\xi_2(z)$. *We therefore may assume without loss of generality that* $\frac{1}{4}f_0^2 \neq g_0$ *and, hence, that* $\phi_0 \neq 0$ *in all subsequent analysis.*

The ratio $(s-r)(s-r+1)/(2sp_{0,j})$ of $a_{s,j}$ to $a_{s-r,j}$ in the recurrence relation (1.12) indicates that, in general, the series (1.9) diverge.[2] In order to describe solutions that have these series as asymptotic expansions, we subdivide the plane into sectors S_k, $k = 0, \pm 1, \pm 2, \ldots$, defined as follows. Let $\sigma = \operatorname{ph} \phi_0$; then

$$S_k = \left\{ z : \frac{(k-\frac{1}{2})\pi - \sigma}{r} \leq \operatorname{ph} z \leq \frac{(k+\frac{1}{2})\pi - \sigma}{r} \right\}; \tag{1.15}$$

see Figure 1.1.

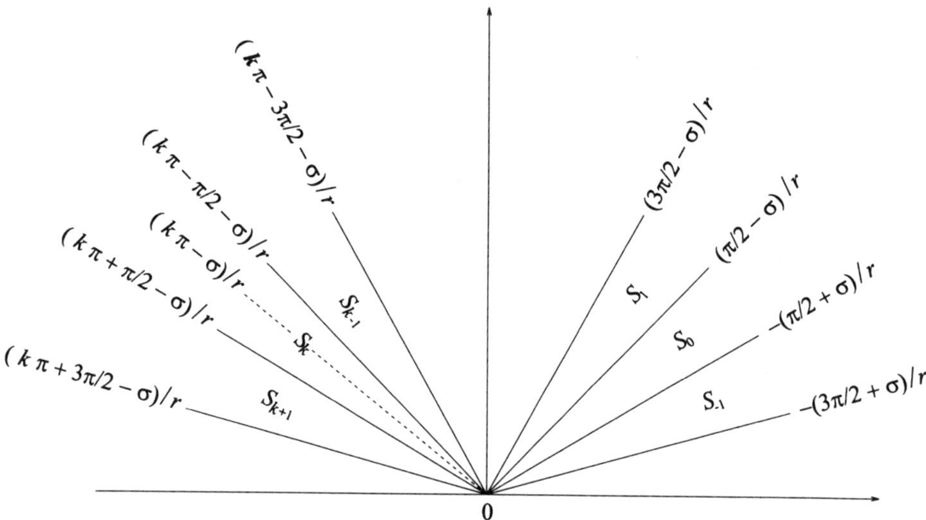

FIGURE 1.1. z-plane. Sectors S_k. Values of $\operatorname{ph} z$ are given at ends of rays.

The significant feature of these sectors is that for sufficiently large $|z|$, the real part of $\xi_2(z) - \xi_1(z)$ is positive or negative at interior points of S_k according as k is even or odd. This follows from the relation

$$\xi_2(z) - \xi_1(z) \sim 2\phi_0 z^r / r, \qquad z \to \infty,$$

obtained from (1.10).

Now define $\hat{S}_k$ to be any closed sector that is properly interior to $S_{k-1} \cup S_k \cup S_{k+1}$. For example, $\hat{S}_0$ could be taken to be the sector

$$-\left(\tfrac{3}{2}\pi + \sigma - \delta\right)/r \leq \operatorname{ph} z \leq \left(\tfrac{3}{2}\pi - \sigma - \delta\right)/r,$$

where δ is an arbitrary small positive constant.

Theorem 1.1. (i) *For each even integer* k, *there exists a unique solution* $w_k(z)$ *of* (1.1) *such that*

$$w_k(z) \sim e^{\xi_1(z)} z^{\mu_1} \sum_{s=0}^{\infty} \frac{a_{s,1}}{z^s}, \qquad z \to \infty \text{ in } \hat{S}_k. \tag{1.16a}$$

[2] See also Theorem 4.1 below.

(ii) *For each odd integer k, there exists a unique solution $w_k(z)$ of (1.1) such that*

$$w_k(z) \sim e^{\xi_2(z)} z^{\mu_2} \sum_{s=0}^{\infty} \frac{a_{s,2}}{z^s}, \qquad z \to \infty \text{ in } \hat{S}_k. \tag{1.16b}$$

Any branches may be chosen for $\sigma \equiv \operatorname{ph} \phi_0$ in (1.15) and z^{μ_1}, z^{μ_2} in (1.16), provided that they are used consistently.

Theorem 1.1 can be derived from the theorem of [15] by suitable choice of the path $\mathcal{P}_k$ in this theorem. Thus, in the present notation, if we take $\hat{S}_k$ to be the sector

$$\hat{S}_k = \left\{ z : \frac{(k-\frac{3}{2})\pi - \sigma + \delta}{r} \leq \operatorname{ph} z \leq \frac{(k+\frac{3}{2})\pi - \sigma - \delta}{r} \right\}$$

and make the transformation $\zeta = \phi_0 z^r$, then for all sufficiently large z in $\hat{S}_k$, the path $\mathcal{P}_k$ can be taken as the map of a path $\mathcal{Q}_k$ in the ζ-plane comprising an infinite segment of the real axis and segments of one or two straight lines at angles $\pm\frac{1}{2}\delta$ to the imaginary axis. Figures 1.2, 1.3, for example, depict $\mathcal{Q}_k$ when k is even and $(k\pi - \sigma)/r \leq \operatorname{ph} z \leq (k\pi + \frac{1}{2}\pi - \sigma)/r$, $(k\pi + \frac{1}{2}\pi - \sigma)/r \leq \operatorname{ph} z \leq (k\pi + \frac{3}{2}\pi - \sigma - \delta)/r$, respectively. See also Lemma 13.1 of [13], Chapter 6.

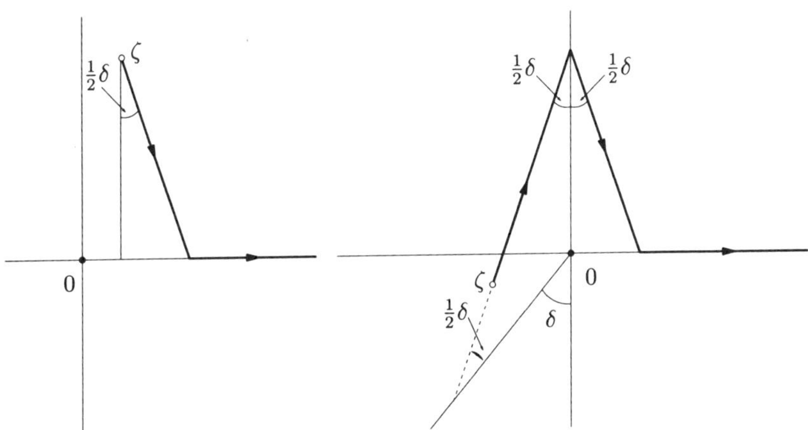

FIGURE 1.2. ζ-plane. Path $\mathcal{Q}_k$ when $k\pi \leq \operatorname{ph}\zeta \leq (k+\frac{1}{2})\pi$, k even.

FIGURE 1.3. ζ-plane. Path $\mathcal{Q}_k$ when $(k+\frac{1}{2})\pi \leq \operatorname{ph}\zeta \leq (k+\frac{3}{2})\pi - \delta$, k even.

2. The connection formula problem

Although, for each value of k, Theorem 1.1 provides information on the solution $w_k(z)$ only in the sector $\hat{S}_k$, this solution can be continued analytically to all values of $\operatorname{ph} z$. In general, $w_k(z)$ has a branch-point at infinity.

Among any three solutions a linear relation holds for all values of z. In particular,

$$w_{k+1}(z) = C_k w_k(z) + B_k w_{k-1}(z), \tag{2.1}$$

where B_k and C_k are constants. The value of B_k is easily found by letting $z \to \infty$ on an interior ray in S_k. On this ray, $w_k(z)$ is recessive and the other two solutions are dominant with exactly the same asymptotic form. Hence $B_k = 1$, and (2.1) reduces to

$$w_{k+1}(z) = C_k w_k(z) + w_{k-1}(z). \tag{2.2}$$

The coefficient C_k is more difficult to calculate in general. For later convenience, we sometimes set

$$C_k = e^{(-)^k k\omega\pi i/r} A_k, \tag{2.3}$$

where

$$\omega = \mu_2 - \mu_1; \tag{2.4}$$

then

$$w_{k+1}(z) = e^{(-)^k k\omega\pi i/r} A_k w_k(z) + w_{k-1}(z). \tag{2.5}$$

Either set of constants $\{C_k\}$ or $\{A_k\}$, $k = 0, \pm1, \ldots$, may be called the ***Stokes multipliers*** (at infinity) for the differential equation (1.1).

In passing, we note that if we know the C_k (or A_k) for all values of k, then it is possible to determine the asymptotic behavior of any solution $w_j(z)$, say, in any sector S_k, say. Suppose, for example, $k > j$. It is readily verified that

$$w_j(z) = \Lambda_k w_{k-1}(z) + \Lambda_{k-1} w_k(z), \tag{2.6}$$

where the constants Λ_{k-1} and Λ_k are found by application of the recurrence relation

$$\Lambda_{n+1} = -C_n\Lambda_n + \Lambda_{n-1}, \qquad n = j+2, j+3, \ldots, k-1, \tag{2.7}$$

beginning with $\Lambda_{j+1} = 1$ and $\Lambda_{j+2} = -C_{j+1}$. Once Λ_k and Λ_{k-1} have been found, the (compound) asymptotic expansion of $w_j(z)$ in the sector $\hat{S}_{k-1} \cap \hat{S}_k$ is obtained from (2.6) by substituting the known expansions (1.16) of $w_{k-1}(z)$ and $w_k(z)$ in this sector. Obviously from Figure 1.1, we can always arrange that $\hat{S}_{k-1} \cap \hat{S}_k$ includes the sector

$$\left(k\pi - \tfrac{1}{2}\pi - \sigma\right)/r \le \operatorname{ph} z \le \left(k\pi - \sigma\right)/r,$$

that is, the right half of S_k when viewed from the origin. To cover the left half of S_k, we continue the recurrence (2.7) one step further, to $n = k$, and then apply

$$w_j(z) = \Lambda_{k+1} w_k(z) + \Lambda_k w_{k+1}(z). \tag{2.8}$$

The purpose of the present paper is to describe two methods for computing the coefficients C_k and A_k in the connection formulas (2.2) and (2.5), one asymptotic, the other numerical.

The asymptotic method is developed in §§3, 4, 5 and is based on expansions of the coefficients $a_{s,1}$ and $a_{s,2}$ for large s. Methods of this kind are already known; see, for example, [6–11]. Other analytical methods also exist [5, 18]. The novelty of our approach is that we employ inverse factorial series in place of the more usual inverse power series for the asymptotic expansions of $a_{s,1}$ and $a_{s,2}$. *The advantage of the inverse factorial expansions is that the coefficients are available explicitly.* In fact, they are simple multiples of the earlier coefficients $a_{0,1}, a_{1,1}, a_{2,1}, \ldots, a_{0,2}, a_{1,2}, a_{2,2}, \ldots$. Therefore, it is possible to evaluate the Stokes multipliers to high accuracy with relatively little analytical and computational effort. In §6, we supply two numerical examples to illustrate this feature.

The second method for evaluating the Stokes multipliers is based on direct numerical integration of the differential equation along suitably chosen paths in the complex plane. It is outlined in §7 and applied to the numerical examples previously treated in §6.

3. Asymptotic method for the Stokes multipliers: singularities of unit rank

In this section, we assume that $r = 1$. The expressions (1.10) for $\xi_1(z)$ and $\xi_2(z)$ reduce to

$$\xi_1(z) = \lambda_1 z, \qquad \xi_2(z) = \lambda_2 z, \tag{3.1a,b}$$

where λ_1, λ_2 are the zeros of the quadratic polynomial $\lambda^2 + f_0\lambda + g_0$. Accordingly,

$$\lambda_2 - \lambda_1 = \pm(f_0^2 - 4g_0)^{\frac{1}{2}}, \tag{3.2}$$

and is nonzero by hypothesis (§1). The exponents μ_1 and μ_2 are given by

$$\mu_1 = \frac{f_1\lambda_1 + g_1}{\lambda_2 - \lambda_1}, \qquad \mu_2 = \frac{f_1\lambda_2 + g_1}{\lambda_1 - \lambda_2}, \tag{3.3a,b}$$

and the recurrence relation (1.12), with $j = 1, 2$, respectively, reduces to

$$(\lambda_1 - \lambda_2)sa_{s,1} = (s - \mu_1)(s - 1 - \mu_1)a_{s-1,1} + \sum_{j=1}^{s}\{\lambda_1 f_{j+1} + g_{j+1} - (s - j - \mu_1)f_j\}a_{s-j,1}, \tag{3.4a}$$

$$(\lambda_2 - \lambda_1)sa_{s,2} = (s - \mu_2)(s - 1 - \mu_2)a_{s-1,2} + \sum_{j=1}^{s}\{\lambda_2 f_{j+1} + g_{j+1} - (s - j - \mu_2)f_j\}a_{s-j,2}, \tag{3.4b}$$

again with the starting values $a_{0,1} = a_{0,2} = 1$. We also have $\phi_0 = \frac{1}{2}(\lambda_2 - \lambda_1)$, $\sigma = \mathrm{ph}(\lambda_2 - \lambda_1)$. The sectors S_k, $k = 0, \pm1, \ldots$, are defined by

$$S_k = \left\{z : \left(k - \frac{1}{2}\right)\pi - \sigma \le \mathrm{ph}\, z \le \left(k + \frac{1}{2}\right)\pi - \sigma\right\}.$$

Next, we observe that $w_k(e^{-2j\pi i}z)$ is also a solution of the differential equation for any integer j, and from Theorem 1.1 it follows that

$$w_{k+2j}(z) = e^{2j\mu_1\pi i}w_k(e^{-2j\pi i}z), \qquad k \text{ even}, \tag{3.5a}$$

$$w_{k+2j}(z) = e^{2j\mu_2\pi i}w_k(e^{-2j\pi i}z), \qquad k \text{ odd}. \tag{3.5b}$$

On combining these results with (2.5), with $r = 1$, and (2.4), we deduce that

$$A_k = A_0, \quad k \text{ even}; \qquad A_k = A_1, \quad k \text{ odd}.$$

Now suppose that the differential equation is normalized in such a way that

$$\lambda_2 - \lambda_1 = 1. \tag{3.6}$$

This always can be arranged, if necessary, by replacing z with $z/(\lambda_2 - \lambda_1)$. Then $\phi_0 = \frac{1}{2}$, $\sigma = 0$, and the sectors S_k become

$$S_k = \left\{z : \left(k - \frac{1}{2}\right)\pi \le \mathrm{ph}\, z \le \left(k + \frac{1}{2}\right)\pi\right\}.$$

Furthermore, the new values of C_k and A_k are $(\lambda_2 - \lambda_1)^{(-)^k\omega}$ times their old values.[3]

In [12], we proved that in the present circumstances the following theorem holds.[4]

---

[3]In forming $(\lambda_2 - \lambda_1)^{(-)^k\omega}$, the branch of ph $(\lambda_2 - \lambda_1)$ has to be σ.

[4]The notations $w_1(z)$, $w_2(z)$, C_1, and C_2 in [12] now are denoted by $w_0(z)$, $w_1(z)$, $-C_1$, and C_0, respectively.

Theorem 3.1. *Let m be an arbitrary fixed nonnegative integer. Then as $s \to \infty$,*

$$a_{s,1} = (-)^{s-1}\frac{A_1}{2\pi i}\sum_{j=0}^{m-1}(-)^j a_{j,2}\Gamma(s+\omega-j) + \mathcal{O}\{\Gamma(s+\omega-m)\}, \tag{3.7a}$$

$$a_{s,2} = -\frac{A_0}{2\pi i}\sum_{j=0}^{m-1} a_{j,1}\Gamma(s-\omega-j) + \mathcal{O}\{\Gamma(s-\omega-m)\}, \tag{3.7b}$$

where ω is defined by (2.4).

Equations (3.7) can be regarded in two ways. If A_0 and A_1 are known, then (3.7) provide an easy way of computing $a_{s,1}$ and $a_{s,2}$ for large s.

Alternatively, if we regard equations (3.4) as a way of generating $a_{s,1}$ and $a_{s,2}$ recursively for arbitrary large s, then A_0 and A_1 can be estimated via

$$A_0 = -2\pi i \lim_{s\to\infty}\frac{a_{s,2}}{\Gamma(s-\omega)}, \qquad A_1 = 2\pi i \lim_{s\to\infty}\frac{(-)^{s-1}a_{s,1}}{\Gamma(s+\omega)}, \tag{3.8a,b}$$

or more accurately from

$$A_0 = -2\pi i a_{s,2}\Big\{\sum_{j=0}^{m-1} a_{j,1}\Gamma(s-\omega-j)\Big\}^{-1} + \mathcal{O}(s^{-m}), \tag{3.9a}$$

$$A_1 = (-)^{s-1}2\pi i a_{s,1}\Big\{\sum_{j=0}^{m-1}(-)^j a_{j,2}\Gamma(s+\omega-j)\Big\}^{-1} + \mathcal{O}(s^{-m}). \tag{3.9b}$$

It is the second point of view that we adopt in this paper. By choosing values of s and m that are large (but not unduly large), it is possible to compute A_0 and A_1 from (3.9) to very high accuracy.

4. Asymptotic method for the Stokes multipliers: singularities of arbitrary rank

We now proceed to the generalization of Theorem 3.1 to the case of arbitrary rank r.

Corresponding to (3.5), we have

$$w_{k+2jr}(z) = e^{2j\mu_1\pi i}w_k(e^{-2j\pi i}z), \qquad k \text{ even}, \tag{4.1a}$$

$$w_{k+2jr}(z) = e^{2j\mu_2\pi i}w_k(e^{-2j\pi i}z), \qquad k \text{ odd}. \tag{4.1b}$$

From these results and (2.4), (2.5), it follows that

$$A_{k+2jr} = A_k, \tag{4.2}$$

for all integers k and j. Accordingly, it suffices to determine a set of $2r$ consecutive Stokes multipliers.

With $\xi_1(z)$ and $\xi_2(z)$ defined as in §1, we follow the terminology of Dingle [3], and call $\xi_2(z) - \xi_1(z)$ the *singulant* (with respect to $z = \infty$) of the differential equation (1.1). The first step is to renormalize the differential equation in such a way that the singulant is simply z^r; compare (3.1) and (3.6) in the case $r = 1$. This can be achieved in various ways. The simplest, in principle, is to take a new independent variable x defined by

$$x^r = \xi_2(z) - \xi_1(z) = 2z^r\sum_{s=0}^{r-1}\frac{\phi_s}{(r-s)z^s}; \tag{4.3}$$

compare (1.10). For large x, we can expand z in a convergent power series of the form

$$z = x\sum_{s=0}^{\infty}\frac{c_s}{x^s}, \tag{4.4}$$

where, for example,

$$c_0 = \left(\frac{r}{2\phi_0}\right)^{1/r}, \qquad c_1 = -\frac{\phi_1}{(r-1)\phi_0}, \tag{4.5a,b}$$

$$c_2 = \frac{\phi_1^2}{2(r-1)\phi_0^2 c_0} - \frac{\phi_2}{(r-2)\phi_0 c_0}, \tag{4.5c}$$

and higher coefficients can be found by means of standard procedures for reversion of power series. The problem with this approach is that reversion is cumbersome; even with the aid of available software packages, the evaluation of c_s is slow when s is large. Following [10], Section III.3, we circumvent this difficulty by truncating the expansion (4.4) after r terms. Thus, instead of x, we use the variable $\tilde{z}$ defined implicitly by

$$z = \tilde{z}\sum_{s=0}^{r-1}\frac{c_s}{\tilde{z}^s}, \tag{4.6}$$

with the condition $c_0\tilde{z} \sim z$ as $z \to \infty$. The effect of this modification is to replace (4.3) by

$$\xi_2(z) - \xi_1(z) = \tilde{z}^r - \frac{rc_r}{c_0} + \mathcal{O}\left(\frac{1}{\tilde{z}}\right), \tag{4.7}$$

the term $\mathcal{O}(1/\tilde{z})$ here actually being a power series in $1/\tilde{z}$.

In terms of the variable $\tilde{z}$, the differential equation (1.1) transforms into

$$\frac{d^2w}{d\tilde{z}^2} + \tilde{f}(\tilde{z})\frac{dw}{d\tilde{z}} + \tilde{g}(\tilde{z})w = 0, \tag{4.8}$$

where

$$\tilde{f}(\tilde{z}) = -\left(\frac{dz}{d\tilde{z}}\right)^{-1}\frac{d^2z}{d\tilde{z}^2} + \frac{dz}{d\tilde{z}}f(z), \qquad \tilde{g}(\tilde{z}) = \left(\frac{dz}{d\tilde{z}}\right)^2 g(z). \tag{4.9a,b}$$

From (1.2) and (4.6), we see that $\tilde{f}(\tilde{z})$ and $\tilde{g}(\tilde{z})$ can be expanded in the form

$$\tilde{f}(\tilde{z}) = \tilde{z}^{r-1}\sum_{s=0}^{\infty}\frac{\tilde{f}_s}{\tilde{z}^s}, \qquad \tilde{g}(\tilde{z}) = \tilde{z}^{2r-2}\sum_{s=0}^{\infty}\frac{\tilde{g}_s}{\tilde{z}^s},$$

these series converging for all sufficiently large values of $|\tilde{z}|$. In particular, we have

$$\tilde{f}_0 = c_0^r f_0, \qquad \tilde{g}_0 = c_0^{2r} g_0, \qquad \tilde{g}_1 = c_0^{2r-1}\{g_1 + (2r-2)c_1 g_0\}.$$

Since not all of f_0, g_0, and g_1 vanish, the same is true of $\tilde{f}_0$, $\tilde{g}_0$, and $\tilde{g}_1$. Furthermore,

$$\tilde{\phi}_0 \equiv \left(\tfrac{1}{4}\tilde{f}_0^2 - \tilde{g}_0\right)^{\frac{1}{2}} = c_0^r\phi_0 = \tfrac{1}{2}r.$$

On applying Theorem 1.1, we see that if $\tilde{S}_k$ denotes the sector

$$\frac{(k-\frac{3}{2})\pi + \delta}{r} \le \operatorname{ph}\tilde{z} \le \frac{(k+\frac{3}{2})\pi - \delta}{r},$$

then equation (4.8) has solutions $\tilde{w}_k(\tilde{z})$ such that, as $\tilde{z} \to \infty$ in $\tilde{S}_k$,

$$\tilde{w}_k(\tilde{z}) \sim e^{\tilde{\xi}_1(\tilde{z})}\tilde{z}^{\tilde{\mu}_1} \quad \text{or} \quad \tilde{w}_k(\tilde{z}) \sim e^{\tilde{\xi}_2(\tilde{z})}\tilde{z}^{\tilde{\mu}_2}, \tag{4.10}$$

according as k is even or odd. Furthermore, because $\tilde{w}_k(\tilde{z})$ is recessive when $\tilde{z} \to \infty$ in the central third of $\tilde{S}_k$ and $w_k(z)$ is recessive when $z \to \infty$ in the central third of $\hat{S}_k$, it follows that

$$\tilde{\mu}_1 = \mu_1, \qquad \tilde{\mu}_2 = \mu_2, \tag{4.11}$$

$$\xi_1(z) - \tilde{\xi}_1(\tilde{z}) = b_1 + \mathcal{O}(\tilde{z}^{-1}), \quad \xi_2(z) - \tilde{\xi}_2(\tilde{z}) = b_2 + \mathcal{O}(\tilde{z}^{-1}), \quad \tilde{z} \to \infty, \tag{4.12}$$

where b_1, b_2 are constants and, hence,

$$w_k(z) = e^{b_1} c_0^{\mu_1} \tilde{w}_k(\tilde{z}) \quad \text{or} \quad w_k(z) = e^{b_2} c_0^{\mu_2} \tilde{w}_k(\tilde{z}), \tag{4.13}$$

according as k is even or odd. Next, since $\tilde{\xi}_1(\tilde{z})$ and $\tilde{\xi}_2(\tilde{z})$ are polynomials in $\tilde{z}$ of degree r with no constant term, it follows from (4.7) and (4.12) that $\tilde{\xi}_2(\tilde{z})-\tilde{\xi}_1(\tilde{z}) = \tilde{z}^r$, exactly (as required), and also that

$$b_1 - b_2 = \frac{rc_r}{c_0}. \tag{4.14}$$

Lastly, let $\{\tilde{A}_k\}$ be the set of Stokes multipliers associated with (4.8) at $\tilde{z} = \infty$, so that

$$\tilde{w}_{k+1}(\tilde{z}) = e^{(-)^k k\omega\pi i/r} \tilde{A}_k \tilde{w}_k(\tilde{z}) + \tilde{w}_{k-1}(\tilde{z}), \tag{4.15}$$

with ω again defined by (2.4); compare (2.5) and (4.11). Then from (4.13) and (4.14), we deduce that these multipliers are related to the original multipliers A_k by the formula[5]

$$A_k = e^{(-)^{k-1} rc_r/c_0} c_0^{(-)^k \omega} \tilde{A}_k. \tag{4.16}$$

From here until the end of §5, *we shall assume that the preliminary transformation of the form* (4.6) *has been made, if needed; in consequence, the normalizing condition*

$$\xi_2(z) - \xi_1(z) = z^r \tag{4.17}$$

is satisfied.

We observe in passing that when (4.17) holds, the definitions of §1 simplify, in that $\phi_0 = \frac{1}{2}r$, $\phi_s = 0$ $(1 \le s \le r-1)$, and $\sigma = 0$.

Theorem 4.1. *Let m be an arbitrary fixed nonnegative integer. Then with the condition* (4.17), *the coefficients $a_{s,1}$ and $a_{s,2}$ defined in* §1 *have the asymptotic expansions as $s \to \infty$*

$$a_{s,1} = -\frac{1}{2r\pi i} \sum_{k=0}^{r-1} A_{2k+1} \sum_{j=0}^{m-1} a_{j,2} e^{(2k+1)(s-j)\pi i/r} \Gamma\left(\frac{s+\omega-j}{r}\right) + \mathcal{O}\left\{\Gamma\left(\frac{s+\omega-m}{r}\right)\right\}, \tag{4.18a}$$

$$a_{s,2} = -\frac{1}{2r\pi i} \sum_{k=0}^{r-1} A_{2k} \sum_{j=0}^{m-1} a_{j,1} e^{2k(s-j)\pi i/r} \Gamma\left(\frac{s-\omega-j}{r}\right) + \mathcal{O}\left\{\Gamma\left(\frac{s-\omega-m}{r}\right)\right\}, \tag{4.18b}$$

where $\omega = \mu_2 - \mu_1$.

---

[5] Again, the branch of $\operatorname{ph} c_0$ used in forming $c_0^{(-)^k \omega}$ in (4.16) is $-(\operatorname{ph} \phi_0)/r$, where ϕ_0 pertains to the original equation (1.1).

This theorem is proved in §5. In the remainder of the present section, we describe how it can be applied to compute the A_k.

The $\mathcal{O}$-terms on the right-hand sides of (4.18) contribute relative errors $\mathcal{O}(s^{-m/r})$ as $s \to \infty$. We assume that s and m are chosen sufficiently large to render these contributions negligible compared with the desired precision in the A_k. On replacing s in (4.18a) by rs, $rs+1$, ..., $rs+r-1$, in turn, and ignoring the error terms, we arrive at the system of r equations for A_1, A_3, ..., A_{2r-1}

$$\begin{aligned} \sum_{k=0}^{r-1} b_{0,2k+1} A_{2k+1} &= a_{rs,1}, \\ \sum_{k=0}^{r-1} b_{1,2k+1} A_{2k+1} &= a_{rs+1,1}, \\ &\vdots \\ \sum_{k=0}^{r-1} b_{r-1,2k+1} A_{2k+1} &= a_{rs+r-1,1}, \end{aligned} \tag{4.19}$$

where

$$b_{n,2k+1} = \frac{(-)^{s-1}}{2r\pi i} e^{(2k+1)n\pi i/r} \sum_{j=0}^{m-1} a_{j,2} e^{-(2k+1)j\pi i/r}\, \Gamma\Big(s + \frac{n+\omega-j}{r}\Big). \tag{4.20}$$

In a similar way, we find that

$$\begin{aligned} \sum_{k=0}^{r-1} b_{0,2k} A_{2k} &= a_{rs,2}, \\ \sum_{k=0}^{r-1} b_{1,2k} A_{2k} &= a_{rs+1,2}, \\ &\vdots \\ \sum_{k=0}^{r-1} b_{r-1,2k} A_{2k} &= a_{rs+r-1,2}, \end{aligned} \tag{4.21}$$

where

$$b_{n,2k} = -\frac{1}{2r\pi i} e^{2kn\pi i/r} \sum_{j=0}^{m-1} a_{j,1} e^{-2kj\pi i/r}\, \Gamma\Big(s + \frac{n-\omega-j}{r}\Big). \tag{4.22}$$

Each system (4.19), (4.21) may be solved by standard numerical procedures for linear algebraic equations. To investigate the conditioning of these systems, we replace each coefficient $b_{n,k}$ by the corresponding dominant term on the right-hand side of (4.20) or (4.22), that is, we take $m = 1$. In this way, we find that (4.19) has the approximate form

$$\begin{array}{ccccccccc} A_1 & + & A_3 & +\cdots+ & A_{2r-1} & = & (-)^{s-1}\dfrac{2r\pi i a_{rs,1}}{\Gamma(s+\frac{\omega}{r})}, \\ e^{\pi i/r}A_1 & + & e^{3\pi i/r}A_3 & +\cdots+ & e^{(2r-1)\pi i/r}A_{2r-1} & = & (-)^{s-1}\dfrac{2r\pi i a_{rs+1,1}}{\Gamma(s+\frac{1+\omega}{r})}, \\ \vdots & & \vdots & & \vdots & & \vdots \end{array}$$

$$e^{(r-1)\pi i/r}A_1 + e^{(r-1)3\pi i/r}A_3 +\cdots+ e^{(r-1)(2r-1)\pi i/r}A_{2r-1} = (-)^{s-1}\frac{2r\pi i a_{rs+r-1,1}}{\Gamma(s+\frac{r-1+\omega}{r})}.$$

This is a Vandermonde system of equations, and its condition number in the infinity norm is easily deduced from the result of [4, Example 6.4] to be r. Hence the system (4.19) is well conditioned. In a similar way, we may show that the same is true for (4.21).

5. Proof of Theorem 4.1

The proof of Theorem 4.1 is an extension of that of Theorem 2.1 in [12]. With the solutions $w_k(z)$ defined as in §1, we set

$$v_k(z) = e^{-\xi_1(z)}z^{-\mu_1-1}w_k(z). \tag{5.1}$$

Then

$$v_{k+1}(z) = C_k v_k(z) + v_{k-1}(z); \tag{5.2}$$

compare (2.2).

Lemma 5.1. *Let ρ be any constant that exceeds a. Then*

$$2\pi i v_0(z) = \sum_{k=0}^{r-1} C_{2k+1}\int_{\rho e^{(2k+1)\pi i/r}}^{\infty e^{(2k+1)\pi i/r}} \frac{v_{2k+1}(t)}{t-z}dt - \sum_{k=0}^{r-1}\int_{\rho e^{(2k-1)\pi i/r}}^{\rho e^{(2k+1)\pi i/r}} \frac{v_{2k}(t)}{t-z}dt, \tag{5.3}$$

valid when z lies in the annular sector $|z| > \rho$, $|\mathrm{ph}\, z| < \pi/r$.

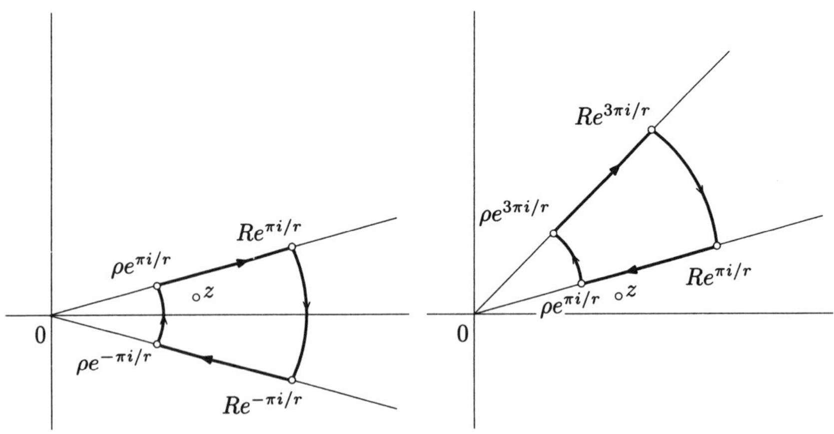

FIGURE 5.1. t-plane. Contour $\mathcal{C}_0$.

FIGURE 5.2. t-plane. Contour $\mathcal{C}_1$.

Proof. Let R be any constant that exceeds $|z|$. Then, from Cauchy's integral formula, we have

$$2\pi i v_0(z) = -\int_{\mathcal{C}_0} \frac{v_0(t)}{t-z}dt, \tag{5.4}$$

where $\mathcal{C}_0$ is the closed contour depicted in Figure 5.1. From (1.16a) and (5.1), with $k=0$, we see that $v_0(t) = \mathcal{O}(t^{-1})$ uniformly as $t \to \infty$ in the sector $|\operatorname{ph} t| \le \pi/r$. Accordingly, on letting $R \to \infty$, (5.4) becomes

$$2\pi i v_0(z) = -\left(\int_{\rho e^{\pi i/r}}^{\infty e^{\pi i/r}} - \int_{\rho e^{-\pi i/r}}^{\infty e^{-\pi i/r}} + \int_{\rho e^{-\pi i/r}}^{\rho e^{\pi i/r}}\right)\frac{v_0(t)}{t-z}dt.$$

In the first of these integrals, we substitute for $v_0(t)$ by means of (5.2) with $k=1$. This yields

$$\begin{aligned}2\pi i v_0(z) = C_1\int_{\rho e^{\pi i/r}}^{\infty e^{\pi i/r}} \frac{v_1(t)}{t-z}dt - \int_{\rho e^{-\pi i/r}}^{\rho e^{\pi i/r}} \frac{v_0(t)}{t-z}dt \\ + \int_{\rho e^{-\pi i/r}}^{\infty e^{-\pi i/r}} \frac{v_0(t)}{t-z}dt - \int_{\rho e^{\pi i/r}}^{\infty e^{\pi i/r}} \frac{v_2(t)}{t-z}dt.\end{aligned} \tag{5.5}$$

We now integrate $v_2(t)/(t-z)$ around the closed contour $\mathcal{C}_1$ depicted in Figure 5.2, and again let $R \to \infty$. From (1.16a) and (5.1), with $k=2$, we see that $v_2(t) = \mathcal{O}(t^{-1})$ uniformly as $t \to \infty$ in the sector $\pi/r \le \operatorname{ph} t \le 3\pi/r$. Hence, we obtain

$$\int_{\rho e^{\pi i/r}}^{\infty e^{\pi i/r}} \frac{v_2(t)}{t-z}dt = \int_{\rho e^{3\pi i/r}}^{\infty e^{3\pi i/r}} \frac{v_2(t)}{t-z}dt + \int_{\rho e^{\pi i/r}}^{\rho e^{3\pi i/r}} \frac{v_2(t)}{t-z}dt.$$

Then by application of (5.2), with $k=3$, we derive

$$\int_{\rho e^{\pi i/r}}^{\infty e^{\pi i/r}} \frac{v_2(t)}{t-z}dt = -C_3\int_{\rho e^{3\pi i/r}}^{\infty e^{3\pi i/r}} \frac{v_3(t)}{t-z}dt + \int_{\rho e^{3\pi i/r}}^{\infty e^{3\pi i/r}} \frac{v_4(t)}{t-z}dt + \int_{\rho e^{\pi i/r}}^{\rho e^{3\pi i/r}} \frac{v_2(t)}{t-z}dt.$$

Substituting into (5.5) by means of this equation, we obtain

$$\begin{aligned}2\pi i v_0(z) = C_1\int_{\rho e^{\pi i/r}}^{\infty e^{\pi i/r}} \frac{v_1(t)}{t-z}dt + C_3\int_{\rho e^{3\pi i/r}}^{\infty e^{3\pi i/r}} \frac{v_3(t)}{t-z}dt - \int_{\rho e^{-\pi i/r}}^{\rho e^{\pi i/r}} \frac{v_0(t)}{t-z}dt \\ - \int_{\rho e^{\pi i/r}}^{\rho e^{3\pi i/r}} \frac{v_2(t)}{t-z}dt + \int_{\rho e^{-\pi i/r}}^{\infty e^{-\pi i/r}} \frac{v_0(t)}{t-z}dt - \int_{\rho e^{3\pi i/r}}^{\infty e^{3\pi i/r}} \frac{v_4(t)}{t-z}dt.\end{aligned} \tag{5.6}$$

We may regard (5.5) as the first stage in a cycle of substitutions and (5.6) as the second stage. We may continue the substitutions until we reach the rth stage, and then observe that

$$\int_{\rho e^{-\pi i/r}}^{\infty e^{-\pi i/r}} \frac{v_0(t)}{t-z}dt = \int_{\rho e^{(2r-1)\pi i/r}}^{\infty e^{(2r-1)\pi i/r}} \frac{v_{2r}(t)}{t-z}dt,$$

this being a consequence of the relation

$$v_{2r}(t) = v_0(te^{-2\pi i}),$$

obtained from (4.1a) and (5.1). Therefore, (5.3) is precisely the result that is obtained on completion of the rth stage. □

Lemma 5.2.

$$2\pi i a_{s,1} = -\sum_{k=0}^{r-1} C_{2k+1} \int_{\rho e^{(2k+1)\pi i/r}}^{\infty e^{(2k+1)\pi i/r}} v_{2k+1}(t) t^s dt + \sum_{k=0}^{r-1} \int_{\rho e^{(2k-1)\pi i/r}}^{\rho e^{(2k+1)\pi i/r}} v_{2k}(t) t^s dt. \quad (5.7)$$

The derivation of this result from Lemma 5.1 is similar to the derivation of Lemma 3.2 of [12] from Lemma 3.1 of [12]. We omit the proof.

To complete the proof of Theorem 4.1, we observe from (1.16b) and (5.1) that for each k

$$v_{2k+1}(t) = e^{\xi_2(t)-\xi_1(t)} t^{\omega-1} \Big\{ \sum_{j=0}^{m-1} \frac{a_{j,2}}{t^j} + \mathcal{O}\Big(\frac{1}{t^m}\Big) \Big\}$$

as $t \to \infty$ in $\hat{S}_{2k+1}$ and, in particular, as $t \to \infty$ along the ray $\operatorname{ph} t = (2k+1)\pi/r$. By hypothesis, $\xi_2(t) - \xi_1(t) = t^r$, hence

$$\int_{\rho e^{(2k+1)\pi i/r}}^{\infty e^{(2k+1)\pi i/r}} v_{2k+1}(t) t^s dt = \sum_{j=0}^{m-1} a_{j,2} \int_{\rho e^{(2k+1)\pi i/r}}^{\infty e^{(2k+1)\pi i/r}} e^{t^r} t^{s+\omega-j-1} dt$$
$$+ \int_{\rho e^{(2k+1)\pi i/r}}^{\infty e^{(2k+1)\pi i/r}} e^{t^r} \mathcal{O}\big(t^{s+\omega-m-1}\big) dt,$$

where the $\mathcal{O}$-term is uniform for all positive integer values of s. Taking a new variable τ defined by $t = \exp\{(2k+1)\pi i/r\}\tau^{1/r}$, we find that the right-hand side of the last equation becomes

$$\frac{e^{(2k+1)\omega\pi i/r}}{r} \sum_{j=0}^{m-1} a_{j,2} e^{(2k+1)(s-j)\pi i/r} \int_{\rho^r}^{\infty} e^{-\tau} \tau^{(s+\omega-j-r)/r} d\tau$$
$$+ \mathcal{O}\Big(\int_{\rho^r}^{\infty} e^{-\tau} \tau^{(s+\Re\omega-m-r)/r} d\tau \Big).$$

As in [12], §4, we may replace each lower limit ρ^r by zero without disturbing the uniformity of the $\mathcal{O}$-term with respect to s. Thus, we obtain

$$\int_{\rho e^{(2k+1)\pi i/r}}^{\infty e^{(2k+1)\pi i/r}} v_{2k+1}(t) t^s dt = \frac{e^{(2k+1)\omega\pi i/r}}{r} \sum_{j=0}^{m-1} a_{j,2} e^{(2k+1)(s-j)\pi i/r} \Gamma\Big(\frac{s+\omega-j}{r}\Big)$$
$$+ \mathcal{O}\Big\{\Gamma\Big(\frac{s+\Re\omega-m}{r}\Big)\Big\}, \qquad s \to \infty. \quad (5.8)$$

To establish (4.18a), we substitute into the first sum in (5.7) by means of (2.3), (5.8) and then observe that the second sum is $\mathcal{O}(\rho^s)$ as $s \to \infty$ and therefore is absorbable in the estimate $\mathcal{O}\big[\Gamma\{(s+\Re\omega-m)/r\}\big]$. Lastly, in consequence of Stirling's formula, $\mathcal{O}\big[\Gamma\{(s+\Re\omega-m)/r\}\big] \subseteq \mathcal{O}\big[\Gamma\{(s+\omega-m)/r\}\big]$. Equation (4.18b) may be proved in a similar manner, and the proof of Theorem 4.1 is complete.

Remark. Using another approach, Immink [7] constructed integral representations of Stieltjes type for solutions of linear differential equations of any order; compare Lemma 5.1. From these representations, she then obtained asymptotic approximations for the Stokes multipliers that in effect supply the dominant terms of the expansions in Theorem 4.1. In other words, in the case of second-order equations, Immink's results correspond to ours with $m = 1$. This is an important difference, however, because the restriction to $m = 1$ renders the approximations much weaker for numerical purposes; compare the examples in §6 below.

6. Examples

Example 1. We take

$$\frac{d^2w}{dz^2} + (1 - z^2)\frac{dw}{dz} + (1 - z^4)w = 0. \tag{6.1}$$

In the notation of §1, we have $f(z) = 1 - z^2$, $g(z) = 1 - z^4$, and hence $r = 3$. For the formal series solutions (1.9), we find that

$$\xi_1(z) = \frac{1-\sqrt{5}}{6}z^3 + (\tfrac{\sqrt{5}}{10} - \tfrac{1}{2})z, \qquad \xi_2(z) = \frac{1+\sqrt{5}}{6}z^3 - (\tfrac{\sqrt{5}}{10} + \tfrac{1}{2})z, \tag{6.2}$$

and

$$\mu_1 = \tfrac{1}{5}\sqrt{5} - 1, \qquad \mu_2 = -\tfrac{1}{5}\sqrt{5} - 1, \qquad \omega \equiv \mu_2 - \mu_1 = -\tfrac{2}{5}\sqrt{5}. \tag{6.3}$$

Thus, the singulant $\xi_2(z) - \xi_1(z) = \frac{1}{3}\sqrt{5}z^3 - \frac{1}{5}\sqrt{5}z$. Since this is not a monomial, Theorem 4.1 is not immediately applicable. Accordingly, we transform (6.1) as indicated in §4. On setting

$$x^3 = \tfrac{1}{3}\sqrt{5}z^3 - \tfrac{1}{5}\sqrt{5}z$$

and taking the cube root, we find that

$$x = \frac{5^{\frac{1}{6}}}{3^{\frac{1}{3}}}z - \frac{1}{3^{\frac{1}{3}}5^{\frac{5}{6}}}z^{-1} + \mathcal{O}(z^{-3}), \qquad z \to \infty.$$

Hence by reversion,

$$z = \frac{3^{\frac{1}{3}}}{5^{\frac{1}{6}}}x + \frac{1}{3^{\frac{1}{3}}5^{\frac{5}{6}}}x^{-1} + \mathcal{O}(x^{-3}), \qquad x \to \infty,$$

thus

$$c_0 = 3^{\frac{1}{3}}5^{-\frac{1}{6}},\ c_1 = 0,\ c_2 = 3^{-\frac{1}{3}}5^{-\frac{1}{6}},\ c_3 = 0.$$

Our choice of new independent variable is therefore $\tilde{z}$, defined implicitly by

$$z = \frac{3^{\frac{1}{3}}}{5^{\frac{1}{6}}}\tilde{z} + \frac{1}{3^{\frac{1}{3}}5^{\frac{5}{6}}}\tilde{z}^{-1}; \tag{6.4}$$

compare (4.6). In the transformed differential equation

$$\frac{d^2w}{d\tilde{z}^2} + \tilde{f}(\tilde{z})\frac{dw}{d\tilde{z}} + \tilde{g}(\tilde{z})w = 0, \tag{6.5}$$

the coefficients are given by (4.9). We find that

$$\tilde{f}(\tilde{z}) = -c_0^3\tilde{z}^2 + \tfrac{4}{5}c_0 - \frac{4}{25c_0\tilde{z}^2} + \frac{1}{125c_0^3\tilde{z}^4} - \left(1 - \frac{1}{5c_0^2\tilde{z}^2}\right)^{-1}\frac{2}{5c_0^2\tilde{z}^3}, \tag{6.6}$$

$$\tilde{g}(\tilde{z}) = -c_0^6\tilde{z}^4 - \tfrac{2}{5}c_0^4\tilde{z}^2 + \tfrac{26}{25}c_0^2 - \frac{46}{125\tilde{z}^2} + \frac{26}{625c_0^2\tilde{z}^4} - \frac{2}{3125c_0^4\tilde{z}^6} - \frac{1}{15625c_0^6\tilde{z}^8}. \tag{6.7}$$

Formal series solutions are

$$e^{\tilde{\xi}_1(\tilde{z})}\tilde{z}^{\mu_1}\sum_{s=0}^{\infty}\frac{\tilde{a}_{s,1}}{\tilde{z}^s}, \qquad e^{\tilde{\xi}_2(\tilde{z})}\tilde{z}^{\mu_2}\sum_{s=0}^{\infty}\frac{\tilde{a}_{s,2}}{\tilde{z}^s}, \tag{6.8}$$

where μ_1 and μ_2 are as in (6.3) and

$$\tilde{\xi}_1(\tilde{z}) = -\tfrac{1}{2}(1 - \frac{1}{\sqrt{5}})\tilde{z}^3 - \tfrac{2}{5}c_0\tilde{z}, \qquad \tilde{\xi}_2(\tilde{z}) = \tfrac{1}{2}(1 + \frac{1}{\sqrt{5}})\tilde{z}^3 - \tfrac{2}{5}c_0\tilde{z}. \tag{6.9}$$

$s = 33$	A_0	A_1	A_2	A_3
$m = 1$	$-4.28024360i$	$0.53504119 + 0.13182434i$	$-1.59057354 - 1.25459872i$	$-2.16118253i$
$m = 10$	$-4.87003491i$	$0.50940646 + 0.15648251i$	$-1.60891229 - 1.02017197i$	$-2.38919826i$
$m = 19$	$-4.87002156i$	$0.50940850 + 0.15647932i$	$-1.60891135 - 1.02017656i$	$-2.38916059i$
$m = 28$	$-4.87002160i$	$0.50940850 + 0.15647933i$	$-1.60891136 - 1.02017655i$	$-2.38916077i$
$m = 37$	$-4.87002160i$	$0.50940850 + 0.15647933i$	$-1.60891136 - 1.02017655i$	$-2.38916077i$

TABLE 6.1. Approximations for the Stokes multipliers of (6.1).

In consequence, $\tilde{\xi}_2(\tilde{z}) - \tilde{\xi}_1(\tilde{z}) = \tilde{z}^3$ as expected and as required by (4.17).

With the aid of the software package MAPLE V [1], we computed numerically the Taylor series expansions of the functions $\tilde{p}_j(\tilde{z})$ and $\tilde{q}_j(\tilde{z})$ associated with (6.5); compare (1.13) and (1.14). From these results, we generated the coefficients $\tilde{a}_{s,1}$ and $\tilde{a}_{s,2}$ via (1.12), proceeding as far as $s = 101$. Sample values are

$$
\begin{aligned}
\tilde{a}_{0,1} &= 1, & \tilde{a}_{0,2} &= 1,\\
\tilde{a}_{1,1} &= -0.39691860, & \tilde{a}_{1,2} &= 0.25184962,\\
\tilde{a}_{2,1} &= 0.033329236, & \tilde{a}_{2,2} &= -0.087257074,\\
\tilde{a}_{3,1} &= -0.053431001, & \tilde{a}_{3,2} &= 0.33387567,\\
\tilde{a}_{4,1} &= 0.10293154, & \tilde{a}_{4,2} &= 0.21695963,\\
\tilde{a}_{5,1} &= -0.029902385, & \tilde{a}_{5,2} &= -0.052190874,\\
&\cdots & &\cdots\\
\tilde{a}_{101,1} &= -6.3158988 \times 10^{34}, & \tilde{a}_{101,2} &= 1.2029605 \times 10^{35}.
\end{aligned}
$$

To compute the Stokes multipliers $\{\tilde{A}_k\}$ associated with (6.5), (4.19) and (4.21) were set up numerically with $s = 33$ and various values of m in (4.20) and (4.22). The two sets of three simultaneous linear algebraic equations were solved for the $\{\tilde{A}_k\}$. Subsequently, the desired multipliers $\{A_k\}$ for (6.1) were obtained by use of the identity

$$A_k = \left(\tfrac{1}{3}\sqrt{5}\right)^{(-)^k \frac{2}{15}\sqrt{5}} \tilde{A}_k; \tag{6.10}$$

compare (4.16).

Final results for $m = 1$, 10, 19, 28, and 37 are presented in Table 6.1. Since $A_4 = -\overline{A_2}$ and $A_5 = -\overline{A_1}$ (compare (2.5) and (4.2)), we omit the results for A_4 and A_5. The agreement of the entries in the last two rows indicates that, to the present accuracy, the neglect of the $\mathcal{O}$-terms in equations (4.18) is justified after the stage $m = 28$ is reached. We infer that these entries give the correct values of A_k to eight decimal places.

Example 2. We take the first example in [10], which is the system

$$x^3 \frac{dW}{dx} = \begin{bmatrix} 1 + \frac{4}{3}x^2 & \frac{1}{2}x \\ 2x & 2 + x - x^2 \end{bmatrix} W. \tag{6.11}$$

In [10], the asymptotic analysis applies to the case $x \to 0$. In terms of $z = 1/x$, the system becomes

$$\frac{dW}{dz} = \begin{bmatrix} -z - \frac{4}{3}z^{-1} & -\frac{1}{2} \\ -2 & -2z - 1 + z^{-1} \end{bmatrix} W. \tag{6.12}$$

On decomposing $W = [X, Y]^T$, we obtain the simultaneous equations

$$\frac{dX}{dz} + \Big(z + \frac{4}{3z}\Big)X + \tfrac{1}{2}Y = 0, \qquad \frac{dY}{dz} + 2X + \Big(2z + 1 - \frac{1}{z}\Big)Y = 0. \tag{6.13a,b}$$

Eliminating Y, X, in turn, we find that

$$\frac{d^2X}{dz^2} + \Big(3z + 1 + \frac{1}{3z}\Big)\frac{dX}{dz} + \Big(2z^2 + z + \tfrac{5}{3} + \frac{4}{3z} - \frac{8}{3z^2}\Big)X = 0, \tag{6.14a}$$

$$\frac{d^2Y}{dz^2} + \Big(3z + 1 + \frac{1}{3z}\Big)\frac{dY}{dz} + \Big(2z^2 + z + \tfrac{8}{3} + \frac{4}{3z} - \frac{1}{3z^2}\Big)Y = 0. \tag{6.14b}$$

Equations (6.14a,b) each have an irregular singularity of rank 2 at infinity. On applying the theory of §1, we find that there are solutions X_k, Y_k of (6.14a,b), respectively, with the properties

$$\begin{aligned} &k \text{ even:} \quad X_k \sim e^{-z^2-z}z^{-1}, \quad Y_k \sim e^{-z^2-z}, \quad z \to \infty \text{ in } \hat{S}_k, \\ &k \text{ odd:} \quad X_k \sim e^{-\frac{1}{2}z^2}z^{-\frac{1}{3}}, \quad Y_k \sim e^{-\frac{1}{2}z^2}z^{-\frac{4}{3}}, \quad z \to \infty \text{ in } \hat{S}_k, \end{aligned} \tag{6.15}$$

where $\hat{S}_k = \{\, z : (\frac{1}{2}k - \frac{3}{4})\pi + \delta \le \operatorname{ph} z \le (\frac{1}{2}k + \frac{3}{4})\pi - \delta \,\}$. (Thus $\sigma = 0$ for both differential equations.) Moreover, from (6.15), it is clear the solution Y of (6.13a,b) that corresponds to $X = X_k$ is $Y = (-)^k 2Y_k$, and also that

$$\begin{bmatrix} X_k & X_{k-1} \\ (-)^k 2Y_k & (-)^{k-1}2Y_{k-1} \end{bmatrix} \tag{6.16}$$

is a fundamental matrix solution of (6.12). Any other fundamental matrix solution can be expressed in the form

$$\begin{bmatrix} X_k & X_{k-1} \\ (-)^k 2Y_k & (-)^{k-1}2Y_{k-1} \end{bmatrix} C, \tag{6.17}$$

where C is a non-singular constant matrix [17, §2.3]. In particular,

$$\begin{bmatrix} X_{k+1} & X_k \\ (-)^{k+1}2Y_{k+1} & (-)^k 2Y_k \end{bmatrix} = \begin{bmatrix} X_k & X_{k-1} \\ (-)^k 2Y_k & (-)^{k-1}2Y_{k-1} \end{bmatrix} \begin{bmatrix} C_{11}^{(k)} & C_{12}^{(k)} \\ C_{21}^{(k)} & C_{22}^{(k)} \end{bmatrix}, \tag{6.18}$$

say. We set ourselves the task of computing the scalar constants $C_{11}^{(k)}$, $C_{12}^{(k)}$, $C_{21}^{(k)}$, and $C_{22}^{(k)}$.

By comparing the asymptotic behavior of the two sides of (6.18) as $z \to \infty$ in the sector $\frac{1}{2}k - \frac{1}{4}\pi < \operatorname{ph} z < \frac{1}{2}k + \frac{1}{4}\pi$, we immediately conclude that $C_{11}^{(k)} = C_{k,X} = -C_{k,Y}$, $C_{12}^{(k)} = C_{21}^{(k)} = 1$, and $C_{22}^{(k)} = 0$. Here $\{C_{k,X}\}$ and $\{C_{k,Y}\}$ denote the "C-type" Stokes multipliers of equations (6.14a,b), respectively; compare (2.2). Hence, (6.18) reduces to

$$\begin{bmatrix} X_{k+1} & X_k \\ (-)^{k+1}2Y_{k+1} & (-)^k 2Y_k \end{bmatrix} = \begin{bmatrix} X_k & X_{k-1} \\ (-)^k 2Y_k & (-)^{k-1}2Y_{k-1} \end{bmatrix} \begin{bmatrix} C_{k,X} & 1 \\ 1 & 0 \end{bmatrix}, \tag{6.19}$$

and we also observe that the Stokes multipliers of (6.14a,b) differ only in sign.

We apply the method of §4 to compute the Stokes multipliers for (6.14a). We have $r = 2$ and find that $\omega = \frac{2}{3}$, $c_0 = \sqrt{2}$, $c_1 = -1$, $c_2 = \frac{1}{4}\sqrt{2}$. Accordingly, our transformation variable $\tilde{z}$ is defined by

$$z = \sqrt{2}\tilde{z} - 1. \tag{6.20}$$

$s=30$	$C_{0,X}$	$C_{1,X}$	$C_{2,X}$	$C_{3,X}$
$m=1$	$13.114172i$	$7.2724007-0.95787147i$	$-0.22234619-0.12837163i$	$4.4657414-5.8191481i$
$m=9$	$14.849803i$	$7.2773761+0.30624016i$	$-0.20091135-0.11599622i$	$3.3734763-6.4555127i$
$m=17$	$14.849851i$	$7.2773721+0.30622089i$	$-0.20091164-0.11599639i$	$3.3734910-6.4554995i$
$m=25$	$14.849851i$	$7.2773721+0.30622084i$	$-0.20091164-0.11599639i$	$3.3734910-6.4554995i$
$m=33$	$14.849851i$	$7.2773721+0.30622084i$	$-0.20091164-0.11599639i$	$3.3734910-6.4554995i$

TABLE 6.2. Approximations for the Stokes multipliers of (6.14a).

Since this is a linear transformation, the calculations are simpler than in Example 1. After computing the "A-type" Stokes multipliers $\{\tilde{A}_k\}$ of the transformed differential equation, the $C_{k,X}$ are obtained by use of the identity

$$C_{k,X} = e^{(-)^k(\frac{1}{3}k\pi i - \frac{1}{2})} 2^{(-)^k \frac{1}{3}} \tilde{A}_k; \tag{6.21}$$

compare (2.3) and (4.16).

Final results are presented in Table 6.2 for the case when $s = 30$ in (4.19)–(4.22) and $m = 1$, 9, 17, 25, and 33 in (4.20) and (4.22). Similar conclusions may be drawn concerning accuracy to those drawn above for Table 6.1.

7. Direct numerical methods for the Stokes multipliers

In principle, the calculation of the Stokes multipliers C_k and A_k defined in §2 by direct integration of the differential equation (1.1) is quite simple. Let z_0 be a point in S_{k-1} sufficiently close to infinity to enable $w_{k-1}(z_0)$ and $w'_{k-1}(z_0)$ to be computed to a prescribed accuracy from (1.16a) or (1.16b) and their differentiated forms. Similarly, let z_1 be a point in the interior of $S_k \cup S_{k+1}$ that is sufficiently close to infinity to enable $w_k(z_1)$ and $w_{k+1}(z_1)$ to be computed from (1.16). By numerical integration, starting with the initial values $w_{k-1}(z_0)$ and $w'_{k-1}(z_0)$, the value of $w_{k-1}(z_1)$ is obtained. Then

$$C_k = \frac{w_{k+1}(z_1) - w_{k-1}(z_1)}{w_k(z_1)}. \tag{7.1}$$

The difficulty in this approach is that it is prone to numerical instability. If z_1 is taken to be an interior point of S_k, then $w_{k-1}(z_1)$ and $w_{k+1}(z_1)$ will be almost indistinguishable numerically, and $w_k(z_1)$ will be exponentially small in comparison. This means that severe cancellation will occur in evaluating the right-hand side of (7.1), and consequently little or no precision will remain in the computed value of C_k. On the other hand, if z_1 is taken to be in S_{k+1}, then the computation of $w_{k-1}(z_1)$ will be unstable if the integration path lies in the neighborhood of infinity, because on parts of it (in fact within the left-hand half of S_k), $w_{k-1}(z)$ decays rapidly compared with other solutions of the differential equation.

The difficulty is overcome if the real part of the singulant $\xi_2(z) - \xi_1(z)$ is monotonic on the integration path. However, the construction of such a path is not straightforward in general. For reasons given above, it cannot be confined to the neighborhood of infinity, and it may be dependent on the distribution of turning points and the other singularities of the differential equation. In these cases, [14] may be helpful. Although this reference is devoted to the problem of calculating the Stokes multipliers asymptotically when there is a large parameter present in the differential equation, it includes an investigation of the topology of the curves along which $\Re\{\xi_2(z) - \xi_1(z)\}$ is monotonic. In addition, the Appendix in [14] supplies a numerical method for computing these curves.

A modification to this procedure is to make the same preliminary transformation of independent variable as that described in §4 to reduce $\xi_2(z) - \xi_1(z)$ to the monomial form z^r. This greatly simplifies the task of finding integration paths on which $\Re\{\xi_2(z) - \xi_1(z)\}$ is monotonic, although it may do so at the expense of introducing an extra singularity into the differential equation at $z = 0$.

Consider again Example 1 of §6. We may integrate numerically either (6.1) or (6.5). The only singularity of the former is at $z = \infty$, but the singulant is $\frac{1}{3}\sqrt{5}z^3 - \frac{1}{5}\sqrt{5}z$. On the other hand, the latter equation has $\tilde{z}^3$ as singulant, but it has a second singularity at the origin. For illustration with this example, we compromise by integrating (6.1) numerically along rays through the origin on which $\Re(z^3)$ is monotonic. This combines the simplifying features of the two possibilities, but at the risk of introducing some instability into the computations.

In the numerical integration, we start with $z_0 = 11$ and we compute $w_0(z_0)$ and $w_0'(z_0)$ by taking 11 terms in (1.16a) and its differentiated form. We obtain $w_0(z_0) = 1.0137883 \times 10^{-121}$ and $w_0'(z_0) = -7.6141442 \times 10^{-120}$. By differentiation of (6.1), we see that the coefficients of the Taylor series expansion

$$w_0(z) = \sum_{s=0}^{\infty} d_s(z - z_0)^s \tag{7.2}$$

are given by $d_0 = w_0(z_0)$, $d_1 = w_0'(z_0)$, and

$$\begin{aligned}(s+1)(s+2)d_{s+2} &= (s+1)(z_0^2 - 1)d_{s+1} + (z_0^4 + 2sz_0 - 1)d_s \\ &\quad + (4z_0^3 + s - 1)d_{s-1} + 6z_0^2 d_{s-2} + 4z_0 d_{s-3} + d_{s-4},\end{aligned} \tag{7.3}$$

$s = 0, 1, 2, \ldots,$ where we set $d_s = 0$ if $s < 0$. Taking the first 40 terms of (7.2) and its differentiated form, we approximate $w_0(z)$ and $w_0'(z)$ at $z = z_0 - \frac{1}{20}$. Again, we compute the Taylor series expansion of $w_0(z)$ at $z = z_0 - \frac{1}{20}$, and with this expansion, we approximate $w_0(z)$ and $w_0'(z)$ at $z = z_0 - \frac{2}{20}$. After 220 steps, we obtain $w_0(0) = 0.81045660$ and $w_0'(0) = -0.16426746$. We then continue this process along the ray $\operatorname{ph} z = \frac{2}{3}\pi$. After 220 steps in this direction, we arrive at $z_1 = 11\exp(\frac{2}{3}\pi i)$ with $w_0(z_1) = (3.8675043 + 3.3107321i) \times 10^{311}$.[6]

To compute C_1 from (7.1), we also need $w_1(z_1)$ and $w_2(z_1)$. These quantities can be found by use of the expansions (1.16). Again with 11 terms, we obtain $w_1(z_1) = (-8.2587430 + 4.8022021i) \times 10^{311}$. In comparison, $w_2(z_1)$ is negligible. Accordingly, (7.1) yields

$$C_1 = 0.17576723 + 0.50307920i$$

and, hence, from (2.3), we obtain

$$A_1 = \exp(-\tfrac{2}{15}\sqrt{5}\pi i)C_1 = 0.50940850 + 0.15647933i.$$

This agrees with the result given in the last two rows in Table 6.1, indicating that the possible instability in integrating the differential equation along the chosen path was not realized.

Another general and reasonably stable variant of the method of numerical integration, and one that will extend more readily to differential equations of higher order, is as follows. As in Lemma 5.1, let ρ again denote a constant that exceeds the radius of convergence of each of the power series (1.2a), (1.2b). Also, let z_j $(j = k-1,\ k,\ k+1)$

[6]This procedure for the numerical integration of (6.1) is, of course, the well-known Taylor series method [2, §6.3]. We have used it simply for illustration; other methods could equally well be employed.

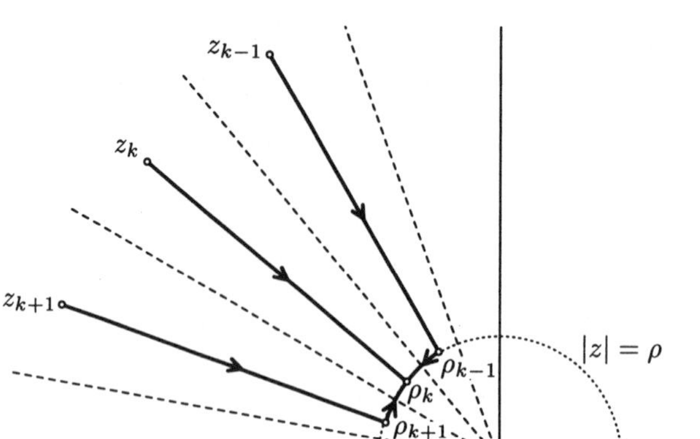

FIGURE 7.1. Paths for numerical integration (second method).

be a point in S_j sufficiently close to infinity to enable $w_j(z_j)$ and $w_j'(z_j)$ to be computed from (1.16a), (1.16b), their differentiated forms, and $\rho_j = \rho \exp(i \operatorname{ph} z_j)$; see Figure 7.1. Starting with the initial values $w_j(z_j)$ and $w_j'(z_j)$, we integrate inwards along the ray $\operatorname{ph} z = \operatorname{ph} z_j$ to compute $w_j(\rho_j)$ and $w_j'(\rho_j)$ for $j = k-1,\ k,\ k+1$. We then may compute $w_{k-1}(\rho_k)$ and $w_{k+1}(\rho_k)$ by integrating along arcs of the circle $|z| = \rho$. (This will be stable provided that ρ can be chosen to be sufficiently small.) Lastly, C_k is found from formula (7.1) with z_1 replaced by ρ_k throughout.

All of the entries in Tables 6.1 and 6.2 were recomputed by at least one of the two methods described in the present section, and numerical agreement was satisfactory in all cases. We would add that the computations needed in these direct numerical methods are considerably longer than those used in the asymptotic method described in §4.

8. Summary and conclusions

In §1, we summarized the theory of the asymptotic solutions of the form

$$e^{\xi_1(z)} z^{\mu_1} \sum_{s=0}^{\infty} \frac{a_{s,1}}{z^s}, \qquad e^{\xi_2(z)} z^{\mu_2} \sum_{s=0}^{\infty} \frac{a_{s,2}}{z^s},$$

in which $\xi_1(z)$ and $\xi_2(z)$ are polynomials, for linear second-order differential equations having an irregular singularity at $z = \infty$. In §2, we discussed the problem of finding the linear identities that hold among any three asymptotic solutions of these types. The coefficients in these identities are the so-called Stokes multipliers. The case of a singularity of rank unity was considered in §3, and asymptotic expansions of $a_{s,1}$ and $a_{s,2}$ for large s were supplied in series of inverse factorials. These expansions then may be used to compute the Stokes multipliers quite simply.

In §4, the corresponding asymptotic expansions of $a_{s,1}$ and $a_{s,2}$ for large s were stated for a singularity of arbitrary rank r, and it was shown how to use the results to compute the Stokes multipliers by solving two sets of r simultaneous linear algebraic equations. §5, is devoted to the proof of the asymptotic expansions of the coefficients $a_{s,1}$ and $a_{s,2}$ stated in §4. Two numerical examples were furnished in §6, one for a singularity of rank 3, the other for a system of two first-order differential equations having a singularity of rank 2.

In §7, we described another method for calculating the Stokes multipliers based on procedures for direct numerical integration of the differential equation. Potential problems of numerical instability were outlined, together with ways of overcoming this instability. The examples given in §6 were recomputed using this method.

Both methods we have described are very powerful, and both may be capable of extension to differential equations, or systems of differential equations, of order higher than two.

Acknowledgments. The authors are indebted to Professors D. A. Lutz and Y. Sibuya for supplying several references and Professor B. L. J. Braaksma for helpful discussions.

References

1. B. W. Char, K. O. Geddes, G. H. Gonnet, B. L. Leong, M. B. Monaghan, and S. M. Watt, *Maple V Library Reference Manual*, Springer-Verlag, New York, 1991.
2. S. D. Conte and C. de Boor, *Elementary Numerical Analysis: An Algorithmic Approach* (3d ed.), McGraw-Hill, New York, 1980.
3. R. B. Dingle, *Asymptotic Expansions: Their Derivation and Interpretation*, Academic Press, London, 1973.
4. W. Gautschi, *Norm estimates for inverses of Vandermonde matrices*, Numer. Math. **23** (1975), 337–347.
5. F. L. Hinton, *Stokes multipliers for a class of ordinary differential equations*, J. Math. Phys. **20** (1979), 2036–2046.
6. R. Hoeppner, *Über die Reihenreste der Lösungen linearen Differentialgleichungen in der Nähe stark singulärer Punkte*, Ph. D. thesis, Universität Strasbourg, 1994.
7. G. K. Immink, *A note on the relationship between Stokes multipliers and formal solutions of analytic differential equations*, SIAM J. Math. Anal. **21** (1990), 782–792.
8. W. B. Jurkat, D. A. Lutz, and A. Peyerimhoff, *Birkhoff invariants and effective calculations for meromorphic linear differential equations. I*, J. Math. Anal. Appl. **53** (1976), 438–470.
9. ———, *Birkhoff invariants and effective calculations for meromorphic linear differential equations, II*, Houston J. Math. **2** (1976), 207–238.
10. M. Loday-Richaud, *Calcul des invariants de Birkhoff des systèmes d'ordre deux*, Funkcial. Ekvac. **33** (1990), 161–225.
11. D. A. Lutz and R. Schäfke, *Calculating connection coefficients for meromorphic differential equations*, [Manuscript.]
12. A. B. Olde Daalhuis and F. W. J. Olver, *Exponentially improved asymptotic solutions of ordinary differential equations. II Irregular singularities of rank one*, Proc. Roy. Soc. London Ser. A **445** (1994), 39–56.
13. F. W. J. Olver, *Asymptotics and Special Functions*, Academic Press, New York, 1974.
14. ———, *General connection formulae for Liouville-Green approximations in the complex plane*, Philos. Trans. Roy. Soc. London Ser. A **289** (1978), 501–548.
15. F. W. J. Olver and F. Stenger, *Error bounds for asymptotic solutions of second-order differential equations having an irregular singularity of arbitrary rank*, SIAM J. Numer. Anal. Ser. B **2** (1965), 244–249.
16. W. J. Trjitzinsky, *Analytic theory of linear differential equations*, Acta Math. **62** (1933), 167–226.
17. W. Wasow, *Asymptotic Expansions for Ordinary Differential Equations*, Interscience, New York, 1965. Reprinted by Krieger Publishing Co., Huntington, New York, 1976.
18. C. Zhu and H. Nakamura, *Stokes constants for a certain class of second-order ordinary differential equations*, J. Math. Phys. **33** (1992), 2697–2717.

Institute for Physical Science and Technology, University of Maryland, College Park, Maryland 20742, U.S.A.

E-mail: aod@olgao.umd.edu, olver@bessel.umd.edu

Methods and Applications of Analysis
4 (4) 1997, pp. 375–403

Asymptotic solutions of linear ordinary differential equations at an irregular singularity of rank unity

F. W. J. Olver

Abstract. New existence theorems are constructed for the asymptotic solutions of linear ordinary differential equations of arbitrary order in the neighborhood of an irregular singularity of rank 1 with distinct characteristic values. Advantages over existing results include more extensive regions of validity, explicit and realistic bounds for the remainder terms in the asymptotic expansions, and greater simplicity. In general the regions of validity are maximal.

1. Introduction

This investigation is aimed at homogeneous linear ordinary differential equations having an irregular singularity, which we may suppose without loss of generality to be located at the point at infinity in the complex plane ($\mathbb{C}$). We may represent these equations in the forms

$$Lw \equiv \frac{d^n w}{dz^n} + f_{n-1}(z)\frac{d^{n-1}w}{dz^{n-1}} + f_{n-2}(z)\frac{d^{n-2}w}{dz^{n-2}} + \cdots + f_0(z)w = 0, \qquad (1.1)$$

$$\frac{d\mathbf{w}}{dz} = \mathbf{F}(z)\mathbf{w}, \qquad (1.2)$$

for example. In (1.1), $n-2$ is an arbitrary nonnegative integer and the coefficients $f_\ell(z)$, $\ell = 0, 1, \ldots, n-1$, are analytic in a punctured neighborhood of infinity. In (1.2), $\mathbf{w}$ is a column vector of length n and $\mathbf{F}(z)$ is an $n \times n$ matrix whose elements are analytic in a punctured neighborhood of infinity; again $n \geq 2$. As is well known, an equation having either of the forms (1.1), (1.2) can be transformed into the other.[1] Consequently, to any asymptotic theory applicable to one of these forms, there is a corresponding theory for the other. In our investigation, we concentrate on the scalar equation (1.1), partly because almost all recent literature for general n applies to the vector form (1.2), but more importantly because the matrix approach has had the weakness of treating all asymptotic solutions as having the same character and enjoying only a common region of validity.

Without loss of generality, we shall suppose that the irregular singularity is located at the point at infinity. Let r be the least nonnegative integer for which all of the functions $z^{(\ell-n)(r-1)}f_\ell(z)$ are analytic at ∞. When $r = 0$, infinity is either an ordinary point or a regular singularity [7, Chapter 7]. We shall not be concerned with this case.

Received November 28, 1996, revised March 18, 1997.
1991 *Mathematics Subject Classification*: 34E05.
Key words and phrases: asymptotic expansions, canonical sectors, error bounds, Liouville-Neumann series, remainder terms, variational operator, Volterra integral equation.

[1] More precisely, only special forms of (1.2) are equivalent to (1.1); conversely, each element of a solution vector of (1.2) satisfies a different form of (1.1) in general [26, §1].

In other cases when r exists, we say that ∞ is a singularity of the differential equation of *rank* r.

For $n = 2$, there is a well-developed and frequently applied theory of asymptotic solutions, complete with error bounds; see, for example, [15], [16, Chapter 7], [18]. Also for $n = 2$ and $r = \infty$ (that is, when at least one of the coefficients $f_\ell(z)$ has an essential singularity), the asymptotic forms of the solutions, again with error bounds, can be found by application of the Liouville-Green approximation theorems given in [16, Chapter 6]. By comparison, and as explained more fully in a companion paper [14], existing theories for higher values of n are disappointing in some ways. Regions of validity are unnecessarily restricted, there is a lack of information about bounds for the remainder terms, and the differing natures of the asymptotic solutions are not revealed.

The purpose of the present paper is to supply a more comprehensive theory for arbitrary values of n in the case $r = 1$. New forms of asymptotic existence theorems are stated and proved, and explicit bounds for the remainder terms are constructed.

The paper is arranged as follows. In §2, we construct formal series solutions of (1.1) in descending powers of z, with the recurrence relation for the coefficients expressed in explicit form. The main asymptotic existence theorems are stated in §3. The proof of these theorems begins in §4 with the construction of an approximating differential equation with known solutions. In §5, we derive a singular Volterra integral equation that is satisfied by the remainder term associated with any chosen formal expansion. This equation is solved in a Liouville-Neumann series in §§6–8, complete with upper bounds on the sum of the series. This analysis is an extension of that given in [16, Chapter 7] for the case $n = 2$, but is considerably more difficult; it owes much to an earlier investigation of F. Stenger [19]. In §9, the bounds found in §§6–8 for the remainder term are discussed and simplified (at a cost of some sharpness). The proof of the asymptotic existence theorems of §3 is completed in §10. Lastly, in §11, we discuss the extent of the regions of validity and the asymptotic nature of the error bounds.

2. Formal solutions

By hypothesis, the singularity of equation (1.1) at infinity is of rank 1. Hence the coefficients $f_\ell(z)$ can be expanded in power series

$$f_\ell(z) = \sum_{s=0}^{\infty} \frac{f_{s\ell}}{z^s}, \qquad \ell = 0, 1, \ldots, n-1, \tag{2.1}$$

that converge on an open annulus $|z| > a$, say. We also can extend (2.1) to $\ell = n$, by defining $f_{0n} = 1$ and $f_{sn} = 0$ $(s \geq 1)$.

Formal solutions of (1.1) in descending powers of z are the so-called normal solutions

$$w(z) = e^{\lambda z} z^{\mu} \sum_{s=0}^{\infty} \frac{a_s}{z^s}, \tag{2.2}$$

in which λ, μ, and the coefficients a_s are constants. Formal differentiation yields

$$w^{(\ell)}(z) = e^{\lambda z} z^{\mu} \sum_{s=0}^{\infty} \frac{a_s^{(\ell)}}{z^s}, \qquad \ell = 1, 2, \ldots, \tag{2.3}$$

where

$$a_s^{(\ell)} = \lambda a_s^{(\ell-1)} + (\mu - s + 1) a_{s-1}^{(\ell-1)},$$

with the understanding that $a_s^{(0)} = a_s$ and coefficients of negative suffix vanish. By induction,

$$a_s^{(\ell)} = \sum_{p=0}^{\ell} \binom{\ell}{p} \lambda^{\ell-p} (\mu - s + 1)_p \, a_{s-p} \tag{2.4}$$

where $(\mu - s + 1)_p$ is the usual Pochhammer symbol for the ascending factorial $(\mu - s + 1)(\mu - s + 2) \cdots (\mu - s + p)$.

On substitution into (1.1) by means of (2.1), (2.2), and (2.3) and equating coefficients of $e^{\lambda z} z^{\mu - s}$, we obtain

$$\sum_{\ell=0}^{n} \sum_{k=0}^{s} f_{k\ell} a_{s-k}^{(\ell)} = 0.$$

Then by substituting into this equation using (2.4) and interchanging the order of summation, we find that

$$\sum_{p=0}^{n} \sum_{k=0}^{s-p} \binom{\mu - s + k + p}{p} \phi_k^{(p)}(\lambda) a_{s-k-p} = 0 \tag{2.5}$$

where $\phi_k^{(p)}(\lambda)$ denotes the pth derivative of the polynomial

$$\phi_k(\lambda) = \sum_{\ell=0}^{n} f_{k\ell} \lambda^{\ell}. \tag{2.6}$$

If we now replace k by $k - p$ in (2.5) and again interchange the order of summation, we obtain

$$\sum_{k=0}^{s} a_{s-k} \sum_{p=0}^{\min(k,n)} \binom{\mu - s + k}{p} \phi_{k-p}^{(p)}(\lambda) = 0. \tag{2.7}$$

Without loss of generality, set $a_0 = 1$. Then with $s = 0$, equation (2.7) reduces to the *characteristic equation*

$$\phi_0(\lambda) = 0. \tag{2.8}$$

Next, on taking $s = 1$ in (2.7) and using (2.8), we obtain the *indicial equation*

$$\mu \phi_0'(\lambda) + \phi_1(\lambda) = 0. \tag{2.9}$$

For higher values of s, we note that as a consequence of (2.8), the lower limit in the outer sum in (2.7) may be replaced by unity. Then changing s and k into $s + 1$ and $k + 1$, respectively, solving for a_s, and using (2.9), we arrive at

$$s \phi_0'(\lambda) a_s = \sum_{k=1}^{s} a_{s-k} \sum_{p=0}^{\min(k+1,n)} \binom{\mu - s + k}{p} \phi_{k+1-p}^{(p)}(\lambda), \quad s \geq 1. \tag{2.10}$$

The n roots $\lambda_1, \lambda_2, \ldots, \lambda_n$, say, of (2.8) are the *characteristic values*. Equation (2.9) yields the corresponding values $\mu_1, \mu_2, \ldots, \mu_n$, say, of μ, the *indices* or *exponents*.

Lastly, equation (2.10) determines the corresponding coefficients $a_{s1}, a_{s2}, \ldots, a_{sn}$, say, for $s = 1, 2, \ldots$. In this way, we have n formal solutions

$$w_j(z) = e^{\lambda_j z} z^{\mu_j} \sum_{s=0}^{\infty} \frac{a_{sj}}{z^s}, \qquad j = 1, 2, \ldots, n, \tag{2.11}$$

each being normalized by the condition $a_{0j} = 1$. As is well known, the process fails if, and only if, $\phi_0'(\lambda) = 0$, that is, if the characteristic equation has multiple roots. *We shall not pursue these cases in the present paper.*[2]

Owing to the presence of the binomial coefficients on the right-hand side of (2.10), the coefficients a_s will usually grow as factorials as $s \to \infty$; compare [17]. In consequence, the formal series (2.11) diverge in general.

3. Main theorems

The sectors of validity of the asymptotic solutions that correspond to the formal solutions (2.11) depend on the configuration of the λ's in $\mathbb{C}$. We introduce the following definitions. Write

$$\theta_{jk} = \text{ph}(\lambda_k - \lambda_j), \qquad k \neq j. \tag{3.1}$$

To remove the ambiguities in the choice of these angles, let $\mathcal{I}$ be any prescribed half-closed interval of length 2π—the closure may be on the left or on the right. The unique set of the $n(n-1)$ angles θ_{jk} that belong to $\mathcal{I}$ we call the *canonical set* of the $\text{ph}(\lambda_k - \lambda_j)$ corresponding to $\mathcal{I}$. Next, for each j, let

$$\alpha_j = \min_{k \neq j} \theta_{jk}, \qquad \beta_j = \max_{k \neq j} \theta_{jk}. \tag{3.2}$$

Then

$$0 \leq \beta_j - \alpha_j < 2\pi\ . \tag{3.3}$$

We call the open sector

$$\mathcal{S}_j(\mathcal{I}) = (z : -\tfrac{3}{2}\pi - \alpha_j < \text{ph}\ z < \tfrac{3}{2}\pi - \beta_j) \tag{3.4}$$

the *canonical j-sector* corresponding to $\mathcal{I}$. As a consequence of (3.3), the angle of $\mathcal{S}_j(\mathcal{I})$ lies in the half-closed interval $(\pi, 3\pi]$. Thus, $\mathcal{S}_j(\mathcal{I})$ exceeds half a Riemann sheet, but cannot exceed one and a half Riemann sheets.

In a similar manner, let

$$\alpha = \min_{k \neq j} \theta_{jk}, \qquad \beta = \max_{k \neq j} \theta_{jk}, \tag{3.5}$$

the minimum and maximum now being taken over all possible values of j and k. Then

$$\pi \leq \beta - \alpha < 2\pi\ . \tag{3.6}$$

(The left-hand inequality follows from the fact that in a canonical set, θ_{kj} is either $\theta_{jk} + \pi$ or $\theta_{jk} - \pi$.) We call the open sector

$$\mathcal{S}(\mathcal{I}) = (z : -\tfrac{3}{2}\pi - \alpha < \text{ph}\ z < \tfrac{3}{2}\pi - \beta) \tag{3.7}$$

[2]An approach for handling these exceptional cases is to make a simple change of variable, for example, $z = \zeta^2$ or other power of ζ. For general formal solutions when the characteristic equation has multiple roots, see [20], [22], [24] and [26, Chapter 5].

the *canonical sector* corresponding to $\mathcal{I}$. Again, as a consequence of (3.6), $\mathcal{S}(\mathcal{I})$ exceeds half a Riemann sheet, but cannot exceed one Riemann sheet. It also is evident that[3]

$$\mathcal{S}(\mathcal{I}) = \mathcal{S}_1(\mathcal{I}) \cap \mathcal{S}_2(\mathcal{I}) \cap \cdots \cap \mathcal{S}_n(\mathcal{I}). \tag{3.8}$$

Theorem 3.1. *For a given interval $\mathcal{I}$ and for each $j = 1, 2, \ldots, n$, there exists a unique solution $w_j(\mathcal{I}|z)$ of* (1.1) *such that*

$$w_j(\mathcal{I}|z) \sim e^{\lambda_j z} z^{\mu_j} \sum_{s=0}^{\infty} \frac{a_{sj}}{z^s} \tag{3.9}$$

as $z \to \infty$, uniformly in any closed sector properly interior to $\mathcal{S}_j(\mathcal{I})$. Furthermore, this asymptotic expansion can be differentiated $n-1$ times in the same circumstances, and the n solutions $w_j(\mathcal{I}|z)$ are linearly independent.

Theorem 3.2. *In any canonical sector $\mathcal{S}(\mathcal{I})$, there exist linearly independent and unique solutions $w_j(\mathcal{I}|z)$, $j = 1, 2, \ldots, n$, such that* (3.9) *applies for each j as $z \to \infty$ uniformly in any closed sector properly interior to $\mathcal{S}(\mathcal{I})$.*

Theorems 3.1 and 3.2 are proved in §§4–10, and in the process, we shall construct bounds for the remainder terms in the asymptotic expansions and their differentiated forms. We observe here that except for the uniqueness property pertaining to the common sector $\mathcal{S}(\mathcal{I})$, Theorem 3.2 follows immediately from Theorem 3.1. Conversely, Theorem 3.1 could be deduced from Theorem 3.2 by repeated use of connection formulas; however, this approach does not yield bounds for the remainder terms.

The special case of these theorems when $n = 2$ is well known; see, for example, [16, Chapter 7]. For higher values of n, the existing literature supplies results that are essentially equivalent either to Theorem 3.2, e.g., [2], [3], or to forms of Theorem 3.2 that are weaker insofar as the region of validity and uniqueness property are concerned, e.g., [5], [22], [26].[4] See also the surveys included in [8], [25]. As suggested in §1, this emphasis on a common region of validity for all solutions rather than separate regions for individual solutions may well be a consequence of the matrix approach to systems of equations. However, as demonstrated in [14], the increased regions of validity furnished by the stronger result, Theorem 3.1, are very important in applications, including the computation of solutions outside the neighborhood of infinity.

4. Differential equation satisfied by leading terms

Three general methods are available to prove Theorems 3.1 and 3.2. The first is to seek integral representations of the solutions in the form of generalized Laplace transforms. This approach was used, for example, by Birkhoff [3], and it also underlies more recent developments based upon summation of the formal divergent series by Borel-Laplace transforms, for example, [1], [11], [21]. The second method is to solve an integral equation satisfied by the remainder term in the asymptotic expansion. This is used, for example, in [5, Chapter 5], [16, Chapter 7], [19], [20], [26, Chapters 4 and 5]. Lastly, convergent expansions in series of inverse factorials can be constructed for the solutions, see, for example, [23], [24]. We shall adopt the second method because of its

[3]It can happen that $\mathcal{S}_j(\mathcal{I}) = \mathcal{S}(\mathcal{I})$. This is the case when all the λs are collinear, and λ_j is not an endpoint of the line.

[4]An important exception is the work of Stenger [19], [20]. These papers seem to have been overlooked by later writers.

directness, and also because it lends itself more readily to the construction of bounds for the remainder term.

As a preliminary step, we need to construct an approximating differential equation with known solutions. For this purpose, we derive an equation $\widehat{L}w = 0$ of the form (1.1) that is satisfied exactly by the functions

$$\widehat{w}_j(z) = e^{\lambda_j z} z^{\mu_j}, \qquad j = 1, 2, \ldots, n, \tag{4.1}$$

where λ_j and μ_j are determined as in §2.

One way to proceed is as follows.[5] Let $\widehat{L}_m w = 0$ be a linear differential equation of order m satisfied by $\widehat{w}_1(z), \widehat{w}_2(z), \ldots, \widehat{w}_m(z)$. Then

$$\widehat{L}_{m+1} w = e^{-\lambda_{m+1} z} z^{-\mu_{m+1}} \left\{ \left(\widehat{L}_m \widehat{w}_{m+1}\right) \frac{d}{dz} \left(\widehat{L}_m w\right) - \left(\widehat{L}_m w\right) \frac{d}{dz} \left(\widehat{L}_m \widehat{w}_{m+1}\right) \right\}. \tag{4.2}$$

Beginning with

$$\widehat{L}_1 = \frac{d}{dz} - \left(\lambda_1 + \frac{\mu_1}{z}\right),$$

we can calculate the operators $\widehat{L}_2, \widehat{L}_3, \ldots,$ by successive application of (4.2) until $\widehat{L}_n$ is obtained. Then dividing $\widehat{L}_n$ by its coefficient of $(d/dz)^n$, we arrive at the desired operator $\widehat{L}$ in the form

$$\widehat{L} = \left(\frac{d}{dz}\right)^n + \widehat{f}_{n-1}(z) \left(\frac{d}{dz}\right)^{n-1} + \cdots + \widehat{f}_0(z). \tag{4.3}$$

The coefficients $\widehat{f}_\ell(z)$, $\ell = 0, 1, \ldots, n-1$, are rational functions of z that can be expanded in series

$$\widehat{f}_\ell(z) = \sum_{s=0}^{\infty} \frac{\widehat{f}_{s\ell}}{z^s}, \qquad \ell = 0, 1, \ldots, n-1, \tag{4.4}$$

convergent on an annulus $|z| > \widehat{a}$, say.

An alternative procedure that leads to a direct recurrence relation for generating the coefficients $\widehat{f}_{s\ell}$ is as follows. On referring to equations (2.8) and (2.9), we see that the polynomials $\phi_0(\lambda)$ and $\phi_1(\lambda)$, corresponding to the desired equation $\widehat{L}w = 0$, have to be the same as before. As a consequence, in the expansions (4.4), we have

$$\widehat{f}_{0\ell} = f_{0\ell}, \quad \widehat{f}_{1\ell} = f_{1\ell}, \quad \ell = 0, 1, \ldots, n-1. \tag{4.5}$$

To determine the remaining coefficients $\widehat{f}_{s\ell}$, we start from the equations $\widehat{L}w = 0$ and (4.4), and retrace the analysis of §2, distinguishing corresponding quantities by the addition of hats when they differ from the originals. For example, from (2.10), we derive

$$s\phi_0'(\lambda)\widehat{a}_s = \sum_{k=1}^{s} \widehat{a}_{s-k} \sum_{p=0}^{\min(k+1,n)} \binom{\mu - s + k}{p} \widehat{\phi}_{k+1-p}^{(p)}(\lambda).$$

Clearly, our objective is achieved if we can arrange that $\widehat{a}_s = 0$ when $\lambda = \lambda_j$, $\mu = \mu_j$, $j = 1, 2, \ldots, n$, and $s \geq 1$.

[5] Suggested to the author by A. B. Olde Daalhuis. T. M. Dunster [6] gives the result in the case $n = 2$.

On setting $\widehat{a}_1 = 0$ and bearing in mind that $\widehat{a}_0 = a_0 = 1$, we have

$$\widehat{\phi}_2(\lambda) + \binom{\mu}{1}\phi_1'(\lambda) + \binom{\mu}{2}\phi_0''(\lambda) = 0,$$

that is,

$$\sum_{\ell=0}^{n-1} \widehat{f}_{2\ell}\lambda^\ell + \binom{\mu}{1}\sum_{\ell=1}^{n-1} f_{1\ell}\ell\lambda^{\ell-1} + \binom{\mu}{2}\sum_{\ell=2}^{n-1} f_{0\ell}\ell(\ell-1)\lambda^{\ell-2} + \binom{\mu}{2}n(n-1)\lambda^{n-2} = 0.$$

The condition that this equation is satisfied for $\lambda = \lambda_j$, $\mu = \mu_j$, $j = 1, 2, \ldots, n$, is expressed conveniently in matrix notation:

$$\mathbf{\Lambda}\widehat{\mathbf{F}}_2 + \mathbf{M}_1\frac{\partial\mathbf{\Lambda}}{\partial\lambda}\mathbf{F}_1 + \mathbf{M}_2\frac{\partial^2\mathbf{\Lambda}}{\partial\lambda^2}\mathbf{F}_0 + \mathbf{M}_2\frac{\partial^2\boldsymbol{\lambda}}{\partial\lambda^2} = \mathbf{0} \tag{4.6}$$

where

$$\mathbf{\Lambda} = \begin{bmatrix} 1 & \lambda_1 & \cdots & \lambda_1^{n-1} \\ 1 & \lambda_2 & \cdots & \lambda_2^{n-1} \\ \vdots & \vdots & \vdots & \vdots \\ 1 & \lambda_n & \cdots & \lambda_n^{n-1} \end{bmatrix}, \tag{4.7}$$

$$\boldsymbol{\lambda} = [\lambda_1^n, \lambda_2^n, \ldots, \lambda_n^n]^T, \quad \mathbf{M}_p = \operatorname{diag}\left[\binom{\mu_1}{p}, \binom{\mu_2}{p}, \ldots, \binom{\mu_n}{p}\right], \tag{4.8a,b}$$

$$\mathbf{F}_k = \left[f_{k0}, f_{k1}, \ldots, f_{k,n-1}\right]^T, \quad \widehat{\mathbf{F}}_k = \left[\widehat{f}_{k0}, \widehat{f}_{k1}, \ldots, \widehat{f}_{k,n-1}\right]^T, \tag{4.9a,b}$$

and

$$\frac{\partial}{\partial\lambda} = \frac{\partial}{\partial\lambda_1} + \frac{\partial}{\partial\lambda_2} + \cdots + \frac{\partial}{\partial\lambda_n}. \tag{4.10}$$

Since

$$\det\mathbf{\Lambda} = \prod_{k>j}(\lambda_k - \lambda_j) \neq 0, \tag{4.11}$$

by hypothesis, equation (4.6) determines $\widehat{\mathbf{F}}_2$, and hence its elements $\widehat{f}_{20}, \widehat{f}_{21}, \ldots, \widehat{f}_{2,n-1}$, finitely and uniquely.

The process may be continued, setting $\widehat{a}_2 = 0, \widehat{a}_3 = 0, \ldots$, in turn. By induction, we may verify that

$$\begin{aligned}\mathbf{\Lambda}\widehat{\mathbf{F}}_{s+1} &+ \mathbf{M}_1\frac{\partial\mathbf{\Lambda}}{\partial\lambda}\widehat{\mathbf{F}}_s + \mathbf{M}_2\frac{\partial^2\mathbf{\Lambda}}{\partial\lambda^2}\widehat{\mathbf{F}}_{s-1} + \cdots + \mathbf{M}_{s-1}\frac{\partial^{s-1}\mathbf{\Lambda}}{\partial\lambda^{s-1}}\widehat{\mathbf{F}}_2 \\ &+ \mathbf{M}_s\frac{\partial^s\mathbf{\Lambda}}{\partial\lambda^s}\mathbf{F}_1 + \mathbf{M}_{s+1}\frac{\partial^{s+1}\mathbf{\Lambda}}{\partial\lambda^{s+1}}\mathbf{F}_0 + \mathbf{M}_{s+1}\frac{\partial^{s+1}\boldsymbol{\lambda}}{\partial\lambda^{s+1}} = \mathbf{0}, \quad 1 \le s \le n-1,\end{aligned} \tag{4.12}$$

and

$$\mathbf{\Lambda}\widehat{\mathbf{F}}_{s+1} + \mathbf{M}_1\frac{\partial\mathbf{\Lambda}}{\partial\lambda}\widehat{\mathbf{F}}_s + \cdots + \mathbf{M}_{n-1}\frac{\partial^{n-1}\mathbf{\Lambda}}{\partial\lambda^{n-1}}\widehat{\mathbf{F}}_{s+2-n} = \mathbf{0}, \quad s \ge n. \tag{4.13}$$

These equations enable each of the vectors $\widehat{\mathbf{F}}_s$, $s = 2, 3 \ldots$, to be found finitely and uniquely by recurrence, with the recurrence relation involving no more than n consecutive $\widehat{\mathbf{F}}$'s.

5. Integral equation for the remainder term

Let S be an arbitrary positive integer. From (1.1) and (2.1), we see that the function

$$e^{-\lambda z} z^{-\mu} L\left\{e^{\lambda z} z^{\mu} \sum_{s=0}^{S-1} \frac{a_s}{z^s}\right\} \tag{5.1}$$

is analytic on the annulus $|z| > a$. Furthermore, by referring to (2.7) and recalling that the lower limit in the outer sum can be changed to $k = 1$, we see that in the expansion of the function (5.1) in descending powers of z, the coefficients of $1, z^{-1}, \ldots, z^{-S}$ all vanish, and that of z^{-S-1} is given by the right-hand side of (2.10) with $s = S$. Hence,

$$L\left\{e^{\lambda_j z} z^{\mu_j} \sum_{s=0}^{S-1} \frac{a_{sj}}{z^s}\right\} = e^{\lambda_j z} z^{\mu_j} \left\{\frac{S\phi_0'(\lambda_j) a_{Sj}}{z^{S+1}} + O\left(\frac{1}{z^{S+2}}\right)\right\} \tag{5.2}$$

as $z \to \infty$, uniformly $\forall$ ph z.

Let us write

$$w(z) = e^{\lambda_j z} z^{\mu_j} \sum_{s=0}^{S-1} \frac{a_{sj}}{z^s} + R_{Sj}(z) \tag{5.3}$$

where $w(z)$ is assumed to be a solution of (1.1). Then,

$$L\{R_{Sj}(z)\} = -e^{\lambda_j z} z^{\mu_j} T_{Sj}(z) \tag{5.4}$$

where $T_{Sj}(z)$ is the content of the braces on the right-hand side of (5.2). Thus $T_{Sj}(z)$ is analytic on the annulus $|z| > a$, and $T_{Sj}(z) = O(z^{-S-1})$ as $z \to \infty$. Our main objective is to show that with the right choice of $w(z)$ in (5.3), the operator L can be inverted, and hence that $R_{Sj}(z) = e^{\lambda_j z} z^{\mu_j} O(z^{-S})$ as $z \to \infty$ under suitable restrictions in $\mathbb{C}$. We shall achieve this goal by a method similar to that used in [15], [19].

We compare the given equation $Lw = 0$ with $\widehat{L}w = 0$, defined in §4, with the known solutions (4.1). We also shall write

$$L = \widehat{L} + L_2, \tag{5.5}$$

so that L_2 is the operator

$$L_2 = \sum_{\ell=0}^{n-1} \{f_\ell(z) - \widehat{f}_\ell(z)\} \left(\frac{d}{dz}\right)^{\ell}. \tag{5.6}$$

Using the decomposition (5.5) and applying the method of variation of parameters [4, §8], we see that there is a solution of (5.4) that satisfies the singular Volterra integral equation[6]

$$\begin{aligned} R_{Sj}(z) = &\sum_{k=1}^{n} \widehat{w}_k(z) \int_{\Omega_k(z)} \frac{\widehat{W}_k(t)}{\widehat{W}(t)} L_2\{R_{Sj}(t)\}\, dt \\ &+ \sum_{k=1}^{n} \widehat{w}_k(z) \int_{\Omega_k(z)} \frac{\widehat{W}_k(t)}{\widehat{W}(t)} e^{\lambda_j t} t^{\mu_j} T_{Sj}(t) dt. \end{aligned} \tag{5.7}$$

[6]This may be verified directly with the aid of the identities (5.13) below.

Here $\widehat{W}(z)$ denotes the Wronskian determinant

$$\widehat{W}(z)=\begin{vmatrix} \widehat{w}_1(z) & \widehat{w}_2(z) & \cdots & \widehat{w}_n(z) \\ \widehat{w}_1'(z) & \widehat{w}_2'(z) & \cdots & \widehat{w}_n'(z) \\ \vdots & \vdots & \vdots & \vdots \\ \widehat{w}_1^{(n-1)}(z) & \widehat{w}_2^{(n-1)}(z) & \cdots & \widehat{w}_n^{(n-1)}(z) \end{vmatrix}, \tag{5.8}$$

and $\widehat{W}_k(z)$ is the determinant obtained by replacing the kth column of $\widehat{W}(z)$ by $[0,0,\ldots,0,1]^T$; thus

$$\widehat{W}_k(z)=\begin{vmatrix} \widehat{w}_1(z) & \cdots & \widehat{w}_{k-1}(z) & 0 & \widehat{w}_{k+1}(z) & \cdots & \widehat{w}_n(z) \\ \vdots & \vdots & \vdots & \vdots & \vdots & \vdots & \vdots \\ \widehat{w}_1^{(n-2)}(z) & \cdots & \widehat{w}_{k-1}^{(n-2)}(z) & 0 & \widehat{w}_{k+1}^{(n-2)}(z) & \cdots & \widehat{w}_n^{(n-2)}(z) \\ \widehat{w}_1^{(n-1)}(z) & \cdots & \widehat{w}_{k-1}^{(n-1)}(z) & 1 & \widehat{w}_{k+1}^{(n-1)}(z) & \cdots & \widehat{w}_n^{(n-1)}(z) \end{vmatrix}. \tag{5.9}$$

Lastly, the integration path $\mathcal{Q}_k(z)$ runs from $t=z$ to $t=\infty\exp(-i\theta_{jk})$ where θ_{jk} belongs to the canonical set introduced in §3 when $k\neq j$, and $\theta_{jj}=\frac{1}{2}(\alpha_j+\beta_j)$. We assume that z and $\mathcal{Q}_k(z)$ lie in the intersection of the canonical j-sector $\mathcal{S}_j(\mathcal{J})$ with the annuli $|z|>a$, $|z|>\widehat{a}$. Furthermore, we assume that the branches of ph t used in forming the fractional powers $t^{\mu_1}, t^{\mu_2},\ldots,t^{\mu_n}$ are continuous on $\mathcal{Q}_k(z)$.

We shall solve equation (5.7) by the standard procedure for constructing a Liouville-Neumann series expansion

$$R_{Sj}(z)=\sum_{s=0}^{\infty}h_s(z) \tag{5.10}$$

by the method of successive approximations. Subsequently, we shall verify directly that this series converges, and that its sum is a solution of the inhomogeneous differential equation (5.4).

We define the functions $h_s(z)$, $s=0,1,\ldots$, by[7]

$$h_0(z)=\sum_{k=1}^{n}\widehat{w}_k(z)\int_{\mathcal{Q}_k(z)}\frac{\widehat{W}_k(t)}{\widehat{W}(t)}e^{\lambda_j t}t^{\mu_j}T_{Sj}(t)dt, \tag{5.11}$$

and

$$h_s(z)=\sum_{k=1}^{n}\widehat{w}_k(z)\int_{\mathcal{Q}_k(z)}\frac{\widehat{W}_k(t)}{\widehat{W}(t)}L_2\{h_{s-1}(t)\}\,dt,\quad s\geq 1. \tag{5.12}$$

We observe that if we replace the last row of the determinant (5.8) by $[\widehat{w}_1^{(\ell)}(z), \widehat{w}_2^{(\ell)}(z),\ldots,\widehat{w}_n^{(\ell)}(z)]$ and then expand along this row, we obtain the identities

$$\sum_{k=1}^{n}\widehat{w}_k^{(\ell)}(z)\widehat{W}_k(z)=\begin{cases}0, & \ell=0,1,\ldots,n-2,\\ \widehat{W}(z), & \ell=n-1.\end{cases} \tag{5.13}$$

[7]For simplicity, we have not indicated the dependence of the functions $h_s(z)$ on S and j in the notation. We also are assuming that the integrals in (5.11), (5.12), and subsequent equations in this section all converge. This is confirmed later.

Hence, on differentiating (5.11) and (5.12), we have, for $\ell = 0, 1, \ldots, n-1$,

$$h_0^{(\ell)}(z) = \sum_{k=1}^{n} \widehat{w}_k^{(\ell)}(z) \int_{\mathcal{Q}_k(z)} \frac{\widehat{W}_k(t)}{\widehat{W}(t)} e^{\lambda_j t} t^{\mu_j} T_{Sj}(t) dt, \tag{5.14}$$

$$h_s^{(\ell)}(z) = \sum_{k=1}^{n} \widehat{w}_k^{(\ell)}(z) \int_{\mathcal{Q}_k(z)} \frac{\widehat{W}_k(t)}{\widehat{W}(t)} L_2 \{h_{s-1}(t)\} dt, \quad s \geq 1, \tag{5.15}$$

and for $\ell = n$,

$$h_0^{(n)}(z) = \sum_{k=1}^{n} \widehat{w}_k^{(n)}(z) \int_{\mathcal{Q}_k(z)} \frac{\widehat{W}_k(t)}{\widehat{W}(t)} e^{\lambda_j t} t^{\mu_j} T_{Sj}(t) dt - e^{\lambda_j z} z^{\mu_j} T_{Sj}(z), \tag{5.16}$$

$$h_s^{(n)}(z) = \sum_{k=1}^{n} \widehat{w}_k^{(n)}(z) \int_{\mathcal{Q}_k(z)} \frac{\widehat{W}_k(t)}{\widehat{W}(t)} L_2 \{h_{s-1}(t)\} dt - L_2 \{h_{s-1}(z)\}, \; s \geq 1. \tag{5.17}$$

From (5.14) and (5.15) it follows that

$$L_2 \{h_0(z)\} = \sum_{k=1}^{n} L_2 \{\widehat{w}_k(z)\} \int_{\mathcal{Q}_k(z)} \frac{\widehat{W}_k(t)}{\widehat{W}(t)} e^{\lambda_j t} t^{\mu_j} T_{Sj}(t) dt, \tag{5.18}$$

$$L_2 \{h_s(z)\} = \sum_{k=1}^{n} L_2 \{\widehat{w}_k(z)\} \int_{\mathcal{Q}_k(z)} \frac{\widehat{W}_k(t)}{\widehat{W}(t)} L_2 \{h_{s-1}(t)\} dt, \quad s \geq 1. \tag{5.19}$$

6. Further preliminaries

In order to bound the functions $h_s(z)$ introduced in §5, and their derivatives, we need upper bounds for the functions that appear on the right-hand sides of equations (5.14) to (5.19), and also further restrictions on the integration paths $\mathcal{Q}_k(z)$. Let b be an arbitrarily chosen constant that exceeds the quantities a and $\widehat{a}$ introduced in §§2 and 4. Then there exists a finite constant B_{Sj} such that

$$|T_{Sj}(t)| \leq S B_{Sj} |t|^{-S-1} \tag{6.1}$$

when $|t| \geq b$.

Next, for $\ell = 0, 1, \ldots, n-1$, we have

$$\widehat{w}_k^{(\ell)}(z) = e^{\lambda_k z} z^{\mu_k} \left\{ \lambda_k^{\ell} + O(z^{-1}) \right\}, \quad z \to \infty \tag{6.2}$$

(with the conventional understanding that $\lambda_k^{\ell} = 1$ when $\lambda_k = \ell = 0$). Hence

$$\left| \widehat{w}_k^{(\ell)}(z) \right| \leq D_{k\ell} \left| e^{\lambda_k z} z^{\mu_k} \right|, \quad |z| \geq b, \tag{6.3}$$

where $D_{k\ell}$ is an assignable finite constant. Since, also

$$f_\ell(z) - \widehat{f}_\ell(z) = O(z^{-2}), \quad z \to \infty,$$

(compare (2.1), (4.4), and (4.5)), it follows that

$$L_2 \{\widehat{w}_k(z)\} = e^{\lambda_k z} z^{\mu_k - 2} O(1), \quad z \to \infty. \tag{6.4}$$

Therefore, there is another finite constant G_k such that[8]

$$|L_2 \{\widehat{w}_k(z)\}| \leq G_k \left| e^{\lambda_k z} z^{\mu_k - 2} \right|, \quad |z| \geq b. \tag{6.5}$$

[8]An upper bound for G_k can be calculated with the aid of (6.3), (4.12), (4.13), and the use of vector and subordinate matrix norms [27, page 56].

For the determinants $\widehat{W}(t)$ and $\widehat{W}_k(t)$, we have from (4.7), (4.11), (5.8), (5.9), and (6.2)

$$\widehat{W}(t) = e^{(\lambda_1+\lambda_2+\cdots+\lambda_n)t} t^{\mu_1+\mu_2+\cdots+\mu_n} \left\{\det \mathbf{\Lambda} + O(t^{-1})\right\}, \quad t \to \infty, \tag{6.6}$$

and

$$\widehat{W}_k(t) = C_k e^{-\lambda_k t} t^{-\mu_k} \widehat{W}(t) \left\{1 + O(t^{-1})\right\}, \quad t \to \infty, \tag{6.7}$$

where

$$C_k = \left\{\prod_{s\neq k} (\lambda_k - \lambda_s)\right\}^{-1}. \tag{6.8}$$

We also know from Liouville's formula [4, §7] that $\widehat{W}(t)$ is nonvanishing when $|t| > \widehat{a}$. Accordingly, there is a finite constant $\widehat{C}_k$ such that

$$\left|\widehat{W}_k(t)/\widehat{W}(t)\right| \le \widehat{C}_k \left|e^{-\lambda_k t} t^{-\mu_k}\right|, \quad |t| \ge b. \tag{6.9}$$

For the integration paths $\mathcal{Q}_k(z)$, we impose the following conditions:

(i) $\mathcal{Q}_k(z)$ *lies in the annulus* $|t| \ge b$.
(ii) *As* t *moves along* $\mathcal{Q}_k(z)$ *away from* z,

$$\operatorname{Re}\{(\lambda_k - \lambda_j)t + (\mu_k - \mu_j)\ln t\}, \quad k \neq j,$$

is nondecreasing.

As a consequence of the second condition, we are assured that

$$\left|e^{(\lambda_j-\lambda_k)t} t^{\mu_j-\mu_k}\right| \le \left|e^{(\lambda_j-\lambda_k)z} z^{\mu_j-\mu_k}\right|, \quad t \in \mathcal{Q}_k(z). \tag{6.10}$$

Let us write

$$\nu_j = \max_{k\neq j} \left|\frac{\mu_k - \mu_j}{\lambda_k - \lambda_j}\right| \tag{6.11}$$

and assume that Condition (i) is satisfied. Then by following the analysis of [15, §7], the roles of t and k in that reference now being played by $e^{i\theta_{jk}}t$ and $-(\mu_k - \mu_j)/\{2|\lambda_k - \lambda_j|\}$, respectively, we see that Condition (ii) is certainly satisfied if we take b large enough to ensure that $b \ge \nu_j\sqrt{2}$ and also require that the angle between the direction of $\mathcal{Q}_k(z)$, as t moves along $\mathcal{Q}_k(z)$ away from z, and the direction ph $t = -\theta_{jk}$ lies in the interval $[-\frac{1}{2}\pi + \kappa_j, \frac{1}{2}\pi - \kappa_j]$ where

$$\kappa_j \equiv \sin^{-1}(\nu_j/b) \in [0, \tfrac{1}{4}\pi]. \tag{6.12}$$

The actual paths $\mathcal{Q}_k(z)$ that we use depend on the value of $\beta_j - \alpha_j$ and the value of $\theta \equiv \operatorname{ph} z$. We shall need to distinguish between three main cases as follows.

Case I. $\beta_j - \alpha_j \in [0, \pi - 2\kappa_j], \quad \theta \in [-\frac{1}{2}\pi - \alpha_j + \kappa_j, \frac{1}{2}\pi - \beta_j - \kappa_j]$.

Case II. $\beta_j - \alpha_j \in [0, \pi - 2\kappa_j], \quad \theta \in (-\frac{3}{2}\pi - \alpha_j + \kappa_j, -\frac{1}{2}\pi - \alpha_j + \kappa_j] \cup$
$[\frac{1}{2}\pi - \beta_j - \kappa_j, \frac{3}{2}\pi - \beta_j - \kappa_j)$.

Case III. $\beta_j - \alpha_j \in [\pi - 2\kappa_j, 2\pi - 4\kappa_j], \quad \theta \in (-\frac{3}{2}\pi - \alpha_j + \kappa_j, \frac{3}{2}\pi - \beta_j - \kappa_j)$.

It will be observed that in the case $n = 2$, we have $\alpha_j = \beta_j$, hence Case III does not arise.

7. Solution of the integral equation in Cases I and II

Case I is depicted in Figure 7.1. In this and subsequent diagrams, each ray from the origin is labelled with its angular direction and $\theta = \mathrm{ph}\, z$.

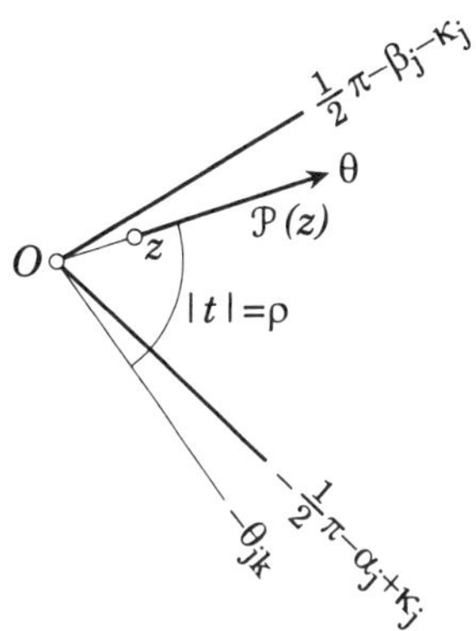

FIGURE 7.1. t-plane. $0 \le \beta_j - \alpha_j \le \pi - 2\kappa_j$ and $-\frac{1}{2}\pi - \alpha_j + \kappa_j \le \theta \le \frac{1}{2}\pi - \beta_j - \kappa_j$.

We first show that if, for all k,

$$S > \mathrm{Re}(\mu_j - \mu_k), \tag{7.1}$$

then in (5.14) and (5.18), we can deform $\mathcal{Q}_k(z)$ into the outward ray $\mathcal{P}(z)$ from z, that is,

$$\mathcal{P}(z) = \{t : \mathrm{ph}(t - z) = \theta\}. \tag{7.2}$$

For large $|t|$, we have

$$\{\widehat{W}_k(t)/\widehat{W}(t)\}e^{\lambda_j t}t^{\mu_j}T_{Sj}(t) = O\{e^{-(\lambda_k-\lambda_j)t}t^{\mu_j-\mu_k-S-1}\};$$

compare (6.1) and (6.7). Consider the circular arc $|t| = \rho$ running from ph $t = -\theta_{jk}$ to ph $t = \theta$. Suppose first that $k \neq j$. Then on this arc, ph $\{(\lambda_k - \lambda_j)t\} \equiv \theta_{jk}$+ph t runs from 0 to $\theta_{jk} + \theta$. Now

$$\theta_{jk} + \theta \in [\theta_{jk} - \tfrac{1}{2}\pi - \alpha_j + \kappa_j,\ \theta_{jk} + \tfrac{1}{2}\pi - \beta_j - \kappa_j] \subseteq [-\tfrac{1}{2}\pi + \kappa_j, \tfrac{1}{2}\pi - \kappa_j] \tag{7.3}$$

since $\alpha_j \le \theta_{jk} \le \beta_j$. Hence, $\left|e^{-(\lambda_k-\lambda_j)t}\right| \le 1$. Obviously the last inequality continues to apply when $k = j$. Hence, from (7.1), the integrals around this arc of the integrands on the right-hand sides of (5.14) and (5.18) vanish as $\rho \to \infty$. □

We next observe that as a consequence of (7.3), Conditions (i) and (ii) of §6 are satisfied by the choice $\mathcal{Q}_k(z) = \mathcal{P}(z)$ as long as $|z| \ge b$. Hence, on substituting into (5.14) and (5.18) by means of (6.1), (6.3), (6.5), (6.9) and then applying (6.10), we obtain

$$\left|h_0^{(\ell)}(z)\right| \le B_{Sj}D_\ell\left|e^{\lambda_j z}z^{\mu_j}\right|\mathcal{V}_{\mathcal{P}(z)}(t^{-S}) \tag{7.4}$$

and

$$\left|L_2\{h_0(z)\}\right| \le B_{Sj}G\left|e^{\lambda_j z}z^{\mu_j-2}\right|\mathcal{V}_{\mathcal{P}(z)}(t^{-S}) \tag{7.5}$$

where

$$D_\ell = \sum_{k=1}^{n} \widehat{C}_k D_{k\ell}, \qquad G = \sum_{k=1}^{n} \widehat{C}_k G_k, \tag{7.6a,b}$$

and $\mathcal{V}$ denotes the variational operator [16, Chapter 1, §11].

Next, consider (5.19) with $s = 1$. We may substitute by means of (7.5). Since

$$\mathcal{V}_{\mathcal{P}(z)}(t^{-S}) = |z|^{-S}, \tag{7.7}$$

[16, Chapter 6, §13], it follows by analysis similar to that used at the beginning of this section that we again may take $\mathcal{Q}_k(z) = \mathcal{P}(z)$. Then substituting by means of (6.5) and (6.9), applying (6.10), and majorizing $\mathcal{V}_{\mathcal{P}(t)}(t^{-S})$ by $\mathcal{V}_{\mathcal{P}(z)}(t^{-S})$, we conclude that

$$\left|L_2\{h_1(z)\}\right| \le B_{Sj}G^2\left|e^{\lambda_j z}z^{\mu_j-2}\right|\mathcal{V}_{\mathcal{P}(z)}(t^{-1})\mathcal{V}_{\mathcal{P}(z)}(t^{-S}).$$

This process may be continued. On the next step, for example, we use

$$\int_{\mathcal{P}(z)} \mathcal{V}_{\mathcal{P}(t)}(t^{-1})\left|t^{-2}dt\right| \le \left\{\mathcal{V}_{\mathcal{P}(z)}(t^{-1})\right\}^2/2.$$

By induction, we may verify that

$$\left|L_2\{h_s(z)\}\right| \le B_{Sj}(G^{s+1}/s!)\left|e^{\lambda_j z}z^{\mu_j-2}\right|\left\{\mathcal{V}_{\mathcal{P}(z)}(t^{-1})\right\}^s\mathcal{V}_{\mathcal{P}(z)}(t^{-S}) \tag{7.8}$$

for $s = 0, 1, \ldots$. Then from (5.15), (6.3), (6.9), and (7.4), we derive

$$\left|h_s^{(\ell)}(z)\right| \le B_{Sj}D_\ell(G^s/s!)\left|e^{\lambda_j z}z^{\mu_j}\right|\left\{\mathcal{V}_{\mathcal{P}(z)}(t^{-1})\right\}^s\mathcal{V}_{\mathcal{P}(z)}(t^{-S}), \tag{7.9}$$

$s \ge 0$, $\ell = 0, 1, \ldots, n-1$.

As a consequence, the series (5.10) converges uniformly on compact sets in the annular sector

$$\left\{\, z:\ |z| \ge b \text{ and } \theta \in \left[-\tfrac{1}{2}\pi - \alpha_j + \kappa_j, \tfrac{1}{2}\pi - \beta_j - \kappa_j\right] \,\right\}.$$

Its sum is therefore analytic within, and continuous on, this sector. That $R_{Sj}(z)$, defined in this way, satisfies (5.4) may be verified with the aid of (5.14)–(5.17). Then the function $w(z)$ defined by (5.3) is a solution of (1.1). Moreover, as a consequence of (7.9), we have

$$\left|\left(\frac{d}{dz}\right)^\ell R_{Sj}(z)\right| \le B_{Sj}D_\ell\left|e^{\lambda_j z}z^{\mu_j}\right|\mathcal{V}_{\mathcal{P}(z)}(t^{-S})\exp\left\{G\mathcal{V}_{\mathcal{P}(z)}(t^{-1})\right\}, \tag{7.10}$$

$\ell = 0, 1, \ldots, n-1$.

We now consider Case II and suppose first that $\theta \in [\frac{1}{2}\pi - \beta_j - \kappa_j, \frac{3}{2}\pi - \beta_j - \kappa_j)$; see Figures 7.2 and 7.3.

Unlike Case I, the paths $\mathcal{Q}_k(z)$ cannot be deformed into the outward ray $\mathcal{P}(z)$ from z for all values of k. (This is true, for example, of the value of k for which $\theta_{jk} = \beta_j$.) However, as long as (7.1) continues to hold, we may for each k deform $\mathcal{Q}_k(z)$ into $\mathcal{P}_1(z)$, where $\mathcal{P}_1(z)$ is the half-line emerging from z parallel to the right-hand boundary of the given sector, that is,

$$\mathcal{P}_1(z) = \{t:\ \mathrm{ph}(t-z) = \tfrac{1}{2}\pi - \beta_j - \kappa_j\}. \tag{7.11}$$

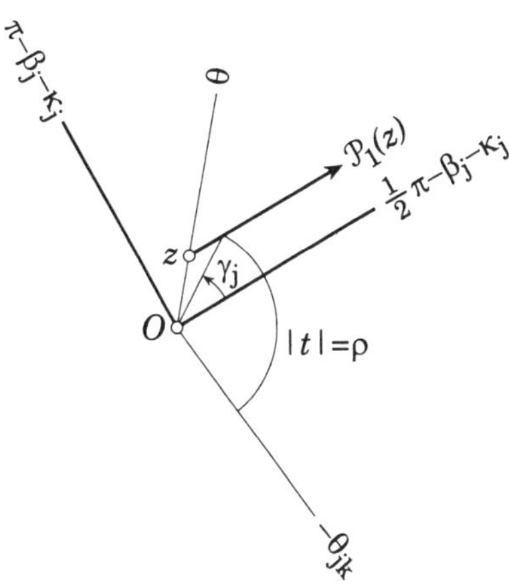

FIGURE 7.2. t-plane. $0 \le \beta_j - \alpha_j \le \pi - 2\kappa_j$ and $\frac{1}{2}\pi - \beta_j - \kappa_j \le \theta \le \pi - \beta_j - \kappa_j$.

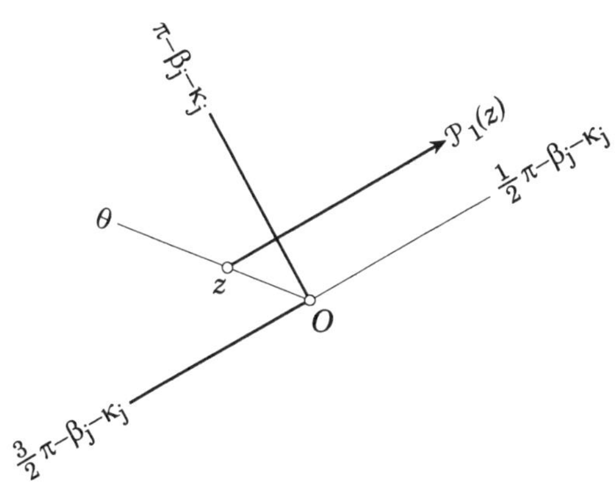

FIGURE 7.3. t-plane. $0 \le \beta_j - \alpha_j \le \pi - 2\kappa_j$ and $\pi - \beta_j - \kappa_j \le \theta < \frac{3}{2}\pi - \beta_j - \kappa_j$.

This may be proved in a similar way to Case I. On the part of the circular arc $|t| = \rho$ between the ray ph $t = -\theta_{jk}$ and $\mathcal{P}_1(z)$, ph t runs from $-\theta_{jk}$ to $\frac{1}{2}\pi - \beta_j - \kappa_j + \gamma_j$ where $0 \le \gamma_j \le O(1/\rho)$ as $\rho \to \infty$. Hence, ph $\{(\lambda_k - \lambda_j)t\}$ runs from 0 to

$$\begin{aligned}\theta_{jk} + \tfrac{1}{2}\pi - \beta_j - \kappa_j + \gamma_j &\in [\tfrac{1}{2}\pi - (\beta_j - \alpha_j) - \kappa_j + \gamma_j, \tfrac{1}{2}\pi - \kappa_j + \gamma_j] \\ &\subseteq [-\tfrac{1}{2}\pi + \kappa_j + \gamma_j, \tfrac{1}{2}\pi - \kappa_j + \gamma_j] \\ &\subseteq [-\tfrac{1}{2}\pi, \tfrac{1}{2}\pi + \gamma_j].\end{aligned}$$

Therefore,

$$-\operatorname{Re}\{(\lambda_k - \lambda_j)\, t\} \le |\lambda_k - \lambda_j|\, \rho \sin \gamma_j = O(1);$$

accordingly, $|e^{-(\lambda_k - \lambda_j)t}|$ is uniformly bounded on the arc as $\rho \to \infty$. □

Next, we observe that Condition (i) of §6 is satisfied if

$$|z| \ge b \text{ when } \tfrac{1}{2}\pi - \beta_j - \kappa_j \le \theta \le \pi - \beta_j - \kappa_j$$

(Figure 7.2), or

$$|z| \ge b \operatorname{cosec}(\tfrac{3}{2}\pi - \beta_j - \kappa_j - \theta) \text{ when } \pi - \beta_j - \kappa_j \le \theta < \tfrac{3}{2}\pi - \beta_j - \kappa_j$$

(Figure 7.3). We also observe that the angle from the ray $\operatorname{ph} t = -\theta_{jk}$ to the direction of $\mathcal{P}_1(z)$ is

$$\tfrac{1}{2}\pi - \beta_j - \kappa_j + \theta_{jk} \in [\tfrac{1}{2}\pi - (\beta_j - \alpha_j) - \kappa_j, \tfrac{1}{2}\pi - \kappa_j] \subseteq [-\tfrac{1}{2}\pi + \kappa_j, \tfrac{1}{2}\pi - \kappa_j].$$

Accordingly, Condition (ii) is satisfied.

The rest of the analysis is similar to that of Case I, with $\mathcal{P}(z)$ replaced everywhere by $\mathcal{P}_1(z)$. In place of (7.10), we have

$$\left|\left(\frac{d}{dz}\right)^{\ell} R_{Sj}(z)\right| \le B_{Sj} D_\ell \left|e^{\lambda_j z} z^{\mu_j}\right| \mathcal{V}_{\mathcal{P}_1(z)}(t^{-S}) \exp\left\{G\mathcal{V}_{\mathcal{P}_1(z)}(t^{-1})\right\}, \tag{7.12}$$

$\ell = 0, 1, \ldots, n-1$.

Lastly, we consider Case II when $\theta \in (-\tfrac{3}{2}\pi - \alpha_j + \kappa_j, -\tfrac{1}{2}\pi - \alpha_j + \kappa_j]$. The diagrams of the t–plane for this case are similar to Figures 7.2 and 7.3 and are omitted.

We now deform $\mathcal{Q}_k(z)$ into the half-line $\mathcal{P}_2(z)$ emerging from z parallel to the left-hand boundary of the given sector:

$$\mathcal{P}_2(z) = \{\, t : \ \operatorname{ph}(t - z) = -\tfrac{1}{2}\pi - \alpha_j + \kappa_j \,\}. \tag{7.13}$$

The final result is given by

$$\left|\left(\frac{d}{dz}\right)^{\ell} R_{Sj}(z)\right| \le B_{Sj} D_\ell \left|e^{\lambda_j z} z^{\mu_j}\right| \mathcal{V}_{\mathcal{P}_2(z)}(t^{-S}) \exp\left\{G\mathcal{V}_{\mathcal{P}_2(z)}(t^{-1})\right\}, \tag{7.14}$$

$\ell = 0, 1, \ldots, n-1$. This is valid when (7.1) holds and

$$|z| \ge b \quad \text{when} \quad -\pi - \alpha_j + \kappa_j \le \theta \le -\tfrac{1}{2}\pi - \alpha_j + \kappa_j,$$

or

$$|z| \ge b \operatorname{cosec}(\theta + \tfrac{3}{2}\pi + \alpha_j - \kappa_j) \quad \text{when} \quad -\tfrac{3}{2}\pi - \alpha_j + \kappa_j < \theta \le -\pi - \alpha_j + \kappa_j.$$

Remark. The analysis in this section could be shortened by appealing to general theorems for solving singular Volterra integral equations given in [16, Chapter 6, §10]. We did not adopt this course since much of the analysis is relevant to the more difficult situation in which $\beta_j - \alpha_j$ exceeds $\pi - 2\kappa_j$. This case is treated in the next section, and the cited theorems no longer apply.

8. Solution of the integral equation in Case III

When $\beta_j - \alpha_j$ exceeds $\pi - 2\kappa_j$, it is no longer possible to deform all the paths $\mathcal{Q}_k(z)$ into a single half-line from z to the point at infinity. Instead, we employ two such half-lines, in fact, the paths $\mathcal{P}_1(z)$ and $\mathcal{P}_2(z)$ defined by (7.11) and (7.13).

Figures 8.1 and 8.2 illustrate the paths $\mathcal{P}_1(z)$ and $\mathcal{P}_2(z)$ when θ lies in the subinterval $[-\pi-\alpha_j+\kappa_j, \pi-\beta_j-\kappa_j]$. Figure 8.1 pertains to the range $\beta_j-\alpha_j \in [\pi-2\kappa_j, \frac{3}{2}\pi-2\kappa_j]$ for which the angle from $\mathcal{P}_1(z)$ to $\mathcal{P}_2(z)$ is in the interval $[0, \frac{1}{2}\pi]$, and Figure 8.2 pertains to the range $\beta_j - \alpha_j \in [\frac{3}{2}\pi - 2\kappa_j, 2\pi - 4\kappa_j]$ for which the angle from $\mathcal{P}_1(z)$ to $\mathcal{P}_2(z)$

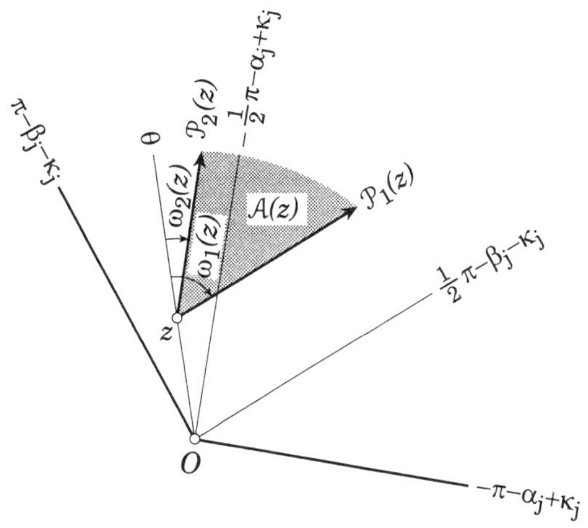

FIGURE 8.1. t-plane. $\pi-2\kappa_j \leq \beta_j-\alpha_j \leq \frac{3}{2}\pi-2\kappa_j$ and $-\pi-\alpha_j+\kappa_j \leq \theta \leq \pi - \beta_j - \kappa_j$.

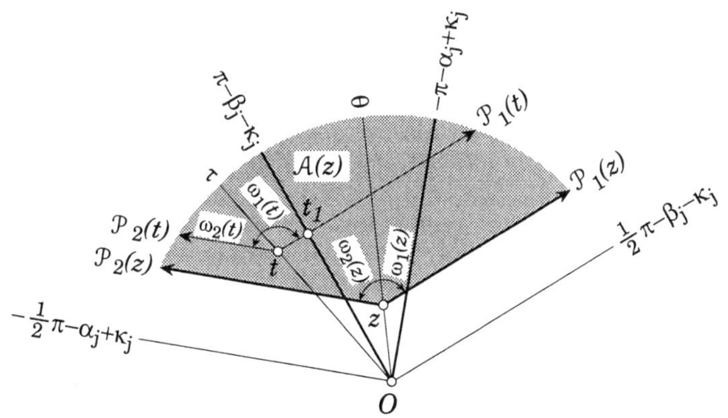

FIGURE 8.2. t-plane. $\frac{3}{2}\pi - 2\kappa_j \leq \beta_j - \alpha_j \leq 2\pi - 4\kappa_j$ and $-\pi - \alpha_j + \kappa_j \leq \theta \leq \pi - \beta_j - \kappa_j$.

is in $[\frac{1}{2}\pi, \pi - 2\kappa_j]$. In a similar manner, Figures 8.3 and 8.4 depict $\mathcal{P}_1(z)$ and $\mathcal{P}_2(z)$ when $\theta \in [\pi - \beta_j - \kappa_j, \frac{3}{2}\pi - \beta_j - \kappa_j)$. The corresponding diagrams for the remaining range $\theta \in (-\frac{3}{2}\pi - \alpha_j + \kappa_j, -\pi - \alpha_j + \kappa_j]$ are similar to Figures 8.3 and 8.4 and are omitted.

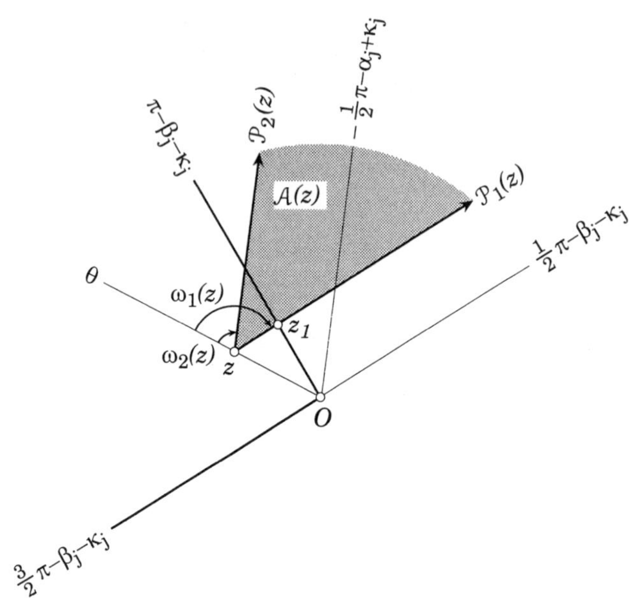

FIGURE 8.3. t-plane. $\pi - 2\kappa_j \le \beta_j - \alpha_j \le \frac{3}{2}\pi - 2\kappa_j$ and $\pi - \beta_j - \kappa_j \le \theta < \frac{3}{2}\pi - \beta_j - \kappa_j$.

In equations (5.14)–(5.19), we take

$$\mathcal{Q}_k(z) = \begin{cases} \mathcal{P}_1(z) & \text{when } \theta_{jk} \in [\frac{1}{2}\alpha_j + \frac{1}{2}\beta_j, \beta_j], \\ \mathcal{P}_2(z) & \text{when } \theta_{jk} \in [\alpha_j, \frac{1}{2}\alpha_j + \frac{1}{2}\beta_j]. \end{cases} \tag{8.1a,b}$$

(If $\theta_{jk} = \frac{1}{2}\alpha_j + \frac{1}{2}\beta_j$, as happens when $k = j$, then we may take $\mathcal{Q}_k(z)$ to be either $\mathcal{P}_1(z)$ or $\mathcal{P}_2(z)$). The justification of these deformations of the integration paths is similar to that given in §7.

In order to satisfy Condition (i) of §6, we need to examine the angles $\omega_1(z)$ and $\omega_2(z)$, say, from ph $t = \theta$ to $\mathcal{P}_1(z)$ and $\mathcal{P}_2(z)$, respectively. These angles are indicated on Figures 8.1–8.4 and are given by

$$\omega_1(z) = \tfrac{1}{2}\pi - \beta_j - \kappa_j - \theta, \qquad \omega_2(z) = -\tfrac{1}{2}\pi - \alpha_j + \kappa_j - \theta. \tag{8.2a,b}$$

Suppose first that $\theta \in [-\pi - \alpha_j + \kappa_j, \pi - \beta_j - \kappa_j]$ (Figures 8.1 and 8.2). Then

$$\omega_1(z) \in [-\tfrac{1}{2}\pi, \tfrac{3}{2}\pi - (\beta_j - \alpha_j) - 2\kappa_j] \subseteq [-\tfrac{1}{2}\pi, 0],$$

and

$$\omega_2(z) \in [-\tfrac{3}{2}\pi + \beta_j - \alpha_j + 2\kappa_j, \tfrac{1}{2}\pi] \subseteq [0, \tfrac{1}{2}\pi].$$

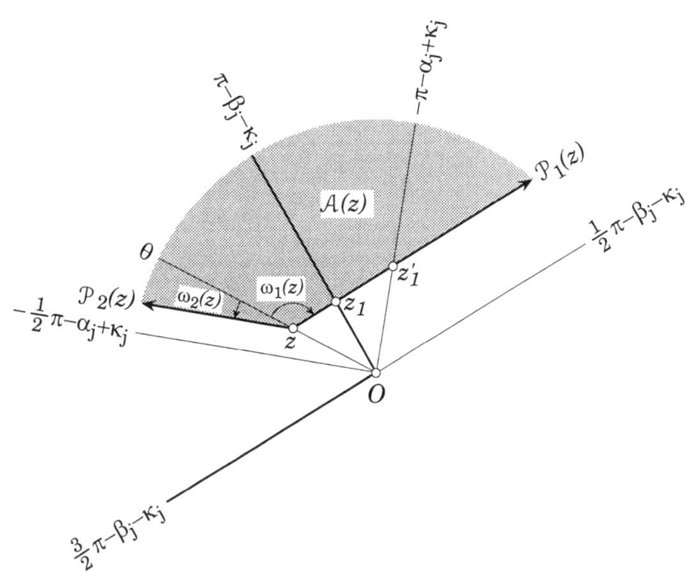

FIGURE 8.4. t-plane. $\frac{3}{2}\pi - 2\kappa_j \le \beta_j - \alpha_j \le 2\pi - 4\kappa_j$ and $\pi - \beta_j - \kappa_j \le \theta < \frac{3}{2}\pi - \beta_j - \kappa_j$.

Accordingly, Condition (i) is satisfied when $|z| \ge b$.

Next, suppose that $\theta \in [\pi - \beta_j - \kappa_j, \frac{3}{2}\pi - \beta_j - \kappa_j)$ (Figures 8.3 and 8.4.), then

$$\omega_1(z) \in (-\pi, -\tfrac{1}{2}\pi].$$

Also,

$$-\omega_1(z) - \omega_2(z) = 2\theta + \alpha_j + \beta_j \in [2\pi - (\beta_j - \alpha_j) - 2\kappa_j, 3\pi - (\beta_j - \alpha_j) - 2\kappa_j) \subseteq [2\kappa_j, 2\pi),$$

and

$$-\omega_1(z) + \omega_2(z) = -\pi + \beta_j - \alpha_j + 2\kappa_j \in [0, \pi - 2\kappa_j].$$

These three equations show that $|\omega_2(z)| \le |\omega_1(z)| < \pi$, and hence that Condition (i) is satisfied when $|z| \ge b \operatorname{cosec}\{\pi + \omega_1(z)\}$, that is, $|z| \ge b \operatorname{cosec}(\frac{3}{2}\pi - \beta_j - \kappa_j - \theta)$.

On carrying out a similar analysis for the remaining range $\theta \in (-\frac{3}{2}\pi - \alpha_j + \kappa_j, -\pi - \alpha_j + \kappa_j]$ and summarizing the results, we see that Condition (i) of §6 is satisfied when

$$|z| \ge b, \quad -\pi - \alpha_j + \kappa_j \le \theta \le \pi - \beta_j - \kappa_j, \tag{8.3}$$

$$|z| \ge b \operatorname{cosec}(\tfrac{3}{2}\pi - \beta_j - \kappa_j - \theta), \quad \pi - \beta_j - \kappa_j \le \theta < \tfrac{3}{2}\pi - \beta_j - \kappa_j, \tag{8.4}$$

$$|z| \ge b \operatorname{cosec}(\theta + \tfrac{3}{2}\pi + \alpha_j - \kappa_j), \quad -\tfrac{3}{2}\pi - \alpha_j + \kappa_j < \theta \le -\pi - \alpha_j + \kappa_j. \tag{8.5}$$

That Condition (ii) of §6 is satisfied in these circumstances again follows as in §7.

With the choice (8.1), we find that on substituting into (5.14) by means of (6.1), (6.3), and (6.9), and applying (6.10), we have

$$\left|h_0^{(\ell)}(z)\right| \leq B_{Sj}\left|e^{\lambda_j z} z^{\mu_j}\right| U_{Sj\ell}(z). \tag{8.6}$$

Here

$$U_{Sj\ell}(z) = \widehat{D}_{1\ell}\mathcal{V}_{\mathcal{P}_1(z)}(t^{-S}) + \widehat{D}_{2\ell}\mathcal{V}_{\mathcal{P}_2(z)}(t^{-S}), \tag{8.7}$$

with

$$\widehat{D}_{1\ell} = \sum\nolimits_1 \widehat{C}_k D_{k\ell}, \quad \widehat{D}_{2\ell} = \sum\nolimits_2 \widehat{C}_k D_{k\ell} \tag{8.8}$$

where $\sum_1$ denotes the sum over those values of k for which $\mathcal{Q}_k(z) = \mathcal{P}_1(z)$, and $\sum_2$ denotes the sum over those values of k for which $\mathcal{Q}_k(z) = \mathcal{P}_2(z)$. Similarly, from (5.18), we derive

$$|L_2\{h_0(z)\}| \leq B_{Sj}\left|e^{\lambda_j z} z^{\mu_j-2}\right| V_{Sj}(z) \tag{8.9}$$

where

$$V_{Sj}(z) = \widehat{G}_1\mathcal{V}_{\mathcal{P}_1(z)}(t^{-S}) + \widehat{G}_2\mathcal{V}_{\mathcal{P}_2(z)}(t^{-S}) \tag{8.10}$$

and

$$\widehat{G}_1 = \sum\nolimits_1 \widehat{C}_k G_k, \qquad \widehat{G}_2 = \sum\nolimits_2 \widehat{C}_k G_k. \tag{8.11a,b}$$

Before we can continue to the next step, we need to show that (8.9) and (8.10) remain valid when z is replaced by t with $t \in \mathcal{P}_1(z) \cup \mathcal{P}_2(z)$, that is, t lies on the boundary of the closed sector $\mathcal{A}(z)$ obtained by rotating $\mathcal{P}_1(z)$ around z in the positive sense to $\mathcal{P}_2(z)$. $\mathcal{A}(z)$ is indicated by the shading in Figures 8.1–8.4. Since the angle $-\pi + \beta_j - \alpha_j + 2\kappa_j$ of $\mathcal{A}(z)$ is less than π, both $\mathcal{P}_1(t)$ and $\mathcal{P}_2(t)$ lie in $\mathcal{A}(z)$. Hence, if (8.3)–(8.5) apply, then $\mathcal{P}_1(t)$ and $\mathcal{P}_2(t)$ each satisfy Conditions (i) and (ii) of §6; as a consequence z may be replaced by t in (8.9) and (8.10). Then from (5.19) with $s = 1$, we derive

$$\begin{aligned} |L_2\{h_1(z)\}| &\leq B_{Sj}\left|e^{\lambda_j z} z^{\mu_j-2}\right| \sum_{k=1}^{n} \widehat{C}_k G_k \int_{\mathcal{Q}_k(z)} V_{Sj}(t)\left|t^{-2}dt\right| \\ &\leq B_{Sj}\left|e^{\lambda_j z} z^{\mu_j-2}\right| \widehat{V}_{Sj}(z) V_{1j}(z) \end{aligned} \tag{8.12}$$

where

$$\widehat{V}_{Sj}(z) = \sup_{t\in\mathcal{A}(z)} V_{Sj}(t). \tag{8.13}$$

On the following step, we have

$$\begin{aligned} |L_2\{h_2(z)\}| &\leq B_{Sj}\left|e^{\lambda_j z} z^{\mu_j-2}\right| \sum_{k=1}^{n} \widehat{C}_k G_k \int_{\mathcal{Q}_k(z)} \widehat{V}_{Sj}(t) V_{1j}(t)\left|t^{-2}dt\right| \\ &\leq B_{Sj}\left|e^{\lambda_j z} z^{\mu_j-2}\right| \widehat{V}_{Sj}(z)\widehat{V}_{1j}(z)V_{1j}(z). \end{aligned}$$

(Here we have used the fact that $\mathcal{A}(t) \subseteq \mathcal{A}(z)$ when $t \in \mathcal{A}(z)$.)

The cycle of steps may be continued, and we may verify by induction that

$$|L_2\{h_s(z)\}| \leq B_{Sj}\left|e^{\lambda_j z} z^{\mu_j-2}\right| \widehat{V}_{Sj}(z)\left\{\widehat{V}_{1j}(z)\right\}^{s-1} V_{1j}(z).$$

As a consequence,

$$|L_2\{h_s(z)\}| \le B_{Sj}\left|e^{\lambda_j z} z^{\mu_j - 2}\right| \widehat{V}_{Sj}(z)\{\widehat{V}_{1j}(z)\}^s; \tag{8.14}$$

this result also holds for $s = 0$ by virtue of (8.9). Then from (5.15), we obtain

$$\left|h_s^{(\ell)}(z)\right| \le B_{Sj}\left|e^{\lambda_j z} z^{\mu_j}\right| \widehat{V}_{Sj}(z)\{\widehat{V}_{1j}(z)\}^{s-1} U_{1j\ell}(z), \quad s \ge 1. \tag{8.15}$$

Summation of (8.6) and (8.15) yields the desired bound:

$$\left|\left(\frac{d}{dz}\right)^\ell R_{Sj}(z)\right| = \left|\sum_{s=0}^{\infty} h_s^{(\ell)}(z)\right| \le B_{Sj}\left|e^{\lambda_j z} z^{\mu_j}\right| \left\{U_{Sj\ell}(z) + \frac{\widehat{V}_{Sj}(z) U_{1j\ell}(z)}{1 - \widehat{V}_{1j}(z)}\right\}, \tag{8.16}$$

provided that $\ell = 0, 1, \ldots, n-1$ and $\widehat{V}_{1j}(z) < 1$. The other conditions needed for the validity of this result are (7.1) and (8.3)–(8.5).

9. Evaluation and simplification of the error bounds

In this section, we digress on the problem of evaluating the bounds that were constructed in §§7 and 8 for the remainder term $R_{Sj}(z)$ and its derivatives. Besides the intrinsic interest of these bounds for computational purposes, the results we derive here ease the understanding of the completion of the proof of the theorems of §3 in the next section.

All of the bounds in §§7 and 8 involve the variation of the function t^{-S} along half-lines in $\mathbb{C}$, S being a positive integer. The general parametric equation of such a line $\mathcal{Q}(z)$ that does not intersect the origin can be written

$$\mathcal{Q}(z) = \{\, t : t = z(1 + ve^{i\sigma}),\ 0 \le v < \infty \,\} \tag{9.1}$$

where $z(\neq 0)$ is the endpoint of $\mathcal{Q}(z)$, and $\sigma \in (-\pi, \pi)$ is the angle of slope of $\mathcal{Q}(z)$ to the ray ph $t = \theta$; see Figures 9.1 and 9.2.

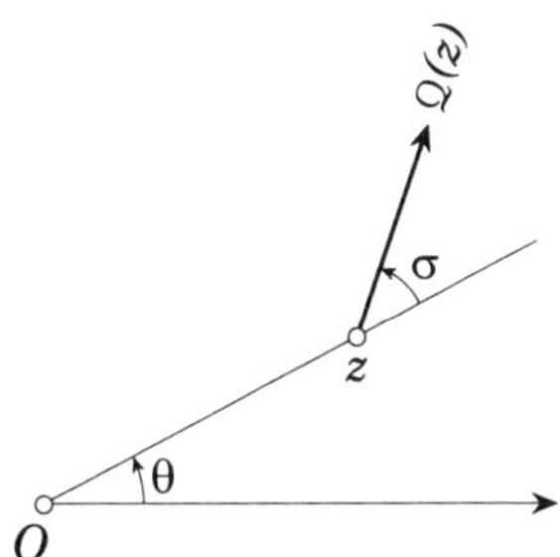

FIGURE 9.1. $\mathcal{Q}(z)$ when $0 \le |\sigma| \le \frac{1}{2}\pi$.

By definition,

$$\mathcal{V}_{\mathcal{Q}(z)}(t^{-S}) = S\int_{\mathcal{Q}(z)} \left|\frac{dt}{t^{S+1}}\right| = \frac{S}{|z|^S}\int_0^\infty \frac{dv}{|1 + ve^{i\sigma}|^{S+1}}$$
$$= \frac{S}{|z|^S}\int_0^\infty \frac{dv}{(1 + 2v\cos\sigma + v^2)^{(S+1)/2}}. \tag{9.2}$$

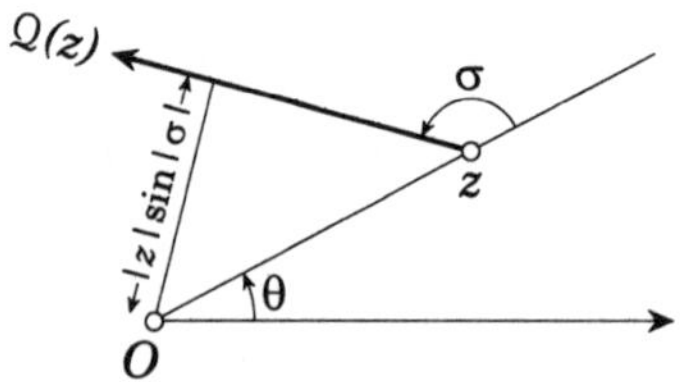

FIGURE 9.2. $\mathcal{Q}(z)$ when $\frac{1}{2}\pi \leq |\sigma| < \pi$.

On taking a new integration variable ψ defined by

$$v + \cos\sigma = \sin\sigma \cot\psi,$$

we obtain

$$\mathcal{V}_{\mathcal{Q}(z)}(t^{-S}) = I_S(\sigma)|z|^{-S} \tag{9.3}$$

where

$$I_S(\sigma) = \frac{S}{(\sin\sigma)^S} \int_0^\sigma (\sin\psi)^{S-1} d\psi. \tag{9.4}$$

For example,

$$I_1(\sigma) = \frac{\sigma}{\sin\sigma}, \qquad I_2(\sigma) = \frac{1}{\cos^2(\frac{1}{2}\sigma)}, \tag{9.5}$$

and for higher values of S, we have the recurrence relation

$$S\sin^2\sigma I_{S+1}(\sigma) = (S+1)I_{S-1}(\sigma) - (S+1)\cos\sigma, \qquad S \geq 2. \tag{9.6}$$

These identities can be used to generate $I_S(\sigma)$ analytically. For numerical purposes, however, there is some obvious instability lurking in the forward application of (9.6) when $|\sigma|$ is small.

We also observe from (9.2) that when $\sigma = 0$,

$$\mathcal{V}_{\mathcal{Q}(z)}(t^{-S}) = |z|^{-S}; \tag{9.7}$$

furthermore, $\mathcal{V}_{\mathcal{Q}(z)}(t^{-S})$ is an increasing function of $|\sigma|$. The latter observation enables us to construct simple, and not too unrealistic, bounds for $\mathcal{V}_{\mathcal{Q}(z)}(t^{-S})$. From the Beta function integral, we have

$$I_S(\tfrac{1}{2}\pi) = \chi(S) \tag{9.8}$$

where

$$\chi(S) = \pi^{1/2}\Gamma(\tfrac{1}{2}S + 1)/\Gamma(\tfrac{1}{2}S + \tfrac{1}{2}). \tag{9.9}$$

Hence,

$$\mathcal{V}_{\mathcal{Q}(z)}(t^{-S}) \leq \chi(S)|z|^{-S}, \quad |\sigma| \leq \tfrac{1}{2}\pi. \tag{9.10}$$

When $|\sigma| \geq \frac{1}{2}\pi$, the shortest distance from the origin to $\mathcal{Q}(z)$ is $|z|\sin|\sigma|$; compare Figure 9.2. Accordingly,

$$\mathcal{V}_{\mathcal{Q}(z)}(t^{-S}) < 2\chi(S)|\operatorname{cosec}\sigma|^S|z|^{-S}, \quad \tfrac{1}{2}\pi \leq |\sigma| < \pi. \tag{9.11}$$

This inequality also is given in [16, Chapter 6, §13], and this reference may be consulted for further information concerning the function $\chi(S)$.

We now may substitute straightforwardly by means of (9.7), (9.10), and (9.11) into the bounds for $(d/dz)^\ell R_{Sj}(z)$ that were obtained in §§7 and 8. For brevity, we denote

$$\left(\frac{d}{dz}\right)^\ell R_{Sj}(z) = B_{Sj} D_\ell e^{\lambda_j z} z^{\mu_j - S} R, \tag{9.12}$$

again for $\ell = 0, 1, \ldots, n-1$. Assuming that (7.1) continues to apply, we now state the final bounds for Cases I and II. In these results, the quantities b and κ_j are defined in §6, G in §7, and $\chi(S)$ in the present section.

Case I. $\beta_j - \alpha_j \in [0, \pi - 2\kappa_j], \quad \theta \in [-\frac{1}{2}\pi - \alpha_j + \kappa_j, \frac{1}{2}\pi - \beta_j - \kappa_j]$.

$$|R| \le \exp(G|z|^{-1}), \qquad |z| \ge b. \tag{9.13}$$

Case IIa. $\beta_j - \alpha_j \in [0, \pi - 2\kappa_j], \quad \theta \in [-\pi - \alpha_j + \kappa_j, -\frac{1}{2}\pi - \alpha_j + \kappa_j] \cup [\frac{1}{2}\pi - \beta_j - \kappa_j, \pi - \beta_j - \kappa_j]$.

$$|R| \le \chi(S)\exp(\tfrac{1}{2}\pi G|z|^{-1}), \quad |z| \ge b. \tag{9.14}$$

Case IIb. $\beta_j - \alpha_j \in [0, \pi - 2\kappa_j], \quad \theta \in (-\frac{3}{2}\pi - \alpha_j + \kappa_j, -\pi - \alpha_j + \kappa_j]$.

$$|R| \le 2\chi(S)\operatorname{cosec}^S(\theta + \tfrac{3}{2}\pi + \alpha_j - \kappa_j)\exp\{\pi G \operatorname{cosec}(\theta + \tfrac{3}{2}\pi + \alpha_j - \kappa_j)|z|^{-1}\},$$
$$|z| \ge b\operatorname{cosec}(\theta + \tfrac{3}{2}\pi + \alpha_j - \kappa_j). \tag{9.15}$$

Case IIc. $\beta_j - \alpha_j \in [0, \pi - 2\kappa_j], \quad \theta \in [\pi - \beta_j - \kappa_j, \frac{3}{2}\pi - \beta_j - \kappa_j)$.

$$|R| \le 2\chi(S)\operatorname{cosec}^S(\tfrac{3}{2}\pi - \beta_j - \kappa_j - \theta)\exp\{\pi G \operatorname{cosec}(\tfrac{3}{2}\pi - \beta_j - \kappa_j - \theta)|z|^{-1}\},$$
$$|z| \ge b\operatorname{cosec}(\tfrac{3}{2}\pi - \beta_j - \kappa_j - \theta). \tag{9.16}$$

In Case III, however, the analysis is less direct. We need to distinguish six subcases, as follows:

Case IIIa. $\beta_j - \alpha_j \in [\pi - 2\kappa_j, \frac{3}{2}\pi - 2\kappa_j], \quad \theta \in [-\pi - \alpha_j + \kappa_j, \pi - \beta_j - \kappa_j]$ (Figure 8.1).

Case IIIb. $\beta_j - \alpha_j \in [\frac{3}{2}\pi - 2\kappa_j, 2\pi - 4\kappa_j], \quad \theta \in [-\pi - \alpha_j + \kappa_j, \pi - \beta_j - \kappa_j]$ (Figure 8.2).

Case IIIc. $\beta_j - \alpha_j \in [\pi - 2\kappa_j, \frac{3}{2}\pi - 2\kappa_j], \quad \theta \in (-\frac{3}{2}\pi - \alpha_j + \kappa_j, -\pi - \alpha_j + \kappa_j]$ (not illustrated).

Case IIId. $\beta_j - \alpha_j \in [\frac{3}{2}\pi - 2\kappa_j, 2\pi - 4\kappa_j], \quad \theta \in (-\frac{3}{2}\pi - \alpha_j + \kappa_j, -\pi - \alpha_j + \kappa_j]$ (not illustrated).

Case IIIe. $\beta_j - \alpha_j \in [\pi - 2\kappa_j, \frac{3}{2}\pi - 2\kappa_j], \quad \theta \in [\pi - \beta_j - \kappa_j, \frac{3}{2}\pi - \beta_j - \kappa_j)$ (Figure 8.3).

Case IIIf. $\beta_j - \alpha_j \in [\frac{3}{2}\pi - 2\kappa_j, 2\pi - 4\kappa_j]$, $\quad \theta \in [\pi - \beta_j - \kappa_j, \frac{3}{2}\pi - \beta_j - \kappa_j)$ (Figure 8.4).

Lemma 9.1. *Assume* $t \in \mathcal{A}(z)$ *(as defined in §8). Then* $\mathcal{V}_{\mathcal{P}_1(t)}(t^{-S})$ *and* $\mathcal{V}_{\mathcal{P}_2(t)}(t^{-S})$ *are bounded by*

$$\chi(S)|z|^{-S} \text{ in Case IIIa;} \qquad 2\chi(S)|z|^{-S} \text{ in Case IIIb;}$$
$$2\chi(S)\operatorname{cosec}^S(\theta + \tfrac{3}{2}\pi + \alpha_j - \kappa_j))|z|^{-S} \text{ in Cases IIIc and IIId;}$$
$$2\chi(S)\operatorname{cosec}^S(\tfrac{3}{2}\pi - \beta_j - \kappa_j - \theta)|z|^{-S} \text{ in Cases IIIe and IIIf.}$$

The proof of this lemma involves only elementary geometry, but is not entirely obvious. For illustration, we supply the proof in Cases IIIb and IIIf. For brevity, we denote ph t by τ.

Case IIIb. From (8.2), we derive

$$\omega_1(z) \in [-\tfrac{1}{2}\pi, \tfrac{3}{2}\pi - (\beta_j - \alpha_j) - 2\kappa_j] \subseteq [-\tfrac{1}{2}\pi, 0],$$

and

$$\omega_2(z) \in [-\tfrac{3}{2}\pi + \beta_j - \alpha_j + 2\kappa_j, \tfrac{1}{2}\pi] \subseteq [0, \tfrac{1}{2}\pi].$$

Hence, from (9.10),

$$\mathcal{V}_{\mathcal{P}_1(z)}(t^{-S}), \quad \mathcal{V}_{\mathcal{P}_2(z)}(t^{-S}) \leq \chi(S)|z|^{-S}.$$

Similarly, when $t \in \mathcal{A}(z)$ and $-\pi - \alpha_j + \kappa_j \leq \tau \leq \pi - \beta_j - \kappa_j$, we have

$$\mathcal{V}_{\mathcal{P}_1(t)}(t^{-S}), \quad \mathcal{V}_{\mathcal{P}_2(t)}(t^{-S}) \leq \chi(S)|t|^{-S} \leq \chi(S)|z|^{-S}. \tag{9.17}$$

Next, if $t \in \mathcal{A}(z)$ and $\pi - \beta_j - \kappa_j \leq \tau \leq -\frac{1}{2}\pi - \alpha_j + \kappa_j$, then

$$\omega_2(t) \equiv -\tfrac{1}{2}\pi - \alpha_j + \kappa_j - \tau \in [0, -\tfrac{3}{2}\pi + \beta_j - \alpha_j + 2\kappa_j] \subseteq [0, \tfrac{1}{2}\pi - 2\kappa_j].$$

Hence, (9.17) continues to apply in the case of $\mathcal{V}_{\mathcal{P}_2(t)}(t^{-S})$. For $\mathcal{V}_{P_1(t)}(t^{-S})$, let t_1 be the intersection of $\mathcal{P}_1(t)$ with ph $t = \pi - \beta_j - \kappa_j$; see Figure 8.2. Then from (9.11), we have

$$\mathcal{V}_{\mathcal{P}_1(t)}(t^{-S}) < 2\chi(S)|t_1|^{-S} \leq 2\chi(S)|z|^{-S}.$$

The analysis in the remaining case, that is $t \in \mathcal{A}(z)$ and $\frac{1}{2}\pi - \beta_j - \kappa_j \leq \tau \leq -\pi - \alpha_j + \kappa_j$, is similar.

Case IIIf. Let z_1 and z_1' be the intersections of $\mathcal{P}_1(z)$ with ph $t = \pi - \beta_j - \kappa_j$ and ph $t = -\pi - \alpha_j + \kappa_j$, respectively; see Figure 8.4. From (9.11), it is clear that if $t \in \mathcal{A}(z)$, then

$$\mathcal{V}_{\mathcal{P}_1(t)}(t^{-S}) < 2\chi(S)|z_1|^{-S}.$$

Next, suppose that $t \in \mathcal{A}(z)$ and $-\pi - \alpha_j + \kappa_j \leq \tau < \frac{3}{2}\pi - \beta_j - \kappa_j$. Then

$$\omega_2(t) \in (-2\pi + \beta_j - \alpha_j + 2\kappa_j, \tfrac{1}{2}\pi] \subseteq (-\tfrac{1}{2}\pi, \tfrac{1}{2}\pi].$$

Hence, from (9.10),

$$\mathcal{V}_{\mathcal{P}_2(t)}(t^{-S}) \leq \chi(S)|t|^{-S} \leq \chi(S)|z_1|^{-S}.$$

Alternatively, assume that $t \in \mathcal{A}(z)$ and $\frac{1}{2}\pi - \beta_j - \kappa_j \leq \tau \leq -\pi - \alpha_j + \kappa_j$. Then from (9.11),

$$\mathcal{V}_{\mathcal{P}_2(t)}(t^{-S}) < 2\chi(S)|z_1'|^{-S} \leq 2\chi(S)|z_1|^{-S}.$$

Lastly, from Figure 8.4, we note that

$$|z_1| = |z| \sin(\tfrac{3}{2}\pi - \beta_j - \kappa_j - \theta). \qquad \square$$

With the aid of Lemma 9.1 and the identities $\widehat{D}_{1\ell}+\widehat{D}_{2\ell} = D_\ell$, $\widehat{G}_1+\widehat{G}_2 = G$, we now may construct bounds for $|R|$ in Case III analogous to those given by (9.13)–(9.16) in Cases I and II. They are as follows:

Case IIIa.

$$|R| \le \frac{\chi(S)}{1 - \frac{1}{2}\pi G|z|^{-1}}, \qquad |z| > \max(b, \tfrac{1}{2}\pi G). \tag{9.18}$$

Case IIIb.

$$|R| \le \frac{2\chi(S)}{1 - \pi G|z|^{-1}}, \qquad |z| > \max(b, \pi G). \tag{9.19}$$

Cases IIIc and IIId.

$$|R| \le \frac{2\chi(S)\operatorname{cosec}^S(\theta + \frac{3}{2}\pi + \alpha_j - \kappa_j)}{1 - \pi G \operatorname{cosec}(\theta + \frac{3}{2}\pi + \alpha_j - \kappa_j)|z|^{-1}},$$
$$|z| > \max(b, \pi G)\operatorname{cosec}(\theta + \tfrac{3}{2}\pi + \alpha_j - \kappa_j). \tag{9.20}$$

Cases IIIe and IIIf.

$$|R| \le \frac{2\chi(S)\operatorname{cosec}^S(\frac{3}{2}\pi - \beta_j - \kappa_j - \theta)}{1 - \pi G \operatorname{cosec}(\frac{3}{2}\pi - \beta_j - \kappa_j - \theta)|z|^{-1}},$$
$$|z| > \max(b, \pi G)\operatorname{cosec}(\tfrac{3}{2}\pi - \beta_j - \kappa_j - \theta). \tag{9.21}$$

10. Completion of the proof of Theorems 3.1 and 3.2

We now seek uniform O-estimates for the remainder term $R_{Sj}(z)$ and its derivatives as $z \to \infty$ in the closed sector

$$\mathcal{S}_j(\mathcal{J}, \delta) = (\ z : -\tfrac{3}{2}\pi - \alpha_j + \delta \le \operatorname{ph} z \le \tfrac{3}{2}\pi - \beta_j - \delta\ ). \tag{10.1}$$

Here δ is an arbitrary constant that we shall restrict to the interval

$$0 < \delta < \pi - \frac{1}{2}(\beta - \alpha); \tag{10.2}$$

compare (3.6).

The constant b introduced in §6 has to exceed both of the quantities a and $\widehat{a}$ introduced in §2 and §4 and also satisfy $b \ge \nu_j\sqrt{2}$ where ν_j is defined by (6.11). At this stage, we restrict b further, if necessary, by requiring

$$b \ge \nu_j \max\{\sec(\tfrac{1}{4}\beta_j - \tfrac{1}{4}\alpha_j), \operatorname{cosec}\tfrac{1}{2}\delta\}. \tag{10.3}$$

Then from (6.12), it follows that

$$\beta_j - \alpha_j \le 2\pi - 4\kappa_j, \tag{10.4}$$

and

$$2\kappa_j \le \delta. \tag{10.5}$$

The last inequality shows that

$$\mathcal{S}_j(\mathcal{J}, \delta) \subseteq (\ z : -\tfrac{3}{2}\pi - \alpha_j + 2\kappa_j \le \operatorname{ph} z \le \tfrac{3}{2}\pi - \beta_j - 2\kappa_j\ ).$$

Accordingly, if $z \in \mathcal{S}_j(\mathcal{I},\delta)$ and $|z|$ is sufficiently large, then the conditions for the applicability of the results given in §9 for Cases I, II, and III are all satisfied. Furthermore,

$$\operatorname{cosec}(\theta + \tfrac{3}{2}\pi + \alpha_j - \kappa_j) \le \operatorname{cosec}\kappa_j \text{ in Cases IIb, IIIc, and IIId,}$$
$$\operatorname{cosec}(\tfrac{3}{2}\pi - \beta_j - \kappa_j - \theta) \le \operatorname{cosec}\kappa_j \text{ in Cases IIc, IIIe, and IIIf.}$$

We conclude that if $z \to \infty$ in $\mathcal{S}_j(\mathcal{I},\delta)$, then for each $\ell = 0, 1, \ldots, n-1$,

$$\left(\frac{d}{dz}\right)^{\ell} R_{Sj}(z) = e^{\lambda_j z} z^{\mu_j} O(z^{-S}) \tag{10.6}$$

uniformly with respect to ph z. We observe also that the condition (7.1) can be removed for (10.6); in those cases in which $S \le$ Re $(\mu_j - \mu_k)$, we may re-expand

$$R_{Sj}(z) = e^{\lambda_j z} z^{\mu_j} \sum_{s=S}^{S'-1} \frac{a_{sj}}{z^s} + R_{S'j}(z)$$

where S' satisfies (7.1); compare (5.3).

In particular, with $\ell = 0$, equation (10.6) shows that there is a solution of the differential equation (1.1) whose asymptotic expansion to S terms within the sector $\mathcal{S}_j(\mathcal{I},\delta)$ agrees with the formal expansion (2.11). However, we constructed this solution starting from (5.3) and (5.7), which suggests that it may depend on the choice of S. Denoting it by $w_{Sj}(z)$, we have

$$w_{Sj}(z) = e^{\lambda_j z} z^{\mu_j} \left\{ \sum_{s=0}^{S-1} \frac{a_{sj}}{z^s} + O\left(\frac{1}{z^S}\right) \right\} \tag{10.7}$$

as $z \to \infty$ in $\mathcal{S}_j(\mathcal{I},\delta)$. To complete the proof of Theorems 3.1 and 3.2, we need to show that $w_{Sj}(z)$ is independent of S, and also that the solution with the property (10.7) is unique.

We first observe that in the intersection

$$\mathcal{S}(\mathcal{I},\delta) \equiv \{\, z : -\tfrac{3}{2}\pi - \alpha + \delta \le \text{ph}\, z \le \tfrac{3}{2}\pi - \beta - \delta \,\} \tag{10.8}$$

of the sectors $\mathcal{S}_j(\mathcal{I},\delta)$, $j = 1, 2, \ldots, n$, we have a set of n solutions $w_{Sj}(z)$, $j = 1, 2, \ldots, n$, that enjoy the property (10.7) for each j. We also know that (10.7) is $n-1$ times differentiable. On constructing the Wronskian of these solutions, we see that

$$\begin{aligned} &\mathcal{W}\{w_{S1}(z), w_{S2}(z), \ldots, w_{Sn}(z)\} \\ &\qquad = (\det \mathbf{\Lambda}) e^{(\lambda_1+\lambda_2+\cdots+\lambda_n)z} z^{\mu_1+\mu_2+\cdots+\mu_n}\{1 + O(z^{-1})\} \end{aligned}$$

as $z \to \infty$ in $\mathcal{S}(\mathcal{I},\delta)$ where $\mathbf{\Lambda}$ is defined by (4.7). Since $\mathbf{\Lambda}$ is nonsingular, the n solutions are linearly independent.

To prove that for each j, $w_{Sj}(z)$ does not depend on the choice of S, we observe that as a consequence of (10.2), $\mathcal{S}(\mathcal{I},\delta)$ exceeds half a Riemann sheet. Accordingly, the doubly-infinite line

$$\text{Re}\,\{(\lambda_k - \lambda_j)z\} = 0, \qquad k \ne j,$$

divides the interior of $\mathcal{S}(\mathcal{I},\delta)$ into either two or three open sectors. On at least one of these sectors, Re $\{(\lambda_k - \lambda_j)z\} > 0$, and on another, Re $\{(\lambda_k - \lambda_j)z\} < 0$. Let us denote the difference between any two solutions that are asymptotic to $e^{\lambda_j z} z^{\mu_j}$ as $z \to \infty$ in $\mathcal{S}(\mathcal{J}, \delta)$ by $\Delta w_j(z)$. Then

$$\Delta w_j(z) = \sum_{k=1}^{n} A_{jk} w_{Sk}(z) \tag{10.9}$$

where the A_{jk} are constants. When $k \neq j$, we may show that any one of these coefficients $A_{j\hat{k}}$, say, vanishes, as follows. Let $z \to \infty$ along a ray $\mathcal{R}$ in $\mathcal{S}(\mathcal{J}, \delta)$ on which (i) Re $\{(\lambda_p - \lambda_q)z\} \neq 0$ for all unequal values of p and q, and (ii) Re $\{(\lambda_{\hat{k}} - \lambda_j)z\} > 0$. It then follows that $A_{jk} = 0$ for those values of k for which $e^{\lambda_k z} z^{\mu_k}$ dominates $e^{\lambda_j z} z^{\mu_j}$ on $\mathcal{R}$. Since this includes $\hat{k}$, we have $A_{j\hat{k}} = 0$. Accordingly, (10.9) reduces to

$$\Delta w_j(z) = A_{jj} w_{Sj}(z).$$

It then follows that $A_{jj} = 0$ by letting $z \to \infty$ in $\mathcal{S}(\mathcal{J}, \delta)$. Thus $w_{Sj}(z) = w_j(\mathcal{J}|z)$, say, where $w_j(\mathcal{J}|z)$ is independent of S.

This completes the proof of Theorems 3.1 and 3.2.

11. Summary and conclusions

In this paper we have constructed new existence theorems for the asymptotic solutions of linear ordinary differential equations of arbitrary order in the neighborhood of an irregular singularity of rank 1, on the assumption that the characteristic values are distinct. Advantages of the new theorems include more extensive regions of validity and availability of explicit bounds for the remainder terms. The theorems also will serve as a starting point for constructing hyperasymptotic expansions of the solutions on the lines of [9], [10], [12], [13], instead of the Borel-Laplace transform approach used in [11]. The only paper that has significant overlap with the present one is that of Stenger [19]. The theorems in this paper apply to systems of equations, rather than a single equation; more importantly, the regions of validity are not as extensive as those in the present paper, and the accompanying error bounds are not evaluated in explicit form. (On the other hand, Stenger's results are not restricted to singularities of unit rank nor to the case when the characteristic values are unequal.)

The asymptotic existence theorems are stated in §3 and proved in §§4–10. In the proof, it becomes necessary to distinguish three cases, Case I, Case II, and Case III, as defined at the end of §6. Error bounds for these cases, expressed in terms of variations of negative powers of z along certain straight-line paths in $\mathbb{C}$, are given by (7.10) in Case I, (7.12) and (7.14) in Case II, and (8.16) in Case III. Bounds for these variations are constructed in §9, leading to simpler bounds for the error terms, given by (9.12)–(9.16) and (9.18)–(9.21).

At this stage, two questions naturally arise.

First, are the new regions of validity given in §3 actually maximal? As a rule, the answer to this question is in the affirmative. This can be seen by analogy with the well-understood situation when $n = 2$ [12], [15], [16, Chapter 7], as follows.

The sector of validity $\mathcal{S}_j(\mathcal{J})$ of the expansion (3.9) of the solution $w_j(\mathcal{J}|z)$ always contains the nonempty closed sector

$$\mathcal{T}_j(\mathcal{J}) = (\ z : -\pi - \alpha_j \leq \text{ph}\ z \leq \pi - \beta_j\ ).$$

On each boundary of $\mathcal{T}_j(\mathcal{J})$, there is at least one solution $w_k(\mathcal{J}|z)$, say, over which $w_j(\mathcal{J}|z)$ achieves maximum dominance as $|z| \to \infty$, that is, the argument $(\lambda_k - \lambda_j)z$

of the function $\exp\{(\lambda_k - \lambda_j)z\}$ is real and negative. For example, on ph $z = \pi - \beta_j$, this is the solution, or solutions, for which $\theta_{jk} = \beta_j$. As ph z increases or decreases without restriction, the form of the asymptotic expansion of $w_j(\mathcal{J}|z)$ keeps changing, in accordance with the Stokes phenomenon. In this way, a multiple of $w_k(\mathcal{J}|z)$ is introduced as ph z crosses the corresponding boundary of $\mathcal{T}_j(\mathcal{J})$.[9] As ph z continues to increase (or decrease), then at first $w_j(\mathcal{J}|z)$ continues to dominate $w_k(\mathcal{J}|z)$; accordingly, the contribution of the multiple of $w_k(\mathcal{J}|z)$ is absorbable in the O-estimates for the remainder terms associated with the expansion (3.9). However, this situation ends as soon as we reach the boundary of $\mathcal{S}_j(\mathcal{J})$ because on crossing this boundary the relative dominance of $e^{\lambda_j z}z^{\mu_j}$ and $e^{\lambda_k z}z^{\mu_k}$ is reversed. This means that unless the corresponding Stokes multiplier for $w_k(\mathcal{J}|z)$ is zero, the validity of (3.9) indeed does cease at the boundary of $\mathcal{S}_j(\mathcal{J})$.

The second question we address is: how sharp are the error bounds we have derived? Consider the most favorable situation first, Case I. In (9.12) and (9.13), the constants B_{Sj}, D_ℓ, and G are defined in §§6–7. By comparing (5.2)–(5.4) and (6.1), we see that when b is large,

$$B_{Sj} \simeq |\phi_0'(\lambda_j)a_{Sj}|.$$

Similarly, from (6.2) and (6.3),

$$D_{k\ell} \simeq |\lambda_k|^\ell,$$

and from (6.7)–(6.9),

$$\widehat{C}_k \simeq |C_k| = 1/|\phi_0'(\lambda_k)|.$$

Substitution into (7.6a) then yields

$$D_\ell \simeq \sum_{k=1}^{n} \frac{|\lambda_k|^\ell}{|\phi_0'(\lambda_k)|}.$$

In (9.13), the actual value of G is not critical since the factor $\exp(G|z|^{-1})$ approaches 1 as $|z| \to \infty$. On combining the foregoing approximations, we see that if $a_{Sj} \neq 0$, then for large $|z|$, the ratio of the error bound furnished by (9.12) and (9.13) to the asymptotic form of the actual error is asymptotic to

$$\frac{|\phi_0'(\lambda_j)|}{|\lambda_j|^\ell} \sum_{k=1}^{n} \frac{|\lambda_k|^\ell}{|\phi_0'(\lambda_k)|}, \qquad \ell = 0, 1, \ldots, n-1. \tag{11.1}$$

We may regard (11.1) as the overestimation factor for our bound. When $n = 2$, this factor reduces to 2 when $\ell = 0$ and to $(|\lambda_1| + |\lambda_2|)/|\lambda_j|$ when $\ell = 1$ (provided that $\lambda_j \neq 0$ in the latter case). These values agree with those already available when $n = 2$; compare [16, Chapter 7, Theorem 12.1]. We also observe that owing to the quantities $|\phi_0'(\lambda_k)|^{-1}$ in (11.1), the overestimation factor will become large if any of the characteristic values are close together. This is to be expected since our results cease to apply when any of the λ's coalesce.

In Cases II and III, the asymptotic estimates of the error bounds (9.14), (9.18), and (9.19) contain extra factors of $\chi(S)$ or $2\chi(S)$. Since $\chi(S) \sim (\frac{1}{2}\pi S)^{\frac{1}{2}}$ as $S \to \infty$, these factors increase the overestimation factors by a moderate amount. More severe are the effects of the cosecants raised to the power S that appear in (9.15), (9.16),

[9]See also [11, equation (2.13)], and [14, equation (8.7)].

(9.20), and (9.21). However, as in the case $n = 2$, this kind of deterioration is to be expected because we are approaching the boundaries of the regions of validity.

This concludes one part of the present investigation. Other parts are [11] and [14]. In [11], hyperasymptotic expansions are obtained for the solutions, but with smaller regions of validity than those furnished by Theorems 3.1 and 3.2. (However, as noted in [11], these regions can be increased by application of connection formulas.) In [14], we investigate more deeply the nature of the asymptotic solutions and develop methods for their computation for all values of z and not merely in certain sectors in the neighborhood of the singularity. Both [11] and [14] also include new methods for computing the associated Stokes multipliers.

Acknowledgments. This research was stimulated by a workshop on *Exponential Asymptotics* held at the Isaac Newton Institute for Mathematical Sciences in Cambridge, U.K. from January 1995 through June 1995. The author is pleased to acknowledge the support of the Institute and of an EPSRC Visiting Fellowship for this period. He also thanks the referees for suggestions concerning the presentation of the results.

References

1. W. Balser, B. L. J. Braaksma, J.-P. Ramis, and Y. Sibuya, *Multisummability of formal power series solutions of linear ordinary differential equations*, Asymptotic Anal. **5** (1991), 27–45.
2. W. Balser, W. B. Jurkat, and D. A. Lutz, *Birkhoff invariants and Stokes' multipliers for meromorphic linear differential equations*, J. Math. Anal. Appl. **71** (1979), 48–94.
3. G. D. Birkhoff, *Singular points of ordinary linear differential equations*, Trans. Amer. Math. Soc. **10** (1909), 436–470.
4. J. C. Burkill, *The Theory of Ordinary Differential Equations*, Second edition, Oliver and Boyd, Edinburgh, 1962.
5. E. A. Coddington and N. Levinson, *Theory of Ordinary Differential Equations*, McGraw-Hill, New York, 1955.
6. T. M. Dunster, *Error bounds for exponentially improved asymptotic solutions of ordinary differential equations having irregular singularities of rank one*, Methods Appl. Anal. **3** (1996), 109–134.
7. E. L. Ince, *Ordinary Differential Equations*, Longmans, Green, London and New York, 1927. Reprinted by Dover, New York, 1956.
8. W. B. Jurkat, *Meromorphe Differentialgleichungen*, Lecture Notes in Mathematics No. 637, Springer-Verlag, Berlin, 1978.
9. B. T. M. Murphy and A. D. Wood, *Hyperasymptotic solutions of second-order ordinary differential equations with a singularity of arbitrary integer rank*, Methods Appl. Anal. [In press.]
10. A. B. Olde Daalhuis, *Hyperasymptotic solutions of second-order linear differential equations II*, Methods Appl. Anal. **2** (1995), 198–211.
11. ———, *Hyperasymptotic solutions of higher order linear differential equations with a singularity of rank one*, Proc. Roy. Soc. London Ser. A. [In press.]
12. A. B. Olde Daalhuis and F. W. J. Olver, *Exponentially improved asymptotic solutions of ordinary differential equations. II Irregular singularities of rank one*, Proc. Roy. Soc. London Ser. A **445** (1994), 39–56.
13. ———, *Hyperasymptotic solutions of second-order linear differential equations I*, Methods Appl. Anal. **2** (1995), 173–197.
14. ———, *On the asymptotic and numerical solution of linear ordinary differential equations*, SIAM Rev. **40** (1998) [In press.]
15. F. W. J. Olver, *On the asymptotic solutions of second-order differential equations having an irregular singularity of rank one, with an application to Whittaker functions*, SIAM J. Numer. Anal. Ser. B **2** (1965), 225–243.
16. ———, *Asymptotics and Special Functions*, Academic Press, New York, 1974. Reprinted by AK Peters, Wellesley, 1997.

17. ———, *Asymptotic expansions of the coefficients in asymptotic series solutions of linear differential equations*, Methods Appl. Anal. **1** (1994), 1–13.
18. F. W. J. Olver and F. Stenger, *Error bounds for asymptotic solutions of second-order differential equations having an irregular singularity of arbitrary rank*, SIAM J. Numer. Anal. Ser. B **2** (1965), 244–249.
19. F. Stenger, *Error bounds for asymptotic solutions of differential equations I. The distinct eigenvalue case*, J. Res. Nat. Bur. Standards Sect. B **70** (1966), 167–186.
20. ———, *Error bounds for asymptotic solutions of differential equations. II. The general case*, J. Res. Nat. Bur. Standards Sect. B **70** (1966), 187–210.
21. B. Yu. Sternin and V. E. Shatalov, *Borel-Laplace Transform and Asymptotic Theory: Introduction to Resurgent Analysis*, CRC Press, Boca Raton, 1996.
22. W. J. Trjitzinsky, *Analytic theory of linear differential equations*, Acta. Math. **62** (1934), 167–226.
23. ———, *Laplace integrals and factorial series in the theory of linear differential and linear difference equations*, Trans. Amer. Math. Soc. **37** (1935), 80–146.
24. H. L. Turrittin, *Convergent solutions of ordinary linear homogeneous differential equations in the neighborhood of an irregular singular point*, Acta. Math. **93** (1955), 27–66.
25. V. S. Varadarajan, *Linear meromorphic differential equations: a modern point of view*, Bull. Amer. Math. Soc. (N.S.) **33** (1996), 1–42.
26. W. Wasow, *Asymptotic Expansions for Ordinary Differential Equations*, Wiley (Interscience), New York, 1965. Reprinted by Krieger, Huntington, 1976 and Dover, New York, 1987.
27. J. H. Wilkinson, *The Algebraic Eigenvalue Problem*, Clarendon Press, Oxford, 1965.

Institute for Physical Science and Technology and Department of Mathematics, University of Maryland, College Park, Maryland 20742, U.S.A.
E-mail: `olver@bessel.umd.edu`

SIAM REV.
Vol. 40, No. 3, pp. 463–495, September 1998

ON THE ASYMPTOTIC AND NUMERICAL SOLUTION OF LINEAR ORDINARY DIFFERENTIAL EQUATIONS*

A. B. OLDE DAALHUIS† AND F. W. J. OLVER‡

Abstract. An investigation is made of the nature of asymptotic solutions of homogeneous linear differential equations of arbitrary order in the neighborhood of a singularity of unit rank. We introduce a classification of the solutions into two types, explicit and implicit. For the former there exists a sector on which the solution is dominated by all independent solutions as the singularity is approached. No such sector exists for implicit solutions. In consequence, the two types of solution have different uniqueness properties. Another difference is that error bounds for the asymptotic expansions of explicit solutions are generally stronger than those for implicit solutions.

We also investigate the computation of the solutions by numerical integration of the differential equation. It is shown that it is the exception rather than the rule for the integration process to be stable, particularly so for implicit solutions. To overcome these instabilities we develop boundary-value methods, complete with error analysis.

Numerical examples illustrate the computation of both explicit and implicit solutions, and also the associated Stokes multipliers.

Key words. asymptotic expansions, boundary-value methods, error bounds, irregular singularity, perturbation analysis, remainder terms, stability, Stokes multipliers, Taylor-series method

AMS subject classifications. 34E05, 65L10, 65L20

PII. S0036144597315341

1. Introduction. It is well understood how to construct asymptotic solutions of linear homogeneous ordinary differential equations of the second order

$$\frac{d^2w}{dz^2} + f(z)\frac{dw}{dz} + g(z)w = 0$$

in the neighborhood of an irregular singularity (that is, a point in whose neighborhood the solution cannot be expanded in convergent series of powers and logarithms); see, for example, [18], [20], [23]. When the singularity is at infinity and of positive integer rank, asymptotic expansions of solutions in descending powers of z or $z^{\frac{1}{2}}$ are available complete with maximal regions of validity in the complex plane $\mathbb{C}$ and explicit error bounds. For infinite rank we have the Liouville–Green approximation. These theories are in frequent use by applied mathematicians, theoretical physicists, and other scientists and engineers. Quite recently, beginning with a seminal paper of M.V. Berry [2], there has been a surge of interest in re-expanding the remainder terms in these expansions into so-called exponentially-improved and hyperasymptotic forms. These re-expansions yield greatly increased precision, together with enlarged regions of validity in the complex plane. They also provide a more satisfactory explanation of the Stokes phenomenon, including direct asymptotic methods for computing the connection coefficients, or Stokes multipliers; see [3], [8], [12], [13], [15], [16], [17], [25].

The situation for differential equations of higher order is quite different. There is, indeed, a very extensive body of literature on asymptotic solutions that goes back to

*Received by the editors January 22, 1997; accepted for publication (in revised form) August 18, 1997.

http://www.siam.org/journals/sirev/40-3/31534.html

†Department of Mathematics and Statistics, King's Buildings, University of Edinburgh, Edinburgh EH9 3JZ, UK (adri@maths.ed.ac.uk).

‡Institute for Physical Science and Technology and Department of Mathematics, University of Maryland, College Park, MD 20742 (olver@bessel.umd.edu).

the nineteenth century. However, it is fair to comment that almost all of it belongs to the realm of pure mathematics. The main objective in this earlier work has been to construct existence theorems in as general a form as possible, with an emphasis on the elimination of all cases of failure. Applications, or at any rate nontrivial applications, of the general theory are rare.[1] An applied mathematician confronted with a differential equation of order higher than two faces a formidable task in understanding and applying this theory. In older papers, for example [4], [9], [29], [30], this is because of their length and intricacy. In more recent contributions—see, for example, those cited in the extensive survey [31]—it is because of the depth and abstraction of new concepts such as multisummability and resurgence.

Now even if our applied mathematician is willing to invest the time needed to understand and apply existing theory he or she still risks disappointment. Qualitatively, the regions of validity for individual solutions are usually far from being maximal, nor does the theory yield an understanding of two quite different types of asymptotic solutions that occur with equations of order higher than two. Quantitatively, the theory lacks any information about the remainder term other than that relatively it is $\mathcal{O}(z^{-s})$, where z^{-s} is the first neglected power in the expansion.[2]

To illustrate these observations, consider what happens when the main existence theorems given in Wasow's well-known text [32, section 12] are applied to Bessel's equation

$$\frac{d^2w}{dz^2}+\frac{1}{z}\frac{dw}{dz}+\left(1-\frac{\nu^2}{z^2}\right)w=0,$$

in which ν is a parameter and the singularity under consideration is the one at infinity. We learn that as $z \to \infty$ in any closed sector of angle less than π there are solutions $w_1(z)$ and $w_2(z)$ having asymptotic expansions of the form

$$w_1(z) \sim e^{iz} z^{-\frac{1}{2}} \sum_{s=0}^{\infty} \frac{a_{s1}}{z^s}, \qquad w_2(z) \sim e^{-iz} z^{-\frac{1}{2}} \sum_{s=0}^{\infty} \frac{a_{s2}}{z^s},$$

in which a_{s1}, a_{s2}, $s = 0, 1, \ldots,$ are constants; compare [32, section 13]. What we do not learn is that the accuracy yielded by these expansions can vary enormously over the chosen sector,[3] that each asymptotic expansion actually holds in a closed sector of angle arbitrarily close to 3π, and, last, that with these increased sectors of validity the solutions are unique. The situation for differential equations of higher order is similar, especially insofar as regions of validity and accuracy are concerned.

Further difficulties may lie in store. For an applied mathematician the computation of an asymptotic expansion is often just the initial step in evaluating the wanted solution. Elsewhere the solution needs to be computed, for example, by numerical integration of the original differential equation. As we shall see equations of higher order are highly unstable and it is the exception, rather than the rule, to be able to integrate directly.

[1] An exception is [24]. However, the differential equations in this reference are solvable in terms of Mellin–Barnes integrals, and the asymptotic expansions of the solutions are obtained from these integral representations rather than directly from the differential equation.

[2] Again, an exception is the work of Stenger [27], [28]. These important papers appear to have been overlooked by most subsequent writers. Compare [22].

[3] It can happen that the accuracy of a solution is extremely good at one boundary but almost nonexistent as we approach the other.

The purpose of our investigation is to remedy the deficiencies we have just described. In [22] new, and easily understood, asymptotic existence theorems are proved for singularities of rank one. The regions of validity are maximal, in general, and the asymptotic expansions are accompanied by strict and explicit bounds on the remainder terms. In the present paper we discuss the qualitative nature of the asymptotic solutions furnished by the theorems of [22], distinguishing two types which we call explicit and implicit. We also show how to integrate the defining differential equation numerically in a stable manner by application of boundary-value methods, and how to compute the Stokes multipliers numerically.

In [14] hyperasymptotic expansions of the solutions are found by successive re-expansions of integral representations of the remainder terms based on the Borel–Laplace transform—again in the case of a singularity of rank unity. The results are a generalization of those supplied in [13], [16] in the case $n = 2$. These hyperasymptotic expansions greatly increase the attainable precision, and will lead to a further enlargement of the regions of validity. They also supply asymptotic expansions for the Stokes multipliers and shed additional light upon the qualitative nature of the asymptotic solutions.

2. Asymptotic existence theorems. We are concerned with the differential equation

$$\frac{d^n w}{dz^n} + f_{n-1}(z)\frac{d^{n-1}w}{dz^{n-1}} + f_{n-2}(z)\frac{d^{n-2}w}{dz^{n-2}} + \cdots + f_0(z)w = 0. \tag{2.1}$$

We assume, without loss of generality, that the singularity is located at $z = \infty$, and since it is to be of rank one this means that the coefficients $f_l(z)$, $l = 0, 1, \ldots, n-1$, can be expanded in power series

$$f_l(z) = \sum_{s=0}^{\infty} \frac{f_{sl}}{z^s}$$

that converge for all sufficiently large values of $|z|$. Formal series solutions of (2.1) are given by

$$e^{\lambda_j z} z^{\mu_j} \sum_{s=0}^{\infty} \frac{a_{sj}}{z^s}, \qquad j = 1, 2, \ldots, n, \tag{2.2}$$

where $a_{0j} = 1$ and the characteristic values λ_j, indices μ_j, and remaining coefficients a_{sj} are found by formal substitution in (2.1); see [22, section 2]. Thus, for example, λ is a root of the equation

$$\phi_0(\lambda) = 0,$$

and the corresponding μ is given by

$$\mu\phi_0'(\lambda) = -\phi_1(\lambda),$$

where

$$\phi_0(\lambda) = \lambda^n + \sum_{l=0}^{n-1} f_{0l}\lambda^l, \qquad \phi_1(\lambda) = \sum_{l=0}^{n-1} f_{1l}\lambda^l.$$

As in [22] we assume that

$$\lambda_j \neq \lambda_k, \qquad j \neq k, \tag{2.3}$$

and we suppose that $\mathcal{J}$ denotes any prescribed half-closed interval of length 2π. We define θ_{jk}, $j \neq k$, to be the (unique) value of $\mathrm{ph}\,(\lambda_k - \lambda_j)$ that lies in $\mathcal{J}$ and we call $\{\theta_{jk}\}$, $j \neq k$, the canonical set of the $\mathrm{ph}\,(\lambda_k - \lambda_j)$ corresponding to $\mathcal{J}$.

Continuing to follow [22], we define

$$\alpha_j = \min_{k \neq j} \theta_{jk}, \qquad \beta_j = \max_{k \neq j} \theta_{jk}, \tag{2.4}$$

and

$$\mathcal{S}_j(\mathcal{J}) = \{z : -\tfrac{3}{2}\pi - \alpha_j < \mathrm{ph}\, z < \tfrac{3}{2}\pi - \beta_j\}. \tag{2.5}$$

Next,

$$\alpha = \min_{k \neq j} \theta_{jk}, \qquad \beta = \max_{k \neq j} \theta_{jk}, \tag{2.6}$$

the minimum and maximum now being taken with respect to j as well as k, and

$$\mathcal{S}(\mathcal{J}) = \{z : -\tfrac{3}{2}\pi - \alpha < \mathrm{ph}\, z < \tfrac{3}{2}\pi - \beta\}. \tag{2.7}$$

THEOREM 2.1. *For a given interval $\mathcal{J}$ and for each $j = 1, 2, \ldots, n$,* (2.1) *has a unique solution $w_j(\mathcal{J}|z)$ such that*

$$w_j(\mathcal{J}|z) \sim e^{\lambda_j z} z^{\mu_j} \sum_{s=0}^{\infty} \frac{a_{sj}}{z^s} \tag{2.8}$$

as $z \to \infty$ uniformly in any closed sector properly interior to $\mathcal{S}_j(\mathcal{J})$. This asymptotic expansion can be differentiated $n-1$ times in the same circumstances, and the n solutions $w_j(\mathcal{J}|z)$ are linearly independent. Furthermore, the sectors of validity $\mathcal{S}_j(\mathcal{J})$ are maximal in general.

THEOREM 2.2 (see [4], [11]). *There exist n linearly independent and unique solutions $w_j(\mathcal{J}|z)$, $j = 1, 2, \ldots, n$, such that* (2.8) *applies as $z \to \infty$ uniformly in any closed sector properly interior to $\mathcal{S}(\mathcal{J})$.*

Theorem 2.1 (which is new) and Theorem 2.2 are proved in [22]. One of the advantages of Theorem 2.1 over existing results, including those of [32, section 12], is that it supplies much larger regions of validity. As we shall see in examples in later sections, these increased regions are very important in applications. Another advantage of Theorem 2.1 is that the proof given in [22] yields strict and realistic bounds for the remainder terms.

Can a set of solutions exist with the property (2.8) in an *arbitrary* sector of sufficiently small angle?

THEOREM 2.3 (see [32]). *Let S be any ray*[4] *or any closed sector of angle less than π. Then there is a set of linearly independent solutions $w_j(z)$, $j = 1, 2, \ldots, n$, such that*

$$w_j(z) \sim e^{\lambda_j z} z^{\mu_j} \sum_{s=0}^{\infty} \frac{a_{sj}}{z^s} \tag{2.9}$$

as $z \to \infty$ uniformly in S.

[4]Here and elsewhere by "ray" we mean, as usual, a straight line joining the origin to the point at infinity.

This result is a weaker form of Theorem 2.2 and is derivable from it by appropriate choice of $\mathcal{J}$. But unlike Theorem 2.2 the set of solutions in Theorem 2.3 may not be unique. However, if we permit the angle of $\mathcal{S}$ to be π and assume that the boundaries of $\mathcal{S}$ do not coincide with any of the anti-Stokes lines (that is, rays on which $\theta_{jk} + \operatorname{ph} z$ is an odd multiple of $\frac{1}{2}\pi$), then a set of solutions with property (2.9) exists and is unique; compare, for example, [22, section 10].

3. Classification of solutions. Suppose first that

$$0 \leqslant \beta_j - \alpha_j < \pi. \tag{3.1}$$

We introduce the following subsectors of $\mathcal{S}_j(\mathcal{J})$, three open and two closed:

$$\begin{aligned}
\mathcal{D}_j^-(\mathcal{J}) &= \{z : -\tfrac{3}{2}\pi - \alpha_j < \operatorname{ph} z < -\tfrac{1}{2}\pi - \beta_j\},\\
\mathcal{S}_j^-(\mathcal{J}) &= \{z : -\tfrac{1}{2}\pi - \beta_j \leqslant \operatorname{ph} z \leqslant -\tfrac{1}{2}\pi - \alpha_j\},\\
\mathcal{R}_j(\mathcal{J}) &= \{z : -\tfrac{1}{2}\pi - \alpha_j < \operatorname{ph} z < \tfrac{1}{2}\pi - \beta_j\},\\
\mathcal{S}_j^+(\mathcal{J}) &= \{z : \tfrac{1}{2}\pi - \beta_j \leqslant \operatorname{ph} z \leqslant \tfrac{1}{2}\pi - \alpha_j\},\\
\mathcal{D}_j^+(\mathcal{J}) &= \{z : \tfrac{1}{2}\pi - \alpha_j < \operatorname{ph} z < \tfrac{3}{2}\pi - \beta_j\}.
\end{aligned}$$

They have the following properties:

(i) If $z \to \infty$ along any ray in $\mathcal{R}_j(\mathcal{J})$ and $w_k(z)$, $k \neq j$, is a solution of (2.1) that has the series (2.2), with $j = k$, as its asymptotic expansion along the given ray (Theorem 2.3), then $(\lambda_j - \lambda_k)z$ has unbounded negative real part, and so

$$w_j(\mathcal{J}|z)/w_k(z) \to 0.$$

(ii) If $z \to \infty$ along any ray within[5] $\mathcal{S}_j^-(\mathcal{J}) \cup \mathcal{S}_j^+(\mathcal{J})$, then there is at least one nontrivial solution $w(z)$ of (2.1) such that

$$w(z)/w_j(\mathcal{J}|z) \to 0,$$

and at least one solution $\tilde{w}(z)$ of (2.1) such that

$$w_j(\mathcal{J}|z)/\tilde{w}(z) \to 0.$$

(To construct $w(z)$ in the case of $\mathcal{S}_j^-(\mathcal{J})$, take k to be any of the integers that satisfies $\theta_{jk} = \alpha_j$. Then $w(z)$ is a solution that has the series (2.2), with $j = k$, as its asymptotic expansion along the given ray. For $\tilde{w}(z)$ take k to be any of the integers that satisfies $\theta_{jk} = \beta_j$. Similarly for $\mathcal{S}_j^+(\mathcal{J})$.)

(iii) If $z \to \infty$ along any ray in $\mathcal{D}_j^-(\mathcal{J}) \cup \mathcal{D}_j^+(\mathcal{J})$ and $w_k(z)$, $k \neq j$, is a solution of (2.1) that has the series (2.2), with $j = k$, as its asymptotic expansion along the given ray (Theorem 2.3), then (similar to (i))

$$w_k(z)/w_j(\mathcal{J}|z) \to 0.$$

Because of these properties, we call $\mathcal{R}_j(\mathcal{J})$ the *recessive sector* of $w_j(\mathcal{J}|z)$ within $\mathcal{S}_j(\mathcal{J})$, and $\mathcal{D}_j^-(\mathcal{J})$ and $\mathcal{D}_j^+(\mathcal{J})$ *dominant sectors* for $w_j(\mathcal{J}|z)$. The two closed sectors $\mathcal{S}_j^-(\mathcal{J})$ and $\mathcal{S}_j^+(\mathcal{J})$ are called *intermediate sectors* for $w_j(\mathcal{J}|z)$.

[5]By "within" we exclude the boundaries. When $\beta_j = \alpha_j$ the sectors $\mathcal{S}_j^-(\mathcal{J})$ and $\mathcal{S}_j^+(\mathcal{J})$ degenerate into single rays, and no ray exists within their union.

Now suppose that

$$\pi \leqslant \beta_j - \alpha_j < 2\pi. \tag{3.2}$$

Then except possibly when $\beta_j - \alpha_j = \pi$ there is always a nontrivial solution $w(z)$ such that

$$w(z)/w_j(\mathcal{J}|z) \to 0$$

as $z \to \infty$ along a given ray $\mathcal{R}$ within $\mathcal{S}_j(\mathcal{J})$. This can be seen as follows. Let $\mathcal{R}$ be $\operatorname{ph} z = \psi$, and in Theorem 2.3 take $\mathcal{S}$ to be $\mathcal{R}$. If $\psi \in (-\frac{3}{2}\pi - \alpha_j, -\frac{1}{2}\pi - \alpha_j)$, then we take $w(z) = w_k(z)$ where k is such that $\theta_{jk} = \alpha_j$; if $\psi \in (\frac{1}{2}\pi - \beta_j, \frac{3}{2}\pi - \beta_j)$, then we take $w(z) = w_k(z)$ where k is such that $\theta_{jk} = \beta_j$. Last, except when $\beta_j - \alpha_j = \pi$ the union of the intervals $(-\frac{3}{2}\pi - \alpha_j, -\frac{1}{2}\pi - \alpha_j)$ and $(\frac{1}{2}\pi - \beta_j, \frac{3}{2}\pi - \beta_j)$ is $(-\frac{3}{2}\pi - \alpha_j, \frac{3}{2}\pi - \beta_j)$.

We introduce the following new classifications.[6] When (3.1) is satisfied, we call $w_j(\mathcal{J}|z)$ an *explicit solution* on $\mathcal{S}_j(\mathcal{J})$; when (3.2) applies, we call $w_j(\mathcal{J}|z)$ an *implicit solution* on $\mathcal{S}_j(\mathcal{J})$. We note that implicit solutions cannot exist when $n = 2$, because in this case $\alpha_j = \beta_j$.

As we have just seen, the most important difference between explicit and implicit solutions is that the former possess recessive sectors but the latter do not.[7] To put this another way, explicit solutions can be specified uniquely by their asymptotic behavior along a single ray, whereas to ensure uniqueness of an implicit solution its asymptotic property might need to extend over a nondegenerate sector, for example, the sector $\mathcal{S}(\mathcal{J})$ of Theorem 2.2.

Another difference between explicit and implicit solutions is that error bounds for their asymptotic expansions (2.8) are generally weaker for implicit solutions; this can be seen by inspection of the results supplied in [22, section 9].

Finally, as we shall see in later sections, there are significant differences in the numerical methods for computing the two types of solution.

To provide a geometric interpretation of explicit and implicit solutions, let Λ denote the convex hull of the points $\lambda_1, \lambda_2, \ldots, \lambda_n$ in $\mathbb{C}$. If λ_j is an interior point of Λ, or a boundary point of Λ other than a vertex, then condition (3.2) applies and in consequence $w_j(\mathcal{J}|z)$ is an implicit solution. Alternatively, if λ_j is a vertex of Λ, then it is always possible to choose $\mathcal{J}$ in such a way that $w_j(\mathcal{J}|z)$ is an explicit solution. However, other choices of $\mathcal{J}$ can result in the corresponding solution $w_j(\mathcal{J}|z)$ being implicit. These possibilities are illustrated in the next section.

4. Example. Let us suppose $n = 4$, $\lambda_1 = \frac{1}{2}$, $\lambda_2 = 2\frac{1}{2}$, $\lambda_3 = i$, $\lambda_4 = -i$; see Figure 4.1.

Here the convex hull Λ is the triangle $\lambda_2\,\lambda_3\,\lambda_4$. Since λ_1 is interior to Λ, $w_1(\mathcal{J}|z)$ is an implicit solution, whatever the choice of $\mathcal{J}$.

Suppose we take $\mathcal{J} = \mathcal{J}_1 \equiv (-\frac{5}{4}\pi, \frac{3}{4}\pi]$. Then the angles θ_{jk} are distributed as in Figure 4.2.

The region of validity $\mathcal{S}_1(\mathcal{J}_1)$ for $w_1(\mathcal{J}_1|z)$ is the unshaded reflex sector in Figure 4.3. In this diagram the labels $-\frac{3}{2}\pi - \theta_{14}$ and $\frac{3}{2}\pi - \theta_{13}$ denote the phase angles of the boundary rays. Next, from Figure 4.2[8] we see that the condition $\beta_j - \alpha_j < \pi$ is fulfilled

[6]These classifications differ from the "extreme" and "interior" solutions of Stenger [27].

[7]On the other hand, implicit solutions can have dominant sectors in $\mathcal{S}_j(\mathcal{J})$. An example is provided by the solution $w_2(\mathcal{J}_2|z)$, defined in the next section, for which $\frac{1}{2}\pi - \theta_{23} < \operatorname{ph} z < -\frac{1}{2}\pi - \theta_{24}$ is a dominant sector.

[8]Figure 4.2 and all other figures in this section are drawn to scale.

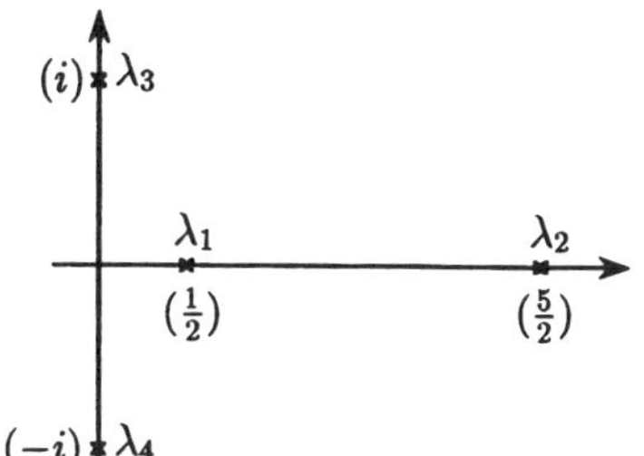

FIG. 4.1. *Affixes of the* λ*'s in* $\mathbb{C}$.

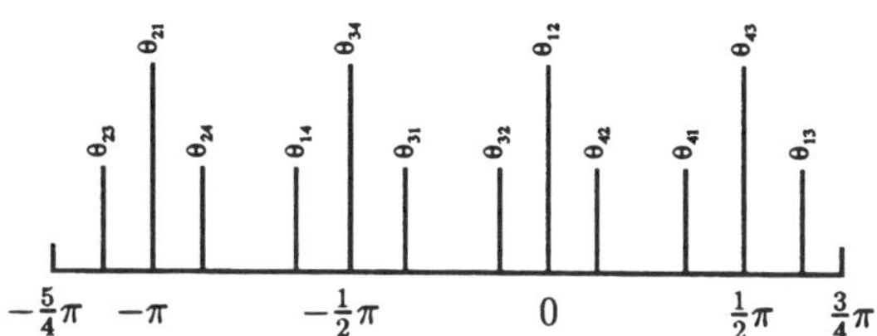

FIG. 4.2. *Angles* θ_{jk} *when* $\mathcal{J} = \mathcal{J}_1 = (-\frac{5}{4}\pi, \frac{3}{4}\pi]$.

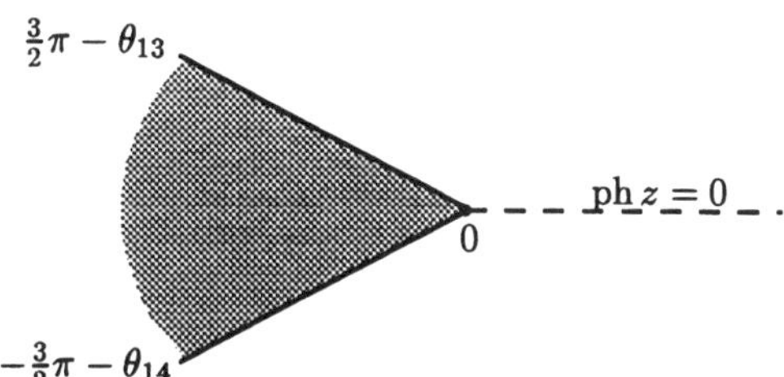

FIG. 4.3. *Sector* $\mathcal{S}_1(\mathcal{J}_1)$.

when $j = 2, 3, 4$. Hence $w_2(\mathcal{J}_1|z)$, $w_3(\mathcal{J}_1|z)$, $w_4(\mathcal{J}_1|z)$ are all explicit solutions. Their sectors of validity $\mathcal{S}_j(\mathcal{J}_1)$ occupy two Riemann sheets and are indicated on Figures 4.4, 4.5, 4.6, respectively. Again, the boundary rays are labeled with their phase angles, and we have also indicated the recessive sectors $\mathcal{R}_j(\mathcal{J}_1)$, the dominant sectors $\mathcal{D}_j^-(\mathcal{J}_1)$, $\mathcal{D}_j^+(\mathcal{J}_1)$, and the intermediate sectors $\mathcal{S}_j^-(\mathcal{J}_1)$, $\mathcal{S}_j^+(\mathcal{J}_1)$.

Next, let us suppose instead that $\mathcal{J} = \mathcal{J}_2 \equiv [-\pi, \pi)$. The angles θ_{jk} are now distributed according to Figure 4.7.

The only angle that has changed from Figure 4.2 is θ_{23}, which has increased by 2π. This means that Figures 4.3, 4.5, and 4.6 are unaffected when $\mathcal{J}_1$ is replaced by $\mathcal{J}_2$, and hence that $w_1(\mathcal{J}_2|z) = w_1(\mathcal{J}_1|z)$, $w_3(\mathcal{J}_2|z) = w_3(\mathcal{J}_1|z)$, $w_4(\mathcal{J}_2|z) = w_4(\mathcal{J}_1|z)$. However, $w_2(\mathcal{J}_2|z)$ is a new solution whose region of validity $\mathcal{S}_2(\mathcal{J}_2)$ is the unshaded sector in Figure 4.8. Moreover, this solution is implicit.

Third, we take $\mathcal{J} = \mathcal{J}_3 \equiv (-\pi, \pi]$ (the principal interval for phase angles). This increases both θ_{21} and θ_{23} by 2π from the values depicted in Figure 4.2; see Figure 4.9. Again, this does not affect the solutions for $j = 1, 3, 4$. But $w_2(\mathcal{J}_3|z)$ is another implicit solution whose region of validity $\mathcal{S}_2(\mathcal{J}_3)$ is the unshaded sector in Figure 4.10.

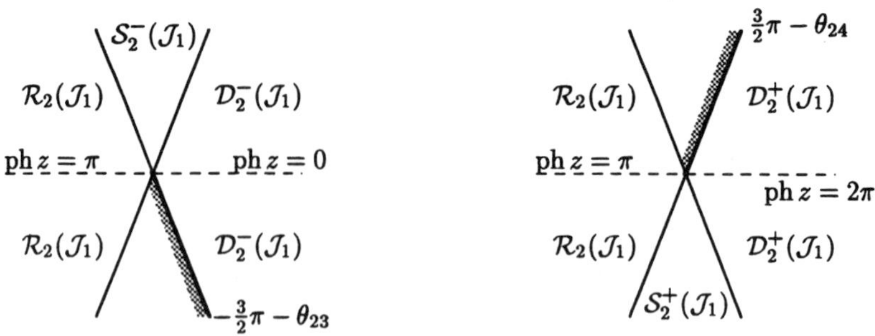

FIG. 4.4. *Sectors for* $w_2(\mathcal{J}_1|z)$.

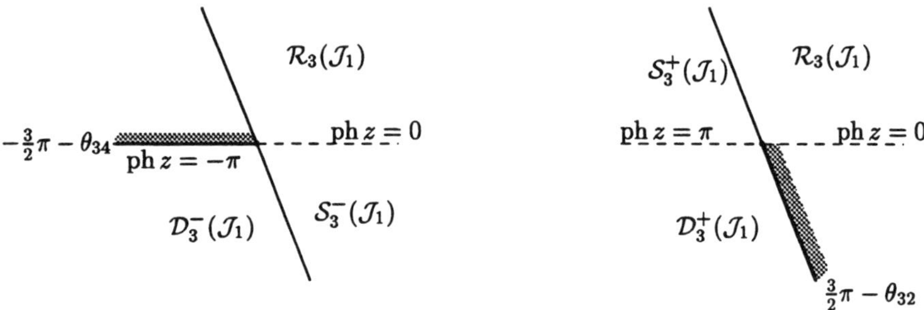

FIG. 4.5. *Sectors for* $w_3(\mathcal{J}_1|z)$.

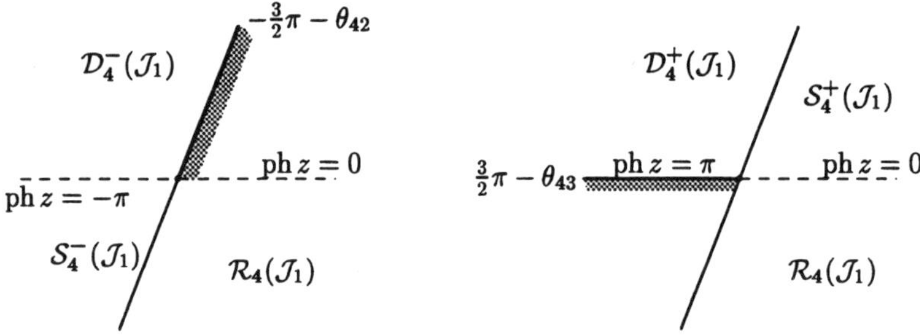

FIG. 4.6. *Sectors for* $w_4(\mathcal{J}_1|z)$.

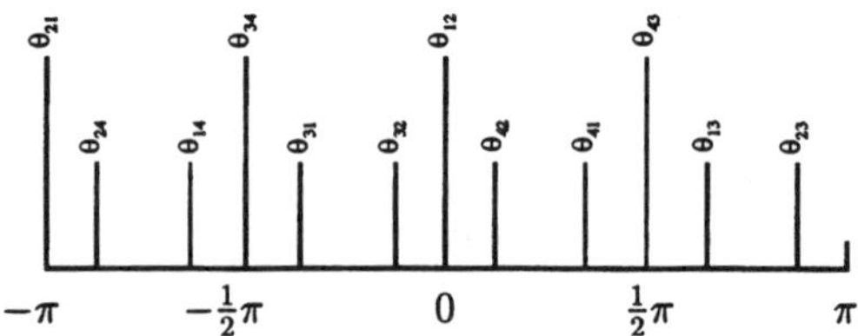

FIG. 4.7. *Angles* θ_{jk} *when* $\mathcal{J} = \mathcal{J}_2 = [-\pi, \pi)$.

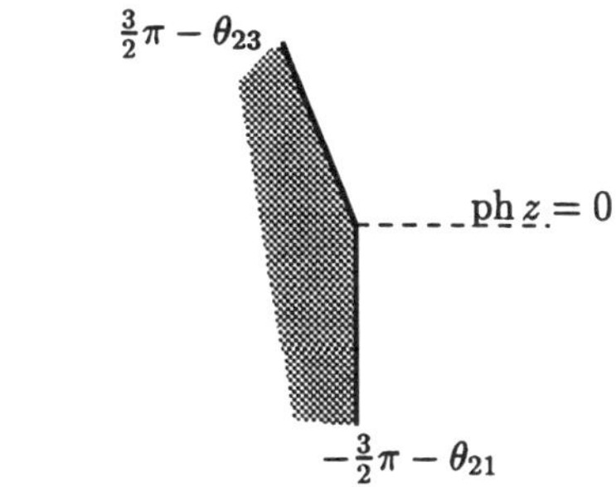

FIG. 4.8. *Sector* $\mathcal{S}_2(\mathcal{J}_2)$.

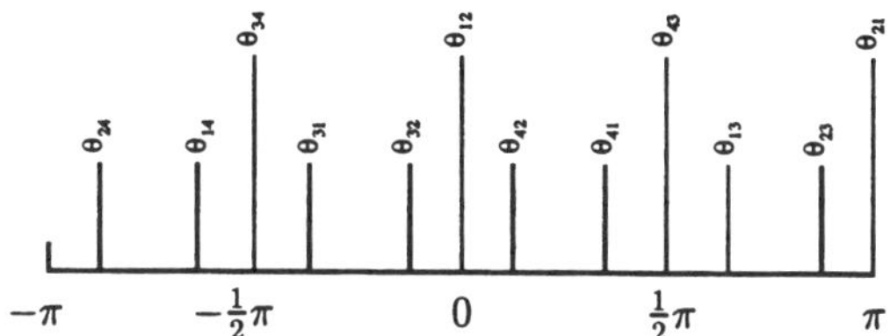

FIG. 4.9. *Angles* θ_{jk} *when* $\mathcal{J} = \mathcal{J}_3 = (-\pi, \pi]$.

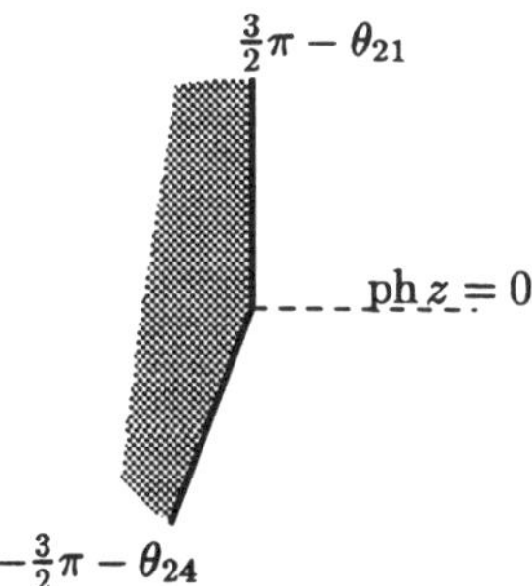

FIG. 4.10. *Sector* $\mathcal{S}_2(\mathcal{J}_3)$.

The process may be continued, but for $j = 2$ we have exhausted the possible geometrical configurations of the sectors, and the corresponding solutions are simple continuations of the ones we have already described. For example, if $\mathcal{J}_4 = (-3\pi, -\pi]$, then the diagram for the sector $\mathcal{S}_2(\mathcal{J}_4)$ coincides with the unshaded sector in Figure 4.10 and $w_2(\mathcal{J}_4|z) = e^{2\pi i \mu_2} w_2(\mathcal{J}_3|ze^{-2\pi i})$. For the general differential equation of order n with a singularity of rank one, the number of configurations of the sectors of validity of a solution $w_j(\mathcal{J}|z)$ with varying $\mathcal{J}$ can be up to $n-1$.

We also record for later reference the region of validity of a second solution of w_1 type, given by $w_1(\mathcal{J}_5|z)$ where $\mathcal{J}_5 = (-\frac{7}{4}\pi, \frac{1}{4}\pi]$; see Figure 4.11.

Perhaps it should be stressed that although $w_2(\mathcal{J}_1|z)$, $w_2(\mathcal{J}_2|z)$, and $w_2(\mathcal{J}_3|z)$ are solutions of the same differential equation having the same asymptotic expansions with overlapping sectors of validity, nevertheless they are different solutions of the equation as a rule. Only if at least one of the common sectors $\mathcal{S}(\mathcal{J}_1)$, $\mathcal{S}(\mathcal{J}_2)$, or $\mathcal{S}(\mathcal{J}_3)$

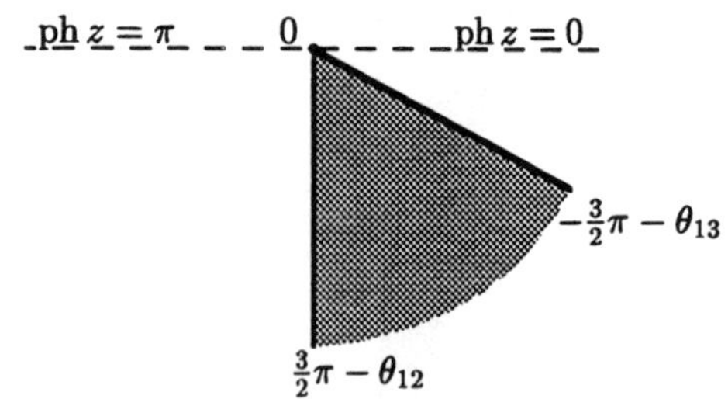

FIG. 4.11. *Sector* $\mathcal{S}_1(\mathcal{J}_5)$.

were included in each of $\mathcal{S}_2(\mathcal{J}_1)$, $\mathcal{S}_2(\mathcal{J}_2)$, and $\mathcal{S}_2(\mathcal{J}_3)$ could we appeal to Theorem 2.2 and conclude that the three solutions are the same, and it is easily seen that this is not the case. In fact, if any two of the solutions were the same, this would imply that the expansions (2.8) are valid in larger sectors than those given in Theorem 2.1, and we know that this cannot happen in general.

Similar comments apply to the solutions $w_1(\mathcal{J}_1|z)$ and $w_1(\mathcal{J}_5|z)$, and in section 8 we illustrate numerically the difference between these two solutions.

5. Computation of explicit solutions. Let the annulus on which the coefficients $f_0(z)$, $f_1(z), \ldots, f_{n-1}(z)$ in (2.1) are analytic be denoted by

$$\mathcal{A} = \{z \, : \, |z| > a\}.$$

Three general procedures are available for the computation of a solution $w(z)$ of (2.1) on $\mathcal{A}$: (i) numerical summation of the asymptotic expansion of $w(z)$; (ii) numerical solution of the differential equation (2.1); (iii) use of connection formulas. Since (iii) is used only to extend results obtained by (i) and (ii) to other ranges of $\operatorname{ph} z$ we shall not discuss it further. In theory both (i) and (ii) are quite simple; in practice they are prone to severe problems of instability. In this section and the next we explain these instabilities and show how they may be overcome.

In the case of (i) the problem is to ensure that the remainder term in the asymptotic expansion is negligible to the required precision. Perhaps it needs to stressed that it is the remainder term and not the first neglected term in the asymptotic expansion that controls the accuracy. The error bounds supplied in [22] and the hyperasymptotic expansions of [14] and [16] indicate that for a given value of $|z|$ the absolute value of the ratio of the remainder term to the first neglected term may increase from moderate values near the center of the sector of validity to very large values near the boundaries. To put this another way, the closer we are to the boundaries of the sector of validity, the larger the value of $|z|$ has to be in order to achieve a specified precision from the asymptotic expansion. (This is partly why we need to know the maximum sectors of validity.)

In the case of (ii) the problem is to ensure that the cumulative effect of the rounding errors does not become so large as to destroy the precision in the wanted solution. Each integration step along a chosen path $\mathcal{P}$, say, introduces a set of rounding errors. In effect, these contaminate the wanted solution by small multiples of members of a set of independent solutions. Consequently, only when the wanted solution is growing on $\mathcal{P}$ at least as fast as all other solutions can we be assured of stability.

In order to test for stability in (ii), we need to be able to measure the relative rate of growth of solutions. We adopt the following definitions. Let $w_j(z)$ and $w_k(z)$ be solutions with asymptotic forms $w_j(z) \sim e^{\lambda_j z} z^{\mu_j}$ and $w_k(z) \sim e^{\lambda_k z} z^{\mu_k}$ as $z \to \infty$ on $\mathcal{P}$. If $\Re\{(\lambda_j - \lambda_k)z\} \to +\infty$ as $z \to \infty$ on $\mathcal{P}$, then we say that $w_j(z)$ *dominates* $w_k(z)$ as $z \to \infty$ on $\mathcal{P}$; equivalently, $w_k(z)$ *is dominated by* $w_j(z)$ as $z \to \infty$ on $\mathcal{P}$. Second, if $|\Re\{(\lambda_j - \lambda_k)z\}|$ is bounded as $z \to \infty$ on $\mathcal{P}$, we say that $w_j(z)$ *matches* $w_k(z)$ as $z \to \infty$ on $\mathcal{P}$. It should be appreciated that the term "matches" does not imply that the ratio $|w_k(z)/w_j(z)|$ is bounded. In fact if $\Re(\mu_k - \mu_j) > 0$, then generally $|w_k(z)/w_j(z)| \to \infty$ as $z \to \infty$ on $\mathcal{P}$. However, because this kind of growth is algebraic rather then exponential, the resulting instability can be tolerated as a rule. In other words the term "matches" admits a weak form of instability.[9]

Consider now an explicit solution $w_j(\mathcal{J}|z)$, as defined in section 3. Since the angle separating the boundaries of the recessive sector $\mathcal{R}_j(\mathcal{J})$ from the corresponding boundaries of the total region of validity $\mathcal{S}_j(\mathcal{J})$ is π, $\mathcal{R}_j(\mathcal{J})$ lies well within $\mathcal{S}_j(\mathcal{J})$. Accordingly, the computation of $w_j(\mathcal{J}|z)$ from its asymptotic expansion will be stable in $\mathcal{R}_j(\mathcal{J})$.

From property (i) of section 3 it is seen that as z moves *away* from ∞ along any ray in $\mathcal{R}_j(\mathcal{J})$ the wanted solution $w_j(\mathcal{J}|z)$ grows faster than any of the independent solutions $w_k(z)$, $k \neq j$. Hence we may compute initial values $w_j(\mathcal{J}|z)$, $w_j'(\mathcal{J}|z), \ldots$, $w_j^{(n-1)}(\mathcal{J}|z)$ from the expansion (2.8) and its differentiated forms at a point $z = z_\infty$ sufficiently close to infinity in $\mathcal{R}_j(\mathcal{J})$ to control the remainder terms, then integrate step by step from z_∞ towards the origin in a stable manner. In this way we can arrive at a point z_0 in $\mathcal{A}$ such that $\operatorname{ph} z_0 = \operatorname{ph} z_\infty$ and $|z_0|$ is small compared with $|z_\infty|$; see Figure 5.1.

Next, we make the reasonable assumption that there is no rapid growth in the solutions around arcs of the circle $|z| = |z_0|$. Accordingly, we may integrate (2.1) from z_0 around such an arc in the positive sense until we reach a point z_0'', say, in the dominant sector $\mathcal{D}_j^+(\mathcal{J})$. In $\mathcal{D}_j^+(\mathcal{J})$, $w_j(\mathcal{J}|z)$ grows at least as fast as any other solution as we approach ∞, hence we may integrate along outward rays. The complete directed path $\mathcal{P}$ on which integration of (2.1) is stable is indicated on Figure 5.1. Similar considerations apply to the other dominant sector $\mathcal{D}_j^-(\mathcal{J})$.

It remains to consider the intermediate sectors $\mathcal{S}_j^-(\mathcal{J})$ and $\mathcal{S}_j^+(\mathcal{J})$. Let $\mathcal{L}'$ be the part of a fixed ray in either of these sectors that extends to ∞ from a point z_0' on the arc $|z| = |z_0|$. Except possibly when $\mathcal{L}'$ coincides with one of the boundaries of $\mathcal{S}_j^-(\mathcal{J})$ or $\mathcal{S}_j^+(\mathcal{J})$ it is not possible to integrate (2.1) in either direction on $\mathcal{L}'$ because there is always at least one solution that grows faster than $w_j(\mathcal{J}|z)$; see property (ii) of section 3. In order to devise a stable algorithm for computing $w_j(\mathcal{J}|z)$ on $\mathcal{L}'$ we adapt the boundary-value algorithms used by D.W. Lozier [10] and F.W.J. Olver [19] for solving difference equations.[10]

Let $w_k(z)$, $k = 1, 2, \ldots, n$, be a set of n independent solutions of (2.1) such that $w_k(z) \sim e^{\lambda_k z} z^{\mu_k}$ as $z \to \infty$ on $\mathcal{L}'$, with the proviso that $w_j(z) = w_j(\mathcal{J}|z)$. Assume that as $z \to \infty$ on $\mathcal{L}'$, $m-1$ of the solutions dominate $w_j(z)$, q solutions match $w_j(z)$, and the remaining $n - m - q$ solutions are dominated by $w_j(z)$. Here m and q are arbitrary integers such that $1 \leqslant m \leqslant n$ and $0 \leqslant q \leqslant n - m$.

Following [10] we prescribe $m - 1$ boundary conditions, for example, $w_j(z)$, $w_j'(z), \ldots, w_j^{(m-2)}(z)$ at a point $z = z_\infty'$ on $\mathcal{L}'$ sufficiently close to ∞ to enable the asymptotic expansion (2.8) and its differentiated forms to be applied. We also pre-

[9] An alternative formulation that would avoid the notion of weak instability is to replace $\Re\{(\lambda_j - \lambda_k)z\}$ by $\Re\{(\lambda_j - \lambda_k)z + (\mu_j - \mu_k)\ln z\}$ in the definitions. This makes the choice of integration paths $\mathcal{P}$ more complicated, however; compare [22, section 6].

[10] See also [6] for further references.

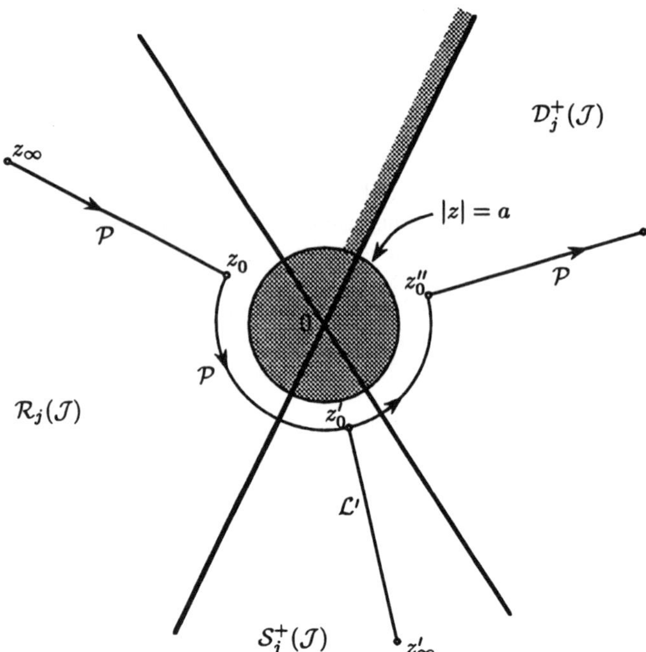

FIG. 5.1. *z-plane. Integration paths for explicit solutions.*

scribe $n-m-q$ boundary conditions, for example, $w_j(z)$, $w_j'(z), \ldots, w_j^{(n-m-q-1)}(z)$ at $z = z_0'$; these are available from the numerical integration already carried out around the arc $|z| = |z_0|$. This choice of boundary conditions has the effect of eliminating the $m-1$ unwanted dominating solutions at ∞, and the $n-m-q$ unwanted dominated solutions at ∞. We need $q+1$ further conditions to select $w_j(z)$ from the set of $q+1$ matching solutions. (In the common case $q = 0$, for example, this means that we need one extra condition to normalize $w_j(z)$.) These further conditions can be distributed at z_0' and z_∞' in various ways, but the analysis is simplest when we place them at one end or the other. Thus we take the $q+1$ further conditions to be either $w_j^{(n-m-q)}(z_0')$, $w_j^{(n-m-q+1)}(z_0'), \ldots, w_j^{(n-m)}(z_0')$, or $w_j^{(m-1)}(z_\infty')$, $w_j^{(m)}(z_\infty'), \ldots, w_j^{(m+q-1)}(z_\infty')$.

In section 7 we show how to solve these boundary-value problems numerically by means of the Taylor-series method. In the remainder of the present section we demonstrate that the boundary-value problems we have just formulated are well posed, in the sense that small perturbations in the boundary values induce only small perturbations in the computed solution. This justifies the replacement of the asymptotic conditions at ∞ by the chosen conditions at the finite points z_0' and z_∞'. However, it needs to be stressed that the particular choices we have made above are critical: in section 8 we demonstrate by means of examples that the other possible combinations of boundary values at z_0' and z_∞' can lead to severe instabilities.

We begin by relabeling the solutions, if necessary, so that the one we want is $w_m(z)$; furthermore, as $z \to \infty$ on $\mathcal{L}'$, $w_1(z)$, $w_2(z), \ldots, w_{m-1}(z)$ dominate $w_m(z)$; $w_{m+1}(z)$, $w_{m+2}(z), \ldots, w_{m+q}(z)$ match $w_m(z)$; $w_{m+q+1}(z)$, $w_{m+q+2}(z), \ldots, w_n(z)$ are dominated by $w_m(z)$. Our prescription for the boundary values then becomes either

$$w_m(z'_\infty),\ w'_m(z'_\infty),\dots,w_m^{(m-2)}(z'_\infty),\quad w_m(z'_0),\ w'_m(z'_0),\dots,w_m^{(n-m)}(z'_0), \tag{5.1}$$

or

$$w_m(z'_\infty),\ w'_m(z'_\infty),\dots,w_m^{(m+q-1)}(z'_\infty),\quad w_m(z'_0),\ w'_m(z'_0),\dots,w_m^{(n-m-q-1)}(z'_0). \tag{5.2}$$

Suppose that we first adopt the conditions (5.1) and then perturb these values by small relative amounts $\varepsilon_1,\ \varepsilon_2,\dots,\ \varepsilon_{m-1}$ in the case of those at z'_∞ and by small absolute amounts $\varepsilon_m,\ \varepsilon_{m+1},\dots,\ \varepsilon_n$ in the case of those at z'_0. The difference between the true solution of the boundary-value problem and the perturbed solution is another solution $w(z)$ of (2.1). Let it be expressed in the form

$$w(z) = a_1w_1(z) + a_2w_2(z) + \cdots + a_nw_n(z). \tag{5.3}$$

Then the coefficients $a_1,\ a_2,\dots,a_n$ satisfy the equations

$$\begin{aligned}
&a_1w_1(z'_\infty) + a_2w_2(z'_\infty) + \cdots + a_nw_n(z'_\infty) = \varepsilon_1 w_m(z'_\infty),\\
&a_1w'_1(z'_\infty) + a_2w'_2(z'_\infty) + \cdots + a_nw'_n(z'_\infty) = \varepsilon_2 w'_m(z'_\infty),\\
&\qquad\vdots\\
&a_1w_1^{(m-2)}(z'_\infty) + a_2w_2^{(m-2)}(z'_\infty) + \cdots + a_nw_n^{(m-2)}(z'_\infty) = \varepsilon_{m-1} w_m^{(m-2)}(z'_\infty),\\
&a_1w_1(z'_0) + a_2w_2(z'_0) + \cdots + a_nw_n(z'_0) = \varepsilon_m,\\
&a_1w'_1(z'_0) + a_2w'_2(z'_0) + \cdots + a_nw'_n(z'_0) = \varepsilon_{m+1},\\
&\qquad\vdots\\
&a_1w_1^{(n-m)}(z'_0) + a_2w_2^{(n-m)}(z'_0) + \cdots + a_nw_n^{(n-m)}(z'_0) = \varepsilon_n.
\end{aligned}$$

Let $D_{m,n}(z'_0)$ denote the determinant

$$D_{m,n}(z'_0) = \begin{vmatrix} w_m(z'_0) & \cdots & w_n(z'_0)\\ \vdots & \ddots & \vdots\\ w_m^{(n-m)}(z'_0) & \cdots & w_n^{(n-m)}(z'_0)\end{vmatrix}, \tag{5.4}$$

and assume for the moment that

$$D_{m,n}(z'_0) \neq 0. \tag{5.5}$$

If D denotes the determinant of the above system of linear algebraic equations for $a_1,\ a_2,\dots,a_n$, then by examining the relative rates of growth of the solutions $w_1(z)$, $w_2(z),\dots,w_n(z)$ for large z on $\mathcal{L}'$ and selecting the dominant $(m-1)\times(m-1)$ minor from the first $m-1$ rows of D we conclude that as $z'_\infty \to \infty$ on $\mathcal{L}'$

$$D \sim D_{m,n}(z'_0)\begin{vmatrix} w_1(z'_\infty) & \cdots & w_{m-1}(z'_\infty)\\ \vdots & \ddots & \vdots\\ w_1^{(m-2)}(z'_\infty) & \cdots & w_{m-1}^{(m-2)}(z'_\infty)\end{vmatrix},$$

and hence

$$D \sim D_{m,n}(z'_0) \prod_{1\leqslant k<l\leqslant m-1} (\lambda_l - \lambda_k) \prod_{k=1}^{m-1} w_k(z'_\infty). \tag{5.6}$$

Next, by application of Cramer's rule we see that

$$Da_l = \varepsilon\mathcal{O}(z_\infty'^{\mu}) \prod_{k=1}^{m}{}' w_k(z_\infty'), \qquad 1 \leqslant l \leqslant m-1, \tag{5.7}$$

and

$$Da_l = \hat{\varepsilon}\mathcal{O}(1) \prod_{k=1}^{m-1} w_k(z_\infty'), \qquad m \leqslant l \leqslant n. \tag{5.8}$$

Here ε denotes the infinity norm for the perturbations $\varepsilon_1, \varepsilon_2, \ldots, \varepsilon_n$; $\hat{\varepsilon}$ denotes the infinity norm for the perturbations $\varepsilon_m, \varepsilon_{m+1}, \ldots, \varepsilon_n$; the prime on products means that the factor corresponding to $k = l$ is to be omitted; μ denotes a generic constant with nonnegative real part. (Actually μ here will be $\mu_k - \mu_m$ for some value of k in the set $m, m+1, \ldots, m+q$.)

If $1 \leqslant l \leqslant m-1$, then on dividing (5.7) by (5.6) we obtain

$$a_l w_l(z_\infty') = \varepsilon\mathcal{O}(z_\infty'^{\mu}) w_m(z_\infty'). \tag{5.9}$$

This means that the term $a_l w_l(z)$ in (5.3) contributes at worst a weak instability at $z = z_\infty'$. And because $w_m(z)$ grows faster than $w_l(z)$ as we proceed from z_∞' to z_0' the same is true for all the other values of z on $\mathcal{L}'$.

Alternatively, if $m \leqslant l \leqslant n$, then from (5.6) and (5.8) we have

$$a_l = \hat{\varepsilon}\mathcal{O}(1). \tag{5.10}$$

Again, since $w_m(z)$ either matches or dominates $w_l(z)$ as we proceed from z_0' to z_∞', the term $a_l w_l(z)$ can contribute only weak instability anywhere on $\mathcal{L}'$.

On combining these results we conclude that the conditions (5.1) correspond to a well-posed boundary-value problem on $\mathcal{L}'$, or at worst a weakly unstable problem when $\Re\mu$ is positive.[11]

When the condition (5.5) is violated, the foregoing analysis breaks down. However, $D_{m,n}(z)$ cannot vanish for all values of z in the neighborhood of $z = z_0$. (If it did, then it would be identically zero everywhere, in contradiction of the asymptotic relation

$$D_{m,n}(z) \sim e^{(\lambda_m+\lambda_{m+1}+\cdots+\lambda_n)z} z^{\mu_m+\mu_{m+1}+\cdots+\mu_n} \prod_{m\leqslant k<l\leqslant n} (\lambda_l - \lambda_k) \tag{5.11}$$

as $z \to \infty$ on $\mathcal{L}'$.) Hence we can perturb z_0' slightly on $\mathcal{L}'$ so as to satisfy (5.5) before setting up the boundary-value problem. See also section 8.1 below.

The analysis of the boundary-value problem prescribed by (5.2) is similar. The conclusions are the same, except that condition (5.5) is replaced by

$$D_{m+q+1,n}(z_0') \neq 0. \tag{5.12}$$

There does, however, remain a possible stability problem for the intermediate sectors. When $\beta_j - \alpha_j$ is close to π, the outer boundaries of $\mathcal{S}_j^-(\mathcal{J}) \cup \mathcal{S}_j^+(\mathcal{J})$ approach the boundaries of $\mathcal{S}_j(\mathcal{J})$. Accordingly, on rays $\mathcal{L}'$ in $\mathcal{S}_j^-(\mathcal{J}) \cup \mathcal{S}_j^+(\mathcal{J})$ close to these

[11]In the common case $q = 0$, that is, when none of the other solutions $w_k(z)$ matches $w_m(z)$ as $z \to \infty$ on $\mathcal{L}'$, μ is zero and weak instability cannot occur.

boundaries the evaluation of $w_j(\mathcal{J}|z)$ ($w_m(z)$ when relabeled) and its derivatives from their asymptotic expansions will be unstable. One way of overcoming this difficulty is to use the more accurate hyperasymptotic expansions of [14]. Another is to use connection formulas. However, it is interesting to note that this instability affects the solution of the boundary-value problem (5.1) only when z is in the vicinity of z'_∞.[12] This can be seen as follows.

Since the values of $w_m(z'_\infty)$, $w'_m(z'_\infty), \ldots, w_m^{(m-2)}(z'_\infty)$ are inaccurate, the perturbation norm ε in equations (5.7) and (5.9) is no longer small. Nevertheless, in (5.9) the effect of a large ε is soon offset as z moves away from z'_∞ towards z'_0: this is because $w_l(z)$ decays more rapidly than $w_m(z)$ when $1 \leqslant l \leqslant m-1$. For the other values of l equations (5.8) and (5.10) are unaffected, since the perturbation norm $\hat{\varepsilon}$ continues to be small.

Similar analysis may be applied to the boundary-value problem corresponding to (5.2), but here the conclusion is different: instability in the values of $w_m(z)$ and its derivatives at z'_∞ affects the computed values of $w_m(z)$ for all values of z on $\mathcal{L}'$ and not just those in the vicinity of z'_∞. *Accordingly, conditions* (5.1) *are to be preferred to* (5.2).

6. Computation of implicit solutions. In the previous section we saw that once we are able to generate values of an explicit solution and its derivatives around a circular arc of moderate radius in the annulus $\mathcal{A}$, we can compute this solution elsewhere in $\mathcal{A}$ either by direct integration or by solving an appropriate boundary-value problem. The same is true of implicit solutions. However, we are unable to begin the process in the same way because there is no recessive sector. Instead, we start by setting up a boundary-value problem, but of a different type.

Let the solution $w_j(\mathcal{J}|z)$ of section 2 be implicit. Since (3.2) applies the angle of $\mathcal{S}_j(\mathcal{J})$ lies in the interval $(\pi, 2\pi]$. Accordingly, we can find two fixed rays $\mathcal{L}$, $\mathcal{L}'$, say, with the following properties:

(i) $\mathcal{L}$, $\mathcal{L}' \subset \mathcal{S}_j(\mathcal{J})$.

(ii) The angle from $\mathcal{L}$ to $\mathcal{L}'$ is π.

(iii) Neither $\mathcal{L}$ nor $\mathcal{L}'$ coincides with any of the anti-Stokes lines, that is, $\theta_{jk} + \operatorname{ph} z$ is not an odd multiple of $\frac{1}{2}\pi$ on $\mathcal{L}$ or $\mathcal{L}'$ for all unequal values of j and k.

Let $\mathcal{H}$ be the closed half-plane bounded by $\mathcal{L} \cup \mathcal{L}'$ that lies in $\mathcal{S}_j(\mathcal{J})$. From the paragraph following Theorem 2.3 there exists a set of unique solutions $w_k(z)$, $k = 1, 2, \ldots, n$, such that $w_k(z) \sim e^{\lambda_k z} z^{\mu_k}$ as $z \to \infty$ uniformly in $\mathcal{H}$; furthermore $w_j(z) = w_j(\mathcal{J}|z)$. Next, $\Re\{(\lambda_k - \lambda_j)z\}$ is nonzero when $k \neq j$ and $z (\neq 0)$ lies on $\mathcal{L} \cup \mathcal{L}'$. Let $m-1$, with $2 \leqslant m \leqslant n-1$, be the number of values of k for which $\Re\{(\lambda_k - \lambda_j)z\}$ is positive on $\mathcal{L} \setminus \{0\}$. Then $m-1$ of the solutions $w_k(z)$ dominate $w_j(\mathcal{J}|z)$ as $z \to \infty$ on $\mathcal{L}$, and are dominated by $w_j(\mathcal{J}|z)$ as $z \to \infty$ on $\mathcal{L}'$. For the other $n-m$ solutions the dominance vis-à-vis $w_j(\mathcal{J}|z)$ is reversed.

As in section 5, we eliminate the dominant solutions on $\mathcal{L}$ by prescribing $m-1$ boundary values at a point z_∞ on $\mathcal{L}$ sufficiently close to ∞ to enable the asymptotic expansion (2.8) and its differentiated forms to be applied. These values can be $w_j(\mathcal{J}|z_\infty)$, $w'_j(\mathcal{J}|z_\infty), \ldots, w_j^{(m-2)}(\mathcal{J}|z_\infty)$. Similarly, to eliminate the dominant solutions on $\mathcal{L}'$ we prescribe $w_j(\mathcal{J}|z'_\infty)$, $w'_j(\mathcal{J}|z'_\infty), \ldots, w_j^{(n-m-1)}(\mathcal{J}|z'_\infty)$, where z'_∞ is on $\mathcal{L}'$ and again sufficiently close to infinity to enable (2.8) and its differentiated forms to be applied. One extra boundary condition is needed to normalize the wanted solution. This can be, e.g., $w_j^{(m-1)}(\mathcal{J}|z_\infty)$ or $w_j^{(n-m)}(\mathcal{J}|z'_\infty)$. Either of the resulting sets of n

[12] Compare also a similar phenomenon in the solution of difference equations [10], [19].

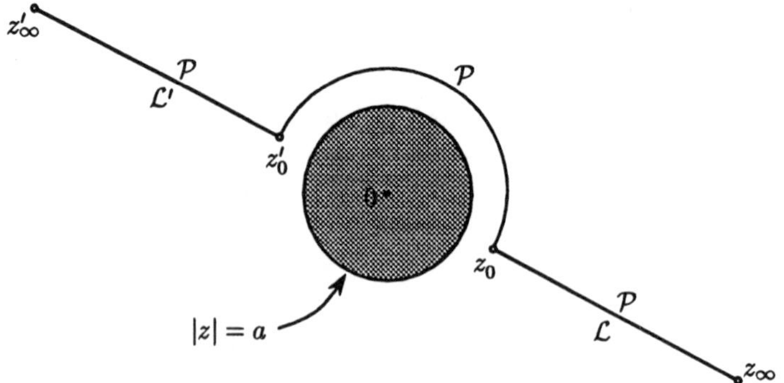

FIG. 6.1. *z-plane. Integration path $\mathcal{P}$ for implicit solutions.*

conditions is taken in conjunction with an integration path $\mathcal{P}$ in $\mathcal{A} \cap \mathcal{S}_j(\mathcal{J})$ joining z_∞ and z'_∞, and comprising parts of the rays $\mathcal{L}$ and $\mathcal{L}'$ together with a semicircular arc; see Figure 6.1.

As in section 5 we need to demonstrate that the boundary-value problems formulated above are well posed. The method is similar. Let us relabel the solutions so that the one we want, $w_j(\mathcal{J}|z)$, is $w_m(z)$; furthermore, $w_1(z), w_2(z), \ldots, w_{m-1}(z)$ dominate $w_m(z)$ as $z \to \infty$ on $\mathcal{L}$, and $w_{m+1}(z), w_{m+2}(z), \ldots, w_n(z)$ dominate $w_m(z)$ as $z \to \infty$ on $\mathcal{L}'$. Our boundary-value prescriptions become either

$$(6.1) \quad w_m(z_\infty),\ w'_m(z_\infty), \ldots, w_m^{(m-2)}(z_\infty), \quad w_m(z'_\infty),\ w'_m(z'_\infty), \ldots, w_m^{(n-m)}(z'_\infty),$$

or

$$(6.2) \quad w_m(z_\infty),\ w'_m(z_\infty), \ldots, w_m^{(m-1)}(z_\infty), \quad w_m(z'_\infty),\ w'_m(z'_\infty), \ldots, w_m^{(n-m-1)}(z'_\infty).$$

Let us first adopt (6.1) and then perturb these values by small relative amounts $\varepsilon_1, \varepsilon_2, \ldots, \varepsilon_n$, respectively. The corresponding perturbation in the solution is again given by (5.3), where now

$$\begin{aligned}
a_1 w_1(z_\infty) &+ a_2 w_2(z_\infty) + \cdots + a_n w_n(z_\infty) = \varepsilon_1 w_m(z_\infty),\\
a_1 w'_1(z_\infty) &+ a_2 w'_2(z_\infty) + \cdots + a_n w'_n(z_\infty) = \varepsilon_2 w'_m(z_\infty),\\
&\vdots\\
a_1 w_1^{(m-2)}(z_\infty) &+ a_2 w_2^{(m-2)}(z_\infty) + \cdots + a_n w_n^{(m-2)}(z_\infty) = \varepsilon_{m-1} w_m^{(m-2)}(z_\infty),\\
a_1 w_1(z'_\infty) &+ a_2 w_2(z'_\infty) + \cdots + a_n w_n(z'_\infty) = \varepsilon_m w_m(z'_\infty),\\
a_1 w'_1(z'_\infty) &+ a_2 w'_2(z'_\infty) + \cdots + a_n w'_n(z'_\infty) = \varepsilon_{m+1} w'_m(z'_\infty),\\
&\vdots\\
a_1 w_1^{(n-m)}(z'_\infty) &+ a_2 w_2^{(n-m)}(z'_\infty) + \cdots + a_n w_n^{(n-m)}(z'_\infty) = \varepsilon_n w_m^{(n-m)}(z'_\infty).
\end{aligned}$$

As $z_\infty \to \infty$ and $z'_\infty \to \infty$ we see by selecting dominant minors that the determinant D of this system of equations satisfies

$$D \sim \begin{vmatrix} w_1(z_\infty) & \cdots & w_{m-1}(z_\infty) \\ \vdots & \ddots & \vdots \\ w_1^{(m-2)}(z_\infty) & \cdots & w_{m-1}^{(m-2)}(z_\infty) \end{vmatrix} \times \begin{vmatrix} w_m(z'_\infty) & \cdots & w_n(z'_\infty) \\ \vdots & \ddots & \vdots \\ w_m^{(n-m)}(z'_\infty) & \cdots & w_n^{(n-m)}(z'_\infty) \end{vmatrix}$$

and hence

$$D \sim \prod_{1\leqslant k<l\leqslant m-1} (\lambda_l - \lambda_k) \prod_{m\leqslant k<l\leqslant n} (\lambda_l - \lambda_k) \prod_{k=1}^{m-1} w_k(z_\infty) \prod_{k=m}^{n} w_k(z'_\infty); \tag{6.3}$$

compare (5.6). Again, by application of Cramer's rule we find that

$$Da_l = \varepsilon \mathcal{O}(1) \prod_{k=1}^{m}{}' w_k(z_\infty) \prod_{k=m}^{n} w_k(z'_\infty), \qquad 1 \leqslant l \leqslant m-1,$$

and

$$Da_l = \hat{\varepsilon}\mathcal{O}(1) w_m(z'_\infty) \prod_{k=1}^{m-1} w_k(z_\infty) \prod_{k=m}^{n}{}' w_k(z'_\infty), \qquad m \leqslant l \leqslant n,$$

where ε, $\hat{\varepsilon}$, and the primes on the products have the same significance as in section 5. From these equations and (6.3) we deduce that

$$a_l w_l(z_\infty) = \varepsilon \mathcal{O}(1) w_m(z_\infty), \qquad 1 \leqslant l \leqslant m-1, \tag{6.4}$$

$$a_l w_l(z'_\infty) = \hat{\varepsilon} \mathcal{O}(1) w_m(z'_\infty), \qquad m \leqslant l \leqslant n. \tag{6.5}$$

Hence by reasoning similar to that of section 5 we conclude that the conditions (6.1) correspond to a well-posed boundary-value problem for the wanted solution $w_m(z)$. By similar analysis, or by appealing to symmetry, we reach the same conclusion for conditions (6.2). We also note in passing that the problems as presently formulated are free from the phenomenon of weak instability.

The main objective in solving the foregoing boundary-value problems is to generate values of $w_j(\mathcal{J}|z) \equiv w_m(z)$, and its derivatives, on the semicircular arc depicted in Figure 6.1. Once we have these values we can integrate along a longer arc of the same radius if needed. And as already indicated, we can generate values of $w_j(\mathcal{J}|z)$ elsewhere in $\mathcal{S}_j(\mathcal{J})$ by setting up boundary-value problems similar to these already described for explicit solutions.

A remaining difficulty arises when one or both of the rays $\mathcal{L}$, $\mathcal{L}'$ happen to be close to a boundary of $\mathcal{S}_j(\mathcal{J})$. Again, this causes instability in the evaluation of $w_j(\mathcal{J}|z)$ and its derivatives from their asymptotic expansions. As in section 5 this difficulty can be overcome by using instead the hyperasymptotic expansions of [14]. Alternatively, we may rotate $\mathcal{L}$ and $\mathcal{L}'$ away from the boundaries of $\mathcal{S}_j(\mathcal{J})$.[13] The latter approach is illustrated by numerical examples in section 8.

7. Numerical implementation of the boundary-value problems by the Taylor-series method. The method we use for solving the differential equation (2.1) numerically over a finite path $\mathcal{P}$ in the complex plane is based on analytic continuation by Taylor-series expansions. We choose this method because of its mathematical simplicity, not because of its efficacy.

Let $\mathcal{P}$ be subdivided at nodal points t_p, $p = 0, 1, \ldots, P$, P being arbitrary and t_0 and t_P coinciding with the endpoints. As indicated in Figure 7.1 these nodes need not be equispaced.

Let $w(z)$ be the solution we are computing on $\mathcal{P}$. By Taylor's theorem

$$w(t_{p+1}) = \sum_{s=0}^{\infty} \frac{\tau_p^s}{s!} w^{(s)}(t_p), \tag{7.1}$$

[13]This may be at the price of reintroducing the phenomenon of weak instability.

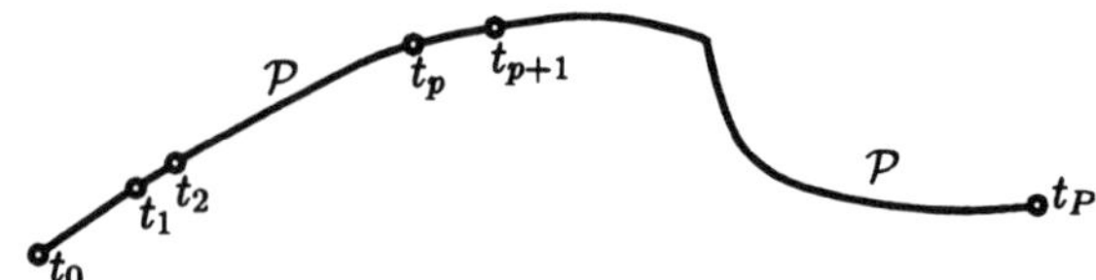

FIG. 7.1. *z-plane. Integration path $\mathcal{P}$ with nodes $t_0, t_1, \ldots, t_P$.*

where $\tau_p = t_{p+1} - t_p$. All derivatives of $w(z)$ can be expressed in terms of $w(z)$ and its first $n-1$ derivatives by use of (2.1) and its differentiated forms. In this way we find that

$$w^{(s)}(z) = \sum_{l=0}^{n-1} F_{sl}(z) w^{(l)}(z), \tag{7.2}$$

where

$$F_{sl}(z) = \delta_{sl}, \qquad s = 0, 1, \ldots, n-1, \tag{7.3}$$

δ_{sl} being the usual Kronecker symbol, and

$$F_{sl}(z) = F_{s-1,l-1}(z) + F'_{s-1,l}(z) - f_l(z) F_{s-1,n-1}(z), \qquad s = n, n+1, \ldots, \tag{7.4}$$

with the understanding that $F_{s,-1}(z) = 0$. These equations enable the functions $F_{sl}(z)$ to be generated recursively.

If we now substitute into the expansion (7.1), and its first $n-1$ differentiated forms, by means of (7.2) we obtain

$$\begin{bmatrix} w(t_{p+1}) \\ w'(t_{p+1}) \\ \vdots \\ w^{(n-1)}(t_{p+1}) \end{bmatrix} = \mathbf{G}(\tau_p, t_p) \begin{bmatrix} w(t_p) \\ w'(t_p) \\ \vdots \\ w^{(n-1)}(t_p) \end{bmatrix},$$

$\mathbf{G}(\tau, z)$ being an $n \times n$ matrix whose $(k+1, l+1)$th element is given by

$$G_{kl}(\tau, z) = \sum_{s=0}^{\infty} \frac{\tau^s}{s!} F_{s+k,l}(z). \tag{7.5}$$

Clearly $\mathbf{G}(\tau, z)$ depends only on the coefficients in the original differential equation and not on its solutions.

We may now cast all the boundary-value problems into a single matrix form. Let $\mathbf{X}$ be the column vector of length $nP+n$ whose elements $x_1, x_2, \ldots, x_{nP+n}$ are defined by

$$x_{np+l+1} = w^{(l)}(t_p), \qquad l = 0, 1, \ldots, n-1, \qquad p = 0, 1, \ldots, P. \tag{7.6}$$

Then

$$\mathbf{GX} = \mathbf{0}, \tag{7.7}$$

where $\mathbf{G}$ is the $(nP) \times (nP+n)$ matrix

$$(7.8) \qquad \mathbf{G} = \begin{bmatrix} -\mathbf{G}(\tau_0, t_0) & \mathbf{I} & \mathbf{0} & \cdots & \mathbf{0} & \mathbf{0} \\ \mathbf{0} & -\mathbf{G}(\tau_1, t_1) & \mathbf{I} & \cdots & \mathbf{0} & \mathbf{0} \\ \vdots & & \ddots & & & \vdots \\ \vdots & & & \ddots & & \vdots \\ \mathbf{0} & \mathbf{0} & \mathbf{0} & \cdots & -\mathbf{G}(\tau_{P-1}, t_{P-1}) & \mathbf{I} \end{bmatrix},$$

in which $\mathbf{I}$ denotes the $n \times n$ unit matrix.

Equation (7.7) represents a set of nP homogeneous linear algebraic equations in the $nP+n$ quantities $x_1, x_2, \ldots, x_{nP+n}$. The remaining n equations that are needed are supplied by the boundary values of $w(z)$ and its derivatives at $z = t_0$ and $z = t_P$. Suppose that (as in (5.1) and (6.1)) the values of $w(z)$, $w'(z), \ldots, w^{(m-2)}(z)$ are given at $z = t_0$ and the values of $w(z)$, $w'(z), \ldots, w^{(n-m)}(z)$ are given at $z = t_P$. Then we move all terms in (7.7) that contain the known elements $x_1, x_2, \ldots, x_{m-1}, x_{nP+1}, x_{nP+2}, \ldots, x_{nP+n-m+1}$ to the right-hand side and delete columns $1, 2, \ldots, m-1$ and $nP+1, nP+2, \ldots, nP+n-m+1$ from the matrix $\mathbf{G}$. In this way we arrive at a system of nP inhomogeneous linear algebraic equations for the remaining nP unknowns. These can be solved by stable algorithms, for example, Gaussian elimination with pivoting. Moreover, the error analysis of Wilkinson [33, Chapter 4] indicates that the net effect of rounding errors made during the process of solution is equivalent to small perturbations in the boundary values, and we have already demonstrated in sections 5 and 6 that these have no adverse effects on the final solutions.

We observe in passing that although we constructed equation (7.7) as a discrete formulation of a boundary-value problem, it also includes initial-value problems, that is, direct step-by-step integration by the Taylor-series method. (This is used for explicit solutions; compare section 5.) We have only to set $m = n+1$, that is, to regard $x_1, x_2, \ldots, x_n$ as the known elements of the vector $\mathbf{X}$.

8. Numerical examples. As in [14] we use the equation

$$(8.1) \qquad w^{(4)}(z) - 3w^{(3)}(z) + \left(\tfrac{9}{4} + \tfrac{1}{2}z^{-2}\right) w^{(2)}(z) - \left(3 + \tfrac{3}{4}z^{-2}\right) w'(z) + \left(\tfrac{5}{4} + \tfrac{9}{16}z^{-2}\right) w(z) = 0.$$

Here $n = 4$ and

$$\lambda_1 = \tfrac{1}{2}, \qquad \lambda_2 = 2\tfrac{1}{2}, \qquad \lambda_3 = i, \qquad \lambda_4 = -i,$$

as in section 4 above. We also have $\mu_1 = \mu_2 = \mu_3 = \mu_4 = 0$.[14] We address the following problems: computation of the explicit solution $w_3(\mathcal{J}_1|z)$, the implicit solutions $w_1(\mathcal{J}_1|z)$ and $w_1(\mathcal{J}_5|z)$, and the Stokes multipliers for these solutions. Again, as in section 4, $\mathcal{J}_1 = (-\frac{5}{4}\pi, \frac{3}{4}\pi]$ and $\mathcal{J}_5 = (-\frac{7}{4}\pi, \frac{1}{4}\pi]$. In the notation of [14] the three solutions are denoted respectively by $w_3(z, \eta)$ where $\eta \in (\theta_{32}, \theta_{34}+2\pi)$, $w_1(z, \tilde{\eta})$ where $\tilde{\eta} \in (\theta_{13}, \theta_{14}+2\pi)$, and $w_1(z, \hat{\eta})$ where $\hat{\eta} \in (\theta_{12}, \theta_{13})$. Here the θ_{jk}'s are elements of $\mathcal{J}_1$; compare Figure 4.2.

All computations have been carried out with the aid of the Maple computer algebra package [7].

[14] In this example, the fact that the μ's are all equal eliminates the phenomenon of weak instability as described in section 5.

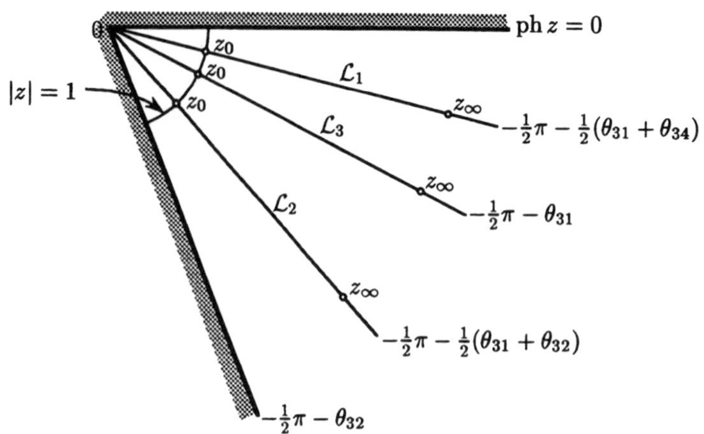

FIG. 8.1. *z-plane. Sector* $\mathcal{S}_3^-(\mathcal{J}_1)$.

8.1. Computation of $w_3(\mathcal{J}_1|z)$. The recessive, intermediate, and dominant sectors for $w_3(\mathcal{J}_1|z)$ are indicated in Figure 4.5. We shall compute this solution along the rays $\mathcal{L}_k$, $k = 1, 2, 3$, defined by

$$\mathcal{L}_1: \quad \text{ph}\, z = -\tfrac{1}{2}\pi - \tfrac{1}{2}(\theta_{31} + \theta_{34}) = (-0.073791808825217\ldots)\pi,$$
$$\mathcal{L}_2: \quad \text{ph}\, z = -\tfrac{1}{2}\pi - \tfrac{1}{2}(\theta_{31} + \theta_{32}) = (-0.263232338029795\ldots)\pi,$$
$$\mathcal{L}_3: \quad \text{ph}\, z = -\tfrac{1}{2}\pi - \theta_{31} = (-0.147583617650433\ldots)\pi.$$

These rays all lie within the intermediate sector $\mathcal{S}_3^-(\mathcal{J}_1)$. Following section 5, with a slight change of notation, we set up boundary-value problems on segments $z_0 z_\infty$ of the $\mathcal{L}_k$; see Figure 8.1.

The points z_∞ must be sufficiently close to ∞ to enable $w_3(\mathcal{J}_1|z)$ and its derivatives to be computed accurately from the asymptotic expansion (2.8) and its differentiated forms. Since the least value of $|\lambda_3 - \lambda_k|$ for $k = 1, 2, 4$ is $\frac{1}{2}\sqrt{5}$ we know from [14, section 7] that as $s \to \infty$ the coefficient a_{s3} is of order $\Gamma(s)(\frac{1}{2}\sqrt{5})^{-s}$. The optimum value of s in (2.8) with $j = 3$ is therefore $\text{int}[\frac{1}{2}\sqrt{5}|z|]$. We also know from [22, sections 9 and 11] that in $\mathcal{S}_3^-$ the truncation error in (2.8) will be a moderate-sized multiple of the first neglected term. If we take $|z| = 21$, then $s = 23$ and $\Gamma(s)(\frac{1}{2}\sqrt{5})^{-s}|z|^{-s} = 10^{-10.5}$, approximately. In consequence, with $|z_\infty| = 21$ and optimum truncation we expect the asymptotic expansions to yield an accuracy of 10 to 11 significant figures.

To compute $w_3(\mathcal{J}_1|z)$ and its derivatives at points z_0 located on the unit circle, we first integrated (8.1) step by step along the line $\Re z = 1$ in the recessive sector $\mathcal{R}_3(\mathcal{J}_1)$ from $z = 1 + 21i$ to $z = 1$. Initial values at $1 + 21i$ were computed from optimized truncations of (2.8) and its differentiated forms; again we expect 10 to 11 significant figures of accuracy. The number of integration steps used was 40, with 33 terms in the Taylor-series expansions. After reaching $z = 1$ the numerical integrations were continued around the unit circle in the negative sense until the points z_0 were reached. Table 8.1 gives the computed values of $w_3(\mathcal{J}_1|z)$ and its first three derivatives at $z = z_\infty$ and $z = z_0$.

Let us now formulate the three boundary-value problems.

TABLE 8.1
Boundary values.

	$k = 1$	$k = 2$	$k = 3$
$w_3(\mathcal{J}_1\|z_\infty)$	-1.51275494452 $+124.669025707i$	-400949.161514 $+5150793.49233i$	11981.5059205 $-864.921239606i$
$w_3'(\mathcal{J}_1\|z_\infty)$	-124.700874467 $-1.52375642435i$	-5150780.63814 $-402476.436336i$	862.752991977 $+11984.0676324i$
$w_3''(\mathcal{J}_1\|z_\infty)$	1.53751505085 $-124.731246351i$	403901.980634 $-5150659.74367i$	-11986.3488809 $+860.437593603i$
$w_3'''(\mathcal{J}_1\|z_\infty)$	124.759795718 $+1.55376687272i$	5150452.33765 $+405224.297031i$	-858.019580055 $-11988.3453158i$
$w_3(\mathcal{J}_1\|z_0)$	0.744821677641 $+0.969999123059i$	1.69742528458 $+1.15792900686i$	1.03055344919 $+1.12648184224i$
$w_3'(\mathcal{J}_1\|z_0)$	-0.975020770943 $+0.786740941215i$	-1.19794681343 $+1.79377841622i$	-1.14224918609 $+1.08844394262i$
$w_3''(\mathcal{J}_1\|z_0)$	-0.835188443653 $-1.026470383747i$	-1.82847299744 $-1.35231345912i$	-1.13609041664 $-1.22655108060i$
$w_3'''(\mathcal{J}_1\|z_0)$	1.149127536878 $-0.812921942425i$	1.46284549206 $-1.61957544301i$	1.36318987942 $-1.05174536609i$

As $z \to \infty$ on $\mathcal{L}_1$, the solution $w_3(\mathcal{J}_1|z)$ is dominated by $w_1(\mathcal{J}_1|z)$ and $w_2(\mathcal{J}_1|z)$, and dominates $w_4(\mathcal{J}_1|z)$. In the notation of section 5 we have $m = 3$, $q = 0$. Accordingly, our stable prescriptions (5.1) and (5.2) for the boundary values become $w_3(\mathcal{J}_1|z_\infty)$, $w_3'(\mathcal{J}_1|z_\infty)$, $w_3(\mathcal{J}_1|z_0)$, $w_3'(\mathcal{J}_1|z_0)$ and $w_3(\mathcal{J}_1|z_\infty)$, $w_3'(\mathcal{J}_1|z_\infty)$, $w_3''(\mathcal{J}_1|z_\infty)$, $w_3(\mathcal{J}_1|z_0)$. Using an obvious notation we call these prescriptions [2,2] and [3,1], respectively.

On $\mathcal{L}_2$ $w_3(\mathcal{J}_1|z)$ is dominated by $w_2(\mathcal{J}_1|z)$ and dominates $w_1(\mathcal{J}_1|z)$ and $w_4(\mathcal{J}_1|z)$. Hence $m = 2$, $q = 0$, and our stable prescriptions are [1,3] and [2,2].

Lastly, on $\mathcal{L}_3$ $w_3(\mathcal{J}_1|z)$ is dominated by $w_2(\mathcal{J}_1|z)$, matches $w_1(\mathcal{J}_1|z)$ and dominates $w_4(\mathcal{J}_1|z)$. Hence $m = 2$, $q = 1$, and our stable prescriptions are [1,3] and [3,1].

We applied the method described in section 7, in each case taking 41 nodal points and 33 terms in the Taylor-series expansions.

To illustrate the stability theory of section 5 we actually solved the boundary-value problem in each of the cases $k = 1, 2, 3$ with all five possible prescriptions [0,4], [1,3], [2,2], [3,1], and [4,0]. The results are compared graphically in Figures 8.2, 8.3, and 8.4.

In these diagrams the horizontal scale corresponds to the nodal points and the vertical scale represents the logarithm to base 10 of the relative precision (rp)[15] when compared with the **[2,2]** solution when $k = 1$, and the **[1,3]** solution when $k = 2, 3$.[16] Predicted stable prescriptions are indicated in boldface type.

We first observe from the graphs that in each of the cases $k = 1, 2, 3$, the rp's of the solutions for the prescriptions given in bold nowhere exceeds $10^{-10.3}$. This implies agreement to between 10 and 11 significant figures. We can claim that this stability confirms the conclusions of the perturbation analysis of section 5, provided we can verify that conditions (5.5) and (5.12) are satisfied. This can be carried out straightforwardly. For example, when $k = 1$ and 3, condition (5.12) reduces to

[15]By "relative precision" of two nonzero real or complex numbers x and $\hat{x}$, say, we mean $|\ln(x/\hat{x})|$. When x and $\hat{x}$ are nearly equal this quantity is almost indistinguishable numerically from the relative errors $|(x/\hat{x}) - 1|$ and $|(\hat{x}/x) - 1|$. One advantage of rp is that it is a metric. See [21].

[16]We selected the "basis" solution in each case in accordance with the preference stated in the final sentence of section 5.

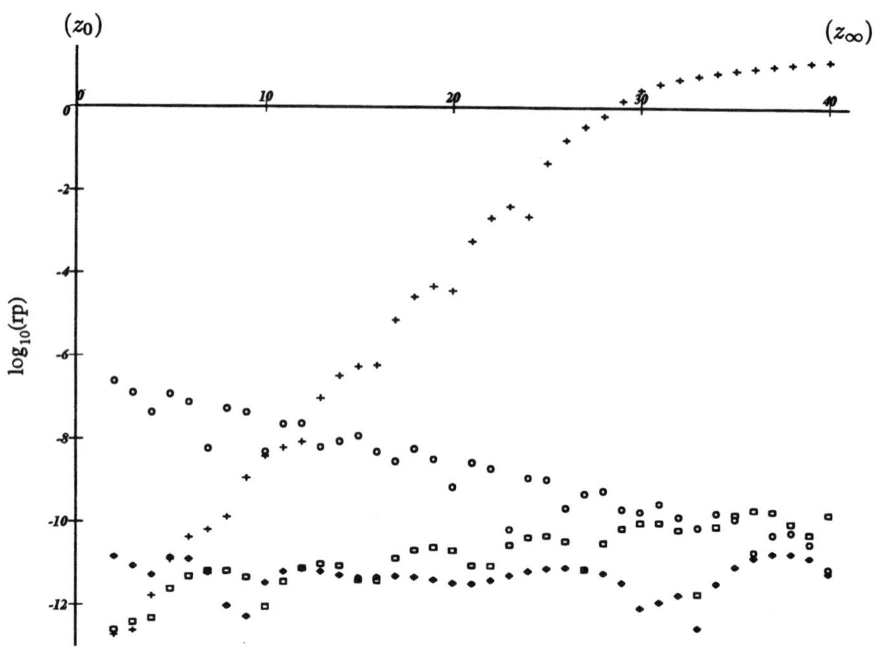

FIG. 8.2. $k = 1$. *Relative precision (rp) compared with* **[2,2]** *solution.* [0,4] +++. [1,3] □□□. **[3,1]** ◇◇◇. [4,0] ○○○.

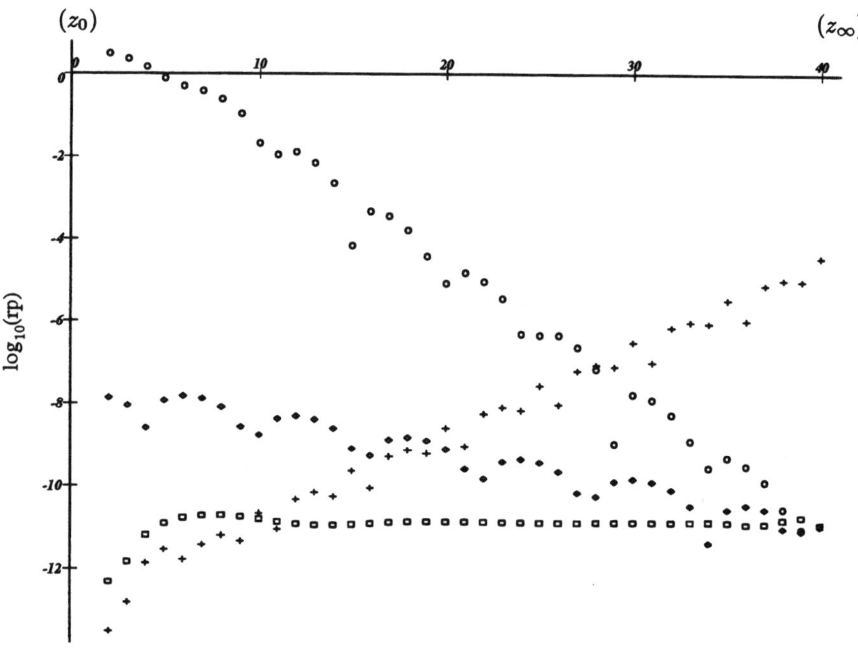

FIG. 8.3. $k = 2$. *Relative precision (rp) compared with* **[1,3]** *solution.* [0,4] +++. **[2,2]** □□□. [3,1] ◇◇◇. [4,0] ○○○.

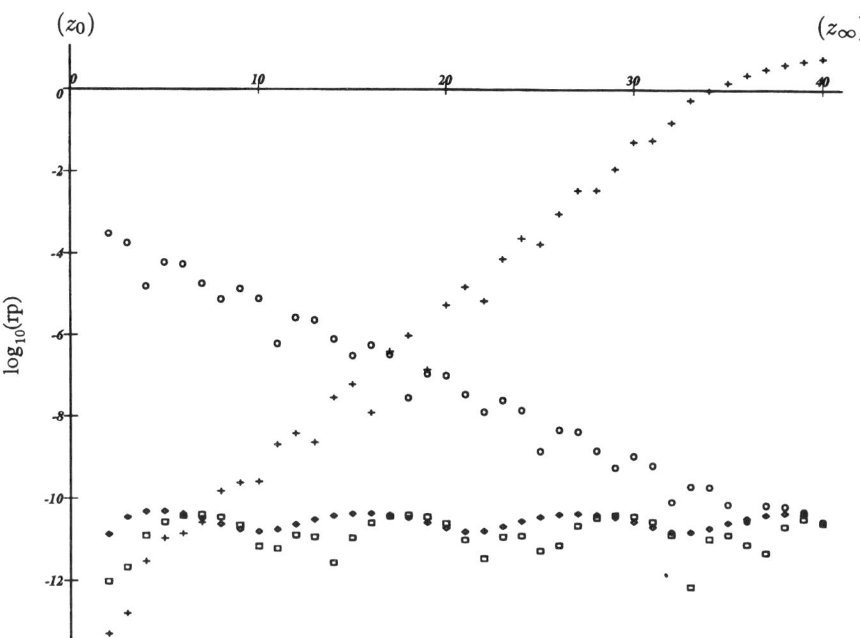

FIG. 8.4. $k = 3$. *Relative precision (rp) compared with* **[1,3]** *solution.* [0,4] +++. [2,2] □□□. **[3,1]** ◇◇◇. [4,0] ○○○.

$w_4(\mathcal{J}_1|z_0) \neq 0$. And since $w_4(\mathcal{J}_1|z)$ is the complex conjugate of $w_3(\mathcal{J}_1|z)$ numerical values of $w_4(\mathcal{J}_1|z_0)$ are available from Table 8.1. We could also compute $D_{m+q+1,n}(z_0)$ when $k = 2$, and $D_{m,n}(z_0)$ when $k = 1, 2, 3$ with the aid of the computations of the implicit solution $w_1(\mathcal{J}_1|z)$ given in section 8.2 below. However, the direct verification of conditions (5.5) and (5.12) is not really necessary. We can argue that if there is severe cancellation in evaluating any of the determinants $D_{m,n}(z_0)$ and $D_{m+q+1,n}(z_0)$, then there will be a corresponding loss of precision in the computed solution of the boundary-value problem; compare (5.6), (5.7), (5.8). This loss will show up when we compare results for the stable prescriptions.

We also observe from Figures 8.2, 8.3, and 8.4 that the other configurations of the boundary values are less stable, especially [0,4] and [4,0], that is, when the differential equation is integrated step by step along $\mathcal{L}_k$ starting from z_0 and z_∞, respectively. The only exception is the [2,2] prescription in the case $k = 3$. Figure 8.4 indicates that this is another stable prescription, and this may be confirmed by a similar perturbation analysis to that given in section 5. The only difference is that condition corresponding to (5.5) and (5.12) is more complicated.

8.2. Computation of $w_1(\mathcal{J}_1|z)$. As we noted at the beginning of section 6, the main problem in the computation of an implicit solution is the generation of a set of values for the solution and its derivatives for moderate values of z, for example, on the unit circle.

Figure 8.5 depicts $\mathcal{S}_1(\mathcal{J}_1)$ and the anti-Stokes lines associated with $w_1(\mathcal{J}_1|z)$ within this sector. The values of $\operatorname{ph} z$ on these lines are $-\frac{1}{2}\pi - \theta_{12}$, $\frac{1}{2}\pi - \theta_{13}$, $-\frac{1}{2}\pi - \theta_{14}$, $\frac{1}{2}\pi - \theta_{12}$, that is, $-\frac{1}{2}\pi$, $(-0.147583617650433\ldots)\pi$, $(0.147583617650433\ldots)\pi$, $\frac{1}{2}\pi$, re-

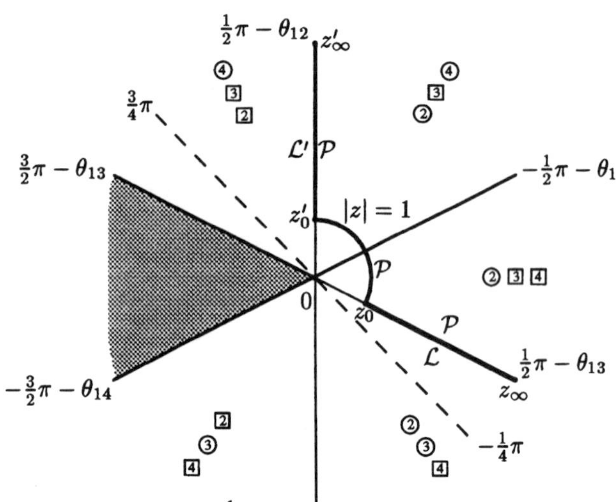

FIG. 8.5. *Sector $\mathcal{S}_1(\mathcal{J}_1)$ and anti-Stokes lines for $w_1(\mathcal{J}_1|z)$. Dominating solution ○. Dominated solution □.*

spectively. We also indicate, by means of circles and squares enclosing the numbers 2, 3, 4, the relative dominance of $w_1(\mathcal{J}_1|z)$ compared with the other asymptotic solutions $w_j(z)$, $j = 2, 3, 4$, in the various sectors into which $\mathcal{S}_1(\mathcal{J}_1)$ is subdivided by the anti-Stokes lines. For example, as $z \to \infty$ in the sector $\operatorname{ph} z \in (-\frac{1}{2}\pi - \theta_{12}, \frac{1}{2}\pi - \theta_{13})$ the solution $w_1(\mathcal{J}_1|z)$ dominates $w_4(z)$ and is dominated by $w_2(z)$ and $w_3(z)$.

A straightforward choice of the rays $\mathcal{L}$ and $\mathcal{L}'$ that fulfills conditions (i), (ii), and (iii) of section 6 is given by $\operatorname{ph} z = -\frac{1}{4}\pi$ and $\operatorname{ph} z = \frac{3}{4}\pi$, respectively; see the broken rays on Figure 8.5. Since two solutions dominate $w_1(\mathcal{J}_1|z)$ as $z \to \infty$ on $\mathcal{L}$ and the other dominates $w_1(\mathcal{J}_1|z)$ as $z \to \infty$ on $\mathcal{L}'$, we may prescribe either two boundary values at ∞ on $\mathcal{L}$ and another two at ∞ on $\mathcal{L}'$, or three boundary values at ∞ on $\mathcal{L}$ and one at ∞ on $\mathcal{L}'$; compare (6.1) and (6.2) with $m = 3$. The difficulty associated with this choice is that the ray $\operatorname{ph} z = \frac{3}{4}\pi$ lies fairly close to the left-hand boundary $\operatorname{ph} z = \frac{3}{2}\pi - \theta_{13}$ of $\mathcal{S}_1(\mathcal{J}_1)$. In consequence, the truncation error associated with (2.8) may be quite large compared with the first neglected term [22, sections 9 and 11]. To put this another way, on $\operatorname{ph} z = \frac{3}{4}\pi$ the value of $|z|$ needed in (2.8) to attain a specified precision in $w_1(\mathcal{J}_1|z)$ may lead to a matrix $\mathbf{G}$ of very large order in the implementation of the boundary-value problems described in section 7.

To ease this difficulty we modify the integration path $\mathcal{P}$ prescribed in section 6 by rotating the rays $\mathcal{L}$ and $\mathcal{L}'$ away from the boundaries of $\mathcal{S}_1(\mathcal{J}_1)$ as far as possible. Thus we permit $\mathcal{L}$ and $\mathcal{L}'$ to coincide with the anti-Stokes lines $\operatorname{ph} z = \frac{1}{2}\pi - \theta_{13}$ and $\frac{1}{2}\pi - \theta_{12}$, respectively. The path $\mathcal{P}$ becomes $z_\infty z_0 z'_0 z'_\infty$, as indicated in Figure 8.5. Here z_∞ and z'_∞ are points on the new choices of $\mathcal{L}$ and $\mathcal{L}'$, respectively, and sufficiently close to ∞ to achieve the desired precision in the asymptotic expansions; whereas z_0 and z'_0 are the points on $\mathcal{L}$ and $\mathcal{L}'$, respectively, of unit modulus. The perturbation analysis of section 6 needs appropriate modification, of course. We omit details, but the conclusion remains the same, that is, with the prescriptions

$$w_1(\mathcal{J}_1|z_\infty),\ w'_1(\mathcal{J}_1|z_\infty),\ w_1(\mathcal{J}_1|z'_\infty),\ w'_1(\mathcal{J}_1|z'_\infty), \tag{8.2}$$

or

$$w_1(\mathcal{J}_1|z_\infty),\ w_1'(\mathcal{J}_1|z_\infty),\ w_1''(\mathcal{J}_1|z_\infty),\ w_1(\mathcal{J}_1|z_\infty'), \tag{8.3}$$

the boundary-value problem is well posed. Again, using an obvious notation we denote these prescriptions by [2,2] and [3,1], respectively.

In the expansion (2.8) the coefficient a_{s1} is of the same order of magnitude as a_{s3} when $s \to \infty$, since the minimum value of $|\lambda_1 - \lambda_k|$ for $k = 2, 3, 4$ is $\frac{1}{2}\sqrt{5}$; compare section 8.1. Hence the optimum value of s is again $\operatorname{int}[\frac{1}{2}\sqrt{5}|z|]$. With $|z_\infty| = |z_\infty'| = 21$ and $s = 23$, we find that

$$\left\{\begin{aligned} w_1(\mathcal{J}_1|z_\infty) &= -166.032669262 + 11920.4947572i,\\ w_1'(\mathcal{J}_1|z_\infty) &= -85.8240663779 + 5962.26128988i,\\ w_1''(\mathcal{J}_1|z_\infty) &= -43.9888664278 + 2982.08492335i,\\ w_1'''(\mathcal{J}_1|z_\infty) &= -22.4147729568 + 1491.47920007i, \end{aligned}\right. \tag{8.4}$$

$$\left\{\begin{aligned} w_1(\mathcal{J}_1|z_\infty') &= -0.470325599934 - 0.882592135685i,\\ w_1'(\mathcal{J}_1|z_\infty') &= -0.235021330696 - 0.441048831648i,\\ w_1''(\mathcal{J}_1|z_\infty') &= -0.117463406537 - 0.220386937696i,\\ w_1'''(\mathcal{J}_1|z_\infty') &= -0.058721855399 - 0.110121144466i. \end{aligned}\right. \tag{8.5}$$

In the case of z_∞ the truncation errors will be comparable with the first neglected terms, hence the values (8.4) will be accurate to an rp of about $10^{-10.5}$. For z_∞', however, the angle between $\operatorname{ph} z_\infty'$ and the boundary $\operatorname{ph} z = \frac{3}{2}\pi - \theta_{13}$ of $\mathcal{S}_1(\mathcal{J}_1)$ is less than $\frac{1}{2}\pi$. Because of this, the error bounds in [22] indicate that the remainder terms may be considerably larger than the first neglected terms. A way to estimate the magnitude of these remainder terms is to observe that the effect of crossing the Stokes line $\operatorname{ph} z = \pi - \theta_{13}$ is to switch on a multiple of a w_3-type solution in the compound asymptotic expansion of $w_1(\mathcal{J}_1|z)$; compare (8.7) below or [14, equation (2.13)]. At z_∞' the rp of this contribution is of the order $|e^{(\lambda_3-\lambda_1)z_\infty'}|$, that is, about $10^{-9.1}$.

In applying the method of section 7, we used 96 nodal points on $\mathcal{P}$ (41 each on $\mathcal{L}$ and $\mathcal{L}'$ and 16 on the arc $|z| = 1$). We again took 33 terms in the Taylor-series expansions. Furthermore, to illustrate our stability theory we solved the boundary-value problem with all five possible configurations [0,4], [1,3], **[2,2]**, **[3,1]**, [4,0] of the boundary values. (Again, bold face is used to indicate the predicted stable prescriptions.) The results are compared graphically in Figure 8.6.

The rp agreement between the results for the **[2,2]** and **[3,1]** prescriptions is nowhere worse then $10^{-9.0}$, which is consistent with the expected accuracy. Figure 8.6 also demonstrates the strongly unstable nature of the other configurations [0,4], [1,3], and [4,0].

Another way of confirming the overall accuracy of the results for the stable prescriptions is to repeat the solution of the boundary-value problems taking $|z_\infty|$ and $|z_\infty'|$ to be 22 instead of 21. The rp's of the two pairs of results are graphed in Figure 8.7.

8.3. Computation of $w_1(\mathcal{J}_5|z)$ and Stokes multipliers. The sector of validity of the asymptotic expansion (2.8) for $w_1(\mathcal{J}_5|z)$ is depicted in Figure 4.11. The computation of this solution is very similar to that of $w_1(\mathcal{J}_1|z)$ described in section

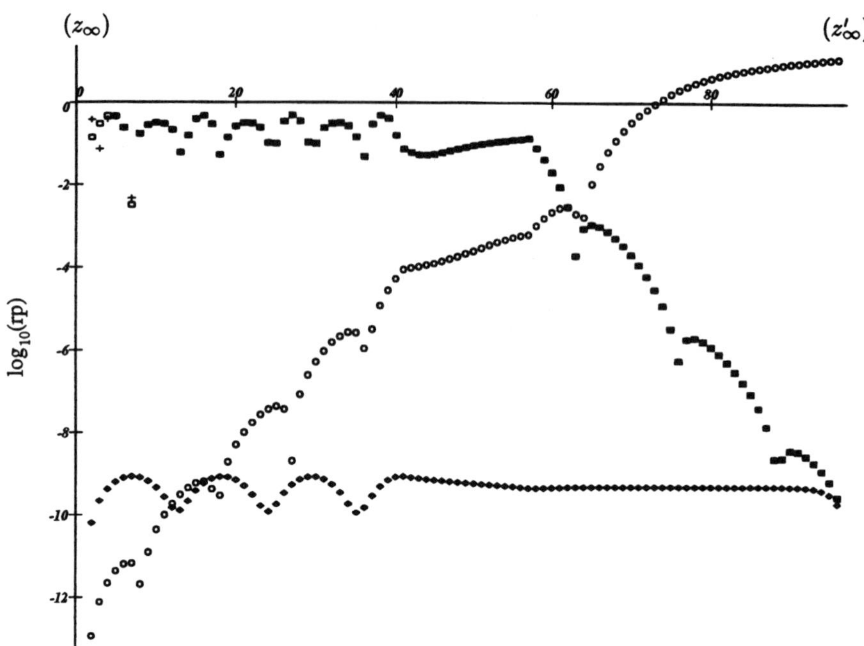

FIG. 8.6. *Relative precision compared with* **[3,1]** *solution.* [0,4] +++. [1,3] □□□. **[2,2]** ◇◇◇. [4,0] ○○○.

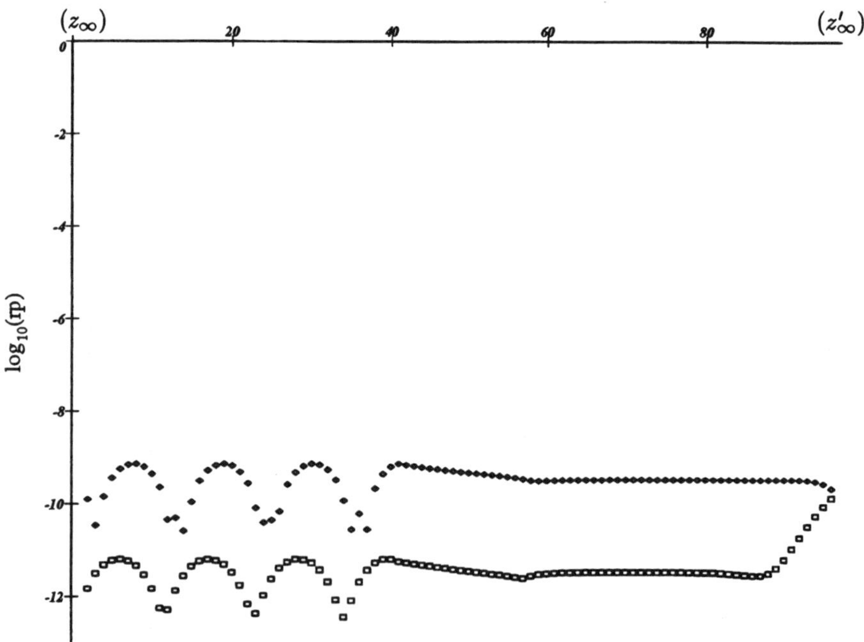

FIG. 8.7. *Relative precision of solutions computed with* $|z_\infty|$, $|z'_\infty| = 21$ *compared with* $|z_\infty|$, $|z'_\infty| = 22$. **[2,2]** ◇◇◇. **[3,1]** □□□.

8.2. As integration path $\mathcal{P}$ we chose segments $\mathcal{L}$ and $\mathcal{L}'$ of the anti-Stokes lines $\operatorname{ph} z = \frac{1}{2}\pi - \theta_{12}$ and $\frac{1}{2}\pi - \theta_{14}$, that is, $\frac{1}{2}\pi$ and $(1.147583617650433\ldots)\pi$, respectively, together with an arc of the unit circle. On $\mathcal{P}$ the stable prescriptions of the boundary values are (8.2) and (8.3), where z_∞ and z'_∞ now denote points on the new $\mathcal{L}$ and $\mathcal{L}'$, respectively, and $\mathcal{J}_1$ is replaced by $\mathcal{J}_5$. With these prescriptions we find that the two solutions agree at all nodal points of $\mathcal{P}$ to within rp $(10^{-10.9})$. Also, with (8.3) the computed values of $w_1(\mathcal{J}_5|z)$ and its derivatives at $z = 1$ are, to 12 decimal places,

$$\begin{aligned}
w_1(\mathcal{J}_5|1) &= 1.559211749708 + 0.361875533446i,\\
w_1'(\mathcal{J}_5|1) &= 0.462444256610 + 0.062542541088i,\\
w_1''(\mathcal{J}_5|1) &= 0.307610738357 - 0.382858981984i,\\
w_1'''(\mathcal{J}_5|1) &= 0.654470902265 - 0.064103473814i.
\end{aligned}$$

The remaining task that we set ourselves is to compute the Stokes multipliers K_{j1}, $j = 2, 3, 4$, that appear in the connection formula

$$w_1(\mathcal{J}_5|z) = K_{11}w_1(\mathcal{J}_1|z) - K_{21}w_2(\mathcal{J}_1|z) - K_{31}w_3(\mathcal{J}_1|z) - K_{41}w_4(\mathcal{J}_1|z). \tag{8.6}$$

The intersection of the regions of validity of the asymptotic expansions (2.8) for the solutions $w_1(\mathcal{J}_1|z)$ and $w_1(\mathcal{J}_5|z)$ is the half-plane $(-0.147583617650433\ldots)\pi < \operatorname{ph} z < (0.852416382349567\ldots)\pi$. Since this includes part of the sector $\mathcal{D}_2^-(\mathcal{J}_1)$ on which $w_2(\mathcal{J}_1|z)$ is the overall dominant solution (see Figure 4.4) it follows that $K_{21} = 0$. Similarly $K_{41} = 0$. Then by letting $z \to \infty$ on e.g. $\operatorname{ph} z = 0$, we see that $K_{11} = 1$. Accordingly, (8.6) reduces to

$$w_1(\mathcal{J}_5|z) = w_1(\mathcal{J}_1|z) - K_{31}w_3(\mathcal{J}_1|z). \tag{8.7}$$

To evaluate the remaining coefficient K_{31} we record the values of $w_1(\mathcal{J}_1|z)$ and $w_3(\mathcal{J}_1|z)$ and their derivatives at $z = 1$, obtained from the computations described in sections 8.1 and 8.2:

$$\begin{aligned}
w_1(\mathcal{J}_1|1) &= 1.507148034892, & w_3(\mathcal{J}_1|1) &= 0.563772745472 + 0.787060869387i,\\
w_1'(\mathcal{J}_1|1) &= 0.828705288934, & w_3'(\mathcal{J}_1|1) &= -0.784587089739 + 0.593751821492i,\\
w_1''(\mathcal{J}_1|1) &= 0.380693420216, & w_3''(\mathcal{J}_1|1) &= -0.638771231423 - 0.810743127323i,\\
w_1'''(\mathcal{J}_1|1) &= 0.236045121243, & w_3'''(\mathcal{J}_1|1) &= 0.905293130731 - 0.661049014756i.
\end{aligned}$$

On substituting into (8.7) and its first three differentiated forms by means of the foregoing results, then solving for K_{31}, we obtain the following values:

$$\begin{aligned}
&-0.335184743572 - 0.173943736289i, && -0.335184743179 - 0.173943736979i,\\
&-0.335184742552 - 0.173943736932i, && -0.335184742742 - 0.173943736886i.
\end{aligned}$$

That these values all agree to almost nine decimal places furnishes a powerful check on the accuracy of the computations.

These results may also be compared with

$$K_{31} = -0.335184718109 - 0.173943694726i,$$

obtained in [14, section 8] by a completely different method. Its estimated accuracy is known to be slightly less than that we have attained above.

9. Use of Cauchy's integral formula. One of the most time-consuming operations in our implementation of the algorithms described in sections 5–7 is the solution of equation (7.7) by Gaussian elimination with pivoting. Various procedures exist for speeding up this operation, including Zahar's method of block LU decomposition [6], [35], alternating pivoting [26], and parallel algorithms [34]. In this section we outline another approach based on Cauchy's integral formula.[17] This is applicable to the computation of explicit solutions in intermediate sectors and to the computation of implicit solutions after the main boundary-value problem has been solved.

Let $w(z)$ be a solution of (2.1), and $\mathcal{C}$ be a simple closed contour on which numerical values of $w(z)$ and its first $n-1$ derivatives are known at P nodal points t_1, $t_2, \ldots, t_P$ enumerated in the positive sense around $\mathcal{C}$. If $w(z)$ is analytic on domain $\mathcal{G}$ that contains $\mathcal{C}$ and its interior then

$$w(z) = \frac{1}{2\pi i}\int_{\mathcal{C}} \frac{w(t)}{t-z}\,dt \tag{9.1}$$

for any point z interior to $\mathcal{C}$. We assume that the points $t_1, t_2, \ldots, t_P$ form the vertices of a simple polygon $\mathcal{C}'$, say, and that $\mathcal{G}$ contains $\mathcal{C}'$ and its interior as well as the disks

$$|t - t_p| \leqslant \tfrac{1}{2}\max\left(|t_p - t_{p-1}|, |t_{p+1} - t_p|\right), \qquad p = 1, 2, \ldots, P,$$

where $t_0 = t_P$ and $t_{P+1} = t_1$. Then in (9.1) we may replace $\mathcal{C}$ by $\mathcal{C}'$, provided that now z is interior to $\mathcal{C}'$. We obtain

$$w(z) = \frac{1}{2\pi i}\int_{\mathcal{C}'} \frac{w(t)}{t-z}\,dt = \frac{1}{2\pi i}\sum_{p=1}^{P}\int_{\frac{1}{2}t_p+\frac{1}{2}t_{p-1}}^{\frac{1}{2}t_p+\frac{1}{2}t_{p+1}} \frac{w(t)}{t-z}\,dt.$$

On expanding $w(t)$ in its Taylor series centered at t_p and integrating term by term, we arrive at

$$w(z) = \frac{1}{2\pi i}\sum_{p=1}^{P}\sum_{s=0}^{\infty} \frac{w^{(s)}(t_p)}{s!}\phi_s(t_p, z), \tag{9.2}$$

where

$$\phi_s(t_p, z) = \int_{\frac{1}{2}t_p+\frac{1}{2}t_{p-1}}^{\frac{1}{2}t_p+\frac{1}{2}t_{p+1}} \frac{(t-t_p)^s}{t-z}\,dt, \tag{9.3}$$

the integration path in (9.3) comprising two straight lines that meet at $t = t_p$.

If we also need the values of the derivatives of $w(z)$, then corresponding to (9.2) we have

$$w^{(l)}(z) = \frac{1}{2\pi i}\sum_{p=1}^{P}\sum_{s=0}^{\infty} \frac{w^{(l+s)}(t_p)}{s!}\phi_s(t_p, z), \qquad l = 1, 2, \ldots, n-1. \tag{9.4}$$

A potential problem in using the expansions (9.2) and (9.4) numerically is severe cancellation. This will occur when $w(t)$ and its derivatives vary greatly in magnitude as t passes around $\mathcal{C}$. A simple way of overcoming this difficulty in the present context is to rescale the solution $w(z)$ by extracting the exponential factor $e^{\lambda z}$ that appears in its asymptotic expansion as $z \to \infty$.

[17] Suggested to the writers by T. M. Dunster.

A second problem is to generate numerical values of the integrals $\phi_s(t_p, z)$ in a stable manner. On substituting in (9.3) by means of the identity $t - t_p = (t - z) + (z - t_p)$, we obtain the recursion formula
(9.5)

$$\phi_s(t_p, z) = \frac{1}{s}\left(\frac{1}{2}t_{p+1} - \frac{1}{2}t_p\right)^s - \frac{1}{s}\left(\frac{1}{2}t_{p-1} - \frac{1}{2}t_p\right)^s + (z - t_p)\phi_{s-1}(t_p, z), \qquad s \geqslant 1.$$

When $|z - t_p| \leqslant 1$, this relation can be used in a forward direction without loss of absolute precision, starting from

$$\phi_0(t_p, z) = \ln\left(\frac{t_p + t_{p+1} - 2z}{t_p + t_{p-1} - 2z}\right). \tag{9.6}$$

Alternatively, if $|z - t_p| > 1$ then we can maintain absolute precision in the ϕ's by applying (9.5) in a backward direction. For this purpose we need a starting value $\phi_S(t_p, z)$, say. On splitting the integration path in (9.3) at t_p and integrating by parts, we find that

$$\begin{aligned}\phi_s(t_p, z) = {} & \frac{\left(\frac{1}{2}t_{p+1} - \frac{1}{2}t_p\right)^{s+1}}{(s+1)\left(\frac{1}{2}t_p + \frac{1}{2}t_{p+1} - z\right)}\left\{1 + \mathcal{O}\left(\frac{1}{s}\right)\right\} \\ & - \frac{\left(\frac{1}{2}t_{p-1} - \frac{1}{2}t_p\right)^{s+1}}{(s+1)\left(\frac{1}{2}t_p + \frac{1}{2}t_{p-1} - z\right)}\left\{1 + \mathcal{O}\left(\frac{1}{s}\right)\right\}, \qquad s \to \infty.\end{aligned} \tag{9.7}$$

Accordingly, if we restrict $|t_{p+1} - t_p| < 2\ \forall p$, then $\phi_s(t_p, z) \to 0$ as $s \to \infty$. In consequence, for any chosen precision a starting value for the backwards recursion may be taken to be $\phi_S(t_p, z) = 0$, where S may be estimated with the aid of (9.7).

Example. Let us compute $w(z) = e^{-iz}w_3(\mathcal{J}_1|z)$, where $w_3(\mathcal{J}_1|z)$ is defined as in section 8. As $\mathcal{C}$ we use the contour depicted in Figure 9.1.

We take the following 228 nodal points

$$t_p = (21 - \tfrac{1}{2}p)i, \quad p = 1, \ldots, 40, \qquad t_{p+40} = e^{(\frac{1}{2} - \frac{1}{16}p)\pi i}, \quad p = 1, \ldots, 16,$$
$$t_{p+56} = (-1 - \tfrac{1}{2}p)i, \quad p = 1, \ldots, 40, \qquad t_{p+96} = 21e^{(\frac{1}{132}p - \frac{1}{2})\pi i}, \quad p = 1, \ldots, 132.$$

Note that $|t_{p+1} - t_p| \leqslant \frac{1}{2}\ \forall p$.

From Figure 4.5 it is evident that $w_3(\mathcal{J}_1|z)$ can be computed in a stable manner by step-by-step integration of equation (8.1) from $z = t_0(= 21i)$ to $z = t_{96}(= -21i)$. The same is therefore true when we integrate the corresponding differential equation satisfied by $w(z)$, given by

$$w^{(4)} + (4i - 3)w^{(3)} - \left(\frac{15}{4} + 9i - \frac{1}{2z^2}\right)w^{(2)} + \left(6 + \frac{1}{2}i + \frac{i - \frac{3}{4}}{z^2}\right)w' + \frac{\frac{1}{16} - \frac{3}{4}i}{z^2}w = 0.$$

Initial values at t_0 are found from the expansion

$$w(z) \sim \sum_{s=0}^{\infty} \frac{a_{s3}}{z^s}, \qquad z \to \infty, \tag{9.8}$$

and its differentiated forms. We used 24 terms in (9.8) and 50 terms in the Taylor series. We expected this to yield 10 to 11 significant figures of accuracy. This was

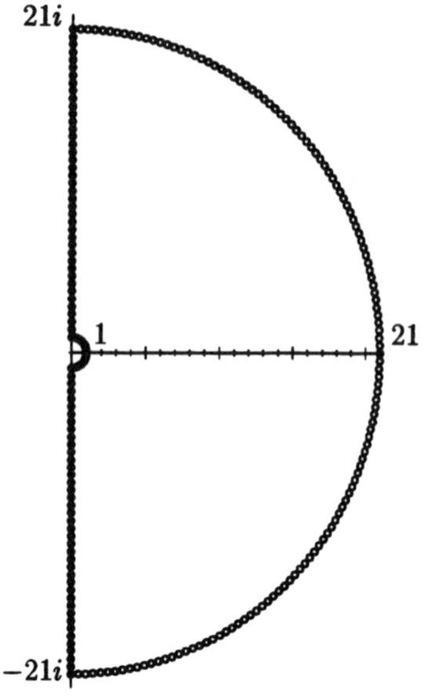

FIG. 9.1. *Contour of integration and nodal points.*

confirmed by comparing the integrated value of $w(t_{96})$ with that obtained by summation of (9.8). The discrepancy amounted to $1.96 - 0.70i$ units in the eleventh decimal place.

For the remaining nodal points t_p, $p = 97, \ldots, 228$, we computed $w^{(s)}(t_p)$, $s = 0, 1, 2, 3$, from (9.8) and its differentiated forms, again taking 24 terms in each expansion.

For the value of z in (9.2) we chose $z = 5e^{(-\frac{1}{2}\pi - \theta_{31})i}$. This lies within the intermediate sector $\mathcal{S}_3^-(\mathcal{J}_1)$ (Figure 4.5) and also on the ray $\mathcal{L}_3$ (Figure 8.1). Note that $|z - t_p| \geqslant 4\ \forall p$. If we take $s = 15$, then the magnitudes of the two terms on the right-hand side of (9.7) are smaller than 10^{-11}. This means that we can take $\phi_s(t_p, z) = 0$ for $s = 15, 16, \ldots$ and compute $\phi_0(t_p, z), \ldots, \phi_{14}(t_p, z)$ by applying (9.5) in the backward direction, starting with $\phi_{15}(t_p, z) = 0$. Thus our approximation to $w(z)$ is given by

$$\frac{1}{2\pi i} \sum_{p=1}^{228} \sum_{s=0}^{14} \frac{w^{(s)}(t_p)}{s!} \phi_s(t_p, z). \tag{9.9}$$

We still need values for $w^{(s)}(t_p)$, $s = 4, \ldots, 14$, $p = 1, \ldots, 228$. We computed these via (7.2).

For each term in (9.9) we expect to have 10 to 11 figures accuracy. Since there are 3420 of them and many are of comparable magnitude, we may expect 8 to 9 figures in the computed sum

$$e^{-iz} w_3(\mathcal{J}_1|z) = w(z) = 1.003682188248 - 0.022896650530i.$$

In comparison, the boundary value method of section 8.1 yields

$$e^{-iz} w_3(\mathcal{J}_1|z) = 1.003682221629 - 0.022896628018i,$$

confirming the expected accuracy of 7 to 8 decimals of the Cauchy-integral method.

10. Summary and conclusions. In this paper we have examined the nature and computation of asymptotic solutions of homogeneous linear differential equations of arbitrary order having an irregular singularity at the point of infinity. We have distinguished two types of solution, which we call explicit and implicit. They differ in both their uniqueness properties and method of computation.

Explicit solutions can be specified completely by their asymptotic form along a single ray. In general, implicit solutions do not enjoy this property, and to ensure uniqueness their asymptotic form may need to be maintained uniformly over a non-degenerate sector of sufficiently large angle.

Explicit solutions can be computed by step-by-step integration of the defining differential equation in sectors in which they are overall recessive or dominant. Elsewhere it is necessary to employ a boundary-value method in order to achieve stability. On the other hand, it may be necessary to solve as many as two boundary-value problems to compute an implicit solution at a chosen point in $\mathbb{C}$ in a stable manner.

Examples given in the paper include the numerical computation of both explicit and implicit solutions and also of the associated Stokes multipliers. Although we believe that this paper may be the first to address the general stability problem in the numerical evaluation of solutions of linear ordinary differential equations of arbitrary order, the evaluation of Stokes multipliers has been considered by many writers; see, for example, [1], [5], [11], [14]. In particular, [14] supplies hyperasymptotic expansions of the coefficients of the Poincaré expansions that generalize the results of [17] for the case $n = 2$ and as in [17] facilitate a direct numerical approach. This is probably the most effective method for computing Stokes multipliers unless numerical values of the actual solutions are also needed. Moreover, whichever method is used for the Stokes multipliers, the computations are somewhat intricate, and it is valuable to have completely independent methods for checking purposes.

In describing the computation of solutions we have concentrated on demonstrating the feasibility of the numerical algorithms we have introduced. However, in section 9 we touch on ways to optimize these algorithms, and also examine the possible use of Cauchy's integral formula to reduce the total amount of computation.

We have restricted the discussion in the present paper to singularities of rank unity having distinct characteristic values. However, the classification of the solutions and methods of computation will carry over to singularities of higher rank and to coalescing characteristic values. A preliminary need is the development of more general asymptotic existence theorems on the lines of [22].

Acknowledgments. This research was stimulated by a workshop on *Exponential Asymptotics* at the Isaac Newton Institute for Mathematical Sciences in Cambridge, U.K. from January 1995 through June 1995. The authors are pleased to acknowledge the support of the Institute, the Netherlands Organisation for Scientific Research (NWO) and the British Engineering and Physical Sciences Research Council (EPSRC) for this period, and the Institute for Physical Science and Technology of the University of Maryland for visits in 1996 and 1997 by the first author. The authors also thank R.V.M. Zahar for helpful comments and some of the references, and the referee for improvements in the presentation.

REFERENCES

[1] W. Balser, W.B. Jurkat, and D.A. Lutz, *Birkhoff invariants and Stokes' multipliers for meromorphic linear differential equations*, J. Math. Anal. Appl., 71 (1979), pp. 48–94.

[2] M.V. Berry, *Uniform asymptotic smoothing of Stokes's discontinuities*, Proc. Roy. Soc. London Ser. A, 422 (1989), pp. 7–21.

[3] M.V. Berry and C.J. Howls, *Hyperasymptotics*, Proc. Roy. Soc. London Ser. A, 430 (1990), pp. 653–668.

[4] G.D. Birkhoff, *Singular points of ordinary linear differential equations*, Trans. Amer. Math. Soc., 10 (1909), pp. 436–470.

[5] B.L.J. Braaksma, *Multisummability and Stokes multipliers of linear meromorphic differential equations*, J. Differential Equations, 92 (1991), pp. 45–75.

[6] J.R. Cash and R.V.M. Zahar, *A unified approach to recurrence algorithms*, in Approximation and Computation, R.V.M. Zahar ed., Internat. Ser. Numer. Math., 119, Birkhäuser, Boston, 1994, pp. 97–120.

[7] B.W. Char, K.O. Geddes, G.H. Gonnet, B.L. Leong, M.B. Monaghan, and S.M. Watt, *Maple* V *Library Reference Manual*, Springer-Verlag, New York, 1991.

[8] T.M. Dunster, *Error bounds for exponentially improved asymptotic solutions of ordinary differential equations having irregular singularities of rank one*, Methods Appl. Anal., 3 (1996), pp. 109–134.

[9] M. Hukuhara, *Sur les points singuliers des équations différentielles linéaires*, II, J. Fac. Sci. Hokkaido Imp. Univ., Ser. 1, 5 (1937), pp. 123–166.

[10] D.W. Lozier, *Numerical Solution of Linear Difference Equations*, Report NBSIR 80–1976, National Bureau of Standards, Washington D.C., 1980. (Available from National Technical Information Service, Springfield, VA 22161.)

[11] D.A. Lutz and R. Schäfke, *Calculating connection coefficients for meromorphic differential equations*, Complex Variables Theory Appl., 34 (1997), pp. 145–170.

[12] B.T.M. Murphy and A.D. Wood, *Hyperasymptotic solutions of second-order ordinary differential equations with a singularity of arbitrary integer rank*, Methods Appl. Anal., 4 (1997), pp. 250–260.

[13] A.B. Olde Daalhuis, *Hyperasymptotic solutions of second-order linear differential equations* II, Methods Appl. Anal., 2 (1995), pp. 198–211.

[14] A.B. Olde Daalhuis, *Hyperasymptotic solutions of higher order linear differential equations with a singularity of rank one*, Proc. Roy. Soc. London Ser. A, 454 (1998), pp. 1–29.

[15] A.B. Olde Daalhuis and F.W.J. Olver, *Exponentially improved asymptotic solutions of ordinary differential equations.* II *Irregular singularities of rank one*, Proc. Roy. Soc. London Ser. A, 445 (1994), pp. 39–56.

[16] A.B. Olde Daalhuis and F.W.J. Olver, *Hyperasymptotic solutions of second-order linear differential equations* I, Methods Appl. Anal., 2 (1995), pp. 173–197.

[17] A.B. Olde Daalhuis and F.W.J. Olver, *On the calculation of Stokes multipliers for linear differential equations of the second order*, Methods Appl. Anal., 2 (1995), pp. 348–367.

[18] F.W.J. Olver, *On the asymptotic solutions of second-order differential equations having an irregular singularity of rank one, with an application to Whittaker functions*, SIAM J. Numer. Anal. Ser. B, 2 (1965), pp. 225–243.

[19] F.W.J. Olver, *Numerical solution of second-order linear difference equations*, J. Res. Nat. Bur. Standards Sect. B, 71 (1967), pp. 111–129.

[20] F.W.J. Olver, *Asymptotics and Special Functions*, Academic Press, New York, 1974. Reprinted by AK Peters, Wellesley, 1997.

[21] F.W.J. Olver, *A new approach to error arithmetic*, SIAM J. Numer. Anal., 15 (1978), pp. 368–393.

[22] F.W.J. Olver, *Asymptotic solutions of linear ordinary differential equations at an irregular singularity of rank unity*, Methods Appl. Anal., 4 (1997), pp. 375–403.

[23] F.W.J. Olver and F. Stenger, *Error bounds for asymptotic solutions of second-order differential equations having an irregular singularity of arbitrary rank*, SIAM J. Numer. Anal. Ser. B, 2 (1965), pp. 244–249.

[24] R.B. Paris and A.D. Wood, *Asymptotics of High Order Differential Equations*, Pitman Res. Notes Math. Ser. 129, Longman Scientific & Technical, Harlow, and Wiley, New York, 1986.

[25] R.B. Paris and A.D. Wood, *Stokes phenomenon demystified*, Bull. Inst. Math. Appl., 31 (1995), pp. 21–28.

[26] J.K. Reid and A. Jennings, *On solving almost block diagonal (staircase) linear systems*, ACM Trans. Math. Software, 10 (1984), pp. 196–201.

[27] F. Stenger, *Error bounds for asymptotic solutions of differential equations* I. *The distinct eigenvalue case*, J. Res. Nat. Bur. Standards Sect. B, 70 (1966), pp. 167–186.

[28] F. Stenger, *Error bounds for asymptotic solutions of differential equations.* II. *The general case*, J. Res. Nat. Bur. Standards Sect. B, 70 (1966), pp. 187–210.

[29] W.J. TRJITZINSKY, *Analytic theory of linear differential equations*, Acta Math., 62 (1934), pp. 167–226.

[30] H.L. TURRITTIN, *Convergent solutions of ordinary linear homogeneous differential equations in the neighborhood of an irregular singular point*, Acta Math., 93 (1955), pp. 27–66.

[31] V.S. VARADARAJAN, *Linear meromorphic differential equations: a modern point of view*, Bull. Amer. Math. Soc. (N.S.), 33 (1996), pp. 1–42.

[32] W. WASOW, *Asymptotic Expansions for Ordinary Differential Equations*, Wiley (Interscience), New York, 1965. Reprinted by Krieger, Huntington, 1976 and Dover, New York, 1987.

[33] J.H. WILKINSON, *The Algebraic Eigenvalue Problem*, Clarendon Press, Oxford, 1965.

[34] S.J. WRIGHT, *Stable parallel algorithms for two-point boundary-value problems*, SIAM J. Sci. Statist. Comput., 13 (1992), pp. 742–764.

[35] R.V.M. ZAHAR, *A generalization of Olver's algorithm for linear difference systems*, in Asymptotic and Computational Analysis, R. Wong, ed., Marcel Dekker, New York, 1990, pp. 535–551.

Methods and Applications of Analysis
Vol. 6 No. 2, 1999, pp. 165–174

On the uniqueness of asymptotic solutions of linear differential equations

F. W. J. Olver

Dedicated to Richard Askey on the occasion of his 65th birthday and in celebration of his many contributions to classical analysis

Abstract. We consider the characterization of solutions of a linear differential equation of arbitrary order in the neighborhood of an irregular singularity of rank unity, on the assumption that the characteristic values are distinct. We show that some solutions can be defined uniquely simply by their asymptotic behavior along a single ray, whereas for other solutions the asymptotic behavior must be maintained along two rays to ensure uniqueness. The results are needed in the construction of algorithms for the computation of solutions.

1. Introduction

We consider solutions of the differential equation

$$\frac{d^n w}{dz^n} + f_{n-1}(z)\frac{d^{n-1}w}{dz^{n-1}} + f_{n-2}(z)\frac{d^{n-2}w}{dz^{n-2}} + \cdots + f_0(z)w = 0 \tag{1.1}$$

in the neighborhood of the point at infinity, on the assumptions that $n \geq 2$ and the coefficients $f_\ell(z)$, $\ell = 0, 1, \ldots, n-1$, are analytic at infinity, that is, they can be expanded in power series of the form

$$f_\ell(z) = \sum_{s=0}^{\infty} \frac{f_{s\ell}}{z^s} \tag{1.2}$$

that converge for all sufficiently large values of $|z|$. Thus the singularity of equation (1.1) at infinity is no worse than an irregular singularity of rank 1.

Formal solutions of (1.1) are given

$$e^{\lambda_j z} z^{\mu_j} \sum_{s=0}^{\infty} \frac{a_{sj}}{z^s} \qquad j = 1, 2, \ldots, n, \tag{1.3}$$

with $a_{0j} = 1$. The *characteristic values* λ_j, *indices* μ_j, and remaining coefficients a_{sj} are obtained by substituting into (1.1) by means of (1.2), (1.3), and the differentiated forms of (1.3), and equating coefficients. We shall restrict our attention to the case in which the λ_j are distinct; however, the main conclusions in this paper will carry over to more general situations.

In order to describe the sectors in which the formal solutions furnish asymptotic expansions of actual solutions for large z, we denote

$$\theta_{jk} = \text{ph}\,(\lambda_k - \lambda_j), \qquad k \neq j, \tag{1.4}$$

Received May 8, 1998, revised Augest 17, 1998.
1991 *Mathematics Subject Classification.* 34E05.
Key words and phrases: anti-Stokes lines, asymptotic expansions, differential equations, equidominant solutions, explicit solutions, implicit solutions, recessive solutions, singularities, uniqueness.

resolving the ambiguity in the choice of these phase angles by requiring θ_{jk} to lie in a prescribed, but arbitrary, half-closed interval $\mathcal{I}$ of length 2π. Next, we define $\mathcal{S}_j(\mathcal{I})$ to be the open sector

$$\mathcal{S}_j(\mathcal{I}) = \left\{z \, : -\frac{3}{2}\pi - \alpha_j < \operatorname{ph} z < \frac{3}{2}\pi - \beta_j\right\}, \tag{1.5}$$

in which

$$\alpha_j = \min_{k \neq j} \theta_{jk}, \qquad \beta_j = \max_{k \neq j} \theta_{jk} \, . \tag{1.6}$$

Theorem 1.1. *For each $j = 1, 2, \ldots, n$, there exists a unique solution $w_j(\mathcal{I}|z)$ of* (1.1) *with the property*

$$w_j(\mathcal{I}|z) \sim e^{\lambda_j z} z^{\mu_j} \sum_{s=0}^{\infty} \frac{a_{sj}}{z^s} \tag{1.7}$$

as $z \to \infty$, uniformly in any closed sector properly interior to $\mathcal{S}_j(\mathcal{I})$. This asymptotic expansion can be differentiated $n - 1$ times in the same circumstances, and the n solutions $w_j(\mathcal{I}|z)$ are linearly independent. Furthermore, the sectors of validity $\mathcal{S}_j(\mathcal{I})$ are maximal, in general.

This theorem is proved in [5], and this reference includes strict bounds for the remainder terms in the expansion (1.7) and its differentiated forms.

The conditions of Theorem 1.1 (and also Theorems 2.1 and 2.2 below) require the property (1.7) to hold uniformly on sectorial domains in order to ensure the uniqueness of the solution $w_j(\mathcal{I}|z)$. The purpose of the present paper is to simplify this condition. We seek unbounded point sets $\mathcal{T}$ in $\mathbb{C}$, for example rays, such that if $w(z)$ is a solution of (1.1) with either the property

$$w(z) \sim e^{\lambda_j z} z^{\mu_j}, \qquad z \to \infty \quad \text{on } \mathcal{T} \, , \tag{1.8a}$$

or the stronger property

$$w(z) \sim e^{\lambda_j z} z^{\mu_j} \sum_{s=0}^{\infty} \frac{a_{sj}}{z^s}, \qquad z \to \infty \quad \text{on } \mathcal{T} \, , \tag{1.8b}$$

then

$$w(z) = w_j(\mathcal{I}|z) \, . \tag{1.9}$$

Another way of characterizing solutions uniquely is by their hyperasymptotic behavior along a single ray [2]. The advantage of the present approach is that it provides a basis for the boundary-value methods needed in the numerical computation of the solutions anywhere in $\mathbb{C}$, not merely in the neighborhood of the singular point; see [3].

2. Preliminary results

The common region of validity of the expansion (1.7) for $j = 1, 2, \ldots, n$ is given by

$$\mathcal{S}(\mathcal{I}) = \mathcal{S}_1(\mathcal{I}) \cap \mathcal{S}_2(\mathcal{I}) \cap \cdots \cap \mathcal{S}_n(\mathcal{I}), \tag{2.1}$$

that is,

$$\mathcal{S}(\mathcal{I}) = \left\{z : -\frac{3}{2}\pi - \alpha < \operatorname{ph} z < \frac{3}{2}\pi - \beta\right\}, \tag{2.2}$$

where

$$\alpha = \min_{k \neq j} \theta_{jk}, \qquad \beta = \max_{k \neq j} \theta_{jk}, \tag{2.3}$$

the minimum and maximum now being taken over all possible values of j and k.

Theorem 2.1. *There exist linearly independent and unique solutions $w_j(\mathcal{I}|z)$, $j = 1, 2, \ldots, n$, such that* (1.7) *applies as $z \to \infty$, uniformly in any closed sector properly interior to $\mathcal{S}(\mathcal{I})$.*

This theorem follows immediately from Theorem 1.1, except for the uniqueness property associated with the smaller sector $\mathcal{S}(\mathcal{I})$. The proof of this property was supplied in [5, §10].

The following results were stated in [3, §2] and also appear in earlier literature (see [1] for Theorem 2.2 and [6, Chapter 4] for Theorem 2.3). Since they are important in subsequent analysis we include brief proofs here for completeness. As usual, by an "anti-Stokes line" we mean a ray on which $\theta_{pq} + \operatorname{ph} z$ is an odd multiple of $\frac{1}{2}\pi$ for at least one unequal pair of values of p and q.

Theorem 2.2. *Let $\mathcal{Z}$ be an arbitrary closed sector of angle π whose boundaries do not coincide with anti-Stokes lines. Then there is a set of linearly independent and unique solutions $w_j(z)$, $j = 1, 2, \ldots, n$, such that*

$$w_j(z) \sim e^{\lambda_j z} z^{\mu_j} \sum_{s=0}^{\infty} \frac{a_{sj}}{z^s} \tag{2.4}$$

uniformly as $z \to \infty$ in $\mathcal{Z}$.

Theorem 2.3. *Let $\mathcal{Z}$ be an arbitrary ray or an arbitrary closed sector of angle less than π. Then there is a set of linearly independent (but not necessarily unique) solutions $w_j(z)$, $j = 1, 2, \ldots, n$, such that* (2.4) *applies uniformly as $z \to \infty$ in $\mathcal{Z}$.*

Proof of Theorem 2.2. Let $\mathcal{Z}$ be bounded by the rays $\operatorname{ph} z = \phi - \pi$ and $\operatorname{ph} z = \phi$. In Theorem 2.1 take $\mathcal{I} = (-\frac{1}{2}\pi - \phi, \frac{3}{2}\pi - \phi]$. Then it is easily verified that $-\frac{3}{2}\pi - \alpha + \delta \le \phi - \pi$ and $\frac{3}{2}\pi - \beta - \delta \ge \phi$ where α and β are defined by (2.3) and δ is the smaller of

$$\min_{k \ne j}\left(\theta_{jk} + \frac{1}{2}\pi + \phi\right), \qquad \min_{k \ne j}\left(\frac{3}{2}\pi - \phi - \theta_{jk}\right),$$

the minima being taken over all possible values of j and k. Because $\theta_{jk} \in (-\frac{1}{2}\pi - \phi, \frac{3}{2}\pi - \phi]$ and $\theta_{jk} + \phi$ cannot be an odd multiple of $\frac{1}{2}\pi$, δ is necessarily positive. Accordingly $\mathcal{Z} \subset \mathcal{S}(\mathcal{I})$ and the existence of the $w_j(z)$ follows from Theorem 2.1. The uniqueness property is again proved as in [5, §10]. □

The condition that the boundaries of $\mathcal{Z}$ are not anti-Stokes lines cannot be omitted from Theorem 2.2. An example is provided by Bessel's equation

$$\frac{d^2 w}{dz^2} + \frac{1}{z}\frac{dw}{dz} + \left(1 - \frac{\nu^2}{z^2}\right) w = 0.$$

Here $n = 2, \lambda_1 = i, \lambda_2 = -i, \mu_1 = \mu_2 = -\frac{1}{2}$, and the anti-Stokes lines are the positive and negative parts of the real axis. Using the well-known properties of the solutions $H_\nu^{(1)}(z)$ and $H_\nu^{(2)}(z)$ of this equation [4, Chapter 7], we can prove, for example, that no solution exists that is asymptotic to $e^{iz} z^{-1/2}$ uniformly in the sector $-\pi \le \operatorname{ph} z \le 0$, except when the parameter ν is half an odd integer. [1]

Proof of Theorem 2.3. Theorem 2.3 is an immediate consequence of Theorem 2.2, inasmuch as any closed sector of angle less than π is always properly interior to a sector of angle π whose boundaries are not anti-Stokes lines. □

[1] This is a consequence of the Stokes phenomenon. When the Stokes ray $\operatorname{ph} z = -\frac{1}{2}\pi$ is crossed, a multiple of the solution that is exponentially small on that ray is switched on. This multiple vanishes iff 2ν is an odd integer.

Theorem 2.3 can also be deduced directly from Theorem 2.1, as follows. Let the boundaries of $\mathcal{Z}$ be the rays ph $z = \phi_1$ and ph $z = \phi_2$, with $0 \le \phi_2 - \phi_1 < \pi$. (By permitting $\phi_2 - \phi_1 = 0$ we include the case in which $\mathcal{Z}$ is a ray.) In Theorem 2.1 take $\mathcal{I} = (-\pi - \frac{1}{2}\phi_1 - \frac{1}{2}\phi_2, \pi - \frac{1}{2}\phi_1 - \frac{1}{2}\phi_2]$. Then it is easily verified that $\mathcal{Z}$ is properly interior to $\mathcal{S}(\mathcal{I})$, and the result follows. (The uniqueness property has now been sacrificed.)

The final topic in this section is the relative behavior, as $z \to \infty$, of any two distinct members $w_j(z)$ and $w_k(z)$ of the set of solutions furnished by Theorem 2.3 in the case when $\mathcal{Z}$ is the single ray $\mathfrak{L}$, given by

$$\mathfrak{L} = \{z : \ z = te^{i\theta}, \ 0 < t < \infty\}. \tag{2.5}$$

We have three cases to consider:

$$\text{(i) } \operatorname{Re}\{(\lambda_k - \lambda_j)z\} \ne 0 \text{ on } \mathfrak{L},$$
$$\text{(ii) } \operatorname{Re}\{(\lambda_k - \lambda_j)z\} = 0 \text{ on } \mathfrak{L}, \text{ and } \operatorname{Re}\mu_k \ne \operatorname{Re}\mu_j.$$
$$\text{(iii) } \operatorname{Re}\{(\lambda_k - \lambda_j)z\} = 0 \text{ on } \mathfrak{L}, \text{ and } \operatorname{Re}\mu_k = \operatorname{Re}\mu_j.$$

In Case (i) if, for example, $\operatorname{Re}\{(\lambda_k - \lambda_j)z\}$ is negative on $\mathfrak{L}$, then $w_k(z)/w_j(z) \to 0$ as $z \to \infty$ and we say that *$w_j(z)$ dominates $w_k(z)$ exponentially as $z \to \infty$ on $\mathfrak{L}$*. Similarly in Case (ii) if, for example, $\operatorname{Re}(\mu_k - \mu_j)$ is negative, then again $w_k(z)/w_j(z) \to 0$ as $z \to \infty$, but this time we say that *$w_j(z)$ dominates $w_k(z)$ algebraically as $z \to \infty$ on $\mathfrak{L}$*. Lastly, in Case (iii) $|w_k(z)\backslash w_j(z)| \to$ a nonzero constant as $z \to \infty$, and we say that *$w_j(z)$ and $w_k(z)$ are equidominant on $\mathfrak{L}$*.

Uniqueness problems are not difficult to resolve when only exponential dominance is involved. To handle other cases we shall make frequent use of the following result:

Lemma. *On a given ray $\mathfrak{L}$ no nontrivial linear combination of a set of equidominant solutions can be dominated by a member of the set.*

Proof. Let the solutions be enumerated in such a way that the equidominant set is $w_p(z), w_{p+1}(z), \ldots, w_q(z), p$ and q being integers such that $1 \le p < q \le n$, and let

$$w(z) = A_p w_p(z) + A_{p+1} w_{p+1}(z) + \cdots + A_q w_q(z), \tag{2.6}$$

where the A's are constants. Let us assume that

$$w(z) = o\{w_k(z)\}, \qquad z \to \infty \text{ on } \mathfrak{L}, \tag{2.7}$$

where $p \le k \le q$. Then we have to prove that $A_p = A_{p+1} = \cdots = A_q = 0$.

By hypothesis

$$\lambda_j e^{i\theta} = a + ib_j, \qquad \mu_j = c + id_j, \qquad j = p, p+1, \ldots, q,$$

where a, b_j, c, and d_j are real constants, a and c being independent of j, and the b_j being unequal. Hence on $\mathfrak{L}$

$$e^{\lambda_j z} z^{\mu_j} = e^{(a+ib_j)t} \, t^{c+id_j} \, e^{i\theta c - \theta d_j}. \tag{2.8}$$

On replacing the w's in (2.6) and (2.7) by means of their limiting forms, and then substituting by means of (2.8), we find that

$$\sum_{j=p}^{q} \hat{A}_j e^{ib_j t} \, t^{id_j} = o(1) \tag{2.9}$$

as $t \to \infty$, where

$$\hat{A}_j = e^{-\theta d_j} A_j, \qquad j = p, p+1, \ldots, q. \tag{2.10}$$

Now let σ be an arbitrary constant such that

$$0 < \sigma < \frac{2\pi}{\max|b_j - b_k|}, \tag{2.11}$$

the maximum being taken over j, $k \in [p, q]$. In (2.9) set $t = (\tau + s)\sigma$, with $s = 0, 1, \ldots, q - p$ in turn, and then let $\tau \to \infty$. Since

$$t^{id_j} = \left\{(\tau + s)\sigma\right\}^{id_j} = (\sigma\tau)^{id_j}\left\{1 + O(\tau^{-1})\right\},$$

uniformly for $s = 0, 1, \ldots, q - p$, we have

$$\sum_{j=p}^{q} \hat{A}_j e^{ib_j\sigma\tau}(\sigma\tau)^{id_j} = o(1),$$

$$\sum_{j=p}^{q} \hat{A}_j e^{ib_j\sigma\tau + ib_j\sigma}(\sigma\tau)^{id_j} = o(1),$$

....

$$\sum_{j=p}^{q} \hat{A}_j e^{ib_j\sigma\tau + i(q-p)b_j\sigma}(\sigma\tau)^{id_j} = o(1).$$

This is a system of $q - p + 1$ inhomogeneous equations for the $q - p + 1$ unknowns $\hat{A}_p$, $\hat{A}_{p+1}, \ldots, \hat{A}_q$. The determinant D, say, of this system is given by

$$D = e^{i(b_p + \cdots + b_q)\sigma\tau}(\sigma\tau)^{i(d_p + \cdots + d_q)} \prod_{p \le j < k \le q} \left(e^{ib_k\sigma} - e^{ib_j\sigma}\right).$$

Clearly $|D|$ is independent of τ, and in consequence of (2.11) and the fact that $b_j \neq b_k$ when $j \neq k$, $|D|$ does not vanish. Applying Cramer's rule and letting $\tau \to \infty$ we deduce that $\hat{A}_p = \hat{A}_{p+1} = \cdots = \hat{A}_q = 0$, and hence from (2.10) $A_p = A_{p+1} = \cdots = A_q = 0$. □

3. Explicit solutions

In [3] new classifications of the asymptotic solutions given by Theorem 1.1 were introduced, as follows. If $\beta_j - \alpha_j \in [0, \pi)$, then the corresponding solution $w_j(\mathcal{I}|z)$ is said to be *explicit*. Alternatively, when $\beta_j - \alpha_j \in [\pi, 2\pi)$, $w_j(\mathcal{I}|z|)$ is said to be *implicit*. In the explicit case $\mathcal{S}_j(\mathcal{I})$ contains the nonempty open sector

$$\mathcal{R}_j(\mathcal{I}) = \left\{z : -\frac{1}{2}\pi - \alpha_j < \text{ ph } z < \frac{1}{2}\pi - \beta_j\right\}. \tag{3.1}$$

This is called the *recessive sector* for $w_j(\mathcal{I}|z)$, because if $z \to \infty$ along any chosen ray $\mathfrak{L}$ in $\mathcal{R}_j(\mathcal{I})$, then $w_j(\mathcal{I}|z)$ is dominated, indeed dominated exponentially, by any solution with asymptotic form $e^{\lambda_k z} z^{\mu_k}$ $(k \neq j)$ on $\mathfrak{L}$.

When $n = 2$ we have $\beta_j = \alpha_j$; hence both asymptotic solutions are explicit, and it is easily seen (and already well known) that $w(z)$ is specified uniquely by (1.8a) with $\mathcal{T} = \mathfrak{L}$, provided again that $\mathfrak{L} \subset \mathcal{R}_j(\mathcal{I})$. We begin this section by proving that this result holds for explicit solutions for all values of n.

To simplify notation we may suppose that $j = 1$, so that (1.8a) becomes

$$w(z) \sim e^{\lambda_1 z} z^{\mu_1}, \qquad z \to \infty \text{ on } \mathfrak{L}, \tag{3.2}$$

with $\mathfrak{L} \subset \mathcal{R}_1(\mathcal{I})$. Also, we let $w_1(z), w_2(z), \ldots, w_n(z)$ denote solutions furnished by Theorem 2.3 with $\mathcal{Z} = \mathfrak{L}$. Then constants $A_1, A_2, \ldots, A_n$ exist such that

$$w(z) = A_1 w_1(z) + A_2 w_2(z) + \cdots + A_n w_n(z) . \tag{3.3}$$

Suppose first none of the solutions are equidominant on $\mathfrak{L}$. Then they may be ranked in order of dominance, and by relabelling $w_2(z), w_3(z), \ldots, w_n(z)$, if necessary, we may suppose that the ascending order of rank is given by $w_1(z), w_2(z), \ldots, w_n(z)$. On dividing (3.3) by $w_n(z)$, letting $z \to \infty$ on $\mathfrak{L}$ and using (3.2), we see immediately that $A_n = 0$. Similarly $A_{n-1} = A_{n-2} = \cdots = A_2 = 0$, and $A_1 = 1$. Since $w_1(\mathcal{I}|z)$ satisfies (3.2) it follows that any solution that satisfies (3.2) must be the same as $w_1(\mathcal{I}|z)$.

In the general case we group the sets of equidominant solutions in blocks when we arrange the solutions $w_1(z), w_2(z), \ldots, w_n(z)$ in ascending order of dominance on $\mathfrak{L}$. If we follow the previous method of proof, and $w_p(z), w_{p+1}(z), \ldots, w_q(z)$ is the first block of equidominant solutions that we encounter, then we have $1 < p < q \leq n$ and

$$A_p w_p(z) + A_{p+1} w_{p+1}(z) + \cdots + A_q w_q(z) = o\{w_p(z)\}$$

as $z \to \infty$ on $\mathfrak{L}$. Accordingly, from the Lemma of §2 $A_p = A_{p+1} = \cdots = A_q = 0$. Similarly for the other blocks, and the remainder of the proof is completed as before. We have therefore proved the following result:

Theorem 3.1. *Let $\mathfrak{L}$ be any ray within the recessive sector $\mathcal{R}_j(\mathcal{I})$ of an explicit solution $w_j(\mathcal{I}|z)$ of* (1.1). *Then condition* (1.8*a*), *with $\mathcal{T} = \mathfrak{L}$, implies* (1.9).

If we substitute (1.8b) for (1.8a), then we may permit $\mathfrak{L}$to coincide with a boundary of $\mathcal{R}_j(\mathcal{I})$:

Theorem 3.2. *Let $\mathcal{L}$ be any ray in the closure of the recessive sector $\mathcal{R}_j(\mathcal{I})$. Then condition* (1.8*b*), *with $\mathcal{T} = \mathfrak{L}$, implies* (1.9).

Proof. The difference in the proof of this result from that of Theorem 3.1 stems from the possibility that if $\mathfrak{L}$ coincides with a boundary of $\mathcal{R}_1(\mathcal{I})$, then there are members of the set $w_2(z), w_3(z), \ldots, w_n(z)$ that are equidominant with, or dominated algebraically by, $w_1(z)$ as $z \to \infty$ on $\mathfrak{L}$. Let the latter set be $w_2(z), w_3(z), \ldots, w_p(z)$ where $1 \leq p \leq n$, and assume that in nondescending order of dominance the complete set of solutions is given by

$$w_2(z), w_3(z), \ldots, w_p(z), w_1(z), w_{p+1}(z), w_{p+2}(z), \ldots, w_n(z) .$$

On following the proof of Theorem 3.1 we first conclude that equation (3.3) reduces to

$$w(z) = A_2 w_2(z) + \cdots + A_p w_p(z) + A_1 w_1(z) + A_{p+1} w_{p+1}(z) + \cdots + A_q w_q(z), \tag{3.4}$$

where $p \leq q \leq n$ and the solutions $w_1(z)$, $w_{p+1}(z), \ldots, w_q(z)$ are equidominant on $\mathfrak{L}$. Hence on using the assumption (1.8b) with $j = 1$ we have

$$(A_1 - 1) w_1(z) + A_{p+1} w_{p+1}(z) + \cdots + A_q w_q(z) = o\{w_1(z)\}$$

as $z \to \infty$ on $\mathfrak{L}$. Application of the Lemma of §2 then shows that $A_1 - 1 = A_{p+1} = \cdots = A_q = 0$, so that (3.4) reduces to

$$A_2 w_2(z) + \cdots + A_p w_p(z) = w(z) - w_1(z). \tag{3.5}$$

Again, from (2.4) and (1.8b) with $j = 1$ in both cases, it follows that the right-hand side of (3.5) is $O(e^{\lambda_1 z} z^{\mu_1 - m})$, where m is an arbitrary integer. This estimate may be included in $o\{w_2(z)\}$ by choosing m large enough, and proceeding again as in the proof of Theorem 3.1 we conclude that $A_2 = A_3 = \cdots = A_p = 0$. □

4. Implicit solutions

Unlike explicit solutions, in general it is not possible to characterize an implicit solution $w_j(\mathcal{I}|z)$ by its asymptotic behavior along a single ray $\mathcal{L}$. This is because for all choices of $\mathcal{L}$ in the sector $\mathcal{S}_j(\mathcal{I})$ of asymptotic validity there is always a nontrivial solution of (1.1) that is dominated exponentially by $w_j(\mathcal{I}|z)$ as $z \to \infty$, the only possible exception arising when $\beta_j - \alpha_j = \pi$ [3, §3]. However, two rays, suitably restricted, always suffice:

Theorem 4.1. *Let $\mathcal{Z}$ be a nondegenerate closed sector within $\mathcal{S}_j(\mathcal{I})$ with boundaries $\mathfrak{L}$ and $\mathfrak{L}'$. Assume that either: (i) $\mathcal{Z}$ is of angle less than π; or (ii) the angle of $\mathcal{Z}$ is π and neither $\mathfrak{L}$ nor $\mathfrak{L}'$ is an anti-Stokes line of* (1.1). *Assume also that in Case (i) no nontrivial solution of* (1.1) *is dominated exponentially by $w_j(\mathcal{I}|z)$ on both $\mathfrak{L}$ and $\mathfrak{L}'$ as $z \to \infty$. Then condition* (1.8*b*), *with $\mathcal{T} = \mathfrak{L} \cup \mathfrak{L}'$, implies* (1.9).

Proof. The proof of Theorem 4.1 is similar to the proofs of Theorem 3.1 and 3.2, and proceeds as follows. With the given conditions there is a set of linearly independent solutions $w_k(z)$, $k = 1, 2, \ldots, n$, such that

$$w_k(z) \sim e^{\lambda_k z} z^{\mu_k} \sum_{s=0}^{\infty} \frac{a_{sk}}{z^s}$$

as $z \to \infty$ on both $\mathfrak{L}$ and $\mathfrak{L}'$. This is a consequence of Theorem 2.3 in Case (i) and Theorem 2.2 in Case (ii). We may express $w(z)$ in the form

$$w(z) = A_1 w_1(z) + A_2 w_2(z) + \cdots + A_n w_n(z), \tag{4.1}$$

in which the A's are constants. If we let $z \to \infty$ on $\mathfrak{L}$, then it follows that $A_k = 0$ for those values of $k (\neq j)$ for which $w_k(z)$ dominates, or is equidominant with, or is algebraically dominated by, $w_j(z)$ on $\mathfrak{L}$, and $A_j = 1$. Similarly $A_k = 0$ for those values of $k(\neq j)$ for which $w_k(z)$ dominates, or is equidominant with, or is algebraically dominated by, $w_j(z)$ on $\mathfrak{L}'$ (and $A_j = 1$). In both Cases (i) and (ii) only the term $w_j(z)$ survives on the right-hand side of (4.1). And since $w_j(\mathcal{I}|z)$ satisfies (1.8b) with $\mathcal{T} = \mathfrak{L} \cup \mathfrak{L}'$ it follows that (1.9) applies. □

It should be observed that Theorem 4.1 actually applies to any of the solutions $w_j(\mathcal{I}|z)$. If $w_j(\mathcal{I}|z)$ is explicit, then the theorem provides a way of specifying $w_j(\mathcal{I}|z)$ uniquely by its asymptotic behavior on two rays that lie outside its recessive sector.

There is one case in which an implicit solution can be characterized by its asymptotic behavior along a single ray:

Theorem 4.2. *Assume that $\beta_j - \alpha_j = \pi$ and*

$$\mathfrak{L} = \left\{ z : ph\ z = -\frac{1}{2}\pi - \alpha_j \left(= \frac{1}{2}\pi - \beta_j \right) \right\}.$$

Then condition (1.8*b*), *with $\mathcal{T}\mathfrak{L}$, implies* (1.9).

The proof of Theorem 4.2 is essentially the same as that of Theorem 3.2. In fact, Theorem 4.2 may be regarded as a limiting form of Theorem 3.2, because as $\beta_j - \alpha_j \to \pi$ the boundaries of the recessive sector $\mathcal{R}_j(\mathcal{I})$ coalesce into $\mathfrak{L}$.

5. Examples

We first note that the conditions of Theorem 4.1 can always be satisfied by taking $\mathfrak{L}$ and $\mathfrak{L}'$ to be within $\mathcal{S}_j(\mathcal{I})$ and the images of each other in the origin, provided that they are not anti-Stokes lines. For numerical purposes, however, it is sometimes desirable to locate $\mathfrak{L}$ and $\mathfrak{L}'$ instead along anti-Stokes lines.

Thus in [3, §8.2] to compute an implicit solution $w_1(\mathcal{I}_1|z)$ of a certain fourth-order differential equation, rays $\mathfrak{L}$ and $\mathfrak{L}'$ were used along anti-Stokes lines as depicted in Figure 8.5 of this reference. On $\mathfrak{L}$ only multiples of the solution $w_4(z)$ are dominated exponentially by $w_1(z)$, and on $\mathfrak{L}'$ only multiples of $w_3(z)$ are dominated exponentially by $w_1(z)$. In consequence the conditions of Theorem 4.1 (Case(i)) of the present paper are satisfied; accordingly $w_1(\mathcal{I}_1|z)$ is defined uniquely by its asymptotic behavior on $\mathfrak{L}$ and $\mathfrak{L}'$. This is the underlying reason that in [3] we were able to place the boundary values for computing $w_1(\mathcal{I}_1|z)$ on $\mathfrak{L}$ and $\mathfrak{L}'$. (Even so, as in [3] perturbation analysis is needed to determine precisely how the n necessary boundary values must be distributed on $\mathfrak{L}\cup\mathfrak{L}'$ to ensure stability in the computation of the wanted solution.)

Another interesting situation is to suppose that all the λ's lie on the imaginary axis (and are, of course, distinct). An example is provided by the differential equation

$$\frac{d^5w}{dz^5} + \left(\frac{4}{z} - \frac{1}{z^3}\right)\frac{d^4w}{dz^4} + 5\frac{d^3w}{dz^3} + \frac{7}{z}\frac{d^2w}{dz^2} + 4\frac{dw}{dz} + \left(\sin\frac{1}{z}\right)^2 w = 0. \tag{5.1}$$

Here $\lambda_1 = -2i$, $\lambda_2 = -i$, $\lambda_3 = 0$, $\lambda_4 = i$, $\lambda_5 = 2i$; correspondingly, $\mu_1 = -\frac{3}{2}$, $\mu_2 = -\frac{1}{2}$, $\mu_3 = 0$, $\mu_4 = -\frac{1}{2}$, $\mu_5 = -\frac{3}{2}$. Let us take $\mathcal{I} = (-\pi, \pi]$. Then for the extreme values of λ we have, from (1.6), $\alpha_1 = \beta_1 = \frac{1}{2}\pi$ and $\alpha_5 = \beta_5 = -\frac{1}{2}\pi$. Accordingly, the corresponding solutions $w_1(\mathcal{I}|z)$ and $w_5(\mathcal{I}|z)$ are explicit. For the remaining solutions we have $\alpha_j = -\frac{1}{2}\pi$ and $\beta_j = \frac{1}{2}\pi$, $j = 2, 3, 4$. Accordingly, $w_2(\mathcal{I}|z)$, $w_3(\mathcal{I}|z)$, and $w_4(\mathcal{I}|z)$ are implicit. Next, as $z \to \infty$ on ph $z = 0$ there is no exponential dominance among the five solutions, and by applying Theorems 3.2 and 4.2, we conclude that condition (1.8b), with $\mathcal{T}$ taken to be ph $z = 0$, determines $w_j(\mathcal{I}|z)$ uniquely in all cases; in particular, for the overall dominant solution $w_3(\mathcal{I}|z)$ on ph $z = 0$. It also follows from the Lemma of §2 that if we were to modify equation (5.1) in such a way that the λ's are unchanged, but the μ's all have equal real parts, then the weaker condition (1.8a) can be substituted for (1.8b).

6. Conclusions

We have shown that at an irregular singularity of rank 1, with unequal characteristic values, an explicit solution of the differential equation is always defined uniquely by its asymptotic expansion along any ray in the closure of the recessive sector of the solution. For an implicit solution, the asymptotic behavior needs to be maintained on two rays, in general, in order to specify the solution uniquely.

Acknowledgement. The author is indebted to A. B. Olde Daalhuis and the referee for helpful comments.

References

1. D. Lutz and R. Schäfke, *On the remainders of the asymptotic expansion of solutions of differential equations near irregular singular points*, Complex Variables Theory Appl. **26** (1994), 203–212.
2. A. B. Olde Daalhuis, *Hyperasymptotic solutions of higher order linear differential equations with a singularity of rank one*, Proc. Roy. Soc. London, Ser. A **454** (1998), 1–29.
3. A. B. Olde Daalhuis and F.W.J. Olver, *On the asymptotic and numerical solution of linear ordinary differential equations,* SIAM Review **40** (1998), 463–495.
4. F.W.J. Olver, *Asymptotics and Special Functions*, Academic Press, New York, 1974. Reprinted by AK Peters, Wellesley, 1997.
5. ———, *Asymptotic solutions of linear ordinary differential equations at an irregular singularity of rank unity*, Methods Appl. Anal. **4** (1997), 375–403.

6. W. Wasow, *Asymptotic Expansions for Ordinary Differential Equations*, Wiley (Interscience), New York, 1965. Reprinted by Krieger, Huntington, 1976, and Dover, New York, 1987.

Institute for Physical Science and Technology and Department of Mathematics, University of Maryland, College Park, Maryland 20742
E-mail: olver@bessel.umd.edu

LIST OF PUBLICATIONS BY F. W. J. OLVER

Papers Included in This Collection

1. Transformation of certain series occurring in aerodynamic interference calculations, *Quart. J. Mech. Appl. Math.* **2** (1949), 452–457.
2. A new method for the evaluation of zeros of Bessel functions and of other solutions of second-order differential equations, *Proc. Cambridge Philos. Soc.* **46** (1950), 570–580.
3. A further method for the evaluation of zeros of Bessel functions and some new asymptotic expansions for zeros of functions of large order, *Proc. Cambridge Philos. Soc.* **47** (1951), 699–712.
4. Some new asymptotic expansions for Bessel functions of large orders, *Proc. Cambridge Philos. Soc.* **48** (1952), 414–427.
5. Note on the asymptotic expansion of generalized hypergeometric functions, *J. London Math. Soc.* **28** (1953), 462–464.
6. The asymptotic solution of linear differential equations of the second order for large values of a parameter, *Philos. Trans. Roy. Soc. London Ser. A* **247** (1954), 307–327.
7. The asymptotic expansion of Bessel functions of large order, *Philos. Trans. Roy. Soc. London Ser. A* **247** (1954), 328–368.
8. The asymptotic solution of linear differential equations of the second order in a domain containing one transition point, *Philos. Trans. Roy. Soc. London Ser. A* **249** (1956), 65–97.
9. Uniform asymptotic expansions of solutions of linear second-order differential equations for large values of a parameter, *Philos. Trans. Roy. Soc. London Ser. A* **250** (1958), 479–517.
10. Uniform asymptotic expansions for Weber parabolic cylinder functions of large orders, *J. Res. Nat. Bur. Standards* **63B** (1959), 131–169.
11. Error bounds for the Liouville-Green (or WKB) approximation, *Proc. Cambridge Philos. Soc.* **57** (1961), 790–810.
12. Error bounds for first approximations in turning-point problems, *J. Soc. Indust. Appl. Math.* **11** (1963), 748–772.
13. Error bounds for asymptotic expansions in turning-point problems, *J. Soc. Indust. Appl. Math.* **12** (1964), 200–214.
14. On the asymptotic solutions of second-order differential equations having an irregular singularity of rank one, with an application to Whittaker functions, *J. Soc. Indust. Appl. Math. Ser. B Numer. Anal.* **2** (1965), 225–243.
15. Error bounds for asymptotic solutions of second-order differential equations having an irregular singularity of arbitrary rank, *J. Soc. Indust. Appl. Math. Ser. B Numer. Anal.* **2** (1965), 244–249. (With F. Stenger.)

16. Error analysis of phase-integral methods. I. General theory for simple turning points, *J. Res. Nat. Bur. Standards* **69B** (1965), 271–290.
17. Error analysis of phase-integral methods. II. Application to wave-penetration problems, *J. Res. Nat. Bur. Standards* **69B** (1965), 291–300.
18. Numerical solution of second-order linear difference equations, *J. Res. Nat. Bur. Standards* **71B** (1967), 111–129.
19. Bounds for the solutions of second-order linear difference equations. *J. Res. Nat. Bur. Standards* **71B** (1967), 161–166.
20. Error bounds for the Laplace approximation for definite integrals, *J. Approx. Theory* **1** (1968), 293–313.
21. Why steepest descents? *SIAM Rev.* **12** (1970), 228–247. Reprinted in *Special Functions and Wave Propagation, Studies in Applied Mathematics* **6** (D. Ludwig and F. W. J. Olver, eds.), Society for Industrial and Applied Mathematics, Philadelphia, PA, 1970, pp. 44–63.
22. A paradox in asymptotics, *SIAM J. Math. Anal.* **1** (1970), 533–534.
23. Note on backward recurrence algorithms, *Math. Comp.* **26** (1972), 941–947. (With D. J. Sookne.)
24. Error bounds for stationary phase approximations, *SIAM J. Math. Anal.* **5** (1974), 19–29.
25. Unsolved problems in the asymptotic estimation of special functions. In *Theory and Application of Special Functions* (R. A. Askey, ed.), Academic Press, New York, 1975, pp. 99–142.
26. Second-order linear differential equations with two turning points, *Philos. Trans. Roy. Soc. London Ser. A* **278** (1975), 137–174.
27. Legendre functions with both parameters large, *Philos. Trans. Roy. Soc. London Ser. A* **278** (1975), 175–185.
28. Improved error bounds for second-order differential equations with two turning points, *J. Res. Nat. Bur. Standards* **80B** (1976), 437–440.
29. Second-order differential equations with fractional transition points, *Trans. Amer. Math. Soc.* **226** (1977), 227–241.
30. Connection formulas for second-order differential equations with multiple turning points, *SIAM J. Math. Anal.* **8** (1977), 127–154.
31. Connection formulas for second-order differential equations having an arbitrary number of turning points of arbitrary multiplicities, *SIAM J. Math. Anal.* **8** (1977), 673–700.
32. Asymptotic behavior of integrals of Bessel functions of high order, *Utilitas Math.* **12** (1977), 225–239. (With M. L. Glasser.)
33. Sufficient conditions for Ackerberg-O'Malley resonance, *SIAM J. Math. Anal.* **9** (1978), 328–355.
34. General connection formulae for Liouville-Green approximations in the complex plane, *Philos. Trans. Roy. Soc. London Ser. A* **289** (1978), 501–548.

35. Asymptotic approximations and error bounds, *SIAM Rev.* **22** (1980), 188–203.
36. Whittaker functions with both parameters large: uniform approximations in terms of parabolic cylinder functions, *Proc. Roy. Soc. Edinburgh Sect. A* **86** (1980), 213–234.
37. A posteriori error bounds for Gaussian elimination, *IMA J. Numer. Anal.* **2** (1982), 377–406. (With J. H. Wilkinson.)
38. Beyond floating point, *J. Assoc. Comput. Mach.* **31** (1984), 319–328. (With C. W. Clenshaw.)
39. Generalized exponential and logarithmic functions, *Comput. Math. Appl.* **12B** (1986), 1091–1101. (With C. W. Clenshaw, D. W. Lozier and P. R. Turner.)
40. Level-index arithmetic operations, *SIAM J. Numer. Anal.* **24** (1987), 470–485. (With C. W. Clenshaw.)
41. Error bounds for linear recurrence relations, *Math. Comp.* **50** (1988), 481–499.
42. Closure and precision in level-index arithmetic, *SIAM J. Numer. Anal.* **27** (1990), 1295–1304. (With D. W. Lozier.)
43. On Stokes' phenomenon and converging factors. In *Asymptotic and Computational Analysis* (R. Wong, ed.), *Lecture Note in Pure and Applied Mathematics* **124**, Marcel Dekker, New York, 1990, pp. 329–355.
44. Uniform, exponentially improved, asymptotic expansions for the generalized exponential integral, *SIAM J. Math. Anal.* **22** (1991), 1460–1474.
45. Uniform, exponentially improved, asymptotic expansions for the confluent hypergeometric function and other integral transforms, *SIAM J. Math. Anal.* **22** (1991), 1475–1489.
46. Exponentially-improved asymptotic solutions of ordinary differential equations I: The confluent hypergeometric function, *SIAM J. Math. Anal.* **24** (1993), 756–767.
47. Airy and Bessel functions by parallel integration of ODEs. In *Proc. Sixth SIAM Conference on Parallel Processing for Scientific Computing*, **v. 2** (R. F. Sincovec et al., eds.), 1993, 530–538. (With D. W. Lozier.)
48. Asymptotic expansions of the coefficients in asymptotic series solutions of linear differential equations, *Methods Appl. Anal.* **1** (1994), 1–13.
49. The generalized exponential integral. In *Approximation and Computation* (R. V. M. Zahar, ed.), *International Series of Numerical Mathematics* **119**, Birkhäuser, Basel, 1994, 497–510.
50. Exponentially improved asymptotic solutions of ordinary differential equations. II Irregular singularities of rank one, *Proc. Roy. Soc. London Ser. A* **445** (1994), 39–56. (With A. B. Olde Daalhuis.)
51. On an asymptotic expansion of a ratio of Gamma functions, *Proc. Roy. Irish Academy Sect. A* **95** (1995), 5–9.
52. Hyperasymptotic solutions of second-order linear differential equa-

tions I, *Methods Appl. Anal.* **2** (1995), 173–197. (With A. B. Olde Daalhuis.)
53. On the calculation of Stokes multipliers for linear differential equations of the second order, *Methods Appl. Anal.* **2** (1995), 348–367. (With A. B. Olde Daalhuis.)
54. Asymptotic solutions of linear ordinary differential equations at an irregular singularity of rank unity, *Methods Appl. Anal.* **4** (1997), 375–403.
55. On the asymptotic and numerical solution of linear ordinary differential equations, *SIAM Rev.* **40** (1998), 463–495. (With A. B. Olde Daalhuis.)
56. On the uniqueness of asymptotic solutions of differential equations, *Methods Appl. Anal.* **6** (1999), 165–174.

Other Papers — Not Included in This Collection

A1. Note on a paper by H. Bateman, *J. Appl. Phys.* **17** (1946), 1127.
A2. Solution of differential equations by recurrence relations, *Math. Tab. Wash.* (now *Math. Comp.*) **5** (1951), 34–39. (With C. W. Clenshaw.)
A3. The evaluation of zeros of high-degree polynomials, *Philos. Trans. Roy. Soc. London Ser. A* **244** (1952), 385–415.
A4. The asymptotic expansion of Legendre functions of large order. Abstract. In *Proceedings of the International Congress of Mathematicians* **2**, North-Holland, Amsterdam, 1954, p. 152.
A5. The use of economized polynomials in mathematical tables, *Proc. Cambridge Philos. Soc.* **51** (1955), 614–628. (With C. W. Clenshaw.)
A6. Errors in asymptotic solutions of linear ordinary differential equations, *Quart. Appl. Math.* **14** (1956), 218–219.
A7. Linear differential equations of the second order with a large parameter, *J. Soc. Indust. Appl. Math.* **7** (1959), 306–310.
A8. Two inequalities for parabolic cylinder functions, *Proc. Cambridge Philos. Soc.* **57** (1961), 811–822.
A9. Error bounds for asymptotic expansions, with an application to cylinder functions of large argument. In *Asymptotic Solutions of Differential Equations and their Applications* (C. H. Wilcox, ed.), Wiley, New York, 1964, pp. 163–183.
A10. Error analysis of Miller's recurrence algorithm, *Math. Comp.* **18** (1964), 65–74.
A11. Error bounds for asymptotic expansions of special functions in the complex plane. In *Error in Digital Computation* (L. B. Rall, ed.), **2**, Wiley, New York, 1965, pp. 55–75.
A12. Evaluation of special functions. In *Proceedings of IFIP Congress 65*, **2** (W. A. Kalenich, ed.), Spartan Books, Washington DC, 1966, pp. 604–605.

A13. An extension of Miller's algorithm, *Apl. Math. No. 2*, **13** (1968), 174–176.

A14. Recent error analysis of asymptotic solutions of linear differential equations. In *International Conference on Differential Equations* (H. A. Antosiewicz, ed.), Academic Press, New York, 1975, pp. 636–645.

A15. Uniform asymptotic expansions and singular perturbations. In *Asymptotic Methods and Singular Perturbations* (R. E. O'Malley, Jr., ed.), *SIAM-AMS Proceedings* **10**, American Mathematical Society, Providence, RI, 1976, pp. 105–117.

A16. A new approach to error arithmetic, *SIAM J. Numer. Anal.* **15** (1978), 368–393.

A17. Asymptotic approximations for parabolic cylinder functions, *J. Phys. B: Atom. Molec. Phys.* **11** (1978), L531–L533. (With C. Lozano.)

A18. An unrestricted algorithm for the exponential function, *SIAM J. Numer. Anal.* **17** (1980), 310–331. (With C. W. Clenshaw.)

A19. Unrestricted algorithms for generating elementary functions. In *Fundamentals of Numerical Computation (Computer-Oriented Numerical Analysis)* (G. Alefeld and R. D. Grigorieff, eds.), *Computing Suppl.* **2**, Springer-Verlag, New York, 1980, pp. 131–140.

A20. The general connection-formula problem for linear differential equations of the second order. In *Singular Perturbations and Asymptotics* (R. E. Meyer and S. V. Parter, eds.), Academic Press, New York, 1980, pp. 317–343.

A21. Extended-range arithmetic and normalized Legendre polynomials, *ACM Trans. Math. Software* **7** (1981), 93–105. (With J. M. Smith and D. W. Lozier.)

A22. Further developments of rp and ap error analysis, *IMA J. Numer. Anal.* **2** (1982), 249–274.

A23. Associated Legendre functions on the cut, *J. Comput. Phys.* **51** (1983), 502–518. (With J. M. Smith.)

A24. Error bounds for arithmetic operations on computers without guard digits, *IMA J. Numer. Anal.* **3** (1983), 153–160.

A25. Error analysis of complex arithmetic. In *Computational Aspects of Complex Analysis* (H. Werner, L. Wuytack, E. Ng and H. J. Bunger, eds.), D. Reidel Publishing Company, Dordrecht, 1983, pp. 279–292.

A26. Unrestricted algorithms for mathematical functions. In *Rend. Sem. Mat. Univ. Politec. Torino*, Special Issue (1985), pp. 237–248.

A27. Error bounds for polynomial evaluation and complex arithmetic, *IMA J. Numer. Anal.* **6** (1986), 373–379.

A28. Simplified error bounds for Newton's rule. In *Rev. Téc. Fac. Ingr. Univ. Zulia* **9**, Edición Especial (1986), pp. 71–77.

A29. Unrestricted algorithms for reciprocals and square roots, *BIT* **26** (1986), 476–492. (With C. W. Clenshaw.)

A30. The level-index number system. In *Bull. Inst. Math. Appl.* **22** (1986), pp. 182–185.

A31. A closed computer arithmetic. In *Proceedings of the Eighth Symposium on Computer Arithmetic* (M. J. Irwin and R. Stefanelli, eds.), IEEE Computer Society Press, Washington DC, 1987, pp. 139–143. Reprinted in *Computer Arithmetic*, **v. 2** (E. Swartzlander, Jr., ed.), IEEE Computer Society Press, Los Alamitos, 1990, pp. 360–364.

A32. Implementation of level-index arithmetic using partial table look-up. In *Proceedings of the Eighth Symposium on Computer Arithmetic* (M. J. Irwin and R. Stefanelli, eds.), IEEE Computer Society Press, Washington DC, 1987, pp. 144–147. (With P. R. Turner.)

A33. Closure and precision. In *Numerical Analysis and Parallel Processing* (P. R. Turner, ed.), *Lecture Notes in Mathematics* **1397**, Springer-Verlag, New York, 1989, pp. 124–130.

A34. Generalized exponentials and logarithms; surface fitting; conclusions. In *Numerical Analysis and Parallel Processing* (P. R. Turner, ed.), *Lecture Notes in Mathematics* **1397**, Springer-Verlag, New York, 1989, pp. 156–164.

A35. Rounding errors in algebraic processes — in level-index arithmetic. In *Reliable Numerical Computation* (M. G. Cox and S. Hammarling, eds.), Clarendon Press, Oxford, 1990, pp. 197–205.

A36. Converging factors. In *Wave Asymptotics* (P. A. Martin and G. R. Wickham, eds.), Cambridge University Press, 1992, pp. 54–68.

A37. Exponentially-improved asymptotic solutions of ordinary differential equations. In *Ordinary and Partial Differential Equations* (B. D. Sleeman and R. J. Jarvis, eds.), **4**, Longman Scientific and Technical, Harlow, Essex, 1993, pp. 238–247.

A38. Numerical evaluation of special functions. in *Mathematics of Computation 1943–1993: A Half-Century of Computational Mathematics* (W. Gautschi, ed.), *Proceedings of Symposia in Applied Mathematics* **48**, American Mathematical Society, Providence, RI, 1994, pp. 79–125. (With D. W. Lozier.)

A39. Advances in the asymptotic and numerical solution of linear ordinary differential equations. In *Recent Advances in Differential Equations* (H.-H. Dai and P. L. Sachdev, eds.), *Pitman Research Notes in Mathematics Series* **386**, Addison Wesley Longman, Harlow, Essex, 1998, pp. 3–14.

A40. Practical problems in the solution of high-order linear differential equations. In *Tricomi's Ideas and Contemporary Applied Mathematics, Atti dei Convegni Lincei* **147**, Accademia Nazionale dei Lincei, Rome, 1998, pp. 239–249.

A41. On the reversion of an asymptotic expansion and the zeros of the Airy functions, *SIAM Rev.* **41** (1999), 762–773. (With B. Fabijonas.)

Books (or Parts of Books)

B1. *Modern Computing Methods, National Physical Laboratory Notes on Applied Science* **16**, Her Majesty's Stationery Office, London, 1957. (With L. Fox, E. T. Goodwin, J. G. L. Michel, and J. H. Wilkinson.) Second edition 1961. (With C. W. Clenshaw, E. T. Goodwin, D. W. Martin, G. F. Miller, and J. H. Wilkinson.)

B2. *Royal Society Mathematical Tables*, **v. 7**, Bessel Functions, Part III: Zeros and Associated Values, Cambridge University Press, 1960 (Editor).

B3. *National Physical Laboratory Mathematical Tables*, **v. 6**, Tables for Bessel Functions of Moderate or Large Orders, Her Majesty's Stationery Office, London, 1962.

B4. Bessel functions of integer order. In *Handbook of Mathematical Functions, National Bureau of Standards Applied Mathematics Series* **55**, U.S. Government Printing Office, Washington DC, 1964, pp. 355–433.

B5. *Studies in Applied Mathematics*, **v. 6**, *Special Functions and Wave Propagation*, Society for Industrial and Applied Mathematics, Philadelphia, PA, 1970 (Co-editor).

B6. *Asymptotics and Special Functions*, Academic Press, New York, 1974. Reprinted by AK Peters, Ltd., Wellesley, MA, 1997. Russian translation: Izdatel'stvo Nauka, Moscow, 1990.

B7. *Introduction to Asymptotics and Special Functions*, Academic Press, New York, 1974. Russian translation: Izdatel'stvo Nauka, Moscow, 1978.

B8. Asymptotic methods. In *Handbook of Applied Mathematics* (C. E. Pearson, ed.), Van Nostrand Reinhold, New York, 1974, pp. 645–710. Second edition 1983, pp. 631–696.

Book Reviews

C1. "Coulomb Wave Functions", by A. R. Curtis: *Royal Society Mathematical Tables*, **v. 11**, Cambridge University Press, 1964. Reviewed by F. W. J. Olver for *Math. Comp.* **19** (1965), 341–342.

C2. "The Special Functions and Their Approximations", two volumes, by Y. L. Luke: Academic Press, New York, 1969. Reviewed by F. W. J. Olver for *SIAM Rev.* **14** (1972), 181–183.

C3. "Mathematics for the Analysis of Algorithms", by D. H. Greene and D. E. Knuth: *Progress in Computer Science*, **v. 1** (second edition), Birkhäuser, Boston, 1982. Reviewed by F. W. J. Olver for *COMPEL* **3** (1984), 53–54.

C4. "Computation with Recurrence Relations", by Jet Wimp: Pitman, Boston, 1984. Reviewed by F. W. J. Olver for *Math. Comp.* **47** (1986), 371–372.

C5. "Linear Turning Point Theory", by Wolfgang Wasow: *Applied Mathematical Sciences*, **v. 54**, Springer-Verlag, New York, 1985. Reviewed by F. W. J. Olver for *SIAM Rev.* **28** (1986), 433–435.
C6. "Theory of Difference Equations: Numerical Methods and Applications", by V. Lakshmikantham and D. Trigiante: *Mathematics in Science and Engineering*, **v. 181**, Academic Press, New York, 1988. Reviewed by F. W. J. Olver for *Amer. Sci.* **77** (1989), 294–295.
C7. "Mathematical Function Library for Microsoft-FORTRAN", by United Laboratories, Inc.: Wiley, New York, 1989. Reviewed by F. W. J. Olver for *Math. Comp.* **56** (1991), 879–885.
C8. "Special Functions: An Introduction to the Classical Functions of Mathematical Physics", by N. M. Temme: Wiley, New York, 1996. Reviewed by F. W. J. Olver for *SIAM Rev.* **39** (1997), 355–356.

PERMISSIONS

Part 1

1. Transformation of certain series occurring in aerodynamic interference calculations. Reprinted with permission of the publisher, Oxford University Press, from *Quart. J. Mech. Appl. Math.*, Copyright © 1949, Vol. 2, pp. 452–457.

2. A new method for the evaluation of zeros of Bessel functions and of other solutions of second-order differential equations. Reprinted with permission of the publisher, Cambridge University Press, from *Proc. Cambridge Philos. Soc.*, Copyright © 1950, Vol. 46, pp. 570–580.

3. A further method for the evaluation of zeros of Bessel functions and some new asymptotic expansions for zeros of functions of large order. Reprinted with permission of the publisher, Cambridge University Press, from *Proc. Cambridge Philos. Soc.*, Copyright © 1951, Vol. 47, pp. 699–712.

4. Some new asymptotic expansions for Bessel functions of large orders. Reprinted with permission of the publisher, Cambridge University Press, from *Proc. Cambridge Philos. Soc.*, Copyright © 1952, Vol. 48, pp. 414–427.

5. Note on the asymptotic expansion of generalized hypergeometric functions. Reprinted with permission of the publisher, London Mathematical Society, from *J. London Math. Soc.*, Copyright © 1953, Vol. 28, pp. 462–464.

6. The asymptotic solution of linear differential equations of the second order for large values of a parameter. Reprinted with permission of the publisher, The Royal Society, London, from *Philos. Trans. Roy. Soc. London Ser. A*, Copyright © 1954, Vol. 247, pp. 307–327.

7. The asymptotic expansion of Bessel functions of large order. Reprinted with permission of the publisher, The Royal Society, London, from *Philos. Trans. Roy. Soc. London Ser. A*, Copyright © 1954, Vol. 247, pp. 328–368.

8. The asymptotic solution of linear differential equations of the second order in a domain containing one transition point. Reprinted with permission of the publisher, The Royal Society, London, from *Philos. Trans. Roy. Soc. London Ser. A*, Copyright © 1956, Vol. 249, pp. 65–97.

9. Uniform asymptotic expansions of solutions of linear second-order differential equations for large values of a parameter, Reprinted with permission of the publisher, The Royal Society, London, from *Philos. Trans. Roy. Soc. London Ser. A*, Copyright © 1958, Vol. 250, pp. 479–517.

10. Uniform asymptotic expansions for Weber parabolic cylinder functions of large orders. Reprinted with permission of the publisher, National Bureau of Standards (now National Institute of Standards and Technology), from *J. Res. Nat. Bur. Standards*, Copyright © 1959, Vol. 63B, pp. 131–169.

11. Error bounds for the Liouville-Green (or WKB) approximation. Reprinted with permission of the publisher, Cambridge University Press, from *Proc. Cambridge Philos. Soc.*, Copyright © 1961, Vol. 57, pp. 790–810.

12. Error bounds for first approximations in turning-point problems. Reprinted with permission of the publisher, Society for Industrial and Applied Mathematics, from *J. Soc. Indust. Appl. Math.*, Copyright © 1963, Vol. 11, pp. 748–772.

13. Error bounds for asymptotic expansions in turning-point problems. Reprinted with permission of the publisher, Society for Industrial and Applied Mathematics, from *J. Soc. Indust. Appl. Math.*, Copyright © 1964, Vol. 12, pp. 200–214.

14. On the asymptotic solutions of second-order differential equations having an irregular singularity of rank one, with an application to Whittaker functions. Reprinted with permission of the publisher, Society for Industrial and Applied Mathematics, from *J. Soc. Indust. Appl. Math. Ser. B Numer. Anal.*, Copyright © 1965, Vol. 2, pp. 225–243.

15. Error bounds for asymptotic solutions of second-order differential equations having an irregular singularity of arbitrary rank. Reprinted with permission of the publisher, Society for Industrial and Applied Mathematics, from *J. Soc. Indust. Appl. Math. Ser. B Numer. Anal.* Copyright © 1965, Vol. 2, pp. 244–249. (With F. Stenger.)

16. Error analysis of phase-integral methods. I. General theory for simple turning points. Reprinted with permission of the publisher, National Bureau of Standards (now National Institute of Standards and Technology), from *J. Res. Nat. Bur. Standards*, Copyright © 1965, Vol. 69B, pp. 271–290.

17. Error analysis of phase-integral methods. II. Application to wave-penetration problems. Reprinted with permission of the publisher, National Bureau of Standards (now National Institute of Standards and Technology), from *J. Res. Nat. Bur. Standards*, Copyright © 1965, Vol. 69B, pp. 291–300.

18. Numerical solution of second-order linear difference equations. Reprinted with permission of the publisher, National Bureau of Standards (now National Institute of Standards and Technology), from *J. Res. Nat. Bur. Standards*, Copyright © 1967, Vol. 71B, pp. 111–129.

19. Bounds for the solutions of second-order linear difference equations. Reprinted with permission of the publisher, National Bureau of Standards (now National Institute of Standards and Technology), from *J. Res. Nat. Bur. Standards*, Copyright © 1967, Vol. 71B, pp. 161–166.

20. Error bounds for the Laplace approximation for definite integrals. Reprinted with permission of the publisher, Academic Press, Inc., from *J. Approx. Theory*, Copyright © 1968, Vol. 1, pp. 293–313.

21. Why steepest descents? Reprinted with permission of the publisher, Society for Industrial and Applied Mathematics, from *SIAM Rev.*, Copyright © 1970, Vol. 12, pp. 228–247. Reprinted in *Special Functions and Wave Propagation, Studies in Applied Mathematics*, Vol. 6 (D. Ludwig and F. W. J. Olver, eds.), Society for Industrial and Applied Mathematics, Philadelphia, PA, 1970, pp. 44–63.

22. A paradox in asymptotics. Reprinted with permission of the publisher, Society for Industrial and Applied Mathematics, from *SIAM J. Math. Anal.*, Copyright © 1970, Vol. 1, pp. 533–534.

23. Note on backward recurrence algorithms. Reprinted with permission of the publisher, American Mathematical Society, from *Math. Comp.*, Copyright © 1972, Vol. 26, pp. 941–947. (With D. J. Sookne.)

24. Error bounds for stationary phase approximations. Reprinted with permission of the publisher, Society for Industrial and Applied Mathematics, from *SIAM J. Math. Anal.*, Copyright © 1974, Vol. 5, pp. 19–29.

25. Unsolved problems in the asymptotic estimation of special functions. Reprinted with permission of the publisher, Academic Press, Inc., in *Theory and Application of Special Functions*, Copyright © 1975, pp. 99–142 (R. A. Askey, ed.).

26. Second-order linear differential equations with two turning points. Reprinted with permission of the publisher, The Royal Society, London, from *Philos. Trans. Roy. Soc. London Ser. A*, Copyright © 1975, Vol. 278, pp. 137–174.

27. Legendre functions with both parameters large. Reprinted with permission of the publisher, The Royal Society, London, from *Philos. Trans. Roy. Soc. London Ser. A*, Copyright © 1975, Vol. 278, pp. 175–185.

28. Improved error bounds for second-order differential equations with two turning points. Reprinted with permission of the publisher, National Bureau of Standards (now National Institute of Standards and Technology), from *J. Res. Nat. Bur. Standards*, Copyright © 1976, Vol. 80B, pp. 437–440.

Part 2

29. Second-order differential equations with fractional transition points. Reprinted with permission of the publisher, American Mathematical Society, from *Trans. Amer. Math. Soc.*, Copyright © 1977, Vol. 226, pp. 227–241.

30. Connection formulas for second-order differential equations with multiple turning points. Reprinted with permission of the publisher, Society for Industrial and Applied Mathematics, from *SIAM J. Math. Anal.*, Copyright © 1977, Vol. 8, pp. 127–154.

31. Connection formulas for second-order differential equations having an arbitrary number of turning points of arbitrary multiplicities. Reprinted with permission of the publisher, Society for Industrial and Applied Mathematics, from *SIAM J. Math. Anal.*, Copyright © 1977, Vol. 8, pp. 673–700.

32. Asymptotic behavior of integrals of Bessel functions of high order. Reprinted with permission of the publisher, Utilitas Mathematica Publishing, Inc., from *Utilitas Math.*, Copyright © 1977, Vol. 12, pp. 225–239. (With M. L. Glasser.)

33. Sufficient conditions for Ackerberg-O'Malley resonance. Reprinted with permission of the publisher, Society for Industrial and Applied Mathematics, from *SIAM J. Math. Anal.*, Copyright © 1978, Vol. 9, pp. 328–355.

34. General connection formulae for Liouville-Green approximations in the complex plane. Reprinted with permission of the publisher, The Royal Society, London, from *Philos. Trans. Roy. Soc. London Ser. A*, Copyright © 1978, Vol. 289, pp. 501–548.

35. Asymptotic approximations and error bounds. Reprinted with permission of the publisher, Society for Industrial and Applied Mathematics, from *SIAM Rev.*, Copyright © 1980, Vol. 22, pp. 188–203.

36. Whittaker functions with both parameters large: uniform approximations in terms of parabolic cylinder functions. Reprinted with permission of the publisher, The Royal Society of Edinburgh, from *Proc. Roy. Soc. Edinburgh Sect. A*, Copyright © 1980, Vol. 86, pp. 213–234.

37. A posteriori error bounds for Gaussian elimination. Reprinted with permission of the publisher, Oxford University Press, from *IMA J. Numer. Anal.*, Copyright © 1982, Vol. 2, pp. 377–406. (With J. H. Wilkinson.)

38. Beyond floating point. Reprinted with permission of the publisher, Association for Computing Machinery, Inc., from *J. Assoc. Comput. Mach.*, Copyright © 1984, Vol. 31, pp. 319–328. (With C. W. Clenshaw.)

39. Generalized exponential and logarithmic functions. Reprinted with permission of the publisher, Elsevier Science Ltd., from *Comput. Math. Appl.*, Copyright © 1986, Vol. 12B, pp. 1091–1101. (With C. W. Clenshaw, D. W. Lozier and P. R. Turner.)

40. Level-index arithmetic operations. Reprinted with permission of the publisher, Society for Industrial and Applied Mathematics, from *SIAM J. Numer. Anal.*, Copyright © 1987, Vol. 24, pp. 470–485. (With C. W. Clenshaw.)

41. Error bounds for linear recurrence relations. Reprinted with permission of the publisher, American Mathematical Society, from *Math. Comp.*, Copyright © 1988, Vol. 50, pp. 481–499.

42. Closure and precision in level-index arithmetic. Reprinted with permission of the publisher, Society for Industrial and Applied Mathematics, from *SIAM J. Numer. Anal.*, Copyright © 1990, Vol. 27, pp. 1295–1304. (With D. W. Lozier.)

43. On Stokes' phenomenon and converging factors. Reprinted with permission of the publisher, Marcel Dekker, Inc., N.Y., in *Asymptotic and Computational Analysis* (R. Wong, ed.), *Lecture Notes in Pure and Applied Mathematics*, Copyright © 1990, Vol. 124, pp. 329–355.

44. Uniform, exponentially improved, asymptotic expansions for the generalized exponential integral. Reprinted with permission of the publisher, Society for Industrial and Applied Mathematics, from *SIAM J. Math. Anal.*, Copyright © 1991, Vol. 22, pp. 1460–1474.

45. Uniform, exponentially improved, asymptotic expansions for the confluent hypergeometric function and other integral transforms. Reprinted with permission of the publisher, Society for Industrial and Applied Mathematics, from *SIAM J. Math. Anal.*, Copyright © 1991, Vol. 22, pp. 1475–1489.

46. Exponentially-improved asymptotic solutions of ordinary differential equations I: The confluent hypergeometric function. Reprinted with permission of the publisher, Society for Industrial and Applied Mathematics, from *SIAM J. Math. Anal.*, Copyright © 1993, Vol. 24, pp. 756–767.

47. Airy and Bessel functions by parallel integration of ODEs. Reprinted with permission of the publisher, Society for Industrial and Applied Mathematics, in *Proc. Sixth SIAM Conference on Parallel Processing for Scientific Computing*, Copyright © 1993, Vol. 2, pp. 530–538. (R. F. Sincovec et al., eds.) (With D. W. Lozier.)

48. Asymptotic expansions of the coefficients in asymptotic series solutions of linear differential equations. Reprinted with permission of the publisher, International Press, Cambridge, MA, from *Methods Appl. Anal.*, Copyright © 1994, Vol. 1, pp. 1–13.

49. The generalized exponential integral. Reprinted with permission of the publisher, Birkhäuser Verlag AG., in *Approximation and Computation* (R. V. M. Zahar, ed.), *International Series of Numerical Mathematics*, Copyright © 1994, Vol. 119, pp. 497–510, Birkhäuser, Basel.

50. Exponentially improved asymptotic solutions of ordinary differential equations. II. Irregular singularities of rank one. Reprinted with permission of the publisher, The Royal Society, London, from *Proc. Roy. Soc. London Ser. A*, Copyright © 1994, Vol. 445, pp. 39–56. (With A. B. Olde Daalhuis.)

51. On an asymptotic expansion of a ratio of Gamma functions. Reprinted with permission of the publisher, The Royal Irish Academy, Dublin, from *Proc. Roy. Irish Academy Sect. A*, Copyright © 1995, Vol. 95, pp. 5–9.

52. Hyperasymptotic solutions of second-order linear differential equations I. Reprinted with permission of the publisher, International Press, Cambridge, MA, from *Methods Appl. Anal.*, Copyright © 1995, Vol. 2, pp. 173–197. (With A. B. Olde Daalhuis.)

53. On the calculation of Stokes multipliers for linear differential equations of the second order. Reprinted with permission of the publisher, International Press, Cambridge, MA, from *Methods Appl. Anal.*, Copyright © 1995, Vol. 2, pp. 348–367. (With A. B. Olde Daalhuis.)

54. Asymptotic solutions of linear ordinary differential equations at an irregular singularity of rank unity. Reprinted with permission of the publisher, International Press, Cambridge, MA, from *Methods Appl. Anal.*, Copyright © 1997, Vol. 4, pp. 375–403.

55. On the asymptotic and numerical solution of linear ordinary differential equations. Reprinted with permission of the publisher, Society for Industrial and Applied Mathematics, from *SIAM Rev.*, Copyright © 1998, Vol. 40, pp. 463–495. (With A. B. Olde Daalhuis.)

56. On the uniqueness of asymptotic solutions of linear differential equations. Reprinted with permission of the publisher, International Press, Cambridge, MA, from *Methods Appl. Anal.*, Copyright © 1999, Vol. 6, pp. 165–174.